D1239398

Farmers in a Changing World

Yearbook of Agriculture • 1940

THE YEARBOOK OF AGRICULTURE
1940

UNITED STATES DEPARTMENT OF AGRICULTURE

UNITED STATES GOVERNMENT PRINTING OFFICE

FOR SALE BY THE
SUPERINTENDENT OF DOCUMENTS
WASHINGTON, D. C.
PRICE $1.50

Foreword

THIS YEARBOOK on economic and social conditions in agriculture in the United States today was prepared under the direction of the former Secretary of Agriculture, Henry A. Wallace, and there is little that I can add to his Foreword, which follows and which was written before the book went to press.

So swiftly have events moved in recent months that some of the book will undoubtedly be "dated" before it is published. The whole question of foreign trade, for example, is in a state of flux, and the country is now plunged in a vast preparedness program that will affect employment and wages, and therefore the farmer's domestic market.

Underneath even these great changes, however, there are continuing agricultural problems, some of which have been building up for decades. In a deeper sense, indeed, modern wars result from some of the very causes back of farm distress.

In the main, then, these studies of present-day agricultural problems are underlined rather than outdated by recent events.

CLAUDE R. WICKARD, *Secretary of Agriculture.*

September 15, 1940.

TO BUILD an economic democracy that will match our political democracy, our people must have the facts.

Few agencies have been as persistent in digging out facts as the Department of Agriculture. Its scientists have a long and honorable record in this never-ending quest, and they have added much to human knowledge in fields that are vital to every one of us.

In our recent agricultural Yearbooks on genetics, on soils, on nutrition we have tried to sum up what the scientists have discovered and at the same time to show how imperfect our knowledge is—what great frontiers are still to be explored.

The investigations of the Department of Agriculture are not confined to the natural sciences. Under the necessities of modern life—many of them arising out of the revolutionary discoveries of science—the Department has had to pay more and more attention to economic and social problems as well. It has been building up a notable body of knowledge in these fields.

This book tries to deal with these problems as the previous Yearbooks dealt with some of the great problems in the natural sciences—to sum up needs, methods, results, and at the same time indicate shortcomings.

Of course, people are not so ready to agree on the meaning of economic and social facts as on the meaning of facts in the natural sciences. And even when they agree on the facts, they are not so ready to agree on what should be done about them. True, the human element is never entirely absent in any science, but it is far more important here, where it sometimes takes extreme forms of passion and prejudice.

That does not relieve any of us of the duty of trying to discover the facts in the scientific spirit and to deal with them wisely. It makes the duty all the more urgent. One of the great solvents of passion and prejudice, which between them have pushed civilization dangerously close to the brink of disaster, is the scientific spirit.

I believe that on the whole this book has been written in that spirit. It is a sincere effort to contribute to economic democracy in these United States. But I would also be the first to acknowledge that it has human shortcomings.

I should like to think it is a step, even if a halting one, toward that marriage of the social and the natural sciences which I believe can be one of the great contributions of democracy to civilization.

HENRY A. WALLACE, *Secretary of Agriculture.*

June 15, 1940.

Contents

Part 4. Farm Organizations

Part 5. What Some Social Scientists Have to Say

Part 6. Democracy and Agricultural Policy

Part 7. Essentials of Agricultural Policy

APPENDIX

1940 Yearbook Committee

M. L. Wilson, *Extension Service*, Chairman

Howard R. Tolley, *Bureau of Agricultural Economics*

Gove Hambidge, *Office of Information*

The advice and assistance of many specialists were freely sought by the committee in planning the book. In particular, thanks are due to L. C. Gray, F. F. Elliott, John R. Fleming, O. V. Wells, Carl C. Taylor, Bushrod W. Allin, O. E. Baker, and Paul H. Johnstone.

Editor of the Yearbook—Gove Hambidge

Assistant Editor—Marion Julia Drown

A NECESSARY POSTSCRIPT

Since the preparation during 1939 of most of the material in this book, the international situation has changed swiftly and tragically. The thoughts and lives of people all over the world have had to be reoriented to these changes. Unquestionably the turn of world events will profoundly affect the problems of agriculture in the United States in ways not entirely predictable. The reader should keep this in mind in everything that follows.

Yet the underlying theme of the book—the necessity in the modern world for constant and adequate adjustment to change—is powerfully emphasized by these recent events. The lesson should be well learned by a generation that has seen within half a lifetime the two greatest wars and the greatest depression as well as many of the greatest scientific advances and political upheavals in all history. Furthermore, the fundamental problems of our agriculture are not likely to be lessened by the changing international situation. They are more likely to be intensified, and there will be more need than ever to meet them with courage and intelligence in order that we may strengthen our country to the utmost.

Organization of the United States Department of Agriculture

Claude R. Wickard, *Secretary of Agriculture*
Paul H. Appleby, *Under Secretary*
Grover B. Hill, *Assistant Secretary*

Director of Information,
M. S. Eisenhower.

Director of Extension Work,
M. L. Wilson.

Director of Finance,
W. A. Jump.

Director of Personnel,
Roy F. Hendrickson.

Director of Research,
James T. Jardine.

Director of Marketing,
Milo R. Perkins.

Solicitor,
Mastin G. White.

Land Use Coordinator,
M. S. Eisenhower.

Office of Plant and Operations,
Arthur B. Thatcher, *Chief.*

Office of C. C. C. Activities,
Fred W. Morrell, *Chief.*

Office of Experiment Stations,
James T. Jardine, *Chief.*

Office of Foreign Agricultural Relations,
Leslie A. Wheeler, *Director.*

Agricultural Adjustment Administration,
R. M. Evans, *Administrator.*

Bureau of Agricultural Chemistry and Engineering,
Henry G. Knight, *Chief.*

Bureau of Agricultural Economics,
H. R. Tolley, *Chief.*

Agricultural Marketing Service,
C. W. Kitchen, *Chief.*

Bureau of Animal Industry,
John R. Mohler, *Chief.*

Commodity Credit Corporation,
Carl B. Robbins, *President.*

Commodity Exchange Administration,
Joseph M. Mehl, *Chief.*

Bureau of Dairy Industry,
O. E. Reed, *Chief.*

Bureau of Entomology and Plant Quarantine,
Lee A. Strong, *Chief.*

Farm Credit Administration,
A. G. Black, *Governor.*

Farm Security Administration,
C. B. Baldwin, *Administrator.*

Federal Crop Insurance Corporation,
Leroy K. Smith, *Manager.*

Forest Service,
Earle H. Clapp, *Acting Chief.*

Bureau of Home Economics,
Louise Stanley, *Chief.*

Library,
Claribel R. Barnett, *Librarian.*

Bureau of Plant Industry,
E. C. Auchter, *Chief.*

Rural Electrification Administration.
Harry Slattery, *Administrator.*

Soil Conservation Service,
H. H. Bennett, *Chief.*

Surplus Marketing Administration,
Milo R. Perkins, *Administrator.*

Farmers in a Changing World—A Summary

by GOVE HAMBIDGE[1]

THERE was a small band of men and women on a little ship, journeying toward an unknown future—an unknown land, in fact, where they dreamed of building a new, freer life. The ship was small and frail; it hardly crawled along the interminable sea; it wallowed in calms and was nearly smashed by storms. To the courageous little band the possibility of ever reaching the new land must sometimes have seemed remote. Often they must have thought longingly of the familiar, comfortable things they had left behind. The future must at times have seemed dark, and the days through which they were living bitter with uncertainty and hardship.

They did not give up. They did not turn the ship back. They did reach the new land. Their descendants conquered a continent and built a civilization.

This was more than 300 years ago, and the circumstances are different today. Yet we, who inherit what these people won, are also on a journey toward an unknown future. We also often look back longingly to the old familiar ways. To us too the future sometimes seems dark, and the days through which we are living filled with uncertainty and hardship. We too have dreams which at times we think we shall never attain.

Men have been through such experiences uncounted times in human history. It is true that today the circumstances are different. The circumstances are always different.

But the human beings who must deal with new circumstances are not essentially different. Courage, toughness of mind and body, fear of change and of the unknown, and a certain indomitable idealism that in the end conquers fear—these are still the heritage with which human beings face new conditions and problems. And the ends we strive for are not so essentially different. We no longer have the frontiers of a continent to conquer; that much has been done by the men and women of courage who were our forebears. But who will say there is not work for every man and woman on the frontiers of a better civilization?

This volume may be considered as a log book of a journey toward a future that must always remain inscrutable to human beings. Like its predecessors in the present series of Yearbooks of Agriculture, it is essentially a record of exploration.

The Yearbooks for 1936 and 1937, both entitled "Better Plants and Animals," told what scientists are doing to create improved forms of life for human use. "Soils and Men" (1938) told what is being discovered about soils and what these findings mean in human terms. "Food and Life" (1939) was a record of explorations in human and animal nutrition, where many new trails have been blazed in recent years.

[1] Gove Hambidge is Principal Research Writer, Office of Information.

"Farmers in a Changing World" records explorations along the social and economic frontiers of agriculture.

The year 1940 marks the end of a decade that has seen more swift and far-reaching changes in agricultural viewpoints and policy than perhaps any other decade in the history of the United States. Yet this decade does not stand alone as something cut off from the past. It simply felt the cumulative effect of the longer period of change, beginning near the turn of the century, during which agriculture has been virtually revolutionized by modern science.

That agricultural policy had to keep step with new needs resulting from profound disturbances throughout the world everyone will agree. Everyone will also agree that the needs have not been fully met. This is reason enough why the situation in agriculture should be summed up and reexamined as a whole at the close of so eventful a decade. From such a summing up and reexamination it is possible that we may be able to detect certain mistakes, discern trends and forces a little more clearly, see a few steps along the road ahead of us, and gain a little more wisdom. And more wisdom is the most fundamental need.

Most though not all of the 54 articles in the book were prepared by workers in the Department of Agriculture whose job it is to conduct research in agricultural problems and to carry out laws relating to agriculture passed by the Congress of the United States. There is a sprinkling of articles by writers who are not in the Department—mostly specialists in various branches of social science.

A certain unity of viewpoint will be evident throughout most of the book, but there are also a good many differences. The book does not represent official policy; it makes no claim to final wisdom; it simply explores agricultural problems, and the reader will sometimes find official policies treated with skepticism, controversial viewpoints defended, and things discussed that do not enter into any policy. It would have been possible to avoid such differences. But the great merit of democracy, we Americans believe, is that it not only permits but encourages the expression of different viewpoints. We think this is essential if social and economic problems are to be dealt with intelligently. The Yearbook might well have gone further in that direction than it has, but it would take more than one volume to give all the facts and viewpoints on such a wide variety of subjects.

Keeping these conditions in mind, the reader should discount or disagree with whatever he wishes in the book and bring his own thinking to bear on the points at issue. If there were complete understanding and agreement on all the problems in modern agriculture there would be no need for books about them; and if this were an autocracy instead of a democracy, there would be no need for discussion—problems would be settled by decree. In fact, there are few other countries left in the world where such a book as this could now be published.

SOME FUNDAMENTAL TRENDS

It goes without saying that such a book reflects the conditions of our time. A historian mulling over it in the future will no doubt think some of the material as quaint as beaver hats and tight breeches seem to us. He will smile at some of the problems his ancestors took so seriously. But this will be only because, in his day, those problems will have given place to others that are crucial in their turn.

Whether or not any specific policy developed during the past 10 years will continue during the next 10, certain trends or viewpoints have emerged during this decade that will amost certainly continue to influence policy. Different people would see these trends differently. To the editor who has had to view as a whole the large amount of material in this book a few viewpoints seem particularly fundamental.

(1) Most important of all, of course, is a remarkably widespread recognition of the fact that we do face profound changes and that we must do something to adjust ourselves to them. The symptoms of these changes are discussed again and again in the pages of this book. Among them are mechanization, vast dislocations caused by war, disruption of foreign markets, change from debtor to creditor status as a nation, soil damage on a large scale, the end of the frontier of free land. It is clear that the world we live in is far less "safe and sane" than the world of our fathers and grandfathers. Many things they took for granted we cannot take for granted. Agriculture is not in a mood to shirk the need for strengthening our economy to meet this less safe and less sane world, and this feeling of urgency has had a powerful effect on policy making in recent times.

(2) There is a sharpened recognition of the interrelationships in the modern world. This shows up in a great many ways—perhaps most notably in widespread reiteration of the fact that the agricultural problem is only part of a more inclusive national economic problem. More and more people realize, for example, that the well-being of agriculture depends to a large extent on the amount and the steadiness of employment in industry; that city and country are linked together in a thousand ways; that events on the other side of the earth profoundly affect farmers in the United States.

One of the powerful practical results of this recognition of interrelationships is a trend toward broader planning in the solution of economic problems. It rests on some such basis as this: What seem like separate problems are often found to be only parts of some larger problem; you cannot solve the parts by themselves; you have to work toward a solution of the whole problem; and this cannot be done without comprehensive planning. This kind of reasoning is back of the effort to work out procedures for soil conservation that begin with the individual farmer and go on up through the community, the county, the State, the region, to the Nation as a whole.

The reader of this book will note a fundamental conflict in agricultural thought which cannot be resolved until we reach sufficient maturity in our thinking to consider agriculture and industry as a single unit. The conflict can be simply put: On the one hand we push forward agricultural efficiency, with the inevitable consequence that fewer people are needed for production; on the other, we advocate inefficiency, or at any rate tolerate it, by an extension of subsistence farming as the only way to take care of those who are displaced by improved techniques. M. L. Wilson frankly recognizes this dilemma in his article, Beyond Economics. To the extent that it is unresolved, we can only acknowledge that men are the slaves rather than the masters of their own machines.

(3) There is an increased awareness of what might be called the human aspect of agricultural problems. This too shows up in many ways, but most strikingly in the attention given to the so-called disadvantaged groups among our farmers.

Hitherto the problems of commercial farmers have almost completely dominated agricultural thinking and policy. These problems still bulk very large, as they should, but they no longer tell the whole story. In the last few years Americans have become aware of a rather startling fact: A third to a half of the farm families in the United States contribute little to our commercial supply of food and raw materials. They have little to sell; they are unable to compete in the commercial market; they live for the most part in great poverty; many of them are homeless migrants. They seem to have little economic function. But they produce relatively more children than any other group, and as a consequence an increasing percentage of the American citizens of the future will be exposed to a childhood background that is in many cases appalling.

The analogy of this growth of functionless human beings in society with the growth of functionless cells in the human body produced by cancer is inescapable, and we have been forced to give attention to it for much the same reason that medicine has been forced to give attention to cancer. But these are not cells that can be cut out with a knife or killed with lethal rays. They are men and women and children—individuals and families with the same needs, longings, and possibilities as the rest of us. Together, they are the reverse side of the picture of wonderful technological progress that has enabled fewer and fewer farmers in the modern world to do the necessary work of production.

(4) There is a marked tendency to enlarge the meaning of science by bringing it to bear upon social as well as physical or biological problems. Time was when the Department of Agriculture was mainly a conglomeration of bureaus engaged in research in engineering, chemistry, genetics, microbiology, and the application of these "natural" sciences to farming. The result was a steady, sometimes an amazing, increase in efficiency. But this achievement, notable as it has been, did not serve to keep agriculture out of trouble. It became glaringly evident that science, in the sense in which the term has been commonly used, is not sufficient to insure a sound agriculture.

Economics entered the picture long ago in response to the imperative need for orderly economic information. Now sociology, anthropology, psychology, political science are all beginning to come in. What does this mean? It means a recognition that our idea of science was much too narrow. All of our attention was concentrated on the science of material things. But the greatest discoveries about gasoline, steel, rubber, fertilizers, bacteria, insects, however much they contribute to better production, tell us little about how to live wisely. In fact, they often complicate living enormously—individual living and social living. Seeing the effects of this complication, we have come to realize that there are other great areas about which we are badly in need of scientific knowledge. We need to know a great deal more about such vital problems as what kind of environment human beings need for their best development; how to create such an environment;

why we human beings so often make a mess of our affairs in spite of all our great achievements; how to stop making a mess of them. The scientific viewpoint, with its insistence on facts and on discovering the true causes of effects rather than relying on authority, opinion, prejudice, superstition, and brute force, has been the most powerful problem-solving tool man ever had, and it remains the most hopeful. Can we apply it to a much wider range of problems? [1] Can we use it to learn about human life and human relationships, as well as about things? If we can, our present civilization is only a crude beginning of what is possible.

(5) There is a tendency to put a new, conscious emphasis on all that is denoted by the word "democracy." This is the result of the impact of world events on American thinking. Democracy is fast disappearing in many parts of the world; we are the more determined to cling to it ourselves. It is being bitterly attacked from many quarters; we are the more determined to make it something worth defending. We ourselves seem to be faced by certain urgent necessities—for broader planning, for more effective administration—which elsewhere seem to have hastened the downfall of democracy. We believe democracy can meet the challenge without being weakened in its fundamental tenets.

In agriculture, this tendency is evident in an increased effort to root policies and programs in the soil of our own native traditions and ways. Americans are reexamining their origins and looking into the meaning of democracy more intensively than at any time since the Republic was founded.

SUMMARY OF THE YEARBOOK

As in the case of previous volumes in the series, the Yearbook will be summarized in the pages that follow.

The book is divided into 7 parts. Part 1, The Farmer's Changing World, is a history of agriculture in the United States from the colonial period through 1939, with special emphasis on changing needs and conditions that have shaped national policies during these centuries. Part 2, Agriculture and the National Welfare, deals with relationships between producers and consumers, agriculture and industry, farm people and city people. Part 3, The Farmer's Problems Today and the Efforts to Solve Them, is a comprehensive survey of current agricultural problems and current efforts to solve them. These problems fall into several different groups—soil conservation and land use; farm management; foreign and domestic markets; credit, insurance, and taxation; rural standards of living; tenancy and labor. Part 4, Farm Organizations, reports the viewpoints and recommenda-

[1] An illuminating point may be noted here. The physical and biological scientist rejects opinion, prejudice, superstition, and brute force out of hand. He would dismiss as sheer superstition, for example, the idea that you must carry a rabbit's foot in your pocket to come out well in your undertakings. The social scientist considers opinion, prejudice, superstition, and brute force as facts which we have to study and with which we must deal, since they have enormous effects on individuals and society. He would say: "Certain people believe in the necessity of carrying a rabbit's foot. How many people? Where did the belief come from? Why do they hold to it? What effect does it have on their behavior and attitudes? Does the belief make it difficult for them to understand important facts? Should it be changed? How can it be changed? What will be the effect on their behavior and attitudes if it is changed?" The example given is trivial, but there are many similar situations that are overwhelmingly important. The social scientist has the same attitude toward these situations that a physicist would have toward a problem in physics.

223761°—40——2

tions of three national organizations of farmers in the United States—viewpoints that are sometimes opposed to, sometimes in favor of, specific policies. In Part 5, What Some Social Scientists Have to Say, a few representatives of different social sciences view agriculture as a whole from their particular angles. Part 6, Democracy and Agricultural Policy, deals with the relationship of policy making to democratic processes. Part 7, Essentials of Agricultural Policy, is an attempt to sum up what has gone before in terms of today's and tomorrow's policies.

Part 1. The Farmer's Changing World

How simple the farmer's problem would be, Elliott points out in the first article in this section, if there were no such thing as change in the world—no changes in soils, cultural practices, markets, population, birth rates, and a thousand other things.

But the principal fact the farmer faces is that all these things do change. There have been enormous changes in a comparatively few years, and he has had to adjust himself to them.

For instance, in 1920 farmers had to feed a total population of 105 million people (excluding exports for populations abroad); now the same number of farmers feed 132 million here. Around 1920, people used 27 pounds of citrus fruits a year per capita; now their habits have changed and they use 47 pounds. In 1919 farm income was 16.9 billion dollars; in 1932 it was 5.3 billion. In 1919 farmers received 4 billion dollars for exports; in 1932, they got 590 million. Twenty years ago there were 26 million horses and mules to be fed on farms; now there are fewer than 16 million. Since 1900 machinery has greatly reduced the need for human labor in production. In the same period of time, farmers have come to demand a better standard of living in many ways, and this has meant a need for more cash.

Such changes have brought crucial problems—how to get greater stability and security within agriculture, how to adjust agriculture to the rest of our economy, how to conserve our soil resources, what to do about the large numbers who have succumbed in the economic struggle. Whatever approach we take toward these problems, we run some risk. But "neither policy making by explosion," Elliott says, "such as occurs when the orderly processes of government fail, nor policy making by executive action, such as occurs when the experts and administrators make decisions without the citizen's participation, is likely to occur in a society where democratic practice is reasonably in accord with democratic theory. . . . If we are to preserve the democratic process, it is absolutely necessary that the farmer play an important part and have a direct voice in the formulation of farm policy as well as in its execution."

The main question is whether the farmer shall try to meet modern problems entirely by himself, as an individual, or whether he shall get together with others so that all may act as a group for certain desired objectives. Farmers have insisted during recent years on group action. The legislation they won is a sharp departure from previous policy in the United States. It raises issues that need to be thoroughly examined.

Old Ideals Versus New Ideas in Farm Life

Johnstone's primary interest as a historian is to trace out people's ways of living and their attitudes and institutions, and to discover why they lived and thought as they did. This is folk history. It helps us to understand ourselves. He digs into many sources to find out about such things.

There have been vast changes in the 150 years of United States history—from the sickle to the combine, the ox to the tractor, 4 million people to 132 million, a rural civilization to an industrial civilization, free land to scarce, high-priced land. These changes, Johnstone points out, "have profoundly influenced the very essence and character of rural living. Even the philosophies, the ideas of right and wrong, have in some cases taken on a wholly new shape and character."

The Republic was born in what has come to be known as the Age of Reason or the Age of Enlightenment. In the earlier feudal period, traditional ways of doing things were hardly ever questioned; they were eternally right and natural and could not be improved. In the Age of Enlightenment, intelligent people believed that reason could show us better ways. There was an aggressive search for these better ways. In agriculture, new methods of cultivation were developed. Washington and Jefferson were among those who put aside traditional prejudices and tackled agricultural problems scientifically.

Agricultural societies, based upon this spirit, soon sprang up in the new country, along with agricultural fairs and agricultural journals. Such things were new in the world; they were the beginning of a ceaseless agitation for progress and scientific improvement. Over against them was the natural inertia of tradition, which resists novelties. In 75 years after the Revolution, agricultural technology was improved more than it had been in the previous 2,000 years. Farmers accepted new mechanical devices readily; they were much slower to adopt scientific methods, which for a long time were labeled "book farming"; but by the time of the present generation, attitudes had so changed that most practical applications of science are readily accepted by all farmers in a position to profit from them.

Along with this spirit of progress, there was in the early days a strong belief that "those who labor in the earth are the chosen people of God," as Jefferson wrote, and that the cities were corrupt and decadent. Farmers alone were free and independent; farming was man's fundamental pursuit; it was the natural and good life. There was a dislike and disdain of the cities and all their institutions—including trade and banking. Partly this was because so many farm people came from a working-class or peasant background in Europe, whereas the dominant element in the cities came from the European upper classes. Thus the struggling American farmer also tended to link himself with the city laborer and artisan, who worked with his hands. These tendencies, and the conditions of frontier life, helped to develop a robust democratic spirit and a pride in the virtues of labor, industry, and thrift as settlement moved westward. Right and justice were "always on the side of the poor and humble."

Out of the general belief in the idea of progress, which the successes achieved by a vigorous, colonizing people seemed to make a reality, came a strong belief that America was truly the land of opportunity. This attitude was strengthened by the sensational rise in land values along the frontier. It was not entirely fortunate that a boomer spirit developed as one aspect of this optimism. Frequently men took up land, not to farm it permanently, but to clean up on the rising market and go on to the next stopping-off place. The tendency of everyone to expect land values to rise indefinitely contributed to the heavy debt load that agriculture was later to bear, for farms were capitalized on the basis of expectations that did not always pan out.

Another element in the early background of rural America was a vigorous movement for self-education as a means of enriching life. During and after the Civil War this developed further, and local farmers' clubs and discussion groups sprang up in great numbers. Then came the Patrons of Husbandry and the Granger movement on a national scale. At the same time there was a growing agitation for more public schools, and finally for special schools and colleges to teach agricultural science. Education was a political issue in rural communities for a generation or more, until the Morrill Act of 1862 established the agricultural colleges. Education by then had become more than a means of attaining culture. It was considered the road to social and economic advancement. A "success philosophy" had begun to take root in this country.

During the past century, three forces, which Johnstone calls commercialization, urbanization, and technological advance, have been at work to change the character of rural life and along with it some of the most fundamental of the earlier habits, customs, and ideas.

Industrial development in the cities gradually took away the farmer's self-sufficient independence. As the cities grew in size, he had to produce food for increasing numbers of industrial workers—and he did it successfully. He also had to produce agricultural products to be sent to Europe to pay for the European goods and the capital needed for industrial development—and he did this successfully. But in the process he became more deeply involved in a commercial, specialized economy, more closely tied to markets and large-scale industry—which meant to cities. At the same time, his own demands grew; he wanted more of the conveniences industry produced—such things as a sewing machine, kerosene oil, a telephone. Instead of making almost everything for himself, he bought more and more things made in factories. He had to produce more cash products to buy these conveniences.

Thus farming came to be considered increasingly as a commercial pursuit rather than primarily as a way of living—which it was in the old view. Agricultural journals, schools, colleges urged the farmer to take the businessman as his model. There was a widespread drive to introduce bookkeeping and cost accounting in agriculture. The farmer was advised to charge a certain amount against his business as "salary," a certain amount as "interest on investment," just as businessmen did. As this viewpoint was more widely accepted, the whole picture of the farm enterprise changed. A farmer might succeed very well in maintaining himself, but he was not commercially successful unless he made a profit in business terms. By operating on a business basis, he greatly increased his cash income—but also his cash outgo.

These developments inevitably brought other changes in attitudes. For one thing, farmers were no longer so inclined to identify themselves with those city people who worked with their hands; they became more conscious of their status as employers and commercial proprietors. The growing gap between the farmer and the city worker was widened by labor's agitation for shorter hours and higher pay, which offended some of the deepest convictions of the farmer, who had to work long hours on his own enterprise and whose economic return was more closely related than the average urban worker's to the amount of effort he put in. The farmer found himself faced with the business problems of the modern commercial world, and was forced to accept the methods of that world even though the frequent inequalities under which agriculture was practiced placed him at a disadvantage. He was usually in debt, and did not feel that he got a fair share of the national income as compared with the great, rich monopolies and trusts in industry. But in spite of this disadvantage, he had to become a businessman, and when he did, he became conscious of a "labor problem."

Agricultural education fostered the philosophy of commercial success. Although there was a group of educators, among them Kenyon L. Butterfield and Liberty Hyde Bailey, who emphasized cultural values in rural living, on the whole the educational drive was strongly directed toward economic advancement, based on scientific and technical progress. Farmers increasingly sought and applied the advice of technical experts, many of whom were not themselves dirt farmers. Meanwhile, the use of farm machinery increased rapidly, especially after the tractor came in to displace horses; by 1930, farmers were using some $3,300,000,000 worth of agricultural machines. Technical progress in other fields kept pace with these advances.

In brief, ideas and ideals that had become dominant in the United States through commerce and industry inevitably spread to the farmer. He also took more and more kindly to urban standards of living and urban tastes. The mail-order catalogs, the farm magazines with their urban stories and advertisements, and the Hollywood movies have been powerful forces in this development.

Thus a single century brought an almost complete reversal of many old customs and attitudes—highly commercialized farming in place of the old self-sufficient production; emphasis on cash crops in place of the products needed at home; dependence on world economic conditions in place of almost complete independence; acceptance of the desirability of commercial success in place of the older pride in thrift and hard work as the primary virtues; acceptance of urban standards in place of the earlier disdain for them.

None of these changes took place universally and all at once, or without conflict. Indeed, the outstanding fact, Johnstone points out, is that change has meant conflict and struggle. The older generation clings to tradition; old ways are deeply rooted in moral attitudes and ideas of right and wrong; adaptations to new needs and new conditions are made with great difficulty, and they are accompanied by a sense of uncertainty and fear. Because we have been unable to adapt ourselves readily enough and wisely enough to changed conditions, we now have a sharp division between commercial farming and a large noncommercial group that barely subsists; and commercial farmers themselves have great difficulty in meeting the cost of modern living plus the cost of production by modern methods.

But though the lag between old ways and new needs is the chief cause of social maladjustments, the same persistence of the old that brings conflict with the new is also, Johnstone says, the great safeguard of society. For the most enduring of all are the ideals and desires based on fundamental human needs. And these ideals and desires outlast the particular forms and institutions that give them expression and effectiveness in any particular age. Thus, although in times of stress we tend for a time to confuse the temporary form with the essence, and although this loyalty to older forms causes maladjustments, it is in essence a loyalty to basic ideals that may be depended upon to survive changes in outward forms and institutions.

American Agriculture—The First 300 Years

In writing a history of agriculture in this country from the colonial period to the World War, Edwards traces the changing conditions and policies that most affected farmers.

The colonial period, he notes, covered almost two centuries, and its influence lasted much longer. It strongly stamped American habits and institutions. Two characteristics of this period were especially notable. (1) The colonies were predominantly agricultural, and the attitudes of the small farmer characterized the people as a whole. (2) Life was fluid because it was continually beginning over again on the frontier. Frontier isolation tended to make people narrow, but primitive conditions made them resourceful, self-reliant, practical, hard-working. These have been typical American traits.

Englishmen predominated in the 13 Colonies. They came mostly from a rural background where agriculture was not yet highly developed. Their farming methods were not suited to the wilderness, and at first they almost starved in spite of an abundance of wilderness food. Not until they had learned new ways from the Indians did they make a success of the new life. Agriculture in this country became a blend of European and Indian practices and has remained so ever since.

Since landownership was the key to individual success in England, it became equally important in the Colonies. Three ways of acquiring land were especially significant. (1) Under the manorial system, large tracts were granted to individuals, who were practically feudal overlords and collected quitrents from settlers. With such an abundance of land in America, this system was hard to enforce. Eventually manors became plantations and the owners made a profit from slave labor rather than land. (2) Under the New England system, a trading company took title to the land. Settlers were granted rights—usually to an area the size of a township—as a group, not as individuals. Through town meetings, the group acted as a corporation in dividing the land fairly among individuals, and some of it was held in common. This system, designed to be like the Biblical commonwealth, developed group action, compact social communities, democratic institutions. (3) Under the headright system of Virginia and other southern Colonies, any settler had a right to 50 acres of land—equivalent to a dividend on a share of company stock. This system became highly corrupt and was eventually replaced by "treasury rights"—the sale of 50-acre tracts to individuals by the Commonwealth.

Agricultural tools and implements in the Colonies were extremely crude. Labor was scarce, since four freemen out of five were independent farmers. This led to various systems of unfree labor. Many people sold themselves as voluntary indentured servants for 5 to 7 years in order to get to America. Others were involuntary indentured servants for 7 to 10 years—paupers, vagrants, debtors, petty criminals "condemned" to the Colonies, or innocent persons shanghaied by professional kidnapers. Many of these "redemptioners," though poor, came of good stock, accumulated a stake for themselves, became independent and often prosperous. The trade in indentured servants was checked about 1700, and the importation of slaves from Africa then began in earnest. By 1760, slaves made up two-fifths of the population of the southern Colonies; in South Carolina they outnumbered the whites 2 to 1.

At first the colonists grew their crops in the clearings they found; then they began making clearings, using the Indian method of girdling and burning trees. Indian corn became the major crop because of its many advantages, but the European grains were also grown—wheat, rye, barley, oats, buckwheat, peas. Livestock was scarce; all animals had to be imported, and none but the better-financed settlements could afford an adequate supply. As the number of livestock increased, native annual grasses in the clearings proved inadequate for forage, and this led to the importation of timothy, bluegrass, clover.

Almost from the beginning, Edwards points out, there were laws regulating production and marketing, passed either in England or by the Colonies themselves. Some were successful, some visionary. Tobacco production was restricted again and again to prevent glutting the market and to insure the growing of food crops. There were price-fixing agreements for tobacco, official grading, destruction of surpluses. Rice growing was encouraged, and there were laws to fix the exchange value of the product, standardize quality, prevent deceitful packing. The growing of indigo was stimulated by premiums. Bounties were paid for hemp and flax, and growers were subsidized by various Colonies. There were likewise bounties for the production of naval stores, as well as official standardization. Extraordinary efforts, never very successful, were made to encourage silk production, including not only bounties but compulsory planting of mulberry trees. Cotton, sugar, spices, wine, and subtriopical fruits were also subject to stimulative or regulative legislation.

Most of the colonial trade was overseas, but a sizable amount developed between the Colonies. New England quickly became a commercial and shipping center, trading especially with the West Indies and along the coast. The middle Colonies became a fur-trading and grain-exporting region. The South contributed more than any other region to overseas trade, the chief product being tobacco. Several factors interfered seriously with the trade of the Colonies, including a long series of navigation acts, designed to assist in creating a self-sufficient economic empire, which prohibited the shipping of most products anywhere except to England, in English or colonial ships.

Small farmers, backwoodsmen, city laborers, mechanics were the driving force back of the Revolutionary War. In effect, they were revolting against the large landed and commercial interests that represented England in the government of the Colonies. They wanted more liberal land policies; paper money to pay off their debts; an end of absentee landlordism, property qualifications for voting, taxation without representation, expensive justice.

After the war the last vestiges of feudalism were abolished by "frontier 'radicals' like Jefferson." Thereafter land could be held in fee simple. Probably the most important development relating to land was the formation of policies for disposing of the vast western area won from England. Fortunately the States with claims to western land ceded them to the Confederation and this enabled the country to develop as a federation of equal States instead of a system of provinces dependent on the older States. In 1785 and 1787 ordinances were passed that laid down the principles and procedure later followed in the disposition of public land. There were two divergent views from the beginning, one group favoring a cautious and the other a liberal land policy. Gradually the second viewpoint won.

Land policy came to center around three specific issues. (1) Graduation. The best land was settled first, leaving islands of poor land unsold. In 1854 prices were graduated downward on the unsold land. (2) Preemption. At first efforts were made to drive off squatters. Frontier farmers banded together, finally forced enactment of the preemption law in 1841. Settlers could then take up (preempt) land before it was surveyed and placed on sale. (3) Homestead. Conservative leaders as well as eastern landowners and manufacturers opposed a too liberal land policy. Pioneer farmers and land speculators joined forces with labor to have land distributed free to actual settlers; one of their slogans was "Vote yourself a farm." Underneath the political struggle, says Edwards, "lay the conviction that equality of economic power was essential if genuine freedom and democracy were to thrive in America." The bill for free homesteads was passed by the House in 1852, but it became part of the slavery issue and was not finally enacted until 1862.

The opening of new lands and the westward expansion between 1790 and 1850 was marked by one of the greatest migrations in the history of the world. In 1790 there were 4,000,000 people in the United States, of whom 94 percent were in the 13 original States; within 60 years there were 23,000,000 people and 32 States. "Land was the great magnet . . . available almost for the asking . . . an irresistible temptation." The first great trek was into the Old Northwest (bounded by the Ohio, the Great Lakes, and the Mississippi) opened up by the Ordinances of 1785 and 1787. Settlers rushed in even before the surveys were completed. The same wave of migration settled western New York. After 1815, the migration increased, stimulated by depression in Europe and our own Eastern States, the increasingly liberal land policies of the Federal Government, victories over the Indians, the use of steamboats on western rivers, the Louisiana and East Florida purchases. Ohio, Indiana, Illinois, Michigan were soon admitted to the Union.

The immense demand for cotton following the invention of the cotton gin in 1793 pushed planters westward into the Old Southwest, where a plantation aristocracy developed. In 1834 Alabama for the first time took the lead in cotton production away from Georgia, and in 1839 Mississippi led for the first time. The acquisition of the Louisiana Territory in 1803 increased the area of the United States by 140 percent. The westward tide moved into Texas in 1830, bringing annexation and war with Mexico. Before 1850 the Oregon Territory was acquired from England, and Mexico ceded California. Then came the gold rush to the Pacific coast.

The opening of fertile western lands caused a depression in eastern agriculture, made possible the development of industries and cities, had a liberalizing influence on American politics, and above all affected American psychology because of the feeling that the individual always had a chance to start life over again by taking up new land.

The virgin soil of the Old Northwest grew wheat well, and during the 1850's wheat production shifted westward to Illinois, Indiana, and Wisconsin. Corn, marketed in the form of whiskey and hogs, also did well in the new country.

Eastern agriculture went through two major changes by 1860. (1) Prior to 1810, methods were backward except in a few progressive areas, and production for home use was the rule—perhaps mainly because there was no large urban market. Then the growth of cities stimulated production for sale. As a result, better tools and more scientific methods were used, production became more specialized, land values rose, farmers began buying instead of making home and farm equipment. At the same time, young people began leaving the farm for the city. (2) Western competition also forced eastern farmers to specialize. By 1850 there were 7,000 miles of railroads, and shortly thereafter Western States were pouring wool, wheat, pork, beef into eastern markets. Eastern farmers perforce turned to the production of potatoes and other vegetables, orchard fruits, fluid milk, cheese, butter, hay.

Meanwhile, southern agriculture also underwent changes. The application of power to textile manufacturing in England and later in New England resulted in an enormous demand for cotton, and the invention of the cotton gin enabled American producers to meet this demand. More and more the South specialized in cotton, which became the largest export crop of the United States. This expansion revived slavery, which had been on the wane. As soil resources were used up in the eastern areas, growers moved westward, finally reaching the prairie regions of Texas. The Southeast had little to compensate for this loss, and its story, Edwards notes, would have been different had western migration been better regulated.

Of vital importance to farmers was the development of the transportation system, prior to 1860. The Colonies were tardy in road and bridge building. The completion of the Philadelphia-Lancaster Turnpike in 1792 started a boom in turnpike building by private companies, which charged heavy tolls—$12 a ton per hundred miles, on the average. Even with some State aid, however, this did not provide an adequate road system, and in 1808 Jefferson's Secretary of the Treasury, Albert Gallatin, advocated public expenditure for a Nation-wide system of canals, turnpikes, and river improvements. The Cumberland Road (834 miles—$7,000,000) was the major result.

In 1815 a steamboat ascended the Mississippi and Ohio Rivers from New Orleans to Louisville in 25 days. This inaugurated a tremendous expansion. The Northeast and Southwest were bound together by river trade, and the favored cities—particularly New Orleans—grew rapidly. For a long time steamboats were the chief means of travel in settling the West. Coastwise traffic, however, became more important in the long run; by 1860 the value of commodities carried by coastwise vessels was six times that of exports abroad.

Canal building was begun partly to bring inland products to seaports for the steamship traffic. First big project was the Erie Canal, completed in 1825. Before the canal, it had cost $100 to ship a ton of farm products from Buffalo to New York in 20 days; now it cost $15 and the trip was completed in 8 days. Farm prices and land values went up; new cities were born; New York became the biggest American seaport. Other States began canal building, and a series of feeder canals was constructed in the Old Northwest. The whole development greatly stimulated western agriculture, but the cost of the internal improvements was enormous, more than the States could bear. After the panic of 1837, "it became part of the American credo that a public utility could not be built and operated successfully except by private enterprise."

Then came railroads, to challenge the supremacy of canals and eventually win. Western railroad building did not get a good start until 1850, but by 1860 Illinois was the greatest corn State as a result of the opening of the prairies by railroads, and the flour-milling and stock-raising centers inevitably moved westward.

Edwards argues that after 1862, when the Homestead Act was signed, there were many major mistakes in United States land policy. In the first place, the act itself did not and could not do what its supporters had in mind. It offered 160 acres of land free to the settler. This was enough for a farm in the East and Middle West, including even eastern Kansas, Nebraska, and the Dakotas. But by 1862 these areas were largely settled. Homestead lands lay mostly west of the 100th meridian, in areas of low rainfall, where eastern farming methods did not apply; it was obvious to anyone who knew the West that 160 acres was too little for dry-farming or grazing, too much for irrigation. Moreover, there were two competing systems of land disposal in effect. The better lands often were purchased in huge blocks by speculative syndicates, which gouged the farmer. The administration of the land laws was also full of abuses, and fraud and graft were common.

Some of the subsequent land laws also had the effect of encouraging overexploitation of resources by large corporations and other interests. A movement toward conservation began in 1891, when the Timber Cutting Act and the Preemption Act were repealed, the policy of selling the public domain (except special lands) was abandoned, and forest reserves were authorized. The old Forestry Office became a bureau of the Department of Agriculture in 1897. The Carey Act of 1894 provided for irrigation under State auspices; the Reclamation Act of 1902 put the Federal Government into irrigation. Laws passed between 1906 and 1920 reserved all mineral rights for the Government, permitted only carefully regulated leasing. Meanwhile 148,000,000 acres was added to the timberland reservation and Gifford Pinchot inaugurated an active forest conservation policy. Between 1904 and 1916 efforts were made to improve the Homestead Act by granting larger tracts on the inferior western lands that remained undistributed.

If settlement had been better managed as a public policy, says Edwards, there might now be more farm owners, fewer tenants, and far better conservation of national resources. But most people were not then thinking in those terms. The object, natural enough at the time, was to settle and develop the wilderness as rapidly as possible.

Edwards traces the main developments in farm machinery as a major influence shaping the history of American agriculture. Many machines, developed between 1830 and 1860, were being used by farmers before the Civil War—the mechanical reaper (most significant single invention), mechanical raker and binder attachments, the steel plow, the grain drill, the corn drill, the threshing machine. The Civil War was a turning point in mechanization A million farmers were withdrawn from production to fill the biggest army the world had ever seen, and machinery had to be used on a large scale if those left on the farms were to do their job effectively. Thus between 1860 and 1910 there was a general displacement of man labor by horse labor, and additional machines were invented to be run by horses.

After 1910 another great period began, marked by the substitution of mechanical power for horses. In this development too, war (the World War) was a turning point because it demanded greater production by fewer hands (though the farm depression of the 1920's perhaps stimulated mechanization even more through the need to cut production costs to the bone).

By no means all of the increased efficiency of agriculture is due to machines, but they have been a major force in bringing more land under cultivation, making it possible to produce up to and beyond the market demand, enlarging farms, shifting production to level lands, reducing labor requirements, lightening farm toil.

Developments in transportation after 1860 were as important to farmers as those in machinery. When settlement on a large scale was to be undertaken the Federal Government was called on to further it; the same thing happened in the case of railroad expansion. By 1914 "the railroad mileage of the United States . . . exceeded that of all Europe and represented more than a third of the world's total"; it increased eight times while the population was increasing three times. This expansion would not have been possible without Government aid. After 1850 the Government gave more than 159,000,000 acres of land to the railroads and granted two railroads $16,000–$48,000 for each mile of line they constructed. State and local subsidies were extensive and varied. Altogether, perhaps three-fourths of the cost of railway construction was borne by public authorities.

Farmers favored this aid and in addition mortgaged their land to buy railroad bonds, because the railroads promised to bring them unbelievable prosperity. When the extravagant hopes were not realized, the failure was attributed to grasping railroad barons. In fact, many serious charges could rightfully be made against the railroads. To correct the evils, farmers banded together, started the Grange, organized State and local tickets, forced railroad reforms and rate regulation by States and later by the Federal Government. In 1887 the Interstate Commerce Act was passed, in 1903 the Elkins Act, in 1906 the Hepburn Act, in 1910 the Mann-Elkins Act.

From the 1870's to the World War there was a progressive decline in rates. Competition doubtless was more of a factor in the east-west traffic rate reduction. The result was a rapid development of the West. Colonization was actively promoted by the railways. The Northwest and North Central States became the grain kingdom; meat packing was stimulated by the invention of the refrigerator car, which also spread dairy and poultry production westward.

After the Civil War, agriculture went through a long period of revolutionary change and growth, stimulated by mechanical improvements, transportation, the homestead policy, but above all by the expansion of domestic and foreign markets, which in turn resulted from industrialization and the growth of great cities whose workers had to be fed and whose factories demanded raw materials. Cereals were by far the most important commercial crop, making up half the total value of all crops in 1899. Corn production rose from 800,000,000 bushels in 1859 to a peak of over 3,000,000,000 in 1906, wheat from 200,000,000 to over 1,000,000,000 in 1915. Great milling and shipping centers developed near the heart of the grain country. Livestock production was stimulated likewise, and this brought the big livestock trading and packing centers. Butter and cheese making shifted from the farm to the factory to supply the immense demand as the dairy industry moved westward. Incubators and cold storage enabled farmers to meet the urban need for poultry products. The cotton regions, which were in a desperate plight after the Civil War, soon caught up with their 1860 production of 3,841,000 bales, and by 1910 were producing 11,609,000. By 1899 a third of the cotton crop was being used in domestic mills, and in 1909 more cotton was consumed in southern mills than in the northern. Wool production for the domestic market increased in importance. The first eastward shipment of fruit from California was made in 1867; by 1899 the total was 193,000,000 pounds of fresh deciduous fruit a year. The Southern States began sending fruits and vegetables north. Tobacco production grew.

Foreign as well as domestic trade in farm products rose sharply after the Civil War. Though city workers here and abroad benefited from the cheap food supply, many European farmers were ruined by American competition and immense numbers migrated to this country.

The peak of food exports came about 1900; after that there was a rapid decline caused by more effective competition in Europe, the development of new agricultural regions, and tariff and other policies of foreign governments. But the domestic market in the United States was then expanding and the American farmer was able to adjust his production by a gradual shift toward an increased output of sugar, dairy products, fruits, and vegetables. Cotton and tobacco exports also increased. The period 1900–1914 was relatively prosperous for agriculture, since production was fairly well balanced with demand.

The vast expansion in agriculture after the Civil War was entirely in the direction of commercial farming, and this brought a train of new and complex problems. Farmers were thrown into competition with one another; they had to produce at the lowest possible cost; they had to have money for machines and other needs; they found commodity prices set by the new cotton and grain exchanges and the speculators in futures; they were squeezed by high freight rates, by monopolies, by loan sharks, by commission men. The only way they could fight their battles was by organization. So they organized, first in the Granger movement. One major outcome was a rapid growth of cooperative buying, selling, and even manufacturing. These early efforts of the farmer "to perform the function of middleman, manufacturer, capitalist, and banker through cooperative enterprise met with only short-lived success," because of lack of capital, inexperience, fair and unfair competition; but it paved the way for the cooperative movement of later years. In the 1880's came the Northwestern and the Southern Alliances, which started many cooperative enterprises; in 1895 another expansion in cooperative activity began; in 1902 the Farmers' Union was formed, and it developed plans that forecast certain aspects of present-day agricultural thinking. In 1914 the Clayton Act recognized the need for farmer cooperatives, and they have had legal protection ever since.

The post-Civil War period of rapid agricultural expansion also saw the development of a Federal Department of Agriculture. Founded in 1862, it was actually the result of almost a hundred years of preliminary steps. In 1776 there was a tentative proposal for Congress to set up a standing committee to assist agricultural societies. Two decades later Washington proposed a board of agriculture, and a similar proposal was made in 1817. Meanwhile consuls and naval officers abroad were sending back seeds and improved breeds of livestock. In 1836 Henry L. Ellsworth, Commissioner of Patents, undertook to distribute these seeds to farmers. In 1839 Congress appropriated $1,000 for the work, as well as for statistical and other investigations. An Agricultural Division was inaugurated in the Patent Office, and regular appropriations were made after 1847. In 1854 a chemist, a botanist, and an entomologist were employed.

When an independent Department was established in 1862, Isaac Newton, who headed the agricultural work in the Patent Office, became Commissioner and laid the foundations for a broad policy of research and education. Almost from the beginning, therefore, "the Department made notable contributions to the field of scientific agriculture," partly because "men of outstanding ability served as division chiefs and research workers." The Department gradually added divisions, beginning with chemistry, statistics, entomology, in response to need and demand. In 1884 it took on regulatory work in addition to fact-finding and education when the Bureau of Animal Industry was organized to clean up cattle diseases.

The year 1862 also saw the founding of the land-grant colleges under the Morrill Act, and in 1887, under the Hatch Act, Congress authorized a national system of State agricultural experiment stations—several had been started by the States, beginning with Connecticut in 1875—which served as a link between the colleges and the Federal Department. Finally in 1889 the Department was given Cabinet status, and its appropriations were increased, its functions widened. Highly trained explorers went to far countries and brought back valuable crop plants; extensive breeding work got under way; protection of the national forests was undertaken; enforcement of the Food and Drugs Act was given to the Department. After 1900 county demonstration work began, and in 1914, under the Smith-Lever Act, Congress gave financial aid to extension divisions in the State colleges, which were to cooperate with the Federal agency. Meanwhile marketing problems were receiving increased emphasis, and an Office of Markets was created in 1913. Weather reporting and road construction had also become Department functions.

Meanwhile agricultural education also went through a period of early growth until the Land Grant College Act of 1862 granted large amounts of land to the States to be sold for funds to create and maintain agricultural and mechanical colleges. A system of direct Federal subsidies was created by legislation in 1890 and 1907. The colleges had a difficult time at first because of lack of funds, lack of qualified teachers, lack of a sufficient body of agricultural knowledge, and political interference, but they gradually proved their economic and scientific value. They in turn sponsored agricultural courses in the grade schools, beginning with Wisconsin in 1905. Meanwhile agricultural high schools had been started, and eventually (1917) this led to the Smith-Hughes Act, granting Federal funds to the States for agricultural education in the secondary schools.

The development of specialized schools and colleges has had profound effects on agriculture, scientifically, economically, and socially. It is significant, Edwards notes, that at critical points in this development there was always a demand for Federal aid and cooperation.

At the end of his article Edwards sums up the influence of agriculture on governmental policy in the United States.

The Civil War may be considered as a dividing line. Until that time agricultural production was dominant in this country. Events that showed the powerful influence of farmers before the war included the formation of the Democratic-Republican Party in opposition to traders, bankers, speculators; purchase of the Louisiana Territory; the War of 1812, "begun and carried through by ardent expansionists"; abandonment of property qualifications for voting and office holding; public education; destruction of the National Bank, greatest monopoly of its day; the policy of moving Indians beyond the Mississippi; the preemption, graduation, and homestead acts.

After the Civil War, agriculture was on the defensive and business enterprise in the ascendancy. Industrialization got under way in earnest. By 1889, for the first time, the income derived from manufacturing was greater than that from agriculture; since 1910, the income from manufacturing has exceeded that from agriculture in every year, and the United States has ranked first among industrial countries.

Agriculture expanded also and controlled the European market, but farmers never did reap the benefits to anything like the same extent as businessmen. Farmers could not combine to fix prices or control output. As prices fell, their fixed charges rose. Mortgages and tenancy steadily increased. Credit facilities for farmers were lacking, and they suffered from contracted currency. As a result of these and other conditions, frequent farm revolts have characterized the entire period since shortly after the Civil War.

Railroad reform and regulation, won by the Grange, was the first great post-war victory of organized farmers. Even though many of the Granger laws were not enforced and were soon repealed, the battle taught farmers much, brought them into united action, started a far-reaching cooperative movement. An outstanding result of Granger activity, says Edwards, "was the firm establishment of the principle that a State government has power to regulate businesses clothed with a public interest." The Interstate Commerce Act also "marked the entrance of the Federal Government into the sphere of business regulation."

Currency reform—"the same money for the bondholder as for the plowholder"—was another great objective of farmers resulting from the monetary situation after the war. In 1874 a farm group united with labor to form the Independent National Party, which became the Greenback Labor Party in 1878, when it polled a million votes, and in 1888 was absorbed into the Union Labor Party. Meanwhile State Alliances organized in the South in the 1870's eventually united (1888) as the National Farmers' Alliance and Industrial Union. A similar organization, the Northwestern Alliance, was formed in 1880. Both advocated free silver, paper money, tax reform. In 1892 a combination of the Western Alliance and Knights of Labor became the Populist Party, which in 1894 elected seven Congressmen and six Senators. Though the party fought for a considerable list of agrarian measures, it concentrated on free silver in the campaign of 1896 and supported Bryan, who polled 6,500,000 votes. Bryan's defeat marked the end of the Populists as an effective organization.

Though farmers had a measure of prosperity in the early 1900's the agrarian reform movement did not die out but broadened and deepened. Several organizations were formed and two headquarters were established in Washington. The Nonpartisan League eventually became "a force to be reckoned with in the national political arena." Achievements between 1912 and 1920 that resulted from long-standing farm demands included the Federal Reserve Act, the county agent extension system, a Federal Farm Loan Board and 12 regional banks for long-term credit, and subsidies by the Federal Government for vocational agriculture in the public schools.

Agriculture in the World War Period

American agriculture was in the midst of a long period of quiet adjustment to the lack of any more virgin land, and to the new order of machines and commercialization, says Genung, when the war came overnight and forced it into a new pattern. A half-dozen years brought changes that would normally have been spread over generations. "Under the stimulus of price and patriotism—finally of outright inflation—the farm business labored and expanded and provided the sinews" of war. "Then, in the aftermath, it was left high and dry."

The objective of all official policy was to stimulate production, but some semiluxury foods were actually depressed because of the imperative need for bread, heavy meats, fats, sugar, wool. One of the early effects of the war was to change the United States from a debtor to a creditor nation. In September 1914 we owed Europe about $500,000,000. A year later Europe owed us $15,000,000, and 3 months after that, $132,000,000. And this was only the beginning.

The effects of the war on production can best be visualized by considering what happened to different commodities.

Allied bidding for American wheat began as soon as the Russian supply was cut off. The year 1915 saw a billion-bushel crop—the largest before or since. Early in 1915 farmers were getting $1.25 a bushel; by the spring of 1917 they were getting over $2.40. The United States entered the war that year, and the drastic Food and Fuel Control Act went into effect. Thereafter most growers realized $2 a bushel or better. Acreage rose more than half during the war—from 47,000,000 acres in 1909–13 to 74,000,000 in 1919—and production 38 percent (from 690,000,000 bushels to 952,000,000).

During the early years of the war cotton was hurt rather than stimulated, and the total effect was to reduce world consumption of American cotton about 12 percent compared with the years immediately preceding the war. For 3 years beginning in 1917, however, growers averaged over 25 cents a pound, and in 1919, with the price at 35 cents, they had a $2,000,000,000 cotton crop, never equaled before or since. This was largely the result of domestic business activity, inflation, and moderately small crops.

"It was not until toward the close of the war that tobacco exports, prices, and production all soared to comparatively high levels."

Hog production felt the greatest stimulus among the livestock industries. In 1914 prices were about $8 a hundredweight at the farm. In November 1917 the price was pegged by the Food Administration at about $15.50. In the summer of 1919 it was over $19. At the beginning of 1914 there were 53,000,000 head of swine on farms and at the beginning of 1919, 64,000,000. The hog situation raised the price of corn, but the acreage increased very little.

Farm prices for beef cattle rose from $6.24 in 1914 to $9.56 in 1919. Exports went up from 150,000,000 pounds in 1914 to 954,000,000 in 1918. The number of cattle, other than milk cows, on farms increased from 40,000,000 head early in 1914 to 51,000,000 four years later.

Through 1917–18 the price of dairy products rose about 70 percent above pre-war prices. Concentrated milks felt the greatest war stimulus; exports rose from 17,500,000 pounds in the pre-war period to 853,000,000 in 1919.

Sheep production declined somewhat during the war, but prices more than doubled. The poultry industry was depressed, partly because of the high price of feed grains.

The total number of animal units increased by 16 percent during the war, the production of all meat by 23 percent, and the acreage in crops by 13 percent, or about 40,000,000 acres.

The rise in commodity prices was partly the result of world-wide inflation, and this left farmers vulnerable to the shock of deflation after the war. Farm prices ultimately were more than double the pre-war figure, but they fell further and faster than the prices of commodities in general. The gross income of agriculture rose from $7,000,000,000 in 1914 to nearly $17,000,000,000 in 1919. By 1920 it was down to $13,500,000,000.

Meanwhile land values soared during the war and all production costs increased. The bill for hired help more than doubled; the fertilizer bill nearly doubled; the farm-implement bill more than tripled; the bill for livestock feeds more than doubled; taxes doubled, and then kept on going up after 1921; interest paid on farm mortgages more than doubled between 1914 and 1921; freight rates increased; the cost of living went up. In other words, the picture was not all rosy for farmers. They had three profitable years during the war, but neither prices nor profits were high compared with those in industry.

Along with economic changes there were social changes—chiefly a greatly increased exodus of workers from the farm to high-paying industries and to the Army. After the war, young men flowed back to the farms, bought land at peak prices, went into debt, and were caught by deflation a little later.

Huge credits were granted to Europe after the war. When this process stopped, foreign buying fell off and prices crashed. Europe could not pay us in goods because of our tariff policy. Then European countries went nationalist and further throttled trade. The loss of the European market for wheat, pork, and cotton hit our agriculture vitally and suddenly. Meanwhile, the war had also stimulated production in other agricultural countries—Canada, Argentina, Australia, New Zealand—some of which had cheaper land and labor than the United States.

The war proved to be a turning point that compelled a reorientation of our entire farm economy. "The world of abundance and of relatively free exchange," Genung writes, "had turned into one of low buying power, with international trade balked by a barricade of restrictions and political designs."

The Development of Agricultural Policy Since the End of the World War

"The collapse of agricultural prices [in 1920]," Davis writes, "produced vehement protest from farmers everywhere. Existing farm organizations increased their membership and new ones sprang into being. They exerted a pressure on lawmakers and administrators which, continuing through the years, has been primarily responsible for the unparalleled sweep of farm legislation from the early 1920's through 1938 and has carried the Federal Government into fields of farm aid undreamed of when the crisis of 1920 broke."

Davis sees this process as a continuous development in which legislation at any given time grew out of previous proposals and efforts that sometimes had a long history.

As a result of ferment throughout the country, Congress created a Joint Committee of Agricultural Inquiry early in 1921. The inquiry was broad, but the committee's recommendations were too limited to cope with conditions effectively. Overproduction or overmarketing was not considered to be a cause of the price decline. A "farm bloc" was also organized in Congress about this time, and early in 1922 Secretary Henry C. Wallace called a National Agricultural Conference, which was attended by nearly 400 representatives of agriculture and related industries. "Practically all of the notes that have been struck in subsequent agricultural policy were sounded in one way or another in that conference." For example, at the insistence of George N. Peek, a paragraph was included in the conference report urging that Congress and the President "should take such steps as will immediately reestablish a fair exchange value for all farm products with that of all other commodities." Crop insurance and the whole question of Government guaranty of agricultural prices were recommended for study.

Prior to this report, in December 1921, Peek and Hugh S. Johnson, using the slogan "Equality for Agriculture," had proposed a plan for surplus disposal. This plan was studied by cabinet members, officials, economists, and industrial and financial leaders, and later became the basis for the McNary-Haugen bills, which were before Congress in varying forms from 1924 through 1928. Though they were twice vetoed by the President after being passed by Congress, these bills accomplished much in organizing farm support and focusing national attention on the farm problem. The substitutes adopted also added valuable elements to experience.

Against aggressive Government action for farm relief in the period from 1923 to 1926, or indifferent to the issue, were the cooperative marketing associations, the South, the East and the industrial centers, the agricultural colleges, and most of official Washington. Support came from Congress, a small group close to the Secretary of Agriculture, certain individuals and special groups, and finally the national farm organizations. There were lively debates on whether there actually was any surplus of farm products. Both sides failed to recognize three major factors in the situation—the importance of foreign loans in maintaining the export market, the change from debtor to creditor status, and the final closing of the frontier, which had for so long acted as a shock absorber.

Agitation for farm relief got its start in the Northwest, where wheat growers were the first to be hit. Late in 1923, Secretary Wallace publicly proposed an export corporation to dispose of surplus wheat, and growers in the Northwest pressed for action. In the following year, active agitation for farm relief began in the Corn Belt. A long struggle for "equality for agriculture" and "a fair share of the national income" followed. The McNary-Haugen bills, around which most of the struggle centered, embodied two essential ideas: "(1) That the centralizing power of the Federal Government should be used to assist farmers to dispose of the surplus abroad and raise prices to the desired level in the domestic market, and (2) that the loss on the segregated exports was to be paid by the farmers themselves by means of an equalization fee," charged on the first sale or first processing of the commodity.

A number of organizations were started between 1924 and 1928 in connection with the drive for a clearly defined national agricultural policy—among them the aggressive American Council of Agriculture, the Executive Committee of Twenty-two, and the Corn Belt Committee of Farm Organizations. In November 1924 President Coolidge called an agricultural conference, which attacked the surplus-export plan and failed to develop any other program acceptable to farm forces. In 1926 the South for the first time joined the West in agitating for an effective farm-relief program, and southern cooperatives came in.

A debenture plan to enable exporters to pay a higher price for farm products reached Congress in 1926, and in 1927 there were several proposals for a Federal farm board, one of which had Administration support and was endorsed by the Business Men's Commission—a product of the National Industrial Conference Board and the United States Chamber of Commerce. A land-grant college committee also came out, somewhat vaguely, for "favorable and sound" farm legislation. After the President had vetoed the McNary-Haugen bill for the second time, a threatened farm revolt failed to materialize in 1928, largely because the farmers had been promised a general agricultural bill. They got this in the form of the Agricultural Marketing Act of 1929, which created the Federal Farm Board.

The Federal Farm Board attempted to stabilize prices by storing surplus wheat and cotton and withholding them from the market. These operations resulted in heavy losses, and the Board soon began to insist that production must be held in line with actual market demand. Meanwhile the depression struck with full force. The income and capital values of farmers tumbled; banks closed. Additional farm legislation was imperative, and various proposals were made, which culminated in the Agricultural Adjustment Act of 1933.

In effect, this legislation summed up the experience of the previous decade. One of its main features was taken from the domestic allotment plan proposed by M. L. Wilson and John D. Black during the Farm Board period. Their proposal was to let the export surplus take care of itself but to increase returns to farmers on the portion of their crop consumed in this country. This was to be accomplished by issuing certificates to farmers which would be bought by processors at the time they paid for the farm products; but the certificates would cover only products for the domestic market.

Under the Agricultural Adjustment Act, "millions of farmers entered into contracts to reduce acreage in specified surplus crops in return for benefit payments, financed chiefly by processing taxes." Additional legislation setting up marketing quotas for cotton and tobacco was soon incorporated in the Bankhead Cotton Act and the Kerr-Smith Act. In January 1936 the adjustment program was halted by the Supreme Court decision in the Hoosac Mills case, declaring that the power to regulate and control production resided in the States, not in Congress. The result of this decision was a shift to the Soil Conservation and Domestic Allotment Act of 1936. Late in 1937 the need for acreage control again became apparent and resulted in the enactment of the Agricultural Adjustment Act of 1938.

The existing legislation embodies five main features: (1) Provisions for soil conservation, good farm management, and balanced output, the aim being "to keep the total acreage allotments at a level that will insure a normal supply of food and fiber for domestic consumption and export." The work of the Soil Conservation Service complements the work of the Agricultural Adjustment Administration. (2) Loans, marketing quotas, and parity payments. Storage loans are authorized for producers of corn, wheat, cotton, tobacco, and rice. Marketing quotas may be applied, after a favorable vote of producers, in years of excessive supply. Parity payments are authorized under certain conditions to raise the income of producers. (3) Marketing agreements. These are designed to enable farmers and distributors to "establish permanent and rational marketing systems." (4) The diversion of surplus products into domestic and foreign channels, and the development of new uses for agricultural products. This includes the activities of the Federal Surplus Commodities Corporation and the work of four regional laboratories conducting research in new uses. (5) Crop insurance. The Federal Crop Insurance Corporation is authorized to write insurance against loss in wheat yields.

Davis traces the lineage of practically all of these provisions back to proposals and legislation of the previous decade or so, and in some cases further back.

Certain other problems that have come to the front in recent years are being dealt with more or less experimentally in the current farm program. One of them is tenancy. The Bankhead-Jones Farm Tenant Act of 1937 authorized loans for the purchase of small farms on a long-term mortgage basis; in addition, efforts are being made in several States to create better tenancy conditions. Another problem has to do with the large number of rural families who are on the fringe of commercial production or entirely outside it, many of whom are in distress and must be helped to earn a subsistence, at least until further opportunities are open in industrial employment. Work in this field is being carried on by the Farm Security Administration. A third problem is related to the domestic consumption of farm surpluses. Here the food-stamp plan is being used to increase the purchasing power of low-income consumers without going outside regular channels of commercial distribution.

The full story, Davis points out, is not told in these direct measures to aid agriculture, varied as they are. Attitudes and laws regarding taxation, tariffs, international trade, labor, money, credit, banking, and many other things all have a bearing on agricultural problems. Agricultural policy itself is never finally fixed and complete, and it cannot be, because conditions change. It cannot be said that the present laws have solved the problems of agriculture, and presumably they too will be subject to change and displacement. But "a continuous thread runs through the evolution of an agricultural policy, notwithstanding the manifest inconsistencies and contradictions that appear in it."

Part 2. Agriculture and the National Welfare

Agricultural Surpluses and Nutritional Deficits

Cavin starts out by defining what the economists mean by a surplus—the amount by which supplies of a commodity depress the income of producers below the level usual in periods of average prosperity when the different parts of the economy are in balance with one another. Three conditions can cause such a surplus, and each requires a different remedy. (1) Unusually good growing conditions, improved production methods, or some other factor may result in a larger than average crop. The obvious remedy is to withhold some of the crop from the market. But if the surplus becomes chronic, acreage and output must be reduced. (2) Changes in consumption habits may decrease the demand for a product compared with that for competing products. Unless new uses can be found for the product, the only possible remedy is to decrease production and substitute production of products for which there is an increasing demand. (3) A decline in general buying power—as in a depression—or the loss of a foreign market may result in a surplus. In the latter case, reduced production, accompanied by shifts to other types of production, is required. In the case of a depression, however, reduced production is no permanent remedy. It is necessary to restore general business activity.

The amount of a surplus of one or more farm products can be measured, Cavin points out, through the establishment of normal requirements for domestic use, exports, and reserve stocks. These are based on averages for some past period with adjustment for evident trends.

Stiebeling considers surpluses from a different viewpoint—that of the nutritionist. She points out that in the case of certain protective foods—dairy products; leafy, green, and yellow vegetables; foods rich in vitamin C—there may be a market surplus but at the same time a deficit compared with what people need. These deficits exist among low-income groups in all industrialized countries, including the United States.

How much more of these products do we need to make up the nutritional deficits? That depends on what we consider the desirable goal. The answers vary from 10 to 100 percent more for dairy products; 10 to 70 percent for tomatoes and citrus fruits; 80 to 100 percent for certain vegetables. If the nutritional deficits were made up, we could wipe out such scourges as pellagra, beriberi, scurvy; have a population with greater average physical efficiency and longer average life; significantly increase the demand for some important agricultural products. The job is partly one of education, and many agencies, including the Bureau of Home Economics, are busy in spreading knowledge of good nutrition. But education alone is not enough. Incomes and prices are large factors.

Cavin estimates that to raise the nutritional level as Stiebeling suggests would require between 8,000,000 and 40,000,000 additional acres for production, depending on the goal desired. There is no question but that this would largely eliminate agriculture's surplus problem. Farmers could and would do the job, but they could not do it if it meant an additional burden without a fair return.

Farioletti tackles the problem from the standpoint of income. He points out that farmers can no longer depend on population growth to create an expanding market; by 1960 the population may be stable. The market can expand, however, if we can manage to increase consumer purchasing power. One way to do this is to increase the total national income. A national income of $90,000,000,000–$100,000,000,000 (as compared with $69,000,000,000 in 1939) would put everyone to work and greatly increase food consumption. So great a rise in national income, however, cannot be expected to occur quickly, nor would it settle the deficit problem Stiebeling discusses; there would still be large groups with inadequate incomes, unable to purchase all the protective foods they need. For the most dynamic effect on the agricultural market, what is required is enough increase in the incomes of the lowest groups (about 42 percent of all families had incomes under $1,000 in 1935–36) to enable them to reach the dietary level of the next higher group. From the standpoint of agricultural surpluses, a program for consumption adjustment is fully as important as one for production adjustment.

But even increasing the incomes of these lower groups is a long-time business, says Cavin. Aren't there consumption adjustments that can be made in the meanwhile? Yes, we can subsidize consumption (as Stiebeling and Farioletti also suggest) where the need is greatest by two methods—keeping prices low for certain income groups, and distributing some foods free. There are numerous possibilities within this range. In the 4 years 1935–39, nearly 3,000,000,000 pounds of surplus foods were distributed free. Recently, the food-stamp plan was adopted experimentally as an efficient plan for meeting the needs of families on Work Projects Administration jobs or eligible for other public assistance. This plan permits personal choice, reduces waste, and makes use of existing trade channels. It proved to be so successful that it has now been greatly expanded.

One solution or partial solution of the surplus problem does not shut out others. But the problem cannot be settled, Cavin warns, by a simple exercise in arithmetic. The causes are deep-rooted and complex. Nothing less than a national policy involving long-continued effort and probably large expenditures will be needed to solve it.

The Farmer's Stake in Greater Industrial Production

Bean makes a rather close analysis, using numerous figures, of the dependence of agriculture on industrial activity. His point is that "farmers have a vital interest in any program or policy that will help to bring about full employment of the working population in the cities."

At the end of 1939 there were 42 to 44 million available nonagricultural workers in the United States, of whom 35,000,000 were employed, leaving 7 to 9 million unemployed. Since this is about one-fourth of the number employed, it may be said that in order to bring full employment, industrial production should have been about 25 percent greater than it was at the end of 1939.

What, Bean asks, would this 25 percent greater production mean to farmers? He discusses four aspects of this question.

(1) It would relieve the pressure of an excess farm population on the land. Heavy industrial unemployment inevitably takes the form of a back-to-the-land movement. Much of the farm problem is due to the fact that there are too many people sharing the agricultural income. Between 1930 and 1940 the proportion of the population engaged in agriculture failed to decline for the first time in over a hundred years. If previous trends had continued, 16 percent of the

population should have been on the land in 1940; actually, the proportion was 21 percent. On the basis of long-time trends, there should have been 26,000,000 persons living on farms instead of 32,000,000. The excess 6,000,000 (about 20 percent of the total) would under normal conditions have been living in towns and cities. Since this 20 percent is for the most part a low-income group not contributing a great deal to commercial production, transferring them to the cities—that is, giving them industrial employment—would not proportionately raise the incomes of the remaining farmers. What it would do, however, would be to increase the proportion of consumers of farm products in the total population as compared with the proportion of producers of farm products. The total population is 132,000,000. Shifting 6,000,000 out of farming would make the total consuming population four times as large as the farm population, instead of three times as at present.

(2) Full industrial activity would create a larger national income, which would expand domestic consumer expenditures for farm products. An increase of 25 percent in industrial production would raise the national income from $70,000,000,000 (1939) to more than $90,000,000,000. Retail expenditures for food closely parallel the ups and downs of consumer incomes; they average about 20 percent of the income of nonfarm consumers. Thus the increase in national income suggested would mean that about $4,000,000,000 more would be spent for food. About 40 percent of this, or $1,500,000,000, would go to farmers, the remainder to those engaged in distribution. For nonfood products, farmers would probably receive another $500,000,000 with the suggested increase in national income.

(3) Full employment and increased national income would also improve the farmer's foreign market. Imports go up and down with domestic industrial activity. On the basis of past trends, they would increase by about $1,000,000,000 if the national income increased by $20,000,000,000. This would increase foreign buying power for American goods—that is, it would increase exports. Probably about one-fourth of the increased exports would be farm products.

(4) Bean notes that there are certain large if's in these assumptions. Full employment and increased national income would not automatically bring the results outlined for farmers. For instance, the declining foreign market and the declining demand for feed crops for work animals have upset past relationships in the market for farm products, and this has changed the proportion of farm income to national income. Increases in distribution and production costs have operated in the same way. The net result was that in 1939 farm income was short by $2,400,000,000 of being on a par with nonfarm income. About one-third of the shortage ($807,000,000) was made up by Government payments. In other words, there is a price problem involved as well as a problem of improving markets.

Practically all schools of economic thinking today agree that, to some extent at least, new methods are necessary to stimulate recovery, and that these methods involve some governmental action. Groups disagree on the amount and the kind of action required. Leaving out of account extreme views such as those involved in socialism and fascism, Bean distinguishes three main approaches.

(1) Some people argue that in order to increase industrial production, consumer buying power must first be increased. As an example of this approach in its more extreme form, he takes old-age pension plans involving large regular payments to individuals and traces some of their possible results.

(2) A second group believes that production must be stimulated first; increased employment and consumer buying power will then follow. If this were to be fully effective, it would admittedly require widespread economic planning and organized cooperation between many industries as well as between industry, labor, and consumers. Proponents argue that full economic planning could be developed gradually.

(3) A third group takes a middle-of-the-road position, arguing that our economy is too complex for any one approach. They would rely on stimulating the flow of private investment, especially into large-scale industries; increasing public investment, especially in self-liquidating projects and conservation; expanding consumption by such measures as liberalized old-age benefits, in order particularly to increase the purchasing power of low-income groups; reducing maladjustments in prices, labor relations, trade barriers, and other factors. Changes in the tax structure and in the method of handling governmental budgets are corollaries to some of these proposals. The degree of public action required would depend on the extent of cooperation for recovery by industry and labor.

It is unlikely, Bean believes, that the United States will adopt any single program during the next decade. There will be a combination of various approaches. The future is obscure because of developments in Europe, but he holds that we are entitled to have great confidence in our ability to cope with our major economic problems provided we pay special attention to developing domestic markets never yet fully utilized.

The City Man's Stake in the Land

When almost anyone could go into farming, the city man had a direct personal interest in the land. That period ended with the closing of the frontier. Today the city man is aware that the soil means something to him only when he is aroused by dramatic dust-storms or floods. Sometimes these happenings, however, are the effects rather than the causes of maladjustments in agriculture. Actually, the city man's stake in the welfare of agriculture is greater now than it used to be. Chew tells why he thinks this is so.

Pressure of population on the land supply, coupled with farm depression and soil wastage, drives large numbers of country people into city jobs or bread lines, and this inevitably burdens relief rolls in the towns, depresses wage rates, creates problems of housing and sanitation, complicates the task of school authorities, necessitates increased taxation, and causes ill feeling between migrants and residents.

For a long time—even in depressions—there has been a net migration of farm people to the city. Between 1920 and 1930, 4 out of every 10 new workers in the cities came from farms. If these people come out of rural areas marked by poor health, poor housing, and poor education, they will not be adequately fitted for city life; most of them will be unsuited for any job except common labor, and many will become public charges. The city man, then, has a direct interest in rural living standards because large numbers of rural people are going to be his neighbors.

On the other hand, suppose great numbers are held on the farms because they can find no opportunities elsewhere. Something has to be done to help them; 600,000 farm families have been assisted by the Farm Security Administration, for example, and as many more need assistance. Who pays for this necessary rescue work? City people, in the long run. It would be cheaper for them to create conditions that eliminate the need for such wholesale salvaging of human beings by supporting fundamental improvements in agriculture.

Too much tenancy and bad tenancy conditions are one of the signs of agricultural maladjustment. How do they affect the city man? They force many farmers to become wage hands, and this heightens job competition in country and city. They also tend to bring about a shift of farm ownership to city people through failures and foreclosures. The resulting absentee farm management may be inefficient and costly. It may be better for the city man to own the mortgage than the farm because "rent is harder to collect than interest." Foreclosing mortgages is generally a losing business for everyone. Farm prosperity, on the other hand, means that payments to city creditors can be maintained.

Tenancy reform, Chew argues, will mean less competition for farm ownership but better chances for those who want to become owners, and this will benefit both farm and city people.

The country, Chew points out, serves as a double shock-absorber in depressions; it accepts low prices for the necessities of life, and it holds people on the land who cannot find other employment. But there is a heavy penalty for the city man if this shock-absorbing power is abused. Much of the burden of farm relief is due to the fact that such immense numbers of people have been held back on the land. Because of that, agricultural adjustment has to move in two conflicting directions at the same time. It has to adjust production to improve the incomes of commercial farmers, and it has to help great numbers of marginal farmers to make a living—which inevitably means more production even though it is only a small amount in any individual case. These costly contradictory efforts are unavoidable under the circumstances.

There is a way to avoid them, but it lies in the hands of the cities. That way is to provide industrial employment and thus absorb the army of the rural landless. No other solution could compare with this in efficiency. Agricultural adjustment would then be more nearly confined to commercial production and conservation, and it would be comparatively simple and inexpensive.

These are the more fundamental ties between the city man and the land. There are others perhaps less fundamental but more obvious. For example, the poorer the land and the farmers, the less city people can sell in the way of agricultural supplies such as fertilizers and farm machinery. And the more failures there are among farmers, the greater the tax delinquency and the greater the tax burden on city landowners.

The upshot of Chew's argument is that there is no separate agricultural problem which the city man can tackle or leave alone as he chooses. There is a single national economic problem rooted in the use we make of the land, and it is everyone's concern.

Part 3. The Farmer's Problems Today and the Efforts To Solve Them

Agriculture Today: An Appraisal of the Agricultural Problem

In introducing this section of the Yearbook, Wells attempts to give a brief picture of the agricultural situation and the main lines of economic reform that have resulted from it.

He illustrates the economic status of agriculture with four sets of facts and figures.

(1) In the depressions of 1920 and 1929 farm prices fell sooner and further and stayed down longer than nonagricultural prices—a sign of weakness that led to increased organization among farmers and demands for Government aid. (2) The income and the living standards of the farm population are at relatively low levels. About 40 percent of all farm families have incomes under $750 a year—an amount that will barely supply minimum physical and other requirements. Various criteria show what this means in practical terms. Medical and hospital facilities in rural areas compare unfavorably with those in cities. With 31 percent of all the children of school age, farm families receive about 9 percent of the national income; they cannot support schools as good as those city people have. Rural housing conditions, judged by such criteria as sanitary plumbing, running water, electricity, are definitely inferior to those among city populations. Rural dietary standards are low in wide areas. (3) There is a considerable population pressure in many rural areas; for example, over 2,000,000 young people who would normally go elsewhere are now backed up on farms. (4) "The pressure of excess population and . . . exploitive methods of . . . production are taking their toll from the land itself" through erosion, overcropping, and overgrazing.

What causes this situation? Wells suggests that there is no single cause but rather several causes. The export market has declined, restricted immigration and a declining birth rate have slowed down population growth in the United States, and the industrial situation since 1929 has been such as to result in widespread unemployment. Over against the resulting reduced demand are forces that have been actively working toward increased production. These include the nature of the agricultural enterprise itself, the increasing efficiency of agricultural processes, the displacement of work animals by machines, and the damming up of an increasing number of rural young people as a result of industrial unemployment; and, finally, a marketing structure which throws the greater part of the burden of falling prices on the producer and the increasing demand of farm people for a better standard of living are factors that further accentuate the underlying situation.

Efforts to meet this situation follow three general lines: (1) Activities designed to increase incomes for commercial farmers—including all the various methods used under the Agricultural Adjustment Act and the marketing agreements, as well as efforts to improve grading and standardization, reduce interstate trade barriers, reorganize terminal market facilities, reduce freight rates, regulate commodity speculation, encourage cooperative marketing, increase market demand (both domestic and foreign), and improve the agricultural credit system. (2) Activities designed to increase incomes or improve living standards among such groups as migrant laborers, sharecroppers, subsistence farmers, and victims of drought and flood—including the rural rehabilitation program, emergency loans and grants, farm debt adjustments, the tenant-purchase program, medical and community service cooperatives, the financing of water facilities in drought areas, camps for migrant farm workers, feed and seed loans, drought relief, subsistence homesteads, and the rural electrification program. (3) Activities designed to encourage better land use and more efficient farm management—including research and extension work, the acquisition of forest and submarginal lands by public agencies, soil conservation, and forest conservation.

Our Major Agricultural Land Use Problems and Suggested Lines of Action

"However acute the economic problems of our agriculture," says Gray, "we are really one of the most fortunate nations of the world in the opulent relationship of present and prospective population to available agricultural land." For "we are agriculturally self-contained, except for certain tropical products," and it appears likely that our population will become stable at a density of not more than 50 persons to the square mile. In France there are 4 times as many persons to the square mile, in Germany 8 times, in Belgium 14 times. But most of our abundant production comes from a comparatively small proportion of our farms. Various rural areas are decidedly overpopulated in the sense that there are more people in these areas than there are opportunities for making a living.

The nature of our land policy, Gray points out, is fundamentally determined by two things: (1) This Nation believes in promoting the welfare of its citizens as individuals rather than enhancing the power of the state, and it has always emphasized private enterprise and private ownership with a minimum of governmental interference. The object of land policy, then, must be to retain private ownership but to correct its faults. (2) We operate within the framework of a Constitution that limits the powers of Government and is not very explicit in defining what the latter may do to correct faults. Thus it is always necessary in this country to convince legislatures and courts that in particular situations the social welfare is so paramount that individual rights may be justifiably subordinated.

Most of our present-day problems of land use and tenure are due to the fact that the doctrine of individual rights was carried to extremes in the past. Historically, this was probably inevitable. The original idea was that public lands should be put into private hands as rapidly as possible to hasten settlement. Owners then had almost unlimited freedom to dispose of their property as they saw fit, on the theory that "the majority of individuals will act continuously in their own interest, and that individual interest coincides with the social or public interest." That theory often failed to work out well in practice. Much land got into the hands of speculators, who took a generous rake-off before finally passing it on to farmers. Not that the speculator was the big bad wolf of agriculture; farmers often "cleaned up" on rising land values also. Fluctuating land prices go down as well as up, however, as farmers discovered after the World War, when many were caught with excessive capitalization and heavy mortgage debts. Then much farm land passed into the hands of creditors. That is the trouble with speculating in land, which constitutes five-sixths of the farmer's capital investment.

Using farm land as a source of profit has also made for unstable tenancy. The owner who expects to sell when a good opportunity comes along does not feel like arranging long-time leases or making a program for soil improvement. About three farms out of seven are now rented or sharecropped by those who operate them. Largely because of transitory ownership—through inheritance, speculation, foreclosure—"the types of farm tenancy prevailing in the United States are probably the worst in the civilized world," though in many cases, of course, the owner-tenant relationship is wholesome.

The tenancy problem, then, is important in land policy. Steps toward its solution include a credit system suited to the needs of those who are capable of responsible ownership; measures to prevent excessive speculation, which so often causes owners to become tenants; measures to improve the relationships between owners and tenants. One real gap in present land policy is "the lack of an adequate small-holdings program, such as has been developed in a number of other countries."

Other land problems included in Gray's survey are:

The range. Two of the biggest forward steps here are the Taylor Grazing Act and the forming of cooperative grazing districts by stockmen.

Size of holdings. In the Great Plains, homesteads of 320 or 640 acres are too small. Much of the land is held for speculation by absentee owners. Efforts are being made to arrange leases for operators who need more land, but long leases on suitable rental terms are difficult to obtain. In the South, small holdings often make it difficult to change over from cotton to other types of farming.

Submarginal land. It is estimated that half a million farm families "are on land so poor that it will not maintain a decent standard of living," some because of original mistakes, others because of subsequent soil deterioration and timber cutting. In many of these areas the solution will probably have to be an improved self-sufficing economy. Where soil resources are hopelessly insufficient, public purchase of the land and eventual resettlement of families will be involved. As yet there has been no adequate resettlement program.

Tax delinquency. This is especially bad in areas with poor resources and small holdings. Because of tax delinquency, "local governments are seriously embarrassed financially, large areas remain unused or underused, and land titles fall into confusion. . . . More realistic

[tax] procedures, based on adequate land classification, are needed to distinguish the areas adapted to private utilization from those where public administration would be in the public interest."

Undesirable settlement. Settlers have been persuaded to take up land with little regard to the prospects for success. Blue-sky laws, zoning laws, and suitable credit policies can prevent much of this, but "merely restrictive measures are likely to prove less effective than a positive public program for guiding land settlement." The character of such a program, however, would depend fundamentally on the possibilities for absorbing the rural unemployed in industry.

Reclamation. Further reclamation would hardly be needed if agriculture was to be largely commercial. It would be justified under some conditions for self-sufficient farming. Irrigation of small units on existing farms is very worth while and is now going forward with public aid.

Soil conservation. Much worth-while work is being done through public agencies and conservation districts. Some of the most serious obstacles are economic, especially systems of tenure and size of holdings unfavorable to conservation. Subsidies are being used to meet this difficulty in part.

Flood control. The large-scale engineering work of the War Department is now being supplemented by the "upstream engineering" of the Department of Agriculture on tributary streams.

Farm forestry. "The Cooperative Farm Forestry Act passed in 1937 is aimed at providing a comprehensive program of assistance to farmers in making more effective use of their woodlands and conserving their timber."

Major tasks of the immediate future in land policy, Gray believes, are to carry forward the advances already made, modify details where necessary, improve administration, amplify some measures, fill in some serious gaps such as the lack of an adequate small-holdings program for low-income farmers, and integrate the various elements into a real land program.

The Challenge of Conservation

Allin and Foster try to show the real meaning of conservation and its place in American life.

Throughout its early history, the United States was interested in building up certain values, which involved freedom of opportunity on the frontier, the creation of great industries, the peopling of a continent. Our citizens hated European restraints—among them restraints on individual freedom to exploit resources. We went ahead and exploited with unprecedented speed and efficiency. One result was a spectacular wasting of forests and soils.

In recent times, other forces, such as mortgages, tenancy, absentee ownership, the demands of war, and drastically reduced prices, have driven farmers to compel the land to produce more, irrespective of the effects on the land itself.

Over against these developments there has been a slowly growing realization of the need to conserve basic resources. Landmarks in this movement were the establishment in 1871 of a Federal office concerned with fisheries; the beginning in 1873 of demands that ultimately led to the establishment of the Forest Service; creation in 1886 of the forerunner of the Bureau of Biological Survey; the setting up of forest reserves in 1891 and of "national forests" in 1905; the beginning of the Soil Survey in 1899; an Alaskan fisheries act in 1906; establishment of the Inland Waterways Commission and of an office of mining technology in 1907; organization of the National Conservation Commission in 1908.

During the next 20 years, facts were assembled that finally had a powerful effect on the thinking and attitudes of the public. Then came spectacular evidence of the effects of waste in great duststorms and floods, and in the misery of stranded lumbering communities and migrating farmers. In addition, there has been an increased interest in preserving great areas as places where we can get outdoors and find health and recreation.

The intensified drive for conservation during the 1930's resulted in the work of the Soil Conservation Service, the Taylor Grazing Act for better management of the range, the Civilian Conservation Corps.

Agricultural—soil, forest, and range—conservation, Allin and Foster point out, is no negative thing. It is not like withdrawing your money from circulation and burying it in a hole in the ground. Its primary concern is not simply to ration the use of resources between present and future generations. Rather it strives for a better living both today and tomorrow. It seeks these goals by reducing waste and by using farming, forestry, and range practices that maintain and build up long-time productivity.

The authors hold that conservation in this sense can be called a new frontier for American activity. It means looking on our land as a place in which to settle down and live—to develop in new ways the old American dream of freedom and abundance—to invest idle money and idle labor in the truest kind of production and defense.

They list several problems of conservation that together constitute a difficult challenge—but no greater than those we have met in the past. The farmer, they point out, is a key figure in this movement because of his position on the land. "In fact the farmer has such a large share of the conservation job that it is only fair for the rest of the people to help him do it."

Our Soil Can Be Saved

Bennett gives some impressive figures on soil waste and argues that this kind of waste is unnecessary. It has been proved that "soil conservation is practical for the United States and that this Nation need not see its land and rural people impoverished."

Soil conservation is now a major goal of American agriculture because farmers have awakened to the need and are themselves taking the initiative in the work. The early demonstration projects of the Soil Conservation Service brought widespread understanding of the value of conservation. Today farmers are rapidly organizing their own soil conservation districts under State laws. These districts at present include more than 150,000,000 acres, and an equal amount is in process of organization. Aside from range lands and public lands, however, only some 22,000,000 of the 300,000,000 cropland acres affected by erosion are as yet covered by intensive conservation work.

The kind of work being done is perhaps more significant than its extent.

Farmers now signed up under cooperative agreements revise their systems of land use on the basis of thorough surveys. "Gradually these areas are being blanketed with complete protection against erosion and with improved farming methods that protect the permanent productivity of the soil." There is a growing collaboration of neighbors and communities in adopting realistic, practical measures even when they go counter to old habits. "Slowly the patterns of land use are changing in accordance with the dictates of conservation."

Careful fitting together of various public programs is responsible for much of the gain made. The agricultural adjustment program, the water facilities program (Pope-Jones Act), the farm-forestry program (Norris-Doxey Act), the rehabilitation loans of the Farm Security Administration, all have helped conservation to move forward. Some of the worst submarginal land (about 11,000,000 acres so far) has been purchased by the Federal Government and turned into pastures, ranges, forests, wildlife preserves, and public recreation areas.

Soil conservation efforts face several major difficulties. (1) It is impossible to bring expert advice and assistance to all the individual farmers who are eager for it. (2) Many farmers think that the use of conservation methods will lower their income—though the evidence indicates that it at least maintains and sometimes increases income. (3) Natural conservatism prevents many farmers from adopting new methods. (4) There has not been sufficient research as yet to show what the best methods are in all cases. (5) Economic factors militate against the adoption of conservation practices. For example, tenants who move to a new place every year or so have little or no incentive to preserve and protect their temporary farms.

The New Range Outlook

Forty percent of the land of the United States, say Chapline, Renner, and Price, consists of prairie, plain, desert, forest, and mountain range land in the West. The 728,000,000 acres comprise four-fifths of the important water-producing area of the West. In this range area as a whole there is a complicated pattern of ownership by individuals, counties, States, and the Federal Government. Crop farming and livestock farming are intermingled, and both have been made increasingly difficult by deterioration of the native forage, which in turn brought widespread erosion. The vegetation is about half as thick as it used to be. It takes 4 acres on the average to graze a cow for a month where it used to take 2. Abandoned cultivated lands have blown. Floods that spread over and ruin good lands are now common. Attempts at dry-farming have failed on at least 15,000,000 acres, and this has led to many social and economic ills. Much land that is valuable to the public for watershed protection is in the hands of private owners who cannot afford restoration measures.

Mostly because of sheer necessity, the people concerned are awakening to the seriousness of the situation. A new outlook is developing, and many concerted measures are being taken to undo the results of drought, overuse, and lack of understanding. It will be years, however, before this new approach will have its full effects.

The authors describe the present corrective measures under five headings.

(1) Research is the key to better range management, which alone can restore forage and soil. Federal and State agencies are now engaged in a broad research program covering climate, soils, vegetation, animal life, range and watershed management, values and uses of plants, artificial revegetation, introduction of new foreign and native species of plants, selection and breeding of improved strains, mass production of seed, erosion control, livestock husbandry. Valuable practices and principles are being worked out as a result of this work. Example: A long-time experiment in the Southwest by the Forest Service has proved that stocking at a rate that would at no time use more than 80 percent of average forage production doubled the grazing capacity of the range, increased the calf crop 50 percent, cut death losses two-thirds or more, and increased the returns per cow. Other principles of management include stocking with the right kinds of livestock, grazing during the proper season, distributing livestock evenly, deferred and rotation grazing, suspended grazing and artificial revegetation on badly deteriorated areas, fence building, development of watering places, eradication of poisonous plants. Widespread success has resulted from using the knowledge developed by experiment and research, but the quest for information has only begun.

(2) A program of disseminating information is being carried out by county agents and State extension specialists. They deal with such practical matters as hay production, herd improvement, care of sick animals, feeding practices, the use of better sires. Yet the principles of better range management are still not widely known.

(3) The Soil Conservation Service has been active in the range area. It has purchased land not suited to cultivation and developed it for better use by the community, allocating or leasing it on the basis of the grazing needs of individuals and associations. In cooperation with the Farm Security Administration, individuals are also helped to enlarge their holdings when they have farms that are too small for successful operation, and to use conservation practices on the new holdings. Complete soil-conservation demonstrations have been carried out on some ranches.

(4) The Agricultural Adjustment Administration has assisted producers to establish and maintain good stands of forage plants and to arrest soil erosion. For example, in 3 years under this program 19,500,000 acres were naturally reseeded by deferred grazing; 258,000 acres were artificially reseeded; over 23,000 springs or seeps were developed and more than 3,800 wells dug; 130,442 acres were contour-listed, furrowed, or subsoiled. Some 14,000 ranchers participated in the program in 1 year.

(5) The Forest Service for 35 years has had charge of 80,000,000 acres of range land within the national forests and has also carried on studies concerning range-land use. Grazing privileges on the national forests are allocated in such a way as to insure conservation and wise use of the land. Some 750 livestock associations as well as community, city, county, and State organizations participate in making plans for the use of this land. In addition to being used by 7,000,000

head of cattle, horses, sheep, and goats, the national-forest range furnishes food for 1,841,000 big-game animals and countless numbers of small-game animals and birds. Conservative practices have brought marked improvement over the national-forest area as a whole.

(6) Some 134,000,000 acres of unreserved and unappropriated public domain are incorporated into 52 grazing districts administered under the Taylor Grazing Act of 1934 and 1936 by the Grazing Service of the Department of the Interior. A cooperative program has been developed, with stockmen and governmental agencies participating, for surveys, classification, range improvement, controlled use through licenses and permits, and consolidation of ownership.

The complex problems of the range, say the authors, can be solved only by a vigorous, coordinated attack with farmers and stockmen participating. The prospects now look hopeful.

Forest-Resource Conservation

Marsh and Gibbons summarize the forest situation from several angles and suggest a broad outline of needs. They hold that forest-resource conservation is one important means of achieving a balanced rural economy. Permanent forest industries would help to support many farmers.

A third of our land area, or 630,000,000 acres, is forest land. This is half again as much as the total cropland. More than half the total land area in the Northeast and the South is forest. Forestry management can make this land an asset rather than a liability.

Forest land serves at least five major purposes: Timber production, watershed protection, recreation, support of wildlife, forage production. In most cases it can be used for two or more purposes simultaneously; in some cases for all five. For example, of the 630,000,000 acres, nearly three-fourths (462,000,000) can be used for commercial timber crops; nearly three-fourths has watershed value; more than half (about 342,000,000 acres) is grazed by domestic livestock; practically all is suitable for wildlife; a very large percentage can be used for recreation. The five uses will be taken up in order.

(1) *Timber use.* The United States now uses about a third of the lumber, more than half the paper, and nearly 40 percent of the wood in all forms consumed in the world. Wood is the basis of an enormous number and variety of industries, and the full possibilities have not been touched. The South leads in commercial timberland, with 203,000,000 of the 462,000,000 acres. Timberlands have not in general been well managed, and depletion, followed by wrecked communities, has been the usual practice. This could be reversed.

(2) *Watershed services.* Probably of more value than the timber crop is the "water crop" and the soil protection assured by forests. Forests reduce the destructiveness of floods, prevent erosion, help to maintain a supply of pure water for domestic use, and are the sources of water for irrigation agriculture. Large areas of forest land are not managed well enough to furnish their maximum watershed services.

(3) *Recreational use.* Forest lands furnish perhaps the most completely rounded outdoor recreation, from picnicking to camping, hunting, and fishing. About 11,000,000 acres are now used exclusively for recreation. The amount could be doubled or trebled; but for

223761°—40——4

maximum accessibility to communities, much other forest land can be opened up for recreation.

(4) *Wildlife production.* The existing wildlife population in most areas is far below what the forests could support in balance with other uses.

(5) *Forage production.* About half the total value of western range livestock is produced on forest and woodland range, and a large proportion of the 12,000,000 cattle and 11,000,000 hogs in the South graze at least part of the time on forest range. Good management is essential for the best returns in both regions.

The ownership of the 630,000,000 acres of forest lands is distributed as follows: Farmers, 185,500,000 (over 29 percent); other private owners, 248,300,000; national forests, 122,000,000; State and community forests, 26,800,000; public domain, 24,000,000; Indian reservations, 12,000,000; national parks and monuments, 6,500,000; other Federal ownership, 5,000,000; total in private ownership, 433,800,000 (70 percent); total in public ownership, 196,300,000 (30 percent). The most critical problems from the standpoint of sustained yield and multiple use are in the privately owned areas, which furnish 95 percent of the commercial timber cut and include perhaps 90 percent of the potential timber-growing capacity of the country.

(1) *Farm woodlands.* Nearly a third of the commercial (not the total) forest land is in farms, mostly in small tracts. Ownership is fairly stable, costs of management relatively small. The income-producing possibilities of farm woodlands are seldom appreciated, but some headway has been made in recent years. About 41,000,000 acres have now been put under some form of forest management; 20,000,000 acres need to be restocked; perhaps 75,000,000 acres need to be rehabilitated, of which 45,000,000 are without organized fire protection.

(2) *Industrial and other nonfarm ownership.* Over 40 percent of the commercial forest land is under this ownership, and 80 percent of it lies east of the Plains. About one-third is in comparatively large holdings. In general, the policy has been to liquidate rather than sustain the timber resources, though in recent years there has been a striking change for the better. Much submarginal and tax-delinquent land has its source in cut-over forests. Many owners cannot afford the expense of good forestry management. Probably 29,000,000 acres is now under some form of management and 85 percent without it.

(3) *Community forests.* These include some 8,000,000 acres. There could be a considerable expansion in this type of ownership with advantage to many communities.

(4) *State forests and parks.* These total about 19,000,000 acres. Practically the entire area is protected against fire and trespass, and much of it has been developed for recreation. The possibilities have hardly been scratched. The South, with two-thirds of the forest land, has only 3 percent of the State forests.

(5) *Public domain, Indian forests, national parks.* The two latter have been given up-to-date forest management. Much remains to be done on the forest lands in the public domain.

(6) *National forests.* These spread over 40 States, Alaska, and Puerto Rico, though mostly concentrated in the Rocky Mountain and

Pacific coast regions. They "represent the first large-scale trial in the United States of public ownership and administration of a great natural resource," and they "are being built up through intensive, carefully planned protection, by planting, and by timber-stand improvement. All cutting is controlled." Dependent communities are stable. Watershed services have been improved (most rivers in the West, and most of the important eastern rivers, head in the national forests). Big game has increased 150 percent since 1924. Recreational facilities could be increased; some 32,000,000 people visited the national forests in a recent year.

Marsh and Gibbons consider in some detail the present and potential timber resources of the United States. Saw timber, both softwood and hardwood, is the most important class. It is "the oldest timber of highest quality—the cream of the forest"—and any sound program of forest management must aim to achieve long rotations of saw timber. Public agencies now own or control 42 percent of the supply, but much of this is in inaccessible locations in the West and only 4 percent is in the East. There is need and opportunity for greater public investment in this resource in the East. Farmers own 13 percent of the saw timber. Other private owners hold 45 percent but supply two-thirds of the present cut. These figures refer to actual resources. Only about two-thirds of the supply of saw timber could be cut profitably under present conditions.

There is an enormous amount of timber that would yield satisfactory pulp, but since much of it is less readily available than foreign supplies, we import half of what we use. Technical progress and sound forestry could greatly increase the domestic cut.

On a national scale, current annual growth of timber is now 11,287,000,000 cubic feet and annual drain (from logging and destructive agencies), 13,463,000,000. The drain, however, is still concentrated in local areas, so that forest industries continue to cut out and close down. The saw-timber stands in the East have only about two-thirds of the volume needed to meet the annual drain.

It is impossible, these authors point out, to estimate future needs accurately. They hold, however, that there is likelihood of increased utilization through technical developments and argue that under favorable price conditions we could play a larger part in supplying world markets. They estimate that the total annual drain perhaps 50 years from now may well be figured conservatively at 21,400,000,000 cubic feet—including a margin of 5,800,000,000 cubic feet for new uses, exports, a safety factor, and losses by fire, insects, and disease. A substantial advance in forestry would be required to achieve and sustain such a yield. They suggest that 100,000,000 acres (yielding 8,400,000,000 cubic feet) would have to be under intensive management; 311,700,000 acres (yielding 13,000,000,000 cubic feet) under extensive management, including adequate fire protection; and 50,000,000 acres (economically unavailable for commercial use) protected without special management. The growing stock in the East would have to be built up to twice the present available stand.

Such a plan would envisage the building up of many forest activities and industries that would serve as the foundation for self-sustaining communities.

Practical steps required would be:

For private forests: (1) Public cooperation including protection against fire, insects, and diseases; forest and forest-products research, which few private owners can afford; forestry extension work, including demonstrations of good management; extension work in marketing and utilizing forest products; benefit payments to farmers under a conservation program; Federal aid for forest planting; development of cooperatives; large-volume credits where needed; forest fire insurance; some improvements in taxation procedure. (2) Public regulation to the extent of enforcing minimum requirements for keeping private lands fairly productive and stopping destruction of forests. (3) Public acquisition "where private forestry will not pay, or where private owners cannot or will not function in the conservation of the forest resource."

For public forests: "All public lands now held or hereafter acquired should be made outstanding examples of good management and public service."

Farm-Management Problems in an Era of Change

After briefly summarizing the main causes of the present situation in agriculture, Johnson considers the possible adjustments a farmer might make to meet his problems. The most difficult, and in a depression period the most common situation is that of the farmer who has to make readjustments not merely to increase his income but to meet pressing obligations and stay in business at all. By ordinary standards his costs of production include: (1) Fixed costs—(a) rent, (b) interest on investment, (c) obsolescence and depreciation, (d) insurance, (e) taxes, (f) wages for himself and family; (2) variable costs—(a) current supplies, (b) hired labor, (c) repairs and replacements. Studies show that when farm prices do not meet these costs of production, the farmer has to neglect his fixed costs. He compromises with landlord and creditor on rent and interest payments, postpones depreciation replacements, drops insurance, lets taxes go delinquent, and takes a minimum living as his only wage. He thus gets down to variable costs as his only expense. But in the end, if the tight situation continues, some of the neglected or postponed fixed costs catch up with him. He cannot, for instance, indefinitely fail to maintain his land, buildings, and equipment, or to meet rent or mortgage payments.

Some of the steps the individual is forced to take under these circumstances are contrary to the long-time interests of agriculture and a menace to the Nation. This is the main reason why public assistance to individuals is justified. Two major factors in which the public has sufficient interest to assist individuals are soil conservation and technological change. Technical progress is socially desirable, but in the transition period it may create great individual hardship through displacement of labor and lowering of prices.

Farm management problems differ region by region, and Johnson dicussses them from this standpoint.

(1) *North Atlantic region.* As a whole, the region shows considerable stability in farm prices and income owing to large nearby markets and a favorable climate. Many farm groups face severe competition from other areas; some have been forced to exist on a self-sufficing

basis. Production is now mostly specialized—dairy products, poultry, fruits, vegetables. Increased production of hay and pasture should reduce feed costs of dairymen, but they may have greater competition from the Lake States. Poultry production is likely to face higher feed costs; it will need to keep up to date with technical developments and adopt the most efficient practices. Vegetable growers will probably meet increased competition from frozen products; they will have to adapt their production closely to local market needs, and increased mechanization may be necessary. Conditions in the apple industry have been changing rapidly, and some orchardmen may find it necessary to add other enterprises. Forestry possibilities should be studied in this region.

(2) *Lake States.* A large part of farm returns come from manufactured dairy products. There are few alternatives, and local markets are not enough to stabilize income. Heavier expenditures for fertilizer will probably be necessary in many areas. Greatest threat is increased competition from other regions. Expenses may be reduced by using more high-quality roughage, less concentrates. More production for home use is highly desirable. Forestry possibilities should be explored.

(3) *Corn Belt.* Production consists mainly of corn, hogs, and beef cattle, and is highly commercialized, requiring a large investment. Land values are high. Heavy fixed costs make farming especially vulnerable in depressions. Many farms are now in the hands of former creditors and are run by tenants who deal with local representatives of absentee owners. Since much of the land is held for resale, long-time adjustments are often difficult. Major influences are technological—hybrid seed corn, rubber-tired tractors, new-type corn pickers—and their effects cannot be entirely foreseen, but there is need for measures to prevent undue hardship for those who cannot readily meet the demands of change.

(4) *The South.* Cotton dominates the farm situation. The outstanding problem is the low average farm income ($162 gross a person a year, 1924–37, as compared with $381 in the rest of the United States). Because of the high proportion of land in cotton and in corn for mule feed, soil erosion has become increasingly serious. Adjustments are difficult because of the small size of farms (30 acres per farm in the eastern cotton States in 1934) and the extreme pressure for cash income. Greater production for home use is a major need. Labor displacement is encouraged by increased mechanization and by reducing tilled crops for soil conservation. The ultimate solution probably lies in employment outside agriculture for large numbers of people, perhaps in combination with part-time farming. Forestry possibilities should be thoroughly explored.

(5) *Great Plains.* The main problem comes from combined drought and depression. The areas of higher risk should probably be shifted back to grazing, under public control. In the better areas, long-time rotations with perennial grasses (wheat-and-grass farming) may be necessary to maintain organic matter in the soil. The problem of feed supplies for livestock in dry years would then have to be met. Crop insurance should help to stabilize income from wheat and might be used for feed crops. Supplemental irrigation is a useful measure.

Public assistance is especially necessary in this region because natural forces are so powerful.

(6) *Mountain and Pacific regions.* Drought and depression have also been important in the Mountain States. An effective conservation program to maintain grass is essential in the ranching areas, and this will necessarily mean less intensive use. Hard-pressed ranchers can probably not make the required adjustments without public assistance at times. High water costs in relation to prices of products are the big problem on irrigation projects—especially with increased competition from other areas for fruit and vegetable growers. More production for home use is desirable.

For agriculture as a whole, the greatest need is for information on the prospects for industrial recovery. If employment opportunities outside of agriculture are to remain closed for the next decade, agriculture will be overcrowded and major attention will have to be given to improving efficiency and increasing incomes on small farms. Greater self-sufficiency and more nonfarm employment seem to offer the best possibilities for those who are at a disadvantage in commercial farming. Shifts in production to raise national dietary standards might be an important factor in increasing labor needs on farms and reducing some surpluses. In any case, there will be need for public action to assist individual adjustments.

The Influence of Technical Progress on Agricultural Production

Everyone knows that scientific and technical progress has revolutionized farming, but there has been no very comprehensive survey of its effects in practical terms. A special committee of the Department of Agriculture made a rather thorough study of this subject, and the findings are summarized by Kifer, Hurt, and Thornbrough.

The results of technical development are most strikingly shown in two facts. In 1870, half of all workers were engaged in agriculture; in 1930, a fifth of all workers. At the same time, this lower percentage of farmers produced almost a fourth more agricultural products per capita of the total population. Yet known techniques and practices are not even now fully used. Agriculture has not completely adjusted itself to such a drastic change, and further adjustments will be necessary in the future as technical progress continues.

Technical advances have been made on four main fronts: (1) Farm power, (2) farm equipment, (3) production practices for crops, (4) production practices for animals.

(1) It has been estimated that in 1935 tractors and trucks did work that would have required the labor of 345,000 persons on farms. More than 11,000,000 work animals were replaced by this form of power between 1915 and 1939. About 1,600,000 tractors are now being used in the United States—double the number reported in 1930—and it seems likely that the trend to less man-and-horse labor will continue. Present trends are toward increased use of general purpose tractors, small tractors for small farms, and rubber-tired tractors. Mechanization has been most complete in the small-grain areas and the Corn Belt, and on such specialized farms as those for dairy, truck, and orchard products. It has lagged in the South and East.

Small tractors will undoubtedly speed the mechanization of small farms. Rubber tires reduce tractor-operating costs and may make it possible in some areas to dispense with motortrucks.

(2) In tillage and seeding equipment the trend has been toward lighter machines for light tractors, machines especially adapted for erosion control, and the combining of tillage, fertilizer distribution, and seeding in one operation. Great strides have been made in harvesting machinery, which reduces the need for seasonal hired labor. Combines for small grain (110,000 in use in 1939) and mechanical pickers for corn are especially notable. Neither the cotton picker nor the sugar-beet harvester can compete as yet with hand labor at current wage rates.

(3) Perhaps even more significant than mechanical developments are those in crop-production technique. In 7 years hybrid corn has replaced open-pollinated varieties on most Corn Belt acreage and on about one-fourth of the national acreage. In 1938 the use of hybrid corn increased production 100,000,000 bushels over what it would have been with older varieties. Hybrid corn increases the advantage of the better areas and is well adapted to mechanical picking. Other notable products of plant breeding are rust-resistant Thatcher wheat, early-maturing grain sorghums to reduce drought risks, new flax varieties that may increase production in the South, superior varieties of sugar beets, soybean varieties that have permitted a rapid expansion in acreage, longer-staple cotton varieties. In fertilizers, important recent developments include more concentrated materials and the correction of soil deficiencies in so-called minor elements; this has conquered some plant diseases formerly not understood. The full effect of more widespread conservation practices on production will probably not be evident for another decade, but the use of cover or green-manure crops and the concentration of production on the better land both tend to increase yields rather quickly.

(4) "Important current developments in the field of livestock production are progeny testing, artificial insemination, correction of nutritional deficiencies, and disease control." Through progeny testing—used in practice only with dairy cows and poultry so far—high-producing ability gradually becomes more widespread. Cross-breeding to take advantage of hybrid vigor is used with some Gulf coast beef cattle and some range sheep, is still experimental with swine. Artificial insemination may speed up the rate at which high-producing ability can be spread; 17 breeding associations are now using it with dairy animals. In animal feeding, recent developments are largely concerned with the correction of mineral and vitamin deficiencies and shifts in forage production that point toward a possible increase in livestock numbers in the South. Death losses in livestock should decrease and productive efficiency should increase with wider use of measures to control diseases and parasites.

In general, technical improvements will tend to raise the volume of farm products for sale, except as low prices and farm programs offset the tendency. The addition of 500,000 tractors on farms would release for cash crops (especially soybeans in the Corn Belt) much land still used for feed for horses. Further use of green-manuring crops could readily increase corn and cotton yields in the South. Corn production in the Corn Belt could be further increased by 100,000,000 bushels a year by the use of hybrid seed. New areas for small-grain production will probably be opened up by plant breeding. On the whole, the primary influence of increased crop production and better animal husbandry would probably be to increase production of livestock in all areas without materially changing present regional advantages. In the South a considerable increase in livestock (31 percent for milk cows, 136 for other cattle, 31 for hogs, 54 for chickens) would be required merely to raise local dietary standards to a desirable level. Outside the South, present trends might increase livestock products for market by 5 percent.

The trend toward reduction in the need for workers in agriculture "seems likely to continue for the next decade at approximately the rate [of] the past 10 years." This would mean displacement of 350,000 to 400,000 workers. Offsetting factors might be lower wage rates, increased production requiring more workers, or more subsistence farming. The displacement of workers is likely to be most serious in the South.

More mechanization and other developments may increase the total investment required in commercial farming. If the small tractor proves economical, the pressure toward larger farms may be lessened and the small farmer would have a better chance to survive. Some changes in farm organization and perhaps in regional specialization may result from current technical trends. One important result of mechanization is an increase in the importance of cash operating costs in the farmer's budget. The tractor farmer has to buy gasoline no matter how hard up he is, whereas he could feed a horse with no immediate cash expense.

On the whole, according to present trends, it will become more difficult for those at low income levels to acquire or even rent farms, but the number wanting to get farms will increase as farm labor is thrown out of work. Of the four possibilities open to displaced tenants and sharecroppers (subsistence farming, part-time farming, wage labor, or relief) the one likely to develop furthest is subsistence farming. In other words, as part of agriculture becomes more dependent on national economic conditions, another part is likely to draw farther away from dependence on other economic groups.

The Place of Forests in the Farm Economy

Commercial farming, Kirkland points out, drove woodlands out of the important place they once occupied when the farm furnished a well-rounded subsistence for the family. It is time they came back. Many farms have some woodland. Some farms are 60 percent woodland. And there are probably more than 150,000,000 acres of nonfarm forests within easy reach of farmers. These farm and nonfarm forest lands can provide products for home use and for sale, and they can provide work. Why, for instance, should a farmer get needed building materials from 2,000 miles away when he could get them at home?

Most farm woodlands have been so badly managed that they produce less than a third or a half of what they could produce. Yet they supply a fourth of the sawlogs in the United States, and forest crops rank tenth among all farm crops in value. In many cases, forest products need not be shipped out of the community—which puts them in an advantageous position in periods of economic maladjustment. Used at home as fuel, building material, fence posts, poles, and for other purposes, these products have a natural "parity value." With little annual labor forest crops keep on adding to their value at a compound interest rate of 2 to 5 percent; no form of production is carried on so largely by nature unaided. Trees in addition conserve the soil.

A major need, if farm woodlands are to be sufficiently improved to realize their full value, is for "personal contacts of some local forest organization with every . . . owner desiring help." Preferably, the forestry man should actually go into the woods and mark the cuttings, as is done in Sweden and Finland.

Actual "forest farms" are new in the United States, but there seems to be an opportunity for them in some forest areas. They have already developed in the naval stores region. On a forest farm, forest products are the primary source of income. The farm should consist of 500 acres or more, of which about 100 acres would be cut annually to remove the equivalent of 5 years' growth. This procedure would assure annual yield. From 5 to 20 percent of the more fertile land should be used for pasture, grain, hay, vegetables, and fruits to make the farm self-sustaining. The woodland part of the farm would require about 1 day's work an acre a year, including all cultural operations, harvesting, and hauling; and as much of this work as possible should be done by the owner.

Many farms have little or no woodland yet need forest products. Many farmers also need part-time employment, especially in the winter, and this could be furnished by local nonfarm forests. Whether privately or publicly owned, these forests should be organized to give maximum benefits to the community.

County planning committees as well as other agencies, Federal, State, and local, are now working on this problem and others connected with the forests. This is a new development that has grown out of a decade of depression. In the Chippewa National Forest in Minnesota, forest work is allotted to the nearby agricultural communities in such a way as to bring the community income up to reasonable standards. There are vast opportunities for such coordination in the United States.

Cooperative organizations can play an important part in this development, as elsewhere in agriculture, by purchasing and operating up-to-date woodworking equipment, grading and otherwise improving the forest products, marketing them locally or elsewhere, and managing the forests. Such a cooperative need not necessarily own forest land itself; it could devise a contract that would be fair to all owners.

Several agencies in the Department of Agriculture—the Forest Service, the Bureau of Plant Industry, the Bureau of Entomology and Plant Quarantine, the Extension Service, the Agricultural Adjustment Administration, the Soil Conservation Service, the Farm Security Administration, the Bureau of Agricultural Economics—are now carrying on farm-forestry work, and provisions have been made for coordinating forestry programs and integrating them with those of the States.

Acreage Allotments, Marketing Quotas, and Commodity Loans as Means of Agricultural Adjustment

Hutson points out that there are two ways of adjusting agricultural supplies to market demands: (1) Permit unlimited production but limit the amount marketed; (2) limit the amount produced. Following experiments with the first method in the 1920's (the Federal Farm Board in the United States; rubber, coffee, sugar abroad), American farmers resorted to the second method in the 1930's. Fundamentally, agricultural adjustment today depends on acreage regulation. Marketing adjustments are supplementary.

Under the Agricultural Conservation program acreage allotments have been determined for cotton, corn, wheat, rice, tobacco, potatoes, peanuts, and for all other soil-depleting crops as a group. Several steps are involved: (1) Determine the acreage for the Nation as a whole, allowing for an excess above normal supplies. (2) Break this down into separate acreage allotments for the States. (3) Break it down further for the counties. (4) Determine the allotments for the individual farms within the counties. Formulas are provided for these steps, including such factors as past production, type of farming, kind of land. The judgment of farmer committees plays a large part locally. The use of allotments is voluntary, depending on the vote of producers, and in fact the method does not control acreage adequately unless at least 75 percent of the producers participate. Payments are made to those who do comply with the allotments. If appropriations have been made, parity payments also are provided for producers of five commodities—corn, wheat, cotton, rice, tobacco.

Marketing quotas to supplement acreage allotments are permitted for cotton, tobacco, wheat, corn, and rice, though they have never been used for wheat or corn. They are easiest to apply with commodities that go through definite channels (cotton gins, tobacco markets) where the marketings can be checked, but would be difficult with products that can be fed to animals on the farm. A marketing quota is essentially an emergency device, to be used when excessive supplies accumulate (cotton 107 percent of normal, wheat 135, corn and rice 110, tobacco 105), and then only if two-thirds of the producers vote for it. Formulas are provided for allocating quotas to producers, and there are penalties for marketing more than the amount fixed. In practice, then, the method has served primarily to prevent producers who do not comply with acreage allotments from throwing on the market more than their fair share of the total production.

Commodity loans are intended to provide reserves of major food and feed crops yet maintain fair prices. Loans are permitted on any agricultural commodity, but specific provisions have been made only for cotton, corn, and wheat. In each of these cases, loans can be made only in years when the price of the commodity goes below a certain percentage of the parity price (52 percent of parity for wheat and cotton, 75 percent for corn), or when the crop exceeds normal domestic and export requirements for the year. Those who have cooperated in the agricultural conservation program get a loan at the rate of 52–75 percent of parity price, depending on conditions; when marketing quotas are in effect, loans are made available to non-cooperators at 60 percent of the rate applicable to cooperators. To prevent the piling up of excessive supplies with possible heavy losses on the loans, provision must be made to bring production in line with needs the following season or to move the current excess into relief or byproduct channels. In the case of corn, this means that production of substitute feed grains also must be kept in line with trade needs. In the case of export crops, if the loan rate is above the export price, exports will be reduced unless steps are taken to make the crops available on the world markets at prices below the loan rates.

The Meaning of Foreign Trade for Agriculture

The key problem of American agriculture, Chew argues, is foreign trade. If we could regain our foreign market, agriculture could readily dispose of its surplus and would need to make only minor changes. If we cannot, we shall be compelled either to retire a large acreage permanently from production or to expand the domestic market to compensate for the loss. Any of these adjustments would be essentially a response to the foreign-trade situation.

But Chew holds that in the modern world there is no permanent solution in trying to make the Nation prosperous through a favorable balance of trade, such as we have had in the past; or in trying to withdraw from the world and become self-contained; or in excessively curtailing production, controlling prices, and subsidizing producers. The only permanent solution is to expand the domestic market enough to absorb much more of our own production and simultaneously to facilitate the consumption of more products from abroad. Two things are involved: (1) An efficient distribution of purchasing power, which will expand the domestic market; (2) a rather large but even exchange of imports for exports without a favorable balance on either side.

Suppose, to take an imaginary example, that you produce a billion dollars' worth of products more than you can consume at home. You can dispose of that billion-dollar surplus by sending it abroad. But if you take imports in exchange you still have a billion dollars' worth of goods to consume—the same amount of surplus, but in a different form. The only way to get rid of that surplus without consuming it is to have it go abroad without an equivalent amount coming back. This is what a favorable balance of trade means, and it is what all surplus nations have struggled to achieve. But they can achieve it only temporarily. Unless they give away their goods, an equivalent must some day come back. Then there is the same old surplus to consume.

Take an extremely oversimplified example. An industrially developed nation sends its surplus abroad in exchange for agricultural products—not an equivalent amount or it would still have a surplus in another form. As long as this continues, it can produce more than it consumes. But meanwhile its industry keeps on expanding. Hence it needs a still larger favorable balance of exports. Then it sends capital as well as goods abroad. The capital is used to build up industry in the agricultural countries. Thus in time these countries become competitors of the very nation they traded with. As more and more countries become industrialized there is an inevitable return flow of goods to the creditor countries, and also fewer and fewer true agricultural areas are left that can freely take factory goods in exchange for farm products. This forces the industrial nations back upon themselves for a food supply, or drives them toward colonial expansion. The result is a desperate struggle among the industrial nations to control the remaining industrally deficit areas of the world, either by outright seizure or as spheres of influence.

Nations faced with a surplus that cannot be exported commonly try to control it by restricting production. But this throws people out of work; it merely changes a surplus of goods into a surplus of labor. Is there, then, no real way out of the difficulty? Chew argues that there is.

Essentially, the impasse is due to the tendency of modern production to outrun consumption. The obvious remedy, then, is to make consumption keep up with production.

The possibility is real; people need the goods produced. The problem is one of mechanics—how to make the distribution of purchasing power as efficient for consumption as modern industry is for production. Once this is done, the surplus, or the equivalent in suitable imports, will be absorbed. There will no longer be any need to struggle hopelessly for a favorable balance of exports over imports. This does not call for self-sufficiency, which would create more unnecessary artificial restrictions. Absorbing our own production completely would mean producing less of certain things that we can produce efficiently, and more of certain things that we cannot produce efficiently. Reciprocal foreign trade obviates this loss of comparative advantage. Foreign trade is good, but it must not be one-sided. Suppose, for example, that after making adjustments in agriculture to give everyone an excellent diet, we still had more wheat than we could consume. It would be sensible to export the surplus and consume the equivalent in imported products. These ought to be mostly industrial products, because the consumption of industrial products can be expanded more easily than the consumption of food.

Fundamentally, the picture Chew gives is one of peaceful international trade based on shifting comparative advantages. He argues that this is not only entirely practical but the only ultimate way out of the modern dilemma. He points out that the United States was never so prosperous as when its total imports as well as its exports were at a high level. The day of the favorable trade balance is gone; or rather, this method can now be maintained only by utter force. The alternative is efficient purchasing power and high consumption per capita in every surplus country, combined with a balanced foreign trade.

Reciprocal Trade Agreements—A New Method of Tariff Making

Wheeler confines his discussion to only one aspect of the trade-agreements program—its potential usefulness as a method of tariff making. He argues that from the standpoint of agriculture, it has certain advantages over the older method of making tariffs. Until the tariff acts of 1922 and 1930, he points out, tariffs in the United States were largely for the benefit of industry, but they affect farmers in three ways.

(1) They restrict imports and thus reduce the amount of exchange with which foreigners can buy our agricultural products. Before the World War this did not greatly matter. We were a debtor country, and foreign nations had plenty of credit here in the form of interest paid on the loans they had made to us. Since the war, the tariff has been a greater handicap to producers of export farm products. The war made us a creditor country, and foreigners had no exchange for agricultural purchases except exports to us. This situation did not become evident, however, until we quit lending money abroad.

(2) By restricting imports the tariff tends to raise the prices of manufactured goods needed by farmers. Before the war this mattered more than at present since fewer of our industries were then able to produce as cheaply as those abroad.

(3) By restricting agricultural imports, the tariff raises prices for farmers in the United States. This mattered very little before the war, since agriculture was primarily on an export basis, and the world price necessarily set the price in the United States. Since the war there have still been relatively few farm products that could be benefited by a tariff, but the list is longer than it was formerly.

Complete free trade is academic. The choice is between different degrees of protection and different methods of making adjustments. The need is for (1) duties based on as unbiased and scientific an appraisal as possible, from the standpoint of national needs, and (2) flexibility and adaptability, so that the United States may be able to cope with the absolute control exercised in foreign countries.

The older method of tariff making provided neither. The tariff was revised about every 10 years, and rates were set on particular products by a cumbersome process of compromises, usually weighted on the side of protected industries rather than of consumers and exporters. When revisions were made, they were usually upward rather than downward.

By comparison, Wheeler argues, the trade-agreements method is far more sensitive to actual needs. Public hearings on a proposed trade agreement are held, and information is gathered, by an interdepartmental committee. Another interdepartmental committee carefully reviews all the information from the hearings and elsewhere and makes recommendations. A third interdepartmental committee goes over these recommendations in detail. Agriculture is represented on all three committees. Only after these steps are negotiations started with the country involved in the proposed agreement. All questions arising during the negotiations are sent back to the third committee.

By this method, each individual product can be carefully considered. Some classes of a product can be treated differently from others. Duties on a product can be reduced during only the part of the year when there is little or no domestic production, or reductions may be made only on specific, limited quantities during a year or part of a year. The interests of export industries can be taken fully into account on the basis of a specific exchange of advantages between the United States and the other country. Finally, there can be quick and effective action, which increases the bargaining power of the United States in meeting the actions of other countries.

Methods of Increasing Agricultural Exports

Boyd says that confining our agriculture entirely to the domestic market, even if domestic purchasing power were considerably increased, would mean not only a great loss in national income but "untold human suffering." Our chief surpluses are still largely surpluses of export products, and if our agriculture is to remain on its traditional base some way must be found to improve foreign trade.

But there is a "very small number of alternative measures for increasing exports." They may be placed in two groups: (1) Measures for increasing foreign purchasing power for our products. This necessarily means taking more goods or services from foreign countries. Even if we again become a net exporter of capital, we shall have to accept more imports. A reversal of the flow of gold into this country would do much to improve world trade generally. But the best permanent plan for increasing foreign purchasing power is through the lowering of the barriers that now interfere with normal international trade. (2) Measures for making more effective use of existing foreign purchasing power. Several such measures have been proposed or tried at various times.

(1) Carefully studying foreign needs and demands and meeting them by more efficient production and distribution—a method that has permanent value.

(2) Eliminating internal restrictions on the free play of world conditions on prices and maintaining satisfactory fiscal arrangements. This method also has permanent value.

(3) Barter may be effective for a short period, to meet an emergency, or to secure certain necessary imports; but a general policy of barter requires highly centralized control over all foreign trade, and as a method of increasing exports it ultimately involves financial losses by the Government or the producers of the exported products or the consumers of the imported products.

(4) Devaluation of currency to lower the value of export products. The usefulness of this method is soon offset by devaluation of foreign currency or higher domestic prices for the products exported.

(5) Lowering the value of export products by various kinds of subsidies to producers or exporters of these products. Such devices must be used with great caution, since they involve retaliation by other governments if they are carried too far and require adequate measures for production control to avoid unmanageable surpluses. It must be remembered that the market for a given product does have definite limits regardless of the price at which it is offered.

(6) Permitting prices of export products to find their own competitive level, but supporting domestic prices at a higher level. This, too, must be accompanied by production control and should be used with caution to avoid interfering with the free play of world conditions.

In effect, then, Boyd says that various familiar schemes for the artificial stimulation of exports should be considered as only temporary; and it should be recognized that, unwisely used, they may accomplish the reverse of what is expected of them. From the long-time standpoint, a healthy foreign trade can be maintained only by permitting international competition to have free play in setting world price levels, lowering trade barriers, eliminating internal restrictions, carefully studying foreign needs, and above all, being willing to accept imports in exchange for exports.

The Industrial Market for Farm Products

Industry, as Van Arsdel points out, has long made extensive use of farm products—cotton, cereal grains, packing-house byproducts, soybeans, wood. Some of these products, however, meet intense competition from synthetic or other raw materials, especially under the drive of modern industrial research, which is entirely impersonal and merely seeks the cheapest and best sources. The only way for farmers to hold or expand the market is to engage in intensified research themselves. Since they are neither organized nor financed like great industrial corporations, they have to call on Government to do most of the job. The Department of Agriculture has in fact conducted this kind of research for many years, with useful results. Recently the work has been expanded, and a comprehensive research program has just started, centered in four regional laboratories at Peoria, New Orleans, Philadelphia, and San Francisco.

Of the many classes of products for which raw materials could be supplied by the farm, six are dealt with by Van Arsdel—rayon, casein and soybean protein products, plastics, motor fuels, starches, vegetable oils. He gives a brief summary of the situation for each class, based on a survey made in 1939.

(1) *Rayon.* World production of 2,000,000,000 pounds (1938) has cut into the markets for cotton, wool, silk. Total production has about doubled every 3 years since 1920, with Japan and Germany forging ahead of the United States since 1936 and in 1938 producing half the world supply. About 9 percent of the textile fibers used in this country are rayon; 9 percent are wool, 2 percent silk, and 80 percent cotton (compared with 86 percent when the use of rayon was just beginning). There are three types of rayon—one made of wood pulp, two made of cotton linters; about 75 percent of United States rayon production is the wood-pulp type, 25 percent the cotton-linters types. Wood-pulp rayon has had the advantage in the low cost and high uniformity of the raw material. Manufacturers of the cotton-linters types would like to use wood pulp but have not yet solved certain chemical difficulties. The proportion of cotton-linters rayon has been increasing rapidly in this country in recent years and will probably continue to increase. Total rayon production will also increase, but probably at a slower rate than in the past. Future developments are likely to depend on research.

(2) *Casein and soybean proteins.* About 20,000–30,000 tons of casein, requiring over 1,000,000,000 pounds of skim milk (1 percent of total milk production), is now used for glue, cold-water paints, paper coatings, molded articles (chiefly buttons). Transparent wrappings were made of casein some years ago, and with improvements might be able to compete with cellulose materials for this purpose. A synthetic textile fiber, somewhat like wool, has been made of casein, but its possibilities are not yet known. Of the United States production of soybean meal, 95 percent goes for stock feed and fertilizer; less than 5

percent is used for plywood adhesives (largest industrial use), water-resistant coatings, sizes, plastics, cold-water paints, leather finishing. Some of these uses are new; none takes more than a very small percentage of the raw material available. Possibilities for expansion depend on further research and are unpredictable.

(3) *Plastics.* There has been a remarkable growth in the use of plastics in the past 20 years. Cheap methods for making large objects would open up new fields. Most of the raw material is synthetic (from coal, petroleum, limestone, sulfur, salt), but skim milk, oat hulls, vegetable oils, and soybean meal furnish a small percentage, and wood fiber and cotton are used in very large amounts. Synthetic products have certain natural advantages, but research might turn the tables in favor of agricultural raw materials.

(4) *Motor fuels.* Our present petroleum reserves of 17,000,000,000 barrels would be exhausted in 15 years at the present rate of use, but meanwhile rising prices would undoubtedly force other developments, such as the use of oil distilled from shale rock (108,000,000,000 barrels potentially available) and of synthetic fuels from refinery gas, coal gas, water gas, coke-oven gas, and similar abundant sources. Ethyl alcohol is the only fuel of agricultural origin to be used extensively, but others could probably be produced. Blends of ethyl alcohol and gasoline are quite feasible for automobile use. If a blend containing 10 percent of alcohol were universally used in this country, and the alcohol were made from cereal grains, it might require 25,000,000 additional acres in these grains to produce the necessary 2,000,000,000 gallons of alcohol a year. Wood waste, sugarcane bagasse, corncobs, cornstalks, cotton stalks, and cereal straws could all be converted to alcohol. From the supplies of such waste material available for industrial use (135,000,000 tons a year) a maximum of 4,000,000,000 gallons of alcohol could be produced. The great difficulty with alcohol for motor fuel is the cost. At present costs a gasoline-alcohol blend would have to sell for 1 to 2 cents per gallon more than straight gasoline of equal antiknock rating. Nevertheless, research may enable farm crops to furnish part of the huge market for concentrated fuels.

(5) *Starches.* Less than 1 percent of the starch available from corn is now recovered as cornstarch for use in the laundry, rayon, and leather industries and for making sizing, explosives, adhesives, and coloring materials. The potato-starch industry is small and irregular, depending on culls; there is a specialized market in the sizing of paper and textiles. Sweetpotato starch is produced commercially at an experimental cooperative plant in Mississippi; its uses are for sizing textiles, making high-grade dextrin for adhesives, and blending in various food products. A gradual growth may be expected in the traditional uses of starch, but not enough to have a marked effect on crop production. Tremendous quantities of starch are available at comparatively low prices, and an increase of several times the amount now used would not require any expansion in crop acreage. Replacement of the entire quantity of imported starches by sweetpotato starch would require only 200,000 acres.

(6) *Vegetable oils.* About a third of our consumption of fats and oils is industrial—18 percent in soaps and other detergents, 7 percent in drying oils, 8 percent in miscellaneous uses. Inedible tallow,

coconut oil, grease, whale oil go mostly into soaps; linseed, tung, and perilla oils into paint, varnish, linoleum, oilcloth, printing inks. Lines are not sharp, and there is considerable interchange and shifting, depending in part on price levels. Linseed, which used to supply 95 percent of drying oils, now supplies only 60–65 percent; tung, soybean, and perilla oils have replaced it through the development, for example, of fast-drying and waterproof varnishes and enamels. A new competitor in this field is castor oil. The market for drying oils will probably continue to be highly competitive. In the manufacture of soaps and other detergents, animal fats and coconut oil are the preferred materials. Here also competition is very intense. Besides drying oils and soaps, other industrial uses for oils account for several million pounds a year. Each field is highly specialized, and in several fields intensive research is under way. New uses for oils are likely to be developed.

Reducing the Costs of Food Distribution

Everyone knows that the cost of distributing foods is high. In 1938 the farmer got 40 cents of every dollar the consumer spent for food; the other 60 cents went to processors and distributors. Moreover, this cost has been increasing. In the 1913–17 period, farmers got 55 cents of the consumer's dollar and distributors only 45 cents.

How can this great spread be reduced to give farmers a larger share of the retail price?

There can be no material reduction, as many people think, by reducing the distributor's profits. Hoffman and Waugh present figures which indicate that "for most food products probably not over 5 percent of the retail selling price is represented by the combined earnings to capital at all stages in the marketing process." Again, there is no evidence that distribution is becoming less efficient—rather the contrary. Distribution costs might be reduced considerably by decreasing the numerous marketing services consumers now receive, but on the other hand these services presumably add to consumer satisfaction. It can be argued that sizable reductions in distribution costs might be made by reducing the wage rates paid by distributors; studies show that most of the increase in costs since 1913–17 is accounted for by the fact that hourly wage rates have more than doubled since that time. But a heavy cut in wage rates would affect the farmer adversely by reducing the purchasing power of large groups of consumers; and it would be difficult to justify from the standpoint of the general public interest, of which agricultural interests are only a part.

Thus there is little reason to believe that food distribution costs can be greatly reduced within the framework of the present marketing system. This is not to say, however, that even small reductions are not worth while, because they are. Farmers' marketing cooperatives, for example, save money for many farmers though these savings represent only a small part of the total costs of food distribution. Reorganization of terminal and wholesale markets can mean real savings, especially in the case of fresh fruits and vegetables. Savings at the retail end of marketing are particularly important, since the retailer commonly gets from 20 to 35 cents of the consumer's food dollar. In this field the development of chain stores, chains of

223761°—40——5

independents, supermarkets, and milk depots is especially significant.

Labor is the largest item in distribution costs, but there is an alternative to reducing wage rates—namely, to reduce the amount of labor used in food distribution as a whole; and not only the amount of labor but the amount of equipment and of capital to which profits must be paid. There can be no question that there is a very large duplication of marketing facilities. Many plants are not by any means used to capacity. The number of retail stores increased between 1900 and 1935 considerably out of proportion to the increase in population. But to reduce marketing facilities to those actually needed to supply the demands of the public would mean drastic changes in the present marketing system. Much labor would be thrown out of work, as it is with most technical improvements, during the period of transition. Freedom for anyone to go into the food distribution business would be curtailed. Monopolies might be necessary, and that would mean public regulation, as in the case of public utilities. In other words, many factors would be involved besides increased efficiency and reduced distribution costs alone. A thorough reorganization of the marketing system will never come unless the public thinks a fundamental change is absolutely necessary.

Marketing-Agreement Programs as a Means of Agricultural Adjustment

The acreage adjustment method used with major crops is not readily adapted to a number of farm products, including fruits, vegetables, nuts, and milk. But supplies of these products have increased greatly in recent times. Holt and Rubel cite the case of fresh vegetables. There were 500,000 acres in 1919, 1,000,000 in 1926, and about 1,750,000 a year since 1936 (twice as many pounds per person as 20 years ago). Glutted markets with some of the "specialty" crops have not been infrequent; sometimes prices were so low that it did not pay to harvest, and parts of crops were allowed to rot. The experience of cooperatives showed that much might be accomplished through orderly marketing, provided a large enough percentage of the producers would act together. The present marketing-agreement programs simply extend the cooperative marketing principle throughout an industry or an area. This means, however, that producers and handlers must assume certain responsibilities and give up certain individual rights—a difficult achievement.

The marketing-agreement programs are carried out under laws that permit wide variations in practical details to suit local conditions and different commodities. A program is initiated only on the demand of the industry and is put into effect only on a favorable vote of two-thirds of the producers, after public hearings for all interests affected. It combines voluntary and regulatory control to govern the handling (and therefore the handlers) of the commodity. There are three main types of control.

(1) The volume of shipments may be controlled (a) to the entire market for the season; (b) by diverting supplies from one outlet to another (for example, walnuts to other than the domestic unshelled market); (c) by regulating the rate of flow to market in order to smooth out temporary gluts and scarcities and make prices more nearly uniform.

(2) Grades and sizes may be regulated, and certain of these may be kept off the market for a given period.

(3) The shipper may be required to post his prices and not to quote or sell at prices different from those in his schedule. This is not the same as price fixing, since the shipper can post new prices after a reasonable interval.

Regulations limiting the total volume shipped over the season have been the most effective in improving grower prices and were used widely in the earlier years of marketing-agreement programs when consumer purchasing power was at low levels. Regulation of grades and sizes predominates at the present time.

Holt and Rubel point out that the short-time interest of producers—principally increased income—is the immediate objective of marketing-agreement programs. During recent years, however, there has been increasing emphasis on longer-time interests through such means as expanding outlets, developing new uses, eliminating unfair practices, and generally improving marketing institutions and processes. On this basis, the marketing-agreement method may be applicable to a wider field of marketing problems.

Thirty Million Customers for the Surplus

The 30,000,000 customers Perkins has in mind in writing about the food-stamp plan are those who earn an average of $9 a family a week and have great unsatisfied needs for food, clothing, household goods. Two-thirds of them receive some form of public assistance. They spend an average of $1 a week each for food—5 cents a meal. The stamp plan is designed to increase their food purchases by 50 percent—to $1.50 a week, 7½ cents a meal. By the end of 1940, the plan should accomplish this for about 5 million persons in over 200 communities.

Under the plan, all food supplies are distributed through commercial trade channels. Families may buy orange-colored stamps in the same approximate amount as they formerly spent for food in cash. These are good at any grocery store for any food. With every dollar's worth of orange stamps bought, 50 cents in blue stamps is given free; these also are good at any grocery store, but only for foods designated as surplus (mostly dairy and poultry products, fruits, vegetables, meats). The grocer buys these foods from his regular sources. The blue stamps are ultimately redeemed by the Federal Government.

The orange stamps are sold to make sure that those who use them will continue to buy as much food as before. Surplus foods bought with blue stamps, therefore, represent a net increase in the amount eaten, thus assuring farmers of a broader market and undernourished families of better diets. Studies show that where the stamps are used consumption of surplus farm products goes up by large amounts. The full economic effects upon farm income will not be realized until there is a greater national coverage.

A second plan for getting surplus products used consists in giving free, nourishing lunches to school children from low-income families. Nine million children are in need of such supplementary feeding. By the end of 1940 the program should reach six million. The Federal Government contributes the surplus foods; other foods and services are supplied by local agencies.

The recently started cotton-stamp plan works like that for foods, with $1 worth of brown stamps given free to low-income families for each $1 worth of green stamps they purchase. Stamps are exchangeable for cotton goods at retail dry-goods stores. However, in the case of retail sales of cotton goods, only a relatively small part of the consumer's dollar gets back directly to the farmer; most of it goes to employ labor in the manufacture and distribution of cotton goods.

The black plague of the twentieth century, says Perkins, is underconsumption. We must wipe it out if democracy is to survive. The place to begin is with the enormous numbers of people who can afford far too little of what we produce.

Barriers to Internal Trade in Farm Products

By 1786 almost all the Northern States had levied import duties against each other's products. Massachusetts prohibited the importation of some 58 articles from other States. One of the main reasons for the Federal Constitution was to do away with this strangling of interstate trade. The Constitution did in fact make the United States one of the largest free-trade areas in the world, enabling industry to develop mass production for a national market and agriculture to produce wherever conditions were most favorable. Citrus fruits, potatoes, hogs, wheat, cotton, cattle, for instance, all have their special production areas, but their markets are Nation-wide.

After 1929 we began going back to a condition of economic warfare between the States, largely because the loss of foreign trade and the pinch of depression made farmers anxious to save the local market for themselves and shut out everyone else. Burtis and Waugh give as major examples of this economic warfare:

Regulation of motortrucks and merchant truckers. Out-of-State trucks may be required to buy a State license tag or to pay higher ton-mileage taxes than in-State trucks. Kentucky and Tennessee will allow only the lightest trucks to use their roads, thereby interposing a barrier between all States north and south of them. In most cases of high merchant-trucking fees, farmers are exempted. This favors the farmers close to the market. Farmers farther away, who could not afford to haul their own produce the necessary distance, are effectively discriminated against. Railroad freight rates, incidentally, may be so constructed as to discriminate against producers in certain regions.

Regulation of the marketing of dairy products. Milk inspection laws are necessary safeguards of health. Some localities use them to shut out producers from other areas by refusing to inspect farms more than a certain distance away (in one case, as short a distance as 8 miles) or charging a prohibitive fee. At the same time, inspection certificates from other municipalities and States are not accepted.

Margarine taxes. Since Utah started the ball rolling in 1929, half the States have taken to taxing margarine from 5 to 15 cents a pound. Studies indicate that these taxes—which have been upheld by the Supreme Court as revenue measures—greatly reduce sales. Cottonseed oil is an important ingredient in margarine, and southern farmers have threatened to retaliate by discriminating against products of the butter-producing States. Margarine taxes can be an entering wedge for similar action in the case of many other products that compete with home-State products.

Regulation of the sale of alcoholic beverages. Special sales taxes or inspection fees on wines, liquors, or raw materials produced outside the State are used to favor producers within the State—grape growers, for example.

Grading, labeling, and standardization measures. Nonuniform specifications and requirements are perhaps the most serious hindrance to interstate trade among State grading and standardization measures. For instance, Oregon required certain berry-box standards for out-of-State shipments. California made these boxes illegal. In some cases, only eggs produced within the State can be labeled "fresh." Deliberate discrimination against out-of-State products is also to be found in the labeling and grading requirements of some of the States.

Plant and animal quarantines. Like milk inspection, these quarantines are vital protective measures, but they are also sometimes used for purely economic reasons.

Such State barriers can be removed, say Burtis and Waugh, by court action in some cases, by legislative and administrative action in the others. In most instances the latter action will have to be taken by the States, with the Federal Government cooperating to secure uniformity. Several organizations of State officials are now concerned over the problem. What is required most is a widespread and keen appreciation of the advantages and the importance of keeping our great national market open to all American producers.

Standardization and Inspection of Farm Products

When farmers produced mainly for home consumption and trading was by personal contact, Kitchen says, there was little need for standardization and grading. But with the commercialization of agriculture, when buyer and seller might be a thousand miles apart and trading had to be done sight unseen, a common language for trading purposes became necessary. Standards and grades furnish this common language. At first a multitude of local standards grew up; in 1906 there were 133 grade titles for wheat, 63 for corn, 77 for oats, 53 for barley, 10 for rye. The confusion was disastrous to seller and buyer alike. Finally, in 1907, the need for uniform Federal standards was recognized and research began. The Cotton Futures Act was first passed in 1914, the Grain Standards Act and the United States Warehouse Act in 1916, the Food Products Act in 1917, the Cotton Standards Act in 1923, the Tobacco Stocks and Standards Act in 1929, and the Tobacco Inspection Act in 1935. "Under the authority contained in this [and other] legislation the Department has developed standards of quality for most of the important agricultural commodities and has established various types of inspection and supervision to insure their uniform application throughout the country."

All standards are based on extensive research, both on the product itself and on conditions and practices in the trade. They must be so formulated that they can be applied to a product no matter where it is grown or marketed. They must also be uniformly interpreted and applied, which necessitates a corps of carefully trained inspectors.

Most standards are permissive (optional), and the best proof of their value is that they are widely used. In fact, interest in them has broadened to such an extent that there is a growing demand for their use outside the wholesale channels of trade. Thus in 1938 more than 85,000,000 pounds of butter and 720,000,000 pounds of meats were sold in the retail market to consumers under grade labels. Grade standards are also extremely important in market reporting. They have reduced marketing risks, tended to bring production more nearly into line with consumer demands, and greatly facilitated trading in futures, where neither buyer nor seller has any adequate protection unless there are standards.

The problems of standardization, nevertheless, are difficult. They are of four general types. (1) Most important is the problem of measuring quality. Shape, color, flavor cannot be expressed in quantitative terms like weight or size. Hence the need, for example, for butter tasters; hence also the sometimes complicated descriptions of quality. Many ingenious devices have been developed, however, to reduce the element of human error. (2) A problem of another type is the attitude of the trade, which in some instances has opposed uniform standards or has been slow to adopt them. (3) A third problem is the lack of uniformity in the standards and grades established by States. Ten States, for example, have standards for egg sizes, and no two are alike. (4) Finally, there is a very difficult problem in establishing consumer standards that will be simple, understandable, and acceptable.

No set of standards can be regarded as eternal; it must be flexible enough to be changed and refined with changing conditions. Conditions do change in many ways—improvements in practices, new crops or products, production in new areas, weather, new knowledge about values. Thus even if the use of uniform standards were universal, which is far from being the case, there would still be need for the continuous, painstaking research on which they are based.

Cooperative Marketing by Farmers

Cooperative marketing of farm products is now big business—over $2,000,000,000 worth of products sold a year, 2,000,000 farmer members, more than 8,000 associations. Commodities handled, Stokdyk says, include practically everything produced on our farms and ranches. The volume of business has nearly doubled since 1933. The movement is at least 50 years old (24 percent of all cooperatives were over 25 years old in 1936) and has had many ups and downs, but even the failures have added to the experience that made success possible.

A cooperative is a nonprofit organization in the sense that its earnings or savings are returned to the patrons. Control is in the hands of the members, therefore democratic; management is by a board of directors selected from the membership; the usual rule (holding in 86 percent of farmer cooperatives) is one vote to a member. Lower cost, higher quality, better service are the three economic functions of the cooperative. "No influence has been so potent in the economic education of farmers," since a cooperative "cannot succeed without full membership understanding." Meetings, publications, tours, demonstrations, institutes, reports, statistics, special studies, and active cooperation with Federal and State agencies are all used intensively to further education.

Of the three economic objectives, improved quality is brought about through studying market demands and paying returns to growers on a quality basis. Lower costs and better services are brought about by making local marketing units more efficient and thus lowering the margin between terminal prices and local prices. Competitors in turn are forced to narrow their margins and give better service. In other words, the cooperative sets the competitive pace and corrects unsatisfactory conditions. Thereafter its function is to keep conditions satisfactory and to increase its own efficiency. Cooperatives handling specialty crops (as distinct from staples) also perform other functions—advertising to expand markets, timing sales according to demand, distributing the supply among various markets, promoting reasonable dealers' margins, adopting grades and packages to suit consumer incomes. In general, however, cooperatives no longer attempt to cope with the surplus problem, since experience shows that it must be dealt with on an industry-wide basis.

Increasing legislative recognition has been given to cooperatives since the first cooperative statute was enacted in Michigan in 1865. In 1895 a California law authorized the organization of nonstock associations. Every State now has statutes for the incorporation of marketing cooperatives, and courts have recognized the differences between them and general corporations. Their rights have been expanded and safeguarded, notably by the Capper-Volstead Act of 1922, which defined cooperatives clearly and declared that they were not combinations in restraint of trade. A body of case law is being developed under which the rights and liabilities of cooperatives are becoming rather well defined.

The principal types of farmer cooperatives in the United States include:

Dairy products. Lead all other groups in volume of sales ($380,-000,000 in 1933–34, $686,000,000 in 1937–38) and number of members (700,000). Market about 48 percent of all fluid milk, 39 percent of all butter, 25 percent of all cheese.

Poultry products. Sales were $48,000,000 in 1933–34, $91,000,000 in 1937–38; 106,000 members, 194 associations. In addition, 700 other cooperatives handle poultry products as a side line.

Fruits and vegetables. More than 1,100 associations in 48 States; 164,000 members; sales $182,000,000 in 1933–34, $300,000,000 in 1937–38. About 60 percent of all citrus fruit is marketed cooperatively (85–90 percent in the California-Arizona area). Potatoes are handled by cooperatives more widely than any other vegetable. Cooperatives doing more than $1,000,000 worth of business for a commodity are those for citrus fruits ($124,748,000), potatoes, grapes, apples, prunes, strawberries, cranberries, peaches, lima beans, peas, pears, celery, cherries, tomatoes, apricots, lettuce, avocados, olives and olive oil, asparagus, green beans.

Grain. In 1937–38, 2,619 associations, 360,000 members, $475,-000,000 worth of business ($285,000,000 in 1933–34). Coal, feed, salt, and other supplies purchased by local elevators for farmer members have greater value in many cases than the grain handled.

Livestock. Some 900 shipping and marketing associations, 600,000 members, $300,000,000 worth of business ($162,000,000 in 1933–34). Terminal sales agencies now operate in practically all the larger markets, many of the smaller ones, handling about one-fifth of all livestock sold at public stockyards. In 1938, 60 large-scale agencies handled 12,286,914 head.

Wool. In 1937–38, 130 cooperatives handled $11,300,000 worth of wool for 50,000 producers. Most of the business is done by 25–30 large associations.

Cotton. Three types of cooperatives—cotton marketing associations (1938–39, 280,000 members, 1,522,037 bales); cotton gins (400 in Texas and Oklahoma alone in 1937–38, ginning 20–25 percent of the crop); cottonseed-oil mills (6 in operation at present). Total business of all cotton cooperatives in 1937–38 was $110,000,000. The cooperative ginning movement has been growing very rapidly.

Other products. There are cooperatives handling nuts, tobacco, hay, sugar beets, cane-sugar making, maple sirup and sugar, honey, timber, nursery stock, pulpwood, tung oil, broomcorn, fox fur.

The Growth of Farm-City Cooperative Associations

The first rural cooperatives were for marketing farm products. As offshoots of these came a second type, farmers' purchasing cooperatives for handling supplies used in farm production. Quite distinct from both were the consumers' cooperatives—organizations located principally in cities that purchase food, clothing, and other household products for their members. This distinction based on types of goods handled and on membership gradually broke down. Some farmers' societies began to handle products for home use as well as farm supplies. Others admitted city members. Eventually a successful cross was made between some of the farm purchasing cooperatives and city consumer cooperatives. The reasons for this hybrid are simple: (1) Nearly 60 percent of the farm family's expenses are for consumer goods. Why not save on them also through cooperative buying? (2) The larger the membership of a cooperative, the greater the savings. Farm and city people together make a larger membership than either alone.

As Gubin points out, this is a comparatively new development. The number of farm-city cooperatives is still relatively small; most of the members of cooperatives are farmers; farm supplies are still a much larger item in the total cooperative business than consumer goods. Yet the movement is significant because it bridges the gap between two kinds of organizations that had the same purpose—mutual advantage through mass purchasing power—but had grown up to be entirely separate. Many farm cooperative leaders, in fact, have strongly advised against rural cooperatives' taking joint action with the urban organizations. In spite of this opposition, the cross occurred and it has shown hybrid vigor and made a healthy growth.

Gubin cites figures that show the rapid development of rural cooperative buying in general.

In 1915 farmers' purchasing cooperatives (for farm supplies) handled only 2 percent of all the cooperative business done by farmers.

In 1938 they handled 15 percent. In 1913 they did $6,000,000 worth of purchasing business; in 1938-39, $320,000,000 worth. In addition to this, marketing cooperatives handle, buy, and sell $100,000,000 worth of farm supplies a year as a side line, so that the total amount of cooperative purchasing must now be at least $420,000,000 a year. Meanwhile the variety of goods and services handled has notably increased. Feed, seed, and fertilizer still are the most important items and make up about half of the total business. But today 50 percent of the purchasing associations sell some consumer goods—such items as groceries, general merchandise, clothing, fuel, gasoline, and oil—and at least 10 percent do their major business in consumer goods.

How many of the 50 percent handling consumer goods now admit city as well as rural members is not known, but according to Gubin the number has grown rapidly.

In line with this development a number of farmers' purchasing cooperatives formed a Nation-wide wholesale purchasing cooperative to which city organizations were later admitted; and in turn many of the rural cooperatives joined a national cooperative educational association formed originally by urban organizations. Cooperative automobile insurance is another field in which farm and city people have combined, and the growth here has been phenomenal. A few farm-city cooperatives have even gone into production as well as selling—not only mixing fertilizer and preparing feed for livestock but producing paint, bakery products, flour, grease; blending lubricating oil; roasting coffee.

The whole movement is still on a limited scale but it has considerable significance.

The Transportation Problem of Agriculture

Beginning with a brief historical survey, Dewey and Nelson show that agriculture has always played a vital part in solving transportation problems. For example, "the Granger agitation led to the first positive control over railroad rates in this country"—finally culminating in the act to regulate commerce, passed in 1887.

This action, and even the subsequent enlargement and improvement of regulatory legislation, with control in the hands of the Interstate Commerce Commission, proved to be no final answer to the farmers' complaint against unjust freight rates, partly because farmers were unable to meet the expense of bringing adequately prepared cases before the Commission. Another farm protest in the early 1920's resulted in the Hoch-Smith Resolution of 1925, requiring a widespread investigation of freight rates by the Commission with special attention to agricultural products. Here, too, the results were disappointing largely because of the Supreme Court's interpretation of the resolution. Farm dissatisfaction with the viewpoint of the I. C. C. and the railroads during the 1930's led to the passage in 1937 of section 201 of the Agricultural Adjustment Act authorizing the Secretary of Agriculture to make complaints and present economic data to the Commission.

The failure of freight rates in recent years to decline in proportion to the decline in the demand for and prices of farm products, combined with the willingness of the I. C. C. to grant rate increases, has raised several questions in the minds of farmers that require much study and research—among them: Can more of the revenue of the railroads be obtained from other sources than agricultural traffic? Can the revenue requirements of the railroads be reduced by various retrenchments? How can rail rates be made more responsive to economic conditions?

In the effort to overcome the handicap of high freight rates, the authors point out, farmers have stampeded to motortrucks for transportation. Partly as a result, the railroads apparently lost about one-fourth of their potential agricultural tonnage between 1928 and 1938. To meet this competition, the rails were forced to improve services and lower rates on certain products and certain hauls. On other products and hauls where motortrucks could not compete, however—notably in long-haul and transcontinental shipment—rail rates remained high or were even increased. The result has been to place producers in areas distant from their markets at a serious disadvantage and to force shifts in regional relationships.

The transportation problem is much broader than its agricultural aspect. Of particular importance is its relation to economic recovery. Railroad interests argue that we cannot have a healthy economy without healthy railroads, and on this basis they frequently press for higher rates. Farm groups argue that we cannot have healthy railroads without a healthy economy, and they ask what the railroads can contribute to the latter by better managerial methods and by supporting better Government policies.

The pressure to maintain or increase rates is based on the so-called plight of the railroads. About one-third of all companies are in receivership or trusteeship and others have been saved from bankruptcy only by Government loans. Few are paying dividends. Employment has been cut in half since 1920. Depression and competition are important causes of the decline, though other factors have contributed. These authors hold that the railroads are partly to blame for the loss of freight and passenger traffic to competitors in that they failed to see the trend of the times and actually invited competition by maintaining rates. Some lines also have a record of indefensible financial manipulation in the past, and the railroads in general carry a large volume of indebtedness in the form of bonds on which fixed interest charges must be paid. This debt constitutes the largest of the fixed charges of the railroads, and places them under a heavy disadvantage in all difficult economic periods. Other difficulties are due to extravagant construction before 1900, costly terminals in certain large cities, inability to submerge selfish interests and coordinate lines and services (especially terminals).

Since rail service is indispensable to many farmers, they have an interest in profitable railroads, but they are skeptical of the high-rate method of securing necessary profits until everything possible has been done to cut expenses.

When railroads cannot obtain their objectives by increasing rates, Dewey and Nelson note, they seek public regulation of motortrucks, water lines, and other means of transport. Formerly regulation aimed to maintain competition in the public interest; the new kind of regulation apparently aims to restrict competition in the railroads' interest. Actually, these authors indicate, the railroads have much more power to engage in destructive competition and rate cutting than their small, individual rivals; this has been amply proved in the past. Motortruck transportation, on the other hand, is essentially small-scale and highly competitive. Hence, there is serious doubt whether the same kind of regulation should be applied to all types of carriers. "Failure to make proper economic distinctions . . . only postpones socially desirable solutions of the transportation problem." The first effort should be to effect a rationalization of the railroad plant to eliminate uneconomic services.

Agricultural Credit

Johnson points out that whereas farming operations might on the average have been undertaken with an investment of $3,000 in 1900, the amount of capital required in 1930 was more than $8,000. The resulting need of farmers for increased credit facilities was greatly intensified by the sharp drop in farm income and land values beginning in 1930, when many rural banks closed and even farmers in good financial condition found it hard to borrow money. Total farm debt has declined in recent years, first because of foreclosures and enforced scaling down of debts, later because of refinancing and repayments; total farm mortgage debts were $9,600,000,000 in 1930, $7,800,000,000 in 1935, $7,000,000,000 in 1939. Through reduced land values, however, debt now represents a larger percentage of the value of mortgaged farms than formerly—about 30 percent of the value of the land and buildings of owner-operated farms in 1920, about 40 percent in 1930, about 50 percent in 1935. The majority of farms are not mortgaged, but on a comparatively large number of those that are, debt constitutes a heavy burden.

There are three types of financial aid to farmers: (1) Direct grants—essentially relief rather than credit for those who have practically no resources. (2) Loans by Government-subsidized agencies to put farmers who are in a weak financial position on their feet. Such loans should be accompanied by intelligent guidance toward rehabilitation. Assistance of this type has been largely furnished by the Farm Security Administration. (3) Regular business loans based on resources and earnings. It is with this ordinary business credit that Johnson's article is concerned.

To meet the serious situation that faced farmers after 1932, several steps were taken: (1) The Emergency Relief and Construction Act of 1932 set up a temporary regional agricultural credit corporation in each of the Federal land bank districts. (2) The emergency farm mortgage acts of 1933 made funds available for emergency loans and expanded the activities of the Federal land banks (established in 1917). (3) The Farm Credit Administration was established in 1933 to bring all Federal agricultural credit agencies into one unit. (4) The Farm Credit Act of 1933 set up production credit associations to make short- and intermediate-term loans, as well as 12 district banks and 1 central bank to make loans to farmers' cooperatives. (5) The Federal Farm Mortgage Corporation Act of 1934 created a corporation to supplement the facilities of the Federal land banks and the Land Bank Commissioner.

Under the present set-up, then, the country is divided into 12 farm credit districts, in each of which there are: (1) A Federal land bank to make long-term mortgage loans; (2) a production credit corporation, to supervise production credit associations, of which there are now about 500 in the United States making short-term loans; (3) a Federal intermediate credit bank for financing institutions that make short- and intermediate-term loans; (4) a bank for cooperatives, extending credit to cooperative associations.

"Since 1934 the financial position of farmers generally, except in areas affected by drought, has improved." Refinancing in large volume reduced debt charges; the estimated number of foreclosures per thousand farms mortgaged January 1, 1935, declined from 27.8 in 1934 to 16.4 in 1938. Extended or defaulted Federal land bank loans decreased from 48.8 percent in 1933 to 20.5 percent in 1939. Meanwhile other credit agencies (life-insurance companies and banks) have again become active in agricultural lending, indicating renewed confidence. Nevertheless in many regions farmers still face serious problems.

Here are the agencies from which a farmer may seek loans or credit: (1) His district Federal land bank, which may make amortized first mortgages up to 50 percent of the appraised value of the land plus 20 percent of the appraised value of permanent improvements; (2) the Land Bank Commissioner, who, from funds provided by the Federal Farm Mortgage Corporation, may make first and second mortgages up to 75 percent of the appraised normal value of the property; (3) a production credit association, which makes short- and intermediate-term loans, usually secured by a chattel mortgage; (4) the Farm Security Administration; (5) commercial agencies—life-insurance companies, commercial banks, merchants.

Among the problems in agricultural credit, Johnson lays major emphasis on the credit base. "Too much attention has been paid to the value of the collateral . . . and insufficient attention . . . to analyzing the income of the farmer as an indication of his ability to repay." Overemphasis on collateral results in excessive lending during periods of high land values and rising prices. When values and prices go down, the debt is a heavy burden, the farmer may be forced to let land and buildings deteriorate in the effort to meet debt charges, delinquencies are numerous, owners lose their farms, tenancy increases. Attention should also be given to including provisions in mortgage contracts for the upkeep of land and buildings.

"The greatest need," the author concludes, "is to assist farmers in getting out of debt, not deeper into it."

Crop Insurance

Farmers have been able for some time to get commercial insurance on crops against fire and hail. Unfortunately, these are not the greatest risks. What is needed is insurance against all production risks, and this is what the new Federal wheat insurance program provides. The principles involved, as Rowe and Smith point out, are the same as those underlying any insurance. In effect, the large number of farmers who pay premiums in any one year shoulder the loss of those to whom indemnities must be paid; or from another angle, an individual farmer distributes the burdens of his own losses over a number of years. The method, then, is that of self-help on a cooperative basis. The farmers pay premiums to meet the losses; the Federal Government pays administrative expenses as a contribution toward stabilizing agriculture.

The program is handled by the Federal Crop Insurance Corporation—a part of the Department of Agriculture. Offices are in Washington, D. C., Kansas City, Mo., Minneapolis, Minn., Chicago, Ill., and Spokane, Wash. The detailed field work—writing insurance, checking acreage, inspecting crops, adjusting losses—is administered by the same county committees (farmers) that handle the agricultural conservation program, with the help of community committees and the supervision of State committees.

An insured farmer is protected against unavoidable losses to the extent that his crop is smaller than 75 or 50 percent of his average yield, whichever he chooses. Any part of the loss that is due to poor farming is not indemnified. Premiums and indemnities are determined in bushels of wheat and may be paid by warehouse receipts for wheat or by the cash equivalent of the wheat at the current market price. To avoid losses due to price fluctuations, the Government invests cash premiums in wheat and sells such wheat when necessary to pay indemnities. Farmers may pay their premiums by an advance against payments being earned under the agricultural conservation program. Each farm has its own individual premium rate, based in part on its own actual or appraised past record of crop losses and in part on the record of crop losses for the county. Yields and premium rates computed for individual farms by county committees are required to check out in the aggregate with control figures determined for the county from yield and loss data developed in the Department. In some cases, yields are established for different practices on the same farm (summer fallow versus continuous cropping, irrigation versus dry-land farming). A farmer must insure his whole crop, not the part subject to the most risk, and he must insure before seeding, not afterward, when he may realize that loss is imminent. Landlords and tenants have separate policies covering their separate interests. Total losses occurring during the growing season may be settled before harvesttime, but partial losses are not settled until final determination after harvest of the amount of wheat produced. Losses are carefully checked by the county committee and its adjuster.

In 1939, the first year of the program, about 165,000 policies were issued on approximately 7,000,000 acres in 1,289 counties of 31 States. Farmers paid premiums of about 6,700,000 bushels. Crop damage was extensive in the Hard Winter Wheat Belt, where a large acreage was insured, and where fall drought took a heavy toll. Indemnities were paid on 55,800 claims, involving disbursement of 10,000,000 bushels of wheat.

The problems involved are numerous but are being solved: (1) Lack of yield records for individual farms. This will gradually be corrected as data accumulate. (2) Avoiding adverse selection of risks (which would be comparable to insuring only those with heart disease in life insurance). This will always be difficult, but "as new experience is gained, fewer loopholes will be left for those who would take unfair advantage of the program." (3) Desire for temporary advantage on the part of individuals or communities. This will be ironed out by increased premium rates where losses consistently exceed premiums. (4) Adjusting losses. Not so difficult as was anticipated, since the work is done by local people. (5) Reducing costs of operation per policy. Wider participation and simplified procedures will help to accomplish this. Costs will always be relatively high, however, in minor wheat-producing areas and for small acreages.

Experience with the insurance program is still new, and various changes have been suggested. Their merits and demerits are discussed by the authors. The Federal Crop Insurance Act provides for research looking toward insurance on other crops besides wheat. The possibilities with cotton, corn, and citrus fruits have been under investigation so far. Each presents some new and difficult problems.

Rural Taxation

In practically every country in the world, Englund points out, public expenditures have increased rapidly during the past 25 years, partly because of an expansion of government services and subsidies, partly because of the increased cost of goods and services bought with public money. Taxes, which supply the wherewithal for these expenditures, have increased accordingly. Farm real estate taxes have risen steadily since 1900. In 1910 the average tax per $100 of real estate value was 47 cents; in 1930 it was $1.30. After 1929 farm real estate taxes declined in partial but not complete response to falling prices.

The property tax accounts for the major share of State and local revenues but does not contribute to Federal revenues; 92 percent of all local revenues came from this tax in 1938. In recent years, however, other taxes have contributed an increasing share to State revenues. Of the direct taxes paid by farmers in 1934, real estate accounted for 60.2 percent; personal property (livestock, equipment, crops), 10.7; gasoline and automobile licenses, 26.2; income and sales taxes, 2.9. Thus the property tax (real estate and personal) represents 70 percent of the total. Improvement in the property tax is a State matter.

Three main faults are pointed out by Englund.

(1) Large farms and land of high value per acre tend to be underassessed for tax purposes while small farms and land of low value tend to be overassessed. This violates the basic principle of the property tax—that property shall be assessed uniformly in relation to value. Many studies show that tax assessors do not accurately determine the comparative values of different farms. Glaring inequalities remain in spite of the efforts of State boards to promote more uniformity, and they have contributed to tax delinquency in areas where there is much land of low value.

(2) Taxes on "other forms of wealth have in large measure found their way out from under the general property levy," leaving tangible property (especially real estate) to bear the brunt of rising State and local expenditures for such purposes as schools and roads. During the early years of the depression, the limits of the ability of property to bear taxes were apparently reached in many localities. With high taxes and low incomes, the delinquency rate among farmers rose alarmingly. Taxes then had to decline. Schools closed, the

rural educational system was weakened, other rural institutions suffered. Since 1939 the States have placed greater emphasis on the gasoline and motor registration taxes for the construction of roads.

(3) The farm property tax is rigid in relation to income. Between 1925 and 1932, farm income declined 58 percent, but the total real estate tax declined only 11 percent, so that farmers were paying more than twice as high a percentage of their gross income in these taxes.

Englund argues that a resort to general sales taxes to relieve the pressure on property does not help most farmers. An absentee landlord will get some relief from the reduced property tax; a local landowner or a tenant farmer bears an extra burden by paying higher prices for the things he buys. Moreover, in the case of some farm products, the sales tax is not shifted on to the consumer but back to the farmer in the form of lower prices.

In the game of shifting taxes, the farmer is at a disadvantage. He cannot shift the taxes collected from him by demanding higher prices, but many taxes can readily be shifted onto his shoulders.

Englund does not argue that a reduction in taxes on low-value land would necessarily lead to significantly greater efforts at soil conservation; the inducement in many cases would not be large enough. Nor does he think that exempting small homesteads from taxation necessarily promotes small-farm ownership. A homestead-exemption plan may place the farmer at a disadvantage in comparison with the owner of a small home in the city and actually shift more of the county taxes to rural property. In addition, other taxes imposed to make up for homestead exemption may hit the farmer.

Financial aid to farmers from revenues collected largely outside of rural communities go a long way toward counterbalancing direct rural taxes; but on a larger balance sheet the economic contributions of rural people and rural resources to the national economy as a whole may outweigh by far the help they receive. The question whether farm property should bear a smaller proportion of the tax burden for the local and State services and improvements demanded by modern communities must be judged in some such over-all framework as this. The modern trend in public finance, Englund observes, seems to be toward converting a larger part of private income into public revenue and a distribution of public benefits without too close questioning as to whether the benefits go to exactly the place from which the tax money came. It is the function of public policy to see that both costs and benefits are fairly distributed.

Rural Electrification

In view of the mechanical efficiency and the high standard of living in the United States, it is amazing that 90 percent of our farms did not have central-station electrical service as late as 1935. At that time, Beall points out, practically 100 percent of the farms in Holland had electricity, 90 to 95 percent in France, 90 percent in Germany and Japan, 85 percent in Denmark, 65 percent in Sweden, and 60 percent in New Zealand. What was the cause of the remarkable lag in the United States, in the face of the fact that farmers actively desired electrical service? Simply, says Beall, that private utility companies, who own and control over 90 percent of the industry, did not need the rural market. Since it was much less profitable than the city market, rural rates remained high and rural lines were constructed only on conditions that were too burdensome for the average farmer to meet. There was little or no incentive to work out methods that would enable and encourage farmers to use electric service. At the rate of progress of rural electrification during the previous decade, it would have taken 50 years to bring electricity to half the farms in the United States.

In 1934 both the Mississippi Valley Committee and the National Resources Board urged that the only way to speed up rural electrification was for the Federal Government to assume active leadership. In 1935 the Rural Electrification Administration was established to push an active program. In the 4½ years from the middle of 1935 to the end of 1939, the number of farms with electric service jumped nearly 130 percent; that is, more was accomplished in rural areas in this short period than in all the previous decades since electricity first began to be used. By the end of 1939, 25 percent of all farms were electrified. The principal borrowers of R. E. A. funds have been cooperative associations of local farmers, who organized for this purpose and took 92 percent of the R. E. A. loans.

The Rural Electrification Administration does not itself construct, own, or operate lines or sell equipment. It merely lends money and furnishes technical advice and assistance. Loans are self-liquidating within 25 years at low interest rates, and they may be made to "persons, corporations, States, Territories, municipalities, people's utility districts, and cooperative, nonprofit, or limited-dividend associations," for constructing lines or power plants (very few of the latter have been necessary; in most cases, already existing sources of current are used), wiring premises, acquiring and installing electrical and plumbing appliances and equipment.

Economical methods developed by R. E. A. especially for rural areas are largely responsible for the success of the program. They include:

(1) *Area coverage.* Every farm in an area is covered instead of a few selected farms, as hitherto. This distributes costs, develops the maximum load, permits mass-production methods in constructing lines.

(2) *Simplified and standardized line construction.* This has cut costs in half—from $1,500–$1,800 a mile under previous methods down to $800 a mile today. New techniques departing from urban practice include vertical construction with elimination of cross arms on poles and use of half the number of poles by doubling the span.

(3) *Other technical advances.* There have been several of these, including a simplified meter which can be read by farmers, thereby greatly reducing this cost, and a new low-cost small-capacity service unit which will bring lights and small appliances within the reach of low-income farmers for about $1 a month. (Minimum bills for regular service range from $2.50 a month in the South to $3.50 to $4 in the North.)

In spite of the accomplishments so far and the greater public interest in rural electrification, there is an enormous amount of work still to be done. After all, 3 farms out of 4 in the country as a whole still do not have electricity. Though in 9 States half or more of the farms are now electrified, in 12 others the number is 1 in 10 or even less. "Already there are over 200 separate uses for electric power on the farm, and the list continues to grow. While many of those uses relate primarily to household activities, a substantial number of them are directly concerned with labor-saving, cost-reducing, and income-producing equipment for farm operations." Others are of value to the entire community—electricity in schools and churches, for example, or power for cooperative local industries using farm products as raw material.

New Conditions Demand New Opportunities

Certain aspects of the general farm situation in the United States are not pleasant to contemplate, but as potential causes of increasing trouble in the future they must be faced resolutely and handled intelligently. Smith gives a broad survey of these problems as an introduction to several following articles that deal with them in more detail. Essentially he lays down two propositions that challenge agricultural leadership.

(1) It is part of our national tradition that a man could start as a farm hand, save a little money, rent a farm, save some more money, and finally own the farm. Opportunity was open to anyone; our people were not frozen into classes and castes such as still exist in the Old World. Is this true today? Any candid view of present-day agriculture shows that opportunities to climb the agricultural ladder are far more limited than they used to be. The conditions that have closed off opportunities for large numbers of rural people are described in other articles. Their net result, whether we like it or not, is that it has become increasingly difficult for a man to advance from laborer to tenant, tenant to owner. The first challenge to agricultural leadership, then, is whether we shall permit a large part of the rural population of the United States to become permanently set in laborer, sharecropper, and tenant classes, contrary to everything we have believed in.

(2) It has been estimated from 1930 census data that even in 1929 half of all farmers had cash incomes averaging $415 a year; more than a fourth had cash incomes averaging $195 a year. The cash part of the income had to meet payments on mortgage, interest, taxes, feed and fertilizer bills, replacement of tools and work stock. The remainder, if any, was available for food, clothing, furniture, medical care, education, and so on. In other words, there is beyond question a large "poverty class" in agriculture. The second challenge is whether we shall let this poverty become permanently fixed on these people, who are concentrated in certain regions but are also found in every State.

Smith argues that those who are better off must give increased attention to a vigorous search for means to release the "disadvantaged" groups from oppressive poverty, not only for humanitarian reasons but because (1) by increasing their purchasing power we could greatly expand our domestic market; (2) they furnish a disproportionate share of the Nation's children, which means that more and more people will grow up with unhealthy bodies and poorly educated minds; (3) democracy needs a strong backbone—and its backbone is still the rural people.

223761°—40——6

That there is no simple solution of the problem he concedes readily. He notes that all efforts to stabilize agriculture and improve the land as well as all efforts to expand industrial production and employment have an indirect but real effect on the disadvantaged groups. But we cannot wait for these; we must also use more direct measures. Among those that should contribute to improvement are:

(1) Efforts to encourage landownership and reduce tenancy through an extension of measures such as are included in the Bankhead-Jones Farm Tenant Act.

(2) More attention to equitable leasing arrangements between landlords and tenants.

(3) Rehabilitation of families who are down but not out, through such methods as those used by the Farm Security Administration.

(4) Purchase of submarginal land by the Government and assistance to the families living on it in finding new locations.

(5) Resettlement projects—purchasing good land (usually large farms) and dividing it into family-sized farms or turning it over to a cooperative group.

(6) Development of rural industries to furnish part-time employment for stranded families, including sustained-yield forest programs and subsistence homesteads developed on new patterns.

(7) A rural public-works program to supplement the earnings of low-income farmers—and also to conserve natural resources.

(8) Measures to improve the welfare of farm laborers and sharecroppers.

(9) A large-scale rural housing program.

(10) Provision of better educational opportunities for rural children.

(11) Much more attention to sanitation, adequate medical and dental care, and hospitalization in many rural areas.

(12) In a still broader field, policies for assisting farm families to make adjustments to technological change. In the long run, the welfare of all farm families as well as efficiency in production will have to be considered in attempting to measure efficiency in agriculture.

"The problem," Smith concludes, "seems to be to determine what kind of agriculture and rural life we want, and then to set ourselves to the task of bringing it about."

The Rural People

Baker and Taeuber study what is happening among whole populations—vast groups of people regionally and nationally distributed. From this study they have picked out six major trends now occurring in the rural population of the United States.

(1) Culturally, our people are becoming more and more alike. Country folk, for instance, are strongly subject to city influences, partly because at least half the people in the United States now live within a couple of hours by automobile of a city of 100,000 or more. Within the rural areas themselves groups that formerly had quite distinctive customs of their own are disappearing. Foreign-born groups, for example, are being replaced by second-generation Americans.

(2) Economically, on the other hand, we are becoming more sharply separated. In general, the North is more prosperous agriculturally

than the South, yet there are some prosperous areas in the South and many poor areas in the North. In 1929 nearly half the farms produced only about 11 percent of the products sold or traded, and two-thirds of the less productive ones were in the South. Apparently the number of very small farms (many of which are inadequate) is increasing; so is the number of very large farms.

(3) The birth rate has been declining until now the number of births is no longer sufficient to permanently maintain the population. There is a surplus of 50 percent annually among farm people, however, and a deficit of 25–30 percent annually in the larger cities. In the future, then, cities can grow or maintain themselves only by drawing on the country. Since about half the natural increase in the total population now occurs in the South, the poorer sections of the country are bound to furnish an increasing proportion of our people; the smallest proportion will be furnished by the professional and business classes in the large cities.

(4) The number of middle-aged and old people is increasing in proportion to the number of young people.

(5) At least twice as many young people are maturing each year in rural areas as would be required to maintain the number of farm operators at a stationary figure. A large number of these young people are backing up on farms with little chance for employment either in commercial agriculture or in cities. In the absence of migration to the cities, there may be 7,500,000 more people of working age (18–65) on farms by 1955 than there are at present. This is the reservoir from which cities can draw their future increase.

(6) Migration from farm to city has been sharply reduced since 1930, and some cities have had a net migration to rural areas. The tendency to remain on farms has been most marked in areas of the fewest agricultural opportunities; in other words, the poorest areas have been the shock absorbers for depression.

On the basis of these trends, Baker and Taeuber urge the need for a national policy specifically related to rural-urban migration. They point out that whenever opportunities improve, cities will again receive large numbers of rural migrants; therefore they are profoundly concerned with the conditions from which these migrants come. Rural communities, on the other hand, are profoundly concerned with the cities as potential sources of employment for the increasing numbers of rural people. The authors suggest three lines of action:

(1) "Raising the level of living in areas from which migrants will be recruited." Rural migrants from the poorest backgrounds are difficult to absorb into city life. Since in general their condition is not likely to be improved by an expansion in commercial farm production, direct means must be adopted in the form of "a subsistence program for home production on the largest possible scale consistent with the conservation of land resources." The program should include rural industries, home industries, public works, and public services. Such a program would improve health and morale as well as making assimilation into the cities easier.

(2) Increasing educational opportunities. "Many of the children now being reared in rural areas will ultimately live elsewhere." They are not now being equipped with the knowledge and skills they will

need for effective adjustment, so that in many cases they press on the unskilled labor market and live under slum conditions.

(3) "More effective guidance of migrants to areas of greater opportunity." Too many people at present leave home and seek work elsewhere on the basis of "tips, rumors, hunches, and indefinite promises"; or they travel hundreds of miles for very temporary jobs. Many difficulties would be eliminated by an adequate system of information. Public efforts should also be coordinated better than they are; in some cases they retard migration where it should be encouraged, in others they encourage it without adequate assurance of opportunities elsewhere.

Patterns of Living of Farm Families

That widely used phrase, "standard of living," means little unless it is translated into concrete, practical terms of food, housing, clothing, and the other items for which people exchange their incomes. Monroe attempts to give a concrete picture of "standards of living" on our farms in these terms, drawing material from recent surveys and using three income levels in 1935–36 as examples.

(1) The middle group would include farm families with incomes of $1,000 to $1,250 a year, or an average of $1,127. (This included 11.7 percent of all farm families; 56.6 percent of all relief and nonrelief farm families had incomes of less than $1,000 a year.) Of the average income, $634 was in money; $493 was in the form of housing, food, fuel, ice, and other items furnished by the farm. At the end of the year one-third of these families were "in the red"; two-thirds broke even or were ahead of the game; but deficits were larger than savings so that the group as a whole was actually behind.

Of the total value of family living in this group, 47 percent ($537) was represented by food; two-thirds of it was food produced on the farm and one-third food bought for cash ($194). About 2 families out of 3 had good or fair diets; 1 out of 3 had a deficient diet. Housing varied a great deal in different regions, but for the country as a whole about 1 home in 6 had less than 1 room per person. About 5 out of every 6 families had no running water, 9 out of 10 no indoor toilet, 4 out of 5 no electric lights, 7 out of 8 no central heating system, 3 out of 5 no refrigerator of any kind, 19 out of 20 no mechanical refrigerator, 7 out of 10 no telephone, 5 out of 10 no radio. All of these figures are very much higher than for the comparable city group. On the other hand, 7 out of 10 of the farm families had an automobile (as compared with 3 out of 10 in a metropolis—Chicago), and more than 9 out of 10 did home canning, putting up an average of 200 quarts of food. The farm families spent an average of $104 a year for clothing, distributed somewhat like this: Wife, $16 for a winter coat, worn for 5 years; $4.50 for a good dress, worn 2 years; $1.35 for an everyday dress, worn 1 year; $6 for 2 pairs of shoes, worn 1 year; husband, $19 for a wool suit, worn 4 years; $3 for a mackinaw, worn 3 years; $14 for an overcoat, worn many years (13 out of every 14 bought no overcoat); $2.80 for work shoes, worn less than a year. Medical care averaged $50 per family (about half the estimated cost of adequate care on a group basis); education and reading matter, $18; personal care (toilet articles, barber shop, etc.), $17. It might be noted that rural schools spent an average of $67 per pupil, city schools, $108.

(2) The higher economic group might be represented by families with incomes of $2,500 to $3,000 a year, averaging $2,716. (This group included 2.6 percent of all farm families; 93 percent of all farm families had incomes less than $2,500.) In this group, the money income was three times as great ($2,028) as in the middle group; income in the form of housing, food, etc. ($688), was two-fifths higher. Much more was saved or put back into the farm—an average of $777 for the year compared with a deficit of $10 for the middle group. All the families could have had good diets, though some did not. About 9 out of 10 homes had at least 1 room per person, but fewer than half of the families had running water, and 2 out of 3 had no indoor toilet or central heating plant. Three out of four families owned their farms. About $190 a year was spent for clothing per family. Most of the families (96 percent) canned food, putting up an average of 262 quarts.

(3) Two groups are selected to represent families with low incomes—a group of farm operators with incomes of $250–$500 (average, $440), and a group of Negro sharecroppers at the same income level.

The farm-operator group received $130 in cash during the year, $310 in farm-furnished housing, food, and other products. Two-thirds of the total value of living was represented by food ($293), though the cash expenditure for food was only $49. At least 1 out of 3 families had deficient diets. More than a third of the houses had only 2 or 3 rooms for the entire family. One family in 100 had an indoor toilet; 1 out of 17 did not have even an outside toilet; 1 out of 17 had running water; 9 houses out of 10 were heated by fireplaces; none had electricity or any kind of ice box; 1 family in 17 had an automobile; $8 in cash a year was spent for all household operating expenses. Clothing cost $31 a year for the whole family (husband $11, wife $9, children or other members $11), medical care $12 (including 68 cents a family a year for the dentist), recreation $1, all other expenses $29.

Among the Negro sharecroppers, cash income averaged $230 a family, income in kind $153. The food consumed had an average value of $221 a year, or around 5 cents per person per meal; 4 families out of 5 had deficient diets. Almost 6 houses out of 10 had less than 1 room per person. No house had an indoor toilet, running water, or electric lights; 1 out of 6 did not have even an outdoor toilet; about 9 houses out of 10 were heated by fireplaces.

Families with incomes under $500—that is, the group just discussed and the group below it—probably included about one-fourth of all farm families, relief and nonrelief.

Overcrowded Farms

"Conservative estimates show that all told 3,000,000 farm families are existing today on abnormally low incomes and at unwholesomely low standards of living," Alexander writes. "Many of these families are just as able and anxious to earn their own way as any other group in America . . . There is nothing fundamentally wrong with the people. The problem is to devise a system that will enable them to become assets instead of liabilities."

The Farm Security Administration is one of the agencies set up to tackle this problem. It operates in several ways.

(1) By making loans to needy farmers who can become self-supporting but who cannot get a loan anywhere else. These are "character" loans, without collateral, for productive purposes, including necessary farm supplies, equipment, livestock. Each loan is based on a definite plan, worked out by the farmer and his wife in cooperation with the F. S. A. county supervisor and home supervisor. Three essentials of such a plan: (a) A rounded program for efficient home production to furnish a balanced diet for an entire year, including canned and stored products and feed for livestock; (b) at least two farm enterprises that will bring in some cash; (c) continued F. S. A. advice and assistance in carrying out the program. By April 30, 1940, some 837,000 families had received such loans. Many had lifted themselves out of a hopeless situation to self-respect and a modest livelihood. More than 114,000 families had fully repaid their loans by that date. A survey of 360,000 borrowers made in December 1939 showed that they had increased their net worth by 26 percent and their net income by 43 percent since coming on the Farm Security Administration program. In addition they had increased the amount of food produced for home consumption from a total value of $54,160,567 to $89,038,910.

(2) Grants are given in emergency cases—there were many during the drought years—for food, clothing, medical care. By April 30, 1940, 540,000 such grants had been made.

(3) When a family is hopelessly in debt, the F. S. A. assists in getting the debts adjusted to a manageable figure.

(4) Among families in need, sickness is a common cause of failure to get ahead. For instance, 575 people in 100 typical needy farm families were found to have 1,300 health handicaps, including among the most serious rickets, tuberculosis, pellagra, and suspected cancer. To meet this problem, health programs have been developed in cooperation with county medical societies. Families pay $15 to $30 a year; the money is pooled to pay private physicians for providing medical care.

(5) Successful efforts have been made by F. S. A. to improve tenure conditions. Among other gains, the number of written as against oral leases has been quadrupled among F. S. A. clients.

(6) Cooperative purchase of relatively expensive items such as machinery and livestock is encouraged. More thoroughgoing cooperative efforts, being tried experimentally, include the running of entire farms by groups of families.

(7) Under the Bankhead-Jones Farm Tenant Act, loans are made to tenants, on a 40-year amortizing mortgage basis, for the purchase of farms.

(8) Some work has been done to improve the condition of migrant laborers by establishing sanitary labor camps and even more permanent small homes with provisions for producing food.

Other agencies also are working in the rural relief field. The Work Projects Administration and the Civilian Conservation Corps have done a good deal. State and local agencies have given direct relief.

"All of these efforts are helping meet the widespread distress," says Alexander. "But altogether, they are falling far short of the need"—

especially in view of the continuing mechanization of agriculture, which pushes workers off the land. At least 500,000 families, for example, who are in need and would be eligible for F. S. A. aid cannot get it. "A long-range program," Alexander insists, "must be worked out"; the only alternative is a dole on an immense scale. In such a program he would include more rehabilitation loans looking toward self-support; outright grants for capital equipment as well as emergencies, where these seem clearly justified; perhaps more cooperative farming. Even this would leave many rural workers who could not possibly be absorbed into any kind of agricultural production. He would set them to work building better rural homes, roads, schools, reforesting, installing sanitary water supplies, and so on. "In a hundred fields, there is ample need for the manpower that is now wasting on the farms."

In conclusion, Alexander summarizes the development of present rural relief programs, beginning with the Federal Emergency Relief Administration and later the Resettlement Administration.

Farm Tenancy

There are, of course, tenants and tenants. Some are tenants by choice, generally well to do, occupying good soil, preferring to invest their capital in livestock and equipment rather than land. Again, some half-million tenants are on farms owned by relatives. But a large number are tenants by necessity, with low incomes and standards of living. In one such group in the South studied by the Farm Security Administration, the average total income was $134.71 a year; value of household goods, $27.86; value of all worldly goods, $305.61; debts, $220.17; average net worth, $85.44. Often such farm families are old local residents. They farm about 20 acres. The mule is the principal asset. Malnutrition and disease are prevalent. Among the 2,865,155 tenant farmers in the United States (42 percent of all farmers) are 716,000 sharecroppers who have no livestock or equipment of their own.

"National strength and solidarity," says Maris, "spring from an independent, contented, home-loving rural citizenry" such as the old American ideal of owner-operated farms aimed to develop. We have moved much too far away from this ideal. The situation is not likely to get better by itself. At the present rate of natural increase, the farm population in the poorest areas will double in 30 years.

What is being done or can be done to come to grips with the tenancy problem?

Matis lists several existing or proposed legislative remedies in the United States. (1) Fourteen States now have laws partially exempting homesteads from taxation, to protect owners of family-size farms. (2) One State has a law protecting mortgagors who default because of crop failure or some other disaster. (3) The Bankhead-Jones Farm Tenant Act helps to set a pattern of family-size farms. (4) The Taylor Grazing Act is "in the direction of better adjustment of users to the land." (5) The soil conservation districts now authorized in many States will indirectly tackle problems of population adjustment. (6) Loans are being made by the F. S. A. in the Great Plains to create adequate family-size farm units. (7) The Iowa Farm Tenancy Committee has recommended a study of differential taxation to encourage the ownership of family-size farms, as well as a tax on capital gains from the sale of land.

Problems of land tenure have not by any means been confined to the United States. In recent years many other countries have been forced to deal with them. Some examples: In England, farmers are assisted in acquiring small holdings, which must be cultivated by the owner and cannot be divided, sold, assigned, or rented. In Ireland, 97 percent of the farmers were tenants in 1870; land-tenure reforms have brought the figure down to 3 percent today. The Scandinavian countries have made marked progress in improving land tenure. The U. S. S. R., of course, has socialized the land—a move that may be compatible with security but not with the American ideal of individual ownership. Mexico has regulated private property rights and bought out large holdings at 10 percent above the assessed value, turning them over to villages or dividing them into family-size farms. Germany has set up a system of "inherited freeholds"—family-size farms which cannot be mortgaged and are passed on from generation to generation.

Among the most significant measures for encouraging ownership of family-size farms in this country is the Bankhead-Jones Farm Tenant Act. Under this act, first-mortgage or deed-of-trust loans are made to carefully selected farm families for 40-year periods at 3 percent interest. Variable payments are provided to ease farmers in years of abnormally low income, but this privilege is withdrawn if abused. County farmer committees pass on the eligibility of applicants and the value of the farms. In 3 years, $75,000,000 has been appropriated for this purpose, and there have been about 30 times as many applicants as loans. Experience with the plan has been very favorable, and it could probably be used advantageously to reduce tenancy from 42 percent down to 20 percent among farmers in the United States. Over a period of 25 years, this would require about 52,000 loans a year. It would be vital to guard against speculative prices if any such large-scale program of farm purchasing were put into effect.

It will be noted that this plan would not bring about the almost complete elimination of tenancy achieved in Ireland. As a matter of fact, a reasonable amount of tenancy has advantages, provided it is on a sound and fair basis; in England, for example, tenants are legally protected and they stay on their farms. In the United States, unsatisfactory leasing customs are deep-rooted, and landlords hesitate to make contracts with propertyless farmers. These difficulties, however, can be overcome; at least, that is the opinion that has come out of conferences on this subject recently held in many States.

Maris suggests as essential, badly needed reforms: (1) Long-term written leases, preferably for 5 years or more, or written annual leases automatically renewed. (2) Compensation to the tenant for improvements he leaves behind, and to the landlord for damage due to negligence. (3) Compensation when either party breaks the agreement on short notice. (4) Provision for arbitrating differences between landlord and tenant.

Farm Labor in an Era of Change

It was taken for granted in the American tradition, Ham notes, "that the man who remained a farm laborer lacked the initiative or capacity to rise to something better"; the farm labor problem was simply to find enough competent hands to do the work. Today surplus rural labor is so common that many people accept it as part of the order of nature. "Once a laborer, always a laborer" is more and more the rule. Among the laborers are found larger numbers than formerly of "normal farm people" as contrasted with the tramps and drifters of earlier days.

Even the regularly employed "hired man" is not quite so well off as he used to be; but the real problem centers on the seasonal labor employed in large-scale specialty farming. In 1929 the average wage bill on 999 farms out of 1,000 was $135 a year; on the other farm it was $13,385. This tenth of 1 percent of all farms (well over a third of them were in California) paid 11 percent of the total agricultural wages. On these large-scale farms, labor conditions are similar to those in factories. Hiring is often done by a labor contractor; the work is routine and carried on by gangs under a foreman; wages are uncertain and may be cut without notice; workers frequently have to travel long distances for temporary jobs. Seasonal workers probably make up half of the farm labor in the United States. "Standards of living are incredibly low," housing is inadequate, medical and sanitary facilities are meager, and the workers are not accepted as a real part of any community.

In spite of the increasingly factorylike character of much farm labor, these workers have been definitely excluded from the gains made by industrial workers in recent years, as represented by the Wagner Labor Relations Act, the Social Security Act, and the Fair Labor Standards Act. In effect, this exclusion from benefits granted to others creates a class of outcasts and stirs up class strife, which farmers may have cause to regret in the long run. Strikes of farm labor have increased and disputes have become bitter. Unions of city workers have begun to take a more aggresive interest in farm labor conditions, feeling that low farm wages are a threat to their own standards.

Possible remedies for this complex and difficult situation include:

(1) The first line of attack, of course, is to improve the farmer's economic status. What he pays depends on what he gets himself.

(2) Equally obvious is the need for increasing employment opportunities in industry. If 2 out of every 5 farm youths can go to the cities for work, as they used to do, there will be less deadly competition for farm jobs.

(3) The present haphazard, inefficient distribution of seasonal labor, with vastly more workers than are needed drawn to certain areas by advertising, can be improved by an effective placement and information service in which State and Federal agencies cooperate.

(4) More continuous employment can be promoted by such means as new crop sequences and perhaps the transfer of some processing operations to the farm.

(5) The living conditions and health of workers can be improved by establishing many more permanent and mobile camp facilities such as

those set up by the Farm Security Administration, better camp inspection, more low-cost housing, more rural medical centers, and other aids.

(6) Where farm labor approaches factory conditions, workers can be given equality under the law, with due regard for certain special needs of agriculture. They could share in old-age and unemployment insurance privileges, suitable wage and other standards, the right of collective bargaining.

Many of the possible improvements in farm labor conditions, Ham points out, must be made by the States. At present, farm workers are quite generally excluded from State labor laws. The States could encourage joint conferences between employers and employees to determine and stabilize wages; they could work out methods for mediation and conciliation in labor disputes. In some areas, public authorities and employers are becoming active in developing such possibilities.

Beyond Economics

Wilson is impressed by the fact that much more is needed to solve our agricultural problems than convincing schemes in the field of economics. He first shows how complex these problems are. No quick or easy scheme such as getting parity prices can simultaneously bring agriculture an adequate income, make up for the loss of foreign markets, reverse the trend toward loss of farm ownership, improve tenancy conditions, lift the mortgage burden, relieve the pressure of too many people on the land, give vitality to the poverty-stricken, save the soil from being wasted, and enable us to use technology instead of being driven by it. What is needed is practically a new pattern of farm life, and such things cannot be achieved suddenly or simply. This country faces a long period of agricultural reform. It is vital that this reform be democratic and that it be marked by tolerance, not bitterness or hatred.

What Wilson calls the "cultural approach" is best adapted, he feels, to bring about this reform. Primarily, the cultural approach emphasizes that people's moral ideas, their habits of thinking and acting, their notions about right and wrong, are just as important in the total life of the country as money or machines or any other material things. We have the machines and methods to create abundance for everyone; we have the most pressing need to create this abundance. But we don't do it. Why? Because habits, traditions, institutions, moral ideas stand in the way at a thousand points. We have an emotional attachment to old ways even when we can see, with our minds, that they cripple us.

Unless reformers with neat blueprints for a better society—and there are many of them—recognize this paramount fact, they are going to get nowhere rapidly. They cannot start with a theory about how the economic system ought to work if only people were different. "The real genius of any feasible reform effort will reside not in its technical competence . . . but rather in its psychological and cultural insight . . . The crux of the problem is moral and psychological." The more candidly these psychological and moral factors are recognized, the more scientific is the approach to social problems.

What are the implications of this viewpoint in dealing with agricultural problems? It means that psychological possibilities would be considered first; that education would be especially important; that wide discussion would be encouraged to stir people up to examine their own attitudes and thinking, to question whether existing institutions are adequate for their needs, to explore their ideals and preferences sincerely.

Wilson is particularly interested in discussing the plight of the surplus farm population. He attacks two extreme viewpoints. According to one viewpoint, we should recognize the efficiency of the Machine Age, mechanize our farming on a huge scale as fast as possible, put surplus farm workers into industry. The trouble with that is that there is no place for them in industry. According to the other viewpoint, we should split agriculture up into small units, largely do away with specialization, make every farm family practically self-sufficient. The trouble with that is that we must have large-scale specialization today to supply raw materials for industry and to feed the industrial population. But why go to either extreme? Why not do both at the same time? All agriculture does not need to be commercial; in fact, that would probably not be efficient. Nor does subsistence agriculture necessarily mean a return to the handcraft age. A small subsistence farm can be as modern as you please, with all kinds of gadgets to give it its own particular efficiency and to help the farmer achieve a decent standard of living. The two kinds of agriculture can exist side by side. As long as we have an agricultural plant geared to produce more than the market will profitably pay for, this is the only way out. It would mean vastly better living for great numbers of people. And it would tend to reduce surpluses.

Subsistence farmers would need some cash income. The widespread establishment of subsistence farming might require, for a time, a frank and open subsidy. But this would be far better than building up a class of under dogs, dangerous for the future of the country. Subsistence farming and part-time farming are urged as a very practical way to take care of the unemployed and all those who are being driven onto relief. But such a plan would not be easy or simple. "It means new kinds of concerns, new kinds of practice, new kinds of knowledge . . . new kinds of pleasures and satisfactions . . . new ideas about life's most basic values . . . [and] a great extension of cooperative activity." Education is the first essential.

Wilson emphasizes the satisfaction of psychic needs—"for security, for self-respect and prestige, for intimate experience, and for a relationship with the unknown"—as being of primary importance among social goals; and he stresses the need for tolerance. "It is insecurity and confusion that drive men into frantic loyalty to extreme ideas and into desperate and harsh oppression of those who disagree with them. . . . This is the greatest danger . . . that confronts the hope of social progress." The preventive is "to increase the security of the vast number of people who are most in need of it" and "to realize that social and economic truths are not absolutes to which mortals have ready access." Our country needs a real social philosophy of its own—not one based on creeds and doctrines that may suit conditions abroad but do not suit those in the United States. We have the materials for such a philosophy.

Part 4. Farm Organizations

Trends in National Farm Organizations

Wing presents a factual report of the growth and the policies of three great national farm organizations—the National Grange, the National Farmers' Educational and Cooperative Union of America (usually called the Farmers' Union), the American Farm Bureau Federation.

Essentially, he points out, the motive back of these organizations is to secure to farmers an increased share of the national income, or economic equality for agriculture. They fear concentrations of power existing in labor and business organizations and realize that "important decisions upon which action is taken are more and more those of bodies of men rather than of single individuals." Though farmers are still far less than 50 percent nationally organized, there seems to be a growing conviction among them that agricultural problems must be dealt with on a national basis. Education and cooperation are stressed by all the great farm organizations, and they have enlisted the interest of many people besides farmers.

The creed of the Grange, founded in 1867, expressed the desire for "equality . . . and justly distributed power." By 1873 it had a foothold in nearly every State. It aggressively and successfully fought what farmers regarded as the abuses of the railroads. Cooperative activities, including milling and manufacturing, were stressed. More than 50 percent of the Grange members today live in New England, New York, Pennsylvania, New Jersey, and Ohio. New England, with 150,000 members, is the stronghold. There are many women members as well as children over 14. The Grange stresses the fact that it is "a family institution before it becomes anything else."

Wing reports an interview with Master Louis J. Taber in the autumn of 1939 on Grange objectives. Taber emphasized the fact that the 8,000 local Granges with 800,000 members are really community centers where public opinion—"the court of last resort in America"—is created. He said the current Grange program has three objectives—keep America out of war, lift farm incomes, make democracy function more efficiently. Lifting farm income involves developing home markets, new markets, foreign markets, and also strengthening the cooperative movement. Government appropriations are a temporary stopgap on the road to fair prices and a fair share of the national income. On the question of democracy, Taber used the Grange as an example, stressing the sense of responsibility it develops in its members, including a great many young people.

The 1940 national legislative program of the Grange includes the following recommendations: Economic justice for agriculture; remove unnecessary restrictions from business; maintain family-size farm, discourage large-scale farming; continue soil conservation program, but divorced from crop control; continue benefit payments till prices reach parity; regulate imports; terminate reciprocal trade agreements; encourage cooperative marketing; remove State trade barriers; encourage research for new crops and new uses of farm products; develop rural education, rural roads, rural electrification; encourage cooperation between agriculture, labor, industry; restore Farm Credit Administration to independent status; continue low interest rates on farm loans; adopt a comprehensive Federal forestry program and aid extension of farm forestry; keep Forest Service in Department of Agriculture; liberalize railroad regulation; retain short-and-long-haul clause; no restrictions on motortruck or waterway transportation; complete St. Lawrence seaway; balance the Federal budget; no general sales tax, no tax-exempt securities, no processing taxes; continue support of agricultural education; no more reclamation at present; pass truth-in-fabrics legislation; continue development of farm-tenancy program; give agriculture representation in mobilization plans; clarify Wage-Hour Act and give agriculture exemptions; modify National Labor Relations Act; continue regulation of "imitation dairy products"; tax certain imported oils and starches; support Federal action to eradicate predatory animals and more vigorous steps to control insect pests; make interstate transport of stolen livestock a Federal offense; do not ratify Argentine Sanitary Pact; increase allotments of American sugar growers; extend crop insurance; enforce antitrust laws; no State medicine; amend Packers and Stockyards Act for better regulation; no block booking and blind selling of motion pictures; enforce law against lotteries; compel aliens to register; continue congressional committee on un-American activities; vigorously enforce Commodities Exchange Act; prevent overcentralization of government; strengthen national defense; avoid entanglement in foreign wars; take profits out of war.

The Farmers' Union began in Texas in 1902. It represents 100,000 farm families (members join as families), is organized in 21 States, has locals in 12 more, puts special emphasis on training juniors and on cooperatives. The Farmers' Union Grain Terminal Association, operating in the spring wheat area, is the largest; other cooperative activities include oil stations, compounding plants, grocery warehouses and wholesale houses, creameries, a factory for agricultural implements, insurance (fire, life, hospitalization), grain terminals, feed mills, cold-storage lockers, livestock marketing and trucking associations, cotton gins, credit unions.

In an interview with Wing early in 1940, John Vesecky, president, emphasized that the Union is built to serve low- and middle-income farmers. Its main objective is to safeguard farm family homes and enable more farmers to become home owners. "Price and income alone will not solve the farm problem"; development of cooperative enterprise is the surest road to economic power for agriculture. Handling one-third of the farm business cooperatively all the way through to the consumer would be enough to do the job. The Union, Vesecky said, favors more aid like that of the Farm Security Administration; refinancing and adjusting farm debts; a tax earmarked for farm benefit payments; no attempts at price fixing.

Current legislative and other recommendations of the Farmers' Union include: No tax qualifications for voting; aid for cooperative hospitals; extension of Federal Farm Mortgage Act; broader powers for A. A. A. county committees; cost of production or parity for farm products domestically consumed; truth-in-fabrics legislation; homestead-tax exemption; graduated land tax; protection of civil liberties (actions of committee on un-American activities deplored);

debt adjustment; a dairy bill; certificate plans for cotton, wheat, flax, rye, barley, rice, other commodities; commodity loans at top figure; separation of soil conservation from commodity income programs; expansion of farm credit program to take in farm tenancy, debt adjustment, land utilization, mortgage refinancing, rehabilitation, emergency relief; transfer of F. C. A. to Department of Agriculture; use of cooperatives for distribution, the Government to keep out of the distribution field; expansion of food-stamp plan, rural electrification, crop insurance; protection of family-size farm; Federal programs to be administered as far as possible by farmers, democratically elected; legislation to encourage and protect cooperatives; protection for domestic agricultural market; all taxes to be based on ability to pay as measured by income; Congress to have power to coin money and regulate its value; no tax-exempt bonds; no restrictions on truck and water transportation; retention of short-and-long-haul clause; cooperation of agriculture and labor; general opposition to war.

Wing gives a brief history of the Farm Bureau as told by Clifford V. Gregory. The Farm Bureau grew indirectly out of the agricultural extension system, established by the Department of Agriculture and the States just before the World War. In the beginning a few county bureaus were organized by farmers to back up the educational work of the county agents. Some of these bureaus federated into State organizations. In 1919, 12 State farm bureaus got together to form a national organization, and formal action was taken early in 1920. The Federation came along just in time to run head on into the long farm depression of the 1920's. In these circumstances it soon passed beyond purely educational work in better production and plunged into the conomic problems of agriculture. In 1932 the Federation called a conference of farm organizations, and this conference proposed a bill embodying price parity, production control, and a processing tax. In 1940 the Farm Bureau has 400,000 members, mostly in the Corn Belt.

Edward A. O'Neal, Farm Bureau president, was interviewed by Wing early in 1940. He stressed the need, in the modern world, for cooperative control of commodities by farmers and cited the A. A. A. program as an effective form of cooperation. The Farm Bureau, he said, does not now believe that the usual types of cooperatives are enough by themselves to solve the farm problem, though in its early days it did hold this viewpoint and started several important cooperatives. Today it believes more strongly than ever in production control and such devices as marketing agreements. O'Neal cited an article by D. Howard Doane as containing ideas with which he agreed. Doane emphasized two things: (1) All production improvements in farming—use of machinery, soil management, livestock management—must contribute to lower cost per unit of product. (2) Production alone does not pay the farmer under present conditions because he competes with individuals who do not figure production costs. He must carry his product through some stages of processing and distribution. Here he can make a profit because his competitors figure costs. The large-scale operator can do this by himself, the small-scale operator through cooperation.

In resolutions adopted in December 1939 the Farm Bureau Federation reiterated its position that the crux of the economic problem in the United States is parity between agricultural and industrial prices; that when this is achieved, it will solve the problem of unemployment; that money spent for other methods of getting recovery will not get results; that there must be appropriations and taxes fully adequate to bring about a fair economic balance between farmers and other groups.

The following recommendations were made in the resolutions: For expansion of cooperative features of the farm credit system and extension of certain types of loans; for coordination of all types of farm credit and all types of commodity programs in two independent Federal boards within or correlated with the Department of Agriculture; for more local coordination of agricultural programs under the Extension Service; for modification of the trade agreements policy; for "only . . . reasonable regulation" of transportation so as to "preserve the inherent advantages" of each type; for arbitration of labor disputes—compulsory in the case of industries handling perishable and semiperishable agricultural products; for definition and clarification of the status of agricultural labor in labor acts; for enforcement of antitrust laws for labor, industry, agriculture; against transfer of Forest Service from Department of Agriculture; for a price-parity policy on the part of the agricultural advisory council; for a special Senate study of monetary problems in relation to price levels; for extension of marketing agreements; for appropriation of adequate funds for tobacco grading; for livestock and poultry feed control legislation; for increased Federal and State research on marketing and distribution problems; for extension of forest conservation with special emphasis on farm forestry; for extension of the fertilizer program of the Tennessee Valley Authority; for a new and thorough study of livestock marketing by the Federation in cooperation with other groups; for truth-in-fabrics legislation; for further sugar legislation; for maintaining and strengthening relations between the Farm Bureau and the Extension Service.

Resolutions on various other aspects of agriculture adopted in 1938 were reaffirmed by the Federation. The following recommendations by the Associated Women of the Federation were approved: For more discussion meetings between rural and urban groups and extension of discussion meetings in general; for use of county Farm Bureaus as clearing houses for farm programs; for further study of and action on national health problems, including nutrition; for extension of rural libraries; for keeping out of the European war; for a broader Federation program of economic education; for continued cooperation with the Associated Country Women of the World.

Each of the three national farm organizations, Wing points out, maintains headquarters in Washington, studies farm legislation, supports or opposes it. Local and State bodies do not always agree with the national organization on objectives, but differences are decreasing. There seems to be a trend toward a division of territory between the three organizations. Each publishes a national newspaper or magazine (National Grange Monthly, National Union Farmer, Nation's Agriculture), and some State units have their own publications. Editors of privately owned farm papers support the farm organizations and wish to see farm organization strengthened.

Wing argues that there is a trend toward unity of viewpoint between the three organizations; they agree on some of the basic principles, if not on details of agricultural programs. It has been said that agriculture presents a more united front than labor or industry. All the national organizations are agreed on the fundamental issue of parity for agriculture, and all encourage and practice cooperation.

Part 5. What Some Social Scientists Have to Say

Cultural Anthropology and Modern Agriculture

The word "anthropology" means literally "the science of man." Cultural or social anthropology emphasizes the study of human societies or "cultures." As Redfield and Warner point out, the cultural anthropologists so far have been concerned with studying primitive or comparatively simple societies—those of American Indians, for example, or Polynesian Islanders, or simple rural communities. From these studies certain conclusions have been drawn that are believed to hold true for any human social organization.

Can the anthropologists use their methods to study far more complex societies such as our own? Redfield and Warner believe this should be possible. The value such work would have is obvious. By and large, most practical studies of modern society are economic. Most of the solutions offered for social problems—including those in agriculture—are strictly economic solutions. Even the most obvious economic remedies don't always work. Why not? Perhaps because other things besides economics are extremely important, and some of them may balk economic efforts.

There is very little scientific understanding of these "other things." If scientific methods can be used by anthropologists to study a complex human society as a whole, they may contribute a good deal to man's ability to create better conditions of living.

Redfield and Warner outline some of the main conclusions of anthropologists. All societies, simple or complex, they point out, have the same general objective—the successful adjustment of men to their environment and to each other. When the adjustment is successful, all aspects of life tend to fit together into a harmonious whole. In primitive communities this harmonious fitting together can be clearly seen. There is little specialization. Most men do the same things in the same way for the same reasons, and these reasons make up their ideas of what is right and wrong. Work, play, religion are all unified; even the planting of corn, for example, is likely to have a religious significance. The community is a unit knit together by common needs and loyalties, and above all by common understanding, shared by everyone.

In a modern complex community, much of this is reversed. There is a high degree of specialization. Men do not do the same things. They have far less understanding of each other and share fewer common loyalties. The community is split up much more into opposing groups with special interests to defend. Moreover, men do not understand the reasons for what they do. They do many things under the compulsion of remote forces, not those within the community itself. Changes due to advances in technology are rapid. Under the circumstances, the sense of values, of what is right and wrong, becomes confused. Life is far from being a harmonious whole, and it may lose much of its meaning. The adjustment of men to their environment and to each other is out of gear.

The authors do not specifically point a moral, but it seems to be this: Some way must be found to transcend the complexity of modern life and give it much more unity and wholeness. Some way must be found to diffuse a common understanding through complex societies and create common ideals and loyalties. Even the best of economic solutions for our difficulties are only part of the story.

Democracy in Agriculture—Why and How?

Likert writes about democracy and agriculture from the standpoint of the social psychologist. Democracy, which is the opposite of dictatorship, he argues, is the form of social organization best calculated to satisfy some of the most fundamental urges of human nature.

But there are three essential requirements if democracy is to work. (1) The majority of citizens must meet situations as mature individuals—which means solving problems "with the brain in full control of the emotions," and taking full responsibility. Dictatorship depends on a certain emotional immaturity—much like the relationship of a child to a parent. (2) Habits of solving problems through democratic processes as well as habits of maturity and self-reliance do not develop all at once. They can be developed only by constant practice. Democracy must furnish adequate opportunities for this practice. (3) Adequate opportunities depend on having democratic machinery at every level of government (local, State, Federal) for dealing with all kinds of problems, and especially the problems that arise suddenly under modern conditions.

But the increased complexity of government today tends to make it less rather than more democratic, partly because legislation must be broad while specific decisions are left to administrators. How can those administrators be sure they are carrying out broad legislation as the people wish? They cannot be sure, Likert argues, except by constantly obtaining an accurate expression of the felt needs and difficulties of those affected by the legislation. The only way to do this accurately, rapidly, and inexpensively is to use the "sampling" method developed in recent years by social scientists.

Likert points out that this method is now being used by the Department of Agriculture with valuable results. Essentially, it consists in putting the question to which an answer is desired to a carefully selected sample of farmers—say, 1,000. Research has proved that the answers given by those 1,000 farmers will not vary more than 5 percent from the answers that would have been given if all farmers had been questioned. But this will not be true unless extraordinary precautions are observed: (1) The sample must be typical, including the same groups in the same proportions as would be found in the whole farm population. (2) Questions must be carefully worded so as not in any way to suggest a certain kind of answer. (3) The

223761°—40——7

interviews from the field must be carefully and accurately analyzed.

With these precautions fully observed, Likert believes, this method is a valuable contribution to democratic procedures, especially during this period of bewildering change.

The Cultural Setting of American Agricultural Problems

As a cultural historian, Turner is interested in explaining our present situation in terms of the development of social institutions and attitudes in the United States.

In the background of any civilization, he begins, there is a fundamental cleavage between city and country. Cities depend on the farm population for their food and raw materials. But they cannot reproduce themselves; they grow by getting people from the country. If this growth is to continue, more and more people must be released from agriculture, which means that agricultural efficiency must increase. Now, cities are the centers of industry, learning, science, art. The growth of all these, then, depends on increased agricultural efficiency, which frees people to do other things than produce food. Obviously such a development has occurred in the United States.

When America was colonized, the new ideas of individualism held by the middle class were becoming dominant in Europe, and the colonists brought these ideas with them. Individualism was strengthened and given a special turn in the new country because of the great abundance of land. Land was the one great resource, available to almost everyone. Cities were small and few.

Under these conditions, American small-scale farmers—the dominant group—were poor and hard-working, but independent. The strong individualism they developed was based on the fact that a man made his own decisions about life and work and took full responsibility for the results. Self-reliance, equal opportunity, individual responsibility—this became the American credo, born of the abundance of land on the frontier. Democracy was real, economically and politically. Of government there was little, for it was not needed.

Meanwhile, however, the cities were growing and the "industrial revolution" was bringing remarkable changes. "Individualism" was the dominant idea in the cities, too. But in industry it had quite a different meaning than it had among farmers. The farmer said, "We shall do what we please and be responsible for the consequences." The city man said, "We shall do what we please, but we cannot be responsible for the consequences." This philosophy Turner calls economic liberalism. It was enough like the frontier credo to be widely accepted, but the results were profoundly different. Under economic liberalism, for instance, industry could wash its hands of responsibility for unemployment or any other consequence of its policies.

Ultimately the frontier and free land disappeared and agriculture became more efficient, less self-sufficient. This did not matter so long as surplus rural people could be absorbed into industry. But gradually, industrial advances completely changed the picture of American life. The proportion of people engaged in farming was enormously reduced. So was the proportion of independent businessmen. On the other hand, the proportion of wage earners and salaried workers enormously increased. Farmers did not sell their labor directly like wage hands, but they sold it indirectly because they became as completely dependent on the cities as wage hands. The great metropolises, meantime, grew bigger and bigger and dominated more and more of the country.

In brief, the city idea of individualism swallowed up the frontier idea. Individualism was lost in the name of individualism. And this produced a profound conflict. People do not change their deepest convictions and attitudes without conflict.

Our struggle today, Turner argues, is to preserve, in a vastly changed world, what was valuable in our tradition of individualism and democracy.

He believes this can be done, but that we must do it in strictly American ways, not by trying to apply foreign isms to our problems. Two things we must accept. One is that all of us are infinitely more dependent on each other, because of the minute subdivision of modern industry, than we ever were in the past; and we can never get back to the old independence. The other is that cities are bound to be the dominant element in modern culture; it cannot be otherwise in a civilization that is so dependent on science and technology. But it is not true that the frontier is lost. We still have a frontier—one even greater than that which gave rise to the American credo. The new frontier is the productive capacity made possible by science. Science has also given us an even greater sense of possible control over human affairs than our forebears had.

What prevents our using this frontier as we used the old one? Mainly, says Turner, a philosophy based almost entirely on the sale of goods and labor in the market place, plus the notion that freedom means not being responsible for the human consequences that result from our acts. Both these handicaps can be got rid of by sticking to the original ideas that made the American credo. Let the frontier of abundance dominate the market place, not vice versa. Let the old strong sense of individual responsibility be reborn as a strong sense of social responsibility. On such a basis we can go ahead, put necessary social controls into effect, use our productive capacities to wipe out the terrible inequalities in standards of living and in opportunity that now cripple us, and participate again in the decisions that affect our lives. And we can do it in ways that are in accord with our own national philosophy.

Under such conditions Turner sees the development of a more unified civilization than any possible hitherto—one in which the old country-city antagonism will gradually disappear.

In the earlier history of the United States, Turner concludes, the existence of a great land frontier was the material element that most influenced our American pattern of thought and behavior. That pattern should find itself equally at home on a great frontier of production.

Education for Rural Life

"If education is to be of real service to farm life and to rural children," says Embree, "we must cease to be awed by traditional subjects and procedures and build our schools on the essential needs of the countryside and the country child." In some ways, education in primitive societies was better than it is with us; it had the merit of training young people directly for the life they were to live. Today we have lost our way in a mass of specializations, each worshipped for its own sake rather than for what it can contribute to happy and successful living.

In building up this country our interest has centered too much in machines, industry, city life, rather than in the land and rural life. This trend, Embree believes, is now changing. "We are at the beginning of what bids fair to be a rural renaissance. Country life is receiving attention . . . unequaled since colonial days . . . The adulation of industrialism . . . has passed its zenith." For rural schools, this means a new opportunity and a new duty.

Embree does not discuss vocational education for agriculture in the high schools or colleges; he is concerned with the common schools, where the education of most rural children ends. The things he emphasizes for teaching in these schools are old—the three R's, manual crafts, the study of nature. These are the basis of all sound education. But, he says, they have been wrongly taught. Children are drilled like so many trained fleas, with no idea of what they are doing or why. Their recitations have nothing to do with real learning or with everyday life. "Subjects are artificially divided into fragments"; sometimes a teacher rushes through a "whole day made up of lessons of less than 15 minutes each"; too many schools "are not educational institutions at all but simply a species of jail for keeping children in order for a few hours each day." "A shocking number of children—especially in the rural regions—do not acquire even an elementary knowledge" of the primary subjects.

If you really learn how to read, says Embree, you can get all the rest of your education by yourself—as Lincoln did. It is the basis of all education. Reading in this sense, as a means of understanding life, is what the schools should teach. The same thing can be said of arithmetic. The tricks of multiplication and division are meaningless unless pupils acquire them as tools to be constantly used in practical situations. As for manual crafts and nature study—there is little danger that they will be learned as tricks, since they can be taught only through actual work and observation. These two fields, he believes, are especially important for rural children not only as ground work for necessary skills and an understanding of farm practice but also for the enrichment of life.

Finally, Embree stresses the community functions of the rural school. In many places the school is now "the only organized social force able to exert general influence." It has a tremendous responsibility as a center for modern knowledge and information leading toward better community life, and it may well become the focal point for cooperative action by many agencies.

The Contribution of Sociology to Agriculture

The "science of society"—sociology—is the youngest of the sciences, and it deals with extremely complex things. But as a great sociologist, Ward, pointed out, if the things with which sociology deals are ever understood so that they can be controlled, "the results . . . in the interest of man are beyond calculation." Only within the past few years, says Taylor, has sociology been called on to give "actual counsel and service" in large social movements and programs. Its greatest contributions are yet to be made, but they will be real ones.

The sociologist studies many of the same things that the economist studies, but he looks at them from quite a different angle. The economist is interested in the efficiency of an institution from the standpoint of production and the exchange of wealth. The sociologist is interested in its structure, its functions, its origin, how it is maintained, how and why it changes, and the effect of all these processes on the lives of all the people involved in them. An understanding of these things is vital to intelligent direction of human affairs.

If problems are to be solved, however, the first step is to discover what they are. Many of the most serious problems of today crept up on us unnoticed. If we had seen them earlier, we might have done something to prevent their becoming critical. One of the sociologist's functions, then, is the active discovery of problems so that trouble can be forestalled.

Taylor divides sociology into several important branches.

(1) *Social organization and social structure.* Organization is the "machinery by which people live their daily lives." Neighborhoods, communities, villages, families, schools, churches, farm organizations, political organizations—all these are tremendously important to rural people. Under the impact of widespread forces, rapid changes are occurring in such organizations. Where are those changes leading? What kinds of organization at various levels would be best suited to modern needs? These are questions that can be studied by sociology.

(2) *Population or social demography.* This branch of sociology studies the numbers, distribution, and composition of populations, the characteristics of its various segments, population trends and their causes and effects. Many agencies, governmental and private, have constant need for the findings—and whenever possible, the predictions —developed from these studies.

(3) *Social ecology or human geography.* For rural sociology, this includes studies of the relation of natural resources and geography to the distribution of people on the land. "The amount of land required or utilized per farm unit . . . affects all social institutions."

(4) *Cultural or social anthropology.* Old habits and attitudes, often obscure and subconscious, are constantly coming into conflict with new needs and new traits. They constitute the major resistance to change, yet they are often the most treasured possession of a society. How can what is good in the old ways be combined with what is good in the new ways to make a better and richer rural life? Cultural anthropology should be able to throw some light on such a question.

(5) *Social psychology.* This field of sociology is concerned with the effects of cultural processes on individual human behavior, and the attitudes and opinions of members of a group. Great advances have been made in recent years in techniques for discovering group attitudes and opinions, and this is especially important in a democracy, where political processes depend on public opinion. Social psychology also deals with the psychology of leadership and of pressure groups.

(6) *Social pathology.* Under this heading Taylor includes the study of sore spots, unhealthy areas in society—"rural slums," rural unem-

ployment, for example. These sore spots are not pleasant. Nor is disease of any kind; but it must be understood if it is to be controlled.

In the past in the United States, "each local community . . . lived an integrated life . . . and was relatively self-sufficient. Today the majority of American farmers have become a part of the 'great society.'" New and far wider "economic, political, social, and cultural relationships have entered rural life . . . [and] changes are taking place more rapidly than in any previous generation." Sociology should help the farmer "to function more successfully in these new areas and processes of association" and to solve some of the conflicts with which he is now constantly faced.

A Philosophy of Life for the American Farmer (and Others)

Many of the characteristics of man, says Hocking, are shared by the animals, but there are several major differences. Man is always planning—he lives in his dreams. He has a peculiarly deep-rooted desire for self-respect or "standing in the community." His basic drives—food-getting, acquisition, sex—are so balanced that they do not enslave him; he alone among the animals can look at the whole of things and ask himself, "Which way do I really prefer to go?" Competing impulses in man are controlled by a dominating purpose, the desire to count for something, and this must be expressed by contributing to human life as a whole through creative activity. Because he is "the only animal that looks at himself and judges himself," man is both "terribly vulnerable to social approval or social ostracism" and at the same time "able to sacrifice almost anything to promote an idea."

Farm life, Hocking believes, offers exceptional opportunities for the human desire to create—to plan and to carry out plans. The farmer is a perpetual pioneer on the frontier between barrenness and fertility, life and death. If with all its satisfactions farming has serious drawbacks, the remedy lies in discovering and developing "the things which make up the good life, whether on the farm or elsewhere." These things Hocking proceeds to discuss.

He puts family life first and argues that farming has superior opportunities for its development because "the area of common life" among the members of the family is greater on the farm than in the city, the outer associations are less numerous, the family "has to find its own way to fun and mutual help." But many a farmer fails in this family life by overburdening his children and leading them to seek escape—explaining too little and consulting too little. Farming should be to a large extent hereditary, but the life must be attractive to him who inherits it. If necessary, the state will have to play a part in making farming a hopeful occupation.

Next among the things that make a good life Hocking puts property, not only for its assurance that "there will be bread and butter tomorrow" but even more for its education of the possessor. Taking care of his own farm teaches a man responsibility and the use of authority; it is a training ground for democracy, which requires that every man have authority and responsibility. The real justification for private property is that "it allows the free expression of personal traits and invites the social judgment which follows mistakes in its use." Thus "any radical change in the form or extent of farm ownership becomes a matter of importance for the state as a whole."

Hocking argues that there may be many changes in farming techniques—as there have been—without harm to fundamental human qualities and values. For the most part, in fact, such changes are desired and are good. The changes in ways of life brought by the spread of city conveniences to the farm are also good on the whole. The real menace is a change in the ownership of property—the development of large-scale, absentee-owned farms, for example, and of a farm laboring class without ownership or hope of ownership. This is the threat to capitalism, for "the right to work" then becomes the biggest thing in life, and if it is not satisfied men turn against capitalism and demand another system; security becomes far more desirable than liberty. Capitalism can survive only on condition that it satisfy the will to work, spread the ownership and use of capital throughout the community, and make the ownership of real property widespread. Farm property, either individually or cooperatively owned, must "continue to do its part in the building of the American individual and democrat."

Economic change is not "inevitable"; there is no mysterious "economic force"; the human will has the final say, and if some circumstances are too much for the individual to cope with, then the community must step in to prevent change in the wrong direction.

Third though not least important in the things that make the good life Hocking puts what he calls "the wider horizon." By this he means the common culture which makes individuals act and feel together on the big issues of life. "There has never been a time so hopeful as the present for making this [common culture] a solid fact for the life of the American farmer." But there is much that needs to be done. He would like, for example, to see the great journals paying much more attention to farm life and reaching farmers more effectively; a greater development of music, community festivals, and especially community dramatic presentations in the country; more interpretation of science for the farmer. Philosophy too should be brought to the farm public, for it is philosophy that invites men to ennoble the day's work. Philosophy and religion tap "the vein of seriousness with which the responsible man wishes to face his more difficult passes of experience."

Part 6. Democracy and Agricultural Policy

Public Information and the Preservation of Democracy

Stedman is primarily concerned with the threat of war to the basic institutions of democracy. In democracy, "differences are settled by a struggle of ideas, with the decision not by bullet but by ballot." In an absolutist state, opponents of the government have no other recourse except force. But "when totalitarianism reaches its ultimate national stage of war and comes into violent collision with democracy," then the latter also adopts dictatorial methods, and may lose the very democracy it sets out to defend.

This natural tendency poses a critical problem, and it centers around maintaining the free flow and the free conflict of ideas.

Stedman argues that the Department of Agriculture has become one of the most efficient of educational agencies, in distributing information not only on such things as scientific farm practices but also on more or less controversial questions such as those connected with specific farm programs. He believes that it has stuck to democratic principles in this work, especially by allowing opponents to be heard. Yet there is always the risk of stacking the cards entirely on one side, and in a crucial situation the temptation to do this will be very strong. His plea is that the Department strengthen itself against this temptation and continue to keep faith with the people by being truthful and factual; avoiding ballyhoo, hysteria, and politics; and leaving the way open for criticism and opposition on controversial issues.

"Here on this continent," he concludes, "the key institutions of democracy continue to function. If the Government . . . strives to build them stronger, then come what may in other parts of the world, democracy and civilization have a chance to survive in this Nation."

Science and Agricultural Policy

"In the last analysis," says Harding, "the form assumed by our social and economic system as a whole, and by agriculture in particular, depends primarily upon discoveries in natural science. The effect of such discoveries is in turn largely determined by the policies we adopt for their utilization."

To begin with, he asks—what is science? It is a method of investigating reality. Faced by a problem, the scientist first formulates a hypothesis, that is, figures out what might be a likely solution. Then he tests this hypothesis by carefully controlled experiments. If the experiments support the hypothesis, he assumes that it is correct; if not, he makes another hypothesis and tests that. From the experimentally proved hypothesis he deduces certain general principles or laws, and finally he relates these to other principles to form a pattern of scientific truth. Throughout this process he never deals with the whole of a thing; he studies only a carefully selected part of it—an abstraction or abstracted part. Moreover, he always makes certain basic assumptions that cannot be proved but that underlie all science. Thus in a sense he is dealing in fictions. He also deals in huge numbers —of atoms or electrons, for example—and since he cannot investigate what actually happens to all the individual items, his findings have only a mathematical probability. But these abstractions and probabilities have great power. They offer us a pattern of truth, map the universe, and save an immense amount of thought and labor. They are more revolutionary in their effects than so-called "radical ideas." Every great development of the Machine Age, as Harding points out, grew out of discoveries in abstract science made by men whom most people would consider impractical.

So much for the natural sciences, such as physics, chemistry, biology. Many people consider that they are the only sciences capable of revealing truth; that the social sciences—economics, sociology, anthropology, for example—are somehow inferior, or not real sciences at all. Harding vigorously combats this idea. He argues that practically every objection made to the social sciences applies just as well, in one way or another, to the natural sciences; and contrariwise, that the things said in support of the natural sciences are also true of the social sciences.

Harding is not writing about science for its own sake, however. He is concerned with its practical effects. Without doubt it is the most powerful force for good and ill in the modern world. Yet society exerts little or no control over its use. We take it casually and let the chips fall where they may; we make little or no effort to use it deliberately for the good of all men or to foresee and guard against the harmful effects of the swift changes brought by science. For example, "originative" discoveries create many new jobs, but "intensive" discoveries come along and wipe them out; 4,000 people die every year in the United States from pellagra, "an easily and economically preventable disease." The great need, Harding argues, is for "a science to make use of science"—to "supervise scientifically the utilization of the knowledge that research produces."

Because of their qualifications, scientists themselves should play a large part in developing such a "science to make use of science." Before that can be done, however, certain attitudes that have been built up by scientists will have to be changed. Harding makes a forthright attack on these attitudes. Scientists hold themselves aloof from judgments of "value," or right and wrong; they say their job is research, and they wash their hands of responsibility for the results of research. This attitude not only does not represent the truth, says Harding; it will end, if the scientists do not watch out, in the liquidation of all disinterested research, and the researchers as well; this has already happened in several countries. Again, science is too much divided up into airtight compartments; specialists are so specialized, and they have developed such fearful jargons, that they cannot even understand each other, let alone being understood by the public. Finally, to quote A. G. Church, "most scientists are ruled by their prejudices and passions in everything except their own small branches of study. . . . The scientist is afraid to be different, timidly afraid to accept the implications of the results of his own work and acquired knowledge, afraid to suggest that his own outlook . . . could with advantage be applied to our political, social, and economic institutions." The result is that others, often far less qualified, make all the important decisions and use the scientist's work for their own ends.

Both British and American scientists, Harding notes, are awakening to these faults and dangers, and some moves are being made to overcome them in the great professional associations of scientists. The Department of Agriculture also is moving in the direction of coordinating research in the natural and the social sciences and using it more fully as a background for urgent agricultural adjustments.

So far, says Harding, we have tried to cram the vast knowledge and potentialities of science into a given social framework. More and more we shall have to make science the framework and work out social arrangements that will fit it and enable us to use it fully for human welfare.

Schools of Philosophy for Farmers

Adjustments in agriculture in recent years raise a lot of fundamental questions. When extension workers found they needed more background to discuss these questions intelligently, the Department of Agriculture agreed to sponsor group discussion meetings, which soon became known as "schools of philosophy." The idea proved to be so popular and worth while that the discussion groups were soon extended to take in farm leaders (especially the farmer committeemen who handle agricultural programs), staff members of most of the bureaus of the Department of Agriculture and the State Agricultural colleges, teachers of vocational agriculture, even professional and businessmen interested in agricultural welfare. Some 70 of these "schools" now have been held in 38 States with an attendance of some 14,000 farm leaders. About 2,000,000 farm people have also been engaged in organized discussion groups throughout the country, and in 37 States farm men and women receive training under State leadership in how to conduct such groups.

No matter how practical the subject, Taeusch says, the discussion groups always get down to fundamental questions somewhere along the line. There are no brakes on what may be discussed. What is all this government regulation doing to our democracy? Can or should government interfere with economic trends? What kind of life will our farm boys and girls lead? Is local planning work taken seriously in Washington or dumped into the wastebasket? Are committeemen elected democractically or hand picked? Isn't there a danger of too much centralization? What is the difference between education and propaganda? These and other questions just as basic and troublesome continually pop up in the meetings and are frankly threshed out, with arguments on both sides. In general, these farm people and farm leaders want most to discuss what's happening in the modern world and what it's all about.

The real significance of the meetings, Taeusch believes, is that they are a valuable training for democracy. The essence of democracy consists in keeping the avenues of discussion open so that people can get together, talk over their problems, and reach a common understanding. But this is easier said than done. There are definite techniques that must be understood if such discussions are to be genuinely democratic, to open people's minds, to lead them on to further constructive inquiry, to help them express themselves fearlessly; and one of the main functions of the schools is to give training in these basic techniques of democracy. Beyond that, they serve the very practical purpose, for extension workers, administrative officials, and farm leaders, of filling some of the gaps left by the educational system.

In response to demand, over 2 million pamphlets have been issued on some of the subjects taken up by discussion groups. They "are frankly controversial, contrary points of view being presented in conversational form, and they include bibliographies." It is a common complaint of people who participate in the meetings, Taeusch says, that they cannot find enough reliable material on the questions discussed, and he suggests that schools and libraries should make an effort to meet this demand.

To maintain the spirit of the parliamentary form of government, he concludes, "is increasingly devolving on us in the United States—especially now that elsewhere the enemies of democracy are in the saddle and riding fast and furiously."

Old and New in Agricultural Organization

The survival of any living thing or of any human institution depends on its ability to change in response to new needs. New needs have pressed urgently upon the Department of Agriculture in recent years. It has had to undergo changes in order to meet them. Eisenhower and Kimmel tell the story of this growth and change.

The Department was created in 1862. For a long time after that its work was almost entirely in the natural sciences, including the farm practices that depend on science. Farmers could not afford the kind of research carried on by industry; in effect, the public hired a Federal agency to do it for them. It also hired State agencies, for the land-grant colleges and universities soon began carrying on agricultural research also. Under the pressure of changing farm needs, economic activities were added to this work—grading, market reporting, crop estimating, economic research. Education and information were always a part of the work, since research findings are useless if no one but a few researchers know about them. In time, the Extension Service, with its Nation-wide system of county agents, was set up as the link in educational work connecting farmers, State agencies, and the Federal agency.

In sum, the Department was a changing institution from the beginning, meeting new needs as they were expressed in popular demand. On the whole, this process was gradual. The crisis of 1929 brought demands of a different nature—explosive and sudden demands for economic action to prevent a total collapse of agriculture. Even these were not quite so sudden as they seemed; agriculture had had its own private depression for 10 years, and the remedies tried after 1929 had practically all been proposed in some form by farm leaders.

At any rate, Congress did pass laws that suddenly threw far-reaching responsibilities upon the Department for administration in new fields. New agencies had to be created quickly to carry out these "action programs," as they have come to be called in professional jargon in contrast with the older research and educational programs. Inevitably, some confusion resulted from the immense scope and the suddenness of these programs designed to meet urgent needs. Different agencies overlapped; there was not always time to gather or integrate all the necessary facts; and programs national in scope were not properly trimmed and fitted to local needs.

Meanwhile, as things settled into better perspective, it became evident that the farm problem could not be solved by a single formula such as that for parity prices. It had as many lives as a cat. There were, in fact, many farm problems—soil erosion, poverty, tenancy, heavy mortgages, oversupplied markets, loss of foreign trade, industrial unemployment, and so on. All of them were interrelated in one way or another, but they had to be attacked by different approaches. Congress passed legislation with that in view and gave the Department still more diverse responsibilities.

The outstanding need then was to pull all these activities together, get some unity into them—hook research up closely with planning, planning with administration; link the various agencies; coordinate national with State and community efforts. First step was to unify farm programs in the southern and then in the northern Great Plains, where drought and depression made conditions especially difficult. Then all land use activities were coordinated through a special Office of Land Use Coordination. This was a long step, since land use is directly or indirectly involved in many agricultural problems. The new office not only tied together various activities within the Department; it also coordinated Department efforts with those of other Government agencies concerned with land use.

A difficult problem still remained unsettled. These widespread national programs inevitably raised the old question of State versus Federal authority and produced some friction and misunderstanding. To iron out these difficulties, a Department committee and a Land Grant College committee finally got together and worked out what has been called the Mount Weather agreement. This agreement was aimed primarily at decentralizing action programs, particularly land use programs. Planning was to begin in local communities, with farmer committees. Next step was at the county level, with county committees; then at the State level, with State committees. All programs requiring national action or participation were finally to be cleared and coordinated through the Federal Department. This was a momentous step in the direction of democratic procedure, local responsibility, and closer cooperation of farmers, technical specialists, and administrators.

It necessitated some reorganization of the Department of Agriculture—"streamlining," some people called it—which was carried out in 1938. A major change was to turn the old Bureau of Agricultural Economics, originally a market research agency, into the central planning agency through which plans and programs could be cleared and dovetailed. The revised Bureau deals with agricultural economics in a truly broad sense. It is engaged in research and advisory work covering practically every economic problem of importance to agriculture, but it is not itself concerned in administering programs.

This, then, is the arrangement that has grown out of the critical experiences and the pressing needs of the past few years. Yet much remains to be done, the authors frankly conclude, if agriculture in our democracy is to meet the challenge presented by the current trend of world affairs.

Cooperative Land Use Planning—A New Development in Democracy

The agricultural programs that have developed since 1930 were at first adapted to local conditions by administrative officials. Very soon, however, farmer committees began to cooperate with some governmental agencies. This worked pretty well, but the cooperation was scattered and uncoordinated. How it was extended on a national basis through the Mount Weather agreement is told in the article by Eisenhower and Kimmel. Foster and Vogel give the details of the methods worked out as a result of this agreement. As they present it, the plan is a gigantic new undertaking aimed at accomplishing in a democratic way whatever over-all planning may be needed by farmers.

In each State there is a State committee headed by the director of agricultural extension, with farm members as well as members representing State and Federal agencies. At the heart of the plan are the county and community committees. The latter are composed almost entirely of farm men and women, often elected to the job at community mass meetings. These public meetings take place at various stages in the planning process and form the democratic base of the procedure.

First step is to hold local public meetings, discuss the whole idea, elect or appoint a community committee with representatives from each neighborhood. Much depends on the caliber of these representatives. The community committee then makes a preliminary study of local problems, draws up a map of land use areas showing the main characteristics of each, especially in relation to their suitability for farming, and makes recommendations. The county committee gets preliminary maps and reports from all the communities, makes necessary adjustments, consults with technical experts, drafts recommendations in a report for the State committee. Further adjustments may then be made after consultation with the county and community committees.

Next stage is to get action on the recommendations, which may involve new programs or modification and coordination of existing programs. Local farmers and every kind of public agency, county, State, or national, concerned with rural problems may be drawn into the unified action program finally decided upon for a county.

The authors illustrate the procedure by giving details of what occurred in Culpeper County, Va., and Ward County, N. Dak., where unified programs have been developed. For example:

Ward County, N. Dak. (hard hit by drought), was divided by the county committee into 23 areas, mostly grouped in two major classes—those suitable for general farming and those suitable for livestock. Greatest problems were in the second group; they included absentee ownership, too-small farms, shortage of capital, overemphasis on cash crops, needed improvements in range management and conservation. County-wide problems in both types of areas included poor tillage methods, feed shortages, short-term leases, overcapitalization, inadequate farm buildings, unequal taxes, heavy tax delinquency, difficulty in financing local government. Broad recommendations were made for a long-range program covering most of these problems, and action has begun in cooperation with local taxing authorities, the State experiment station, the Bureau of Agricultural Economics, school authorities, the county commissioners, the county treasurer, the County Welfare Board, the Farmers' Union, the State Governor, the Farm Security Administration, the Extension Service, and the Biological Survey.

Practical action is not the only worth-while result of this procedure. It has had a very great educational effect. Nor are action programs by any means confined to public agencies. Local people are getting together in many ways to do things themselves. Cooperative purchase or use of purebred sires, power equipment, sawmills, farm supplies, cold-storage locker plants are among the examples of this kind of action.

Looking ahead, the authors see agricultural planning of this type as above all a means to develop competent leadership and skill in democratic processes.

The authors express the belief that more and more will be done by cooperative private action in dealing with farm problems and that this should reduce the need to resort to Government aid. Much attention should be paid to "the possibilities of private action, by farmers among themselves and in cooperation with other private groups, to deal even with such difficult problems as agricultural surpluses, production control, submarginal croplands, reemployment of farmers displaced by technology, and the creation of opportunities for farm youth."

Part 7. Essentials of Agricultural Policy

Some Essentials of a Good Agricultural Policy

Tolley sums up much of the preceding material in the Yearbook from the standpoint of its bearing on agricultural policy.

Agricultural policy, he says, must rest firmly on the desires of the people. Now, what farm people have demanded in every farm revolt since the Civil War is equality for agriculture. But what does this phrase mean? Essentially it means that farm people want as good a chance as any other group to achieve a good life. Going a step further, what does a "good life" mean? It means such things as these: Enough food to be healthy; a decent house to live in; decent clothes to wear; reasonably adequate medical care; means of getting around, because this is an age of movement; means of keeping in touch with the world, because this is an age of highly developed communication; security, in the sense of a chance to get along by one's own efforts; a decent education; personal dignity—a sense of being of some value in the world; opportunities to join with others in social activity and to share the privileges and duties of citizenship in a democracy.

Farm people want a good life in this sense. It is to the Nation's interest that they should have it. But they are still relatively at a disadvantage compared with other groups. Farmers make up a fourth of the population and rear a third of the Nation's children, yet they have only a tenth of the national money income; half of them are inadequately housed and a third poorly clothed; an immense number of them are definitely below the poverty line; few have access to so simple a thing as a library for reading material; schools in the country are relatively inferior.

The farm movement is essentially a struggle to overcome such handicaps. In the struggle, group action is now being used as never before to develop "new devices of consultation, cooperation, and administration looking toward the satisfaction of these demands." The struggle will go on. But Government cannot give people "a good life" by decree; it can only help to equalize opportunities. Local and individual responsibility are vital. Policies expressed in legislation must not only come from the desires of the people in the first place; they must also be constantly judged by the people in the process of administration.

"In the policies of today," says Tolley, "formed as they have been in response to emphatic though generalized instructions of the people as a whole, it is possible to see, at least partly, the shape of some of the things to come."

Two conditions have been especially important in shaping agricultural policy during the past decade: (1) Lack of industrial opportunities has backed people up on the farms; (2) the demand for farm products has not increased as fast as the ability of farmers to produce them. Greater efforts than ever have been made to improve the income of commercial farmers, but these conditions have also forced two other kinds of effort—to do something for those who must stay on the land whether or not they have a commercial function; to develop the great, untapped possibilities of the domestic market as a means of making up for the loss of foreign markets. A third major line of effort forced by current conditions has been concerned with achieving better land use and conservation. Along with these greater issues are many others centering around such things as credit, taxes, land values.

Tolley discusses these various aspects of agricultural policy under five headings.

(1) Efforts to increase buying power include the highly significant food-stamp plan. In effect, this is dumping the surplus on the domestic instead of the foreign market. Our own consumers, instead of consumers abroad, get the benefit in the form of better diets and improved living standards. The plan has met with such popular approval that it seems more likely to be expanded than curtailed.

Efforts to improve the foreign market will depend largely on two things—the achievement of an enduring peace, and the degree of our willingness to import as well as to export.

(2) Control of production and marketing have come in response to the imperative demand of farm groups. There is little chance that it will be discontinued as long as production outruns demand. Acreage control, marketing quotas, commodity loans, marketing agreements all have certain inherent difficulties. These devices are essentially designed to give farmers some of the advantages that labor gets through organization and business through concentration of financial control. With continued experience they are capable of refinement and improvement to overcome weaknesses. They need to be put on a stable financial base.

On another aspect of marketing, economic studies indicate that substantial cuts in distribution costs could be made by changes in the marketing system, but this is largely a question of public demand.

(3) Financial adjustments to improve the condition of farmers have taken many forms. Crop insurance, now being tried with wheat, is a significant new departure. Credit policies, of course, are of major importance. The farm credit system is now reasonably adequate, but there are still problems to be solved—notably in relating credit to land use practices and to security of tenure. There is also need for further development of credit in relation to rural rehabilitation.

(4) It is now generally recognized that conservation problems are closely tied up with economic and social conditions in agriculture. Educational campaigns are not enough to solve them. But progress toward better patterns of land use will probably be slow. It is likely that conservation will be even more intimately connected with other agricultural adjustments than it is now. In the case of certain submarginal lands, Federal acquisition is difficult; there is a chance for States and counties to step in and do a constructive job. What to

do with the people living on land too poor to furnish a livelihood remains a knotty problem. The older generation in many cases will have to remain while effort is concentrated on opening up opportunities for the younger generation.

(5) The great problems of social adjustment within agriculture cannot be ignored, and it is here that new ground is most likely to be broken in the next decade. A third to a half of the farmers in the United States are poverty-stricken. Many more people are now on farms than are needed for commercial production, and the number is increasing steadily. It is not the American way to hand out doles to these people, but there are several lines of effort that fit our traditions. The most likely include (a) more attention to the needs of the small-scale producer in acreage allotments, benefit payments, soil-conservation practices; (b) help in moving from tenancy to ownership of family-size farms, and also improvements in tenancy itself; (c) employment on worth-while public works projects especially adapted to rural needs; (d) vocational guidance, and assistance in the form of credit based on character, for those capable of getting a toehold in the commercial system, either as individuals or as cooperative groups; (e) further develpoment of part-time and more or less self-sufficient farming on a modernized basis for those who must remain outside the commercial system. One rather special and urgent problem concerns farm labor—at least the migratory labor used in specialized farming. As the very least that can be done here, public opinion seems to favor decent camps and educational opportunities for the children of workers.

Tolley quotes M. L. Wilson to the effect that our need today is to avoid equally a pigheaded adherence to old ways just because we are used to them, and a violent resort to new ways just because they look like cure-alls.

A policy can be truly called "good" if it deals with the needs of every group in the agricultural population and, by giving the farmers of this generation a chance at the good life, conserves the human and natural resources from which will spring the life of the future.

PART 1

The Farmer's Changing World

The Farmer's Changing World

by F. F. Elliott [1]

TO SHOW how constantly the farmer has to plan to meet changes in the world about him, the author of this article pictures a strange world without change—no changes in weather, soils, production, economic affairs. Such a world would be unrecognizable, since we are accustomed to change as the normal condition of all life. The author then takes up the main economic changes that farmers have to meet—changes in markets, consumer buying habits, prosperity and depression, technology, standards of living. How can such changes be made to bring good rather than evil results? To what extent can we cope with the forces of change as individuals, and to what extent must we take group action? This, the author shows, is the fundamental question we face today, and it is not made less urgent by the present international situation.

WE LIVE in a dynamic world—a world in which physical nature, man's habits and reactions, and man-made institutions are all constantly changing. The problem of adjustment to change for the farmer can be easily visualized by assuming that he operates in a static or stationary economy in which no change takes place. How would a world without change differ from the real world in which the farmer actually operates?

[1] F. F. Elliott is Chief Agricultural Economist, Bureau of Agricultural Economics.

PICTURE AN UNCHANGING WORLD

In the first place, in such a stationary state of affairs, production would remain constant instead of continually fluctuating as it now does. The supply of cotton, wheat, corn, and other feed grains, of fruits and vegetables, and of all livestock and livestock products would be forthcoming in a steady and continuous stream. Each year the amount would be the same. There would be no new technological developments introduced to upset existing cost and price relationships. There would be no change in size of farms, no new land brought into cultivation, no changes in fertilizer treatment or in cultural practices, no additional soil losses to offset, and no new diseases, pests, or other production hazards to combat. There would be nothing, in short, to interfere either with the production or the even and continuous flow of products to market.

On the demand side, prices of products and cost of goods also would remain unchanged. There would be no fluctuations in business activity or in employment. No new synthetic products or new processes would be introduced to replace those already in use. There would be no change in export outlets either for agricultural or for industrial commodities. Likewise, there would be no change in birth or mortality rates, no further piling up of old-age groups, and no changes in the geographic distribution of the population. Moreover, standards of living, consumption habits, attitudes, and opinions of both rural and urban people would remain the same. There would be no innovations, no change in styles and fashions. All these things would be completely static or bear a constant relationship to each other.

In such a world the farmer's management problem obviously would be practically nonexistent. What decisions would there be for him to make? How simple his problem would be—and how different from those of the real world in which he operates today! It is only necessary to cite a few specific examples of changes that have occurred over the last decade or so to indicate how striking the contrast really is.

THE CHANGING SCENE OF REALITY

Changes in Markets

Consider first what has happened to the farmer's market, including the prices he has received for his products. In the first place, owing to population growth, he has been confronted with rather significant changes in the size of his total domestic market. He has also been confronted with changes in the composition of that market. This is evidenced by changes in the proportion of people living in cities and on farms, by shifts in the different age groups of the population, and by changes in the dietary habits of the people.

In 1920, for example, the farmer supplied food and fiber for approximately 105 million people, while at the present time he must supply the needs of about 132 million people.

Although the number of people living on farms today is about the same as in 1920, the nonfarm population has increased by about 25 million. As a result of this shift, the farmer's business has become more closely meshed with the nonfarm economy. This has increased the farmer's dependence upon the buying power and habits of the consuming group. At the same time it has subjected him, in an increasing degree, to the sharp ups and downs in business activity and in the general level of employment, which are so characteristic of this sphere of our economy.

Changes in Consumption Habits

In addition to these shifts in the total demand for his products the farmer has had to adjust himself to marked changes in the demand for specific commodities.

This type of change is evidenced by shifts in the per capita consumption of farm products. For example, there has been a decline in per capita consumption of wheat flour from 176 pounds in the period 1920–24 to 154 pounds in 1934–37. The consumption of citrus fruits has risen from 27 to 47 pounds per capita in the same period, and the consumption of canned fruits has risen from 9 to 15 pounds. On the other hand, the consumption of apples has dropped from 55 to 43 pounds. Excluding potatoes, there has been a sharp rise in the consumption of fresh vegetables from an average of 98 pounds during 1920–24 to 126 pounds in the period 1934–37. The increase in consumption of canned vegetables is particularly marked, having risen from 14 to 22 pounds per capita in the same period. There has also been an upward trend in the consumption of dairy products and a decline in the consumption of potatoes and lean meats. Although most of the changes that have taken place in consumption have not placed an excessive burden of adjustment upon farmers, they have added to the general problem and created special problems of expansion and contraction in specific areas.

Prosperity and Depression

The farmer also has felt the impact of industrial prosperity and depression as reflected through sharp fluctuations in the prices and consequently the income he has received. In 1919, for example, the index of prices received by farmers reached a peak of 221 as compared with 100 in the base period 1910–14. Two years later this index figure had slumped to 124. It got back to 147 in 1929 but collapsed again to 68 in 1932. It has since recovered to a post-depression peak of 121 in 1937.

The farmer's income, of course, was affected by these price changes. The gross farm income in 1919 reached the all-time high of 16.9 billion dollars. But in 1921 the farmer was forced to accept an income of only 8.9 billion dollars, barely half of what it had been 2 years before. By 1929 it was up again to 11.9 billion dollars, only to shrink to the ruinous figure of 5.3 billion dollars in 1932. General recovery, combined with a strenuous collective effort on the part of farmers, brought farm income back to slightly over 10 billion dollars in 1937.

These ups and downs in the farmer's prices and income reflect maladjustments in part in agriculture but primarily in the industrial economy, particularly in the structure of prices and the flow of investment.

Even more violent changes have taken place in the farmer's foreign market, reflecting not only the ups and downs of the business cycle and changes in the volume of American foreign lending but also the rise of nationalistic policies of self-sufficiency throughout the world. As a result there has been a sharp drop in the absolute amounts of specific agricultural commodities taken by foreign countries.

In 1919 the American farmer received nearly 4 billion dollars for exported products that required the use of more than 55 million acres of land for their production. In 1932 he received only 590 million dollars for the products of 34 million acres. Despite the subsequent general business recovery during the 1930's, the value of his exports remained low; in 1936 they had a value of less than three-quarters of a billion dollars, and their production required the use of only 20 million acres. Although there has been some recovery, our foreign outlets remain very low as compared with those around the World War period.

Technology and Mechanization

Apart from these sharp changes in markets and demand, the farmer also has had to adjust himself to the impact of rapid technological changes. Although these developments decreased his costs and increased his efficiency, they created new problems. Outstanding has been the increased use of machinery on farms and the substitution of mechanical power for animal power.

Twenty years ago there were more than 26 million horses and mules on farms; today there are fewer than 16 million. This change has resulted from a marked increase in the use of tractors, motortrucks, and automobiles. The number of tractors on farms, for example, had increased from 160,000 in 1919 to close to 1,600,000 in 1939. A change of almost equal magnitude has taken place in the use of motortrucks. With these shifts has come a release of nearly 35 million acres of land the production of which was formerly required to support work stock. The crops produced on this large area now must find a market through other channels, a circumstance that has greatly contributed to the farmer's surplus and price problem.

The increased use of mechanical power with its full complement of seeding, cultivating, and harvesting equipment has resulted in a rather marked increase in the efficiency with which man labor is used. In the period 1898–1902, for example, it required on an average 86 hours of man labor to produce 100 bushels of wheat, whereas in the period 1928–32 less than 50 hours was necessary. This has inevitably resulted in displacement of man labor in agriculture, giving rise to the difficult problem of readjustment and relocation of farm laborers elsewhere.

This trend toward mechanization, furthermore, has tended to cause regional shifts in agricultural production, to concentrate production in the most productive areas, and to increase the competition for farmers located on the more broken and unproductive lands.

Combined with mechanization have been other technological developments, such as those in the fields of plant breeding, genetics, and chemical fertilizers. The productivity of agriculture relative to its manpower has been tremendously increased by all these improvements. The development and recent wide adoption of hybrid seed corn is a particularly apt illustration of what is going on in this field.

Although these advances in technology have enabled the farmer to meet some of his problems, they have also created new ones, particularly when he has had to throw his increased output onto markets already glutted or lacking buying power.

Changing Standards

In addition to these changes of an economic and technical nature affecting the income and purchasing power of the farmer, there have been changes that have altered his standard of living and way of life. Along with other groups in the population, he has attempted to raise his standard of living by adopting many of the numerous innovations which have come to be accepted as necessary by other elements in the American population. These include such things as automobiles, radios, electric refrigerators and other electrical appliances, modern heating and plumbing, and the like. The farmer also has demanded better highways, better schools, better facilities for public health, and other public services.

This tendency to keep pace with rising living standards has increased his money outlay both for personal expenditures and for taxes. The problem of maintaining this standard of living, therefore, becomes increasingly one of maintaining his money income. Hence his concern with the recurring fluctuations in industrial buying power and their repercussions on his own money returns.

The farmer is confronted with still other changes, such as fluctuating debt burdens, changing freight and interest rates, the growth of internal trade barriers, and the like, which also are powerful forces that influence his final action. But it is not necessary to pile up further instances of the physical, economic, and social changes impinging upon the farmer to indicate how really difficult is the job of operating a farm.

THE FARMER'S PROBLEMS ARE THE NATION'S PROBLEMS

Little wonder that the farmer, affected by all these changes and the uncertainties attending them, frequently finds himself in difficulty. Moreover, these fluctuating conditions and forces, in addition to creating problems of serious import to the farmer as a managing operator of a going concern, also raise problems and issues of great importance to the Nation as a whole. They touch directly on national policy, involving questions as to both its nature and the form and direction it should take.

It is this phase of the problem with which this discussion is most concerned. What policy or what particular lines of action are best calculated to meet the situation?

(1) What can be done to bring about greater stability within agriculture itself to minimize the adverse effects upon the individual producer of these physical, economic, and social changes? Is unrestricted individual action most likely to achieve this result, or should we pursue a policy of united action? If the latter, what form should it take? Should cooperative action by farmers be purely voluntary, or should it in part be brought about through the use of monetary inducements or the exercise of the police and taxing powers of the State and Federal Governments?

(2) What can or should be done to improve the position of agriculture as a whole in relation to other industries so as to prevent the serious repercussions on farm prices and income produced by wide

swings in business activity and industrial unemployment? Should agriculture adopt measures now used by industry, or should the Federal Government attempt, through regulatory and other legal measures, to bring about a reversal in the present industrial policies of strong central control over production, marketing, and prices, and substitute a policy directed toward greatly expanded output, lower prices, and greater social responsibility?

(3) What policy or line of action is best calculated to result in the general public interest with respect to conservation and the forestalling of the tremendous wastes in both physical and human resources which have such great significance for the future welfare of the Nation? Shall we depend entirely upon educational appeal to awaken and foster a feeling of stewardship in the land in the hope of achieving conservation in that way; or shall we pursue a more direct and positive policy of group action in which benefit payments, zoning restrictions, land use regulations, and other devices are used to supplement the educational effort?

Finally, there is the even more important problem of human conservation. Can we afford to pursue a hands-off policy and disregard the plight of rural people now stranded in poor land areas and living on small worn-out farms; or trying to eke out an existence as croppers or wage hands in the better areas; or, even worse, living as migrants in some lean-to along the highway or in a labor camp? Shall we leave these casualties of the economic system to their fate and hope that somehow or in some way their lot eventually will be improved either through their own efforts or through the slow operation of the economic machine, which eventually may grind its way out of depression to prosperity? Or shall we follow a more positive policy of rehabilitation and reform whereby direct Government assistance will be given these underprivileged people in the way of loans and grants, guidance in relocation and resettlement, and rural conservation works programs, as well as medical care, hospitalization, and other public-service benefits?

What is done about these things obviously has tremendous significance not only for the individuals concerned, but for the Nation as a whole. It also raises questions of serious import to our institutions and our democratic way of life. This is true regardless of whether we follow a policy of laissez faire or one of united or cooperative action.

If, on the one hand, we let things drift and the Government refuses to take direct action, a situation such as that in 1932 may develop, in which the people in desperation will be inclined to take things in their own hands and do something about it. On the other hand, if we follow a policy in which the Government plays an increasing role in the economic and social life of the farmer, issues of equal magnitude will arise. What form, for example, should controls take, and how should they be imposed? Shall policy be formulated and programs be developed and superimposed from above, or shall the farmer take part in determining what is to be done, as well as how it is to be done?

The theory of democracy has always envisaged the citizen as the ultimate maker of policy. Neither policy making by explosion, such as occurs when the orderly processes of government fail, nor policy making by executive action, such as occurs when the experts and administrators make the decisions without the citizens' participation, is likely to occur in a society where democratic practice is reasonably in accord with democratic theory. Hence, if we are to preserve the democratic process, it is absolutely essential that the farmer play an important part and have a direct voice in the formulation of farm policy as well as in its execution.

It will be noted that the principal questions raised here revolve around the issue of individual versus group action. Which of the two is most likely to meet the situation adequately, and which should the Government adopt as its policy?

As a Nation we have traditionally followed a policy of noninterference by the Government in the operating problems of the individual farmer. The choice and combination of enterprises, the methods of production, the time and place of marketing, have been considered as peculiarly in the domain of the individual and outside the realm of government. But it is well known that this policy of private initiative and individual action in agriculture has not always worked out in the past either to the advantage of the individual farmer or to that of the Nation. In operation it has exhibited certain important weaknesses. It has not resulted in widespread conservation of our resources, but on the contrary has made the conservation problem more difficult and actually has sometimes produced disastrous exploitation of resources. It has tended to cut costs and to promote individual farmer efficiency, but at the same time has not maintained prices and income or given security to the mass of the farmers.

No doubt largely because of this, farmers in the early 1930's demanded a new approach. They demanded and got legislation from the national Government that represented a sharp departure from previous policy. It was based on a philosophy of group action. It specifically authorizes the use of governmental power to restrain or modify the action of the individual, both in the production and in the marketing of agricultural products. It operates on the assumption that this approach and the various procedures developed to give it force and administrative feasibility are necessary if individual farmers as well as the group of which they are a part are to attain that level of prices and income and that standard of living and degree of security which are commensurate with their contribution to the national weal.

No doubt there is a wide difference of opinion with respect to the validity of this assumption and the efficacy of this approach in achieving these ends. The problem is certainly of sufficient importance to warrant a reexamination of the issues involved. Perhaps the most effective way to do this is to resurvey the position of agriculture in relation to our whole national economic and social structure, with a view particularly to determining the forces that tend to affect agriculture adversely. In so doing we should be able to determine how and at what points agriculture is out of balance with the rest of the economy and to appraise the various lines of action most appropriate for meeting the situation. Much of the discussion in subsequent pages in this volume will be devoted to this question.

In recent months a new element has come into the picture—a new World War and our own defense program. This is a development which may have greater significance and more far-reaching implications and consequences to agriculture than any of the other changes previously discussed. It not only will intensify and make more difficult many needed economic and social adjustments, but also may actually endanger our existing institutions and democratic way of life.

The tremendous expenditures projected for armament and other forms of defense undoubtedly will speed up business activity, increase the national income, and absorb large numbers of the unemployed. They also will materially improve the prices of many of our agricultural products. But we should not permit ourselves to be lulled into the false position of assuming that these things are permanently solving our problem of needed agricultural and industrial adjustments. Something like a huge defense program, to be sure, may produce the industrial expansion we have so long needed, but we should remember that industrial expansion induced by increased expenditures for armaments may not be permanent—that it may again fall off as these expenditures are reduced. If such is the pattern, the problem of agricultural adjustment may be rendered more rather than less difficult, and the demand for group action in agriculture may become even more pressing than heretofore.

Old Ideals Versus New Ideas in Farm Life

by PAUL H. JOHNSTONE [1]

WHAT do you as a farmer think of the importance of farming in the general scheme of things? Do you envy city people, or do you tend to look down on them a little? What kind of education do you want, and how would you go about getting it? Do you like farming for its own sake, or do you think it should be considered primarily as a means of making money? How have modern conveniences and comforts affected your attitudes and your life? What do you think the "typical farmer" is like? Would your father and your grandfather have given the same answers to these questions that you do? Here is a rich historical survey of rural attitudes and ways of life in the United States covering just such questions as these, told through a wealth of human-interest material going back to colonial times. The author's interpretations, of course, are his own. They are thought-provoking, but in many cases others might draw different conclusions.

IN THE century and a half since the United States became a nation, our agriculture has moved all the way from the sickle to the combine, from the wooden plow drawn by a yoke of oxen to the

[1] Paul H. Johnstone is Senior Agricultural Historian, Division of Farm Population and Rural Welfare, Bureau of Agricultural Economics.

gang plow powered by a tractor. Our population has grown during this period from 4,000,000 to about 130,000,000; and whereas about 9 out of every 10 persons lived on the farm in the days of the Revolution, today only 1 person in 4 is a farmer. Farm life and work were concerned with more than agriculture then, for the farm family supplied itself with goods provided nowadays by special industries. The family took not only food and fuel, but lumber from the land; it boiled its own sugar, made its own soap, grew its own wool, and wore its own homespun. There were then no large factories nor great financial accumulations; there were no urban and industrial masses to be fed by commercial agriculture. But in 1928 over $63,000,000,000 worth of gross assets were owned by 150 huge corporations; and in 1930 nearly 70,000,000 Americans living in towns and cities of 2,500 or larger, and many more millions in smaller towns, were dependent on the farmer for their food and clothing. A century and a half ago a rich continent of unexploited cheap land awaited the agricultural settler; today there is not enough land to go around.

The economic and technological conditions of American agriculture have in the course of a century or more been altered out of all recognition by thousands of innovations of a drastic and even revolutionary character. These changes have not taken place in a vacuum. Neither farm life, nor any other kind of life, can be divided up. It comes all in one piece and hangs together. The changes that have come to agriculture have not altered just single phases of farm life, leaving everything else untouched. On the contrary, they have profoundly influenced the very essence and character of rural living. Even philosophies and ideas of right and wrong have in some cases taken on a new shape and character. It is the purpose of this article to suggest how the philosophy and social substance of farm life in the United States have altered in response to the tremendous changes that have taken place during the last century in the physical and economic worlds in which we live.

AMERICA'S INHERITANCE FROM "THE AGE OF ENLIGHTENMENT"

The United States was very much the child of the eighteenth century into which it was born. That century was a period of unprecedented social change and intellectual vigor. Most of the ferment of ideas originated in England and France but rapidly penetrated the whole western world. Social and political philosophers felt themselves suddenly free of medieval trammels, and with what seemed to them new and complete freedom from customary ideas they systematized social and political thought according to the abstract rationality [2] of their time. Because of this new faith in the perfectibility of knowledge

[2] The terms "rationality," "rationalistic," and "rationalism" as used in this article are not meant in any technical sense. Rather, they refer generally to the new faith in reason as opposed to the older faith in revelation or tradition. This faith was based partially upon a restless dissatisfaction with the state of things as they were and included confidence that reason and knowledge could effect vast improvements. It was founded also upon the faith that man is a "reasoning" creature of infinite perfectibility who should be expected to act according to the dictates of reason rather than, "unreasonably," according to custom or habit. Rationalism implied that whatever was "natural" or "right" or "just" would be evident as such to man, because of his powers of reason; similarly, because of the supposedly abstract, timeless, and spaceless quality of this rationality, it was conceived to be theoretically possible for man to achieve a kind of perfect and absolute sense of understanding of both nature and the world of men.

and of reason, the period came to be known as the Age of Reason, or the Age of Enlightenment.

Colonial and revolutionary America was not isolated from these influences; rather it participated to the utmost. Our revolutionary and founding fathers reasoned and acted in terms of the philosophy developed in eighteenth-century Europe. The republic they created amounted to a realization of the ideals of eighteenth-century intellectuals.

As with the Nation as a whole, so also with its agriculture. American agriculture has developed under the influence of eighteenth-century tradition. In that early age America was predominantly rural and agricultural, and most of its leaders came from a rural and agricultural background. When they were not themselves farmers or landed proprietors, they generally had at least a rural background and an active interest in agriculture. It was through the agency of men who were at once the civic, intellectual, and agricultural leaders of the young Nation that the beginnings of a new and modern character were planted in the American agricultural world.

One phase of the intellectual atmosphere of eighteenth-century Europe was a fashionable public interest in agriculture that at times attained the proportions of a craze. Princes and princelings, poets and philosophers, and fashionable lords and ladies assumed an ardent interest in agriculture that would have been disdained by people of their rank in an earlier age. Frederick the Great of Prussia loved on occasion to affect rural simplicity and posed as a rustic philosopher-king; George III of England had a model farm and pretended pleasure at the nickname "Farmer George"; the Emperor Joseph of Austria gave a public demonstration of plowing with much ceremony and a beribboned plow; the Dauphin of France (later Louis XVI) did the same; and Marie Antoinette played milkmaid in her doll-house farm at Versailles.

But such faddish extremes were merely froth on the wave of very sober interest in agricultural improvement. Royalty, nobility, landed proprietors, agencies of government, and learned societies fostered serious efforts to improve agricultural practices. Jethro Tull brought to England the "horse-hoe" of southern France and experimented with more intensive methods of cultivation; Lord Townshend improved on Tull's ideas and was the first to practice them successfully. Robert Bakewell began the systematic breeding of cattle and sheep. Such men as these in England, and men like Duhamel du Monceau, the student of forestry, fungus diseases, and insect pests, in France, began to effect substantial progress in husbandry and methods of cultivation through experimentation and the application of rudimentary science. Publicists and theoreticians such as Arthur Young and François Quesnay propagandized the newer methods of cultivation, argued for a better public appreciation of the special agrarian needs, and even developed an economic theory, called physiocracy, along lines particularly favorable to agricultural interests. Physiocracy marked the first notable attempt in history to develop a systematic and coherent theory of economics.

The most prominent men in the political and intellectual life of America aided in planting these ideas in this country. Benjamin Franklin and the American Philosophical Society encouraged the improvement of agricultural methods through the development of labor-saving inventions and the application of science. George Washington corresponded with the English agricultural improvers, Arthur Young and Sir Arthur Sinclair, made Mount Vernon into a model farm, and conducted countless experiments with new plants, new methods, and new machinery. Thomas Jefferson searched Europe for an upland rice, introduced olives into this country, though unsuccessfully, conducted experiments in rotations and soil fertility, undertook novel soil conservation practices, and was possibly the first to devise a mathematical formula for a moldboard of least resistance for plows.

SOME EARLY AMERICAN AGRICULTURAL INSTITUTIONS

Agricultural Societies

Agricultural societies began to spring up in America in imitation of those of Europe. They were inspired by the rationalistic philosophy and agrarian liberalism of the day and were devoted principally to the dissemination of general scientific information and to the encouragement of experimentation with new implements, new plants, and new methods of cultivation. They developed at first under the leadership of prominent men and generally had a select and limited membership drawn from the ranks of wealthy proprietors and distinguished intellectuals and political figures.[3] Among the first were the South Carolina Agricultural Society (1784), the Philadelphia Society for the Promotion of Agriculture (1785), the New York Society for Agriculture, Arts, and Manufactures (1791), followed shortly by the Massachusetts Society for Promoting Agriculture, and many others. The aristocratic nature of these early agricultural societies may be illustrated by the membership of one of them. The Albemarle Agricultural Society, founded at Charlottesville, Va., in 1817, had Thomas Jefferson as its prime mover. James Madison was later to be its president. Of the 30 founding members, besides former President Jefferson, there were 2 future Governors of Virginia, a future United States Senator and Ambassador to Great Britain, a future Justice of the United States Supreme Court, a brigadier general, a future head of the University of Virginia, and several others prominent in the political life of the Old Dominion (*72*).[4]

In the course of time, as the number of agricultural societies grew (about 300 agricultural societies were active in 1852, and in 1860 the United States Agricultural Society listed 941 (*71, p. 23*)), their popular base was broadened. Through their efforts and those of agricultural-fair associations and agricultural journals the ideas of the early and aristocratic agricultural societies were first democratized.

Agricultural Fairs

The agricultural fair as it developed in the first quarter of the nineteenth century has a very mixed ancestry. Its most ancient antecedent was the thoroughly medieval institution of the fair as a

---

[3] A possible exception may be the Kennebec Agricultural Society, founded in 1787, which was purported to have been organized by farmers.

[4] Italic numbers in parentheses refer to Literature Cited, p. 167.

special seasonal market place. Cattle fairs had a long colonial history, and there had been other similar events such as the Strawberry Fair in St. John's Parish in Berkeley County, S. C. An agricultural exhibition of some sort was apparently held in Washington in 1804. George Washington Parke Custis in 1810 began his public sheep shearings at Arlington, across the Potomac from Washington. Custis was essentially imitating the device of the English Coke of Holkham in making the institutional relics of the fair the means of giving a popular demonstration of modern methods of husbandry (*64, p. 5*). What appears to have been the first agricultural fair of a modern kind came probably in 1810, also in the District of Columbia. Many notables attended, including President and Mrs. Madison; and there were prizes for the best exhibits.

It was, however, Elkanah Watson more than anyone else who established the agricultural fair in this country as a lasting institution. After exhibiting publicly two prize merino sheep at his home in Pittsfield, Mass., in 1807, he led in organizing the Berkshire Agricultural Society in 1810; and in 1811 that organization staged its first fair. Thereafter, agricultural fair associations and agricultural societies whose principal purpose was to foster and manage such fairs increased rapidly in numbers and importance, particularly in New England, the Middle Atlantic States, and the new regions to the west. As the membership of these societies grew, the original aristocratic nature was lost, and more and more men of common rank undertook to aid the improvement of agriculture along the lines first advocated by the distinguished and select.

Agricultural Journals

Three early New Jersey newspapers—the New Jersey Gazette (1776), the Rural Magazine (Newark, 1796) and the Newton Farmers' Journal (1797) (*71, p. 28*)—are believed to have been the first American periodicals to publish many articles on agriculture. But it was not until 1810 that America's first full-fledged agricultural journal was founded—the Agricultural Museum (Georgetown, D. C.); it lasted 2 years. In 1819, two agricultural journals made their appearance—the American Farmer (Baltimore) and the Plough Boy (Albany). The New England Farmer (Boston) began publication in 1822, the New York Farmer (New York City) in 1827, the Southern Agriculturist (Charleston, S. C.) in 1828, the Genesee Farmer (Rochester, N. Y.) in 1831, and the Cultivator in 1834. The Prairie Farmer (at first the Union Agriculturist and Western Prairie Farmer) began its long career at Chicago in 1840. By 1850, 40 or more agricultural journals had been established. Many did not last long, but those that survived exerted a great influence. As early as 1837, 3 years after its founding, the Cultivator had an edition of 18,000 and subscribers in almost every State and Territory in the Union.

THE SEED OF A NEW GROWTH

Thus the United States, at the very outset, developed special institutions directed in one or another way to the service and betterment of agriculture—first agricultural societies of an aristocratic nature, then agricultural societies and fair associations on a more popular level, then agricultural journalism. State boards and departments of agriculture, national agricultural organizations, a Federal Department of Agriculture, and a Nation-wide system of State agricultural colleges and experiment stations were to follow. In the present day, when such things are taken for granted, their significance is likely to be overlooked. They were in fact, however, something new under the sun. Agriculture had from the earliest times grown like Topsy. It was wholly traditionalized, conducted automatically according to customs transmitted down the centuries without change or question from father to son. Until the age in which the United States became a nation there had been very little rational and systematic effort to improve agricultural practices, and the overwhelming mass of farmers still employed methods that were very little changed from those employed in ancient Rome. Furthermore, until that age the idea that agriculture might be improved simply did not exist in any effective way. People did things the way things always had been done, and the idea that there might be a better way of doing them, or even an alternative way, simply did not occur to them.

The existence of a growing body of institutions deliberately and directly devoted to the alteration and improvement of agriculture is therefore a fact of tremendous significance in American history. It has meant that there has been within the agricultural world itself a force constantly working to overcome traditional inertias and to direct agriculture into new paths. A stout core of customary resistance has of course remained, but the unrelenting agitation for progress has resulted in an accelerated change that is unprecedented in all previous agricultural history. The story of American agriculture during the last century and of the changes that have taken place in it in that time is to a very large extent the story of the interaction between agricultural leadership on the one hand, striving for improvements and innovations, and the inertias of folkways and informal tradition on the other hand, naturally and inevitably resistant to novelty.

AGRARIANISM

The Tradition

The early leadership of agriculture in America planted the seed of an intellectual tradition that in essence had two parts. The first of these was the idea of progress and scientific improvement. The second was the literary agrarianism derived originally from classic antiquity. Typical of the eighteenth century, these ideas were an integral part of the rising new spirit of that age, in the world at large as well as in the world of farms and farmers.

The agrarianism of classic tradition became the political and social agrarianism of Jefferson:

> Those who labor in the earth are the chosen people of God, if ever He had a chosen people, whose breasts He has made His peculiar deposit for substantial and genuine virtue. It is the focus in which He keeps alive that sacred fire, which otherwise might escape from the face of the earth. Corruption of morals in the mass of cultivators is a phenomenon of which no age nor nation has furnished an example. It is the mark set on those, who, not looking up to heaven, to their own soil and industry, as does the husbandman, for their subsistence, depend for it on casualties

and caprice of customers. Dependence begets subservience and venality, suffocates the germ of virtue, and prepares fit tools for the designs of ambition * * * generally speaking, the proportion which the aggregate of the other classes of citizens bears in any State to that of its husbandmen, is the proportion of its unsound to its healthy parts, and is a good enough barometer whereby to measure its degree of corruption.[5]

Such ideas were in close harmony with the romantic intellectual currents of the day because both were based upon assumptions of the goodness of nature, of natural man, and of simplicity of manners. And they amounted also to a philosophical elaboration of a deep but less articulate distrust of the city widely held among the masses of country people. Regardless of political party, Jeffersonian agrarianism came to be accepted as the expression of the rural social creed.

A cardinal point of the agrarian creed was the concept of the complete economic independence of the farmer. In the days when production on the farm was directed principally to the supply of home consumption needs—when all the food except occasional luxury items, when all the power and housing and fuel and most of the clothing for the farm family were produced upon the farm—the doctrine of rural independence harmonized with reality. It was the doctrine of agricultural leadership, regularly repeated by all rural spokesmen. A typical statement is this excerpt from the Union Agriculturist and Western Prairie Farmer of August 1841:

The farmer is the most noble and independent man in society. He has ever been honored and respected from the days of Cincinnatus, the Roman farmer, to the present time * * * He is not placed in that station which requires him ever to be seeking or courting popular favor, bowing and bowing to this or that man to gain their favor; but he looks upon the earth and the indulgent smiles of Heaven to crown his efforts, resting with the fullest assurance that "seed time and harvest" shall ever continue through all coming time (*3*).

The second important point of the agrarian creed—agricultural fundamentalism, it has been called—was the idea that agriculture is the fundamental employment of man upon which all other economic activities were vitally dependent. This was literary doctrine, but it was also popular belief—was bound to be, perhaps, in a country where three-fourths to nine-tenths of the population lived on farms. And thus farm people generally, and most nonfarm people also, firmly believed that, as General H. K. Oliver declared in 1858—

* * * the whole pulse of commercial and monetary operations is affected by the healthful and unhealthful beatings of the agricultural heart; that stocks and prices in the market and on "change," rise and fall as the agricultural tide ebbs and flows; that, as come the crops, either plenteous or meagre, so darts or limps the gigantic business of the busy world * * * (*65*).

The third and most important point of the agrarian creed was the idea that agricultural life is the natural life, and, being natural, is therefore good. The ever-present corollary was that city life and urban culture are inevitably enervating and corrupt. The first part of this, concerning the inherent goodness of country life, was gener-

[5] United States Bureau of Agricultural Economics. WASHINGTON, JEFFERSON, LINCOLN AND AGRICULTURE. (From Jefferson's Notes on Virginia.) 102 pp. 1937. [Processed.] See p. 48.

ally, so far as it was explicit, a literary or intellectual doctrine. The second, concerning the corruption of the city, was popular belief.

Rural-Urban Antagonisms

There is evidence to indicate that much of the praise of rural life expressed in popular literature was a defensive gesture against real or imagined slurs. Farm journals in those early days were constantly preoccupied with derogatory urban opinions of farm people and rural manners. Farm people were constantly advised by their leaders to be proud of themselves and of their occupation. From this repeated advice it is easy to infer a significant hypersensitiveness, for although it was regularly pointed out that urbanity of manners was superficial at best, and even an indication of shallowness of spirit, frequent exhortation was made to acquire the learning and social grace that would leave no room for such criticism. "There has * * * a certain class of individuals grown up in our land," complained the Cultivator in 1835, quoting the Genesee farmer, "who treat the cultivators of the soil as an inferior caste * * * whose utmost abilities are confined to the merit of being able to discuss a boiled potatoe and a rasher of bacon * * *" (*51*). And Joseph Brayshaw, in an address in 1841 reported by the Union Agriculturist and Western Prairie Farmer, declared that "it is really mortifying to the well-wisher to his country, to see how anxious many of the cultivators of the soil are to leave this occupation, in order to follow some other, which they think will make them gentlemen. Shame upon that gentility which depends only on dress or occupation!" (*43*).

Closely associated with this common resentment against a consciousness of urban disdain was a deep dislike of many of the trappings of aristocracy and the corruptions of the city. Country people have always felt some hostility toward urban cultures. From age to age the specific objects of that hostility have varied; but in the early United States, farm people concentrated their dislike of the city upon the wealthy and aristocratic, upon "dandies" and loafers, and upon bankers, "loan sharks," "land sharks," middlemen, monopolists, and other symbols of an unwelcomed capitalism. In its first issue in June 1819, the Plough Boy in declaring its purposes heaped scorn upon "*female* as well as *male* DANDIES" and detailed its praise of the "real, unsophisticated American; a virtuous, intelligent, brave, hardy, and generous yeoman, who despises alike the trappings of *royalty* or *aristocracy*." Solon Robinson, writing in the Cultivator for May 1838, expressed the typical resentment of farmers against "the butterflies who flutter over them in British broadcloth, consuming the fruits of the sweat of their brows" (*67*). And in November of the same year the Cultivator repeated a common warning to farmers of the dangers in store for them in banks. In the list of "things a farmer should not do" was the following:

> A farmer should shun the doors of a bank as he would the approach of the plague or cholera; banks are for traders and men of speculation, and theirs is a business with which farmers have little to do.

Farm journals made a regular feature of the iniquities of speculators, usurers, and middlemen. There was much outright preaching against the perils of credit dealings, and short tales were told to illustrate this moral. "The Unjust Usurer—A Tale of the Prairie," printed in the Prairie Farmer in 1860 ended on the following note:

> This is no imaginative sketch, but a stern reality. It shows the danger of getting into debt, of the sure ruin that will arise from accumulating interest, and the tender mercies of land-sharks and unjust usurers.

Urban culture was considered bad not only for its possible effect upon country people; it was deemed even more disastrous in its effect upon the poor and the unfortunate within the city itself. It was regularly emphasized that in the city "vice and immorality are held up as examples for the unprovided children of unfortunate families" (*50*). And when a correspondent of the Prairie Farmer ventured in 1849 to praise the "luxuries," the "polished society," and the "investments" possible in the city, he was strongly rebuked for failing to see that city life "*crushes*, *enslaves*, and *ruins so many thousands of our young men*, who are insensibly made the victims of *dissipation*, of *reckless speculation*, and of *ultimate crime*" (*8*).

There was a long historical background for this rural-urban antagonism. It had been especially strong during the colonial period, except in New England. In the middle and southern colonies, the cities were settled and to a large extent governed by the representatives of European commercial houses, sent here to milk the hinterland, and by representatives of European landholders and aristocrats. The upper stratum of the colonial city population, therefore, was identified with European merchants and aristocrats rather than with the American rural settlers whom it exploited.

The farmers and the laboring classes, on the other hand, were for the most part of yeoman and peasant stock and felt akin both because of common origins and common dislike of aristocracy. They had come from a Europe where class lines were relatively rigid to a land of opportunity where they could acquire property and move up the economic ladder. But in many cases they found obstacles in the way of moving up the political and social ladders. The transplanted aristocrats, who came over as members of the ruling class, were slow to recognize the changed situation, even slower to find it desirable. Farmers tended therefore to become progressives and rebels in order to reinforce the economic opportunity of the New World with social and political opportunity as well. Out of long resentment against aristocracy and privilege, the basic belief was developed and perpetuated that virtue is the characteristic of the poor and humble. This good agrarian doctrine linked the struggling farmer with the urban laborer. But it was inconsistent with prevailing Calvinistic doctrine, which said by implication that virtue was rewarded by material blessings, and tended to link the successful farmer with the successful city dweller.

Regional Differences in Rural-Urban Relationships

In New England the proportion and importance of representatives of European aristocracy and commercial interests was very much less than in the Crown Colonies farther south, at least until Massachusetts lost her charter. Furthermore, the population distributed itself in townships, where the people lived in the town and went into the fields to farm. The community of interests within the town cut across occupational lines. There was much part-time farming and part-time manufacturing or business. Since many people were therefore part of both the rural and the urban occupational groups at the same time, the whole pattern tended to minimize both the differences and the antagonisms between those who earned a living by farming and those who earned one by trading or manufacturing. This township plan of living based on community of interests and the political democracy that developed through it fostered a sense of equality that was relatively little disturbed by class antagonisms.

In the middle Colonies, which were largely settled by the parceling out of large estates, the township plan never developed, and the county, an unwieldy social unit in those days of slow transportation, became the political unit. It was in these Colonies that the isolated farmstead which was to be the pattern on western homestead lands was first found. With isolated farmsteads rural-urban antagonism increased, because a sharp division of functions between the city and the country developed. The city seemed to exist as a parasite on the country.

In the South, where the plantation system developed side by side but in successful competition with the yeoman's subsistence homestead, the only function served by the city was as a marketing and transshipping point for the cash crops of the plantations. The city seemed only the agent of remote and somewhat parasitic commercial interests with whom the planters were often at odds. Agrarian liberalism was in the air, and the great plantation owners snatched it up as a rationalization of their own position. Thus, because it was somehow easy for the proprietors of vast estates to believe the praise of humble yeomen applied to themselves, the anomaly of a liberal gentry developed.

The Democratic Character of American Agrarianism

The United States has never had a peasant agriculture, and farm people in this country have never had the sense of inferiority and awkward rusticity of a European peasantry. There was, undoubtedly, a certain crudity of manners that the inevitable rawness and privation of the frontier engendered. And there is, indeed, much evidence that rural people were aware of the cultural inadequacies and the lack of refinement so frequent in their very young civilization and that they resented snobbish criticisms from the city and the seaboard. But that resentment did not spring from any feeling of innate inferiority. Rather, there developed among the small freehold farmers along the frontier a spirit of lusty democracy and social equality. Aristocracies of birth and wealth were left behind in the East. Along the line of westward expansion especially, everyone was close to both poverty and wealth. Wages were generally high in proportion to the cost of becoming a proprietor. Class lines did not exist, hardships were routine, and every man's hands were calloused. The resentments of these frontier agricultural people were directed principally against the lily fingers of the idle, the posturing of aristocrats, and the devious devices of those who lived by manipulation rather than by creative labor. For themselves they knew that toil was preparation for security, and crudity the prelude to refinement. Probably no people ever built so many schools and churches on such a slender margin above the necessities of existence. Homespun was still a sign of virtue, but this did not mean that some day they would not wear silk.

There was a great deal of shifting back and forth between farming and town trades. The carpenter and the blacksmith probably had been farmers and might well become farmers again; the farmer down the road had perhaps worked for a while as a bootmaker. The traditional household practice of crafts that advancing technology was just then beginning to displace by factory industry made this possible. Few people, therefore, were ever far removed either from farming or from commerce and industry.

As settlement moved farther west into prairie lands, subsistence practices became difficult and even impossible, and farmers were forced into commercial production, with increasing dependency upon distant markets, intermediate middlemen, and transportation facilities. There was ordinarily very little local industry with which the agriculture and the farm people of a community could be economically linked and socially bound. The farmers of these regions therefore tended to identify themselves according to a vocational and economic grouping rather than by neighborhood or social classification.

Another factor that influenced the growth of attitudes and institutions in the agricultural West, where the predominant rural culture of this age was developed, was the fact that a large proportion of its pioneers and settlers were the disinherited of the older East. The rebellious suspicion felt by so many toward the East from which they had fled helped to direct hostility toward wealth and aristocracy and ease and polish, all of which long remained as symbols of the East.

THE VIRTUE OF LABOR

The famous French observer of American life, Alexis de Tocqueville, was impressed 15 years later by the fact that labor was so highly esteemed as an economic necessity that it became a social necessity and a moral virtue. There is nothing about this that seems very notable to us today, for it is a part of common American belief. But it looked new and strange to Europeans who were used to the aristocratic tradition that work is degrading.

> Among a democratic people, where there is no hereditary wealth, every man works to earn a living, or has worked, or is born of parents who have worked. The notion of labour is therefore presented to the mind on every side as the necessary, natural, and honest condition of human existence. Not only is labour not dishonourable among such a people, but it is held in honour: the prejudice is not against it, but in its favour. In the United States a wealthy man thinks that he owes it to public opinion to devote his leisure to some kind of industrial or commercial pursuit, or to public business. He would think himself in bad repute if he employed his life solely in living (*70, p. 162*).

Industry and thrift were considered cardinal virtues to a degree that was perhaps unprecedented in many previous centuries of Occidental history. There was no aristocracy on the frontier to establish ease as a social distinction, and hard, grubbing toil was generally necessary for even the barest maintenance of life.

Gain without toil was considered unnatural, and reverence for labor was heightened by religious sanction taken from the Bible. Thus the Cultivator reminded its patrons in 1836 that "the Lord God took the man and put him into the Garden of Eden, *to dress it and keep it;* and He further told him, 'in the sweat of thy face shalt thou eat bread, and thou shalt *till the ground* from whence thou art taken' " (*2*). The concept of the necessity and the honor of labor penetrated ideas of rearing the young, in whom the habits of industry should be inculcated from an early age. "There is no greater defect in educating children," declared the Farmer's Monthly Visitor in 1846, "than neglecting to accustom them to work. It is an evil that attaches mostly to large towns and cities" (*6*). Much of the literary effort of that day celebrated the honor and profit of labor. "Labor—An Ode," was the title of the following verses by George Bungay in the New England Farmer, 1857:

> Toil swings the axe, and forests bow;
> The seeds break out in radiant bloom;
> Rich harvests smile behind the plow,
> And cities cluster round the loom;
> Where towering domes and tapering spires
> Adorn the vale and crown the hill,
> Stout Labor lights its beacon fires,
> And plumes with smoke the forge and mill.
>
> The monarch oak, the woodland's pride,
> Whose trunk is seamed with lightning scars,
> Toil launches on the restless tide,
> And there unrolls the flag of stars;
> The engine with its lungs of flame,
> And ribs of brass and joints of steel,
> From Labor's plastic fingers came,
> With sobbing valve and whirring wheel.

Work Was Work in Town and Country Alike

Wherever the small freehold pattern prevailed, rural people tended strongly to identify themselves with all labor, whether strictly agricultural or not. The word "labor" referred to all creative work with the hands, and "laborer," though sometimes used specially to distinguish the unskilled worker from the "mechanic," was ordinarily understood to include the farmer. This was the early spirit of the agrarian liberalism that developed as the tide of westward movement pushed civilization beyond tidewater-plantation areas and the older coastal regions. It was perhaps the only popular and long-enduring indigenous liberalism that America has yet known. It was a spirit rankled by the privilege of wealth and birth, that saw right and justice always on the side of the poor and humble.[6]

---

[6] See following verses:

> Tell me not that he's a poor man,
> That his dress is coarse and bare;
> Tell me not his daily pittance
> Is a workman's scanty fare.
> Tell me not his birth is humble,
> That his parentage is low;
> Is he honest in his actio ns?
> That is all I want to know.
>
> Let it be a low, thatch'd hovel;
> Let it be a clay-built cot;
> Let it be a parish work-house—
> In my eye it matters not.
> And, if others will disown him
> As inferior to their caste,
> Let them do it—I befriend him
> As a brother to the last (*13*).

Repeatedly, it was stated in farm journals that the hard-working, law-abiding poor man was "a thousand times more respectable than the wealthy idler, the educated spendthrift, the callous miser, or the fashionable fool"; and that "* * * the modest female, whether seamstress, book-folder, press tender, storekeeper, or even house servant," was "* * * infinitely more respectable than the extravagant wife * * * than the thoughtless votary of fashion, than the butterfly flirt" (*12*).

There is much significance in the fact that the agitation for agricultural education that developed during the 1830's included mechanical or industrial education as a matter of course. The desired establishments were frequently referred to by farmer spokesmen as "manual labor schools," to provide "industrial education"; and they were urged as a benefit to "the laboring classes," or in the interest of developing "educated labor." The frequent present-day combination of engineering and agricultural colleges is a historical vestige of this once prevailing community of interest between farmers and urban workers.

Agricultural journals gave sympathetic attention to the interests of urban crafts, and it is sometimes difficult to determine whether a periodical was an agricultural journal or a crafts and labor journal. This was particularly true in New England. The community of interest was sometimes evident even in the name, as in the case of the journal that for 10 years after 1848 was called The Plough, the Loom and the Anvil (subtitled, "An American Farmers' Magazine and Mechanics' Guide") until in 1858 it became simply the American Farmers' Magazine.

There was frequently an exultant optimism in the expressions of the nobility and accomplishments of labor. Those who with their own hands carved farms from the forest and with their own eyes saw the wilderness transformed into a peaceful and productive countryside, with roads and railroads and schools and flourishing towns, could appreciate labor's accomplishments and also believe in unending improvement and progress. The eighteenth-century doctrine of progress had taken root and flourished in America as in no other country in the world. The unequaled opportunity that America offered, the rapid expansion and growth, and the rise in material living standards were so evident that what had been a new and startling idea in early eighteenth-century Europe appeared in nineteenth-century America to be an eternal truth. There was a lusty pride in labor that was associated with the buoyant confidence in progress, for it was conceived that by the labors of the farmer and the mechanic the United States would be made into an ever-prosperous and ever-glorious land of the free.[7]

---

[7] The following verses were written for the Prairie Farmer in 1860:

The Farmers are coming, make room, make room,
The Farmers are coming, make room, make room,
They're felling our forests, enriching our lands,
Improvement is ever the work of their hands:
All hail! to the Farmer, our brave pioneer,
Whose praises resounding are heard far and near.
O! who is so noble and gen'rous as he,
In city, or village, or woodland, or lea?
The Farmer is coming, make room, make room,
The Farmer is coming, make room, make room,
The Farmer, our country's true, resolute friend,
To help, or to fight for, to bless, or defend!

* * *

[Footnote continued on p. 124.]

THE IDEA OF PROGRESS

The idea of progress was a basic element in the creed of early America, both rural and urban. It was not merely an opinion reached by calm deliberation. It had begun, indeed, as an intellectual doctrine but soon became an unreasoned basic attitude, an assumption that the very law of nature itself compelled man and society to go on improving indefinitely. It was, however, ordinarily considered that America was the peculiarly favored domain of progress. The idea of progress was implicit in all the thought and activity of the intellectual and scientific leadership of agriculture; the search for an improved agricultural technology assumed both the possibility and the desirability of such advance. "Machines for abridging human labour are especially desired in America," declared Dr. Nicholas Collin, Rector of the Swedish Churches in Pennsylvania, before the American Philosophical Society in 1789—

as there can be no competition between them and the arms of industrious labour, while these have full employ on her extensive lands; which must be the case for ages. Agriculture has the first claim to the exertions of mechanical genius, as the principal source of national prosperity. * * * Among important desiderata we may place these—A machine for sowing broadcast * * * another for cutting drains * * * an apparatus for clearing new lands * * * so that the trees may be pulled out of the ground, cut in convenient pieces, and heaped; a better instrument for reaping than the common sickle, such for example as the cradling scythe of Northern Europe * * * (*45*).

The doctrine of technological progress, from being merely the idea of a few intellectuals, rapidly became a widely accepted popular assumption. The extent to which this was true is illustrated by an incident related by de Tocqueville:

It can hardly be believed how many facts naturally flow from the philosophical theory of the indefinite perfectibility of man, or how strong an influence it exercises even on men who, living entirely for the purposes of action and not of thought, seem to conform their actions to it, without knowing anything about it. I accost an American sailor, and I inquire why the ships of his country are

---

[Footnote Continued from 123.]

Mechanics are coming, make room, make room,
Mechanics are coming, make room, make room,
For labor is pleasure, and labor is health,
Each better than honor, or wisdom, or wealth;
O, shout! for the laboring man of our time,
Who, 'neath his own fig tree and clustering vine,
Can laugh at adversity's wild dashing waves,
And count those who "live by their wits" among slaves!
  Brave Labor is coming, make room, make room,
  Brave Labor is coming, make room, make room,
Our altars were made by the laborer free,
Who toiled as he shouted for dear liberty!

True Progress is coming, make room, make room,
True Progress is coming, make room, make room,
She comes to the West of our earliest dreams,
Where cradled in beauty, broad lakes and clear streams,
Where Science enchantment e'er loveth to fling,
And Genius spreads broadly her radiant wing;
Where Glory is only the beacon of life,
And Peace is our refuge from carnage and strife.
  True Progress is coming, make room, make room,
  True Progress is coming, make room, make room.
'Tis found in the cottage, the palace, the hall,
Watchword of the noble, the gifted—of all!

built so as to last but for a short time; he answers without hesitation that the art of navigation is every day making such rapid progress, that the finest vessel would become almost useless if it lasted beyond a certain number of years. In these words, which fell accidentally and on a particular subject from a man of rude attainments, I recognize the general and systematic idea upon which a great people directs all its concerns (*70, p. 34*).

The United States thus accepted broadly and popularly, at an early period, the idea of indefinite technological progress. In that youthful age, the United States was in fact unusually disposed to accord at least some welcome to almost any innovation, because she was herself an innovation inclined lustily to impatience with methods and traditions that had only age and custom to recommend them. It seems probable that the readiness to accept technological novelties developed more rapidly among some urban, industrial, and commercial groups than in the more remote rural areas. But the ever-present reform element of agricultural leadership was not surpassed by any in its zeal for progress and kept up a ceaseless and impatient agitation for improvement, regularly insisting that—

The characteristic of the present day is *reformation* and general improvement in the agricultural department—in the sciences and arts—by general diffusion of agricultural and scientific knowledge and by "*elevation* and *refinement of intellect*" (*31*).

Rapid Development of Mechanical Devices

A distinction must be made between the adoption of new labor-saving mechanical devices and of new procedures of cultivation. American farmers were relatively quick to see the advantages of the former. Except for what they learned from the Indians, the American colonists employed agricultural implements and methods that were very little changed from those in common use in the days of ancient Rome. Then suddenly, in the space of half or three-quarters of a century, agricultural technology was improved vastly more than in the full space of the 2,000 previous years.

In the last quarter of the eighteenth century, the very crude plows were made of wood according to rule-of-thumb ideas that varied greatly from one locality to the next. Metal points were in use in a few places. The restless and progressive spirit of the eighteenth century had, however, discovered the inefficiency of the wooden plow, particularly as an instrument for breaking sod and new land, and many inventive minds both in Europe and America were playing with the idea of a better plow made of iron. In 1793 Thomas Jefferson worked out on mathematical principles a formula for a metal moldboard of least resistance, which could have been used by local blacksmiths to make better plows, but wasn't. The first patent for a cast-iron plow was granted to Charles Newbold of New Jersey in 1797. Probably the first patent for steel and wrought-iron plows was granted in 1808. As the western lands opened up and there was increased need for strong plows for breaking prairie sod, it became a practice for farmers and local blacksmiths to face their plows with old saw blades. Finally in the 1830's steel plows became a common reality when John Lane, in 1833, and John Deere, in 1837, began their commercial manufacture. Soon, in all but a few remote places, the old wooden plow was a thing of the past.

In the first days of the Republic, grain and hay were still cut with a bare sickle. At some undetermined date in the last quarter of the eighteenth century the cradle for the scythe was first introduced into America and came into common use early in the nineteenth century. Although Cyrus McCormick began to work on the problem of inventing a grain reaper as early as 1809, the first serviceable machine was patented in 1831 by William Manning. Obed Hussey in 1833 and McCormick in 1834 obtained patents for reapers, which were gradually improved until by the time of the Civil War McCormick's much improved and very practical machine had come into wide use. The first patent for a portable threshing machine attachable to a reaper was taken out in 1837 by Hiram A. and John A. Pitts, but although this idea of the combine was in men's minds then, it did not become a practical reality until three-quarters of a century later, first in Californiε and then in the Palouse. The grain binder made its appearance in the fifties, and the Marsh harvester was first patented in 1858.

Small grain was, of course, sown broadcast in the early days, and corn was planted by hand. George Washington had been among the many who experimented unsuccessfully with mechanical devices to replace broadcasting by hand. Finally, in the years after 1840, a practical seeder was evolved, and the grain drill soon became a common and working reality. A practical corn planter was patented in 1853 by George W. Brown, and a two-horse straddle-row cultivator was patented in 1856. Thus the ox-drawn hoe of the seventeenth-century vineyards of southern France that became Jethro Tull's "horse-hoe" in eighteenth-century England finally evolved toward the riding cultivator so familiar to latter-day Americans.

The cotton gin first patented by Eli Whitney in 1793 was rapidly improved and widely adopted, and it made possible the vast increase in cotton production from 4,000 bales in 1790 to 3,841,000 bales in 1860. Liebig's Organic Chemistry in Its Applications to Agriculture and Physiology (*63*) appeared in 1840 and soon became the basis for the new science of soil chemistry. The mechanical principles of the modern grain elevator were first employed by Joseph Dart in Buffalo, N. Y., in 1842; and grades of wheat were first indicated on grain elevator receipts in Chicago in 1857. In 1817 the Erie Canal was begun, and a 20-year era of canal building was ushered in that opened eastern and foreign markets to much of the western and frontier land. In 1829 Stephenson proved the practicability of railroads, and by 1860 30,000 miles of track had been constructed. The modern world of technology and industry and commerce was approachig at an accelerating pace.

Rural enthusiasm for mechanical progress was by no means confined solely to advances in agricultural technology. Farmer spokesmen expressed frequently their marveling approval of new industrial machinery. Thus in commenting upon a new power loom installed for making carpets in Massachusetts, the Farmer's Monthly Visitor in 1845 saw fit to prophesy that—

> in a few years hence, when the use of the power loom becomes general, we will be able to carpet every house in the United States and England, at one-half the price that it has heretofore cost! (*5*).

Only very occasionally did there appear in print a nostalgic protest against the march of machines like this lament in the Prairie Farmer in 1860:

> Patent right machines are fatal to poetry. * * * Singer's Sewing Machine that *never* sings is no compensation for the loss of the blue eyed girls that sewed and sang in the old homesteads. * * * Wooden harvesters do not sing harvest songs; iron mowers do not drink from cold springs, nor with Sancho Panza bless HIM who invented sleep. The poets and the prophets are a brotherhood, but the poets and the *profits* are strangers, forever.

Very generally, however, the articulate opinion of farm leaders and rural people welcomed mechanical progress with ever-increasing enthusiasm and growing faith in the future wonders that science would perform. The common attitude corresponded to that expressed in an address before the Illinois and Wisconsin Dairymen's Association in 1868:

> Up to within twenty-five years the farmer's life has been but little removed from serfdom. His many hardships conspired to make the farmer feel his inferiority, and rank his calling in the lowest scale of the professions. He now finds himself emerging from this slough; iron and wood are made to perform wonders, and brain is of more account on the farm than muscle. We are on the threshold of grand results in agriculture (*74*).

Resistance to "Book Farming"

Although labor-saving mechanical devices were generally welcomed and adopted relatively fast, nonmechanical technology encountered stubborn resistance. Agricultural science a century ago had in fact very little to offer aside from new machines, unless it was enthusiasm and faith, and for a long time labored under the disadvantage of the contemptuous label, "book farming." In the year the Cultivator was founded (1834), its editors received the following counsel from an early subscriber:

> I think in the *Cultivator* you ought to dwell continually on the importance of science to agriculture; I mean of all the applicable science the world has got. * * * We want to see the application of geological and chemical science to the different processes in agriculture (*1*).

That they needed the advice is questionable; that they followed it is certain. Book farming was advocated steadily by every agricultural journal of the day. But only a few farmers—generally the more prosperous ones—were ready to risk following the practices advocated in the name of science by agricultural societies and farm journals. For this fervent few, however, science held an appeal that was more than the lure of profit alone.

THE VOGUE OF NATURE STUDY

Avocational interest in science under the name of nature study was one of the great vogues of the day. Observation of nature of either a systematic or poetical kind was considered to be both intellectually and morally elevating. This vogue of nature study was a manifestation of some of the most influential and widely prevailing intellectual currents of the age. This was the age of Wordsworth, of Emerson and Thoreau, of Darwin, and of Corot—of nature poems and nature studies and nature paintings and of monumental progress in natural science. As an amateur interest, nature study was inspired by a mixture of scientific rationalism and the romantic concept of the essential and divine goodness of nature. As such it expressed the moralizing ideals of physical science developed in the age before intricate specialization and professionalization took science away from the layman.

For those who went to school beyond the early grades, the pedagogy of that age saw in botany a study wherein both intellectual and moral development could be simultaneously pursued. Chemistry was much studied, but it was considered more severely practical; the biological sciences retained by far the greater amateur esteem. Nature-study clubs were formed among those not in school but with cultural aspirations. The farm journals regularly featured special articles on science—simplified versions of Liebig's Chemistry, special departments for spreading general scientific information, as, for instance, "Chemistry for the Million," a regular feature in the Plough, the Loom, and the Anvil in the fifties; and regular departments devoted to nature lore as, for example, "The Naturalist" column in the Country Gentleman in the sixties. Farmers were regularly urged to make their homes beautiful by planting flowers and ornamental shrubs, and to make their souls gracious by close observation of nature's practices. Typical of this is the advice of the Cultivator in 1842:

> The farmer * * * should remember that every tree, shrub and flower he cultivates, constitutes a new link of attachment to bind him to his home, and render that home more delightful. They multiply our means of enjoyment, they make additions to our stock of knowledge, they invite us to a more intimate communion with nature, and they prevent the concentration of the mind on wealth, and the narrow selfishness that is too often its attendant (*4*).

Although the vogue of nature study had its most obvious important effect in furthering the acceptance of science, it was related closely to many significant moral ideas. The idea gained wide adherence that, as the Prairie Farmer expressed it in 1850 (*9*), "A true lover of nature, and enlightened Horticulturist *cannot be a bad man.* Even those who cultivate trees and flowers as a trade, and who commence with narrow minds and dark souls, grow better and wiser men by the practice of their art."

BELIEF IN THE TRIUMPH OF THE GOOD

Logically essential to the doctrine of progress and to the prevalent ideas of the goodness of nature was the moral optimism of the age. This moral optimism amounted to a belief that the universe is morally ordered and that for that reason good is inherently stronger than evil and will therefore inevitably triumph. This faith had theological, philosophical, and literary foundations of great dignity and prestige. Like the idea of progress and the romantic attitudes toward nature, it developed with the intellectual element; also like them its essence was popularized during the nineteenth century. The phenomenal increase of literacy in that period accelerated to an unprecedented degree the rapidity with which intellectual traditions were transferred to the masses. Metaphysical speculation and aesthetic elaboration were distilled into the earthy slogans of the people. "Behind every cloud there's a silver lining," "Right is bound to win out in the end," "Children (or dogs) are good judges of human nature," and "A true lover of nature (or of children, or of animals, or of music, or of good books) can't be an evil man" were popular applications of the intellectualized moral optimism of Berkeley, Rousseau, and Wordsworth.

RISING LAND VALUES AND BOOMER PSYCHOLOGY

But certain folk beliefs logically similar to intellectualized ideas seem to have developed independently. Perhaps the reason for this was that widely prevailing characteristics of the age in which they evolved determined the general nature of both. A case in point is that of boomer psychology—one of the most important of all the influences that have shaped the course of American agricultural development—which very obviously grew up out of the peculiar set of circumstances in which millions of Americans lived their everyday lives. Boomer psychology, although in a logical sense merely an extension of the idea of progress, was much less the product of any intellectual vogue than of the everyday experience of a people feverishly colonizing a rich and unexploited continent in an age of unprecedented world-wide commercial expansion.

This was the land of opportunity, and all Americans knew it. Here were land and independence and freedom from the old oppressions for all those who had the will and courage to make their own life. Here was the chance to find a home and happiness and security. And there was pride in being a citizen of this booming land.[8]

---

[8] This pioneer exultance was told in the Michigan Emigrant's Song, printed in the Detroit Courier in 1831, shortly after Michigan was admitted to the Union, later reprinted in the New England Farmer in 1871:

Come all ye Yankee Farmers,
Who'd like to change your lot,
Who've spunk enough to travel
Beyond your native spot,
And leave behind the village
Where Pa' and Ma' do stay,
Come follow me and settle
In *Michigania.*

I've hearn of your *Penobscot,*
Way down in parts of *Maine,*
Where timber grows in plenty,
But darn the bit of grain;
And I have hearn of *Quoddy,*
And your *Piscataqua,*
But these can't hold a candle
To *Michigania.*

* * * * * * *

And there's your Massachusetts,
Once good enough, be sure;
But now she's always laying on
Taxation or manure;
She costs you pecks of trouble,
But de'il a peck can pay;
While all is scripture measure
In *Michigania.*

* * * * * * *

What country ever growed up
So great in little time,
Just popping from the nurs'ry
Right into like its prime;
When *Uncle Sam* did wean her,
'Twas but the other day,
And now she's quite a Lady,
This *Michigania.*

* * * * * * *

[Footnote continued on p. 130.]

From the earliest days of frontier expansion, sensational rises in land value were the repeated experience of pioneer farmers. Villages sprang up overnight and rapidly became thriving towns. Population grew, roads came in, river traffic opened up. Settlement, commercial development, and speculation increased land prices, sometimes phenomenally. Out of the experience of witnessing and being part of this expansion, the idea developed that land prices would always rise, population always increase, towns always grow larger. Farming in new regions therefore more often than not assumed a speculative nature founded upon a universal confidence in rising land values. Morris Birkbeck in 1817 described this phenomenon as follows:

> The merchant invests his profits, and the professional man his savings, in the purchase of uncultivated lands. The farmer, instead of completing the improvement of his present possessions, lays out all he can save in entering more land. In a district which is settling, this speculation is said to pay on the average, when managed with judgment, fifteen percent. Who then will submit to the toils of agriculture, further than bare necessity requires, for fifteen percent? Or who would loan his money, even at fifteen percent, when he can obtain that interest by investing it in land? (*39, p. 85*).

Birkbeck had been deeply impressed earlier by the sensational rises in land value in eastern Ohio:

> On entering the State of Ohio from Wheeling, we find a country beautiful and fertile, and affording to a plain, industrious and thriving population, all that nature has decreed for the comfort of man * * *. It is also fully appropriated and thickly settled; and land is worth from twenty to thirty dollars per acre. An advance of a thousand percent, in about ten years! * * * looking forward for the interest of our families * * * we must pass on, until we reach the country where good land is to be purchased at the Government price of two dollars per acre; and which, in return for a few temporary privations, increases in value in a similar ratio (*40, p. 50*).

And he told how towns sprang up out of what had been the wilderness:

> On any spot where a few settlers cluster together * * * some enterprising proprietor finds in his section what he deems a good scite for a town, he has it surveyed and laid out in lots, which he sells, or offers for sale by auction.
>
> The new town then assumes the name of its founder:—a store-keeper builds a little framed store, and sends for a few cases of goods; and then a tavern starts up, which becomes the residence of a doctor and a lawyer, and the boarding-house of the store-keeper, as well as the resort of the weary traveller: soon follow a blacksmith and other handicraftsmen in useful succession: a schoolmaster, who is also the minister of religion, becomes an important accession to this rising community. Thus the town proceeds, if it proceeds at all, with accumulating force, until it becomes the metropolis of the neighbourhood. Hundreds of these speculations may have failed, but hundreds prosper; and thus trade begins and thrives, as population grows around these lucky spots; imports and exports maintaining their just proportion. One year ago the neighbourhood of this very town of Princeton, was clad in "buckskin;" now the men appear at church in good blue cloth, and the women in fine calicoes and straw bonnets (*40, pp. 98–99*).

[Footnote continued from p. 129.]

Then come ye Yankee Farmers,
  Who've mettle hearts like me,
And elbow-grease in plenty,
  To bow the forest tree;
Come take a "Quarter Section,"
  And I'll be bound you'll say,
This country takes the rag off,
  This *Michigania.*

The third verse quoted has reference to the widespread belief of the day that fertilization of the soil was a confession of lack of fertility and an indication that it was time to move on to new, and therefore better, land. This attitude was undoubtedly the result of the presence of so much cheap land and of the lack of a long tradition of permanent agriculture such as existed in Europe.

De Tocqueville was among those who first noted the character that was given to American agriculture and rural life by the speculative and commercial optimism that pervaded the land. Coming from a country where land descended from father to son for generations and even centuries, he was in a position to be impressed by the impermanence that resulted from the boomer psychology and commercial enthusiasm that in agriculture was peculiar to America. His observations obviously did not apply to some parts of New England or to much of the older South where a landed aristocracy had taken root in the soil, but they were pertinent to most of the newer country.

It seldom happens that an American farmer settles for good upon the land which he occupies: especially in the districts of the far west he brings land into tillage in order to sell it again, and not to farm it: he builds a farmhouse on the speculation, that, as the state of the country will soon be changed by the increase of population, a good price will be gotten for it (*70, p. 168*).

In some of the older regions, there was a pronounced rise in land values during the eighteenth century (*38, p. 70*). In the ante bellum South, land values were seldom consistently high, and in general rose and fell with business cycles; but settlement of new areas was there as everywhere accompanied by pronounced increases in land valuation (*55, p. 642 ff.*). Benjamin Horace Hibbard's History of Agriculture in Dane County, Wisconsin indicates that in many cases there the price of land tripled or quadrupled between 1845 and 1855, and doubled again in the next 10-year period (*59, p. 195 et passim*). In Iowa the average value of an acre of improved land increased from $6.09 in 1850, to $11.91 in 1860, to $20.21 in 1870; thence it rose more slowly, to $43.31 in 1900, before booming to $96 in 1910, $134 in 1915, and $255 in 1920 (*56, p. 4*). Land booms were frequently promoted by large owners of land and land speculators from the earliest times, and by canal and railroad interests later.

There were in those older days many manifestations of a boomer spirit quite modern in form. Thus a eulogist of the agricultural wonders of California reported to the Commissioner of Patents in 1851 that—

On land owned and cultivated by Mr. James Williams, an onion grew to the enormous weight of twenty-one pounds. On this same land a turnip was grown which equalled exactly in size the top of a flour barrel. On land owned and cultivated by Thomas Fallen, a cabbage grew which measured, while growing, 13 feet 6 inches around its body * * *. At Stockton a turnip weighed one hundred pounds. In the latter city, at a dinner for twelve persons, of a single potato, larger than the size of an ordinary hat, all partook, leaving at least the half untouched (*75, p. 4*).

In the course of time it became the prevailing fashion to be "a booster, not a knocker." Such wide, unquestioning adherence was developed for the assumptions that unlimited growth and expansion and increased prosperity were the natural disposition of things that to suggest even mildly that such might not forever be the case meant in most communities to be branded as a dangerous eccentric. This extraordinary optimism was probably necessary to the great rapidity with which the second half of the continent was settled, civilized, and tied together. But it gave to American agriculture a speculative and impermanent character that was to be the cause of many later evils. It contributed heavily to an increase in farm capitalization and debt load that could not be justified or liquidated unless the anticipated growth and expansion continued indefinitely—which turned out not to be the case.

The moral aspects of our agricultural traditions, deriving as they did from times of greater stability, implied an ideal of a permanent agriculture neither speculative nor highly commercialized. The little farm, well-tilled, highly sufficient unto itself, with no binding ties to the town and market place and untouched by the vagaries and passions of the changing world, was the assumption upon which the qualities of security, serenity, and independence were imputed to the agricultural life. This moral tradition, perpetuated in its idealized form principally by agricultural journals and writers and other farm leaders, has served by its persistence to develop a conflict in agricultural ideas because of its inconsistency with the speculative and commercial tendencies that were growing up in modern American agriculture.

THE VOGUE OF SELF-EDUCATION

The doctrine of progress meant more than confidence in technological progress alone; it meant, just as vitally, a faith in human perfectibility. Although many Americans were the disinherited of older lands, once in America they were not submissive; although they resented the trappings of wealth, the symbols of ease, and the pedantry of a learning they did not possess, they were not willing meekly to accept inferior status. They would not accept what they did not have as symbols of superiority, but they aspired to those things no less.

A significant proportion of farm people shared enthusiastically in the vogue of self-education and self-improvement that prevailed widely a century ago. This popular passion for self-education originated in New England, if it can be said to have had any geographical point of origin. It was a part of the flowering of New England culture and owed much to transcendentalism, the literary and philosophical movement inspired and led by Ralph Waldo Emerson. England shared and had even begun the self-education movement. But nowhere in the world did the idea of self-improvement arouse such popular enthusiasm as in the United States; and no other group in the United States was more receptive to the ideal of self-improvement than the farm people.

Probably the most famous instance of the self-education vogue is suggested by the picture in everyone's mind of the youthful Abraham Lincoln doing sums on a wooden shovel with a piece of charcoal by the flickering light from the fireplace. But to Lincoln's contemporaries, the most notable personification of the ideals of the self-improvement vogue in America in its early period was Elihu Burritt (1810–78), "the learned blacksmith." Burritt as a young man became an accomplished linguist and student of letters while working as a blacksmith in a Connecticut town. With a book propped beside the anvil and studying long hours by candlelight after the working day was ended, he learned all of the western European languages, delved into their literature, and in the end even wrote a Sanskrit grammar—the first to be written in this country. He exalted manual labor and gave impressive lectures on the subject of its dignity. He insisted that he practiced such intellectual cultivation not as a means of rising above his station but rather to ennoble it, and that such intellectual activity was no more than befitting a working man's status. On these grounds he refused an offer of formal education at Harvard. He engaged in correspondence on a high intellectual plane with many leaders in American thought. In the 1840's his interests began to expand into social and humanitarian affairs, and he devoted himself in later life to furthering such causes as abolition, world peace, and freedom of immigration (*46*). Of such a character were the ideals of self-education and self-improvement set before rural Americans in the 1830's and 1840's.

The Cultivator carried on a constant campaign to educate farmers, not only in practical concerns immediately related to farming but also in matters concerning intellectual and moral development. The prospectus for volume 8 (1841) described the purposes for which the journal was established in the following terms:

> The Cultivator was established to improve and elevate the Agriculture of the country; to give a proper tone to the morals and mind of the farmer; to show him the dignity and importance of his profession; to store his mind with useful knowledge, and convince him that while all classes are and must be more or less dependent on each other, he alone of the whole can make any near approach to independence. If there is one thing more than another, which in this country gives a man superiority over his fellow men, it is knowledge. * * *

Readers of agricultural journals were advised on the merits of various English, Latin, and Greek grammars. Farm youths were urged to read ancient and modern histories, Good's Book of Nature, Dick's Christian Philosophy, Paley's Natural Theology, expositions of the Constitution, and works on political science and ethics, as well as to keep abreast of the news with a "good family newspaper." One of the most frequently repeated arguments was that "the laboring man, as regards the acquisition of knowledge, has almost as good advantages as the man whose whole employment is study—if he was but aware of the fact, and would improve his opportunities" (*47*).

Growth of Farmers' Clubs

In the course of time, reading and study for cultural ends—for the enrichment of life—was more and more urged for groups rather than for lone individuals. Lone study by candlelight was still suggested for those whose aim was to get ahead in the world. But for general intellectual improvement it was advised that families spend their evenings reading and discussing good books, or that they form neighborhood clubs for that purpose. During the Civil War, and especially in the years immediately following, neighborhood farmers' clubs sprang up in great numbers. The common purposes were to overcome the isolation which was, significantly, for the first time being widely regarded as a social handicap, and to cultivate the intellectual interests and capacities of rural people. Both the motives and the methods of these farmers' clubs are evident in an article describing how to organize and conduct them that was printed in both the Country Gentleman and the New England Farmer in 1871:

> The long evenings are now at hand, and the farmer, finding a little leisure after the labors of the day, looks about him for some means of pleasure and

223761°—40——10

amusement wherewith to occupy the time. He will find no more profitable way to spend an occasional evening than in the meetings of a wide-awake Farmers' Club. * * * Here he can in a measure obtain that Mental Culture which is so much neglected by those who labor day after day upon their farms. * * * Mind needs contact with mind to rub it into activity * * *. These Farmers' Clubs then, are just what is needed to draw the farmers together, and to give them an opportunity to bring their minds in contact * * *.

The Exercises of the Club should be varied to suit the tastes of different members. Discussions upon familiar farm topics should generally be held each evening, and every member should take part in them. * * * Essays upon the subjects which are to be considered, may be prepared and read by those who have a taste for putting their thoughts in writing. It is a good practice to assign topics six months or a year before hand, so that those who are to prepare essays may have ample time to "read up" their subject, or to experiment upon it on their farms * * * (*54*).

It is more than mere coincidence that the growth of community farmers' clubs came in the same period with the first rapid development of the Patrons of Husbandry. The Granger movement grew out of the same common desires and aspirations and ministered to the same needs, and in many instances the formation of a local farmers' club turned out to be a preliminary to the establishment of a Grange affiliated with the national organization. Thus the impulse to enrich rural life proceeded according to the familiar sequence of individual effort first, then local group action, and finally national organization.

The vogue of self-education should not be confused with the contemporary craze for refinement. Once the worst hardships of pioneer life were overcome, or as soon as progress permitted some leisure, small-town people and many of the more prosperous farmers sought to cultivate refinement in manners and gracious accomplishments. The job of refinement was in the forties and fifties frequently considered the special duty of young ladies, who were encouraged to cultivate the arts of fancy needlework, music, and home decoration. The French language and literature were also fashionable; and there was emphasis upon delicacy and even upon a kind of anemic fragility of manners in imitation of the pallid heroines common to some of the extremes of literary romanticism. But among most farm people there was a wave of strong feeling against such forms of refinement. Farm journals and other spokesmen for farm people expressed much outraged indignation at the excesses of this vogue. The common opinion was that: "The piano and lace frame are good in their places; and so are ribbons, frills, and tinsel, but you cannot make a dinner of the former, nor a bed blanket of the latter." And the rural reaction to the young lady who was the end product of this urban vogue of refinement was well expressed in a salty satire on "The Modern Young Lady" in the Prairie Farmer in 1860. This young lady at 10 in the morning—

Slowly * * * rises from her couch, the while yawning, for being compelled to rise so horrid early. Languidly she gains her feet, and oh! what a vision of human perfection appears before us! Skinny, bony, sickly, hipless, thighless, formless, hairless, teethless. What a radiant belle! What an ideal beauty! What an inspiration for an aspiring poet! What a model for a sculptor! What a tempting bait for some hopeless bauch! The ceremony of enrobing commences. In goes the dentist's naturalization efforts; next the witching curls are fastened to her "classically molded head." Then the womanly proportions are properly adjusted; hoops, bustles, & c., follow in succession, then a profuse quantity of whitewash, together with a "permanent rose tint" is applied to a sallow complexion; and lastly the "killing" wrapper is arranged on her systematical and matchless form. The modern young lady is complete. But this is not all. The modern young lady is accomplished. She is talented. She can entertain an army of masculines. She is well versed in literary topics. Praises Milton, because she knows its safe. Never speaks of Byron—thinks he is immodest. Knows there is a number in Greek called duol, a tense called aorist, and a grammatical verb called tuptoo. She converses in French, can make "killing eyes," and say "*je pense a toi.*" She can thump immoderately on the piano; can scream up to E flat pure, head voice; can carry her chest notes down to F. She sings any quantity of those "sweet things of Madame Stockhausen's, but always has an awful cold." She "launches into the world of fashion;" considers herself quite a belle; falls in love with a pair of mustaches; thinks said mustaches are the "sweetest she ever saw;" mustaches is flattered by her smiles; thinks her vastly entertaining and asks "pa;" "pa" consents, and the twain are made one. Mustaches rejoices in the effigy of his painted squaw, and modern young lady, finds too late, that it takes a fool to make a fool.

THE DRIVE TO DEMOCRATIZE EDUCATION

The genuine vogue of self-education and self-improvement among farmers and working people was in a sense only an incident of their long campaign for enhanced educational opportunity. No sooner had agricultural fairs and farm journals begun to democratize book farming and improve methods of cultivation than agitation was begun for the establishment of schools and colleges that would give formal education in agricultural science. The drive for special agricultural education was joined to the growing and wider demand for a broad extension of common-school and general education. Farm leaders and spokesmen of the agricultural interests had unanimously a profound faith in education and an eager hunger for it. Education of a cultural nature was considered essential to their ideal of the dignity of agriculture and necessary to the proud independence and civic responsibilities of the farmer in a free republic; education of a practical nature was essential to the adoption of the improved methods of cultivation that science was revealing. For more than a generation, until the passage of the Morrill Land Grant College Act of 1862, education was the most constant and prominent political cause advocated by farmers and their leaders.

The Lyceum movement was the first phase of the organized drive for education for farmers and working-class people. Its father was Josiah Holbrook (1788–1854), who after trying his hand at conducting an industrial school in 1819 and an agricultural school at Derby, Conn., in 1824, hit on the idea of the Lyceum in 1826. Lyceums rapidly became very popular, and by arousing intellectual interests among rural people served to promote a desire for wider opportunity for formal education. By 1831 Lyceums in approximately 900 towns served to bring distinguished and learned men as lecturers before farmer and small-town audiences (*71, pp. 31–32*).

In the 1820's, agricultural spokesmen confined themselves generally to demands for State financial aid to agricultural societies and fair associations, which were in their way devoted to the dissemination of information concerning better farming methods. New York in 1819, New Hampshire in 1820, and Georgia in 1837 established State boards of agriculture, and Massachusetts in 1819 and Ohio in 1839 gave financial assistance for the encouragement of agriculture through the medium of State-wide organizations of agricultural societies. The principal purpose of these organizations and appropriations was in all cases educational.

Public-school education meanwhile was being rapidly extended in the cities. Boston led by including a high school in its city educational system in 1821. In the following years, public-school education was rapidly expanded in the principal cities and towns. The educational revival in the cities, with Horace Mann as its greatest leader, flourished through the twenties, thirties, forties, and fifties.

In general, the popular demand for a broadening of educational opportunities by the establishment of public schools grew out of the democratic ideals of the people and constituted a protest against the aristocratic practices and purposes that characterized most of the private schools of that day. Private schools were generally available only to the children of families of means, and their educational methods were designed to give class-conscious "gentlemen" a literary and linguistic polish. Thus the movement for a broadened educational system was led by progressives and reformers and was politically dependent upon the mass support of the poorer classes of people because of the consistent opposition of most wealthy and conservative groups. Education being a common cause of farmers in the country and working and poor people in the city, their forces were joined in the fight for it.

Agricultural leaders, agricultural societies, and agricultural journals carried on an unceasing campaign for education. Beginning in 1823 when Judge Jesse Buel introduced the first bill to establish an agricultural college in New York State, this agitation continued in a mounting crescendo. Many manual-labor schools, and agricultural schools and academies such as the Gardiner Lyceum at Gardiner, Maine, the Agricultural Seminary at Derby, Conn., and the Boston Asylum and Farm School were first established privately in response to the growing demand for popular education. Rensselaer Institute, Washington (now Trinity) College of Hartford, Conn., Bussey Institution of Roxbury, Mass., Amherst College, Farmers' College at College Hill, Ohio, and other private institutions quickly offered or featured studies especially intended for farmers and mechanics.

But the growing agitation for Government support of agricultural education, of which first Elkanah Watson and later Judge Buel were important leaders, was finally rewarded by the legal establishment in Michigan in 1837 of a State university as an integral part of the public-school system. Instruction in agriculture was specified in the act establishing the university as an essential part of the curriculum; but for some years the desire for agricultural instruction was not actually realized because of lack of funds. Finally, in 1855, an agricultural college was established in Michigan separate from the university, and students were admitted in 1857. In 1853, after a long struggle and many disappointments, the New York State Agricultural College was founded by legislative act. Maryland passed an act to establish and endow an agricultural college in the State of Maryland in 1856; and in the next year Pennsylvania gave $25,000 to match an equal sum raised by private subscription for the establishment of an agricultural college on the site of the present Pennsylvania State College.

Finally the inadequacy of State financing led to Federal support through the Morrill Act of 1862. The extent to which the drive for agricultural and mechanical education was the common purpose of both farmers and urban working people, as well as the degree to which it was a reaction against the aristocratic temper of the prevailing forms of higher education, is indicated by the words of Jonathan Turner, of Illinois:

> The industrial class need a * * * system of *liberal education* for their own class, and adapted to their own pursuits; to create for them an INDUSTRIAL LITERATURE, adapted to their professional wants, to raise up for them *teachers* and *lecturers*, for subordinate institutes, and to elevate them, their pursuits, and their posterity to that relative position in human society for which God designed them (*61, p. 69*).

It is easily observable that by the time the agitation for formal agricultural education had grown to effective proportions it had acquired a strong tendency to emphasize practical ends and aims. Intellectual improvement for its own sake declined in importance, and the idea of training for vocational and professional efficiency gained in proportion.

Education as a Means of Personal Advancement

Many forces joined from the very outset to alter slowly yet fundamentally the ideals and motives of education and self-improvement. The ideal of intellectual cultivation for its own sake began to give way to utilitarian motives almost before it was fully established. It did not, of course, completely disappear; it is present even today. Yet the very urgency of describing attractively the benefits of self-education led to claims that personal advancement up the social and economic ladder was the purpose of education.

The regularly repeated argument of advocates of education and self-improvement was that great men were once poor boys who by hard work and discipline had made themselves great.[9] And there was repeated appeal to the established and very real idea of opportunity. Optimism, respect for industry and accomplishment, and hunger for wide esteem for the class of hard-working common men reshaped educational desires into aspiration for mundane success. This was expressed in the Country Gentleman in 1862 as follows:

> Hold on! don't give up; in our country no social prejudices prevail which prevent the humble dyer from becoming the learned and skillful chemist; no barriers exist which deprive those whom the chances of life have made rude and unlettered, from becoming shining lights in the world of science. Most great inventors have sprung from the ranks of the brave daily workers, and the field is still a wide one, expanding every day; therefore * * * improve your spare hours in mental culture, and reward is certain.

[9] "*The greatest of men have been trained up to 'work with their hands.'* If there is an encouraging sentence in the English language, it is the above. God ordained that man should live by *'the sweat of his face,'* and intelligence can breathe and live only in a being of an active life. Aikenside, the author of 'The Pleasures of Imagination,' was a butcher until twenty-one, and first took to study from being confined in his room, by the fall of a cleaver. Marshal Ney was the son of a cooper; Roger Sherman, Allan Cunningham, and Gifford, were shoemakers; Sir William Herschell was a fifer boy; Franklin, a printer's devil; Ferguson, a shepherd; Ben Johnson [sic] was a bricklayer; James Monroe, the son of a bricklayer; General Knox was the son of a bookbinder; General Green, a blacksmith; General Morgan, a wagoner; Burns, a plough-boy; Bloomfield was a farmer; Frazier, a stone-cutter; Crabbe and Keats, apothecaries; Sir Wm. Blackstone was the son of a silk mercer, and a posthumous child" (*10*).

Implicit in the repeated opportunity stories of poor boys who rose to greatness was the moral that the object of self-improvement was advance in rank. And in general the earthy practicality of the people tended in the long run to give emphasis to ideals that fitted the real desires of everyday life. Psychologically, there is no reason to assume that any contradiction necessarily exists between such variant motives of self-education. And historically it is a fact that they not only could but did live side by side. But what began as a vogue of self-improvement almost entirely for the sake of cultural enrichment of life rapidly became a vogue of self-improvement in order to advance in station. The former never died out, but the latter in the course of time became predominant and contributed to, as well as shared in, the success motif that has colored so much American thought and American life.

The individualistic and success philosophy that motivated much of the agitation for formal education and self-education was revealed in the answer of the Prairie Farmer to a Canadian query regarding the proud and intelligent way in which Americans articulated their opinions.

> The secret is to be found in our Common Schools, Lyceums, and the modes of conducting political canvasses. It is the natural and necessary result, of the doctrine "every man for himself"—that is, his *elevation* or depression, socially or politically, depends entirely upon his own exertions (*36, p. 100*).

Considerable significance is to be attached to the identity and accomplishments of the men who were judged to be great and who were held up as examples to the young. In the period before the Civil War, writers, philosophers, scientists, inventors, and political and military figures predominated among those named as illustrious. Among those most frequently named were Benjamin Franklin, Jeremy Bentham, Shakespeare, Ben Jonson, Linnaeus, George Washington, Robert Burns, and William Cobbett. There was a wide and varying assortment of contemporary governors, senators, and scientists and inventors who had been born poor but through extraordinary effort had made themselves famous and great. Almost never, during this early period, was a financier, industrialist, or businessman so mentioned; but there was a growing tendency to think of attainment in terms of commercial criteria, and this was, in the course of time, to alter the specific ideals of success. It is to be noted that farming was never cited as the vocation of great and illustrious men; models of success were invariably others than farmers. This is significant because farm youth were urged simultaneously to prepare for success and yet to stay on the farm and ignore the false lure and illusory rewards of the city.

Farm youth was already beginning to crowd to the growing towns and cities, thereby arousing the protest that cityward migration has immemorially excited. But among the masses of older rural people, the greatest opportunity was still believed to exist in farming, partly because of eternally expected rises in land values and prices generally, and partly because of the abundance of cheap lands and the financial ease with which one could become a free-holding farmer.

DEMOCRACY AND SECURITY A CENTURY AGO

An aggressively democratic and proud spirit was abroad in the land, combined with a lusty optimism that embraced almost everything from confidence in the future growth of population to faith in the inherent natural goodness and infinite perfectibility of man and society. Although many people were acquiring small fortunes, in rural areas in the nonslave States there were few great inequalities of wealth. A large proportion of the young people moved on to the West or the South or to the city when they came of age; but among the older generation and among those who remained there was much warm neighborliness and an almost complete social equality. There was very little stratification of society. The hired man was as often as not a neighbor's boy who lived in the house, ate with the family, entertained in the parlor, married the boss's daughter, and later established his own farm farther west. The small town itself was in that age much more a part of the agricultural countryside than it was to be later. The storekeeper, the blacksmith, the school teacher, the shoemaker, and the preacher were all farmers in spirit. Their habits of language, patterns of amusement, social usages, and everyday concerns not only were tied to the agricultural life of the community but were actually its product. Family ties were close, kinship meant much, and the family was an economic unit that could if need be face away from depression and survive adversity. The farm home was a Gibraltar of security that without question or faltering harbored the aged and fostered the young until they were ready to seek greater opportunities. Life might be hard and crude, but it was secure. There was nothing in the social code that forced a man to lose his self-respect because of poverty, for no one was far from hardship, and none had excess of ease; and when opportunity was not at hand, it could be found just over the horizon.

Such must be our general picture of farm life a century ago. Just as it does not refer closely to any specific locality, being a generalized picture, neither can it be tied down closely in time. Then, as now and always, society was dynamic and varied, no two years exactly the same, no two places exactly alike. Both the material facts of life and the psychology of men were undergoing continuous alteration. And the very forces and spirit that gave that period its most striking features were destined as they developed to change profoundly the character of agriculture and of rural life.

FORCES OF CHANGE: COMMERCIALIZATION, URBANIZATION, AND TECHNOLOGICAL ADVANCE

The principal alterations in the pattern of agricultural life that have come during the past century may be summarized under the titles of commercialization, urbanization, and technological advance. The forces underlying these changes were present, and in varying degrees operative, a hundred years or more ago; but their total effect upon the everyday life of rural people was by no means then what it later became. Adjustment of the institutions, customs, and attitudes of a people to the slow intrusion of new factors is necessarily a gradual process. Even revolution cannot effect social change any faster than people themselves change; and changes in people living together in society must be measured not in months or years but in terms of generations. Furthermore, the new factors and forces that have been the roots of change did not come all at once and remain constant thereafter; rather, they have been continually insinuated into the total circumstance, in various forms and in varying degrees at different times. There is no present end to them, nor is there ever likely to be. And the social adaptation to one new factor alters the adaptation to the next. Thus there has been a complex and accumulating crescendo that does not even yet seem to have reached the climax of the long sequence of change that began a century or more ago.

The most profound differences between rural life today and a century ago do not in any case consist intrinsically in an increased commercialization, or in a more advanced technology, or in a wider adoption of material things from the city. Many farms then sold as high a proportion of their products as do many commercial farms today. There were farms then that had as much labor-saving equipment as do many farms in this more modern mechanical age. The most profound changes in farm life—those that have had the greatest effect upon the destinies, the course of daily life, and the happiness or unhappiness of farm people—have not been the changes in material things themselves but those involved in the gradual alteration of habits, customs, institutions, and ideas that has constituted the social or cultural adaptation to material change.

The three kinds of change named above—commercialization, urbanization, and technological advance—are by no means intended as mutually exclusive. They are related and interdependent; there could not have been one without the others.

NEW ECONOMIC DEMANDS UPON AGRICULTURE

The extension of industrial technology, the growth of urban markets, the increase of transportation facilities, the general rise in the standard of living—all these and related things have exerted tremendous pressure upon the farmer to become a cog in a vast and infinitely complex economic machine. Urban industry has removed from the farm one by one the industrial functions that once were performed there. The farmer who once wore homespun from his own sheep now wears denim from Oshkosh and cotton shirts from Troy. Soap making is gone; and not one of a thousand farmers who grow wheat eats his own grain. Few farmers build their own houses; and their houses are not lighted with home-made candles or tallow wicks but with kerosene or electricity. Ordinarily they do not sell or barter a variety of produce for the use of nearby townfolk; their customers are 100 or 1,000 or 3,000 miles away.

Commercialization and specialization have been the necessary complements in agriculture to the factory system and mass production in industry. In the space of 60 years, between 1869 and 1929, the annual total of manufactured products turned out by American industries grew in value from about 3⅓ billion dollars to about 70 billions. During this same period, the number of those gainfully employed in agriculture increased slowly from about 6½ to 10¼ millions, while nonagricultural employment quadrupled—from 12 to 48 millions. Vast urban accumulations grew up. In 1870 only a fifth of our people lived in places of 8,000 or more population; but in 1930 roughly half—over 60 millions—were residents of such places. And only a quarter of our people are now on the farm. All this has meant that agriculture must be commercialized, for in no other way could the urban and industrial masses be fed and clothed. It has also involved specialization, to which heavy advantages frequently accrue in production for the market. The rising standard of urban living has had the same commercializing effect as the growth of urban population. The growing demand for fresh fruits and vegetables in winter and the increasing substitution of delicacies for breadstuffs and heavier foods have tended to place a premium upon highly specialized production for special urban markets.

American agriculture was called upon, moreover, to supply a European market as well as a growing domestic demand. In the Civil War period and after, this Nation was still very young financially and industrially. There were few American manufactures with which to pay for the European goods sold in this country. It was largely American agriculture that paid this bill by vast exports of food and fiber for the crowded industrial peoples of Europe.

In the fiscal year 1850–51 total agricultural exports amounted to $146,717,000; from this they climbed gradually to a record figure of $260,280,000 in 1859–60. Cotton was then the single item accounting for most of the total. But after the Civil War, when farm products sold abroad came more and more to include a large quantity of breadstuffs, meats, and fruits, agricultural exports climbed to $296,962,000 in 1869–70, to $694,315,000 in 1879–80, fell back to $634,856,000 in 1889–90, and climbed again to $844,617,000 in 1899–1900. The slight rise to $869,244,000 in 1909–10 was merely a prelude to the tremendous World War expansion that skyrocketed the figure to $3,849,663,000 in 1919–20. During the 1920's, our agricultural exports regularly totaled between $1,500,000,000 and somewhat over $2,000,000,000.

The effect of the growth suggested by these figures was to increase vastly the involvement of American agriculture in a commercialized, specialized, interdependent world economy. American grain and meat production in the latter half of the nineteenth century became a cog in the international economic machine, just as tobacco production had become in the seventeenth and eighteenth centuries and cotton production in the early nineteenth. Thus the dominant American crops—tobacco and cotton, corn, pork, and wheat—became the special products of an agricultural plant geared to the needs of an international and interdependent economy of regional and national specialization.

Without this vast expansion of urban and industrial markets for farm products in both America and Europe the agricultural settlement of our grain-producing areas could neither have proceeded with the same speed nor have developed the same kind of farm economy. It would have had to depend on very limited local markets and would have been forced into diversification rather than specialization, subsistence practices rather than commercial dependency. Thus there has been an irresistible impulse toward specialization and commercialization in American agriculture that was generated by forces as remote and impersonal as population trends, the rising standard of living, and changes in the national economy not only of this but of other countries. Involuntarily, and by dint of circumstances, the farmer has lost much of his old-time independence and has found himself tied to the market, to industry, and to the city.

Self-Sufficiency Gives Way to Interdependence

During the colonial period, the policy of the British Government to discourage manufactures in the Colonies had fostered the development of home industries in the northern and middle Colonies. Both cash and cash crops were scarce. During the 1750's and 1760's, especially after the passage of the Stamp Act, spinning, weaving, knitting, and other household manufacturing became very common. A list of domestic staples made up in 1753 includes more than 160 different articles (*73, pp. 188–189*). In some cases products were not finished in the home. Frequently the spinning was done at home and the weaving by professionals. Shoemaking was sometimes done in shops or by itinerant shoemakers instead of in the home.

It was upon such self-sufficiency that the traditional independence of the farm family was based. Equipped by habit and skill to supply its own needs for food, shelter, and clothing, the farm family could if necessary face away from the world and live completely and even happily upon the products of its own making. But in proportion as industries were transferred from the farm and home into the shop or factory and as rural people began to acquire new tastes for urban products and luxuries their independence was lost.

The shoemaking industry seems to have been among the first to pass into the shop stage, while the textile industry, generally speaking, was one of the last. The manufacture of such items as maple sirup and sugar, furniture, soap, and knit goods and the processing of various foodstuffs remained in the home after other tasks had passed to the factory. Between 1810 and 1840 industry was rapidly removed from the home to the factory. In this period, except in the most remote frontiers, farm families largely ceased to manufacture their own textiles and clothing. Grist-mills, flour mills, and sawmills became common and grew larger as they served increasingly wide areas.

In addition to the loss of home industry, which necessitated cash outlay for products previously supplied right on the farm, new needs were developed. In the Civil War period the sewing machine, based on Howe's patent of 1846 and Singer's patent of 1851, was coming into common use on the finer textiles that were issuing in increasing quantities from the looms of manufacturing towns. At about the same time kerosene began to be used widely for better lighting, and this too increased the need for cash outlay. There were to come telephones (in 1930, 34 percent of all farms reported telephones), electricity, modern plumbing, automobiles (in 1930, 58 percent of all farmers reported automobiles). Many farm families were destined in the first third of the twentieth century to give up home butchering and baking and buy all their meat from the butcher and all their bread from the grocer or baker. Social prestige came more and more to be attached to the possession of various products that were supplied by industry and could be obtained only by cash outlay. Most of these changes and innovations have resulted in a higher standard of living, but they have also involved the surrender of economic independence.

THE INFLUENCE OF FARM BOOKKEEPING

Ever since Arthur Young first used cost accounting as a check for his experiments in England in the late eighteenth century, farm bookkeeping has been advocated by agricultural improvers. At first, the advice was ordinarily in such general terms as: "A clear, precise, and accurate system of book-keeping is an essential feature in an advantageous and well-arranged agricultural undertaking" (*69, p. 106*). But as time passed, the merchant was increasingly appealed to as a model in such matters. Thus the Monthly Journal of Agriculture in 1847 scolded a farmer who was inclined to rule-of-thumb systems of valuation:

Does any one believe that a merchant or manufacturer, interested in a matter connected with his business to the amount of the value to the farmer of any one of these items, would rest until he had ascertained precisely how it bears on his *balance sheet*? (*7*).

In none of their efforts at agricultural improvement have the reformers and leaders of agriculture been more persistent or seemed in the end to have had greater influence than in their drive to enhance the commercial elements of farming practices.

After the Civil War the drive was intensified to induce farmers to think of their farms as a business and of themselves as businessmen. This meant the keeping of books, counting of costs, and determination of farm procedures on the basis of calculated commercial profits. In this vein the Southern Cultivator and Dixie Farmer preached in 1887:

The time has come when the farmer must be a business man as well as an agriculturist. * * * He will have to keep farm accounts, know how much he spends, what his crops cost him, and how much the profit foots up.

It was not agricultural journalism alone that advocated the adoption of bookkeeping methods in farming. When the science of farm management developed, it was based crucially upon cost accounting and calculations of market values. And as agricultural education expanded, the teachings of farm management were increasingly disseminated, first through agricultural colleges and later through agricultural instruction in rural high schools. The direction of this instruction was always toward commercialized agriculture, with emphasis on cost accounting in imitation of urban business practices. Thus a high-school text in farm management printed in 1914 declared:

Farmers are often criticized because they do not "keep books." In the criticism they are compared with the merchant and it is pointed out that the business man keeps books and knows just where he stands. * * * No merchant could long stay in business without some system of accounting to show his debits and credits. *Farm records desirable.* Farm records are just as desirable for the farmer as business accounts are for the merchant (*41, p. 177*).

During the past generation farm bookkeeping and cost accounting have been among the principal reforms advocated by various branches of the Department of Agriculture, modern farm organizations, and State agricultural colleges and extension services. When the American Council of Agriculture and the Committee of Twenty-two met in Des Moines in the summer of 1926, they agreed upon a calculation of annual operating costs of an average 160-acre Iowa farm that included such items as $1,184 interest on value of the land; $1,800 for "operator's salary"; $387 for depreciation on buildings, fences, tile, and water system; $315.56 for depreciation on machinery; $390 for hired labor; and $90.19 for fire and hail insurance. The total annual operating cost of this average 160-acre farm was estimated at $5,601.44 (*53*).

One of the most significant features of calculations of operating cost is the inclusion of such items as interest on land and operating capital, and appraisals of the monetary value of the farmer's own labor. The idea that the farm is an investment on which the farmer should expect to draw interest above and beyond the direct reward for his labor or that the farmer should make a monetary calculation of the value of his labor is an application of principles entirely harmonious with the modern commercial world of the city and industry, but it is a radical departure from the older agrarianism. The emphasis upon a paper concept of ownership, as opposed to a use concept, is obvious; and the remoteness from earlier attitudes which identified the farm as a home providing an opportunity for the production of the necessities of life by the sweat of the brow, where obstacles were natural rather than social, can hardly be exaggerated.

THE FARMER BECOMES A BUSINESSMAN

In spite of all the traditional hostility of rural people to the indirectness of urban economics, most changes in management that have been consciously effected have been sought under the slogan of urban economic efficiency. The farmer was repeatedly told that he was a businessman and that farming was a business. Upon such grounds and in the belief that this was the direction of progress the farmer was urged to specialize, even at the cost of forsaking time-honored subsistence practices. Thus under the progressive slogan, "How we have all advanced," the Prairie Farmer argued in 1868:

> The old rule that a farmer should produce all that he required, and that the surplus represented his gains, is part of the past. Agriculture, like all other business, is better for its subdivisions, each one growing that which is best suited to his soil, skill, climate, and market, and with its proceeds purchase his other needs (*15*).

A prominent agricultural educator and leader who for a generation has been one of the most distinguished spokesmen for modern trends in farm management and progress expressed very well the new point of view in an article written for the Cornell Countryman in 1904:

> Under pioneer conditions the object in agriculture was simply one of maintenance. The problem then, even though strenuous, was yet a simple one. To sow, to bestow a minimum of cultivation, and to harvest, all without regard to either the economy of production or its effects upon fertility—this indeed was simple farming. The only question at the end of the year was whether enough had been produced to last the family and their animals until another year.

Now the object of farming is not primarily to make a living, but it is to make money. To this end it is to be conducted upon the same business basis as any other producing industry. No matter what the yield, it must have been produced at a profit or the farmer is not making money; again, no matter what the profits, the fertility of the land must not be allowed to run down or the capital stock will depreciate and the business will evaporate and come to naught even under conditions of apparent success (*48*).

By developing along such lines American agriculture increased vastly its cash income. But on the other side of the ledger its cash outgo was also increased. By 1929 American farmers paid out annually nearly a billion dollars for feed, over a quarter billion for fertilizer, nearly a billion for labor, nearly three-quarters of a billion for implements and machinery, and nearly fifty million dollars for electricity and power to power companies, exclusive of home generating outfits.

Much of the changed character of the farmer in this age has come about as the result of a long and persistent effort to identify farming directly with business and the farmer with businessmen. Increasing emphasis was given to the merchandizing aspect of farming. In an article entitled "The Farmer as a Merchant," this typical counsel was given in 1887:

Given farms and farmers of equal productive power, the one who sells best will have the best success. The work of farming is only half done when the crop is made out of the ground; sometimes the biggest half is in making the money out of the crop. This branch of farm business needs cultivating; this (the merchant) side of the farmer needs development. Watch and study the markets, and the ways of the marketmen, and dealers in all kinds of goods, and learn the art of "selling well" (*22*).

When agricultural colleges began to carry their work to farmers through farmers' weeks, institutes, and so on, they too preached the ideal of the businessman. The Cornell Countryman announced in 1903 that the Farmers' Institute, held at the agricultural college there, was "a business meeting for business men * * *" (*24*).

In spite of all this, the most familiar stereotype of the farmer continued to be the ancient rubber stamp of the hayseed. Even in farm journals, the tradition remained so strong that cartoon abstractions of the farmer were generally of the hayseed type. Aware of this, the Country Gentleman from July to December of 1921 ran a series of cartoons and comments by nationally prominent cartoonists on the subject "What the Farmer Really Looks Like." Unanimously they agreed that the hayseed abstraction was wholly in error and that the farmer was essentially as modern and as much a businessman as anyone else.

CHANGED ATTITUDES TOWARD LABOR

One of the most significant phases of the long trend toward the identification of farmers with businessmen has been an almost complete reversal in attitudes toward labor. Whereas a century ago farmers generally identified themselves as of the working class and did not ordinarily distinguish themselves from other groups of workers, they have in the course of time acquired an employer consciousness and have developed a strong inclination to regard those who work for wages as of a different class, with other and even hostile interests.

In the period when farmers identified themselves so closely with urban labor, a significant proportion of that labor was still of the pattern of the independent craftsman who owned his tools and shop and sold his product or his services directly to the consumer. A good deal of the time he came closer to being a small businessman than a wage worker in the modern sense. Independent craftsmen of this sort had much in common with farmers that was lost when they became mere factory wage hands.

During the past century, however, urban workers have been losing both economic independence and social status; and farm people, though losing economic independence, have continued to be proprietors in a world in which proprietors are relatively less common than before. Their living standards in terms of industrial products have been rising, and the social status of the more prosperous class of farmers has been greatly improved. A very real differentiation in economic and social position has thus developed between segments of society that once were united in interests and outlook.

Rural Opposition to Organized Industrial Labor

Farmers appear never to have been in a position to sympathize generally with organized industrial labor. So long as urban workers looked like independent craftsmen, their situation could be regarded sympathetically through symbols familiar to the farmer. Thus when in 1851 a group of New England workmen banded together to start a factory of their own, there was sufficient appeal to the farmer to win enthusiastic approval from the agricultural press under the slogan, "Labor is capital" (*11*). But by the time trade unions of a modern character began to develop, the farmer was conscious of himself both as an employer and as a commercial proprietor and was already partly converted to the association of virtue with economic status. Therefore, in spite of his continuing antipathy to trusts and great capital accumulations, he was not prepared to look kindly upon the outlandish innovation of militant unions or the violence incidental to strikes. And labor unions appeared as a companion monster of monopoly, both of which were set to prey upon the farmer. "While labor and capital strive to adjust their differences, the farmer peaceably grows the crops to feed both," was the typical comment of the Farm Journal in 1886 (*20*). At times there was a readiness to believe that capital and labor acted in collusion. Thus the Orange Judd Farmer expressed the opinion in 1903 that:

> Labor and capital engaged in the manufacture of window glass have apparently united to prevent any others going into the business. By this plan manufacturers expect to absolutely monopolize production and shove up prices at will, and under these circumstances they agree to give their help an increase in wages * * *. The farmer feeds them all, and when he gets tired of being robbed by such combinations, he will strike back.

Much of the trouble came from the fact that higher pay and shorter hour agitation by labor unions sometimes offended the rural mind, which out of its own experience had acquired a deep respect for long hours of hard work for humble rewards. The enforced dependence of the urban wage worker has never been sympathetically comprehensible to the farmer with his traditions of independence and individualism. In considering industrial disputes, country people have tended to look upon work as a moral duty, to regard insistence upon conditions and terms of labor as a partial abrogation of that moral duty, and to project their own moral and nonexploitative outlook into the industrial situation. The milder form of this agrarian attitude is suggested by a statement written 30 years ago by L. H. Bailey, one of the grand old men of American agriculture:

> It is doubtful if city industrialism is developing the best type of working-men, considered from the point of view of society. I am glad of all organizations of men and women, whether working-men or not. But it seems to me that the emphasis in some of the organizations has been wrongly placed. It has too often been placed on rights rather than on duties. No person and no people ever developed by mere insistence on their rights. It is responsibility that develops them. The working-man owes responsibility to his employer and to society; and so long as the present organization of society continues he cannot be an effective member of society unless he has the interest of his employer constantly in mind (*37, pp. 139–140*).

The rural hostility toward labor unions has been so well appreciated by some agents of industrial interests that upon occasion farmer groups and representatives have been easily maneuvered into a front position of opposition to labor causes. An example of this was the case of the agitation for repeal of the Adamson eight-hour law about the time of the National Agricultural Conference in Washington in January 1922. When expenditures for the relief of urban unemployed became an issue in recent years, the cleavage between agricultural and labor interests in the rural mind was emphasized still further. Farm people, still clinging to ideals of thrift and industry, and as their own bosses conscious of the ever-present work to be done on their farms, tended to associate all unemployment with the idleness of laziness and to regard huge relief expenditures as prodigal waste.

The Widening Gap Between Proprietors and Hired Hands

Just as, in the course of a century, a social cleavage has developed separating farm people from urban working people, during the same period there has also been a strong tendency toward stratification within rural society, a widening gap between proprietors of farms and those who do farm work for wages. Until a half century or so ago there had not been in the North and West any widely prevailing class distinctions between operators and hired hands. The individual farm proprietor had as likely as not been a hired hand himself at one time; the rungs of the agricultural ladder were still in place, and the hired man likewise would probably be an owner in the course of time. They were social if not economic equals because what one was, the other had been or would be. Furthermore, the tendency of the freehold farmer to identify himself with the under-dog element of society endured in many applications until the collapse of the agrarian revolt in the Populist defeat of 1896. And as long as this attitude endured, the farmer could not with complete consistency separate himself from those who labored hard and honestly with their hands.

But such attitudes and the customs expressing such attitudes in everyday living were due in the course of time to change profoundly as the farmer became more and more a businessman—yet a businessman working under peculiar disadvantages.

All of the agrarian unrest of the post-Civil War period amounted in sum to a protest against the primary dislocation caused by the impact of the new commercialism and industrialism. The frequent statement that it was the farmer as well as the South that lost the Civil War contains an element of important truth. For the Civil War confirmed the protectionist policies of the industrial Northeast and left the farmer no alternative but to buy in a protected, expensive market while having to sell in a cheap world market. With this initial disadvantage, he was forced increasingly by the march of mechanization and rising land prices into ever higher capital investment; and the increasing desire that spread to every hamlet in the land for more of the new products of industrial specialization placed a multitude of new demands upon him. Both factors increased the need for cash, and owing to the farmer's economic disadvantage, both resulted in a growing rural debt load. And always the farmer labored under disadvantages that prevented him from receiving a full share either of his own increased production or of the industrial goods that the improved technology of urban industry made possible. Farm living standards rose, but they did not rise in proportion to the farmer's increased efficiency or as rapidly as those of the urban middle class whose tastes and standards were increasingly important as models for rural emulation.

The farmer was becoming a businessman, but he was doing so under a great disadvantage. The main advantages were beginning to accrue to large-scale organization, and the farmer as a lone individual had to pay tribute. Not only did he get low prices for his products, but he frequently paid excessive freight charges to get his stuff to market because others could combine where he could not. Trusts and monopolies of various kinds upon occasion overcharged him exorbitantly. He bought stocks and bonds to secure market transportation that often failed to materialize. And when he sought redress for grievances, he frequently was thwarted by a wall of corporation legalisms.

He became a small, individual businessman just as the economic world began to be dominated by great and corporate businesses. He might have tried to return to the practices and ideals of an earlier agricultural life, but that was impossible. He was already a cog in the modern economic machine and had to turn as the adjacent cogwheel turned him. He himself wanted modern things; he was in debt; and there was no alternative to muddling through.

Because he was in debt, he participated in the Greenback movement, distrusted the "hard-money" men, and yielded to the lure of 16-to-1. Because distribution by middlemen was generally devious and frequently expensive and was always suspect to traditional agrarian ideals of directness and because he had to pay dearly for his credit, he naturally favored crop-credit and storage schemes such as the Sub-Treasury Plan. Because of the prices he had to pay and because he was still a consistent go-it-alone individualist, trusts and monopolies loomed like monsters.

Although he was the under dog in the struggle against great combinations of industry and finance, the farmer had assimilated the ideas and ideals of opportunity and business success to the extent that he found it just as impossible to join forces with impecunious wage labor below as to sympathize with great accumulations of capital above. And thus, after the great Populist disappointment of 1896, he was heartened by the business revival that followed and recovered courage to face forward again on the path of the new commercialism. It should already have been clear that farmers of the dominant group, from having been proud and rebellious under dogs, were destined, after another brief flurry or two of rebelliousness, to become essentially defenders of the state of things as they are, or even of the state of things as they used to be.

This change in attitudes had been helped along by the increasing awareness among farmers of their own commercial proprietary interests, by the decline of economic self-sufficiency within family units, and by the discovery that regionally and by occupation farm proprietors had common commercial interests generally distinct from all others. The increasing acceptance of commercial ideals, the aspiration for higher material living standards, the faith in economic opportunity, the conversion of the self-improvement vogue into the success idea, and the moral optimism that believed virtue is inevitably rewarded, all combined to foster a rebirth of the Calvinistic notion that the Lord reveals His predilections by the bestowal of mundane favors. Thus the way was slowly prepared for a gradual subscription to the idea that right is the companion of wealth and station rather than of humble poverty, that success is a reward of virtue and failure the penalty of vice.

This change did not come quickly, nor has it ever been logically complete. But in many applications, this realinement of the virtues and the vices proceeded rapidly enough to make typical by the eighties the basic sentiments suggested in the following opinion of the Ohio Practical Farmer in 1885 (*19*): "Here are two grand divisions of society—the honorable and useful, and the poor, the vicious and criminal." Log-cabin birth was long considered a desirable attribute of public men—from 1840 on, practically a prerequisite to Presidential aspiration—because it signified sympathy for the humble; in the course of time it was increasingly considered as proof of having risen. Democratic sentiment thus began to shift from sympathy for the lower stratum to approval of the individual who rose above it. Basic attitudes thus tended to shift from resentment at the existence of privileged social strata toward a belief that social stratification was natural and that moral qualities were somehow correlated with economic levels.

This change has been related to the changing status of the hired man. The increased flow of immigration in the middle of the nineteenth century provided an incident for the first expression of altering attitudes toward hired help. Many of the more indigent newcomers went to work as hired hands and servants, and in many cases much of the hostility toward the strange ways of foreigners was directed toward the ranks they filled. Preceding the discovery by the farmer that he had a labor problem was a period of growing complaint at the supposedly declining quality of hired men and hired girls frequently attributed to their European origin and manners. The neighbor boy and the neighbor girl who had hired out were reported to be supplanted by "a distinct caste," "an inferior class" of foreigners whose incompetence, vice, and ignorance had a "tendency to degrade labor." And the frequent warning was repeated that—

223761°—40——11

While Cincinnatus held the plow, the cultivation of the soil was an honorable employment. But when the prisoners * * * were compelled to hold the plow, the cultivation of the earth became too degrading an employment for the Roman solider or citizen (*35*).

During and after the Civil War the rapid increase in the production of cash crops, particularly in the opening prairie lands where old-fashioned subsistence was impossible, made more emphatic the need for extra labor during busy seasons of the year. Partly as a result of this, the western farm proprietors began upon occasion to complain that the very effectiveness of the agricultural ladder increased their labor difficulties. Thus a subscriber of the Kansas Farmer complained in 1870 that—

Good farm labor is very scarce, from the fact that as soon as young men get a little ahead, in this country of cheap lands, they make arrangements to secure a farm of their own, marry the girl of their choice, and settle down to a staid and quiet life. This is all well enough, but the fact remains that the farmer needs more and better labor, and the question arises how shall he obtain it (*16*).

Hired labor has in fact become a very important consideration to agriculture generally and a personal concern to a substantial proportion of farmers. By 1929, according to census figures, there were over 2,600,000 farmers (nearly 42 percent of the total) who employed hired labor, paying a total cash labor bill in that year of nearly a billion dollars.

In addition to the conditions and facts that tended to place the farmer in the ranks of employers, the influence of farm journals and agricultural-reform agencies of all kinds was in the direction of making the farmer conscious of his status as a real or potential employer with interests different from those who worked on the farm for wages. By the eighties discussion of the "farm labor problem" became a frequent feature of farm journals. When the various branches of economics began to develop special applications to agriculture, farm management and agricultural economics sought to systematize and commercialize the handling of farm labor. Almost invariably the influence of the leaders, intellectuals, and educators and reformers working in agriculture was in the direction of stratifying rural society, because they emphasized making employer-employee relationships formal and contractual.

The mere segregation of labor management as a business problem, as well as the urging of contractual as opposed to personal relationships, has tended to emphasize the diversity of interests and the social differences between employers and employees. The older feeling of equality was dependent upon the informal relationship between proprietor and hired hand, and the careful attention to a legalistic conception of contractual rights and obligations urged upon the farmer has fostered the growth of caste distinction.

In spite of farm-management preachments, relatively few hired hands ever gave or received written contracts, but the spirit prompting the advice spread slowly over the land. It became the practice of farm-management experts to classify farm help into simple groupings, with blanket advice on the over-all virtues and defects of each. Thus a textbook on farm management published in 1921 had a chapter on "Farm Labor" in which hired help was divided into several classifications: White (Irish and Swedish), Negro, Mexican, etc. In such advice as that on "Handling Hobo or Tramp Laborers" there was an unquestioning assumption of deep social stratification.

> These men should be provided with a reasonably warm, dry place to sleep, but as a rule no special housing is needed for them. They are satisfied to furnish their own bedding and sleep on a pile of hay, and to get plain food * * * if ample in quantity and well cooked.
>
> As a class they are easily disgusted with poor machinery, and if an implement continually breaks, they are likely to quit without notice. * * *
>
> These men will not stand crowding or pressing. If any attempt is made to drive them they will quit. Yet they can be held to the daily quitting time, although if over-time or extra work is attempted, a clear understanding must be had and extra money be paid. * * *
>
> Sunday work is usually taboo with the real hobo.
>
> One cannot afford to allow poker playing or gambling of any kind, or tolerate radical talk or preaching by discontented individuals (*32, pp. 520–521*).

Farmers in the traditional pattern of the family farm have generally been generous employers within the limits of their means. Being hard-pressed to make ends meet, they have sometimes had to pay low wages, but when farm prices boomed, as during the World War, good hired hands in the Middle West got as much as $75 to $125 a month with board and room. This fact, however, has not altered the course of the proprietor's growing feeling of separateness from those who work for him or might work for him. The hired hand has moved out of the parlor in most regions and out of the house in many. In some sections in the Middle West, where hired hands lived with the family a generation ago, they now live in town and carry their lunch to work.

This development has been partly the result of a complex of circumstances that has in effect frozen farm help into its inferior status. The old ladder from hiring out to proprietorship has been severely damaged, even working in reverse; and farm hands have in contemporary times become increasingly aware that they are farm hands permanently—not merely climbers on the first of a series of rungs that lead to farm ownership. The famous announcement of the Director of the Census in 1890 about the end of the frontier meant in effect that cheap land was gone and with it the opportunity for the poor man to become a proprietor. For as available land diminished, difficulties were multiplied by increased capital equipment costs. Commerce and industry became the sole remaining hope of the rural disinherited who wished to rise above poverty.

Farmers in general have inclined strongly toward paternalistic treatment of hired help. Although they have grown aware of caste distinctions, they have not in general inclined toward the psychology of exploitation. The attitudes of farmers toward the help they themselves hire has in general been subject to moral considerations of their own that prevent full development of exploitative motives. On this score farmers appear so far to have withstood partially the advice sometimes given by economists and farm-management experts, and they have seldom followed the examples of huge or highly industrial types of agricultural enterprises. The farmer's hostility to labor, where such hostility has really developed, has generally been directed, not against the farm labor with whom he has contact, but rather against urban labor or the urban aspects of labor. In this case, it would seem that the immemorial distrust and dislike for the city has in effect undergone some change in that the specific urban objects of that distrust and dislike have been partially changed. Whereas a century ago the American farmer was inclined to concentrate his suspicion of the city upon the wealthy and aristocratic, he now tends more to look upon the idleness of the unemployed and the tactics of industrial unions as the most prominent symbols of urban corruption.

New Ideas About Success

The increasing acceptance of the success idea has been an important factor in the altering psychology and social institutions of farm people. It was preached with all the zeal of a religion by many popular authors, of whom Horatio Alger was most famous; and it was the social creed of influential publications. Originally an urban phenomenon, it soon penetrated into the country.

Peculiarly enough, the success idea generally repudiated the rugged self-reliance and individualism of the older agrarian creed. There was heavy emphasis usually upon the benevolence of those higher up who would reward young men who were unquestioning and even subservient in their obedience. Farm youths were told repeatedly, in explicit homilies or by implication in juvenile fiction, that by obeying their mothers they would become financially successful and that "a manly young fellow" who is "straight and clean" would be promoted as fast as possible by his employers, out of respect, apparently, for his moral qualities, and because "We always find the best men in the best places" (*58*).

THE PERSISTENCE OF SOME OLDER IDEAS

In very recent times, particularly in the last decade, popular confidence that virtue is inevitably rewarded by economic success has been somewhat dissipated; but the association of economic success with moral qualities remains. A strong tendency to suspect the means whereby great wealth has been acquired still exists. But cheap land and individual opportunity to win independence by thrift and industry were facts of existence for so long that a code of social ethics evolved that, persisting into a later day, seeks to solve the problems of the metropolis and the great society in frontier terms. Thus many believe that the cure for unemployment is hard work and the remedy for technological displacement, old-fashioned moderation and thrift. Both individuals and groups think and act only in terms of their experience. When they are confronted by a situation of crucial importance that is essentially novel, a confusion develops out of which they follow ordinarily one of two general types of behavior. They may appeal to a framework of fantasy, which in the case of social or political problems means faith in some utopian dream. Or they may recur to fragments of past experience connected with established patterns of behavior and, in an effort to escape their sense of inadequacy and insecurity in the new dilemma, emotionalize the older patterns of behavior into eternal standards of right and decency.

Being more at home within the older cultural pattern, farmers and rural people have been more inclined than others to see present difficulties in the light of long-established practices and standards of value. For this reason, the startling new expedients and institutions that have developed within the urban culture to meet new situations that were primarily urban and industrial were bound to arouse a hostile rural reaction in a time of psychological crisis. Relief appropriations have been perhaps the most striking example. Although the country had been acquiring city ways, it was not prepared for such devices. And in its newer forms, the ancient antagonism of the farmer to the city has been directed principally at such innovations and in effect at that stratum of the urban population to whom the farmer once felt most akin.

CHANGING IDEALS IN AGRICULTURAL EDUCATION

Ideals and practices in agricultural education have evolved in conformity with the increasing commercialization of farming and rural life. Agricultural education as originally conceived was to be practical in the sense of being vocational, and aggressively democratic in the sense of being a popular reaction against aristocratic theories of classic education for the few. Yet for a generation or more after the Civil War agricultural colleges failed to be the attraction to farm youth that it had been conceived they would be. The greatest number of farm boys who went to college actually went to study other professions or the liberal arts. Rural people who had faith in and the means to pursue higher education were not generally willing to gamble on agricultural education. There were probably many reasons for this. Many undoubtedly sought professional competence as a means to escape into another occupation. Others retained deep respect for the prestige of old-fashioned academic education. And some may well have suspected that agricultural education had less to offer of a practical nature than had been anticipated. The fact is that agricultural colleges were established before there was a solid and extensive body of agricultural science that could be taught. The agricultural applications of the various sciences had only begun to be worked out, and the best that agricultural colleges could offer was instruction in the basic sciences along the lines followed by academic colleges, with no more than a few incidental references to actual farm practices. In the course of time, agricultural experimentation in the colleges and, after the Hatch Act of 1887, in the experiment stations produced a fund of highly practical and teachable agricultural science; and it seems fair to say that as soon as agricultural colleges had much to offer they had students.

But it was inevitable that, in developing a tangible and applicable body of scientific knowledge, the agricultural colleges should foster specialization and should respond also to the new needs of the farmer created by the increasing economic pressure under which he was forced to operate. Only by conforming to the world could the colleges function within it. But this meant specifically that agricultural education must be purely vocational and technical, measurable only by the success standards of the commercial world. There was probably no real alternative once the frantic race toward commercialism and success ideals was begun.

There has, however, consistently been a conflict in ideals of agricultural education. There has always been a group that sought to include cultural graces and social understanding with purely vocational training. This is the element that in the tradition of the Lyceum, the self-improvement vogue, farmers' clubs and debating and literary societies, the early Grange, the country-life movement, and the Chautauqua movement has sought to improve farm life not only by economic and technological improvement but also by intellectual and social enrichment. Among agricultural educators, Kenyon L. Butterfield and Liberty Hyde Bailey were perhaps the best-known advocates of this intellectual leaven. Within the institutions of agricultural education, this group was not successful in diverting the drift toward increased emphasis upon technical specialization and commercial standards. But its participation in the country-life movement, in farm-life surveys and conferences and rural uplift generally, served nevertheless to hasten the growth of rural sociology as an academic and scientific discipline (*52*).

It is significant that the Country Life Commission was never given the political sanction of congressional support, for the vogue of rural uplift in the early twentieth century was limited principally to educators, clergymen, and small reform groups. It had no strong popular backing and even aroused resentment among many farmers, whose opinion seems to have been that what agriculture needed was more money, and that, with that simple need granted, farmers themselves would be amply able to look out for their own uplift. Social reform in agricultural life had in effect been professionalized; it lacked deep roots in workaday rural society. In the hands of an element largely removed from immediate contact with the soil and not harassed by the same economic difficulties that beset the farmer, it occasionally appeared to the rural mind to be both urban and condescending. The Prairie Farmer in its issue of June 15, 1913, described the continuing rural uplift movement as a case of "too much yeast in the dough," and expressed typical annoyance that—

> There are well up toward a dozen organizations in Chicago that are trying to uplift the farmer. For the most part they are financed and managed by city men.

During the first quarter of the twentieth century, agricultural economics was rapidly attaining academic respectability as well as a wide reputation for being practical. Economics was, in effect, a much more perfect response than uplift to the pressing needs and concerns to which the farmer was then subject.

THE POPULAR ACCEPTANCE OF SCIENCE APPLIED TO AGRICULTURE

The application of the physical sciences to agriculture, although unceasingly advocated throughout the nineteenth century by agricultural leadership, was once generally regarded contemptuously as impractical "book farming" by the masses of farmers. During a century of what was one of the most persistent and intensive propaganda campaigns in history, the benefits of science were advertised to the rank and file of farmers; but only in the present generation has conclusive victory been attained. The intellectuals interested in agricultural progress, farm journals generally, and farm leaders and organizations, with immeasurable faith in scientific progress, have from every quarter urged farmers to adopt the latest scientific devices and methods. When Horace Greeley wrote his book on What I Know of Farming, he dedicated it—

To THE MAN OF OUR AGE, who shall make the first plow propelled by STEAM, or other mechanical power, whereby not less than TEN ACRES PER DAY shall be thoroughly pulverized to a DEPTH OF TWO FEET, at a cost of not more than two dollars per acre * * * (*57*).

In spite of the enthusiasm for science of most agricultural leaders—frequently as extravagant as Horace Greeley's hopes for a steam plow—and in spite of the ready adoption of mechanical devices by all who could afford them, farmers for generations remained generally skeptical of the heralded benefits of science in other forms. The resistance to new methods was slowly worn down, however, by the constant preaching of farm journals and other private agencies. Finally, in the years since the Smith-Lever Act of 1914 and the Smith-Hughes Act of 1917, county-agent work, secondary education in agriculture, and demonstration and extension work generally have broken the last major resistance to agricultural science. A very large number of farmers lack the capital necessary to employ the most modern methods, but the great majority are ready to adopt whatever comes to them under the label of science. To an ever-increasing degree, farmers seek and apply the advice of technical experts, and the lapse of time between laboratory discovery and practical application upon the farm is a mere fraction of what it once was.

Technical Progress in Many Fields

The period between 1864 and 1890 saw the development of the gang plow and the sulky, barbed wire, wheel and two-horse cultivators, spring-tooth and disk harrows, the hay loader and baler, the wire binder, improved reapers, the twine binder and bundle carrier, the silo, the cream separator, and the refrigerator car. By 1890, 910 companies, employing 39,580 men and having a capital aggregating $145,313,997, were engaged exclusively in the manufacture of agricultural machinery. The census estimated that on the 4,564,641 farms enumerated that year there was farm machinery worth half a billion dollars. By 1890 or 1900 most of the major mechanical improvements practicable with horses for power had been developed. With the development of the tractor a great new wave of mechanization began. The 1930 census, taken before the recent great increase of mechanization based on the rubber-tired tractor and supplementary implements, reported 3⅓ billion dollars' worth of farm machinery on about 5,600,000 farms, or nearly $600 per farm.

The technology of plants and animals has developed similarly through introductions from abroad, scientific breeding, and the control of diseases and insects.

This technological progress has resulted in an increase in agricultural wealth so vast and complex that it cannot well be estimated. The agricultural domain has been extended by new varieties of plants resistant to disease, drought, and cold. Yields have been increased.

New plants have been found to supply special needs and to provide products that older plants could not. Losses from disease and pests have been greatly curtailed. Hand-labor requirements have been reduced, sometimes phenomenally, and the amount of land cultivable by a single farm family has been much increased (*60*). The reader will find elsewhere in this Yearbook a much fuller discussion of the nature and effects of agricultural technology (The Influence of Technical Progress on Agricultural Production, p. 509).

Technological advance has fostered specialization by increasing the need for and value of special skills. Technology has made economic specialization possible by counteracting the natural vulnerability to pests and diseases that accompanies concentration and specialization. It has increased the amount of necessary capital investment in equipment and working capital. Thus agricultural science and technology have made the farmer a much more efficient producer of agricultural supplies for the market, but they have also collaborated with other forces in the modern world to make him vitally dependent upon the working of an increasingly complex society.

The laboratory apron is rapidly becoming, for the farmer as for the rest of the world, a priestly vestment of authority. The slogans and fetishes that have accompanied the expansion of science and technology have been accepted along with sober scientific truth. If the judgment of advertisers is an indication, rural as well as city people are impressed by the vitamin content of everything from breakfast food to cold cream, and the approval of white-garbed scientists with test tubes in their hands can be a cogent recommendation of fencing, potash, hybrid corn, tooth paste, or tires for the tractor.

THE DEVELOPMENT OF PROFESSIONAL FARM LEADERSHIP

Traditionally, agriculture has been conducive to democracy. Responsible local leadership has tended to develop more freely and democratically among free-holding farmers than among most other social groupings. But in the process of adjustment to the great society, what was adequate to community organization has sometimes failed to apply on a national scale. A busy farmer may assume civic responsibilities in local matters without prejudice to his farming; but when the level of activity rises to embrace the State, the region, and the Nation, it generally becomes impossible to be both an active leader and a practicing farmer. Since agriculture has been drawn into a national economic orbit, agricultural concerns of the greatest importance have become national problems, and agricultural leadership has tended correspondingly to become national, and therefore professionalized. This professional leadership has been farm-reared; but, in becoming professionalized, it has sometimes grown urban. Farm leaders have of necessity taken urban residence, developed urban associations, become partly urban in outlook. A significant proportion of farm leaders have been farm youth who went to town, made or failed to make a fortune there, and then in later life became leaders of rural reform.

The oldest national farm organization of today—the Grange—illustrates this modern tendency toward urban and professionalized farm leadership. None of the seven founders was by occupation a farmer for more than a small portion of his life. Of the 10 masters of the National Grange (second to eleventh) of whom biographical sketches are given in the official Semi-Centennial History of the Patrons of Husbandry (*34*), only two could be called practicing dirt farmers. Most of the others had spent their youth on the farm, and some engaged in farming as a hobby.

Agriculture has taken its political leadership from the town, too. The great agricultural State of Iowa, for instance, had a total of 419 elected Congressmen between 1844 and 1938. Only 15 of these are identified by the Iowa Official Register as farmers; of the rest, 309 were lawyers, 35 were bankers, 22 were editors, journalists, or publishers, 34 were businessmen (merchants, manufacturers, brokers, nurserymen, grain dealers, lumbermen) and 4 were of the learned professions. Of the total of 15 elected Congressmen who were farmers, 12 were elected to office in the period 1844–90, and not one was elected during the 40 years from 1892 to 1932. The other 3 were elected between 1932 and 1938.

In the far-flung agrarian unrest of the seventies, eighties, and nineties, a substantial proportion of the agricultural leadership rose to prominence directly from the farm. There were Sockless Jerry Simpsons as well as Ignatius Donnellys. And although agricultural leadership has in the course of the last generation or two become increasingly professionalized, there has continued to be much dirt-farmer leadership in purely economic causes. Probably no movement was ever more genuinely indigenous than the farm-holiday movement of the early 1930's. But the contemporary situation is such that noneconomic organizations and causes cannot ordinarily depend upon popular support or leadership from farm people; farm problems have become increasingly technical in nature as well as national in scope, and farm people have generally been content to have others act for them, retaining only a veto power.

PAPER VALUES VERSUS WORK VALUES

Farm people have taken over from urban culture the practice of thinking in terms of money and paper values and of expecting gain to come from mere legal possession. Ownership of the kind residing in the possession of paper, signed, sealed, and attested, has become of itself a morally justifiable claim upon income. This attitude is of course merely in accordance with prevailing institutions and doctrines, and its acceptance by farm people has been aided by the long experience of rising land values as the frontier moved westward and as population grew rapidly. But it is definitely in conflict with older pioneer and agrarian notions, which considered material wealth as the product of toil which by right should be distributed only on the basis of productive work actually performed, on actual possession and use, rather than on the basis of possession of paper symbols and insignia or by their manipulation. The right of corporate or urban groups to receive income from land on the sole basis of legal possession was challenged many times by the rural mind in an earlier period. As time passed, however, this challenge was made less frequently and more and more on the grounds of appeal to other criteria; that is, the rural challenge of corporate and urban income from mere possession of capital was based increasingly on some charge that the capital was not honestly acquired or that it worked public harm rather than on the ground that income from merely legal ownership was wrong in itself, though the latter view was established and respected on the frontier because of the experience of squatters on unopened land.

When agriculture was drawn into the orbit of modern business practices, it was inevitable that modern business ideas and morals should in the course of time extend to the farmer; the farmer merely conformed, generally belatedly, to the changing world. Rationally, at least, he sought tariff benefits for himself only after becoming convinced that industry would never give up its own special tariff benefits. He sought to influence agricultural prices by combination and by political means only after a long and disastrous experience with trusts, monopolies, and administered prices in industry that would not or could not be broken down. The farmer's acceptance of modern capitalistic methods for his own use is in a large measure a defensive gesture.

FARMERS AND MIDDLEMEN

The old agrarian distrust of devious business methods and devices has persisted and has sometimes led to strange contradictions as agriculture has been increasingly commercialized. Dislike of middlemen is as old as history. Medieval law and trade regulations were full of statutes and rules intended to curb the power of middlemen to influence prices. "Middlemen" has essentially the same unfavorable connotation today to many people that "regrators," "forestallers," and "engrossers" had to medieval yeomen. Historically, farmers have been the most consistent of all economic individualists. No group has been more thoroughly or consistently hostile to combination and monopoly and to all that savored of Big Business. Whatever was indirect was under suspicion. This eternal tendency to distrust the agencies of distribution and to suspect them of profiteering is the psychological basis upon which cooperatives have been built.

In the name of a war on speculation, monopoly, and middlemen's unfair profits, producer cooperatives were developed; yet producer cooperatives frequently have declared control of prices an aim. Thus during the campaign for producer cooperatives in 1920, the Prairie Farmer in its issue of September 25 printed an article entitled "Almond Growers Act Like Real Business Men; They Fix Prices and Control Their Product, and Have Run the Speculator to Cover." The article itself, like the title, emphasized the price-fixing role, and told how directors of local associations met annually to fix prices. When in 1926 the Farm Journal told "What the Big Co-op Can Do" (*28*), it emphasized the adjective "big," and declared that, among other things, it—

> * * * can fix, and force buyers to accept fair and uniform grades; can establish its own brands and maintain an exclusive market for them through advertising.
> * * * can afford to hire a trained sales force familiar with markets and "the tricks of the trade" * * *
> * * * can secure and furnish to members reliable figures on production and consumption or probable demand.

* * * can block laws restricting co-operative sales methods, and keep legislative "hands off"; and secure and maintain any necessary tariff protection on its products.

A single farmer or a small co-op cannot do any of these things.

In January 1925 the Pacific Rural Press told with much enthusiasm how California poultry producers' cooperatives entered the market and by manipulative buying raised the price of eggs (*27*). Thus the economic necessity of holding one's own in the highly commercial modern world has forced the farmer to engage as best he can in the very practices which he was once inclined to condemn as the peculiar corruptions of urban economy.

THE COUNTRY ADOPTS CITY WAYS

Rural life has for a century been throwing off the characteristics that once distinguished it so sharply from urban life. The countryside has been undergoing a process of accelerating urbanization for nearly a century. Country people in America have generally aspired to the refinements of middle-class urban culture and have achieved them when possible. Most of the deliberate efforts toward rural improvement during the nineteenth century were inspired by a desire to relieve farm life of the roughness that the frontier had imposed upon it. These efforts mainly followed two lines. One was to increase the creature comforts and conveniences of country life, which in effect meant the adoption of urban devices and methods. The other was to refine and elevate the manners and intellectual concerns of country people upon the model of tastes and predilections in vogue in the city. The changes and improvements effected in rural life during the last century have amounted practically, therefore, to a process of urbanization.

The urbanization of country living has not come about because rural people explicitly desired urban life as such. Rather, the desirable innovations ready for adoption have been those for which urban culture had established a taste. The principal dynamics of the modern situation have originated almost exclusively in the industrial city. Hostility to urban culture as such has not disappeared, although perhaps it has declined and been altered in its manifestations. The rural world has come in large measure to accept urban ideas of success, though it has continued the ancient tradition of decrying rural exodus and deploring the false lures and illusory opportunities of the city.

But in spite of everything, the younger farm people have been attracted to the city and to city traits and behavior; and they have been important agents in the extension of the urban culture to the country. Sympathetic commentators upon the exodus of rural youth have repeatedly explained the exodus in terms of the progressive, up-to-date temper of youth, and the backwardness and conservatism of age; they have urged modernizing—urbanizing—farm equipment and household furnishings as the measure necessary to keep youth on the farm. Here is an example from the Nebraska Farmer of July 1, 1885 (*18*):

In most cases the trouble will be found with the farmer instead of his son * * *.

The old man is content with some improvements on the ideas of fifty years ago. He can't see why any one should want anything better than bare floors, Windsor chairs and cowhide boots. He would as soon go to meeting without a collar as with one. * * *

And now what's the matter with farmer's boys? They live in a new world—the father in an old one. No matter how little schooling they have had, they are better educated than he is. No matter if the father refuses to do more than subscribe to a weekly paper, his boys are fairly posted on all the daily happenings all over the world. He wants to farm after old ideas—they after new ones. * * *

The boys must have things to interest and amuse them. They want books, magazines and newspapers. If there's a chance to fix up a bowling alley let the boys go ahead and make one. * * * If one of the boys has a taste for music help him along with it. Let him have a fiddle, accordeon, organ, or whatever instrument he feels he can bring music out of.

It was realized that the traditional ideas and practices of agriculture did not conform to the commercial temper of the times that was spreading from the city to the country and that many farm boys left the country in order to pursue business careers. This was considered an additional reason for making farming more businesslike. The following typical comment was made in Farm and Fireside in 1907:

Many ambitious farm boys * * * have the business instinct, and they want a chance to develop it, so they turn to the city. * * * if all the farmers of the country would make their occupation more of a business * * * they would not only be more prosperous * * * the ambitious farm boys * * * would stay on the farm.

Commercialization was only one phase of the urbanization of farm life; and it was in effect merely the means whereby farm people could obtain the products of industry that the absorption of urban culture had taught them increasingly to desire. It was generally the case that as the agricultural frontier moved westward there had to be a period of development of the primary necessities and rudimentary capital equipment. For a time the struggle to accomplish this much exhausted the means and the energies of the agricultural settlers. But when these first needs were met, they generally sought the comforts, the refinements, the labor-saving devices, and the pleasures of a less arduous life.

When farm journals first began to print fiction, shortly before the Civil War, the stories that they ran were almost without exception especially written to fit the real or imagined tastes of a rural audience. The heroes were poor young farmers, the heroines were country girls, the villains were wealthy city men; after many vicissitudes rural simplicity and virtue triumphed over urban duplicity and corruption. But by 1900 or shortly thereafter, such fiction as appeared in farm journals—those with a large national circulation were the principal purveyors—was generally the same as that appearing in any class of popular magazines. Rural people thus read fiction based on the cultural assumptions and ideals of the urban reading masses; and country readers followed willy-nilly the vagaries and shifting fads of popular urban fiction.

The country has been motivated to seek some urban refinements as a defense mechanism, adopting customs of the town while continuing to decry them. Thus the Ohio Practical Farmer campaigned in 1885 for better table manners and more social refinement among farmers, protesting meanwhile, perhaps too much, that crude table manners were not a confession of social inferiority.

We do not believe you will find any better manners in the city than in the country, though you may find more awkwardness and restraint in society, simply the result of isolation or lack of society. True politeness, however, does not consist in the observance of arbitrary rules laid down, perhaps, by a brainless fop, but * * * is "kindness expressed in a pleasing manner * * * ." The man who insists that another is a boor because he does not eat pie with a fork, is lacking somewhere in the upper story. And the man who eats pie with his knife because it is the most convenient implement for the purpose, simply manifests good common sense instead of a lack of good breeding. We would make a wide distinction between true refinement and the "polish" of fashionable society (*17*).

There appears to have been among many farm people a continuous resistance to ambition that was risky and to refinements that were expensive. There is evidence that many farmers looked with deep distrust upon the financial dangers of reaching beyond themselves either for new farm machinery or for new comforts of living. This common feeling of distrust and foreboding is suggested in the letter of a Pennsylvania farmer in 1890:

We find many farmers running in debt to "keep even" with their neighbors. Because Jones who owns bank stock and has good machinery, fine musical instruments, fast horses, etc., they think they must have them too, if they have to mortgage the farm to get them (*23*).

The misgiving aroused in the minds of many farmers by the decline of self-sufficiency and the spread of commercialization and urban ways, backward-looking though it sometimes was, amounted to a perception of the social and economic maladjustments that the modern world was bringing to the countryside. The farmer himself, pushed one way by the impact of the new and pulled the other by the persistence of the old, sensed the cultural conflict that was frequently ignored by professional experts, who were for the most part one-sided enthusiasts. Yet the greater force has been in the direction of change, and although there have been many regretful backward glances, farmers have, in their way, adjusted themselves to their times.

Rural free delivery, farm-to-market roads, and parcel post all resulted from agitation by farm leaders strongly supported by the masses of farmers. The mail-order house came in, disseminating widely a taste for the new products of industrial civilization by attractive illustrated catalogs and making new products actually available in remote places. The influence of these catalogs is suggested by the colloquial name for them—"wishing books"—that grew up in some of the more remote regions. Late in the nineties the movement to extend telephone service to the country began; and the building of cooperative lines, sponsored or at least suggested generally by farm organizations or farm journals, gained headway. All these things brought the farmer closer to town and served in the end to extend the town into the country.

Wartime and early post-war prosperity brought an accelerated wave of urbanization to the country that reached an initial climax in a blaze of silk-shirt glory before prices fell in the autumn of 1920. But the trend toward urbanization of country living survived the slump. By the middle 1920's, automobile manufacturers were sure enough of the urbanity of the farmers who read farm journals and bought automobiles to advertise their product as "A regally luxurious motor car * * * beautifully engineered, beautifully built—and stylish as the *Rue de la Paix*." Each new convenience, every new gadget, has bound the country more closely to the town and made it more like the town. Educational effort indicated the virtues of more and still more contrivances to make life easier; and although for most farmers possession of these things was a dream rather than a hope, their existence has been driving ever higher the minimum desired living standard. Farmer visitors to Farm Home Week at Cornell in 1929 were shown a model farm home whose kitchen was described by the Cornell Countryman in the following terms (*29*):

> In the kitchen * * * everything was arranged to give the housewife a convenient, pleasant work room. The electrical apparatus included a refrigerator, a range, a dish washer, and a food mixer. It had that great boon to the farm woman, a complete water system. The water was heated by an electric water heater. The range was one of the kind in whose oven you put the supper and go to town for the groceries and forget about it. The clock turns the heat on and the heat is regulated so that when you come in it is all done. The central light eliminates shadow. The switch for it also had an outlet in the bottom for a flat iron. There were local lights at the sink so you would not be working in your own shadow. There was a power outlet by the table for the food mixer, toaster, or grill, and one by the refrigerator. Every farm woman who saw it probably desired a kitchen like it, so spotlessly white and convenient with all the labor saving devices that are so needed on a farm.

The ephemeral fads and fashions of the city have penetrated to many farms. Beauty columns have entered into the farm press. We find in the Idaho Farmer, April 1935:

> Hands should be soft enough to flatter the most delicate of the new fabrics. They must be carefully manicured, with none of the hot, brilliant shades of nail polish. The lighter and more delicate tones are in keeping with the spirit of freshness.
>
> Keep the tint of your fingertips friendly to the red of your lips, and check both your powder and your rouge to see that they best suit the tone of your skin in the bold light of summer.

It is certain that few farm wives have a chance to heed such "beauty hints," even if they would; but the model is there, and the advice is not all lost, especially on the younger generation.

Several farm journals have for some time sponsored winter tours by farmers; and the idea has spread that farmers should get out and see the world, to broaden their outlook and to give them a vacation, in the urban sense, from the cares of everyday life. Thus, in the syndicated colloquialisms of the Lazy Farmer, from the Idaho Farmer, 1935:

> I planned to take Mirandy Jane and take a trip somewhere by train or in the car, and see some sights, nor have to go to bed of nights until we'd seen most ev'rything, nor have to rise at five, by jing. Us farm folks ought to travel more, we stay at home until we're sore at ev'rything, and raisin' hob, because we're too close to our job. It does us good to git away, when we come back some other day we're fresh in body and in mind, and if the work's a mite behind, we can pitch in and git it done, and, best of all, we've had our fun.

LOSS OF THE OLD WITH ACCEPTANCE OF THE NEW

It should be continually emphasized that the adoption of new things was inevitably followed, sooner or later, by the creation of new customs and new dependencies. This, in turn, involved the desertion of old ways and codes of living. This fact was in one way or another repeatedly observed, generally with regret, because the standards of value and the moral codes that constitute social adaptation to material things always outlive the things themselves. Sometimes, too, the regret was based at least partly upon a sense of social maladjustment, upon a feeling that the efficiency of an older institution had been impaired without a new one rising to take its place. Thus as long ago as 1905 one writer on rural affairs observed (*68*):

> Social matters are not conducted as they once were among farmers. They are following in the wake of other people, and are putting more expense and formality in entertainments than of old. * * *
>
> * * * the "neighbor woman" has gone back on her record. The doctor and hired nurse have come to take her place. She doesn't know now the uses of sage tea and catnip, or of camomile and tansy. She can not take one of her own family through a bilious attack, or spell of colic, as the old-time mother with her garret full of herbs. * * *
>
> It takes more money to live now that people are not so serviceable nor so sociable. Farmers cannot afford to be sociable as sociability is conducted nowadays. * * * People want fine houses and furniture and expensive lighting and heating appurtenances; they want clipped horses and fine carriages, and they try to dress as near like the *elite* as possible, and to entertain their guests as sumptuously as those do who have thrice their wealth. All this is sociability run wild—it will not endure to the end.

When, late in 1929, Farm and Fireside conducted a questionnaire survey among its subscribers to determine the extent of rural social change and of resistance to change, the editors were impressed, more than by anything else, by the evidence of rapid decline of differences between farm and city people. Interpretation of the results of this poll must be consistently qualified by recognition of the fact that the circulation of Farm and Fireside was to a disproportionate degree among the more prosperous strata of rural society and that the opinions of this group would probably not correspond to those of the majority of the whole rural population. It should also be remembered, however, that the more prosperous elements of rural society have generally been in the lead in long-time trends of change. It is this group that has generally been the first to adopt innovations that later attained wide acceptance. Although the Farm and Fireside survey showed rural opinion heavily against easy divorce and repeal of prohibition, 67 percent favored "legalizing doctors to impart birth control methods to married couples who apply jointly"—an opinion that the editors called "a most astonishing departure from old-fashioned standards." The survey also disclosed that articles dealing with "world events and modern thought" were the most popular of all with Farm and Fireside readers. One of the most significant of all was the vote on consolidated schools. It was reported that 78 percent were in favor of them. On this vote Farm and Fireside commented (*30*):

> Distinctly on the side of progress is the vote as to consolidated schools. They cost money, a good deal of money; they represent what old-timers call citified, new-fangled nonsense, but the countryside of America clamors for them, four votes out of five.

What may well be the earliest complete repudiation of the old agrarian social code by a spokesman for agriculture occurred, as might be expected, in a region where farming has been more industrialized and farm life less distinctly rural than in any other large section of the country. In 1915, the Pacific Rural Press reprinted a little story from a midwestern farm paper. This is the story:

> A man and a woman sat together at a theater one afternoon last week. He wore a cheap suit of clothing that fitted him poorly. Her dress was not in the latest mode. Plainly, they were from the country.
>
> Right behind them sat two women of the city. One of them put her lorgnette to her eyes, bent forward and looked critically at the woman in front of her. Then she settled back in her chair and said in a voice evidently intended for the woman in front to hear: "Why do some people have such awful taste as to dress as they used to before the flood?"
>
> The woman in front heard it and her face went red. The man with her heard it too, and he quietly laid his hand upon his companion's arm and patted it lovingly.
>
> A man who sat near, and had heard and seen this little tragedy, told of it afterward. "I knew the man from the country, and his wife," he said. "I know that she is his partner in running that farm. Her vegetables, butter and eggs provide an important part of their income. Now they have come to the city for an outing. To my mind they belong to the class who are really our best people, and the woman behind them with the lorgnette is just a coarse, vulgar frump" (*25*).

This was an almost perfect example of the stereotyped homily that had appeared thousands of times in farm journals for nearly a century in expression of the older agrarian social creed. But the Pacific Rural Press reprinted it only in order to make its modern comment:

> Of course, our Middle West contemporary has to preach upon the text this incident presents, but it needs no sermon here. In the first place, we believe our rural women are relatively better dressed than elsewhere, and therefore the incident would have no local foundation. * * * Our point is that the contrast between rural and urban women in costuming is probably less in California than anywhere else in the world. And we are of the impression also that California rural women are not infrequently outfitted to do the lorgnette act toward the urban women were they not prevented by inborn politeness * * * (*25*).

The Conflict Between the Old and the New

The changes that have been coming to agriculture at a quickening pace in the past two or three generations are more than mere material changes. As things have changed, customs and ideas have changed. Notions of what it is proper to do, right to desire, and judicious to hope are altered under altered circumstances. Conceptions even of right and wrong are changed in the course of time. But moral ideas, though inevitably they change in the long run as the world changes, alter more slowly than most other customs and ideas. The basic attitudes developed in childhood and youth ordinarily cling with us as eternal verities until we die. This is the fundamental reason why every generation of old people inclines to look with uneasiness upon the ways of the young and feels sometimes that the younger generation is headed straight for perdition.

We are not coldly rational beings with minds like calculating machines. Rather we live according to the customs and habits of our cultural inheritance. In the world today are hundreds if not thousands of vastly differing cultures among different peoples, the only common characteristic of which is that the individuals integrated within each one regard their own culture as "right" and "natural." And they generalize upon the particular to the extent of believing beyond question that the standards of value, customs, moral notions, and institutions they have grown up with are inevitable and universal, the product of rational determination as opposed to accidental inheritance. Thus the temporary expedients and ephemeral accommodations that evolve as a means of living together under one set of circumstances almost inevitably become moral codes and concepts of God and nature, of abstract and universal reason. Social adaptation and change to meet new circumstances is therefore bound invariably to result in conflict between old and new institutions, between old and new ideas of right and wrong.

American agriculture has lived through a long series of cultural conflicts during the past century. There has been almost continuous conflict between folkways and folklore on the one hand and applications of scientific rationality on the other. The intellectual and reform elements in agriculture have invariably sought to hasten and to alter the direction of our cultural evolution. There was a conflict in the middle-western agricultural regions in the ante bellum period between the matter-of-fact, severely practical culture, inherited principally from New England and the Middle Atlantic States, and the idealism and optimism fostered by the intellectuals of that period. There has consistently been a conflict between the moral concept of the farmer, developed in part out of older experience but perpetuated by the literary tradition of agrarian fundamentalism, and new realities brought into being by the commercialization of agriculture. Thus the literary tradition has it that the farmer is independent and secure unto himself—which in most cases he has manifestly ceased to be; that he is remote from the ills and corruptions of the market place and unenvious of urban luxuries—which ordinarily he obviously cannot be.

This concept of the farm as a gentle haven from the world's strife is in flat contradiction to the tendencies toward commercialization, mechanization, specialization, and urbanization that are the dominant trends of modern agriculture. And yet it is a fact that this idyllic agrarian fundamentalism has been perpetuated principally by the intellectual and reform elements that have been most active in modernizing American agriculture.

Farm people themselves, genuinely devoted as they may be to country life, have not fooled themselves in this way. They have been too close to the monotony of chores, the dust of harrowing, the threat of drought and pests and disease. Yet among some professional agricultural leaders and educators there has evidently been a desire to idealize rural life in a moral and aesthetic way, and also to see agriculture principally in terms of the most prosperous group of farmers. In order to establish good examples for emulation, or because of class or economic predilections, the farmer has thus been identified with a level of ease, equipment, well-being, and prosperity far above any average for the Nation as a whole. Thus a secondary school text in farm management, written 26 years ago by one of the most capable experts in the field, displayed as the first of many illustrations a photograph with the legend, "An American Farm Home" (*41, p. 8*). The inevitable implication was that the house shown was average or typical. Actually, however, the picture portrayed the hobby farm of a wealthy city man far out of the class of anything that could be called an average or typical farm. In another high-school text on

223761°—40——12

agriculture published in 1939 is a photograph flat-footedly captioned "An airplane view of a typical farm in the North Central Region" (*42, p. 3*). This "typical" farmstead includes a white house of apparently 8 to 10 rooms; a windmill and pump house; a poultry house large enough for at least 1,000 chickens, with incubator and brooder space extra; a dairy barn large enough for 40 or more milk cows in addition to stalls for horses; hog houses to take care of a dozen or more brood sows, and shelter also for shoats; a large milkshed; and in addition one large building that looks like a machinery shed, another apparently a garage or workshop, and another that seems to be a large crib for grain storage.

Incidents of this kind would be trivial were it not that they indicate the frequent confusion of the real and the ideal in thinking about agriculture and that—much more important—they illustrate the social stratification of agricultural ideas that corresponds to the social stratification that has been developing in fact. The majority of educational, reform, and adjustment programs have tended strongly to be directed toward the benefit of a class of farmers who came nearest to corresponding to the abstract conception of the farmer suggested by such illustrations as are noted above.

Thus both the deliberate attempts to improve agriculture and rural life and the untoward, uncontrolled social forces of this age have for the most part concentrated their benefits upon the more prosperous element of the farm population. For only the more prosperous ones have been able to take full advantage of modern technology and commercialism. And while this upper economic stratum has had its living standards raised rapidly, the lower stratum has not been able to follow. As a result the cleavage between the two has grown increasingly wider. The rising proportions of tenancy and farm indebtedness, the growing population pressure in many rural regions, the dramatic migrations of the disinherited are other symptoms of the growing stratification of rural society.

Beyond a doubt the present trends are forcefully directed toward a great split in the agricultural population—the upper group, inclined to take on more and more of the traits of the urban and small-town middle class, while the lower economic stratum seems destined for wage-labor status within a society in which caste consciousness and class lines based on economic means are developing to a rigidity previously unknown among freemen in this country.

The dynamic forces that are most profoundly affecting the nature of rural life today derive from the industrial city and the metropolitan community; and the most central characteristic of these forces is the economic interdependence that modern technology and industrialism have introduced into the country as well as the city. A situation has been created out of which new kinds of economic disparities and social dislocations have developed. Measures conceived in traditional terms, although helpful, have generally failed to achieve any substantial adjustment. The inadequacy of older institutions and arrangements, even as means to attain the substance of older ideals and aspirations, has become more apparent as the modern situation has intensified. As a result the boundless confidence and optimism by which the agricultural domain of this country was first settled and made productive have been increasingly qualified by bewilderment and pessimism, and the former ideal of progress is giving ground to a new ideal of security. The bewilderment and pessimism are likely to endure until the way seems clear to the attainment of security—until institutions develop that within the modern situation can assure the safety of the more lasting needs and desires of men, even though these appear in altered form.

Such is the essence of the vast and complex changes that have taken place in the ideas and ideals of many millions of American farm people. And these changes, it must be emphasized, are not the exclusive products of men's minds—they are what the facts have made them.

LITERATURE CITED

(1) ANONYMOUS.
1834. EXTRACT OF A LETTER TO THE EDITORS. Cultivator 1: 113–114.

(2) ———
1836. TO THE PATRONS OF THE CULTIVATOR. (Letter.) Cultivator 2: 161–162.

(3) ———
1841. [THE FARMER.] Union Agr. and Western Prairie Farmer 1 (8): 63.

(4) ———
1842. THE GARDEN. Cultivator 9: 55–56.

(5) ———
1845. MANUFACTURES AT LOWELL. Farmer's Monthly Visitor 7 (1): 4.

(6) ———
1846. WORK FOR CHILDREN. Farmer's Monthly Visitor 8 (2): 29.

(7) ———
1847. INDIAN CORN: WHAT IS KNOWN AND WHAT IS WANTED TO BE KNOWN ABOUT IT. Monthly Jour. Agr. 2: 537–547.

(8) ———
1850. POETRY AND PROFIT OF CITY LIFE. By a Lover of the Country. Prairie Farmer 10 (1): 18–19.

(9) ———
1850. RANDOM NOTES OF A JOURNEY EAST. (By an old sucker.) Prairie Farmer 10: 180.

(10) ———
1851. HONOR AND PROFIT OF INDUSTRY. New England Farmer 3: 391–392.

(11) ———
1851. LABOR IS CAPITAL. New England Farmer 3: 150.

(12) ———
1853. WHAT IS RESPECTABILITY? Northern Farmer 2: 121.

(13) ———
1858. HUMBLE WORTH. Amer. Farmers' Mag. 12: 634.

(14) ———
1860. GOLD MINES AT HOME. Prairie Farmer (n. s. 5) 21: 148.

(15) ———
1868. HOW WE HAVE ALL ADVANCED. Prairie Farmer (n. s. 21) 37: 17.

(16) ———
1870. HIRED LABOR. Kans. Farmer 7: 138.

(17) ———
1885. REFINEMENT AMONG FARMERS. (Editorial comment on a letter by "An old Subscriber.") Ohio Practical Farmer 67 (12): 198.

(18) ———
1885. SHORT TALK WITH THE BOYS. By M. Quad. Nebr. Farmer 9: 205–206.

(19) ———
1885. WHAT ARE YOU READING? By "Rusticus." Ohio Practical Farmer 67 (8): 127.

(20) Anonymous
1886. cultivation. Farm Jour. 10: 102.

(21) ———
1886. study your business. Farm Jour. 10 (1): 8.

(22) ———
1887. the farmer as a merchant. Farm Jour. 11: 130.

(23) ———
1890. how to economize. Ohio Practical Farmer 77: 442.

(24) ———
1903. the farmers' institute. (Editorial.) Cornell Countryman 1 (1): 14.

(25) ———
1915. two great things in california. Pacific Rural Press 89: 290.

(26) ———
1925. the "divine" law of supply and demand. Ohio Farmer 155: 280.

(27) ———
1925. putting a crowbar under the market. Pacific Rural Press 109: 70.

(28) ———
1926. what the big co-op can do. Farm Jour. 50 (6): 8.

(29) ———
1929. rural electricity and the home. Cornell Countryman 26: 208, illus.

(30) ———
1930. the forces of change. Farm and Fireside 54 (1): 9, 32–38.

(31) A., A. E. A.
1841. "knowledge is power." (Letter.) Cultivator 8: 164.

(32) Adams, R. L.
1921. farm management; a textbook for student, investigator, and investor. 671 pp., illus. New York and London.

(33) Alley, J. P.
1921. what a farmer really looks like. Country Gent. 86 (31): 7.

(34) Atkeson, Thomas Clark.
1916. semi-centennial history of the patrons of husbandry. 364 pp., illus. New York.

(35) B.
1857. female help. New England Farmer (n. s.) 9: 247–248.

(36) B., C. D.
1860. the canadian excursion. Prairie Farmer (n. s. 6) 22: [65], 72, [81], 89, [97], 100–101.

(37) Bailey, L. H.
1911. the country-life movement in the united states. 220 pp. New York.

(38) Bidwell, Percy Wells, and Falconer, John I.
1925. history of agriculture in the northern united states, 1620–1860. 512 pp. Washington, D. C.

(39) Birkbeck, Morris.
1818. letters from illinois. Ed. 3, 114 pp. London.

(40) ———
1818. notes on a journey in america, from the coast of virginia to the territory of illinois. Ed. 4, 156 pp. London.

(41) Boss, Andrew.
1914. farm management. 237 pp., illus. Chicago and New York.

(42) ——— Wilson, Harold K., and Peterson, William E.
1939. american farming; agriculture i. 526 pp., illus. St. Paul, Minn.

(43) Brayshaw, Joseph.
1841. mr. brayshaw's address. (Letter to editor, enclosing address.) Union Agr. and Western Prairie Farmer 1 (8): 59–60.

(44) Carrier, Lyman.
1923. the beginnings of agriculture in america. 323 pp., illus. New York.

(45) COLLIN, NICHOLAS.
1793. PHYSICO MATHEMAĆICAL [SIC] ENQUIRIES. Amer. Phil. Soc. Trans. 3: XIII–XV.
(46) CURTI, MERLE.
1937. THE LEARNED BLACKSMITH; THE LETTERS AND JOURNALS OF ELIHU BURRITT. 241 pp. New York.
(47) D.
1851. STUDY AND LABOR. (Letter to editor.) New England Farmer 3: 210–211.
(48) DAVENPORT, EUGENE.
1904. THE OUTLOOK FOR THE EDUCATED FARMER. Cornell Countryman 1: 204–205.
(49) EDITOR OF FARM AND FIRESIDE.
1916. THE EDITOR'S LETTER . . . Farm and Fireside 39 (22): 2.
(50) G., C. J.
1850. THE COUNTRY AND THE CITY. Prairie Farmer 10: 378–379.
(51) G., W.
1835. QUERY TO FARMERS. Cultivator 1: 189.
(52) GALPIN, CHARLES JOSIAH.
1938. THE DEVELOPMENT OF THE SCIENCE AND PHILOSOPHY OF AMERICAN RURAL SOCIETY. Agr. Hist. 12: 195–208.
(53) GILBERT, A. B.
1926. THESE "FAIR" CROP PRICES. Farm Jour. 50 (11): 10, 48–49.
(54) GILBERT, Z. A.
1871. FARMERS' CLUBS. New England Farmer 5 (2): 81–82.
(55) GRAY, LEWIS CECIL.
1933. HISTORY OF AGRICULTURE IN THE SOUTHERN UNITED STATES TO 1860. 2 v. Washington, D. C.
(56) ——— and LLOYD, O. G.
1920. FARM LAND VALUES IN IOWA. U. S. Dept. Agr. Bul. 874, 45 pp., illus.
(57) GREELEY, HORACE.
1871. WHAT I KNOW OF FARMING; A SERIES OF BRIEF AND PLAIN EXPOSITIONS OF PRACTICAL AGRICULTURE AS AN ART BASED UPON SCIENCE. 321 pp. New York.
(58) GRUNDY, FRED.
1908. WHAT SHALL THE YOUNG MAN DO. Farm and Fireside 32 (5): 3.
(59) HIBBARD, BENJAMIN HORACE.
1904. HISTORY OF AGRICULTURE IN DANE COUNTY, WISCONSIN. Wis. Univ. Bul. 101, pp. [69]–214, illus. (Econ. and Polit. Sci. Ser. v. 1, No. 2, pp. 67–214.)
(60) HURST, W. M., and CHURCH, L. M.
1933. POWER AND MACHINERY IN AGRICULTURE. U. S. Dept. Agr. Misc. Pub. 157, 38 pp., illus.
(61) JAMES, EDMUND J.
1910. THE ORIGIN OF THE LAND GRANT ACT OF 1862 (THE SO-CALLED MORRILL ACT) AND SOME ACCOUNT OF ITS AUTHOR, JONATHAN B. TURNER. Ill. Univ. Studies v. 4, No. 1, 139 pp. Urbana. (Appendix C, The Turner Pamphlet, pp. 45–111.)
(62) KELSEY, DAVID STONE.
1925. KELSEY'S RURAL GUIDE . . . 299 pp. Boston.
(63) LIEBIG, JUSTUS.
1840. ORGANIC CHEMISTRY IN ITS APPLICATIONS TO AGRICULTURE AND PHYSIOLOGY. Ed. from the manuscript of the author, by Lyon Playfair. 387 pp. London.
(64) LOEHR, RODNEY C.
1937. THE INFLUENCE OF ENGLISH AGRICULTURE ON AMERICAN AGRICULTURE, 1775–1825. Agr. Hist. 11 (1): 3–15.
(65) OLIVER, H. K.
1858. EXTRACT FROM AN ADDRESS. Amer. Farmers' Mag. 11 (1): 22–26.
(66) PETTY, FRED L.
1930. SUGAR BEETS AS CASH CROP. Ill. Farmer 78: 563.

(67) Robinson, Solon.
1838. A PROPOSITION, TO FACILITATE AGRICULTURAL IMPROVEMENT. Cultivator 5: 60–61.
(68) Sidney, Mary.
1905. SOCIABILITY AMONG FARMERS. Farm Jour. 29: 109.
(69) Thaer, Albert D.
1844. THE PRINCIPLES OF AGRICULTURE. Transl. by William Shaw and Cuthbert W. Johnson. v. 1. London.
(70) Tocqueville, Alexis C. H. C. de.
1849. THE REPUBLIC OF THE UNITED STATES OF AMERICA, AND ITS POLITICAL INSTITUTIONS, REVIEWED AND EXAMINED. Transl. by Henry Reeves, Esq., with preface and notes by John C. Spencer . . . pt. 2, 355 pp. New York.
(71) True, Alfred Charles.
1929. A HISTORY OF AGRICULTURAL EDUCATION IN THE UNITED STATES 1785–1925. U. S. Dept. Agr. Misc. Pub. 36, 436 pp., illus.
(72) True, Rodney H.
1921. EARLY DAYS OF THE ALBEMARLE AGRICULTURAL SOCIETY. Agr. Hist. Soc. Papers 1: 243–259. Washington, D. C.
(73) Tryon, Rolla Milton.
1917. HOUSEHOLD MANUFACTURES IN THE UNITED STATES, 1640–1860; A STUDY IN INDUSTRIAL HISTORY. 413 pp. Chicago.
(74) Willard, X. A.
1868. [ADDRESS . . . BEFORE THE ILLINOIS AND WISCONSIN DAIRYMEN'S ASSOCIATION.] Prairie Farmer (n. s. 21) 37: 115.
(75) Williams, A.
1852. AGRICULTURE IN CALIFORNIA. [U. S.] Commissioner of Patents Ann. Rpt. 1851: 3–7.

American Agriculture— The First 300 Years

by EVERETT E. EDWARDS [1]

TO UNDERSTAND the form and the spirit, the successes and the problems of agriculture in the United States, it is necessary to go back into the past and study its history from the beginning; for conditions were at work from the start that have left their mark on our practices and institutions until the present day. Here are the highlights of the story from colonial times until the World War—a varied tale of great ambitions and achievements, mistakes and failures, and not a little native American rebellion. At the end the author sums up the influence of agriculture as a dynamic force shaping governmental policy in many fields.

THE COLONIAL PERIOD

FROM the political viewpoint alone the colonial period of American history covered approximately two centuries, and from the point of view of economic and social structures it lasted even longer. To delineate the major characteristics of the colonial era is therefore difficult, owing to the changing conditions involved in such an expanse of time and the wide diversity in the geographical settings of the Thirteen English Colonies along the Atlantic coast of North America.

Two general characteristics, however, do stand out. The social and

---

[1] Everett E. Edwards is Agricultural Economist, Division of Statistical and Historical Research, Bureau of Agricultural Economics. The author wishes to acknowledge the valuable assistance of Hyman Goldenstein of the agricultural history unit in the preparation of this article.

economic structure of all the Colonies was predominantly agricultural. Even in New England, where commerce and industry were most developed, at least nine-tenths of the population were engaged in farming. In the other Colonies the proportion was even greater. The economic life of the southern Colonies ultimately came to be based on large holdings of land, slave labor, and the production of surpluses of exportable staples. The plantation system determined their economy, and the planters dominated the colonial governments; yet the small farmers far outnumbered them, and the economy of this vast group was largely one of self-sufficiency.

In the small-scale farmer of the colonial period were developed and epitomized the attitudes of mind and habits of action which, until recent times at least, have been characteristic of the American people as a national group. Our colonial ancestors were jacks-of-all-trades; at some time or other in their lives—and often even during a single year—they engaged in hunting, trapping, farming, fishing, and sometimes seamanship as well. In short, they were able to turn to any of the various rudimentary economies as the occasion required. The result was a certain cleverness and facility rather than the thoroughness that results from specialization. This versatility, however, served the American people well as they created a multitude of frontiers in their westward march from the Atlantic to the Pacific. These frontiers, it should be emphasized, were both horizontal—that is, westward across the surface of the Continent—and vertical—upward through various stages of social and economic growth—so far as any given area was concerned. In the words of the historian Frederick Jackson Turner, American development exhibited—

> not merely advance along a single line, but a return to primitive conditions on a continually advancing frontier line, and a new development for that area. American social development has been continually beginning over again on the frontier. This perennial rebirth, this fluidity of American life, this expansion westward with its new opportunities, its continuous touch with the simplicity of primitive society, furnish the forces dominating American character (*192, p. 2*).[2]

Like the majority of his descendants, the colonial farmer was constantly preoccupied with the practicalities of existence. His was a struggle to procure the basic necessities. To be sure, he usually did gain comforts over and above a rudimentary existence, but he lacked the time or the stimulus to develop an interest in the aesthetic or the philosophical. There is no indication of his having an appreciation even of the glorious settings which nature had provided as the scene of his activities.

By virtue of necessity the colonial farmer developed a self-reliance, especially as related to the forces of nature, which extended into intense individualism. This is not to say that he did not contribute to community action when a scarcity of labor demanded or when leisure permitted social gatherings. Such association, however, was possible only where there was a semblance of community life.

The lack of opportunities to travel—in either the physical or intellectual sense—also bred a narrow outlook that tended to develop into extreme provincialism.

The colonial farmer was dominated by a generous optimism.

[2] Italic numbers in parentheses refer to Literature Cited, p. 266.

Neither his nondescript past nor his humdrum present provided a basis for boasting, even with his characteristic temerity. Accordingly he always looked to the future, which was unhampered by realities, and let his imagination have full sway.

Owing to the exigencies of their economic existence, our colonial ancestors also came to have a profound and abiding faith in work of some sort, preferably manual, as the duty of every member of a social group. Woe to him who manifested a tendency to shirk his responsibilities, even though the diligence of a parent had amassed for him a modest inheritance which would have permitted his taking a more leisurely way of life.

Background of the English Settlers in America

Among the Europeans who settled in the Thirteen Colonies which England founded or acquired along the North American Atlantic coast, Englishmen predominated. So far as background influences are concerned, it is to the England of the seventeenth—and to a less extent the eighteenth—century that we must look. The mother country was then predominantly rural in its ways of life, and this basic fact must be emphasized in any survey of American colonial agriculture (*82*, *83*). The statement of William Bradford (*30*) that the Pilgrims were "used to a plaine countrie life and ye inocente trade of husbandrey" will serve as a description of the English colonists generally. There was, therefore, a natural predilection on the part of the early English settlers in America to attempt to raise the crops and employ the farming methods that were familiar to them in their homeland.

England of the seventeenth century was comparatively undeveloped agriculturally. Probably not more than a quarter of its land was under cultivation, the remainder being in woods, moors, fens, commons, and parks or warrens. Of the 40 counties in England, only 15 no longer had forests (*61*). There were common lands in abundance and comparatively few fences, plowed fields being separated by balks of earth. In those localities where arable land had been turned into sheep pastures to satisfy the demands of the wool trade, though there were some enclosures, hundreds of acres were grazed by flocks under the supervision of shepherds with their dogs. The "highways" could hardly be so designated; except in the thickly settled regions they may more properly be described as cart or bridle paths. The work of reclamation and enclosure, which changed the surface of the major part of rural England to something approximating the modern scene, took place in the 2½ centuries following the departure of the first English colonists to America. The England which mothered the Thirteen Colonies was relatively untouched by the forces commonly referred to as the industrial and agricultural revolutions.[3]

Trials and Errors of the Early Years

The earliest efforts of the pioneering English colonists to derive a livelihood from the soil can hardly be called agriculture. In general

---

[3] For references on English agriculture, see: EDWARDS, E. E. SELECTED REFERENCES ON THE HISTORY OF ENGLISH AGRICULTURE. U. S. Dept. Agr. Library Bibliog. Contrib. 24, ed. 2, 105 pp. 1939. [Mimeographed.]

their activities resembled those of primitive tribes in the hunting or collection stage of development. All of the initial settlements were to a considerable extent dependent on the native plants and wild animals for food until the first crops could be harvested.

The natural food resources of the Atlantic Coastal Plain varied somewhat according to the latitude, but there was usually an abundance. Berries of various kinds, including blackberries, raspberries, huckleberries, gooseberries, cranberries, and strawberries, and fruits such as wild cherries, grapes, and crab apples, as well as nuts and certain edible roots were available in season. There were also plenty of fish, clams, and oysters, and wild game such as partridges, turkeys, pigeons, geese, and ducks, as well as deer. Yet the early colonists were often on the verge of starvation. Various explanations have been given for this suffering amidst what appears to have been abundance. Basically it was difficult for the first settlers to revert to a different stage of civilization; furthermore, it was difficult to adjust the agriculture of the Old World to conditions in the New.[4]

Contributions of the American Indians

It was not until the English settlers adopted the American Indians' agricultural plants, cultivation and harvesting methods, and processes of food preparation that they were assured of adequate food supplies. Indeed it is not going too far to say that it was the union of American Indian and European farming that produced the beginnings of American agriculture and provided the essential bases for its ultimate development.[5] Furthermore the economic plants domesticated by the American Indian and taken over by the white man constitute, according to a reliable estimate, approximately four-sevenths of the present total agricultural production of the United States, measured in farm values (*181, 182*). A complete list of these plants is extensive, but the most important are maize or corn, cotton (the New World species, *Gossypium barbadense* Linn.), peanuts, pumpkins, squashes, beans, potatoes, sweetpotatoes, tobacco, and tomatoes.

The Indian method of planting corn, potatoes, beans, and other plants of New World origin in hills and then heaping the earth about their stalks during cultivation is still a fundamental process in our present-day farming, just as broadcast seeding is essential in growing the grains of Old World origin. In growing their crops the Indians had neither draft animals nor plowing machinery; all of the work of planting, cultivating, and harvesting was done by hand. They did use pointed and spadelike tools in turning the soil. The white man introduced the ox and the horse to supply power and ultimately developed comparatively elaborate machinery to take the place of manual labor. Yet the fundamental system of cultivation remains essentially the same as the white man found it on his arrival in the New World.

---

[4] For details of the hardships of settlers during the years of adjustment, see Literature Cited (*25, 39, 91*). For additional references see: EDWARDS, E. E. REFERENCES ON AMERICAN COLONIAL AGRICULTURE. U. S. Dept. Agr. Library Bibliog. Contrib. 33, 101 pp. 1938. [Mimeographed.]

[5] EDWARDS, E. E. AGRICULTURE OF THE AMERICAN INDIANS; A CLASSIFIED LIST OF ANNOTATED HISTORICAL REFERENCES WITH AN INTRODUCTION. U. S. Dept. Agr. Library Bibliog. Contrib. 23, ed. 2, 106 pp. 1933. [Mimeographed.] See also Literature Cited (*67*).

Policies of Land Disposition in Colonial America

In seventeenth-century England, landownership was the key that unlocked the door of economic, social, and political privilege, as well as of prestige. It was natural, therefore, that much emphasis should be placed on landownership in the English Colonies. The early explorers for England took possession of most of the North American Continent in the name of the King, and that individual, therefore, theoretically possessed a vast public domain to dispose of as he wished. Although the ways by which land passed from the King into the hands of actual dirt farmers were many and varied, three distinct procedures stand out.[6]

The Manorial System

One of the methods of land disposition may be called the manorial system. The sheer abundance of land naturally suggested establishing hereditary landed estates, and the result was that grants of large tracts were made to friends of the King. In essence, these grants were an attempt to recreate medieval feudalism in the New World, although it had long since outlived its usefulness in the Old. Economically, however, the successful development and operation of landed estates was contingent on securing a substantial revenue from the land. The land available in other ways was so far in excess of the amount immediately needed that those who had the initiative for the adventure to the Colonies did not voluntarily settle on feudal holdings, albeit American versions. The grantees of the large tracts sought to collect quitrents—that is, feudal payments which "quitted" the actual holders of land of all other payments, dues, and services (*26*)—and the result was social friction which did not cease until the quitrents were abolished as an incident of the American Revolution (*110*). In the course of time the manorial holdings largely gave way to plantations, and unfree labor, not land, became the main source of income for the holders of large tracts (*79*).

The New England System

Another distinctive procedure of land disposition was the New England system—a system of vast importance in its influence on the development of national land policies during the nineteenth century. The dominant characteristics of the New England system were community action and the lack of a profit motive in disposing of land (*6*).

The leading New England Colonies were established by trading companies which received extensive grants of land from the Crown and served as, or evolved into, governing bodies. Grants direct from the Crown to individuals were practically unknown in New England, the exception being the Gorges grant of 1639 in what is now the State of Maine. Grants to individuals by the colonial governments were likewise rare—those made were in small amounts and always as a reward for services rendered or anticipated.

To effect the methodical occupation of the New England territory by actual settlers who would develop the natural resources not for the

[6] For the historical literature on the land policies of the colonial period, see: EDWARDS, E. E. REFERENCES ON AMERICAN COLONIAL AGRICULTURE. U. S. Dept. Agr. Library Bibliog. Contrib. 33, 101 pp. 1938. [Mimeographed.] See especially pp. 73-90.

benefit of a few but in the interest of the entire community, reliance was placed on group action and responsibility. When a relatively old and settled community became crowded, at least according to contemporaneous standards, a group wishing to move westward into the wilderness selected representatives to look up a tract, usually contiguous to a settled community, which was deemed suitable for a new settlement. Having found what they needed, they petitioned the colonial government for permission to migrate there. The government, in turn, sent out a committee to examine the tract with reference to its suitability for settlement and to report on the qualifications of the would-be movers—especially of their leaders. If the committee's findings were favorable, the grant was made. The land was usually a rectangular area approximating the traditional American township in size.

The group to which the grant was made became in essence a quasi corporation and proceeded over a period of years to divide the land in severalty among the settlers. Near the center of the tract or in some other strategic location a village was laid out, the focal point being a green with the meeting house, the minister's house, a burial ground, a market place, and a school. From the green extended the village streets with the house lots, which were plots of sufficient size for a dwelling and outbuildings, a dooryard, a garden, and an enclosure for feeding stock.

Then a large block of the grant was roughly surveyed and divided into strips which were distributed among the settlers by lot, each family receiving some of the best as well as some of the poorer land. When these "lots" had been developed into tilled fields, a further—and comparable—division of another block of the grant was made, and so on until all of the land received by the original group had been brought under cultivation. The uncultivated land was used as a common pasture by the community, and one or more herdsmen were employed as public servants to handle the stock.

This plan of land distribution, here described in a rudimentary manner, had important social and political consequences. It developed habits of group action and afforded a compact social life. It facilitated the ideal of a Biblical commonwealth and a Puritan theocracy. The town meeting, at which plans for land distribution were worked out and the officers who cared for the village property were chosen, was a vital factor in the evolution of democracy in America.

The New England way provided an effective and equitable method of distributing large areas of land directly to actual farmers in amounts proportioned to their ability to use the land. During the years when the system of town grants was in full operation—before 1725—land speculation was practically unknown in New England.

The New England system also afforded a security of title that facilitated an orderly settlement of new lands. It provided a sure protection against overlapping surveys and title disputes and made the town or colony responsible for the accuracy of the survey and title. The ease with which new land might be acquired and an independent living assured practically obviated a nonlandholding class and necessitated cooperation among farmers.

Headrights

The idea of headrights—the granting of 50 acres of unoccupied land to immigrants landing in Virginia—grew out of the view that any person who "adventured" himself to America acquired a share in the Virginia Company. Since land was the surplus of which the company could be certain, any dividends from shares in the colonial enterprise might reasonably be expected to be in the form of land. With this beginning, it was only a step to allowing a headright for the importation of others. The system which was developed to dispense headrights remained the principal method of acquiring land in the southern Colonies throughout the seventeenth century (*73, pp. 40–54; 91, pp. 372–408*).

In practice, the system changed greatly from the original conception. It was extended to include the members of a settler's family and his household servants, then white indentured servants, and eventually even slaves. Sea captains and merchants who brought in servants or slaves also acquired and sold headrights on their importations. Indentured servants received headrights on the expiration of their periods of service. Eventually fraud and evasion developed in the administration of the system. Men whose business took them back and forth across the Atlantic customarily received headrights each time they landed in the southern Colonies, and the sea captains even claimed rights for their sailors. Ultimately, at least three persons—a captain, a merchant, and a planter—might acquire a right on the same individual. Finally the applicants for headrights resorted to copying names from old record books and tombstones for use on the required forms, and at about the same time the secretary of the Colony began to sell headrights for 1 to 5 shillings each. The Virginia Council, recognizing realities, then authorized the sale of rights to 50-acre tracts for 5 shillings. This substitution, known as a treasury right, was a reversion in legal theory to the right of acquiring land under the Virginia Company by the purchase of stock, the Commonwealth being regarded as a lineal descendant of the company.

Having secured a headright or a treasury right, the individual located the amount of land to which he was entitled on any part of the unappropriated public domain. Surveys were supposed to be made by public surveyors, but as most of these officers were inexperienced deputies the possibility of error was always present.

So far as the disposition of land was concerned, the southern system left much to individual initiative. A person could select any desirable tract of unappropriated land and have it marked off by a county surveyor under his direction. There was no compulsion to consider the relation of his holding to those of others, and there was ample opportunity to engross the best land, leaving the less fertile soil for the later comers. The system was suited to the needs of a society where large plantations and slave labor, fewer hostile Indians, and a favorable climate permitted the extension and scattering of settlement over the coastal lands. In the hinterland the system enabled the pioneers to locate on the good lands adjacent to streams.

Conditions of Agriculture in the New World

Farm Equipment

The lack of adequate capital affected the supply of farm tools and implements in the early settlements just as it did the number of livestock (*25, 39*). In the documentary materials on the colonial period are occasionally found ideal lists of the various tools which a family contemplating immigration should bring with them, but the actual outfits as indicated in wills were probably inadequate in most instances. The tools and implements most frequently mentioned are hoes, spades, scythes, reaping hooks, shovels, carts, harrows, and plows.

Although a basic implement, plows were scarce during the first half of the colonial period. The Plymouth colony had none for 12 years and during that period was dependent on hoes and mattocks for breaking the soil. The Swedish colony along the Delaware likewise had few tools of any kind until it was taken over by the Dutch in 1655. On the other hand, the farms of Massachusetts Bay had 30 plows by 1636. The early settlers in William Penn's domain around Philadelphia were also relatively well supplied.

The possession of a plow gave the owner what amounted to a distinct profession. He was the plowman of his community, and his services in this capacity were in demand at practically all seasons. In short he was a public benefactor, and many town communities paid bounties to farmers who bought plows and kept them in operating condition.

The plows of the eighteenth century were very heavy and awkward contrivances. The moldboard was not constructed on scientific principles; its iron plating, designed to cut and turn the soil, was rough and uneven, causing excessive friction, and the pull on the drawbar was much greater than it is on that of a modern plow. It took two men, or a man and a boy, using two or three horses or four to six oxen, an entire day to plow 1 to 2 acres. A lighter type of plow was used in cultivating corn. At the close of the eighteenth century, experiments with improved moldboards and cast-iron plowshares were being made.

The procedure and the implements used in harvesting, threshing, and cleaning grain were comparable to those of ancient Palestine as recorded in the Bible. Wheat and sometimes other small grains were reaped with a sickle. Grass and occasionally grain were cut with a scythe. Grain cradles were introduced in the middle Colonies near the end of the eighteenth century, but were unknown in New England until after 1800. A good reaper usually averaged three-fourths of an acre a day, but if the crop was heavy he could not cut more than half an acre. A cradler could cover 2½ acres.

In the middle Colonies, grain was threshed by treading it out with horses; in New England, the flail was used. After threshing, the grain was winnowed as in Biblical times. A few farmers were experimenting with horsepower threshing machines by 1780.

Labor in the English Colonies

Scarcity of labor had even more far-reaching consequences for American social and economic development (*73, 91, 113*). At least four out of five free white men were farmers on their own land. There were two natural outgrowths of this combination of abundant resources and lack of free labor: (1) The credo of the glorification of work, already mentioned as a primary American trait, with the accompanying suspicion of the artistic as unproductive; and (2) various systems of nonfree labor.

Practically all Europeans who had sufficient initiative to emigrate to America were of a type that would not readily submit to the authority of others. The abundance of free land at the back gate of every community stimulated this independence, with the result that there was practically no voluntary hiring out. In the New England and middle Colonies, as in nearly all frontier settlements, the problem of a labor supply was met to some extent by community cooperation. In the southern Colonies, however, where staple crops were raised on large plantations, there was a greater need for a large labor supply, and consequently the greatest number of indentured servants and slaves were found there.

Following the example of the French, and more particularly the Spanish, the English colonists attempted enslavement of the native population, but with little success. There are many instances of Indians being held in some form of bondage in New England, particularly after the wars in which Indians were taken captive. As late as 1706 it was the practice of Massachusetts to sell Indian children under 12 years of age and to enslave the women taken in war. The men, however, refused to bend under the yoke of slavery and were shipped off to the West Indies to be exchanged for Negroes.

Considerably more success in procuring workers was attained through the labor-contract method. This system was deeply rooted in England, where wages had been fixed by statute, minors apprenticed, and vagabonds bound out.

These contracted, or indentured, servants may be divided into two groups—voluntary and involuntary. Voluntary indentured servants were those whose apprenticeship was based on a free contract. They were limited to persons who were so anxious to start a new life in America that they were willing to sell themselves for a period of 5 to 7 years to shipmasters or immigration brokers in payment for their passage. German settlers, and occasionally those of other nationalities, sometimes voluntarily indentured themselves in order to obtain funds to make a more advantageous beginning on the frontier when they were able and ready to set up farming for themselves. Most of these "free-willers" came during the latter part of the seventeenth and early eighteenth centuries. As a type of immigrant they were practically nonexistent by the time of the American Revolution.

The involuntary indentured-servant group was made up of debtors, criminals deported by order of English courts, and unfortunates who had been kidnaped. The vagrancy laws in England during the seventeenth century were extremely harsh; the free movement of labor from one parish to another was forbidden; imprisonment was the penalty for debt; and over 300 crimes were punishable by death. The result of these laws was that the courts and prisons were crowded with paupers, debtors, vagrants, and petty criminals, and many judges felt that shipping these unfortunates to the Colonies was a humanitarian act. Only a few could pay their own passage over, and consequently the vast majority were sold, the term of indenture ranging from 7 to 10 years. Eventually the demand for this type of labor became so great that professional kidnapers seized thousands, particularly in London and other seaport towns, and hurried these victims off to America. During the English civil wars when Cromwell gained ascendancy, many political prisoners also were exiled to the New World.

In general these redemptioners came of good stock. Force of circumstances and social exploitation rather than lack of native ability had kept them poor. As a rule, all they needed was freedom to rise in the social and economic scale. By the terms of their indenture they were promised food, clothing, shelter, medical aid, and the right to own property. For the most part they were well treated, but there were frequent instances of brutality. Masters did not have as strong an economic motive to protect these short-term servants as they did Negro slaves, who were a lifetime investment. At the end of their period of service the redemptioners were to be provided with an outfit as defined in the contract; in the southern Colonies they usually had a headright entitling them to 50 acres of free land. Attesting to the quality of this class as a whole is the fact that thousands of them acquired capital and became prosperous farmers or even planters, as well as mechanics, artisans, and merchants.

There were draw-backs, however, to the use of indentured-servant labor. The initial transportation cost was fairly heavy, the servants had to be acclimated, and the death rate was high, particularly in the last half of the seventeenth century. They provided only a temporary and constantly fluctuating labor supply.

Most of the growth in population of the English Colonies along the Atlantic coast in the seventeenth and eighteenth centuries was the result of natural increase rather than of the influx of indentured servants and slaves. It has been estimated that in 1640 there were 28,000 settlers in the Colonies; in 1660, 85,000; in 1690, 214,000; and in 1770, 2,205,000. Of the immigrants who came after the initial settlements were established, probably one-half landed as indentured servants (*93*, *96*, *137*, *184*).

The first Negro slaves in the English Colonies were landed by a Dutch privateer at Jamestown in 1619. They were sold to the colonial government, which in turn sold them to planters along the James River. It was not until 1630 that a second cargo of Negroes was sold in the Virginia settlements. From 1635 on, a small number was imported nearly every year, partly from England and New Netherlands, but mostly from the West Indies. Despite the shortage of labor, Negroes were not popular at first, and even in 1690 there were only 5,000 in the tobacco Colonies. However, at the end of the seventeenth century the English Government restricted kidnaping and attempted to check the sending of convicts to America. As a result direct slave trade with Guinea developed, and slaveholding began in earnest. It is estimated that there were 400,000 slaves in the Colonies in 1760 and that three-fourths of them were in the southern Colonies. The slaves made up about two-fifths of the entire southern population. They constituted only a small percentage of the inhabitants of North Carolina and Maryland but in South Carolina outnumbered the whites 2 to 1.

In the early days the legal status of the Negroes was vague (*91*). The court records of 1661 speak of Negro servants or merely Negroes and never refer to them definitely as slaves. A few were described as servants for a term of years, others were conceded property rights, and some were liberated by the courts as having served their terms. Nevertheless, holders of Negroes were falling into the custom of considering them servants for life. The more astute saw that, if well directed, Negroes were capable of tending tobacco, rice, indigo, or other staple crops, and with their labor a planter could produce staples at a profit.

Yet even at the time of the American Revolution many southerners were urging the abolition of Negro slavery, and had it not been for the rising interest in sea-island cotton and the problem of the disposition of the Negroes in the Charleston district, manumission might have occurred at that time (*91*).

Slave labor was poorly adapted to the varied activities of economic life in the North. Generally speaking, northern agriculture could not employ gang labor, nor were there any year-round tasks to occupy the slaves. Slavery did prove profitable, however, to Yankee merchants and shipmasters who shared the monopoly of the slave traffic with the British. The usual procedure of the Yankee slave ships—the famous triangular trade— was as follows: The New England vessels carried rum and other commodities to the Slave Coast of Africa and exchanged them for Negroes. This cargo in turn was taken to the plantations of the West Indies or the southern mainland Colonies and exchanged for sugar and molasses or tobacco, which was then taken back to the home port. The "middle passage," that is, the trip between Africa and the West Indies, was where slavery revealed its gloomiest aspect. The Negroes who had been kidnaped in the interior behind the Slave Coast were placed in heavy chains and packed in the holds of the ships, where they suffered during the many slow weeks of transit. It was on this sort of trade that many New England fortunes were founded.

Crops

In growing their first field crops the early colonists turned to the numerous natural clearings or openings of the Atlantic Coastal Plain (*25*, *39*). These openings were found mostly along the banks of rivers and small streams. Many of them were probably old cornfields abandoned by the Indians, while others resulted from the Indian practice of burning underbrush as an aid in hunting.

Shortly, however, the immigrants to the New World had to turn their efforts to clearing land of vegetation, and this proved a formidable task. It continued to be a basic feature of American agriculture until the pioneers of the westward movement had reached the prairies of western Indiana and Illinois. The sunlight had to be admitted to the soil, and the obstructions to tillage, such as stumps, roots, and

223761°—40——13

stones, had to be removed. Whatever may have been their original conception of the task before them, the English settlers soon adopted the Indian method of girdling and burning trees in order to prepare land for cultivation.

As already intimated, Indian corn or maize became the universal crop, owing to its advantages under pioneer conditions of cultivation. Since it was indigenous, there was always reasonable assurance of a successful crop. The manner of cultivating it fitted in with primitive methods of clearing, and therefore it was a labor-saving crop. It also yielded more food per acre than European grains.

Probably all of the crops familiar to the colonists in their homeland were tried at some time or other. Wheat, rye, barley, oats, buckwheat, and peas became important crops, in the order named.

The first attempts to raise wheat were not successful, but by 1640 it became important in New England, judging from the fact that it was received in payment of taxes at that time. The Connecticut Valley with its fertile alluvial soil was the best grain-producing region of New England, and may well be designated as the first wheat belt of America (*25, pp. 92–94*). The middle Colonies also raised wheat and from the very first attempts were more successful. About 1660 the wheatfields of eastern Massachusetts began to be affected by what was called the wheat blast, now recognized as black stem rust. Within a few years it had spread to the Connecticut Valley. In spite of the divers explanations given by learned contemporaries, a general relationship between the presence of common barberry and the "blast" was recognized, and legislation was enacted to encourage the eradication of the bushes. Wheat also became important in the middle Colonies, to such an extent, in fact, that they came to be referred to as the "bread Colonies."

Rye yielded better than wheat on light sandy and gravelly soil and was especially important along the banks of the Delaware, where Swedes and Finns had settled in an attempt to found a New Sweden. Just as this particular specialization was due to a racial emphasis, so was the production of oats. This grain was produced in abundance as feed for livestock, but only after the Scotch-Irish had come in considerable numbers did the colonists of English descent begin to use oats for human food.

Livestock

When the white man first came, the New World had few domesticated animals and none that could be used in conquering and developing the soil. Within the limits of the present continental United States, the dog was the only domestic animal that was practically universal among the Indians, who used dogs for transportation, hunting, protection and companionship, or food, the use differing according to locality. It was therefore necessary for European settlers in America to import livestock from the mother countries. Because of the distance and the small size of ships at that time, there was a pitiful scarcity of livestock in some of the settlements during the early years. The losses incident to transit of the Atlantic Ocean were heavy, and it was difficult for the early settlers to provide forage, shelter, and protection for the animals. Another factor was the amount of capital behind the particular colonizing enterprises. Plymouth, for example, was without cattle for 3 years and had no horses or sheep as late as 1627. The Swedish and Finnish communities along the Delaware were also without an adequate number of livestock for a number of years. The Massachusetts Bay Colony, on the other hand, seems to have had a sufficient supply practically from the start.

Eastern North America did not have an abundant supply of indigenous nutritive forage plants, and it was some time before the early settlers realized this fundamental deficiency. Their livestock was dependent for pasturage on the forage in the open places in the woods where fires had destroyed the underbrush or where natural openings occurred. To the early settlers two native grasses, wild-rye (*Elymus* sp.) and broomstraw (*Andropogon* sp.), looked promising, but it was soon discovered that although cattle could subsist on these in the summer, the hay made from them had too high a proportion of roughage to be adequate for winter feeding. Eventually the familiar forage plants of old England were introduced, either consciously or accidentally, and once started they spread rapidly. Our important hay and pasture plants of today—timothy, bluegrass, and red and white clovers—are thus a product of the initial necessity of the livestock industry in America (*25, pp. 19–20*).

The need of an adequate supply of hay and pasture continued to be a pressing problem not only throughout the seventeenth century but during the eighteenth as well. The cattle were dependent on the annual grasses in the forest openings, and with the increase in numbers of stock the grasses were grazed so short that natural reseeding was prevented. The custom of burning underbrush during the fall months also tended to hold back this process, and droughts further decreased the supply of pasture and hay. As the eighteenth century progressed, more attention was given to what were called "artificial meadows," that is, uplands seeded with red clover, timothy, and other English grasses. This movement was probably inspired by the German-settled communities in the neighborhood of Philadelphia (*177, 178*).

The management of livestock during colonial times, as in most pioneer periods, may be politely described as rudimentary. The problem of confining the animals to definite localities was not easy to solve. Erecting fences required considerable labor and was especially difficult in the middle and southern Colonies where the settlements were largely individual rather than community affairs. In New England, community settlement made common pasturing possible. There the fences were usually around the cultivated fields rather than the pastures, and the community hired one or more herders to watch the livestock. Hogs, being difficult to confine, proved very troublesome, and it is not an exaggeration to say that they were probably the subject of more legislation than anything else in agriculture during the colonial period. There was also much legislation concerning brands and earmarks (*217, 218*).

Livestock received little shelter in the seventeenth century and very little more in the eighteenth. This was largely the current practice in the mother country at that time, and there are indications that the settlers did not immediately realize the effect of the severe American winters on livestock. Besides, the scarcity of labor made it difficult to erect barns or even sheds, and there was also the problem of a feed supply. In the course of the eighteenth century, housing the livestock in winter became a regular practice in New England and New York, but in the Colonies to the south, the livestock continued to shift for themselves as best they could. There was, however, one striking exception—the thrifty German farmers of Pennsylvania kept fewer animals but stabled them during the winter and fed them well.

Colonial Agriculture as Affected by the Policies of England and the Colonies

Contrary to popular belief, legislative regulation of American agricultural production is new only in detail; in principle, it began with our earliest settlements. In accord with the view of other imperial powers of the seventeenth and eighteenth centuries, England expected her colonies to furnish raw materials and serve as a market for the mother country's finished products. Particularly was Britain anxious to stimulate colonial production of commodities for which she was then dependent on other European countries. The measures taken to foster this general policy, commonly known as mercantilism, included tariffs and rebates, subsidies, price regulation, seed distribution, and even acreage control (*20*, *21*, *22*). Conforming in large measure with imperial legislation were enactments of the separate Colonies seeking to stimulate or discourage the raising of certain crops.

The history of tobacco regulation is in many respects the most illuminating example of the methods and effects of mercantilism (*89*). In 1612 it was found that tobacco could be profitably grown in Virginia, and the colonists, stirred by the high returns, began planting it almost to the exclusion of the essential food crops. Sir Thomas Dale, Governor of Virginia, before sailing for England in 1616, found it necessary to order each person to plant at least 2 acres of corn for himself and for each male servant. Tobacco growing continued to increase, however, and the acreage devoted to it was restricted again and again in order to prevent glutting the English market and to insure an adequate food supply.

In response to early high prices farmers in England attempted tobacco raising, but the cost was so great as compared with that of colonial tobacco that various laws were passed between 1619 and 1652 restricting home planting. At the same time, Spanish importations were discouraged by discriminatory tariffs. This gave Virginia, and later Maryland, a monopoly of the English tobacco market, though subject to both custom and excise duties. The supply, however, soon exceeded the demand. Prices were depressed, and because tobacco had become the chief exchange medium for Virginia, price fixing seemed particularly desirable. In February 1631/32, the Virginia Colonial Assembly provided that tobacco exchanged for English goods was not to be sold for less than 6 pence per pound, under penalty of imprisonment. By 1639 production had become so excessive that a crop-curtailment and price-fixing agreement was made between the colonial authorities and the principal merchants. The crops of 1639, 1640, and 1641 were to be limited to 1,200,000 pounds of good quality, and the merchants agreed to accept 40 pounds for each 100 pounds of indebtedness due them. Viewers were appointed to destroy inferior tobacco, and if necessary to burn excess crops, and in exchange the tobacco was to be rated at not less than 3 pence per pound (*91*).

England at first attempted to monopolize all of the colonial tobacco exports, but when it became apparent that such a policy would be ruinous in view of the glutted market, reexportation to other European countries was permitted. The restriction requiring all shipments to be sent to England and then reexported, subjecting them to English as well as foreign custom and excise levies, evoked considerable criticism. To temper the rigor of this policy, an elaborate draw-back system by which part of the tariff was remitted on reexportation was begun in 1631, and after 1723 the entire duty on the reexported commodity was remitted.

The spread of tobacco growing from Virginia to Maryland and North Carolina during the course of the seventeenth century aggravated the surplus problem. As a result, various intercolonial pacts were projected with a view to restricting production. More successful were the efforts at standardizing quality by a system of central warehouses and the inspection of export crops by licensed officials. These provisions were enacted in Virginia in 1730 and in Maryland in 1747.

Despite all attempts at limitation, the volume of tobacco exports grew from 27,750,000 pounds in 1665 to over 100,000,000 on the eve of the Revolution, with a value of £900,000 in 1770. It is probably true that on the whole production was profitable, at least for planters who were able to employ slave labor. One authority holds that it was owing to English restrictions on Continental trade that colonists suffered at periodical intervals from low prices, particularly after 1680, and that this in turn led to the use of slaves. This view has been disputed, however, by others, who stress the the marketing services extended by English merchants, the draw-backs granted the colonists, and the value of the monopoly of the English market (*114*, *208*).

Cotton was not of particular importance in colonial agriculture, though South Carolina was exporting a million pounds annually by the end of the colonial period. Rice and indigo were developed as money crops before the end of the seventeenth century and like tobacco were subject to detailed regulation.

In 1677 the proprietors of South Carolina wrote that they were attempting to secure rice seed for distribution, while an act of the assembly of 1695/96 included rice as one of the commodities that might be tendered in payment of quitrents. Considerable experimentation in rice planting took place in the two decades between 1695 and 1715, and with a surplus available for exporting, the colonists sought to repeal the English tariffs on rice. Portugal and the West Indies offered a profitable market, but the direct trade that resulted was contrary to the purpose of the navigation acts, and in 1704 rice was added to the list of commodities required to be sent to England and subjected to payment of duty before being reexported.

The Portuguese trade, as a result, was greatly diminished, and protest from the colonists took the form of memorials to Parliament and increased smuggling. Parliament relented in 1730 to the extent of permitting direct trade to any part of Europe south of Cape Finisterre in Spain. This encouraged the rice planters to increase production. Later, however, it became apparent that the northern markets were far more important than the southern; in the decade 1730–39, for example, 74 percent of the rice exports went to Holland, Hamburg, Bremen, Sweden, and Denmark. Like tobacco the bulk of the rice crop was then sent to England to be reexported and through draw-back provisions largely escaped British duties.

In the early years of South Carolina, rice was specified as a commodity to be accepted for certain public payments, and legislative decrees attempted to establish its exchange value. There were also laws to prevent deceitful packing and to standardize the quality of exports.

To stimulate the production of indigo, instructions to accept it in place of quitrents were sent to the South Carolina authorities in 1690, and in 1694 an act was passed to provide special encouragement for growing it. It was not until the 1740's, however, that the indigo industry developed to any considerable extent. In 1734 Parliament had placed indigo on the free list, and a decade later the South Carolina Assembly offered a bounty, but the act was repealed after 1 year. Great Britain, in response to petitions from English clothiers and dyers and colonial planters, granted a premium in 1748 that was continued, although at a modified rate, until 1777. This gave the industry a tremendous impetus, and it is said that the indigo planters were able to double their capital every 3 or 4 years. England received the entire indigo crop, which before the Revolution exceeded a million pounds a year (*91*).

Prior to 1700 Great Britain imported all her hemp and flax from the Baltic countries and Holland. To escape this dependence, a bounty of £6 per ton was placed on colonial-grown hemp, and in 1721 it was exempted from duty and the bounty continued for 16 years. These measures had very little effect, but after 1764 there was a revival of interest, and new bounties of £8 per ton of hemp or flax were offered from 1764 to 1771 and of £6 from 1771 to 1778. In addition to these imperial bounties, numerous subsidies were offered by the various Colonies. Despite all the legislation these products never became important items of exportation.

Lumbering and the production of naval stores were essentially agricultural pursuits in the colonial period, being carried on mainly by farmers and planters. Despite the abundance of timber these industries did not develop in America until the opening of the eighteenth century, and then only under the stimulus of the mother country's desire in typical mercantilistic fashion to escape dependence on Baltic imports. A schedule of premiums was drawn up in 1704/5 by Parliament, and arrangements were made for a surveyor of woods to instruct the colonists in methods of naval stores production. In 1713 Parliament further set aside £10,000 to employ skilled people and the necessary tools for fostering the industry.

In all the Colonies the production of tar and pitch as well as the lumbering industry was subject to considerable legislative regulation and aid. Qualitative standards were set up with penalties and officials to enforce adherence.

With the Italian Piedmont alone draining over £200,000 bullion from England for silk, the efforts to raise this product in the Colonies were especially persistent. Numerous mulberry trees were found growing in Virginia, and silkworm eggs were imported by the Virginia

Company from Italy, France, and Spain. The colonial assembly in its first year, 1619, supplemented these efforts by an enactment requiring each man to plant 6 mulberry trees annually for 7 years. In 1654 Armenian silk experts were imported, and in 1656 an allowance of 4,000 pounds of tobacco was voted to one of these experts by the Virginia Assembly. Bounties for production were offered in 1658, and in 1662 every landowner was ordered to plant 10 mulberry trees properly fenced and tended for every 100 acres of land he owned. As late as 1730 it was reported that 300 pounds of raw silk had been exported from Virginia.

The Huguenot settlers of South Carolina were interested in the silk industry, and acts of 1736 and 1744 offered sizable rewards for silk growing. Results were meager, only 651 pounds of raw silk being exported from 1742 to 1755. In Georgia particularly every effort was bent toward stimulating silk production. Foreign experts were sent out by the Trustees of the Colony; a nursery of mulberry trees was established at Savannah, and 4 public filatures—establishments for reeling silk—were erected; books and free instruction were provided; and each grantee of a 500-acre tract had to plant at least 2,000 white mulberry trees. In 1740 membership in the newly established assembly was made conditional upon the planting of 100 mulberry trees, and after 1753 no one was admitted who did not annually produce 15 pounds of silk and conform to the law requiring a certain number of female slaves to be sent to Savannah for instruction in the silk industry. The high point in Georgian silk exports was reached in 1766–67, when 1,084 pounds were shipped out; by 1772–73 the figure had declined to 485 pounds (*91*).

Attempts to grow silk were not confined to the southern Colonies; similar visionary hopes were entertained in the northern Colonies (*25*). Mulberry trees were common, and many families succeeded in actually producing some silk.

Trade and Markets of the English Colonies

By the third quarter of the seventeenth century the main tendencies of colonial trade were already well defined. New England, with its relatively unproductive soil but numerous harbors, excellent resources for shipbuilding, and proximity to the fishing banks, was turning more and more to commercial activities. Its export staples—fish, timber, whale products, grain, and ships—entered into competition for the most part with the products of old England, and consequently New Englanders sought markets in southern Europe and the West Indies. The islands, absorbed as they were in sugar production, afforded a natural outlet for surplus fish, salted meat, timber, and horses, and already the famous three-cornered traffic involving New England rum, African Negroes, and West Indian molasses had begun to develop. Boston and Salem were flourishing shipping centers, not only for the overseas trade but for the coastwise traffic, which more and more was absorbing the energies of New England traders and shippers (*137*).

Of the middle Colonies, the Jerseys and Pennsylvania did not develop until the last quarter of the century. New York, however, under both Dutch and English rule, early turned to fur trading and grain production, and by 1678 Governor Andros reported an annual export of 60,000 bushels of wheat from the Colony. The principal market for this trade was the West Indies. The importance of the middle Colonies as fur-trading and bread-producing regions became more marked by the close of the seventeenth century when the Jerseys and Pennsylvania were also exporting pelts and grain (*4*).

The commerce of the southern Colonies was far more important than that of the other groups during the seventeenth century. The climate, soil, natural resources, and topography adapted the country to the production of the staples demanded by England, and by 1700 southern trade with the mother country was valued at two-thirds that of all the mainland Colonies. Virginia, with its tobacco, was foremost; its great crop was exchanged in England for clothing, iron, wines, and manufactured goods. Maryland, too, became a large exporter of tobacco (*91*).

Foreign trade was by far the most important during the entire colonial era, but domestic trade gradually grew in proportion and significance during the eighteenth century. Overland traffic was difficult because of the lack of transportation facilities. Only a few products—valuable articles of small bulk such as furs, whiskey, iron supplies, and salt—could be carried profitably in this trade. Nearer the coast there was a relatively greater density of population, and centers like Boston, Newport, New York, Philadelphia, Baltimore, and Charleston sponsored market fairs and created a considerable demand by the opening decades of the eighteenth century. Even here, however, water transportation was much cheaper, and the Hudson, Delaware, and Susquehanna Rivers provided excellent arteries of trade. Domestic traffic was largely coastwise. This was due partly to the fact that products were collected at a few important points for shipment to Europe or to the West Indies, while imported articles were distributed to smaller ports. Nevertheless, New England was shipping its own salted meats, cider, fish, and rum to the middle and southern Colonies; by 1714 New York was sending wheat and flour to New England and South Carolina; and before the end of the colonial period, Pennsylvania pig iron and paper and Rhode Island cloth and candles were common in most of the Colonies. With the population only a little over 4,000,000 as late as 1800, the domestic trade could not expand to any great proportions (*114*).

In addition to these early beginnings of internal trade the eighteenth century was marked by the increasing importance of the West Indian traffic. New England came to depend upon the islands for molasses and sugar with which to make rum, a necessary article in its African trade; for currency with which to buy manufactured goods from the mother country; and for a carrying trade—an outlet which used many of her men and much of her capital. So vital was this trade that it continued in spite of the Molasses Act of 1733 and the French and Indian wars of the 1750's. The traffic in African slaves also expanded rapidly with both the West Indies and the mainland (*3*).

Two of the chief obstacles to the expansion of colonial trade were the inadequacy of transportation facilities and the scarcity of metallic money. It has already been pointed out that the overland trade to the interior was negligible owing to conveyance difficulties, though the use of Conestoga wagons rounded at the bottom to prevent the contents from spilling was helpful for short distances and on good roads. The ocean trade too was seriously hampered by the lack of shipping facilities, especially in the South. The vessels sent by the London commission merchants who handled most of the trade usually arrived in the late fall or early winter. The captains leisurely proceeded to collect cargoes from the scattered plantations, and it was not until the following spring that they returned to England. The delay bore heavily on the planters, who in 1659 were paying £6 to £7, or about 18 percent of their gross sales, to send a ton of tobacco to England. After paying the expenses of customs, commissions, freight, and other charges they received only 35 percent of the gross sales, so that shipping costs actually equaled half their net income from the crop. Even as late as 1737, £7 per ton was regarded as low; and in wartime the charge might rise as high as £15. Added to this was the dearth of ships. Merchants tended to send too few rather than too many, since this placed them in a better bargaining position and prevented losses when the tobacco taken did not repay the outlay for the chartered vessels. As long as the planter had a clear account he could exert some pressure on the merchant, but when he fell into debt, as was generally true, he became more and more subject to the will of the commission agent. It is no wonder that the southern planter complained bitterly against the restrictions that kept out Dutch and Portuguese shippers and limited the field to the British and colonials (*91*).

Until far into the eighteenth century piracy was another factor complicating the transport problem. It flourished along the American coast, especially in the West Indies and the Caribbean Sea, where there was plenty of booty and many chances of hiding among the islands. From 1689 on through the eighteenth century England was at war with France, and at various times Spain also was a belligerent. The navies of these countries were kept busy, and the existence of hostilities made possible a good deal of piracy, disguised as legitimate privateering. In 1698 England passed a very stringent law against piracy and employed her navy to act as a convoy for merchant ships. By 1720 the Atlantic Ocean had become relatively safe as a highway of trade.

The absence of an adequate circulating medium also retarded colonial trade. Precious metals were lacking, and the exportation of British coins was forbidden by law. The coins that were circulated came chiefly from Spanish, French, and Portuguese colonies and from the West Indies. Spanish "pieces of eight" were most popular, but since they were subject to "clipping" and "sweating" and might contain varying quantities of metal when minted, their value was hardly stable. Massachusetts from 1652 to 1684 coined the famous "pine tree shilling," worth 75 percent of an English shilling.

In 1690 Massachusetts also issued bills of credit, and soon the other Colonies were printing treasury and land-bank notes. Depreciation was so general that in 1751 Parliament forbade the issuance of paper money in New England and extended the restriction to other Colonies in 1764. Lacking any other medium, the colonists were obliged to resort to barter or staple money for local trade at least. In Virginia and Maryland tobacco was stored in warehouses, and the receipts or notes were recognized as money. Massachusetts made corn and beaver skins legal tender, and the Carolinas used tar and rice. To preserve this currency at a uniform standard was very difficult since the market value of the commodities fluctuated widely (*115, 136*).

More than all else, the navigation acts and the general trend of the mercantilist policy are usually interpreted as having been iniquitous influences on colonial trade. From Adam Smith to the present, writers have insisted that the system violated natural rights and had dire consequences. England was determined to maintain a favorable balance of trade, hoard gold and silver, strengthen native shipping, and employ the Colonies as subsidiary units producing noncompetitive raw materials. The long series of acts passed to promote these ends was a factor in colonial commerce, but to what extent and with what results it is difficult to say (*12*).

The navigation acts were initiated as part of the struggle between England and Holland for the world's carrying trade. The first law was passed in 1645, and was amplified and extended in 1651, 1660, 1663, 1672, and 1696. The act of 1651 is famous for the monopoly it gave the English or colonial shippers in the carrying trade. The act of 1660 added to the monopoly of navigation that of colonial commerce and markets. It prohibited the shipping of sugar, cotton, wool, tobacco, ginger, "fustick," or other dye woods, as well as anything grown, produced, or manufactured on English plantations in America, Asia, or Africa to any place whatsoever except England. The list was expanded in 1706 to include naval stores, including pitch, tar, turpentine, hemp, yards, and masts. Rice was included in the ban during 1706–30, copper ore and furs were added in 1722, molasses in 1733, and whale fins, hides, lumber, iron, raw silk, and pearlash—wood ashes used in soap making—in 1764. Nonenumerated articles, the chief of which were grain, fish, and rum, could be exported anywhere until 1766, but after that only to ports south of Cape Finisterre (*91*).

The acts of 1663, 1673, and 1696 attempted to prohibit the importation of any European goods into the Colonies unless brought via England and in British- or colonial-built and manned ships. To round out this commercial policy, the English Government took steps to control or discourage the few infant industries which sprang up in the Colonies.

While the Old Colonial System stressed the interests of the mother country to the disadvantage of the colonials, the effects on the latter were by no means disastrous (*114*). The Colonies were primarily agricultural, and it was natural that they should devote themselves to the extractive industries. Furthermore, such bounties as those on naval stores and indigo were the determining factor in the production of commodities. The prohibition of tobacco growing in England was beneficial to the planters of Virginia and Maryland, and high duties kept Spanish tobacco out. Similar treatment of other foreign commodities—iron, silk, whale oil, pearlash, and molasses for example—resulted in similar benefits. The duty on commodities bound for the Colonies via England was generally refunded, so that in some cases the colonists could purchase goods more cheaply than could their British brethren. In the case of goods reexported to the Continent the system of draw-backs enabled colonial goods to escape the tariff.

Another moderating influence was the general evasion of the navigation acts, particularly in the first half of the eighteenth century when Robert Walpole's philosophy of "salutary neglect" dominated the attitude of the mother country toward the Colonies. Smuggling was common; courts failed to convict; and later, when admiralty courts were established, the conflict between admiralty laws and the common law courts impeded enforcement. There was also much collusion with imperial customs officials. The Molasses Act of 1733 was a mistake, but economic pressure was too great to permit its enforcement. It remained a dead issue until 1763 at least.

England, moreover, was the natural entrepôt, or distribution center, for the Continental trade. It was the best market for most of the colonial produce; its merchants offered credit facilities for colonial planters; and as Englishmen they could best deal with fellow Englishmen.

It is true there were disadvantages resulting from this regulatory system. While shipbuilding and related industries were stimulated in the northern Colonies, the monopoly of the carrying trade by English and colonial shippers tended, as already shown, to make freight rates high. The middleman's profits for manufactured goods and even for the southern raw-materials trade went into the pockets of the English merchant. Another disadvantage was the constant draining of gold from the Colonies to the mother country. Finally, the more stringent enforcement of the commercial policy after 1763 worked a measure of hardship and aroused resentment (*137*).

AGRICULTURE IN TRANSITION, 1775–1860

Agriculture and the Revolution

It is now generally recognized that the American Revolution was social as well as political. The struggle was waged not only against parliamentary and royal oppression; the enemy included local tyranny as well. Leadership was supplied by merchants and lawyers and planters who had economic as well as ideological differences with England. The driving force of the Revolution, however, was furnished by city laborers and mechanics, small farmers, and backwoodsmen. Often during the "simmering period" the middle-class elements wondered whether their leadership was anything more than nominal, as they found themselves driven more and more to assume a congenitally unpalatable extremist position.

Just as a closed corporation of large landed and commercial interests operated the levers of control in eighteenth-century England, so their prototypes formed the governing caste in America. The constituent elements, most of whom became Loyalists, were the colonial administrators, their friends and clients, the rich planters, the upper clergy, the more prosperous of the professional classes, the merchants whose interests coincided with England's—in short, the most cultivated, the most influential, and the wealthiest. Many rungs below were the smaller merchants, the less prosperous of the professional classes, the indebted planters, the newer families; in this group were Otis, Jay, the two Adamses, Henry, Franklin, Hancock, and Washington. These men cherished a half-expressed ambition to play a more prominent role in political and social life; they were activated also by antagonism to imperial policies that struck at their economic interests. It is equally true that on emotional and intellectual grounds they believed that a greater degree of local control would benefit the Colonies. Yet their alliance with the city and the frontier elements was at best a marriage of convenience. If they shouted against imperial "taxation without representation," still there were many among them who would withhold the suffrage and deny representation in the assemblies to the city landless and the mass of small farmers (*1,131*).

It can also be understood why the agrarian elements should have been attracted to the Revolutionary cause. The backwoodsmen had several grievances against English policy. They resented the Proclamation of 1763, which would have shut off westward expansion; they opposed the prohibition of the issuance of paper money; they sought more liberal land policies; and perhaps most patent of all, they had a sense of local self-sufficiency that was naturally hostile to outside interference.

Their grievances against the colonial governments were even more immediate. The struggle between frontier and seaboard—between old settlements and new—is familiar to every student of society; in the America of a continuously expanding westward movement it is a particularly familiar—perhaps even overworked—theme. In the back country, from Maine to South Carolina, grew up a distinct society composed of small farmers and trappers with little property but considerable courage and initiative. Their philosophy, so far as it was articulate, was democratic and individualistic; it contested the right of the seaboard to exercise political and economic domination. In Virginia it was the Piedmont against the Tidewater; in Pennsylvania, the western farmers against the wealthy Quakers; and in New England, the frontiersmen versus the wealthy coast townsmen.

In the economic sphere the issues at stake were the interests of small, debt-ridden farmers who sought in paper money both an escape and a medium of exchange, as opposed to the creditor and propertied powers of the coast to whom depreciated money meant partial cancellation of loans they had made. In land legislation it was the settler's opposition to absentee landlordism and speculation. Farmers who cleared the land and fought the Indians desired exemption from taxation.

Frontiersmen also took their stand against property qualifications and the careful allotment of representation by means of which colonial governments were controlled before the Revolution. In Pennsylvania, for example, Chester, Bucks, and Philadelphia elected 26 delegates to the assembly, while the five frontier counties although having a considerable majority of the population were allotted only 10 representatives. Virginia's 19,000 voters below the fall line similarly legislated for over 30,000 colonists living elsewhere. These conditions stimulated attempts on the part of the western settlers to break away and form new states in Virginia and the Carolinas. The colonists also charged that tax officials were corrupt and that justice was expensive, slow, and far away.

So far, then, as the small farmers and frontiersmen took up arms in response to their interests, it was a twofold gain that they sought: (1) To strike at imperial control, and (2) to gain a share in local government.

At the opening of the Revolution there were 2,750,000 people in the Colonies; about 700,000 of these were men between the ages of 18 and 60. At no time were more than one-eighth of this number under arms, and during most of this period not more than one-sixteenth. There was widespread apathy concerning the war. The back country did, however, play a role of some importance in the struggle. British armies could not make any permanent conquests in the interior. The failure of Burgoyne in New York is partly attributable to unexpected frontier resistance, and after winning most of his battles Cornwallis lost in the South because he could not hold his gains. George Rogers Clark had a part, in winning the Old Northwest.

On the whole agricultural life went on much as usual. New England, after the first year of the war, except for the occupation of Newport and a few raids along the coast, was free from invasion. New York, New Jersey, and Pennsylvania suffered from the depredations of both armies. This was compensated for by the liberal prices paid in gold by the French and British for supplies from the farmers, many of whom were only too willing to sell.

American agriculture as a whole was stimulated rather than injured by the war. Blockade runners carried Virginia tobacco to Europe, and the last 20 years of the eighteenth century were comparatively a golden age for that crop. In 1774 production totaled 101,800,000 pounds of leaf tobacco; by 1790 the figure had risen to 130,000,000, with one-half of the southern population engaged in or dependent on tobacco growing. Rice cultivation and export also went on with little interruption. In 1778 the first water mill for cleaning and preparing rice for market was erected on the Santee River. The cessation of imperial bounties cut the ground from under the indigo industry, but cotton came to supplant it. The legislatures of Maryland, Virginia, and South Carolina encouraged cotton growing to fill local needs during the war. The same was true of wool production, which was stimulated by interference in trade due to nonimportation agreements and the outbreak of war.

The exodus of the Tories in the course of the war permitted division of many large estates and the abolition of the last vestiges of the feudal system. As late as 1769, five-sixths of the population of Westchester County, N. Y., lived on manor lands. In 1777 the Continental Congress recommended that the Colonies confiscate and sell Loyalist property and invest the proceeds in loan certificates. Little external stimulation was needed; New Hampshire appropriated 28 estates, including that of Governor Wentworth; Massachusetts seized the estates of all who sided with England; New York confiscated the 50,000-acre manor of Sir John Johnson, the Philipse manor of 300 square miles, the Morris estate, and other large holdings, which were broken up and sold in 500-acre lots; and Pennsylvania took over the property of the Penn family. After the Revolution, in response to treaty promises, a few feeble gestures in the direction of remuneration were made. However, the political and social power that went with these great landed holdings was never restored.

Along with confiscation and land division came a more democratic mode of land tenure. Under the leadership of frontier "radicals" like Jefferson, quitrents were abolished; by 1786 entail, by which land was settled permanently on a person and his heirs, had been made illegal in every State but two; and the other aristocrat-fostering device, primogeniture, the exclusive right of inheritance of the first-born, disappeared by 1791 so that a farmer could hold his land in fee simple and dispose of it as he pleased (*133*). A few years after the Revolution, moreover, particularly by the Ordinances of 1785 and 1787, a constructive policy of colonization and land sale and settlement was inaugurated.

National Consciousness and Agriculture

The triumph of the patriot cause in the Revolutionary War brought a quickening of national consciousness in the new country. In every phase of life—political, economic, social, and intellectual—a peculiarly American note was sounded. Having won independence, the leading citizens of the new country seemed resolved not only to create a Nation that had a recognized place among the countries of the world but one with distinctive rather than inherited or borrowed ways of life.

Agriculture too seems to have been affected by this nationalistic movement. Practical farmers in regions where agriculture was rapidly becoming commercialized began to use gypsum on wheatlands and grasslands (*25*, *88*). Clover and other cultivated grasses also came into fairly general use in these regions. Although such changes had no immediate and widespread influence on agricultural production, when considered with the organization of agricultural societies and the beginning of American agricultural literature, they indicate the awakening of a new and enthusiastic interest in agricultural improvement. Washington, Jefferson, and many other prominent leaders were familiar, either by correspondence or by personal observation, with the revolutionary changes that were taking place in the agriculture of England, and the contrast with the stagnant conditions at home was a challenge (*121*, *167*, *195*).

To popularize in America the knowledge of the new methods of farming, leaders organized agricultural societies. The first of these organizations was the Philadelphia Society for Promoting Agriculture founded in 1785 (*189*). Within 15 years similar organizations were at work in Charleston, S. C., Hallowell, Maine, New York City, New Haven, Conn., and Boston, Mass. The membership of these groups consisted for the most part of men of all professions rather than dirt farmers, and the main objective was the dissemination of information concerning the agricultural progress in other countries. These societies were, therefore, literary or learned rather than practical and made few if any direct contributions to actual farming.

These early societies were pioneers, however, in the great task of agricultural education. Their transactions provided the reading public with accounts of the best agricultural practices abroad as well as the results of experiments in scientific agriculture in America.

Land Policies and Democracy, 1785–1862

Many students of American history hold that the laws concerning the disposition of the public domain have been the most significant legislation that the Federal Government has enacted. Certainly these laws have been a vital factor in determining the rate of the westward movement of settlement and the drain of population from older communities; furthermore, the development of manufacturing and its labor supply have been notably affected.

Having won the world-wide conflict which ended in 1763, the English were confronted with the problem of governing and settling the vast empire consisting of what is now Canada and the region westward from the Appalachian Mountains to the Mississippi River. The absence of a strong majority party in the British Parliament and Cabinet in this crucial period precluded the possibility of drafting and executing a well-organized and constructive colonial policy. Furthermore, at this time there were not more than three political leaders in all England who clearly saw the importance of the problem. An added complication was the fact that, with the removal of France as a colonial power in North America, the American colonials breathed more easily and felt more independent.

The halting and little-comprehending efforts to solve this problem of the western empire ended in failure. The struggle which England had carried on in all parts of the world had created a vast debt, and it was natural for the British leaders to contend that the Americans should assume at least part of the responsibility for maintaining military posts on the American western frontier to hold the Indians in check and should help in paying off the national debt. This belief led to a series of financial measures which generated resistance in the American Colonies and led directly to the American Revolution. A factor in this resistance was undoubtedly the economic depression which followed the cessation of war in 1763. Meanwhile westward progress of colonial farmers provoked a series of conflicts with the Indians, and the Imperial Government by the Proclamation of 1763 and supplementary action sought to regulate this movement westward. The treaty of 1783, which recognized American independence, also gave the United States control of the vast domain south of the Great Lakes and west of the Alleghenies, thus leaving to the new Nation the problem which had confronted the mother country in 1763—that of settling and governing this western empire.

Fortunately for the future development of the United States, the States with claims to western land were induced to cede them to the Congress of the Confederation (*2, 111, 112*). Furthermore, after a few preliminary steps Congress enacted the Ordinances of 1785 and 1787. The first of these laid down the basic principles of land disposition to which the United States has adhered, and the second provided the principles of procedure which were generally followed with reference to all territories from the Appalachians to the Pacific. As Frederick Jackson Turner said,

> This federal colonial system guaranteed that the new national possessions should not be governed as dependent provinces, but should enter as a group of sister States into the federation. While the importance of the article excluding slavery has often been pointed out, it is probable that the provisions for a federal colonial organization have been at least equally potential in our actual development. The full significance of this feature of the Ordinance is only appreciated when we consider its continuous influence upon the American territorial and State policy in the westward expansion to the Pacific, and the political preconceptions with which

Americans approach the problems of government in the new insular possessions (*192, p. 132*).

The Federal land policies which developed from the Ordinance of 1785 were conditioned by struggles between different schools of political thought, different sections, and different economic groups (*115*). On one side were those who urged that the Government should dispose of its land with prudence; in the opposite camp were those who demanded a generous land policy. Starting with the first viewpoint in dominance and gradually swinging to the other extreme, the clash of these divergent views constitutes the central theme of the history of American land policies during the eight decades preceding the enactment of the Homestead Act of 1862 (*183, 185, 207*).

During the formulation and enactment of the various land laws, the conflict of interests tended definitely to concentrate on three specific details: The minimum amount of land to be offered for sale; the price per acre; and the terms of payment.

As early as 1800 the political pressure of the frontier farmers, a group traditionally disposed to demand "liberal" land legislation, had begun to show its influence (*185*), and within 20 years their cause had definitely won. Whereas the act of 1796 had specified that the smallest amount purchasable was 640 acres, 80 acres was the minimum unit by 1820, and this in turn was reduced to 40 acres in 1832. The minimum price was reduced from the $2 an acre established in 1796 to $1.25 in 1820. Furthermore, in practice the minimum price tended to become the maximum price, only a few choice areas being bid for higher amounts at auction time. Thus abundance of land, plus a united public opinion, circumvented the intent of the laws.

Only in one respect was there a nominal reversal of this general trend toward a liberalization of the terms of land acquisition. In 1796 the purchaser was required to pay one-half the price in cash within 30 days and the remainder within 1 year. Four years later the credit terms were considerably liberalized—one-fourth cash, one-fourth within 40 days, one-fourth within 2 years, and one-fourth within 4 years. In 1820, owing to the fact that speculators and actual settlers were in arrears amounting to $21,000,000, the credit provisions were repealed and thenceforth immediate cash payment was required.

The history of land legislation during the period under review also tends to center about three political and economic issues—graduation, preemption, and homesteads. The first two were a result of the rapidity with which the public domain had been occupied, and they evolved logically into the third.

The frontier farmers and speculators, having before them what seemed to be an inexhaustible supply of land, selected only the better lands as they pushed westward. Gradually the existence of islands of poorer land which had no buyers became obvious and resulted in a demand to lower its price. Finally in 1854 Congress passed a graduation act reducing the minimum price to $1 an acre on land that had been open to sale for 10 years and to 12½ cents on land that had been listed for 30 years.

The preemption issue evolved from a correlative if opposite situation (*155*). Frontiersmen, becoming impatient of or even being oblivious to the progress of the official land surveys, frequently pushed into the public domain and settled on choice locations without further formality. In doing so they were reverting to the so-called "indiscriminate location" of colonial times. With reference to the land laws, these settlers—usually referred to as squatters—were criminals. When the first townships in Ohio were surveyed there were already a considerable number of settlers in the region, and attempts were made to dislodge them with militia (*101*). The frontier attitude ultimately prevailed to a large extent. The pioneers banded together into claims associations which maintained a list of each member's holdings; they selected a bidder to speak for them at the land auctions and attended the sales as a body pledged to insure the purchase at the minimum price of those lands which were already occupied. Again and again Congress passed laws sanctioning the action of particular groups; and ultimately, in 1841, it enacted the preemption law by which heads of families, men over 21, and widows were allowed to settle on 160 acres of unsurveyed public land with the right to purchase their holdings at the minimum price when the land was actually placed on sale. The Preemption Act of 1841 and the Graduation Act of 1854 were, however, merely preludes to the complete triumph of the advocates of a liberal land policy in 1862, when the homestead principle was enacted into law.

The general idea of free grants of land to actual settlers goes far back into colonial times (*79*). The headright system of land disposition as practiced in the southern Colonies, it will be recalled, embodied the essential features of the homestead principle. Insofar as the quitrent system was unenforceable, it also resulted in actual settlers acquiring land. There was the further precedent of gifts of land to individuals or groups, sometimes as a reward for services rendered to the national welfare or for services anticipated. In all these three procedures settlers got land without money payments.

In spite of these colonial precedents, Congress was slow to abandon the conservative and conserving policies adopted during the two decades immediately following the American Revolution. Many regarded public land as a great national resource which should be administered carefully and prudently with a view toward insuring an income to be used for the well-being of the American people. Many, notably the landowners and manufacturers of the eastern seaboard, opposed liberalization of the land policy. They saw the value of their real estate undermined by the cheaper and newer lands in the West; they also saw western land competing for their labor supply and thus compelling higher wages. The opposition soon rationalized this self-interest and found itself expounding the view that Government generosity with land pauperized the beneficiaries and encouraged laziness. Even as late as 1832 the western leader, Henry Clay, opposed any reduction in the price of public land.

In contrast, the self-interest of the pioneer farmers and land speculators in the West generated a notable enthusiasm for cheap and ultimately free land (*156*, *163*, *164*). To secure effective action, they joined forces with city workers who hoped to escape westward and benefit thereby. In the 1840's the National Reform Association took the leadership, propounding the doctrine that the public land should be distributed in equal amounts to actual settlers (*38*, *51*).

223761°—40——14

One of its most effective pamphlets was entitled "Vote Yourself a Farm," and much emphasis was placed on the idea that land ownership was an essential ingredient of the political philosophy to which the United States was dedicated. Horace Greeley was the patron saint of the association, and the columns of his New York Tribune were an open forum for its use.

At its best the cause of the liberal land policy which came to be epitomized in the idea of free homesteads to actual settlers transcended mere economic self-interest. Many contended that land sold on liberal terms or even given away promoted true democracy. Perhaps the most eloquent spokesman of this view was Senator Thomas Hart Benton of Missouri. It is certain that beneath the passing arguments of the politicians and the pamphleteers lay the conviction that equality of economic power was essential if genuine freedom and democracy were to thrive in America.

The homestead bill introduced by Andrew Johnson passed the House of Representatives in 1852, but complete enactment was destined to be held up for a decade because it became a part of the slavery controversy (*180*). In the first vote a majority of the southern Congressmen had supported the bill, but as sectional tension intensified they veered away, and final passage awaited the withdrawal of the southern representation from Congress after secession (*63*, *101*).

The Pioneers Open New Lands for Agricultural Settlement, 1776–1850

In 1790, when the country's first census was taken, there were approximately 4,000,000 people in the United States. Of these, 94 percent inhabited the 13 original States; only 250,000 had settled in the West of that day—principally in Vermont, Kentucky, Tennessee, and Ohio. By 1850 the Nation boasted 31 States and a population of more than 23,000,000 (*196*). The frontier line had leaped the Mississippi River northward into Minnesota and Iowa, and southward into Texas; skipping the Great Plains, it had followed the trail of gold into California. All this had been effected in one lifetime (*47*, *143*, *154*, *216*).

The migration, one of the greatest in world history, streamed across the Atlantic and swelled through the settled regions of the East. Over 2,000,000 immigrants swarmed in from 1820 to 1850, and in the next 10 years 2,600,000 more arrived. Land was the great magnet. Rich, virgin soil, seemingly unlimited in extent and available almost for the asking—such was the common theme repeated by shipping agents and in letters, pamphlets, newspapers, and handbills. It was an irresistible temptation to farmers sweating over worn-out lands and to city folk who were restless, adventurous, or unsuccessful (*193*).

In the North the first great trek went through western New York and Pennsylvania into the region known as the Old Northwest (*96*, *215*). Bounded by the Ohio, the Great Lakes, and the Mississippi, this area, with the exception of certain reserved sections, had been turned over by the claimant States to the Continental Congress to form a national heritage. The way to settlement was opened by the Ordinances of 1785 and 1787—the most significant legislation passed by Congress under the Articles of Confederation. Immediately after the enactment of the second of these measures the Ohio Co., an association of land speculators, purchased some 2,000,000 acres, paying for them with depreciated soldiers' certificates. In accordance with the bargain, this sale was coupled with the sale of several million acres more to the Scioto Co., a front for certain Congressmen. The third of the groups to undertake settlement of the Ohio country was the Symmes Co., which obtained a contract on similar terms in 1788 (*101, pp. 41–55*).

It was originally planned to delay settlement until the completion of surveys, which in turn were not to be made until the Indian titles had been extinguished. The Indians were with great difficulty persuaded to sign a series of treaties; but, encouraged by British officials, they refused to abide by the terms and prepared to take the warpath, forcing temporary abandonment of the surveys. The land-hungry settlers were not to be daunted, and in December 1787 the first of them left Ipswich, Mass. In the spring of the following year they founded Marietta, north of the Ohio River. A few months later a group of pioneers from New Jersey, under the guidance of Judge John Cleves Symmes, settled near the mouth of the Little Miami River where it flows into the Ohio. Virginians took up the district reserved by their State in 1790, while most of the Connecticut Reserve was sold to the Connecticut Land Co., which in 1796 sent out a small party that founded Cleveland. Thus began the occupation of the vast trans-Appalachian West, a process which continued throughout the nineteenth century (*125, 191*).

In the same wave of migration, western New York was settled. The Catskill and Adirondack Mountains, the forest, and the hostile Iroquois Indians had kept the whites confined to the Hudson and the lower Mohawk Valleys until the close of the Revolution. Soon afterwards pioneers from New Jersey and Pennsylvania followed the Susquehanna and Tioga Rivers north to Seneca Lake and into the heart of New York. At about the same time New Englanders began to push westward from Massachusetts and Vermont. The Holland Land Co. under Robert Morris purchased the region west of Seneca Lake and sold its holdings in smaller tracts to speculators and settlers; east of the lake the State reserved 1,700,000 acres for military bounties. For the most part, however, this entire area was settled by New Englanders.

After 1800 the westward movement assumed momentum. As a result of the pacification of the Indians by Gen. Anthony Wayne and the consequent treaty of Greenville in 1795, the way was cleared for peaceful settlement of the Northwest, particularly after the British gave up their posts on the Great Lakes. The distress in Europe caused by the Napoleonic wars and their aftermath brought hundreds of thousands of immigrants to American shores. Economic depression in the East, due to the embargo, the nonintercourse acts, and the war further stimulated the push westward. There was discontent in the seaboard States, also, especially in New England, because the ruling power was held by old political and religious oligarchies. In the Southern States planters left the worn-out tobacco lands of Virginia and North Carolina and settled on the fresh alluvial soil of the Old Southwest. In doing so they usually drove before them the small pioneer farmers of the uplands, who moved north into the Ohio Valley.

Other factors stimulating migration were the increasing liberality of the Federal Government in its land policy and the wresting of new land cessions from the Indians after the victories of William Henry Harrison in the Northwest and of Andrew Jackson in the Southwest. After 1811, with the launching of the first steamboat on the Ohio River, the pioneers had a more rapid means of transportation. By 1820 there were 60 steamboats on western waters, and in the years that followed, the steamboat was a vital factor in the settlement of the West. Finally, the purchase of the vast Louisiana empire in 1803 and of East Florida in 1819 opened seemingly limitless horizons.

Settlement of the Old Northwest was rapid from the beginning, Ohio being admitted into the Union in 1803. During the next decade Indiana and Illinois became States, and Michigan followed in 1837. In 1810 the region had some 272,000 inhabitants; in 1830, 1,470,000; and in 1860, 6,927,000. Ohio alone had nearly a million people in 1830—more than Massachusetts and Connecticut combined. The growth of the leading cities in the Ohio-Mississippi Valley also reflects the rapidity of settlement. Chicago jumped from a mere fur-trading post to a community of over 100,000 inhabitants between 1830 and 1860, and Cleveland expanded from 6,000 inhabitants in 1840 to 43,000 in 1860. Cincinnati assumed national preeminence in meat packing. This tremendous westward movement was a very serious drain upon the Eastern States, particularly Virginia and Massachusetts where the population remained practically stationary.

Until about 1820 most of the farmers migrating from New England were absorbed along the northern frontier and in western New York (*128*). In Ohio, except in the New England communities around Cleveland and Marietta, most of the settlers came from New York and New Jersey. Indiana and Illinois had many New Englanders in their northern counties but were inhabited for the most part by yeoman farmers from Piedmont Virginia and North Carolina and by the restless pioneer farmers pushed out of Kentucky and Tennessee by more wealthy planters from the seaboard States. The migrations of the Lincoln and La Follette families illustrate this pressure very well.

Though the bulk of the native stock which settled the Mississippi Valley was predominantly from the Southern States, the region north of Tennessee did not take on the same tone as the Old Southwest. The "poor whites" from the South mixed with the New Englanders and the farmers from the Middle Atlantic States to form communities of small farms with few or no slaves and with an abiding faith in democracy (*34*, *124*). Many of the pioneers were Scotch-Irish, and to these was added a large German population. Over half a million Germans came to America between 1830 and 1850 and another million in the decade preceding the Civil War. They were destined to stand by the Union in the struggle between the States and came to be a vital factor in the political development of the Mississippi Valley. The Germans settled chiefly around Cincinnati, in the lake counties of Wisconsin, and in Indiana, Illinois, and Michigan (*76*).

In point of time, migration south of the Ohio into what is now Kentucky and Tennessee preceded the settlement of the Old Northwest. The movement began before the Revolution and continued steadily during the course of the struggle. By 1790 Kentucky had over 70,000 inhabitants, and Tennessee had 36,000. The people of these regions made many attempts to free themselves from the political control claimed by Virginia and North Carolina. Their leaders, John Sevier, James Robertson, and James Wilkinson among others, were in constant intrigue with the Spanish Governor and his agents at New Orleans. However, among the rank and file—chiefly yeoman farmers from Pennsylvania and small farmers pushed out by the wealthy planters of Tidewater Virginia and the Carolinas—loyalty to the United States was stronger, and in 1792 and 1796 Kentucky and Tennessee entered the Union.

The second stage of populating the Old Southwest grew out of the invention of the cotton gin in 1793 and the insatiable demand for cotton. Planters pushed westward seeking land on which they could grow the staple more cheaply and in doing so displaced the pioneer farmers who had preceded them. Unable to refuse the relatively high prices offered by the planters, many sold out and retreated to the mountains to become "poor whites" or pushed on north of the Ohio River or across the Mississippi. Although small farmers continued to constitute the bulk of the population, the political, social, and economic levers in the Southwest were more and more exercised by large planters who developed an aristocracy.

Between 1800 and 1850 Tennessee's population grew from approximately 106,000 to over a million, while Arkansas, having only 14,000 inhabitants in 1820, boasted more than 200,000 three decades later. Simultaneously with the expansion of population westward went the development of cotton production. In 1820 South Carolina and Georgia were the leading cotton States, but after 1834 Alabama and Mississippi, each having grown some 200 percent in the intervening years, became the heart of the cotton kingdom. The profitableness of slave labor on western lands incidentally fastened the institution firmly into southern economy. Other byproducts of the expansion were the Pinckney Treaty with Spain in 1795, which provided for navigation of the Mississippi, deposit rights in New Orleans, and cession of lands between the Yazoo River and the 31° parallel; the acquisition of the Louisiana Territory in 1803; and the purchase of Florida in 1819.

Obtaining the vast territory of Louisana was a particularly monumental stroke of good fortune involving a 140-percent increase in the area of the United States. When Jefferson made the deal there was only a scattered, heterogeneous population in and around New Orleans, chiefly French, Spanish, American, and Indian. Only 10,000 people inhabited upper Louisiana, half of these being Americans who had been lured across the Mississippi by the convenient land laws of Spain and by the rich fur trade centering in St. Louis. The first real knowledge of the size and resources of the trans-Mississippi West resulted from the Lewis and Clark expedition and the explorations of Capt. Zebulon Pike.

After the fur traders the cattle rangers were the first to push into this region, and they were followed by the cotton planters. Together they moved into Texas in the thirties, and the westward tide brought revolution, annexation, and war with Mexico. By the terms of the peace treaty the United States gained a new empire in the southwest beyond the Mississippi.

Before 1850 the Oregon Territory was acquired from England, and California was ceded by Mexico. Gold was discovered in California, and emigrants rushed to the Pacific coast by sea and land. After the gold rush of 1849 there were two frontiers in America. One moved slowly westward from the Mississippi River across the Great Plains, and the other moved eastward from the mountains along the Pacific coast.

The effect of the westward movement on the Eastern States and on American life in general was profound but it is not clearly known in many phases.[7] In the Northeast the opening of fertile lands in the West caused a depression in local agriculture and provided the essential basis for the rise of industrialism and urbanism. As the Ohio and Mississippi Valleys were settled they furnished the industrial centers with both a source of cheap food and a growing market for manufactured goods. A counter claim is that the frontier, by drawing off potential laborers, kept wages high and seriously handicapped the rapid development of American industries; recent studies, however, tend to lessen the weight of this argument. In the South, westward extension no doubt discouraged manufacturing by drawing off the surplus capital. Again, while settlers who undertook cotton production on newly opened lands prospered, those who remained behind suffered greatly from the added competition. Eventually the struggle over the disposition of new territories in relation to slave or free labor provoked the greatest tragedy in American history, the War between the States.

It is generally agreed that the frontier had a liberalizing effect on American politics. Both the Jeffersonian and the Jacksonian movements stemmed in large measure from western influences (*19; 28; 29; 44; 77; 169, pp. 200–219; 192, pp. 243–268; 193, pp. 14–38: 214*). When new State constitutions were drawn up, provisions were made granting to freemen suffrage and office-holding privileges unrestricted by property requirements. Wealth was evenly divided, at least in the first stage of settlement, and this bred a spirit of equality that was reflected in the social and political life. Nevertheless, as has recently been shown, it is easy to overwork this point. Most of the humanitarian reforms of the period were initiated in the older communities where the conditions calling for amelioration were bred and where the leaders were in touch with similar movements in England and on the Continent. The West, however, particularly the Northwest, did support the reforms and embodied many in its legislation. Yet if it were necessary to mention the most important single influence emanating from the West, it would be rather in the realm of the psychological. As long as there was a frontier, men felt that there was always an avenue of escape, a chance to start anew.

Agriculture in the Old Northwest

Until the prairies of western Indiana and Illinois were reached, the farming in pioneer communities west of the Alleghenies was essentially

[7] For the literature evaluating the significance of the westward movement, see: EDWARDS, EVERETT E. REFERENCES ON THE SIGNIFICANCE OF THE FRONTIER IN AMERICAN HISTORY. U. S. Dept. Agr. Library Bibliog. Contrib. 33, 99 pp. 1939. [Mimeographed.]

a repetition of the experience along the Atlantic seaboard during the two centuries of the colonial period. The frontiersman cleared from 1 to 3 acres by girdling and grubbing and then planted the field to vegetables and corn. At this stage the family depended on game and other wild products to supplement the food raised. Maple sugar was also important, but potash was the only cash product. With more land cleared, additional corn and some wheat were added. Gradually a farm capable of producing surpluses for outside markets was developed (*27*).

The responsiveness of wheat to new lands is patent to students of agricultural tendencies, and its development in the region northwest of the Ohio River is an excellent illustration (*17*). New York and Pennsylvania were the leading wheat-producing States during the first quarter of the nineteenth century; but during that time there was a westward shift even within their borders, the Genesee country supplanting the Hudson-Mohawk Valley. Ohio became an important producer of wheat during the thirties, but the big shift westward came during the fifties. Whereas Pennsylvania, Ohio, and New York—in the order named—had been the top-ranking States in 1849, Illinois, Indiana, and Wisconsin took their places within a decade. In that time Wisconsin rose from ninth place to third, and New York and Pennsylvania experienced not only a relative but an absolute decline (*100*). By 1860 the five States of the Old Northwest were supplying about half of the wheat produced in the entire United States. Within the region, the hilly counties of Ohio and the prairies and oak openings of Indiana, Michigan, Illinois, and Wisconsin were the areas of concentration.

When the westward-moving pioneer farmers reached the edge of the prairie in Indiana and Illinois, they hesitated, believing that land which did not support trees was not rich enough to produce farm crops (*150, 175*). The lack of a ready supply of wood for buildings, fences, and fuel was also a factor. The dependence of these frontiersmen on the rivers as avenues of transport to markets and the scarcity of water and lack of shelter for livestock on the prairies also made them reluctant. The thick and heavily matted prairie sod was a formidable challenge to the customary wooden and cast-iron plows, and from three to seven yoke of oxen were required to break new fields. Even then it was two or three seasons before the grass roots had rotted sufficiently so that the fields could be worked easily. Higher prices for grains after 1845, due to conditions in Europe, together with the coming of the railroads, affected the occupation of the prairies. The challenge of the sod led to the development of the steel plow (*45*), and eventually, after experiments with various fencing materials such as sod walls, smooth wire, and Osage hedges, the fence problem was solved by the invention and perfection of barbed wire (*97*).

Corn production, like that of wheat, responded, though less quickly, to the pull of the new lands of the Northwest. In general it tended to occupy a belt directly south of the wheat region, but prior to the end of the sixties a corn belt was not clearly delimited except for special areas, such as the rich bottom lands along the Scioto River and the limestone basins of Kentucky and Tennessee (*119, p. 172*). The census of 1840 revealed Kentucky, Tennessee, and Virginia as the leading corn States, but within two decades the center of concentration had shifted northwestward to Illinois, Ohio, Missouri, and Indiana, with Kentucky and Tennessee in fifth and sixth places. By this time Iowa and the eastern parts of Kansas and Nebraska had become important centers. The older States in the East continued to produce corn for their own needs.

The corn of this northwestward-moving belt was marketed in the form of whiskey and hogs, the first because it was valuable in proportion to bulk and the second because hogs furnished their own motive power. The hogs of the frontier were a special type, essentially a product of the rigors of life in the open and were known aptly as "windsplitters" or razorbacks. Many pioneers raised several hundred hogs a year. If they were left to feed on the forest mast alone, however, besides putting on flesh that was soft and difficult to preserve, they became untractable and without the stamina to survive the rigors of severe winters. It was therefore essential to supplement the mast with corn, and eventually, as markets developed, corn-feeding and marketing hogs became the basic activities of agriculture in the Old Northwest.

In the early nineteenth century the hogs were taken down the rivers on boats to be sold to the plantations in the South or driven overland to eastern markets (*25*). At first the farmers drove their own hogs eastward, but gradually a profession of drovers developed and the trade became standardized. Some herds numbered as many as 5,000 and moved eastward at the rate of 8 or 10 miles a day. Although the ultimate destination was usually Philadelphia, Baltimore, or New York, many herds were taken to the plantations of Tennessee, Virginia, and the Carolinas. This method of marketing declined with the development of meat packing along the Ohio, especially centering about Cincinnati, which became known as "Porkopolis." The coming of the railroads was a final factor ending this trade.

The range-cattle industry has always been associated with the frontier, and the region north of the Ohio River was no exception. As early as 1805 George and Felix Renick of Ohio drove a herd of range cattle overland to Baltimore, where they cleared a profit of over $30 a head (*149*). Their success led to other similar drives, and shortly the marketing of range cattle in the East became a well-defined source of cash income for the farmers in the West of that time. The drives were started in the early spring and continued through the summer. Each night the herds were halted at "drove stands," where food and shelter were provided for both the drovers and their charges. Four-year-old steers were driven slowly and sold directly to the abbatoirs. Three-year-olds were often sold to the farmers in the hinterland of Philadelphia for feeding. By 1840 the farmers of the Ohio Valley had taken over the fattening of their own cattle, and this development became specialized in a zone bounded on the south by the 36° parallel and on the north by the 40° parallel. The bluegrass region of Kentucky and the Scioto Valley were the centers for corn feeding, and many of the leaders in this development were former Virginians who had known of similar methods on the banks of the Potomac in the days of Washington. Eventually these feeders reached out for additional stock from the prairies of Illinois, Iowa, and Missouri and from the wheat farmers to the northward. Before large-scale refrigeration, it was difficult to preserve beef in a palatable form, and beef packing did not develop on a scale comparable with that of pork (*118*). The eastern cattle drives, therefore, continued long after the hog drives had ceased. The advent of railroads after 1850 brought an end to the drives, and the cattle-feeding industry pushed westward to the Corn Belt.

Northeastern Agriculture Confronted With Western Competition, 1775–1860

In the New England and Middle Atlantic States the colonial pattern of agriculture continued dominant until the second decade of the nineteenth century (*25*). Cultivation was extensive and exploitive, tools clumsy, systematic crop rotation and fertilizers generally absent, livestock neglected, and orchards and woodlands badly managed. Each farm was a self-sufficing unit, growing food for home needs and a scant surplus to be exchanged at the local store for salt and sugar (*190*, *204*). For the most part tools and clothing were made in the farm home. In New England wheat had been generally abandoned, except in a few favored regions, and root crops such as potatoes and turnips were noticeably lacking. The prevailing mode of crop rotation was the medieval practice of alternating grain, grass, and fallow. Implements were few in number, most farmers being able to carry all they possessed on their backs, and the plows were home-made wooden contrivances with a plating of iron strips added by the local blacksmith. Oxen were the chief draft animals, and cattle generally were noted more for their hardiness than for beef or dairy production. Between 1801 and 1811 merino sheep were imported from Spain, and the result was a vast improvement in American flocks (*52*, *211*).

To this picture of prevailing agricultural backwardness certain exceptions must be noted. Pennsylvania as late as 1840 was the leading wheat-producing State, and considerable grain was also raised in the Hudson and Mohawk Valleys of New York; the Middle States were to a considerable extent the bread States for New England and the South. Corn was a leading staple in New England the output per acre averaging 25 to 30 bushels; in the Connecticut Valley, it occasionally averaged as high as 40 or 50 bushels. The Connecticut Valley in general was a prosperous farming country still able to raise wheat commercially, and its more progressive farmers used gypsum to restore their soil. Other outstanding areas were the Narragansett country of Rhode Island, where dairying for exportation was extensive, and the western counties of Massachusetts, which produced grain commercially.

With such exceptions it may be repeated that northern agriculture at the opening of the nineteenth century was based on practices comparable to those of old England prior to its agricultural revolution. American farmers had not only failed to avail themselves of the new scientific practices introduced by Bakewell, Tull, and Young—they had even resisted any change. The cheapness of land and the high price of labor also militated against intensive cultivation. However, P. W. Bidwell, a careful investigator of this particular subject (*23*,

24, 152) has insisted that the fundamental cause of this retardation was the lack of markets for surplus production. When the rise of manufacturing resulted in the concentration of a large nonagricultural population in towns and cities a spirit of commercialization became evident in northern agriculture.

This change began after 1810; the population of the Eastern States increased from 3,487,000 in that year to 6,761,000 in 1840; urban centers of over 8,000 inhabitants increased from 3 in 1790 to 33 in 1840; while in southern New England all but 50 of the 479 townships had at least one manufacturing village clustering around a textile mill, an iron furnace, or some other industry. To meet the demand of this new market the farmer turned to lighter and better-designed agricultural tools; the grain cradle displaced the sickle, the iron and later the steel plow superseded the wooden plow, and the cultivator supplanted the hand hoe. Improved machinery brought increased production and decreased labor time and costs. In Pennsylvania and New York the horse replaced the slow-moving ox as the main draft animal.

Creation of a home market brought a shift from general to specialized farming, and each locality tended to concentrate on the products for which its soil, climate, and geographical position were best suited. Market gardening and dairying developed in the immediate vicinity of urban centers, notably around Boston, New York, Philadelphia, Providence, and Newport. Lands were reclaimed, meadows drained, and dry lands irrigated; the soil was repaired by the planting of clover and the use of gypsum; more labor was hired; and the teachings of the new agricultural societies were heeded. One effect of these changes was a sharp rise in land values; an acre outside of Philadelphia brought $150 in 1837, and near New York land prices in some instances increased fourfold between 1800 and 1840. Tenancy also appeared as immigrants leased truck farms before purchasing their own lands. The production of fluid milk to meet town and city needs became prominent in these decades and continued to expand even after the center of dairying had moved westward.

Feeding cattle for beef received increased attention in the East, concentrating in the Connecticut Valley, which supplied the Brighton market near Boston, and in southeastern Pennsylvania. Specialization in butter and cheese making developed chiefly north of New York City and in central New York after the completion of the Erie Canal. Around other cities the sale of fluid milk had largely supplanted cheese and butter production by 1840. Striking improvement was effected in swine husbandry owing to crossing with improved breeds, but there was no marked geographical concentration.

Eastern wool growing enjoyed its greatest prosperity in the decade of the 1830's (*212*). The domestic manufacture of woolen goods was firmly established, and, stimulated by protective tariffs, it increased its output and demand for raw materials. In 1837, 28 of the 38 million pounds of wool used in the mills was of local origin. In 1840 the eastern wool growers owned 60 percent of the country's sheep, but specialization was already well developed. In New England production was limited to Vermont and the hills of western Massachusetts and Connecticut.

Among other changes in northeastern agriculture that came in response to urban needs were the increase in hay production to feed the horses in city and town stables and the growing of potatoes in considerable quantities, particularly in Maine and on Long Island. Farmers also conducted a profitable business in supplying city dwellers with firewood and charcoal and furnishing sand, stone, and timber for buildings.

Now that the farmer received a cash income he turned to factories to supply him with the clothes, tools, and furniture he had formerly made for himself. The decline of household industries had as revolutionary an influence on rural life as the growth of industrialization had on the formation of a wage-earning class. As self-sufficient farming waned, long-established habits and traditions in thinking and living were uprooted. The family as an economic unit became less important, with all that implied for rural mores; farmers' sons and daughters began migrating to mill towns to take up a new way of life. Those who remained behind developed a taste for urban standards of living. Others were stirred to action and turned westward.

In general outline the adaptation of northeastern agriculture to the rise of local markets is valid as painted. The changes did not appear overnight, however, nor did they affect all farmers uniformly. There were many influences retarding the main trend. Ingrained habits tended to keep many farmers in the old ways of producing what they needed for their own uses, buying and selling little. Lack of working capital was another serious hindrance; the farmer marketed his produce once a year and had to maintain his family on the returns until the next year. The country store was the chief source of short-time credit, and interest rates were high because losses were frequent. Where the farmer realized a surplus, he preferred to invest in lands, in larger homes, or in outside enterprises, rather than in labor-saving machinery. Mortgages increased noticeably in number after 1830, but the money was used for paying bills or in outside speculation instead of for financing farm improvements. The imperfect organization of markets was another obstacle; the country merchant, the chief middleman for farm produce, performed his function badly and at a high cost.

While the eastern farmer was still adjusting himself to commercialized agriculture he was faced with a second transforming influence, namely, western competition (*10*). The Erie Canal opened in 1825 and brought steadily increasing quantities of foodstuffs to the eastern markets, but the pressure greatly increased after the railroads reached beyond the Alleghenies. By 1850 there were 7,000 miles of railroad in the country, largely concentrated in the Northeast and Northwest; and 10 years later Minnesota, Iowa, Nebraska, and Kansas were already pouring surpluses eastward. From the West came wool, wheat, and pork in such quantities and at such low prices as to discourage local production. Sheep raising in southern New England declined nearly 50 percent between 1840 and 1850, with a further drop of 35 percent in the next decade. The products of the eastern wheat growers, suffering from soil deterioration and crop blights, could hardly compete with the products of fertile lands newly opened in the West; and by 1840 flour from western wheat was used generally in New England, not only by city folk but by farmers as well.

Before the advent of refrigerator cars the effect of competition in beef and pork production was somewhat tempered, although by 1859 half the beef supply of Massachusetts came from outside New England, and Philadelphia received 32,552 tons of livestock from Pittsburgh over the Pennsylvania Railroad. Between 1840 and 1860 the number of swine in Massachusetts, Rhode Island, and Connecticut fell from 306,000 to 167,000.

Serious as these inroads were, they by no means crowded out eastern production entirely. If local farmers almost completely lost the markets for wheat and wool and to a lesser extent for live cattle and hogs, the advantage of their proximity to industrial centers could not be altogether overcome. More attention was given to growing vegetables and supplying fluid milk. Cheese and butter making increased, and by 1860 New England and the Middle Atlantic States accounted for 70 percent of the country's cheese and close to 50 percent of its butter. In New York, the Nation's leading dairy State, production was centered in the Mohawk and Hudson Valleys, with some expansion into the central counties; Vermont led in New England, although Litchfield County, in western Connecticut, was famous for the fine quality of its cheese; while southeastern Pennsylvania supplied butter and milk for the Philadelphia, Wilmington, and Baltimore markets.

The New England and Middle Atlantic States grew more hay and forage in 1860 than in 1850, although their share of the country's total dropped 15 percent. Corn production increased in New England between 1840 and 1850 but then declined; on the other hand, the crop of potatoes in Maine in 1860 was almost twice as large as that of 1850. A final example of adaptation to city needs was the increased planting of orchards. Horticultural societies were formed, improved varieties of apples planted, and old native fruit trees grafted. By 1847 Oneida County, in the Mohawk Valley, shipped nearly 18,000 barrels of apples.

Eastern agriculture thus underwent two major changes by 1860: First, between 1810 and 1840, in response to the growth of a home market, farmers gradually shifted from self-sufficing to commercialized agriculture. While this process was still unfolding, canals and railroads enabled farmers on rich, virgin, western soil to ship their produce to eastern markets. As a consequence, local farmers were forced to specialize in articles such as milk, butter, cheese, vegetables, fruit, and hay, which, by reason of their perishability or bulk, escaped western competition and enjoyed a ready market in the expanding urban centers close by.

Changes in Southern Agriculture to the Civil War

Despite an ever-growing rivalry with the Northwest, the South continued as the principal center of commercial agriculture from the Revolution to the Civil War. Its preeminence, however, was due chiefly to the rise of cotton production and its expansion into the Old Southwest. Tobacco, the chief staple during the colonial period, fell off greatly in relative importance, its total production remaining stable until about 1850. Indigo cultivation waned, having suffered a deathblow by the removal of the British bounty. Rice farming underwent a transition incident to the adoption of the tide-flow system. Hemp and flax later became crops of some importance in Kentucky and Missouri, and sugar growing achieved considerable success in Louisiana. It was cotton, though, and particularly cotton on western lands, that predominated.

Cotton

During the last half of the eighteenth century the inventions of Crompton, Hargreaves, Arkwright, and Cartwright had revolutionized textile manufacture in England (*46*, *98*, *203*). Spinning and weaving machinery operated by steam or water power and the consequent introduction of the factory system made possible mass production of cotton cloth for a world market. Cotton fiber on an equivalent scale was needed. In colonial times cotton had been grown in the southern Colonies, but only for domestic use. Soil and climate favored the green-seed, short-staple variety, but separation of the seed from the lint was difficult, slow, and expensive because the fiber had to be cut or torn away. Sea-island cotton, a longer-fibered variety, was introduced in 1786. Its seeds were easily removed by running the fiber between rollers that revolved in opposite directions. Although sea-island cotton brought high prices and was raised, often on a large scale, until the Civil War, the acreage devoted to it was limited, as it could be successfully grown only on the lowlands along the southeastern coast.

The cotton gin invented by Eli Whitney in 1793 solved the crucial problem incident to large-scale production of the green-seed, short-staple cotton, and its invention marked a turning point not only in southern agriculture but in American history (*120*). Upland or short-staple cotton became the largest commercial crop in the South and the basis of its economy (*145*, *147*). Each decade cotton production approximately doubled. In 1800, 73,222 bales of cotton was produced; in 1840, 1,347,640; and in 1860, 3,841,416. It overflowed the domestic market and became the largest single export of the United States. In the year beginning October 1809 cotton represented 23 percent of the value of total exports, or a little over $66,000,000; by July 1, 1860, it had increased to 61 percent, or more than $333,000,000. Cotton fed not only the mills of old England but those of New England as well; a major item in the domestic trade was the exchange of southern raw cotton for New England manufactured cloth. As the South concentrated more and more on cotton growing, it also offered a market for northwestern grain and livestock products.

Cotton expansion revived the moribund institution of slavery. In 1794 George Washington had written a friend (*129*): "Were it not that I am principled against selling negroes as you would cattle in the market I would not in 12 months be possessed of a single one as a slave. I shall be happily mistaken if they are not found to be very troublesome species of property ere many years have passed over our heads." The growing of cotton was very well adapted to unskilled, supervised gang labor (*90*); in the 5 years before the Federal prohibition of the slave trade became effective in 1808, South Carolina alone imported 39,000 slaves, and by 1860 its slave population increased to 57.2 percent of the total population. Another institution, the plantation, similarly became prominent, and the three together—cotton, slavery, and the plantation—exercised considerable influence over the political and social as well as the economic structure of the South (*146*).

Cotton growing centered first in the tidewater region of South Carolina and Georgia. The crop proved so profitable that many planters shifted to it from indigo and rice cultivation. As L. C. Gray has pointed out in his monumental work on southern agriculture (*91*), methods of cultivation were crude and wasteful, not because of slave labor but because land was abundant and cheap. Squandering natural resources was as characteristic of the southern planter as of the western pioneer. Cotton growers reached out to the Piedmont of North Carolina and Virginia and then turned southwestward. The War of 1812, the acquisition of East and West Florida, and the removal of Indians to reservations beyond the Mississippi were, in part at least, due to cotton. The heavy black or brown loam soils in the Alabama-Mississippi Black Belt were found to be unsurpassed for cotton, and this region long remained the foremost cotton district in the world. Nevertheless the migration of cotton continued westward into the second area of great cotton production along the lower Mississippi. Even these conquests were not enough, and the land-hungry and restless pushed on to the prairie region of Texas.

Until 1821, over one-half of the cotton had been grown in Georgia and South Carolina. By 1850 Alabama ranked first, Georgia second, Mississippi third, and South Carolina fourth. In 1860 Mississippi, Alabama, and Louisiana produced over one-half of the total cotton crop in the United States, while Texas grew more than South Carolina. In the North, when the Atlantic Seaboard States could not meet the challenge of western agriculture, industrialization was intensified; in the older South no such compensating factor was present, and economically it fell steadily behind the Southwest. Land values declined, and Savannah and Charleston were supplanted by New Orleans and Mobile as trade centers. Even by 1820 the areas first devoted to cotton presented a sorry picture of eroded lands, bare of vegetation except for scrubby growths.

The Southeast blamed its decline on the tariff, the Federal banking policy, the lack of credit facilities, and heavy taxation. All these factors were present, but they did not constitute the crux of the problem. The fundamental difficulty lay in the too-rapid westward expansion. Had there been planned control, southern development might have taken a different course.

The States of the south Atlantic seaboard did attempt to adapt themselves to changing conditions (*33*). Leaders like William Gregg and James Hammond stressed the need for industrial diversification, and a number of textile mills and iron foundries were established. The movement did not progress far—despite hundreds of books, resolutions, and conventions—because the capital available was too closely tied up with landed investments, while the labor supply, whether slave or "poor white," needed wholesale readaptation. It was only after the Civil War, when its agriculture lay in ruins, that the South turned to industry on a large scale. As an alternative to industrial development, an attempt was made to establish the Southeast as the trade center for both the Southwest and the Northwest. Although canals and railroads were built, only a meager success in serving the hinterland was achieved. The Southwest developed its own ports, and the Northwest became tied to the Northeast by the railroads.

Attempts were also made to adjust and reform the agriculture of the Old South to the changed conditions (*54*, *55*, *56*). John Taylor of Caroline sought to halt the retardation of Virginia agriculture (*134*, *179*), and Edmund Ruffin sounded an even more clarion call to action (*56*). His teachings won for him the title "father of American soil science" (*57*), but they failed to stay the tide. When the Old South first felt western competition, it found itself with too much slave labor. Transfer of that surplus westward only strengthened the competition. Finally, in the forties and fifties, when labor was needed for agricultural diversification, slaves were scarce. The Old South could not afford to pay $1,000 to $1,400 for a prime hand and was outbid by the Southwest where fertile lands yielded a much greater output per unit of labor. In desperation the Southeast sought a reopening of the slave trade; though the attempt failed, slave smuggling probably was increased.

More important for later development was the fostering of progressive methods such as deeper plowing, the introduction of new crops, the increased use of labor-saving devices, and the importation of improved breeds of livestock. Agricultural journals and societies were begun and fairs and exhibits held. General farming became a prominent feature of the agriculture of the Border States, and just prior to the outbreak of the Civil War Virginia achieved a moderate prosperity as a result.

Tobacco

Tobacco, the South's chief colonial staple, reached its height in the 1790's, when over half the population of the tobacco States—Virginia, Maryland, and North Carolina—were engaged in or dependent upon its cultivation. It ranked first on the list of American exports in 1790 when the value of tobacco shipped exceeded $4,000,000. After 1800 it declined rapidly in relative importance, and production was stable until 1850. The disturbed trade conditions resulting from the Napoleonic wars, the post-1815 attempt of England to stimulate domestic tobacco production or West Indian importation, the high duties imposed by countries of continental Europe anxious for revenue, and the competition of Cuba, Sumatra, and Colombia, all helped to undermine the position of United States tobacco on the world market. At home, meanwhile, cotton was outbidding tobacco for the available land and labor.

By 1850, however, tobacco production had passed its lowest point and had begun to revive. Flue curing supplanted the old-fashioned, charcoal-fire, open-air methods, while a new yellow-leaf variety, lighter than the old varieties, won popular favor. Between 1850 and 1860 production doubled, North Carolina and Virginia being affected most (*84*, *86*, *109*, *158*, *159*).

Tobacco, like cotton, expanded to new fields in the West in the period before the Civil War. Extractive pioneer cultivation laid waste the older lands, while low prices on the world market called for decreased production costs. It was cheaper to move to fresh soil than to struggle with worn-out fields. Virginia maintained its lead till 1860, but Kentucky was close behind, and Ohio, Tennessee, and Missouri had made a considerable advance. Two important trade and manufacturing centers for tobacco, Louisville and St. Louis, developed in the West.

Sugar

Sugar production, like that of cotton, grew from insignificant proportions to outstrip tobacco in importance. The cane was introduced into Louisiana by Jesuits from Santo Domingo in 1751, but it was not until the last decade of the century that the crop was grown on a commercially significant scale (*31, 145, 147*).

The sugar district centered along the rivers and bayous of southeastern Louisiana, where the soil was rich and the growing season was sufficiently long for the plant to mature. Despite fluctuations due to floods and occasional early frosts, production increased from approximately 20,000 short tons in 1823 to 270,000 in 1861. Unlike most other southern staples, sugar enjoyed the protection of a high tariff, and the industry was highly mechanized; sugar production expanded but little either to the west or to the east. It did extend over to the Brazos River area of Texas and to a lesser degree into Florida and Georgia, but in these States it was relatively insignificant. Though the industry was limited in the main to Louisiana, it affected the Southeast. Many South Carolinians, for example, migrated to Louisiana, taking their laborers with them. In 1811 Wade Hampton established himself on a large plantation at the head of Bayou Lafourche. By 1860 the sugar plantations were using a total of 180,000 slaves; this involved a considerable drain of labor from the Atlantic seaboard and sent slave prices upward.

Rice, Flax, and Hemp

Rice had been a leading agricultural crop along the coast of South Carolina and Georgia during the colonial period and continued to be so down to the Civil War (*16, 50, 99*). Production increased threefold from 1820 to 1850 but suffered a distinct decline in the next decade. In the banner year 1850 South Carolina and Georgia together accounted for almost all the rice grown in the United States. There was some development of the industry in Louisiana, Mississippi, and Alabama, but it was of little consequence. Rice planters felt western competition most when they had to bid for labor on a market dominated by the cotton growers of the Southwest.

At the close of the colonial era flax and hemp were crops of some importance in the local markets of the Southeast. In the next few decades Virginia shipped a sizable quantity of flax to the North, and upper South Carolina also succeeded in raising flax commercially. The extension of cotton cultivation and soil deterioration hampered further development.

Almost from the first settlement of Kentucky, hemp raising was found well suited to the rich limestone areas (*91*). Unusually favorable prices from 1826 to 1828 stimulated production, and hemp growing expanded into middle Tennessee and, during the thirties, into the rich valleys of Missouri. The cotton industry had a considerable interest in hemp, since it was manufactured locally into baling cloth, rope, and clothing for Negroes. In 1859 Kentucky and Missouri together produced more than three-fourths of the 57,000 tons of hemp raised in the United States. Soil deterioration, scarcity of labor, and Russian competition, however, had already influenced Kentucky to turn more toward wheat growing and cattle raising.

Other Southern Crops

While the South raised all of the cotton, rice, and sugar grown in the United States and over 80 percent of the tobacco, its other crops also ranked high. It produced over 50 percent of the country's corn, over 70 percent of the peas and beans, 94 percent of the sweetpotatoes, and a little less than 30 percent of the wheat. In producing each of the principal classes of livestock the South ranked higher per capita than the United States as a whole. Kentucky was famous for its race horses, horned cattle, and Hampshire hogs, while Virginia was a leader in sheep raising. Eighty-six percent of the South's general farming was located in the Border States in 1859.

Social Organization

Recent writings have stressed the point that to divide ante-bellum southern society into planters and poor whites gives a completely false picture (*141*). The landowning class was divided into gradations of small, intermediate, and large farmers, and small, intermediate, and large planters. In 1850 only 18 percent of the South's 569,000 farms and plantations were actually plantations, and this estimate includes as "plantations" many thousands of small cotton and tobacco holdings with but one or two working hands. Even in the Black Belt of Alabama almost 80 percent of the nonslaveholding landowners, who in 1850 constituted 44 percent of the region's agricultural population, owned farms ranging up to 200 acres. Of the slaveholding landowners, over 50 percent owned 10 or fewer slaves and 500 acres of land or less, which classed them as farmers. Together the small planters and the slaveholding and nonslaveholding farmers owned approximately 75 percent of the landed wealth in the Black Belt—the so-called stronghold of the plantation system. As late as 1860 only 348,000 families out of a total of 793,493 white and free colored families owned slaves in the South.

While it is true that the yeoman farmer was more truly characteristic of the landholding class, even in the ante-bellum South, the 2 percent of planters holding estates of more than 50 slaves bulked large economically, politically, and socially (*34*). It was this small predominant group that furnished the Pinckneys, Tyler, Polk, Breckinridge, Claiborne, Hampton, and many others who manipulated the levers of political and social control. Not until the Civil War overthrew the planter aristocracy did the yeoman or dirt farmer begin to come into his own.

Improved Transportation the Key to New Markets

The importance of transportation in American history can hardly be overestimated. As farmers moved westward to conquer the vast

223761°—40——15

empire extending from the Atlantic to the Pacific, internal improvements became one of the most acute problems in governmental policy as well as engineering science. The first settlers along the Atlantic seaboard were dependent upon ocean transportation to Europe for marketing their raw materials and bringing manufactured goods in exchange. As population later pushed into the interior, recourse was had to rivers, roads, canals, and railroads, with a consequent shaping of the economic development of the Nation (*78*). Since most of the trade before the Civil War was in agricultural commodities that were not only bulky but perishable—this was long before the advent of refrigerator cars—rapid, low-cost transportation was particularly essential. Not only the economic life but the very existence and location of settlements were determined in many cases by the availability of transportation facilities. Only after 1850, when railroad building went on so rapidly that railroads preceded the settlers—especially in the trans-Mississippi West—and thus determined the routes of migration, did an adequate solution of the transportation problem seem possible. By shortening distances between various parts of the country, improved transportation laid the basis for nationalism; by stimulating domestic commerce and regional interdependence, it eventually cemented the Federal Union.

The rude log dugout and bark canoe were the first means of transportation on rivers in the colonial period. Later these were supplanted to some extent by flatboats and keelboats, many of which used temporary sails. Although the chief communication between the colonies was by water, Indian trails gradually evolved into routes for travelers on foot or horseback. Roads developed slowly; as late as the Revolution only three roads extended to the north and east from New York City, while only one led west out of Philadelphia. In the South two rude trails extended across the mountains—one through the pass at Harpers Ferry and the other through Cumberland Gap. There were also very few bridges until after the close of the eighteenth century.

General interest and activity in road building was gradually awakened in the years from 1790 to 1820, though definite achievement was limited to the older and more settled communities along the Atlantic seaboard (*64*). Various factors were responsible for the change—the demand of inland farmers for better transportation facilities to market their products; the need of townspeople for cheaper foodstuffs; the prospect of increasing the value of lands in the back country; and the hope of speculators for dividends—this last factor being important and ever present in the movement for internal improvements. The leadership was supplied by individuals who organized private companies and issued stock with which to raise the capital to build turnpikes, expecting dividends to flow from tolls.

Chief among the hard-surfaced or macadamized roads constructed was the Philadelphia-Lancaster Turnpike, 62 miles long, which was built during 1792–94 at a cost of $465,000. The road was a financial success from the start, and the ultimate result was a turnpike-building boom. In the next 30 years 86 companies were chartered in the State of Pennsylvania alone; by 1832 they had built about 2,200 miles of road at a cost ranging from $900 to $7,000 per mile. One hundred and eighty turnpike companies were active in New England in 1810, while some 88 companies built over 3,000 miles of turnpikes in New York between 1800 and 1807. Each of the seaboard cities was anxious to tap its hinterland for a source of agricultural produce and a market for manufactured goods and consequently sought to outstrip the others in developing avenues of transportation.

Although shipping time and costs were greatly reduced as a result of these turnpikes, rates for overland transport were still extremely high. It cost $125 to move a ton of freight overland from Philadelphia to Pittsburgh, while the average charge throughout the country for general merchandise was, according to John Bach McMaster (*125*), probably $10 per ton for each 100 miles. These excessive rates virtually prohibited the transporting of grain and flour more than 150 miles. Another source of complaint was the high toll charges; in New England the average toll was 12½ cents per wagon for every 2 miles. Many farmers preferred using a semblance of trails through swamps and underbrush to submitting to monopolistic extortions. State legislatures in some cases were persuaded to impose a measure of regulatory restraint by setting maximum rates.

Private corporations, even with a certain amount of State aid, could not provide a system of internal improvement adequate to meet national needs. Consequently the people turned to the Federal Government for assistance. Under article 1 of section 8 of the Constitution, Congress was empowered to establish post offices and post roads, raise and support armies, and regulate commerce. This, according to advocates of Government action, was ample authorization in view of the many beneficial results expected to accrue to the general welfare. A network of roads and canals built under Government auspices, they maintained, would stimulate westward settlement, facilitate national defense, and spur the growth of domestic commerce. Such an undertaking was financially possible since in 1806 and at several intervals thereafter there was a surplus in the Federal Treasury.

In response to this pressure Albert Gallatin, Secretary of the Treasury, drew up in 1808 an extensive report to Congress on internal improvements. In it he advocated a Nation-wide system of canals, turnpikes, and river inprovements at a total cost of $20,000,000 to be financed over a 10-year period by the Federal surplus or by the sale of public lands. Coming from such an economy-minded, strict constructionist, the proposal is particularly noteworthy.

The Cumberland Road, extending from Cumberland, Md., to Vandalia, Ill., a distance of 834 miles, was, however, the only major tangible result of this early agitation. The cost to the Federal Government for the construction and maintenance of the Cumberland Road reached almost $7,000,000, but as a highway to the West for both emigration and trade it amply repaid the outlay.

Internal improvements became increasingly a sectional issue, with the North and West favoring Federal aid and the South opposing it. As President, both Madison and Monroe insisted that a constitutional amendment was necessary for further action; John Quincy Adams, who followed, was strongly in favor of Government subsidies, but Congress was opposed. Andrew Jackson, as a westerner, tended to support improvements that were genuinely national in purpose and not "pork-barrel" ventures designed to line the pockets of local speculators. Of the $9,500,000 expended by the Government on roads and canals from 1802 to 1835, two-thirds was disbursed during his administration. The frequently cited Maysville Road veto was due to the intrastate character of that particular project. Under Jackson was also passed the Distribution Act of 1836, designed to rid the Treasury of the surplus by lending the money to the separate States, which were to employ the funds for speculative ventures in road and canal construction. The depression beginning in 1837 brought the movement for Federal aid to a temporary halt, and after the crystallization of opposition in the South the policy finally bogged down in the maze of conflicting constitutional interpretations.

The advent of the steamboat, in 1807, gave river traffic a new importance. Flatboats and keelboats propelled by relays of men who were referred to colloquially as "alligator horses" were useful in downstream trade, and the West was fortunate in having the Mississippi, that 2,000-mile internal artery, for traffic diffusion. By 1810 this trade was valued at $10,000,000 and engaged 2,000 flatboats and keelboats annually. The disadvantages, however, were great—river hazards were numerous, and traffic upstream was almost nonexistent; in 1815 when a steamer ascended the Mississippi and the Ohio from New Orleans to Louisville in 25 days a new chapter in American trade and internal development was opened (*60*).

Steam navigation began under a monopoly patent granted Fulton, Livingstone, and associates, and John Marshall was for once popularly acclaimed when in the case of *Gibbons* v. *Ogden* (1824) he read the Supreme Court's decision invalidating the power of any one State to monopolize river transportation. The next few decades witnessed a tremendous expansion in river navigation by steamboats, particularly in the West. Chief of the water routes were the Mississippi, Ohio, and Missouri Rivers and their main tributaries. By 1851 there were nearly 600 steamboats plying the rivers of the interior. Pittsburgh, Cincinnati, and St. Louis were the main centers of this trade, but New Orleans profited most; from 1830 to 1840 it grew more rapidly in wealth and commerce than any other city. Until canals and railroads broke the tie, this river trade closely bound the Northwest and the Southwest. Western products included flour, bacon, corn, oats, apples, and potatoes. Down to New Orleans from the Ohio Valley came thousands of rafts loaded with corn, hay, and wheat, while from farms of the Cumberland and Tennessee Valleys came tobacco and cotton. By 1852, however, the value of cotton shipped to New Orleans passed that of all other products combined.

Steamboats were an important factor in the settlement of the West, remaining the chief means of travel even after the railroads had come into general use. In 1852 a single ship on one trip carried 500 home-seekers north from New Orleans; the number leaving Pittsburgh on St. Louis boats in 1854 averaged 1,500 each day. The high mark was reached in 1855, when 3,000,000 passengers traveled on Ohio River boats; after that there was a general decline as lines went out of business or moved to more western waters.

The steamboats were never wholly able to overcome many of the obstacles faced by flatboats and keelboats in the Mississippi and Ohio trade. Upstream freight traffic from New Orleans never assumed impressive proportions, and western farmers had to look elsewhere for their imports. The shallow water, strong currents, and falls at Louisville often delayed ships for days. Shoals and bars were numerous, and they shifted frequently; and floating logs often ripped open the hulls of vessels. Ice, floods, boiler explosions, and scourges were also common. According to one calculation, over 1,000 ships had been lost by 1850, and the number of casualties exceeded 2,200 killed and 1,800 wounded. To improve traffic conditions on the Mississippi, Ohio, Missouri, and Arkansas Rivers, the Federal Government appropriated over $3,000,000 between 1822 and 1860; unfortunately the grants were made chiefly before 1844 and dwindled into insignificance when the need was greatest (*130*).

Although less spectacular than western steamboating the coastwise traffic became more important in the long run. New England shippers were most active in the trade. Alien vessels were first placed at a complete disadvantage by the tonnage duties of 1789 and in 1817 were completely excluded by a congressional act. By 1831 the tonnage of vessels in the coasting trade had already exceeded that in American foreign commerce; by 1860 the value of commodities carried in this traffic was six times that of foreign exports. This expansion was due to two factors: (1) Economic specialization and (2) the rise of New York as the leading port. The Northeast became an industrial region supplying the domestic market with manufactured products and receiving in turn food supplies and raw materials, while the Northwest became the granary of the Nation. The pivot of this trade, however, was southern cotton. It was carried to the North to be exchanged for clothes, tools and machinery, furniture, or shoes, or to be reexported from New York to Europe; indeed by 1850 only New Orleans and Mobile ranked above New York in the export of cotton. The coastwise trade in 1852 was valued at over $2,500,000,000, far exceeding that carried by canals, railroads, or western steamboats (*114*).

Steam power was soon applied to the American overseas trade. Its practicability having been proved during the 1830's the Cunard Line from Liverpool to New York was established at the beginning of the next decade. The Federal Government encouraged the organization of American steamship lines by granting subsidies for carrying the mails that were far in excess of the actual cost involved. This system was continued from 1845 to 1858, and under it during this period a total of $14,500,000 was paid out. A competitor of the steamship from 1843 to the Civil War was the clipper ship, with its superior speed and cheaper building and operating costs. Further development of the steamship in transoceanic traffic had to wait upon the era of cheap steel construction.

The movement for artificial waterways or canals arose in part as a response to the successful introduction of steam navigation. From the viewpoint of the seaboard regions, anxious to secure the increasingly important western trade, the problem was to combine steamships with east-west water routes since the great rivers ran in a north-south direction. Despite the improved roads, overland trade was still too slow and too expensive. Meanwhile the West was increasing in population and agricultural production, and the Mississippi River traffic failed to provide an adequate market for its produce or a satisfactory source of manufactured commodities. The further growth of eastern industrialism and western agriculture alike was contingent on adequate interstate transportation facilities.

The building of the Erie Canal marked the opening of the new era, although local canals had been constructed in Virginia and North Carolina before 1800. The idea of a canal connecting the Hudson River and the Great Lakes had occurred to Gouverneur Morris as early as 1777. It was Gov. DeWitt Clinton, however, who finally persuaded the New York Legislature to appropriate the necessary funds in 1817. In addition to the Erie Canal, New York undertook at the same time to build a waterway to Lake Champlain; these were tremendous financial ventures for a State with a population of less than a million and a half. The untiring zeal of DeWitt Clinton was rewarded when the Erie Canal reached its western terminus at Buffalo in 1825. "Clinton's ditch," as it had been derisively nicknamed, extended 363 miles and, together with the Champlain Canal, cost over $10,000,000 (*115*).

Within nine years the cost of building the Erie Canal was paid by the tolls alone; eventually, before these charges were abolished in 1882, more than $120,000,000 was collected. What the canal meant to the northwestern farmer is indicated by the fact that where previously it had cost $100 and taken 20 days to ship a ton of freight overland from Buffalo to New York, now the rate was only $15 a ton, and the time was cut to 8 days. The value of farm produce in western New York doubled, and there was a corresponding increase in the Northwest—with a resultant rise in land values. New cities sprang up overnight in the region of the canal; Utica, Syracuse, and Rochester became large centers. New York City rapidly became the foremost American seaport, its population increasing about 60 percent between 1820 and 1830. Of infinite consequence for the development of the United States was the tie thus knotted between the Northeast and the Northwest.

The example of New York stimulated rival seaboard States to make their bid for western commerce. Pennsylvania was the first. By 1834 this State had completed an elaborate combination of artificial waterways and horse railroads; its 954 miles of canals were the most extensive system in the United States. Though far behind the Erie Canal in volume of trade, the Pennsylvania Canal was the most important route from the upper Ohio to the East. Close to 200 packets and freighters carried produce and passengers on it and the trade between Pittsburgh and Philadelphia in flour, meat products, wool, and tobacco doubled in value.

In the South, Virginia and Maryland undertook canal construction, but with less success. Baltimore sponsored the Chesapeake & Ohio Canal, which terminated at Cumberland, in 1850; the Federal Government contributed a million dollars to this project—one of the very few grants it made in aid of State canals. Though this waterway was useful, the Baltimore & Ohio Railroad soon superseded it in importance. Richmond merchants, also anxious for the western trade, started in 1835 a canal which reached the headwaters of the James River two decades later.

In the Old Northwest to secure the greatest advantage from the

Erie Canal a series of feeder canals was necessary to supplement the rivers flowing toward the Great Lakes. Ohio became the leader, its canal system being outranked only by those of Pennsylvania and New York. Indiana, Illinois, and even sparsely settled Michigan followed suit. The availability of the eastern market led to extended production, quickened westward migration, and increased land cultivation. No longer was the Northwest dependent on a glutted New Orleans market. Western wheat began to feed not only industrial America but England as well.

The costs of internal improvements were staggering, particularly for the less developed States on the frontier.

Private investors in the East and in England subscribed to State securities, and Congress also was induced to contribute. From the public domain alternate sections 5 miles wide on each side of projected canals were granted Indiana, Illinois, and Ohio. To allay opposition, it was argued that the reserved sections would so rise in value as to compensate for the land given gratis.

Expenditures for internal improvements were excessive, and the panic of 1837 pricked the speculative bubble. At least six States were obliged to repudiate part of their debts, while many others stopped interest payments for years. A committee of British bondholders was formed and attempted to induce Daniel Webster to act as its collection agent. Nearly all the States sold their interests to private concerns and retired from the field. It became part of the American credo that a public utility could not be built and operated successfully except by private enterprise. That the State governments should withdraw at this particular juncture—on the eve of railroad development—was of the utmost consequence.

Railroads appeared on the scene to challenge the supremacy of canals just as the latter mode of transportation reached its highest point of usefulness. Being faster and available for year-round use, railroads were soon able to gain the upper hand. Railroad managers hastened the conquest by rate cutting and the purchase and closure of competing canals. The rise in our own time of motor transportation as a rival of the railroads has a touch of poetic justice. Interest in canals has also reawakened recently—witness the Great Lakes-St. Lawrence Waterway project favored by the present administration. Canal transportation is cheaper for heavy freight, and it is maintained that slower marketing may help to prevent glutting the market with agricultural produce.

As the Lancaster Turnpike opened the turnpike era and the Erie Canal began artificial-waterway construction, so the Baltimore & Ohio Railroad ushered in the railroad age in 1828. By 1830 the B. & O. boasted 11 miles of rail, and in the same year the Mohawk & Hudson was begun from Albany to Schenectady. For draft power the railroads used horses and sails at first, but steam locomotives definitely proved their superiority when the "Best Friend of Charleston" attained a speed of 30 miles per hour traveling alone and 16 to 21 miles with four loaded cars. The next year, 1831, the "Tom Thumb" made the 13 miles between Baltimore and Ellicott's Mills in 1 hour, and the managers of the Baltimore & Ohio were converted to steam as a source of power.

On their first appearance railroads evoked considerable opposition. Farmers feared the loss of markets for their horses and hay as well as increased danger from fires along railway routes. Tavern keepers saw the undermining of their business, while military strategists insisted that railroads were inferior to canals for military transport. The superior speed of the railroads gave them easy control of passenger traffic, but commanding the far more important field of freight transportation was another matter. It was relatively easy in New England and the South, where the chief competitor was the carriage trade, but very difficult in the region of the Great Lakes and the Mississippi and near canals of the better type. Figures for 1852 suggest that the railroads at that time carried only one-seventh of the tonnage transported.

Until 1840 railroad building was confined to the seaboard, particularly within southern New England and eastern Maryland. The trans-Allegheny region had only a few miles of isolated railroads. No adequate railroad network was completed by 1850, when a tremendous spurt began. Within 10 years the mileage increased from 9,000 to 30,000 miles. The New York Central was consolidated in 1853; Chicago, by way of the Illinois Central, Michigan Southern, and Lake Shore routes, was brought in touch with New York; the Pennsylvania Railroad reached out to Pittsburgh; while in the South there were connecting railroads from Savannah and Charleston across the mountains to Chattanooga.

Once under way, railway construction increased rapidly, with ensuing consequences in sectional economic alignment. Cincinnati, which had previously depended on the river trade to New Orleans for transportation, in 1857, as a result of railroad connections, sent five times more wheat and corn to northern and eastern than to southern centers. Illinois, by 1860, surpassed Tennessee as the greatest corn State as a result of the opening of the prairie areas by the Illinois Central road. Both the flour-milling center and the stock-raising industry shifted westward. New York City kept growing, while New Orleans began to decline. As in the case of canals, the Northeast bound the Northwest to itself with rails of steel.

Before the break-down of State finances in 1837 the State governments made some gestures in the direction of aiding railroad building. In Massachusetts and Maryland private corporations were granted State assistance, while Michigan and Illinois undertook State construction. Even after the panic years Georgia built the Western and Atlantic, but in general the field was left in the hands of private capital.

The public authorities, however, did not withdraw completely after 1837. In 1838 all railroads were designated by Congress as post roads, while two years earlier maximum rates were fixed for the branch of the Baltimore & Ohio that passed through the District of Columbia. There were proposals to use the army to build a Government railroad to the Mississippi, and at various times Congress voted money for railroad surveys. The separate States, in granting railroad charters, wrote in clauses regulating maximum rates, holding the corporations liable for accidents, and reserving the right to purchase the railroads at a certain price after a given interval.

In the fifties Congress began a system of land grants in connection with railroads such as it had previously attempted with roads and canals (*95*). Illinois, Alabama, and Mississippi were granted alternate sections 6 miles wide on each side of projected routes. This procedure was far more cautious, however, than that which developed after the Civil War. The Illinois Central, for example, was to pay 7 percent of its gross earnings in return for the 2,500,000 acres it received, while the Federal Government doubled the price on the alternate sections that it had reserved to itself. It was not until the South was shorn of its power in Congress that virtual empires of land were given to the railroad magnates as subsidies. A memorial to Congress in 1847, lamenting the growth of railroad combinations and monopolies, and the price-fixing agreement of certain New York, Ohio, and Michigan roads in 1853 foreshadowed post-Civil War trends.

THE AGRICULTURAL REVOLUTION

During the last 100 years, the agriculture of the United States as well as the economic life generally has undergone changes so momentous in their ramifications and consequences that, taken together, they are frequently referred to as the agricultural revolution. In the words of a noted agricultural historian (*174*):

> Agriculture was transformed from a simple, pioneer, and largely self-sufficing occupation into a modern business organized on a scientific, capitalistic, and commercial basis; industry definitely underwent the change from hand labor in the home to machine production in the factory; and the local market was transformed into the world market. This threefold revolution in agriculture, industry, and commerce is the key to the study of the recent history of the United States.

Like all revolutions this vast reorientation of American economic life did not begin suddenly or in all parts of the country simultaneously. It has already been noted that even in the colonial period the activities of many American agricultural communities were directed toward the production of surplus crops for distribution in markets beyond the Atlantic. During the latter half of the eighteenth century the agriculture of England underwent a similar revolution (*153*), and the accompanying desire to utilize the findings of modern science in order to make farming profitable was not without influence among the leaders of the United States in the years immediately following the American Revolution (*195*). While the forces of the agricultural revolution had long been at work, it remained for the Civil War to hasten their fruition. The result was the evolution of a complex economic and social structure whose problems interlink with those of the entire world and challenge the intelligence of all mankind (*169*).

The forces underlying the American agricultural revolution may be epitomized as follows: (1) The passing of the public domain into private ownership by means of liberal land policies; (2) the completion of the westward movement of settlement; (3) the invention and popularization of improved farm implements and machinery; (4) the extension and development of transportation facilities; (5) the migration of industries from the farm to the factory; (6) the expansion of domestic and foreign markets; (7) the establishment of agencies for the promotion of scientific knowledge relating to agriculture—agricultural societies, agricultural fairs, periodicals for farmers, the Federal Department of Agriculture, and agricultural colleges and experiment stations; and (8) the resort to conscious and concerted political organization and action by farmers in an effort to retain an equitable place for agriculture in the economic structure of the Nation.

A concrete result of this agricultural revolution was a quickening of the tendency for certain agricultural crops and commodities to dominate in the regions naturally suited to their production. In its Yearbooks for 1921 through 1925 the Department of Agriculture provided a notable series of articles which include historical descriptions, both textual and graphic, of the westward movement and current location of the agricultural crops and products of the United States.

The remainder of this article, therefore, will be devoted largely to an analysis of the forces which, taken together, constituted the agricultural revolution. Space will not permit a discussion, however, of the development of agricultural societies (*13, 35, 36, 40, 135, 188, 189*), agricultural fairs (*7, 135, 161*), and the agricultural press (*18, 68, 69, 71, 81*). These important elements are briefly treated elsewhere in this volume (Old Ideals Versus New Ideas in Farm Life, p. 111).

Land Policy to 1918; a Perversion of Democratic Aims

On May 20, 1862, President Lincoln, a westerner, signed the Homestead Act. The Republican Party thus completed the bargain it had made in 1860 to insure western support. Under the act, 160 acres of the public domain was offered free to any person who was the head of a family or had reached his majority and who was an American citizen or had filed intentions of becoming one. After proving 5 years of residence or cultivation and paying a nominal registration fee, the homesteader received title. He might, however, by the commutation clause of the act purchase the land after only 6 months of residence, at the prevailing minimum price, usually $1.25 per acre. The required period of residence was raised to 14 months in 1891.

From the vantage ground of the present, the historian can easily see the faults of the homestead law. Its fundamental weakness, according to B. H. Hibbard (*101*), was its complete inadaptability to the region to which it applied. The principle of the small homestead was valid between the Ohio and Missouri Rivers and was reasonable even in Minnesota and the eastern parts of Nebraska, Kansas, and the Dakotas. By 1862, however, these areas were already occupied, and the great bulk of the lands open to homesteading lay west of the 100th meridian, from the Great Plains to the Pacific coast. The average rainfall over most of this region ranges from 10 to 18 inches, falling nuch lower during seasonal and cyclical dry spells. Traditional farming techniques based on the humid soils of the East were unsuitable for these new conditions. Effective land utilization required dry farming, grazing, or intensive cultivation with natural or artificial irrigation. But 160 acres was too much land for irrigated farming, while for dry farming or grazing it was too little.

In addition to being out of touch with the realities of soil and climate, the Homestead Act did not jibe with other land legislation. This idea has been carefully developed by Paul Wallace Gates in his essay, The Homestead Law in an Incongruous Land System (*87*).

He points out that the Government continued the cash sale of land until 1891 and that more land was sold than was homesteaded. Altogether about 100 million acres of Federal lands were on the block. Another 125 million were granted to railroads between 1862 and 1871, with the proviso that homesteaders were to move at least 20 to 40 miles back from projected routes. Rather than suffer from inadequate transportation facilities, many settlers preferred to pay $400 or more for a quarter section. By the Dawes Act of 1887, modified by the Burke Act of 1906 and subsequent measures, some 100 million acres of Indian lands were also opened for sale. Many millions of acres more were turned over to the States to finance colleges according to the Land Grant College Act of 1862.

With such a vast empire purchasable, speculation and land monopolization were in order. Syndicates of foreign or domestic origin purchased in blocks of 100,000 acres or more and generally secured the most desirable lands. Actual settlers were left to take their chances with the free lands, often less fertile or less advantageously located, or to buy at prices set by the speculators, the railroads, or the States. This result was altogether contrary to the expectations of the democratic forces that had fought for free homesteads for 35 years.

Even less satisfactory than the land enactments themselves was their administration. Fraudulent entries were common occurrences. People were regularly employed to file claims which could be turned over to land, timber, or mining companies. Equally flagrant was the practice of staking claims for nonexistent individuals. When land was purchased in large blocks, almost invariably the transaction was accompanied by a measure of graft. The General Land Office, which supervised disposal of the public domain, did not have the organization, the personnel, or the backing to insure careful and honest administration—even if it had had a desire to do so (*65*). So long as rich prizes were in the offing for laxity, and overscrupulousness brought official and public disapproval, the General Land Office was not likely to develop that desire.

Efforts to remedy abuses were slow and ineffectual. Loans were made from time to time to homesteaders affected by droughts and blights. After 1871 the Government ceased its grants to railroad and canal companies and took steps to recover land not actually needed for rights-of-way. Realizing the need for a local supply of lumber, fuel, and fence posts, an attempt was made by an act of 1873, later amended, to stimulate the planting of trees on western prairies. For covering 40 acres with timber, a person could claim the quarter section of which the 40 acres was a part. Unfortunately, to quote Hibbard, "The Timber-Culture Act was framed when there was still some government land in Iowa, a great deal in southwestern Minnesota, and immediately to the west of the Missouri River. But by the time a few years had passed and the Timber-Culture Act got well under way its operation was crowded into the plains and into the semi-arid regions, where it would have been both impossible and undesirable to bring the trees along to the stage required by the government. . . . It was one of the most complete failures, so far as accomplishing what Congress had in mind is concerned, to be recorded in the long list of unfortunate public land acts" (*101; see especially pp. 421–422*).

That a tract of 160 acres was useless in arid regions was quite obvious to anyone who knew the West. President Grant, after visiting the Mountain States in 1875, suggested to Congress that it appoint a commission actually to visit the land and make recommendations based on a first-hand study. Two years later the Desert Land Act was signed. This act offered a 640-acre section at $1.25 per acre to anyone who would irrigate within 3 years. Almost immediately the Land Office began a campaign for the repeal of the measure. The provision for irrigation was vague since it did not specify how much water was to be conducted to the land. On the other hand, effective irrigation farming required considerably more capital than most settlers could command. As it operated, the Desert Land Act of 1877 chiefly benefited the grazing interests and irrigation companies, which engrossed many thousands of acres (*85*).

In 1878 two measures were put into effect for the disposal of public timber and timberlands. By the Timber Cutting Act citizens of specified States and Territories were authorized to cut down trees on the mineral lands of the public domain for mining and agricultural or domestic purposes without charge. However worthy its intent, the measure in effect was a bounty to grasping mill owners and lumber companies.

Even more harmful to the public interest was the Timber and Stone Act which provided for the sale, at $2.50 an acre, of quarter sections of land unsuited for agriculture but valuable for timber. According to reports of the Land Office and the Secretary of the Interior, the act operated to transfer the public timberlands almost directly to large corporations and speculators. Over 13 million acres of the national heritage was thus lost.

The establishment in 1879 of the United States Geological Survey to classify the public resources was a progressive step. Unfortunately a commission created under the same act recommended that the General Land Office be vested with the final responsibility for classification. The work of the Geological Survey until 1906 was confined largely to the preparation of topographical and geological maps and reports.

In 1887–91, under President Cleveland—zealous crusader for honesty in politics—a halt was called to the more flagrant abuses of land administration. When, as a result, the number of claims allowed dropped off, interested groups protested and the trend was reversed in the next administration.

More significant for the future was the attempt made by Congress in 1891 to reform its land policy by the passage of an omnibus bill (*198*). The measure began by repealing the Timber Cutting Act. Next, it specified that a definite plan for irrigation must be presented whenever land was taken up under the Desert Land Office and that at least $3 per acre must be spent for improvements. The Preemption Act, on the statute books since 1841, was repealed, and the policy of selling the public domain, except timber, mineral, and other special lands, was abandoned. Section 24, authorizing the President to set aside forest lands as public reservations, foreshadowed another era.

Toward the close of the century critics became more vehement in attacking laissez faire ideas. Proclaiming new concepts of social control, these progressives helped pave the way for public regulation of railroad practices and the attempted suppression of monopolies. From the same general source came the attack on a land policy that permitted, if it did not actually encourage, the reckless squandering of basic national resources.

As a result of such pressure the movement for conservation got under way. In 1876 the Department of Agriculture was authorized to investigate the country's forest resources and by 1905 the work had evolved into the Forest Service. To its care were entrusted the national forest reserves which Presidents Harrison and Cleveland, acting under the statute of 1891, had already expanded to include almost 40 million acres. An experiment in reclamation was also undertaken; through the Carey Act of 1894 the Federal Government sought to enlist State aid in the settlement and irrigation of arid lands by offering to turn over a maximum of a million acres to each of certain States.

After 1900 the trend toward reform in land policy and administration, as in other phases of national life, became more marked. Theodore Roosevelt assumed leadership and with his dramatic flair impressed the country with the urgent need for a well-rounded program of conservation and reclamation. The Carey Act having proved unsatisfactory, direct Federal activity in promoting irrigation was required by the Reclamation Act of 1902. The money received from land sales was to be set aside as a reclamation fund for developing irrigation projects, the costs of which were to be repaid by the settlers in the ensuing decade. Although the principle of Federal supervision was sound and many desert areas were converted into flourishing farm lands, the measure was not entirely satisfactory and had to be modified repeatedly (*85*).

The first decisive step in protecting the Nation's mineral resources was taken in 1906 when President Roosevelt directed the Secretary of the Interior to withdraw from entry all valuable coal lands. A hardship arose from the fact that mineral lands were often good agricultural areas on the surface. In an effort to serve two purposes, Congress, by acts of 1909 and 1910, authorized agricultural entry for surface rights only, reserving to the Government all mineral rights. Subsurface wealth thus saved to the Nation included not only coal, but iron, phosphate, potash, copper, and other vital resources. The leasing of these deposits to private individuals was permitted under carefully prescribed regulations by laws of 1914, 1917, and 1920.

President Roosevelt added 148 million acres to the public timberland reserves. Systematic efforts to prevent forest fires and to retimber cut-over tracts were undertaken by the Forest Service under Gifford Pinchot. State cooperation was enlisted at a conference of Governors called by the President in 1908, and within 18 months 41 State conservation commissions were appointed and in active operation. The area set aside for national parks under a policy begun in 1872 with the creation of Yellowstone National Park was greatly enlarged.

Under President Taft, the conservation program continued its progress. An act of 1910 facilitated the withdrawal of water-power sites from entry. The following year Congress arranged for the purchase of forest lands near the headwaters of navigable streams in the White

Mountains and the southern Appalachians. Even the intensely bitter Ballinger-Pinchot dispute was from one point of view an encouraging sign. It indicated that public opinion could be aroused to a high pitch of indignation against alleged mishandling of the public wealth (*107*).

Contrary to general opinion, more land was homesteaded in the decades after 1900 than in those preceding. The frontier as a continuous line of settlement came to an end in 1890, as every student since Frederick Jackson Turner has been made aware, but vast tracts of scattered public lands of inferior quality still remained open. To facilitate their settlement Congress tried further modifications of the Homestead Act. In 1904 the Kinkaid Act permitted the granting of 640-acre homesteads in western Nebraska, and 5 years later the Enlarged Homestead Act was passed, making it possible to take 320 acres as a homestead in a number of other States and Territories. The requirement of 5 years of residence prior to issuance of title was cut down to 3 years in 1912. Finally, by the Stock-Raising Homestead Act of 1916, land classified as good only for grazing or forage was to be parceled out in homesteads with a maximum of 640 acres.

The existence of free lands was, according to Turner, the most momentous single factor in the shaping of peculiarly American institutions (*192*). Without subscribing to all the deduced ramifications of that thesis, one may agree that the end of the frontier era closed a significant chapter in the country's history. City laborers may not actually have migrated to western farms to escape industrial exploitation, as the "safety-valve" theory insists, but at least they had shared with other Americans the psychological comfort of looking toward an expanding and seemingly unlimited horizon. Now there was to be no escape to the wilderness or beyond the hills, no endless temporizing with basic social and economic problems. America was obliged to grow up.

Under a wiser and better-administered land system many of the pains of social maturing might have been avoided. It is conceivable, for example, that scientific land planning actually might have achieved the ideal which underlay the conception of the Homestead Act—a wide diffusion of wealth and the creation of a large class of independent proprietors. Instead, 37 percent of the American farmers were already counted as tenants by 1910, and that proportion was to increase in succeeding decades. By holding off land from the market and moderating the rapidity of settlement an equilibrium might have been established and maintained between industrial and agricultural growth and some of the fundamental ills of American agriculture might have been avoided. At least such lands as were not suited to farming should have been closed to cultivation, and programs to combat erosion and floods should have been initiated. The Nation's resources in timber and minerals, had they been better safeguarded, would have increased the social wealth of succeeding generations.

Such reasoning, however, takes no account of prevailing conditions and concepts. It was practically impossible to have foretold in 1860 that within 30 years a half billion acres of the public domain would have been disposed of or reserved for governmental purposes. The land was considered valueless unless it was put under cultivation as rapidly as possible, and the various land acts did help to people the wilderness. To have opposed unregulated settlement would have been considered either a mad perversion or a reflection of some selfish economic interest endangered by western competition. It was not only the lumber and mining companies and the land speculators that demanded a free hand; the mass of the American people, particularly those who looked westward, kept shouting for land and more land. The United States in the generation before 1900 was probably not ripe for any further measures of social control, even though large-scale industry had arisen and shown the value of central planning.

Completion of Westward Movement

By 1850 the westward-moving frontier of settlement had halted at the edge of the Great Plains, owing to the Indian policy inaugurated a generation before and to the fact that the unoccupied region presented a challenge to the accepted methods of agricultural conquest (*206*). It is true that there were already isolated islands of settlement in California, the Willamette Valley, and Utah. Within 40 years the entire territory of the trans-Missouri West was occupied and began to add to the surpluses of agricultural products and to serve as a growing market for manufactured goods (*47, pp. 403–625; 143; 154, ch. 17–42*).

The settlement of the territory extending from the Missouri River to the Pacific Ocean may be resolved into five stages of development. (1) For a time, the region served merely as a roadway to the gold of California and the fertile lands of Oregon. (2) The miners, stimulated to seek new opportunities, turned to the unoccupied valleys and mountain ranges. Their rush into the region of Colorado laid the basis for permanent settlement there. The occupation of Nevada, Arizona, New Mexico, western Montana, Idaho, and eastern Washington followed during the decade of the Civil War. The need of food supplies for the mining camps prompted the beginning of agriculture in the valleys (*53, 213*). (3) The completion of the Union Pacific Railroad in 1869, inaugurated 5 years before as a means of strengthening the bond between the Pacific coast and the North, brought in a flood of hunters who exterminated the buffalo and thus facilitated occupation of the Plains by the range-cattle industry. The success of the Union Pacific encouraged the building of four other similar lines. Thus, the trans-Mississippi West, as contrasted with the East, had facilities for rapid transportation prior to, rather than after, intensive settlement and exploitation (*142*). (4) During the two decades following the close of the Civil War, the Great Plains became the scene of the range-cattle industry, which contributed immeasurably to the romance, color, and folklore of the West (*58, 140, 144*). The railroads made possible the development of this industry; they also brought in homesteaders and other land seekers who disrupted the range and forced the cattlemen to shift to a ranch basis (*59*). (5) Farmers from the East, taking land in accordance with the Homestead Act or buying it from the railroads which had received large grants as subsidies, undertook to occupy the Great Plains and the valleys to the westward (*32, 62*). The fact that much of this land received less than 20 inches of rainfall a year foredoomed the transplanting of eastern ways of agriculture and necessitated the development of new methods and crops (*108, 127, 168*).

Irrigation and dry farming became important in America for the first time, and many problems were passed on to the post-World War generation (*122*, *123*).

Three factors affecting agriculture that accompanied the completion of the westward movement should also be mentioned: (1) The growth of population in that part of the United States settled prior to 1850; (2) the rapid growth of urbanization; and (3) immigration from Europe.

The population of continental United States numbered 23,191,876 in 1850 and 62,947,714 in 1890. By 1920 it had passed the hundred-million mark, totaling 105,710,620. That is to say, the population increased by two and one-half times in 40 years and by four and one-half times in 70 years. Immigration supplied 31,406,943 from 1850 to 1920. Reduced to simple terms, this increase in population meant more farm surpluses; but it also created a greatly expanded home market for agricultural products.

The population of the United States continued to be predominantly rural to the end of the period under review, but the rapid increase and ultimate triumph of urbanization predestined the future of the United States to a quite different social and economic configuration (*171*). The census of 1880 showed that the rural population, including towns and villages with less than 2,500 inhabitants, numbered 35,797,616, or 71.4 percent of the total population. This was more than the population of the entire country in 1860. By 1910 the rural population numbered 49,806,146, which was 54.2 percent of the total. By 1920, however, the census showed that the majority of the American people lived in towns and cities—48.6 percent being classified as rural and 51.4 as urban.

American Agriculture Becomes Mechanized

Through countless centuries agriculture was carried on by hand labor, with only a few simple tools supplemented to a slight extent by animal power (*25*, *pp. 34–37*). This basic pattern continued practically unchanged down to 1830.

In the decades from 1830 to 1860 were crowded inventions and improvements that revolutionized agricultural development (*25*, *pp. 207–216*, *281–305*). After this period food scarcity and famines were no longer accepted as inevitable. Farmers could harness machinery and step up production to the point delimited in capitalistic economy by "effective market demand," or less technically, by the ability of people to buy. The American farmer acquired the power not only to bring forth an abundance of food for every man, woman, and child in the United States but also to contribute to a world surplus.[8] How much of the increased production may be attributed to machinery and how much to the larger acreage under cultivation—though even in that machinery was a causal influence—better methods of cultivation, the use of fertilizers, better seeds, crop rotation, and other factors, it is difficult to determine. The availability of mechanical power was certainly of crucial importance when labor was scarce and land abundant, and it has had a continuing effect on the lowering of prices of farm products by cutting costs of production.

[8] TOLLEY, H. R., and BRODELL, A. P. THE ROLE OF MACHINERY IN THE DEVELOPMENT OF THE AGRICULTURE OF THE UNITED STATES. 11 pp. U. S. Bur. Agr. Econ. 1930. [Mimeographed.]

Probably the most significant single invention introduced in the period from 1830 to 1860 was the mechanical reaper (*74*). Driven by animal power, it displaced many hands at that crucial point in grain production when the work must be completed quickly to save the crop from ruin. The cradle, in general use after 1800, was a great improvement over the sickle, but it was still a hand tool. Many minds in Europe and America worked to perfect a reaper, and more than 50 different models were brought out between 1786 and 1831, when Cyrus McCormick completed his first machine (*132*). Obed Hussey and McCormick patented reapers in 1833 and 1834, respectively (*105*). Within 10 years, during which several improvements were made, McCormick only sold approximately 80 machines and was in a fair way to being outstripped by his rival, Hussey. McCormick, however, had the foresight to move West, seeing a limitless market in the vast, fertile prairies. In 1847 he established his own factory in Chicago and by 1851 was turning out a thousand reapers a year. His profits 6 years later mounted to over a million and a quarter dollars, while Hussey sold out in 1858 for a mere $200,000.

Although the early reaper was crude, it cut by one-third the cost of harvesting. At a trial held in Geneva, N. Y., in 1852, it required 14 men with cradles to do the work of 9 men with a reaper. Of the 9 men, only 2 were needed for the machine and 7 to rake and bind the grain (*160*). When mechanical raker and binder attachments further displaced manpower, the net saving in cost increased two-thirds or more.

Between 1830 and 1860 the plow advanced from the iron to the steel stage. Prior to Jethro Wood's day, the plow in common use was a cumbersome wooden contrivance. In 1814 Wood patented a cast-iron model, and at his death 20 years later farmers had overcome their fear of soil poisoning and thousands were using iron plows.

The iron shares, however, did not scour in the rich, sticky, and heavily root-matted soils of the prairies of the Middle West. In an effort to overcome this, two blacksmiths, John Lane and John Deere, working independently, substituted steel for iron shares (*48*). Lane did not realize the importance of his discovery, but Deere soon moved to Moline, Ill., and began large-scale production. His annual output had reached 10,000 plows by 1857. Although the problem of an adequate and cheap supply of good steel was still unsolved and the East clung to the less expensive iron plow, the contribution of Deere made possible the successful cultivation of the prairies.[9]

Jethro Tull, an early English agricultural reformer, had invented a modern seed drill before the middle of the eighteenth century, but American farmers were still sowing wheat broadcast almost a century later (*11*). In 1799 an American, Eliakim Spooner, patented a mechanical corn planter, but it received very little attention. Not until the 1840's was the manufacture of grain drills begun in this country by William Pennock. By 1860 the wheat drill was in general use in the Middle Atlantic States but it did not become common in the prairie regions until the early seventies. Horse-drawn corn drills also became popular during this time; most noted were the Billings drill, which

[9] Church, Lillian, compiler. history of the plow. U. S. Dept. Agr., Bur. Agr. Engin. Inform. Ser. 48, 16 pp., illus. 1935. [Mimeographed.]

sowed fertilizer with the corn, and the Brown machine, which planted two rows at a time. Mechanical drills combined the two operations of sowing and covering with soil and made for more certain and larger yields.[10]

A few threshing machines of English or Scottish design were imported soon after 1800, but they were easily broken and few persons knew how to repair them. A number of American models were on the market by 1820, but they met with comparatively little success. In the thirties the demand for small inexpensive machines became so great that over 700 different models were being advertised. The Pitts thresher, which successfully combined threshing, separating, and winnowing, marked a turning point, but not until the late forties was it used in the leading wheat fields. After 1850 most of the grain in the prairie regions seems to have been threshed by itinerant machines which could prepare over 300 bushels of wheat for bagging in a single day.[11]

Though all these improved implements were extensively used by 1860, the Civil War was the decisive force in farm mechanization (*106*). The Union Government's mobilization of the largest army which any nation had brought together up to that time necessitated the withdrawal of a million farmers from agricultural production. The men and women left behind on the farms of the North and West had to turn to the new machinery, particularly reapers and threshers, and their success in producing a greater wheat crop than during peacetime proved the utility of the labor-saving devices. By the close of the war, farm machinery had become a necessity for farmers engaged in commercialized agriculture.

The second stage of development, roughly from 1860 to 1910, was marked by the general displacement of men by horses as the motive power for agricultural implements. Horses had already been used before 1860 to provide the motive power for the plow, the grain drill, the hay mower and rake, the reaper, and the thresher. As these implements came into more general use, the number of horses used as draft animals increased correspondingly.

In addition, the new or improved machines marketed in succeeding decades all required horsepower. Among the more prominent of these innovations was the Marsh harvester, patented in 1858, which not only reaped the grain mechanically but delivered it on a table to be bound. Even more important was the invention in 1878 by John F. Appleby of a twine binder. According to Carver (*41*), this machine more than any other made possible increased production of grain by stepping up the speed of harvesting. By 1880, according to the census of that year, about four-fifths of all the wheat grown in the United States was cut by machine.

Improved machines for planting and cultivating were similarly horse-drawn. The sulky and the gang plow were extensively used by 1880 in the wheat-growing regions of the Pacific coast and in the Red River Valley. The spring-tooth harrow was patented in 1877, and

---

[10] CHURCH, LILLIAN, compiler. HISTORY OF GRAIN DRILLS. U. S. Dept. Agr., Bur. Agr. Engin. Inform. Ser. 70, 9 pp., illus. 1935. [Mimeographed.]

[11] CHURCH, LILLIAN, compiler. PARTIAL HISTORY OF THE DEVELOPMENT OF GRAIN THRESHING IMPLEMENTS AND MACHINES. U. S. Dept. Agr.. Bur. Agr. Engin. Inform. Ser. 73, 40 pp., illus. 1939. [Mimeographed.] See also (*160*).

soon there was a growing demand for it in the Eastern and Central States, while after 1892 the disk harrow became popular in the West. The lister, which simultaneously plows and plants the seed in two opposite furrows, was a special device introduced after 1880 for making corn growing possible in the semiarid regions. Mechanical harvesting of corn also replaced hand labor, and in the last decade of the nineteenth century A. S. Peck patented a corn binder.

Although the production of wheat and other small grains, corn and hay benefited most from mechanization, other agricultural products were also affected to a lesser degree. The cotton-seed planter, fertilizer distributor, cotton-stalk cutter, and various specialized types of plows and harrows were introduced in the Cotton Belt. The cotton gin was greatly improved, and the development of a cotton-picking machine was begun. Between 1850 and 1875, dairying too underwent mechanization, and by 1910 centrifugal cream separators and testers, improved churns, and other dairy apparatus had resulted in the transfer of cheese and butter making from the farm to factories.

Just prior to the outbreak of the first World War farm equipment entered still another stage of development, with the substitution of mechanical power for horse power (*15*). Steam engines were first tried, but they were not altogether satisfactory because of their weight and the difficulty of providing fuel and water. About 1905 the gasoline tractor was introduced, and in efficiency, durability, and suitability for the required operations it proved superior to steam.

The tractor was most effective in wheat farming. During the eighties the revolutionary harvester-thresher, or combine, was first tried in the wheat fields of California. The huge machine pulled by 20 to 40 horses completed all the operations from reaping through bagging the wheat and had a daily average capacity of 25 to 45 acres. The combine drawn by steam tractor, which appeared in the nineties, had an even greater average capacity, being propelled at a higher speed than the normal gait of work horses. Both the horse combine and the steam combine were tried in the North Central States, but the demand there was for a smaller and lighter machine. The improved gasoline tractor eventually made possible a redesigning of the combine, which, however, for most economical use still needed a 1,000-acre farm in 1920.

In corn growing, power farming has made plowing and cultivation speedier and less expensive. Whereas a man with a two-horse team could plow from 8 to 10 acres a day, with a tractor and 4-row cultivator he could cover 60 to 65 acres. The horse-drawn corn picker, introduced before 1910, was replaced by a tractor-driven machine. Gasoline power was utilized also for the corn binder and silo filler.

Farm machinery has been used in the United States far more than in any other country, but even here its specific effects cannot be delineated too clearly because of the complexity of the factors involved. Although not the only cause, it has certainly aided the American farmer to achieve the highest production per man (*160*). On the other hand, the widespread use of farm machinery probably postponed the shift from extensive to intensive cultivation, and on a per-acre production basis the American farmer ranked below his European competitor.

Mechanization put a premium on large-scale farming, with the economies incident to such operations (*8*). There was a geographic shift also to lands of relatively level topography and low rainfall. While these conditions were fulfilled in the western part of the United States, they also prevailed in Canada, Australia, and Argentina.

Transportation for the Products of the Farm

The development of domestic transportation facilities from the fifties to the World War centered almost exclusively about the expansion of the railroad industry. In 1860 the United States had 30,000 miles of railroad confined largely to the Northeast; by 1920 the country boasted a network of 253,000 miles covering every section, with some seven separate lines joining the Atlantic and Pacific coasts. The railroad mileage of the United States in 1910 exceeded that of all Europe and represented more than a third of the world's total. While the country's population was increasing three times, railway mileage expanded more than eightfold. In the face of this phenomenal growth the Mississippi River trade declined, and close to 2,000 miles of canals were abandoned by 1900. Waterways did not succumb without a struggle, as will be indicated later, and in certain phases, notably the Great Lakes traffic, enjoyed considerable prosperity. The railroads dominated the post-Civil War era and were interwoven in the political pattern almost as inextricably as in the economic (*75*).

As previously shown, after the panic of 1837 the Federal and State Governments determined to leave the financing and management of public utilities to private interests. They could not shake off responsibility entirely, however; railroads were too obviously and painfully a matter of public concern. The result was that, at least until the depression of 1873, local and State authorities vied with the Federal Government in pouring out lavish subsidies freely to private railroad construction companies. After that a reverse tendency set in and State governments sought to regulate and control railroads, a movement later taken up and extended by the Federal Government.

It is now generally agreed that without Government aid railroad expansion would not have been as great or as rapid. It was not, however, an unmixed blessing. During the 32 years following the initial grant to the Illinois Central in 1850, Congress and the General Land Office actually turned over 155 million acres of the public domain to railroad companies, an area equal to that of the New England States, Pennsylvania, and New York combined (*157*). The Union Pacific and Central Pacific Railroads received financial assistance, $16,000 to $48,000 having been awarded for each mile of railway constructed.

State and local subsidies were more varied; they included land grants, the right of eminent domain, exemption from taxation, loans, money grants, and assistance in floating securities. The railroad companies later defaulted on most of the money loaned, a privilege not extended by the United States Supreme Court to the local governments, which had to shoulder a debt totaling $300,000,000. Adding up these various governmental largesses, one historian concludes that three-fourths of the cost of railway construction was borne by public authorities (*94*).

The farmers had looked with favor on every type of aid given the railroads. They not only accepted the higher taxes necessitated by the local subsidies, but mortgaged their land and equipment to purchase railroad bonds. The railroads promised unbelievable prosperity; they had the power to open Nation-wide and even world-wide markets; they could bring in thousands of settlers to increase land values and create great centers of trade and wealth; they might join field and factory, country and city. It was a bright vision for farmers suffering from declining agricultural prices; that their extravagant hopes were never realized, at least not to the extent expected, they attributed to grasping, iniquitous railroad managers.

Indeed, the embattled agrarians could level and substantiate a host of charges against the railroads. Absentee management, watered stock, flimsy construction, high rates, pooling devices, discriminations between long and short hauls and between shippers and regions, dishonesty, corruption of State legislatures, and incivility—all evils which had been perpetrated by railroad managers—by no means exhausted the list of complaints. If managers attempted to defend themselves on the score that they were protecting the interests of stockholders, it could be pointed out that the inner powers, such as Jay Gould, Daniel Drew, Cornelius Vanderbilt, and their hundreds of imitators, manipulated stocks to their own enrichment; furthermore, the rates charged were based on an excessive capitalization. Competition occasionally brought rates down, but railroad pools removed even this boon. Assuredly the American people in their desire to meet their need for transportation facilities found themselves confronted with problems they had not anticipated. After many vicissitudes, it occurred to the more thoughtful that if railroad managers could band together so could farmers.

The Patrons of Husbandry, or as it is popularly known, the Grange, was founded in Washington, D. C., in 1867. It began as a secret society designed to break down the social isolation of farmers. By 1874 the order had 15,000 local branches and 1,500,000 members; it spread to every section of the country, but particularly to the Middle West. The farmers, having been brought together, naturally began to discuss their common problems, and from that point it was but a step to the launching of cooperatives and the formation of political groups and parties (*35*).

The farmers could not undertake the construction of railroads, so they turned to the Government, which according to democratic theory was their agent. They organized State and local tickets and from 1871 to 1874 elected hundreds of mayors, Governors, and Representatives. The result was the passage of the first mandatory railroad laws ever placed on American statute books. In Illinois, Iowa, Wisconsin, Minnesota, Missouri, Nebraska, and California railroad rates were regulated by legislation and constitutional amendment; pooling, free passes, rebates, and the long- and short-haul evil were prohibited, and enforcing commissions were established. Here again, as in the cooperatives, there was evident a lack of experience, railroad hostility, and increasing apathy as public pressure subsided. In addition, the Supreme Court, in the Wabash decision of 1886, reversed its previous liberal stand in the *Munn* v. *Illinois* ruling of 1876 and held that the

States had no right to regulate interstate commerce, even in lieu of congressional action.

Despite the fulminations of E. L. Godkin in the Nation and of other leading contemporary editors, the Grangers were not "wild-eyed communists" launching a war against private property. They were small-scale American farmers drawn into a new industrial-capitalistic society which they did not understand; but one fact they grasped intuitively—unless they fought to control this new order, it would enslave them and deprive them of their birthright as free Americans. The railroad monopoly was a symbol of the new oppression as well as their most immediate enemy, so the agrarians rose against it; but, as shown in later developments, the struggle was primarily for a society that had a place for the small farmer as well as the great capitalist.

The Granger movement, at least in its economic and political aspects, waned by 1880, but the tradition remained. In 1887, owing largely to western and southern pressure, the Interstate Commerce Act to subject railroads to Federal regulation was passed. When the measure was weakened by judicial decision, the same elements supported the Elkins Act of 1903, which provided for punishing the receiver as well as the giver of rebates, and the Hepburn Act of 1906, which empowered the Interstate Commerce Commission to initiate rates and force adherence, leaving to the carriers the burden of court action, and which also extended the Commission's jurisdiction over express- and sleeping-car companies, pipe lines, switches, spurs, tracks, and terminal facilities. The Mann-Elkins Act of 1910 empowered the Commission to suspend new rates for 10 months pending an investigation and set up a special commerce court to hear railroad cases.

These measures alleviated the worst features of the evil, but to the farmers' new way of thinking they did not solve the problem. In 1892, the People's or Populist Party inserted this plank in its national platform: "Transportation being a means of exchange and a public necessity, the Government should own and operate the railroads in the interests of the people" (*102*).

From the 1870's to the World War there was a progressive decline in railroad rates for both freight and passenger traffic. This was partly in response to legislative regulation, but the competition of railroads and the introduction of various improvements, such as steel rails and labor-saving devices for handling bulky commodities, were even more important factors. In 1880 the average cost of shipping a bushel of wheat from Chicago to New York was 20 cents; in 1910, it had fallen to 9½ cents. The average freight rate per ton-mile was $1.22 in 1883; by 1890 it declined to $0.93, and reached $0.75 in 1900. Passenger rates also decreased, but to a lesser extent.

The effect of these lowered rates was seen in the rapid development of the West. Railroads, anxious to increase transportation revenues and sell their land grants, became active colonizers, spreading propaganda and sending agents to the Eastern States and all over Europe. Glowing pictures were painted, and reduced transportation rates and liberal credit terms on land purchases were offered. The railroad, as Benjamin Harrison observed in 1884, replaced the pack train and Conestoga wagon as the chief vehicle of emigrants to the West. Between 1860 and 1900, the center of the

Nation's population moved from central Ohio to eastern Indiana.

By helping to populate the West and by offering lower freight rates and improved facilities, the railroads were a factor in establishing the Northwest and North Central States as the grain kingdom of the country. The invention of the refrigerator car also spurred the meat-packing industry. After 1869, pork packing was possible in the summer and fresh beef could be shipped freely in any season. The total value of the products in this industry grew from $29,000,000 in 1860 to $4,246,000,000 in 1919. Refrigeration transportation likewise aided the westward extension of the dairy and poultry industries.

With reduced rates and improved facilities, the railroads were able to divert almost completely the agricultural and other bulky commodity trade from the river and canal routes. The high-water mark of river transportation for the lower Mississippi came in 1880 when over a million tons were received and shipped at St. Louis, but this trade fell to 141,000 tons in 1905. The Federal Government attempted to improve river trade by appropriations which mounted to more than $12,000,000 by 1882. Unfortunately, pork-barrel grants were substituted for systematic planning; a Mississippi River Commission established in 1879 urged a flood-control program, but its appropriations were only for higher levees and consequently floods were all the more disastrous when they did occur. In 1899 Congress authorized the removal or remodeling of bridges obstructing navigable streams, but it was not until the War Department took over the project in 1917 that any progress was made. The creation, in 1902, of the Federal Board of Engineers for Rivers and Harbors as a planning and superintending agency marked a turning away from traditional pork-barrel methods. The chief salvation of river traffic, however, was the towboat business. Although barges moved very slowly, so many could be towed at one time that economies were effected in both time and cost.

Canals declined in transportation importance even more than rivers. By 1909, over half the mileage of canals had been abandoned. In an attempt to revive a dwindling trade, the Erie Canal was widened and deepened at a cost of about $200,000,000, but apparently the increase in traffic has not justified the outlay. Railroads are speedier; they are designed to handle large, bulky traffic; their many branch lines touch hundreds of points inaccessible to canals; and the cost of transshipment frequently outweighs the advantages of the lower canal rates.

In contrast with the river and canal traffic, trade on the Great Lakes showed a progressive increase. Despite railroad competition, it increased more than threefold between 1890 and 1910. These fresh-water seas provided a deep and continuous artery of trade for a thousand miles at rates lower than those of the railroads. Grain, lumber, and minerals were the chief commodities carried, and the passage at Sault Ste. Marie, in contrast to the plight of other canals, had become by 1900 the greatest internal waterway in the world, with five times as many ships as passed through the Suez Canal.

The coastwise trade suffered a noticeable decline in the face of railway competition. The opening of the Panama Canal in 1914 aided the water carriers somewhat, although the ship corporations engaged in the coastal trade were actually controlled for the most part by the railroads. Coal, lumber, cotton, and similar bulky commodities have long been the chief items of coastwise traffic.

Compared with the volume of domestic trade, foreign commerce was relatively insignificant, but for agricultural produce foreign markets were of considerable importance, particularly in the period before 1900 and during the World War.

The Migration of Industries From the Farm to the Factory

A distinctive feature of American farm life during the two and a half centuries following the settlement of Jamestown was economic self-sufficiency. Each farm produced practically everything that it consumed—food, clothing, furniture, soap, candles, and the many other articles essential to the farmer and his family (*190, 204*). The transfer of manufacturing from the farm to the factory is the most significant aspect of the transition from self-sufficient to commercial agriculture. It was, furthermore, the central fact of both the agricultural and industrial revolutions.

This migration of industries from the farm to the factory resulted in vast changes in the technical processes of manufacturing; in greatly increased market demands for agricultural commodities due to the growth of large urban centers; and in a tendency toward intensified specialization in agriculture.

The industries that have been transferred from the farm to the factory may be grouped as follows: (1) Food products; (2) textiles and clothing, including boots and shoes; and (3) tobacco and a number of minor products. The first group includes slaughtering and meat packing (*49*), flour milling (*116*), the manufacture of butter, cheese, and other dairy products (*9, 148*), and the canning of fruits and vegetables. Many new industries developed, notably the processing of beet sugar, the baking of bread and pastries, and the making of confections. In 1860 flour and grist mill products were worth $248,580,000 and ranked first among the food-manufacturing industries. In 1919 the initial place had been taken by the slaughtering and meat-packing industry, whose products were worth $4,246,291,000. The products of all food industries in 1919 were valued at $12,438,891,000 and constituted 20 percent of the total value of all American manufactured products.

The transfer of the textile, clothing, and shoe industries likewise has been significant. In 1820 more than two-thirds of the textiles were being produced in individual homes, but within a generation the balance had shifted to the factories in the rising industrial centers (*24*). The processing of tobacco experienced a similar though somewhat less rapid change (*109*).

American Agriculture Acquires New Markets at Home and Abroad (1865–1914)

Prior to 1850, the main emphasis on the southern cotton and tobacco plantations and to a lesser degree in the northeastern wool and fluid-milk industries was on raising a surplus for sale. By that time the same tendency was evident in western cereal and meat production; it was accentuated by the Civil War and brought to full development in the decades immediately following. From the Ohio and Mississippi Rivers to the Pacific coast, vast fertile farming areas were geared to surplus production, with results comparable only to the revolution in industry during the same period. Between 1860 and 1900, over 400 million acres were added to the farm domain, mostly in the trans-Mississippi West, while the income realized from agriculture increased from $3,000,000,000 in 1900 to $5,500,000,000 in 1910.

Many factors combined to produce this phenomenal growth: The application of machinery to agriculture; the free-homestead policy of the Federal Government; improved transportation facilities; a growing labor supply, due mainly to an influx of immigrants; and the utilization of science and industry. Of basic importance was the expansion of markets, both domestic and foreign. It is axiomatic that large-scale agriculture appears, in the first instance, only in response to demand; a farmer has no reason in a money economy for raising crops beyond his immediate family needs unless he can dispose of them profitably. Agriculture utilized machinery and science after the Civil War principally because the tremendous growth in the nonagricultural population created an unparalleled market for food and raw materials. All over the world, the industrial revolution concentrated in urban centers hundreds of millions who had to be fed and clothed, while the processes of manufacturing created a constant demand for cotton, wool, and other agricultural products. It was the good fortune of the western farmer to be particularly blessed with land, labor, machinery, and other resources to meet this need.

Of the farm products grown in the United States after 1860, cereals were by far the most important. In 1899 they constituted almost half of the total value of all crops raised in the country. From 1860 to 1915, the output of corn was increased from a little over 800 million to almost 3 billion bushels; wheat production in the same years rose from 173 million to more than 1 billion bushels (*172*, *194*). Cereal growing was centered in the Northwest and North Central States. Illinois and Indiana were the leading corn States. The substitution of rollers for stones in flour milling encouraged the growing of spring wheat in Minnesota and North Dakota, although by 1909 Kansas had passed Minnesota and was second only to North Dakota (*80*, *116*). The internal grain trade, in turn, was localized in the heart of the Wheat and Corn Belts, particularly in the cities on the Great Lakes and the rivers of the upper Mississippi Valley (*173*). Here sprang up the chief primary cereal warehouses where great supplies of grain and flour were concentrated in the first stage of shipment to the South and East for domestic use or for exportation. Foremost was Chicago, which in 1900 received 350 million bushels of grain and flour and shipped 266 million; Minneapolis was second with receipts of 107 million and shipments of 88 million bushels; other leading markets included St. Louis, Duluth-Superior, Milwaukee, and Toledo. From each of these points radiated a network of railways, which brought in the grain from the fields and then carried it away to the South, East, or West. After 1860 the bulk of trade was no longer confined to the east-and-west route over the Erie Canal, the trunk-line railroads, or the waters of the Mississippi (*114*).

Since freight rates on equal quantities of flour and wheat were about the same, it was found more profitable to transport the finished product than the raw material. As a result, the milling industry tended to be localized near the wheat fields. Minneapolis became the world's greatest milling center, with an annual output of more than 15 million barrels by the end of the century. Duluth-Superior, St. Louis, Milwaukee, Chicago, and Toledo were other major flour-milling cities, just as they were the leading markets for the grain trade.

The extension of railroads to western grazing lands and the rapid increase of corn production in the Mississippi Valley after 1860 spurred the livestock industry. Beef-cattle raising concentrated in the North Central, West-South-Central, and Mountain States; hog growing in the Corn Belt; and sheep raising in the Mountain States. Like the trade in grain, the domestic trade in livestock centered in cities that were within easy reach of the producing regions and at the same time had ready access to the consuming regions. To these primary markets the railroads carried thousands of carloads of cattle, hogs, and sheep to be slaughtered or reshipped to Eastern slaughter-houses.

Cincinnati was the chief meat-packing city prior to 1863, but after that Chicago assumed the lead (*49*). In 1914, Chicago handled almost one-fourth of the country's output, with Kansas City, New York, Indianapolis, and St. Louis following in that order. Pork was the packers' principal product, the dressed weight slaughtered annually exceeding 5 billion pounds; beef was second; and mutton and veal trailed behind. Until the perfection of chilling processes in the early seventies, meat shipped any distance was salted or pickled, and eastern cities depended on importations of live animals for their supplies of fresh meat. With the introduction of the refrigerator car, the trade in dressed beef and mutton grew rapidly in the Central States, and there was a decline in the east-bound shipments of live-stock. The higher railroad rates on livestock as compared with those on meat products further accentuated the change.

The influence of urban concentration was clearly visible in the growth of the dairy business (*9, 117*). Fresh milk had to be supplied each day, and the farmers nearest the great cities, such as New York, Philadelphia, and Chicago, monopolized this form of dairying. The crude home-production methods of butter and cheese making which had formerly prevailed could provide neither the quantity nor the quality of dairy products demanded by city dwellers. Consequently there was a shift to factory production, and by 1869 over a thousand cheese factories extended in a belt from New York to Iowa. In 1879, Wisconsin alone produced more than 19 million pounds of cheese, over eighteen times as much as the total home production in 1859.

At first it was believed that superior dairying was limited to a few scattered regions favored by soil and climate, but agricultural experiment stations proved that butter could be made wherever beef could be grown. Thus the dairy industry spread westward, the refrigerator car providing the necessary transportation facilities to eastern markets. By the end of the century, more than 800 million pounds of butter and over 133 million pounds of cheese were made in the North Central States, Iowa and Wisconsin leading; after 1900, Minnesota began to assume an important place in butter production (*70*). Poultry and eggs were also important items in urban diets, and incubators and cold storage enabled producers to meet market demands for them. The trade in these products was heaviest in the cities of the Corn Belt, from which over half the total output came. In 1901 Chicago received about 2,800,000 cases of eggs, half of which were shipped to eastern cities.

The cotton regions were in a desperate plight in 1865 (*210*). Not only had they suffered the ravages of war, but with the overthrow of slavery and the break-up of the plantation system, they faced the problem of reshaping their entire economy (*138, 219*). However, within 5 years, the Southern States were growing as much cotton as in 1860, and production kept increasing. In 1910 the output of the staple reached 11,609,000 bales as compared with 3,841,000 in 1860, a rise of more than 300 percent. The westward march of cotton is evidenced by the fact that by 1900 Texas was the leading State, with almost 7 million acres devoted to cotton culture and a crop almost equal in size to the total production of the South prior to the Civil War (*5, 66*).

Formerly the bulk of the cotton had been exported to feed English mills, but after the Civil War domestic textile manufacturing grew as rapidly as cotton production, and by 1899 over a third of the cotton crop was used in domestic mills. At first most of the cotton manufacturing was confined to the Northern States, but after 1885 the textile industry began to expand rapidly in the Cotton Belt itself. Southern leaders stressed the need for industrial diversification, and local communities and States offered every inducement to encourage the construction of cotton mills. In 1900, southern factories were consuming three-fourths as much cotton as those in the North, and by 1910, they had taken over the lead in domestic consumption.

Before the advent of the railroad, the cities where cotton was concentrated prior to shipment to seaports were located on navigable streams leading to the Gulf or Atlantic coast. Among the largest of these interior markets were Atlanta, Memphis, Shreveport, Vicksburg, Montgomery, Augusta, and Columbia. After the spread of the railway net into the Cotton Belt, not only were other inland cities able to share in the trade, but river ports themselves declined in importance unless they became railway centers. Houston, St. Louis, Memphis, and Augusta—the most important interior markets in 1898—were all focal points of railroads that passed through the most fertile portions of the Cotton Belt.

Railroads also helped New Orleans to regain its early preeminence as an exporting center, a position which it kept until 1899, when it was replaced by Galveston, the chief market of Texas. These two cities shipped about nine-tenths of the cotton exported through the Gulf of Mexico. On the Atlantic coast the chief ports were Savannah, Norfolk, and Charleston, in that order.

The overland all-rail movement of cotton which began about 1855 became increasingly important after the Civil War. Previously, all cotton shipped to the North was carried by coastwise vessels, but by 1900 the railroads had captured more than a third of the trade. A considerable quantity of the cotton purchased by Canada was sent to the border by rail, and toward the end of the century the growth of cotton exports to Japan stimulated heavy rail movements to the seaports of the Pacific coast.

Although grain, livestock, dairy products, and cotton were the chief commodities in the internal trade, many others were of importance. The production of wool was about five times as great in 1900 as in 1860; the sheep-raising industry shifted after 1880 largely to the Rocky Mountain States, from which wool was sent to the mills of New England, Pennsylvania, and New York.

An interesting trade development of this period was the eastward shipment of fruits from California. The first shipment was made in 1867, and by 1899 the trade amounted to 193 million pounds of fresh deciduous fruits, 95 percent of which was carried in refrigerator cars. During these years, the warmer Southern States also began sending fresh vegetables and fruits to northern cities the year round. Tobacco was another product in great demand in urban communities; Kentucky and North Carolina enjoyed most of the trade, with Louisville becoming the largest leaf-tobacco market in the country in 1865.

As was true of internal commerce, the export trade in agricultural commodities expanded tremendously up to the end of the nineteenth century. A chief item in the trade was grain. So phenomenal was the growth of western production that even during the Civil War, not only were northern armies and civilians fed, but some 138 million bushels of wheat were exported as compared with 39 million from 1856 to 1860. England was the principal market, a fact which has led many historians to the conclusion that western grain kept England neutral.

After the Civil War, the trend of grain exports was upward until the turn of the century. The peak year for corn exports came in 1897 with the shipment of 212 million bushels. Wheat and flour exports reached their maximum in 1901 when over 239 million bushels were shipped, yet only 31.4 percent of that year's crop was exported (*104*). Corn shipments in the peak year accounted for only 8.9 percent of that crop, all the rest being disposed of on the domestic market.

Exports of meat and meat products, which had been relatively insignificant before the Civil War, soon came to rank third in importance. Their value rose from approximately $37,000,000 in 1865 to over $116,000,000 in 1880, and over $179,000,000 in 1900. The packing industries produced more than the home market could readily absorb, and exportation was of considerable importance, particularly in the case of pork products. Refrigerated storage on ocean vessels provided proper transportation facilities.

The results of these huge cereal and meat imports on European social and economic life were of the most fundamental character. On the one hand, the laboring classes in cities were provided with cheap and abundant food. At the same time, however, European farmers, unless protected by tariff barriers, were unable to compete, and many were ruined by declining prices and falling land values (*186*). Great Britain was our chief market, and with free trade prevailing after the repeal of the corn laws in 1846, agriculture there suffered particularly. From 1878 to 1907 wheat acreage in England declined 50 percent. An attempt was made to shift to meat production, and for a time farmers in Great Britain, by concentrating on superior quality, withstood Texan competition, but American meat improved rapidly and even that advantage was soon lost. Continental countries that imported sizable quantities of American foodstuffs suffered similarly. The results were mirrored partly in the tremendous migration from Europe westward during the seventies and eighties, partly in the flocking of farmers to cities, and partly in the agrarian movements that sought relief in governmental policies. A frequently quoted comparison by an Austrian economist likened the effect wrought on European economy by the flow of American agricultural produce to the revolution attendant on the importation of American gold and silver after the discoveries of Columbus.

The peak of this development was reached by 1900; after that, the United States beaan to decline in importance as an exporter of foodstuffs. Fresh-beef shipments fell from 352 million pounds in 1901 to 6 million in 1914; bacon exports dropped from 650 million in 1898 to 194 million in 1913. Wheat averaged only about 80 million bushels annually from 1910 to 1912; while corn exports dropped below 11 million bushels in 1913. Butter and cheese products also dropped from the 79 million pounds exported in 1898 to only 6 million in 1913.

Many factors were responsible for this precipitous decline. European Governments, in an effort to aid their agricultural classes, raised duties and imposed embargoes on sanitary grounds, as in the case of hog products. Continental farmers themselves used more artificial fertilizers and improved the quality of their livestock. After the eighties, new agricultural regions were opened in Russia, Argentina, Australia, and Canada, and their produce began crowding American foodstuffs out of European markets.

At the same time that foreign markets were contracting, the domestic market was expanding. Industrial development in the United States caught up with the overstimulated agricultural development, and as urbanization increased, a larger share of the farm produce was consumed domestically. In 1899 the average number of wage earners in industry totaled 4,700,000; by 1909 it had increased to 6,600,000 (*139*).

The American farmer in turn began to adjust himself more effectively to market demands. The first exuberance of the frontier stage had passed and land values were rising, although there were still millions of acres of free land. There was a gradual trend toward increased sugar production and enlarged output of dairy and horticultural products, and more emphasis was placed on supplying cities with fresh milk and out-of-season fruits and vegetables. The results were highly gratifying to the farmer, for prices rose and his income increased. There was a relatively prosperous period for agriculture from 1900 to 1914, with supply and demand in effective equilibrium. The World War proved an extreme calamity for the American farmer; it induced tremendous overexpansion and renewed dependence on foreign markets.

In contrast to the decline in cereal and meat exports, the shipments of cotton abroad increased 1,584,000 bales between 1905 and 1914. Although India and Egypt appeared as competitors, the natural advantages of the American Cotton Belt gave this country a commanding position. Cotton once more became the chief item in our export trade, as it had been prior to the Civil War. Great Britain alone absorbed one-third of the crop, with Germany and France next in importance (*201*). Just before the outbreak of the World War, an important trade began to develop with Japan, with cotton being exchanged for silk.

Leaf-tobacco exports similarly increased, from over 300 million pounds in 1899 to almost 450 million in 1913. Between 1903 and 1912, one-third of the world's tobacco crop was produced in the United States; the four countries importing most of the American product were Great Britain, Germany, France, and Italy (*201*).

Prior to 1850 most American farmers, particularly those in the West, raised produce to be consumed on the farm or to be exchanged in part at local shops for sugar, salt, and similar articles. After 1850, and especially during and following the Civil War, agriculture, as previously outlined, became a commercialized industry in which farmers raised surplus crops to be sold for cash on national and international markets, depending on outside sources for clothing and in many cases even for food. This transformation created problems of a most complex character for American farmers. They were suddenly harnessed to a vast capitalistic process in which they strove, one with the other, to produce as much as possible at the lowest cost and to realize the largest possible income from the marketed surplus. Since machines were used in the competitive struggle, many farmers mortgaged their lands to buy them; but to pay for them more money was needed, so they ran the machines at full capacity to raise more crops. The larger the surpluses grew, however, the more prices sagged and the less were the relative profits.

New marketing agencies and devices appeared, the blessings of which farmers could not quite appreciate. In 1848, the Board of Trade was established in Chicago, and in 1870 and 1871 cotton exchanges were set up in Liverpool and New York. The farmers suspected that the prices received for their grain and cotton were in large measure determined arbitrarily by transactions at these centers. Moreover, they knew that market quotations were in turn affected by speculators who traded in futures; this was a new device by which speculators could bet on the sizes of forthcoming crops. The farmers were assured that this marketing process helped to establish standards and finance crop movements. They were skeptical, however, expecially when the dealers who purchased the crops in the first instance formed pooling associations to set a common price, while speculators sometimes deliberately manipulated market prices to their own advantage. The developing practice of grading and scoring farm produce was beneficial, if properly administered, but unfortunately the commission merchants and elevator directors were not always scrupulous. As already stated, railroads played an essential part in connecting the farmers with their markets; and railroad managers notoriously abused their power, by discriminating between shippers and sections, setting freight rates as high as the traffic would bear, and forming pools to avoid competition. Further, the more agriculture became commercialized, the more important was credit.

The farmers needed credit to purchase machinery, to make improvements, and to tide them over from one harvest to another, yet the few national banks that existed in rural areas were prohibited from loaning on mortgages. Although State banks, insurance companies, and individuals filled the gap to some extent, many farmers had to rely on loan sharks who charged interest rates of 15 to 25 percent. The crop-lien system, by which the local merchant took a mortgage on a farmer's crop in return for credit, strangled agriculture in the South. Finally, in purchasing their agricultural machinery the farmers found themselves confronted by large companies that kept prices high.

The farmer grew uneasy. He perceived that his produce fed the city hordes and that its exportation helped pay for foreign investments in American manufacturing, transportation, and mining. He was keenly aware of the wealth that was piling up in cities, for his wife and children were demanding the luxuries of city folks. He saw that railroad managers, grain-elevator owners, bankers and loan sharks, farm-machinery monopolists, commission men, and speculators were all flourishing, while he, on whom all these others depended, staggered under an increasing burden that was crushing him into tenancy and serfdom.

When he sought an avenue of escape, he was solemnly advised by economists that he must adjust his output to market demand. This reasoning may have been sound, but how was the farmer to achieve this end? Manufacturers, by combining into trusts or pools, could control prices and output, at least to some degree; they were able, by their corporate might, to squeeze special privileges from the middlemen, and they could, by pouring millions of dollars into advertising, even "educate" the tastes of the ultimate consumer. Similarly, though much less effectively, wage earners organized into unions to raise wages and improve working conditions; but how were farmers—millions of small isolated producers scattered throughout the country—to unite? Not only that, but prices of farm products were set on a world market, and after the eighties American farmers had to compete with millions of farmers in Russia, Argentina, Australia, and India.

However difficult the task of organization may have seemed, it had to be undertaken as the farmers' only method of defense against political and economic oppression. The entrance of agrarianism into the political arena via the Granger movement has already been mentioned. Economic cooperation was also a leading feature of the Grange. Whenever a local Grange was formed, one of the first steps taken was to initiate some form of cooperative buying and selling. Local agencies merged into county or district councils, and these in turn grew into State bodies. Unfortunately, the National Grange failed to take hold in the beginning and work out a comprehensive cooperative program, so that each State Grange was left to its own devices.

The methods used varied; the most general was to employ an agent who would market the farmers' produce most profitably and force the manufacturers to sell more cheaply. In Iowa, where cooperation first achieved marked success, 5 million bushels of grain and large numbers of cattle and hogs were shipped direct to Chicago through Grange agents, effecting a saving of 10 to 40 percent by the end of 1872. On the purchases of farm machinery alone, the State members were said to have saved $365,000. As an example of the difference between individual and cooperative buying, a reaper which had been retailing at $240 was sold to Granges at $140 (*35*).

Grange stores were also common. Stock companies, consisting solely of members of the Grange, were organized to provide the capital. These stores sold to Grangers at very low prices, and the profits, when there were any, were divided proportionally among the stockholders. This system did not work well, as neighboring merchants met the competition and diverted trade from the cooperative stores. More effective was the Rochdale plan, sponsored by the National Grange in 1875. Under this plan, stock was widely distributed in small shares, and savings were effected, not by selling at cost, but by dividing profits among the members according to their purchases. It met with particular success in Texas, where as late as 1887, when the Patrons of Husbandry was in eclipse in other parts of the South and West, there were 150 stores doing an annual business of almost $2,000,000. The Rochdale system was also applied in the Texan Cooperative Association, which handled shipments of cotton, and in the wholesale business in general. In 1887, the Texan Cooperative Association divided almost $20,000 in net profits among its members.

In California, three cooperative banks were established to provide credit at low interest rates to farmers. One of these enterprises saved its members considerable money during a depression in the wheat market by loaning them sufficient funds to enable them to hold their wheat for a rise in the market. In a dozen States, the Grange established successful mutual fire and life insurance companies. Heartened by their success and enjoying full treasuries collected from dues and contributions, many of the Granges launched cooperative factories to manufacture farm implements. In Iowa, during the summer of 1874 about 250 harvesters were manufactured and furnished to members at half the prevailing price. Many other States, particularly Kansas, Wisconsin, and Kentucky, set up factories to turn out plows, cultivators, threshing machines, and other implements used in farming. The National Grange in 1874 authorized its executive committee to purchase machine patents and work out a plan of cooperation with State Granges to manufacture all kinds of farm machinery. Adequate capital for these ventures could not be obtained and the Granges were soon involved in patent suits, so that by the close of 1875 the idea was abandoned.

More successful were the cooperative factories that converted the raw materials produced by farmers into finished products. Cheese and butter factories, linseed-oil factories, pork-packing establishments, and even hemp and cotton mills in the South were projected. Capital for these local enterprises was furnished by the organization of stock companies among Grange members. In some parts of the West, farmers' cooperative creameries and cheese factories had even preceded the rise of the Grange, but their number was greatly increased by the Order.

This attempt of the farmer to perform the function of middleman, manufacturer, capitalist, and banker through cooperative enterprise met with only short-lived success. Lack of capital, inability to work together, lack of business experience on the part of the Grangers, and the competition, fair and unfair, of private merchants and corporations drove most of the cooperatives out of business before 1880. However, the experience had many valuable results. While the undertakings flourished, they saved farmers a considerable amount of money, and they scared the merchants and manufacturers into lowering prices even after the Granger movement had collapsed. Mail-order houses, catering to rural trade, were another outcome, the first one starting business at Chicago in 1872 especially to sell to Grangers. Finally, the Granger experience taught farmers many of the principles and possibilities of cooperation and created a tradition of economic cooperation which has been carried on with increasing vigor down to the present day. The Grange itself, when later revived, returned to cooperative activity in full earnestness.

In the eighties, the Northwestern Alliance and the Southern Alliance, like the Grange in the previous decade, paved the way for united economic as well as political action. A number of grain elevators were established in Minnesota and the Dakotas, and cooperative creameries functioned successfully in Illinois. Much more ambitious, however, was the southern phase: Cooperative stores, elevators, and gins were undertaken by local Alliances and survived over a period of years; cooperative cotton marketing was sponsored in 1886 by the Texas State Alliance; and business agencies were established to make purchases directly from wholesalers and manufacturers. Under C. W. Macune, Texan agrarian leader, a Farmers' Alliance Exchange was organized in Texas to sell farm produce and buy farm supplies. It succeeded in marketing cotton and grain to advantage and in purchasing farm implements at a substantial discount which was passed on to the farmers. So long as the exchange operated on a cash basis, however, it was of no particular benefit to the great mass of farmers who lacked cash. To meet this situation, local Alliances were asked to execute joint notes which, it was hoped, would be accepted as collateral at face value by the banks. The scheme fell through when the banks refused money on the notes, and the exchange was forced into bankruptcy. Other Southern States experimented with the plan in a modified form, the Georgia exchange proving the most successful—in the first year of its existence, it was said to have saved its patrons $200,000 on fertilizers alone. The idea of a national exchange, although widely discussed, was sidetracked in favor of political action (*102*).

Another period of expansion for the cooperatives began in 1895 and continued until 1920. Prior to 1900 at least 950 cooperatives were known to have been organized, and before 1920 over 11,000 had been formed. Cooperative associations for every important type of commodity came into existence, although most important in volume of business during the decade 1910–19 were the grain, dairy, livestock, and fruit and vegetable associations.

In 1915, 65 percent of the active cooperatives were located in the North Central States, and 9 percent in the Southern States (*202*). One reason for this regionalized distribution was the founding, in 1902, of the American Society of Equity in Indiana and of the Farmers' Educational and Cooperative Union, better known as the Farmers' Union, in Texas. Both of these associations gave even more atten-

223761°—40——17

tion than had preceding farmers' organizations to the marketing problem. The Equity Society even attempted to organize farmers into pools, set prices, and monopolize crop marketing. Wheat and tobacco producers were persuaded to sign legally binding pledges to turn over the bulk of their crops to Equity agents, who would withhold the supply from the market until the prices fixed by the society prevailed. Elevators, cold-storage plants, and warehouses were projected for storing the produce, and credit was to be extended to the farmer. Although the scheme eventually fell through, it was both an indication of the lengths to which farmer cooperation might go and a forerunner of current agricultural thinking. A very illuminating discussion of the movement is given by Robert H. Bahmer in the January 1940 issue of Agricultural History (*13*).

The blessing of the Federal Government was first extended to the cooperative movement in 1914. Under the terms of the Clayton Antitrust Act, cooperatives were specifically excluded from prosecution as a monopoly in restraint of trade so long as they operated without capital stock—a restriction dropped in 1922—and refrained from unfair practices. Since then, cooperatives have become a focal point in Federal farm policy.

Development of Federal and State Agencies

The Department of Agriculture

Proposals for the creation of a Federal Department of Agriculture were made as far back as 1776, when two resolutions recommending aid to agriculture were adopted by the Second Continental Congress. One of these resolutions as originally introduced contained a clause, later struck out, proposing the establishment of a standing committee of Congress to "correspond with and assist" the agricultural societies which were to be set up in each of the Colonies (*37*).

Two decades later, George Washington, in his last annual message to Congress, advocated the establishment of a board of agriculture to collect and diffuse information and "by premiums and small pecuniary aids to encourage and assist a spirit of discovery and improvement." The proposal was reported favorably by a House committee but never came to a vote. Again in 1817 a memorial was sent to Congress by the Berkshire Agricultural Society, leader in the movement for progressive farming, petitioning for a national board of agriculture. A bill was drawn up and referred to the Committee of the Whole, but got no further (*92*).

Despite these rebuffs, precedents continued to accumulate. Consuls and naval officers abroad, following the example of Benjamin Franklin, sent home seeds and improved breeds of domestic animals. Merino sheep from Spain were introduced in this way. The practice was officially recognized in John Quincy Adams's administration when all United States consuls were directed to forward rare plants and seeds to Washington. Under Adams, too, a botanical garden was set up and a committee on agriculture was established in the Senate—the House having created a similar committee 5 years earlier, in 1820.

A significant development began in 1836, when Henry L. Ellsworth,

Commissioner of Patents, on his own initiative undertook to distribute seeds obtained from abroad to enterprising farmers. In 1839, Congress answered his plea for aid by appropriating $1,000 for the threefold purpose of collecting agricultural statistics, conducting agricultural investigations, and distributing seeds. With this money Ellsworth inaugurated an Agricultural Division in the Patent Office.

Although appropriations came irregularly in the years immediately following, Ellsworth by his personal interest and zeal kept the work going. In 1 year alone, over 30,000 packages of seeds were given away. The agricultural statistics gathered in connection with the decennial enumeration were published in 1842, with a survey of crop conditions. From 1847 on, Congress made annual appropriations for these activities.

Succeeding Commissioners continued the work of Ellsworth. In 1854, Charles Mason employed a chemist, a botanist, and an entomologist to conduct experiments, Congress having granted the division $35,000. Two years later, a 5-acre garden was obtained and investigations in the cultivation of sorghum and tea were begun.

By 1860, after nearly a century of discussion, the stage was set for the creation of an executive department of agriculture. New forces, including the rise of industrialism, the development of railroad networks, and the introduction of farm machinery, were transforming the Nation's agriculture. Through the work of State and county agricultural societies, the agricultural press, and individuals, at least a beginning had been made in acquainting farmers with the value of scientific agriculture.

The Republican Party, indebted to the agricultural West for its victory in the election of 1860, was pledged to agrarian reform. President Lincoln, in his first message to Congress, called for the immediate establishment of an "agricultural and statistical bureau."

The bill creating the United States Department of Agriculture, which became a law on May 15, 1862, was a compromise between the demands for an organization with Cabinet authority and those calling for a subordinate bureau within the Department of the Interior (*162*). In the hope of establishing an effective agency which might at the same time escape purely political control, an independent Department was voted with a Commissioner at its head.

According to the organic act, the Commissioner was directed "to acquire and preserve in his Department all information concerning agriculture which he can obtain by means of books and correspondence, and by practical and scientific experiments . . . , by the collection of statistics, and by any other appropriate means within his power; to collect, as he may be able, new and valuable seeds and plants; to test, by cultivation, the value of such of them as may require such tests; to propagate such as may be worthy of propagation, and to distribute them among agriculturists" (*197*). Actually, all these powers were in substance identical with those exercised by the Agricultural Division under the Patent Office. The evolutionary growth of the Department is further evident in that the organization and methods in operation under the Patent Office were generally continued. Isaac Newton, chief of the Agricultural Division, was appointed as first Commissioner, and he retained the majority of his former associates.

In his initial annual report, Newton outlined the seven aims he intended to foster. He promised to disseminate knowledge of agricultural improvements and to collect and distribute valuable seeds and plants. He emphasized the necessity of encouraging a spirit of inquiry and cooperation among the farmers. In addition, Newton proposed to further scientific investigation by establishing professorships of botany and entomology and by continuing the task of chemical analysis. Finally, he stressed the importance of organizing an agricultural library and of establishing a museum (*199*).

The last two objectives were realized within a relatively short time. Actually, the library was started in 1840, when a clerk was first appointed to gather statistics and useful agricultural information. When the Department was established this collection of books became its property, and other books were added by purchase and exchange with foreign governments and agricultural societies. By 1871, when the first librarian was appointed, the Department boasted the most complete agricultural library in the country—a collection of more than 8,000 volumes.

A museum was officially established in 1867, when Congress appropriated $10,000 to purchase the private collection of Townend Glover, the entomologist. The Centennial Exposition of 1876 brought large donations from foreign governments. It was not until 1881 that Congress appropriated funds for the erection of a special building in which the entire museum could be housed. (This building was destroyed in 1905 to make room for the present administration building, and the exhibits were scattered.) The essential contribution that an agricultural museum might make was aptly stated by Secretary Rusk in his report for 1889. It should, he maintained, "be an instructive object-lesson of the agricultural products and possibilities of the country, and should be a standard for accurate knowledge and for practical and scientific reference" (*200*).

While the library and the museum served as valuable treasuries for the rapidly growing accumulation of knowledge in agricultural science, the Department was also able to exert an immediate educational force through its publications. The most important of these was the annual report, which, until 1868, included agricultural statistics and essays on special agricultural topics—a practice begun in the Patent Office. After 1868 the contents were limited to digests of the work of the Department and the results of its research, including the reports of special agents. Each volume contained an extensive statistical summary of the year's crop production and of the condition of foreign markets. Had the wealth of information included in the reports reached the hands of the most intelligent farmers, it would have been invaluable in popularizing the latest achievements of agricultural science and gaining the cooperation of the farmers in the work of the Department. Unfortunately, most of the distribution was haphazard.

Of more practical value were the monthly reports of the Department. These contained the latest news on the condition of crops and other timely information. They were sent out to farmers' clubs, State agricultural colleges and societies, and to an individual mailing list. In addition, miscellaneous reports informed the public of special activities of the Department, and beginning in 1883 bulletins were issued by the several divisions dealing with the results of specific investigations.

That the Department was able to make so much headway in the early decades was commendable in view of the many administrative problems it encountered. Remaining outside the Cabinet fold did not protect it from political manipulations. Commissioners were regularly chosen for other than agricultural contributions, although on occasion an appointee possessed the happy combination of political availability and agricultural training. Since it was essential that he remain on good terms with Congress in order to obtain even meager appropriations, the selection of the minor employees of the Department was in large measure political.[12] This criticism, of course, applied more or less to the whole Government service until the establishment of the Civil Service Commission in 1883.

In fashioning its program, the Department had to take account of many conflicting interests. A farsighted minority demanded the pursuit of scientific studies, while the general public insisted on accomplishments of immediate economic benefit. Seed distribution, the most prominent of the Department's activities, was particularly controversial, and it was not until 1924 that the practice was halted by Congress.

Yet in spite of such handicaps the Department made notable contributions to the field of scientific agriculture. Men of outstanding ability served as division chiefs and research workers, and being relatively free from political obligation they built up the Department's prestige. Leaders of this caliber included Townend Glover, entomologist in the Department for the first 15 years, who laid the foundation for the economic approach to the study of insect life; and J. R. Dodge, chief statistician for more than 24 years, who received a gold medal from the French Government for his contributions to the knowledge of practical economics. Dr. H. W. Wiley, in his work on the sugar value of sorghum, conducted the most extensive series of analyses undertaken up to his time in the history of agricultural chemistry, and Dr. D. E. Salmon, chief of the Bureau of Animal Industry, gained a worldwide reputation for his pioneering work in bacteriology.

The organizational structure of the Department was evolved gradually and in response to public need. First of the divisions to be established was the Chemistry Division, set up in 1862. Until 1889 its studies tended to converge about four main subjects: Soils and fertilizers; analyses of the relative compositions of plants raised on the various soils of the country; investigation of food and drug adulteration; and the manufacture of sugar.

The Entomology Division, next created, directed its efforts from the beginning to combating destructive insects. In 1878 Congress recognized the value of such an undertaking by making the first specific appropriation for the investigation "of insects injurious to agriculture," and after 1882 the sum of $20,000 was available annually. C. V. Riley, one of the leading entomologists of the country, was employed

---

[12] CORY, ROBERT H. THE UNITED STATES DEPARTMENT OF AGRICULTURE: A HISTORY OF ITS ESTABLISHMENT, GROWTH, AND ACCOMPLISHMENTS PRIOR TO ITS INCORPORATION INTO THE CABINET IN 1889. Honors Thesis, Yale University. 122 pp. 1936. [Typewritten.] (Copy in files of the Division of Statistical and Historical Research, Bureau of Agricultural Economics.)

and with the exception of a 2-year interval served continuously from 1878 to 1894. A high light of his career which redounded to the credit of the Department was his successul introduction of predaceous insects from Australia to destroy the cottony fruit scale ravaging the orchards of California. This was the first attempt on the part of the Department to apply methods of biological control to the eradication of injurious insects (*103*).

The statistical work, begun in 1863, centered chiefly about crop reporting, already recognized as essential to efficient marketing. Progress was slow, owing to the lack of sufficient funds, inadequate facilities for communication, and the relatively undeveloped state of statistical techniques. Crop estimates were often inaccurate or appeared too late, and this inefficiency provoked considerable criticism among farmers. Later, as the exportation of agricultural products increased, the need for obtaining statistics on foreign markets became increasingly apparent. J. R. Dodge was selected to investigate foreign statistical methods and to report on the possibility of establishing statistical relations with countries abroad.

When Dodge returned from Europe, the statistical division was completely reorganized and the appropriation increased from $10,000 to $80,000. Agents were sent out in the field, and a system of index figures was introduced to indicate relative variations. Considerable progress was made toward the objective of presenting timely and accurate statistics showing current changes in crop areas and conditions. Dodge believed that farmers would learn from the statistics to adjust their production to market demand, but knowledge alone, as later experience testified, was not enough to effect that result.

Up to the establishment of the Bureau of Animal Industry in 1884, the Department was no more than a fact-finding and fact-dispensing agency. The power of regulation was introduced to save our export trade in meat products from total eclipse. During the 1870's the American livestock and dressed-meat industries had overflowed to the European market, but on the charge that the meat was diseased, England and the Continental countries began imposing severe restrictions on imports. Livestock breeders and meat-packing firms were up in arms, and Congress, after a bitter debate, responded by creating the Bureau of Animal Industry to fight contagious diseases among domestic animals and generally supervise meat exports and imports. Permanent quarantine stations were immediately set up near the principal cattle ports, and the Bureau proceeded to wipe out pluero-pneumonia and Texas fever, the two plagues most rampant among domestic cattle. To carry on its fight most effectively, the Bureau was authorized to quarantine areas of infected animals and to condemn and purchase diseased animals. The plagues were conquered after the Bureau of Animal Industry had made a momentous contribution to medical research by its discovery that a micro-organism could be transmitted through the intermediate agency of a carrier, in this case through cattle ticks (*43*).

In a country where there is such diversity of topographical conditions, agricultural research, to be most effective, must be a coordinated national undertaking rooted in regional experiment stations. The land-grant colleges, established as a result of the Morrill Act of 1862, potentially provided a comprehensive system of agricultural research and experimentation, but actually their work lacked coordination. Officials of the Department of Agriculture, perceiving this lack of central direction, proposed a unit in the Department to serve as a clearinghouse for the information obtained by the colleges.

In the meantime, a new type of agency—the experiment station—had arisen and was to prove the vital link between the Department and the colleges. The first State agricultural experiment station was erected at Wesleyan University, Middletown, Conn., in 1875. After 1880 a number of State agricultural colleges established stations. Formal meetings of college representatives were held under the leadership of the Commissioner of Agriculture to coordinate the work of the individual stations for the benefit of the entire Nation. At the convention of 1885 it was voted to seek congressional aid for experiment stations. Two years later a permanent organization under the name of the Association of American Agricultural Colleges and Experiment Stations was set up, and, together with the National Grange, it created Nation-wide sentiment in favor of Government action. Congress responded in 1887 with the Hatch Bill, authorizing a national system of agricultural experimentation, the first of its kind in the world. The act appropriated funds for the establishment of experiment stations in connection with the land-grant colleges to conduct original researches in agricultural science. Section 3 provided that the Commissioner of Agriculture was to stimulate uniformity of method by furnishing forms for the tabulation of results of investigations, by pointing out general lines of inquiry, and by giving advice and assistance. An Office of Experiment Stations was established in the Department to carry out these provisions, and agents were sent to confer with station workers and farmers' clubs throughout the country. A regular publication, the Experiment Station Record, was initiated in 1889 to correlate and publicize the research in progress. The Hatch Act was a notable landmark in the history of the Department, for it insured State cooperation in its research and educational activities.

By 1889 the ground work had been firmly laid and the Department was ready to assume greatly expanded functions. In the 1880's Congress received numerous petitions from the Grange and Alliance groups and from individual farmers stressing the beneficial influence of the Department and urging that it be given Cabinet status. At three separate sessions the House of Representatives approved such a measure by overwhelming majorities. Finally, the Senate concurred, and the law became effective on February 9, 1889. The Commissioner of Agriculture became a Secretary with a place in the Cabinet, but no addition was made to the Department's powers.

The same force of public opinion that won a Cabinet position for the Department of Agriculture obtained for it more generous congressional appropriations. During the first 27 years, the Department's annual expenditures rose from $64,000 to more than $1,000,000. In the next 5 years, between 1890 and 1894, the appropriation increased from $1,708,000 to a little over $2,623,000. With more adequate funds, the Department was able to perform its authorized functions with increased efficiency, and this in turn led Congress to widen its scope of activities.

One aspect of the Department's work that greatly enhanced its prestige was the successful introduction of new plants. Highly trained investigators were sent to Russia, China, North Africa, South America, India, and other parts of the globe. They not only brought back more hardy and productive varieties of plants already grown in this country, but introduced new plant industries that added many millions of dollars to the Nation's agricultural wealth. Concurrently the Department in cooperation with the State experiment stations, undertook extensive researches in plant breeding in order to adapt the foreign plants to domestic soil and weather conditions. Before the World War the Department had succeeded in establishing the navel orange from Brazil in the orchards of southern California, covering the dry-farm lands of the Dakotas and Nebraska with durum wheat brought from Russia, and persuading the farmers of Arizona to plant Egyptian cotton. Foremost among the explorers responsible for such innovations were David Fairchild, N. E. Hansen, and M. A. Carleton (*72*, *166*).

After the turn of the century the Department opened a new field of service to farmers by the inauguration of county demonstration work. Seaman A. Knapp, of the Bureau of Plant Industry, was sent to teach farmers in the South how to raise cotton that would withstand the ravages of the Mexican boll weevil. He established demonstration farms where interested farmers might learn improved methods. The work was extended to noninfested areas by agents assigned to specific districts, but acting under Knapp's guidance. The General Education Board of New York City, interested in promoting better economic conditions in the South's rural areas, agreed to supplement Government funds for the employment of field agents. Later it was found that the work could be done most effectively on a county basis, and farmers and businessmen agreed to help subsidize agents in their counties. The movement spread to the Northern States, where it was directed by the Office of Farm Management in close cooperation with the State agricultural colleges. The many thousands of farmers served by the county agents became warm advocates of a Nation-wide system of extension work (*15*).

Meanwhile the agricultural colleges also sought Government aid for their "institutes" or meetings of farmers where professors outlined progressive agricultural techniques. Congress finally agreed in 1914, under the Smith-Lever Act, to match State grants for extension work. Special extension divisions were to be set up in the State agricultural colleges and were to cooperate with the Extension Office established in the Federal Department of Agriculture. Though all extension work was to be carried on through the State colleges, the Department insisted that Federal funds be used to maintain county agents and that farmers' institutes should not be included in the program under the Smith-Lever Act (*187*).

With the growing public consciousness of national social and economic abuses, after 1890 the Federal Government was granted increased police power to be exercised on behalf of the general welfare. A series of regulatory measures was enacted, and the administrative agencies, including the Department of Agriculture, were called upon to enforce them. In 1905 the Secretary of Agriculture assumed the protection of the national forests. The Department had begun its investigation of the conservation of timber resources as early as 1876, and in 1881 had established a Forestry Division. In 1906 the Department took over the enforcement of the Food and Drugs Act, which empowered it to prohibit the shipment in interstate commerce of adulterated or misbranded foods and drugs; this too was a field in which the Department had pioneered through its Chemistry Division. Early success in fighting animal diseases and regulating the meat-export trade also qualified the Department of Agriculture to administer the Meat Inspection Act of 1907, affecting the quality of meats in interstate trade. In 1908 it also took charge of the inspection and certification of dairy products in the export trade (*42*).

Of these four regulatory measures, three dealt with an aspect of the marketing problem, indicating a new emphasis in the Department's activities. Previously, with the exception of crop reporting and the regulation of meat exports, its work had been concerned almost entirely with stimulating agricultural productivity. The marketing process began to disturb the farmer more and more as he became aware of the gap between the prices he received for his produce and the prices paid by the consumer. Public opinion crystallized in a demand that the Government concern itself with this general problem, and in 1910 Congress authorized the Secretary of Agriculture to "investigate the cost of food supplies at the farm and to the consumer." An appropriation of $50,000 was made in 1913, and within 10 weeks an Office of Markets was created. To this office was entrusted in 1916 enforcement of the Grain Standards Act, the Cotton Futures Act, and the Warehouse Act. The office rapidly grew into the Bureau of Markets and contributed much spadework to the cause of cooperative marketing (*126*, *176*).

From its beginning in 1839 as a division in the Patent Office, to 1917, the Department of Agriculture, according to a reliable estimate, cost the country approximately $285,000,000. That this expenditure was a profitable investment on the whole few will dispute. The Department was not alone in improving farming methods, but it became "the chief and most valuable single agency" (*205*). While remaining fundamentally a research organization, the Department of Agriculture, through an orderly process of growth and in response to public need, had by 1918 undertaken extension work, engaged in such service activities as weather and crop reporting, and supervised Federal road construction and administered regulatory laws (*209*).

Agricultural Education

Formal agricultural education carried on in the schools as a phase of technical or vocational education is relatively new.

The first land-grant college bill introduced in the House of Representatives by Congressman Justin Morrill of Vermont in December 1857 (*165*), was passed by Congress but vetoed by President Buchanan on the grounds of expense and unconstitutionality. The same measure, reintroduced after the Republicans had come into power, was adopted, with minor amendments, and signed on July 2, 1862. Undoubtedly this was the most significant legislation for agricultural education in the United States. The act provided that a State might receive 30,000 acres of the public lands within its borders for each Senator and Representative it had in Congress. The proceeds from the sale of these lands were to be invested and the income used to create and maintain colleges. The curricula of these institutions were to be prescribed by the State legislatures, but the leading object, as stated, was to teach "such branches of learning as related to agriculture and the mechanic arts." Other scientific or classical studies were not to be excluded, however, if they served to promote the "liberal and practical education of the industrial classes in the several pursuits and professions in life" (*188, p. 100*).

The early history of the new colleges was replete with difficulties. In selling their grants, the States competed with the railroad and homestead lands, with the result that in many cases the income derived hardly sufficed to maintain even one department. Aid had to be secured from the State legislatures, and in many cases it was given grudgingly and haltingly, and chiefly in response to pressure from agricultural societies and the Grange. The Federal Government, by the Morrill Act of 1890 and the Nelson amendment of 1907, was induced to provide a subsidy, which by 1911 amounted to $50,000 annually for each State and Territory.

Politics was rife in the determination of whether an endowment was to be used for establishing new departments or schools in existing institutions or to create new agricultural colleges or agricultural and mechanical arts colleges. Politics was also a prominent factor in the selection of college administrators and professors.

Aside from such considerations, there were few qualified teachers in the natural sciences and practically none in agriculture. Most of the available textbooks, moreover, were of European origin, and their contents were not based on American experience. Entrance standards in the new colleges were low, the students being admitted directly from the grades. The general trend of the curriculum varied according to whether the group that favored narrow vocational training or the one that believed in a broad academic education gained the upper hand. A frequent complaint was that the colleges trained youths for urban rather than rural life.

Nevertheless, in spite of their shortcomings, the agricultural colleges made considerable progress. Teachers were trained, equipment was assembled, texts were written, and the economic and scientific values of these schools were demonstrated to the general public. By 1900, most of these colleges were firmly established and attracting rapidly expanding enrollments. The teaching and research became more and more specialized. Summer schools and post-graduate courses were organized for prospective teachers and scientists. As the work of the agricultural colleges progressed and they came into closer touch with the farming people, considerable attention was devoted to the economic and social aspects of farm life. From the agricultural colleges emanated also the movements for experiment stations, the extension work already mentioned, and agricultural education in elementary and secondary schools.

Organized college extension teaching in agriculture dates from 1892 and was part of the general extension-work movement initiated by libraries and universities. As defined in a report of the Association of Agricultural Colleges, extension teaching in agriculture dealt with "subjects having to do with improved methods of agricultural production and with the general welfare of the rural population" and were offered "to people not enrolled as resident pupils in educational institutions" (*188*). Besides special and short courses at colleges, extension work was carried on through lectures, correspondence, publication of bulletins, field experiments, demonstrations, and exhibits at fairs. In 1912, over 7,500 farmers' institutes engaged in extension teaching and attracted a total attendance of 4,000,000 persons. At the same time, the United States Department of Agriculture organized cooperative extension work, as already described.

Closely connected with the extension work were the efforts of the agricultural colleges to aid the movement for the teaching of agriculture in elementary and secondary schools. They initiated nature study and school gardening in city and village schools. To reach the rural schools, they formulated courses of instruction, gave teachers special training at summer-school sessions, and prepared textbooks, manuals, and charts. About 1905, Wisconsin was persuaded to introduce a course in elementary agriculture in its grade schools, and the example was followed by South Dakota and New York. By 1915, the teaching of agriculture in public rural elementary schools was required in more than 20 States, and some instruction was given in practically every State.

As it became evident that the agricultural colleges were destined to become primarily centers of investigation and training of experts, attention was directed to providing systematic agricultural instruction at the secondary level. Only a small proportion of farm children went to college, and of these very few received any considerable amount of agricultural instruction. The courses in elementary schools were helpful, but naturally they could not be very detailed. Most of the manual-labor schools of the pre-Civil War days had disappeared. A new movement for agriculture in secondary schools was begun in the 1880's; in Connecticut, the Storrs Agricultural School was established in 1881, and in 1888 the University of Minnesota organized a well-equipped secondary school on its campus. Other colleges did likewise, and after 1900 the public authorities also began to make appropriations for State, district, or county agricultural schools. The next development was to grant State subsidies to local high schools for introducing courses in agriculture. Virginia began the practice, and 421 public high schools throughout the country had agricultural departments by 1916. Over 73,000 students received some instruction in agriculture during that year through courses at agricultural colleges, State-aided special schools, public high schools, and private schools.

Agricultural instruction was given a practical turn by the rise to prominence of advocates of industrial education. Their general theme was that American youth of noncollege caliber should be required to take fewer "cultural" subjects and should be trained instead along specifically vocational lines. In a sense, this was a return to the Fellenberg philosophy, but with a somewhat broader outlook. The emphasis on practicality attracted many leaders of industry, labor, and agriculture, and in 1906, they formed a National Society for the

Promotion of Industrial Education. The society stimulated public interest in the subject, sponsored State legislation, and drafted bills for Federal aid. The Association of American Agricultural Colleges and Experiment Stations lent its support to the movement, and the campaign culminated in the passage of the Smith-Hughes Vocational Education Act of 1917.

By that measure, funds are granted to States willing to expand their secondary-school systems to include vocational education in agriculture, trade, industries, and home economics. A Federal Board of Vocational Education was set up to cooperate with similar State boards. Plans for expenditures of the Federal funds are submitted by the State agencies for the approval of the Federal Board.

The gradual winning of the mass of farmers to the program of agricultural education tended to encourage improved farm methods, greater productivity, and more general crop diversification. Its social effects were no less significant. Widespread rural education helped to break down the farmers' isolation. It stirred up fresh currents of thought that brought more mobility into rural life. Agriculture was made more attractive to farm youth, having been stamped with academic approval. Altogether, rural education helped to restore the farmers' self-confidence and pride.

From another point of view, the interest of farmers in education indicated a growing maturity in American agriculture. It was a far cry from the western pioneer who skimmed the soil's fertility and then moved on to fresh lands—so long as they were free—to the college-trained specialist familiar with agricultural science and economics. Intensive cultivation began to replace extensive, with a consequent trend toward the laboratory rather than the open frontier.

Finally, it is significant that all the various groups sponsoring agricultural education eventually turned to the Federal Government. Agricultural schools and colleges, organized experimentation, extension work, and elementary and secondary school training in agriculture all began locally, and though the State and local governments have supported them to the present day, in each case Congress was called upon to furnish national leadership and financial aid.

Agrarianism and Agricultural Policy

The struggle to shape national policy with a view to protecting and furthering agricultural interests began with the formation of our Federal system. In the vote on constitutional ratification, the more distinctly rural sections, representing the debtor class, opposed prohibition of State power to issue paper money, and questioned the "sanctification" of contracts. Once launched, the Federal Government, in response to threats of secession from southwestern farmers, was almost immediately obliged to negotiate with Spain for use of the lower Mississippi River and for deposit rights at New Orleans. In domestic policy, the agrarians broke with the Federalist Party on Hamilton's measures, which were designed, as it seemed, to subordinate the interests of a population 95 percent agricultural to the paramount control of an oligarchy of traders, bankers, and speculators. Under the lead of southern planters, notably Jefferson and Madison, the agrarians formed the Democratic-Republican, later known as the Democratic,

Party and gained political control in the Presidential election of 1800.

The followers of Jefferson could not touch the National Bank until 1811 when its charter expired, but they began immediately to retire Government bonds and decrease expenditures. Their greatest achievement was the purchase of the vast Louisiana Territory in 1803. New England's representatives, speaking for the strongly intrenched commercial interests, opposed the purchase as destroying the balance established by the Constitution; they feared that the States carved out of the new possession would outvote the founding States. Later, in the Hartford Convention of 1814, New England secessionists demanded that no new States be admitted into the Union except by a two-thirds vote. The convention itself was called to express New England opposition to a war supposedly fought on behalf of its shipping rights but actually begun and carried through by ardent expansionists—both southern and western (*151*).

Under Jackson, the Democratic Party championed the cause of small farmers and city laborers, as well as planters. In State governments, it forced the abandonment of property qualifications for voting and office holding, established free public education, and abolished imprisonment for debt. In the Federal sphere, it destroyed the National Bank, the greatest monopoly of that day, and carried out the policy of moving Indians beyond the Mississippi where they would not interfere—at least for a time—with land-hungry settlers.

The chief issue agitating the West was liberalization of the land policy. As early as 1824, Senator Thomas Hart Benton of Missouri began the introduction of "graduation bills" designed to reduce the price of slow-selling lands, by progressive stages, to a merely nominal sum. The incipient trade unions and labor parties supported the granting of land to actual settlers at a nominal price, or free of charge, in order to relieve labor competition. In 1829, Thomas Skidmore founded the Agrarian Party among New York workers, with free lands as one of its chief principles, and Horace Greeley filled the columns of the New York Tribune advocating this reform. Jackson, in a message to Congress at the beginning of his second term, urged that "as soon as practicable" public lands should be sold at nominal cost to settlers (*170*). As a result of such pressure, the Preemption Act of 1841 gave actual settlers preference in land sales, and 30 years after its first introduction Benton's graduation bill was adopted.

During the forties and fifties, the southern wing of the Democratic Party largely controlled Federal policy. It lowered the tariff and wrenched new lands from Mexico, but blocked western attempts to secure free homesteads and governmental aid for internal improvements. These issues prevented a political union between the South and the Northwest, and enabled the Republican Party, in 1860, to capture the northwestern vote by a promise of free lands. This pledge was redeemed in 1862 by three measures, later recognized as landmarks in American agriculture: The Homestead Act, granting actual settlers 160 acres free of charge; the act establishing the United States Department of Agriculture; and the Morrill measure creating land-grant colleges.

Up to the Civil War, agriculture was the predominant industry of the Nation. This was reflected in the political as well as in the economic and social life despite the considerable influence wielded by merchants, bankers, lawyers, speculators, shippers, and manufacturers. After the war, agriculture was on the defensive and business enterprise in the ascendancy. The change, with all its revolutionary implications for future development, brought a dynamic, collectivist, urban society, in place of a static, individualist, rural pattern; in that sense, the Civil War was as much a defeat for the Concord farmer as for the southern planter.

By 1890, for the first time, the income from manufacturing was greater than that from agriculture; since 1910, the income from manufacturing has been greater than that from agriculture in every year. Industrialization got under way in earnest during the Civil War; the American entrepreneur had every advantage—unbounded resources, vastly improved machines, a huge reservoir of labor, and an unequaled domestic market. The value of manufactured products shot up from $3,386,000,000 in 1869 to $13,014,000,000 in 1899 (*94*).

Agriculture underwent a parallel transformation, but the farmer never reaped its benefits to any comparable degree. Aided by labor-saving machinery, free lands, and improved transportation facilities, the American farmer, for a time, took control of the world agricultural market. Wheat, pork, and corn poured out of the West to feed Europe as well as the United States, and by 1880 southern cotton again furnished the bulk of the world's cotton supply. This agricultural development was basic in the process of industrialization and urbanization, for without an adequate supply of food and raw materials the factory system would have been impossible.

Yet farmers, as an economic class, fell steadily behind the businessmen. The weaknesses in their position were many. Thousands of small producers could not readily combine to fix prices or control output, even if they had the will to do so. As prices dropped, farmers increased their output, with the result that in some cases the gross as well as relative returns were reduced. On the other hand, fixed charges were increasing. Farmers had to buy machines in order to compete successfully; but as machinery was expensive, the farmer frequently had to mortgage his lands. By 1890, about 28 percent of all American farms operated by owners were under mortgage (*175*). A succession of crop failures or a sharp decline in farm prices meant foreclosure. At the same time, with an influx of settlers, land values rose. In Nebraska, for example, an acre of land formerly valued at $7 or $8 now brought $25 or $30. Tenancy, always present, became much more prominent. The census of 1880—the first to deal with the forms of landownership—revealed that 25.6 percent of the farmers were tenants (*94*). In addition, the farmer suffered from other economic handicaps.

The "robber barons"—or "captains of industry," depending on the point of view—by securing economic power controlled political power. They looked to the Federal Government to safeguard their gains and to yield new sources of wealth. They sought to manipulate tariffs, control banking and currency, escape taxation, grab land subsidies for railroad and timber companies, obtain Government contracts, and prevent governmental interference with the "law of supply and demand"—and they succeeded. Unlike the pre-war planters, they did not enter politics directly, but their control of the political processes, as attested by the Crédit Mobilier, the Whiskey Ring, and the Star Route frauds, was nonetheless effective.

The Granger Movement

The first organization of significance was the Grange, which was inaugurated 2 years after Appomatox. In 1866, President Johnson authorized the Commissioner of Agriculture to send a clerk on a trip of observation through the Southern States. Oliver Hudson Kelley, a Boston Yankee, was chosen, and he had sufficient vision to realize that more was needed than mere recovery from wartime ravages. On his return to Washington, Kelley persuaded five other Government clerks and a fruit grower to organize a secret order of farmers on a national scale, and on December 4, 1867, the National Grange of the Patrons of Husbandry was launched (*36*).

Like every reform movement, it did not enlist all or even a majority of the class it represented, but nearly all the farmers felt its influence to some degree. In the first place, through it farmers were brought together and united in some form of social organization. In their meetings, they discovered their common interests, including similar economic grievances. Gradually, from the heat of discussion a set of tenets which expressed the general view was fashioned. Finally, the more active and militant set out to achieve their objectives in concrete form, and that brought them into the political arena. The entire process was democratic in its truest sense; it sprang from the mass of people and sought to realize its ends through elected leaders and in orderly fashion.

The National Grange, in 1874, asserted emphatically the nonpolitical character of its association and denied that any Grange could be true to its obligations if it so much as discussed political questions. By that time, however, the members had held political meetings outside their Granges, drawn up platforms, and nominated candidates. In 11 Western States, these various Independent, Reform, Anti-Monopoly, or Farmers' Parties had elected large blocs to the legislatures, and already the first mandatory laws regulating railroad rates had been enacted. The tide of political action could not be stemmed while farmers envisioned legislation that would lower freight charges, outlaw railroad discrimination, and substitute governmental credit for dependence on eastern loan sharks. Lack of an adequate money supply, extortionate charges by grain-elevator companies, speculation in grain and cotton, and high tariffs were other evils the Grangers hoped eventually to eradicate by legislative action.

The most immediate contribution of the Granger movement was the enactment of legislation for State regulation of railroads, commonly known as the Granger laws, already discussed. These laws were short-lived, however. Many were repealed within 2 years or went unenforced. The reasons for their failure are varied: The administrative agencies lacked technical skill; the railroad managers dragged the laws through State courts and smeared them in the press; and many communities feared that too drastic action would put a stop to further railroad construction. An equally important factor was the decline of the Grange and the political parties stemming from it.

The collapse of the Granger movement was as rapid as its rise. Between 1874 and 1880, the number of Granges fell from 20,000 to 4,000 (*36*). Too rapid growth had attracted many undesirable elements and resulted in the very difficult problem of proper organizational structure. The strong dislike of farmers for politicians who attempted to use the movement for their own ends led to the acceptance of leaders lacking in political experience, and many costly tactical errors were made. Considerable stress had been laid on the cooperative phase of Granger activity, and its failure dealt the movement a hard blow. Other reasons for the decline were the upswing in prices of farm products and a general lowering of freight rates, both of which relieved the acuteness of farmers' grievances.

The Granger experience was an invaluable political education for the farmers. It trained them to act together and revealed the strength and limitations of their organized might. While almost all the early leaders disappeared into oblivion, the rank and file kept pressing on through a line of agrarian movements that gained in momentum and effectiveness in the course of the century. One very important contribution to American democracy resulting from Granger activity was the firm establishment of the principle that a State government has power to regulate businesses clothed with a public interest. It was affirmed by Justice Waite in the *Munn* v. *Illinois* decision of 1876, a case arising out of the Granger laws, and has remained as a keystone of our constitutional system. The Supreme Court, it is true, withdrew from the States the power to regulate interstate commerce, in 1886. Thereupon, the West and South joined with discontented elements in the East to secure the passage of the Interstate Commerce Act of 1887, which not only brought the railroads under national jurisdiction, but marked the entrance of the Federal Government into the sphere of business regulation—a milestone in American development.

The Greenback Movement

While the Granger agitation was still at its height, another group of agrarians met at Indianapolis, in 1874, to attack the ills of agriculture from another point. Currency reform was the chief prescription of this party, as railroad regulation was the main concern of the Grangers. The money issue was a war legacy; to finance the northern cause, over $433,000,000 had been issued in paper money, or greenbacks; in addition, various series of bonds had been floated bearing interest rates ranging from 4 to 8 percent, and differing in their specifications as to the medium of payment. Some were to be repaid in gold, some in silver, some in gold or silver, while in others no mention was made of a particular currency.

After the war, the Republican Party fumbled about in an attempt to satisfy conservative elements without alienating western voters. The first of the two issues to be decided was in regard to the greenbacks: (1) Were they to be contracted by redemption in metallic money, inflated by further issues, or left as they were to circulate at face value? (2) What currency was to be used to repay the bondholders? The farmer, as a debtor, had considerable at stake in the answers to these questions. If, during the war, he had mortgaged his farm for $1,000, the legal tender he was given was worth probably no more than $600 because of its depreciation. If the greenbacks were to be redeemed in gold, they would immediately rise to par value and the creditor would receive not only a high interest charge, ranging from 8 to 15 percent, but a further profit of $400 on the original loan. With commodity prices dropping, this meant that the farmer would have to raise more corn, wheat, or cotton to meet his debts; but, as production increased, prices dropped. On the other hand, if Government bonds were repaid in gold, it meant an increase in taxation; and it was notorious that rural property was already carrying a heavy tax burden.

In 1868, the agrarian element of the Democratic Party wrote into the platform the so-called Ohio idea calling for redemption of Government bonds in greenbacks. The slogan of the farmers was "The same money for the bondholder as for the plowholder." Not content with working through a major party that necessarily contained conservative interests, the agrarians looked about for allies to form a separate party. They found that laborers suffering from widespread unemployment, accompanying if not caused by contraction of the currency, had formed the National Labor Party, which in 1872 adopted a greenback platform. The panic of 1873 and the failure of the Granger movement to relieve the agricultural depression led to a union of farmers and workers in the Independent National Party. Its candidates in the Presidential election of 1876, however, polled only a little more than 80,000 votes, mainly in the western farm areas rather than in the industrial centers.

Increased unrest and discontent in 1877 gave the party new vigor, and the following year a national convention at Toledo, attended by some 800 delegates, adopted the name of "Greenback Labor." The platform demanded the issue of all money by the Government and in sufficient quantity to meet the needs of farmers and workers. It denounced the demonetization of silver—the so-called "Crime of '73"—and the resumption of specie payments which Congress had voted in 1875, to be effective in 1879. In the elections of 1878—the high-water mark of the movement—Greenback candidates polled close to a million votes. Fifteen members were elected to Congress—6 from the East, 6 from the Middle West, and 3 from the South. Outstanding among the Greenback Congressmen was Gen. James Weaver, of Iowa, who became the party's standard bearer in the next Presidential election.

Despite a valiant campaign, Weaver polled only 309,000 votes. This was due in part to the defection of the workers, who had joined the Knights of Labor. Labor returned again in 1888 to form the Union Labor Party, which absorbed the Greenback agrarians. The platform was much wider in scope than former Greenback programs; it advocated Government ownership of railroads and telegraphs and called for a graduated income tax, direct election of Senators, and woman suffrage. The party, however, failed to capture the industrial strongholds; of the 147,000 votes polled in 1888 about two-thirds came from the West and Northwest and one-third from the South and Southwest.

After this failure the Greenback agitation disappeared from the

223761°—40——18

political scene. The achievements of the organization were notable despite overemphasis on the money issue. It had, for the first time, organized nationally the forces of agrarian discontent; the union of farmers and workers initiated by the Greenbackers was revived in succeeding decades and became the basis for all national reform parties; and finally, it furnished several of the leaders and many of the manifestos of the Populist Party, which became its heir.

The Farmers' Alliances

Farmers' clubs had grown up spontaneously alongside the Granges in the 1870's. In time they were formed into State alliances. In 1887, the Grand State Alliance of Texas joined with the Farmers' Union of Louisiana to form the National Farmers' Alliance and Cooperative Union of America. A year later this organization amalgamated with the Agricultural Wheel of Arkansas, under the name of National Farmers' Alliance and Industrial Union—the change in name indicating a desire to win over the labor element (*102*).

While this development had been going on in the South, a similar movement of independent origin had, by 1880, been launched in the Northwest. It was generally known as the Northwestern Alliance, and its members were active both in establishing cooperatives and in exerting pressure on the major parties.

The two Alliances held meetings at the same time in St. Louis in 1889, with a view to effecting a merger. The attempt failed, but the programs adopted by the separate organizations showed considerable similarity. Both called for free coinage of silver and Government issuance of paper money. They agreed on the need for reducing and equalizing taxation, and reclaiming from railroads all lands held in excess of actual needs. Moreover, both favored Government ownership and operation of the means of communication and transportation. The subtreasury scheme, strongly advocated by the Southern Alliance, called on the Federal Government to establish warehouses where farmers might store nonperishable commodities and receive loans in legal tender equivalent to 80 percent of the value of the deposits. The annual interest rate was to be only 1 percent and the farmer was to have a year to redeem his property. The Northwestern Alliance, to achieve the same ends—increasing money circulation and providing adequate credit facilities—proposed a Federal farm loan bureau with $100,000,000 or more in greenbacks at its disposal to make loans on farms up to 5 percent of their value at 2 percent annual interest (*36*)

In the election of 1890, the Southern Alliance worked through the Democratic Party and succeeded in gaining control of the legislature in five States. In the West, Alliance members organized separate People's, Independent, or Industrial Parties which made particular headway in Kansas and Nebraska.

The Populist Party

Encouraged by this success, the Alliance held a convention with the Knights of Labor at Cincinnati, in 1891, to form a new political party. Some 1,400 delegates attended, a majority of whom represented five Western States; plans were laid to meet the following year to nominate candidates and draft a program. At the convention in Omaha, in

1892, the People's or Populist Party was formally launched on the national scene. Its platform began with a ringing declaration "that the union of the labor forces of the United States this day consummated shall be permanent and perpetual" (*36, pp. 142–143*). It demanded "a national currency, safe, sound, and flexible, issued by the general Government only," free coinage of silver, the subtreasury system, a graduated income tax, postal savings banks, Government ownership and control of railroads and telegraph lines, and abolition of land monopolies. To attract the labor vote, resolutions were adopted favoring the 8-hour day and the abolition of the Pinkerton labor-spy system.

Into the election of 1892, with General Weaver of Greenback fame as its Presidential candidate, the party cast a bombshell by polling more than a million votes and winning 22 electoral votes—the first time since 1860 that a third party had achieved electoral recognition. This success was partially due to the strategy of combining forces with the Republicans in the South and the Democrats in the West. In the congressional election of 1894, the Populists further increased their vote to a million and a half, electing 7 Congressmen and 6 Senators.

The decisive year was 1896, when agrarianism, with labor as an ally, made its supreme bid for power. All the bitterness and unrest of 30 years of economic and political exploitation was compressed in that Presidential campaign. The immediate background was a world-wide depression that was in its worst stage. Labor, suffering from severe unemployment, had organized Coxey's army and had struck at Homestead and Pullman; it was beaten but sullen. Prices of farm products in 1896 were the lowest ever recorded in the United States. Interest rates remained the same, however, and whole sections of farm areas, particularly in Kansas, Nebraska, Iowa, and the Dakotas, suffered foreclosure.

Since the Civil War, national policy, reflecting the dominant industrial class, had almost completely neglected agriculture's plight. Even where legislation had been enacted, it was negated by nonenforcement. Railroad managers had little difficulty in contravening the Interstate Commerce Act; monopolists treated the Sherman Antitrust Act with contempt; and timber and mining corporations helped themselves freely to the country's natural resources regardless of the various land laws. Regulatory legislation, as farmers discovered, had little meaning without a sympathetic administration.

That the leaders chose free silver as the one issue on which to wage the battle proved a fatal error. However, in view of the hardships that the banking and currency systems inflicted on the farmers, the decision is understandable. The high capital requirements for initiating national banks made their extension into rural areas very difficult. The State bank notes had been taxed out of existence in 1865, but the power of national banks to issue notes depended on the amount of Federal bonds they held, and the available supply was being contracted owing to Government refunding programs and the competition of investment houses. Thus, between 1880 and 1890, there was a reported drop of over 50 percent in the amount of national-bank notes in circulation. National banks were forbidden by law, moreover, to lend on mortgages (*94*).

Free silver seemed to provide the only basis for the expansion in currency of which the farmer, as a debtor, stood so sorely in need. The world's annual output of gold declined sharply in the late eighties and early nineties, while the amount of greenbacks in circulation had been fixed by law. The two silver acts—the Bland-Allison Act of 1878 and the Sherman Silver Purchase Act of 1890—had been mere sops and both had been repealed. The money in circulation averaged only $23 per capita in 1890; the Populists demanded $50, a figure which was actually topped in 1920. With cheaper money, credit would have been easier; the farmer would have been freed from the clutches of loan sharks, and the heavy mortgage under which he staggered might have been eased. He would have had money to finance farm improvements and buy machinery. That at least was the hope of the agrarian inflationists.

The Populists, heartened by their strength in 1892 and 1894, looked forward to victory in 1896. They organized State and local committees and sent speakers around the country. Expecting the two major parties to stand for gold, they determined to hold their convention last in order to attract the silver elements in the other parties.

The Republicans nominated McKinley, protégé of Mark Hanna, and opposed the free coinage of silver, "except by international agreement" (*94*). To the Democratic Convention, however, came a strongly determined silver faction. It put through a resolution calling for free and unlimited coinage of both silver and gold at the ratio of 16 to 1 "without waiting for the aid or consent of any other nation." In the closing debate on the party's proposed platform, William Jennings Bryan of Nebraska rose and delivered the speech now favored by schoolboy orators. In that day, however, the words were not only thrilling but revolutionary. When Bryan shouted "You come to us and tell us that the great cities are in favor of the gold standard. We reply that the great cities rest upon our broad and fertile prairies. Burn down your cities and leave our farms, and your cities will spring up again as if by magic; but destroy our farms, and the grass will grow in the streets of every city in the country," he epitomized the defiance agrarianism hurled at the masters of industrialism (*94, p. 313*). The platform was adopted and Bryan acclaimed as the party's leader.

The People's Party met in St. Louis later in the same month. It had been so strongly committed in advance to silver that there was no retreat, and free and unlimited coinage of silver was accepted as the paramount issue of the campaign. The former Populist demands for Government ownership and operation of the means of transportation and communication, conservation of natural resources, and direct election of Senators were repeated, but the subtreasury plan—one of the most constructive measures for agricultural relief—was dropped.

The western Populists were determined that the party, having swallowed the silver issue, should endorse Bryan. In opposition stood the majority of the southern delegates. To them the Democratic Party, which in their section represented the old planters and new industrialists, was anathema; to fuse with the enemy now meant surrendering all the gains the small southern farmers had achieved since the Civil War. They were finally voted down, but only after a concession was made to support Tom Watson of Georgia for Vice

President, rather than the Democratic nominee, Arthur Sewall, a conservative Maine banker. Henry Demarest Lloyd, himself a Populist and one of the wisest political thinkers of his day, in commenting on the convention, called it "the most discouraging experience" of his life. The free-silver movement he denounced bitterly as a "fake" and as "the cowbird of the reform movement" (*94, p. 315*).

Events bore out only too well the predictions of the antifusion Populists. Bryan went down to defeat, though he polled 6½ million votes, and with him went the Populist Party. It never recovered from the blow, although it dragged on until 1912.

Improved economic conditions generally, higher prices of farm products, and rising land values brought farmers a measure of prosperity even before the outbreak of the World War. Nevertheless, the agrarian movement did not die out. No new national farmers' party arose, but various associations were formed emphasizing economic cooperation. Typical of these were the Equity Union, American Society of Equity, Gleaners, and most important of all, the Farmers' Union. In 1910, representatives of the Gleaners and the American Society of Equity joined with several State farmers' organizations to establish a Farmers' National Headquarters at Washington to serve as a lobbying agency. A rival group, the National Board of Farm Organizations, created in 1917, also acted as a lobby for farmers' interests. The Nonpartisan League, established first in North Dakota, and then spreading to Minnesota, South Dakota, Montana, Colorado and Idaho, was by 1919 a force to be reckoned with in the national political arena. It did not set itself up as a separate party, but supported those candidates in the two major parties who agreed to accept the league's principles.

Later Developments

The reform movement that the embattled farmers had begun broadened and deepened. In 1900, La Follette, a liberal Republican, became Governor of Wisconsin, and made the State a laboratory for experimentation in bringing corporations under the control of a people's government. Other States experienced somewhat similar currents, so-called "muckrakers" having exposed the tie-up between corrupt political machines and corporations. The tide swept through the Republican Party with Theodore Roosevelt, admirably fitted by personality if not by intellect, as the reform leader. He induced a spark of life in the almost moribund Sherman Antitrust Act; secured legislation designed to strengthen the powers of the Interstate Commerce Commission; and, most important of all, popularized the need for national conservation and irrigation programs. His successor, the less dramatic Taft, furthered each of these three activities.

In 1912, Roosevelt, having failed to capture the Republican nomination, organized the Progressive Party. The three-cornered race split the Republican ranks, and the Democratic Party under Wilson won the Presidency. The platform written by Bryan, who had remained a power among the Democrats since 1896, promised the farmer reform of the country's banking laws, a lowered tariff, and an attempt at easing rural credits. The Underwood Act of 1913 brought reductions in the tariff, while the justice of Greenback and Populist discontent with the National Bank system was given tardy recognition in the passage of the Federal Reserve Act. In the following year, the Smith-Lever bill, providing for agricultural extension work carried directly to farm communities through county agents, became law (*14*). Two years later, in 1916, a Federal Farm Loan Board was established, and 12 regional farm loan banks were set up to provide long-term credits at moderate rates of interest. Another measure, the Smith-Hughes Act of 1917, authorized Federal subsidizing of the teaching of vocational agriculture and home economics in the high schools. To this extent amends were made to the agrarians.

LITERATURE CITED

(1) Abbott, Wilbur C.
1929. NEW YORK IN THE AMERICAN REVOLUTION. 302 pp., illus. New York and London.

(2) Adams, Herbert Baxter.
1885. MARYLAND'S INFLUENCE UPON LAND CESSIONS TO THE UNITED STATES. 102 pp. Baltimore.

(3) Adams, James Truslow.
1923. REVOLUTIONARY NEW ENGLAND, 1691–1776. 469 pp., illus. Boston.

(4) ———
1928. PROVINCIAL SOCIETY, 1690–1763 . . . Hist. Amer. Life 3, 374 pp., illus. New York.

(5) Agelasto, A. M., Doyle, C. B., Meloy, G. S., and Stine, O. C.
1922. THE COTTON SITUATION. U. S. Dept. Agr. Yearbook 1921: 323–406, illus.

(6) Akagi, Roy Hidemichi.
1924. THE TOWN PROPRIETORS OF THE NEW ENGLAND COLONIES; A STUDY OF THEIR DEVELOPMENT, ORGANIZATION, ACTIVITIES AND CONTROVERSIES, 1620–1770. 348 pp. Philadelphia.

(7) Allix, André.
1922. THE GEOGRAPHY OF FAIRS: ILLUSTRATED BY OLD-WORLD EXAMPLES. Geog. Rev. 12: 532–569, illus.

(8) Altschul, Eugen, and Strauss, Frederick.
1937. TECHNICAL PROGRESS AND AGRICULTURAL DEPRESSION. Natl. Bur. Econ. Res. Bul. 67, 32 pp.

(9) Alvord, Henry E.
1900. DAIRYING DEVELOPMENT IN THE UNITED STATES. U. S. Dept. Agr. Yearbook 1899: 381–402, illus.

(10) Anderson, Russell H.
1932–33. NEW YORK AGRICULTURE MEETS THE WEST, 1830–1850. Wis. Mag. Hist. 16: 163–198, 285–296.

(11) ———
1936. GRAIN DRILLS THROUGH THIRTY-NINE CENTURIES. Agr. Hist. 10: 157–205, illus.

(12) Andrews, Charles M.
1924. THE COLONIAL BACKGROUND OF THE AMERICAN REVOLUTION. 218 pp. New Haven and London.

(13) Bahmer, Robert H.
1940. THE AMERICAN SOCIETY OF EQUITY. Agr. Hist. 14: 33–63.

(14) Baker, Gladys.
1939. THE COUNTY AGENT. 226 pp. Chicago.

(15) Baker, O. E.
1937. A GRAPHIC SUMMARY OF FARM MACHINERY, FACILITIES, ROADS, AND EXPENDITURES. U. S. Dept. Agr. Misc. Pub. 264, 33 pp.

(16) Ball, C. R., and others.
1923. OATS, BARLEY, RYE, RICE, GRAIN SORGHUMS, SEED FLAX AND BUCKWHEAT. U. S. Dept. Agr. Yearbook 1922: 469–568, illus.

(17) BALL, C. R., LEIGHTY, C. E., STINE, O. C., and BAKER, O. E.
1922. WHEAT PRODUCTION AND MARKETING. U. S. Dept. Agr. Yearbook 1921: 77–160, illus.
(18) BARNETT, CLARIBEL R.
1928. THE AGRICULTURAL MUSEUM; AN EARLY AMERICAN AGRICULTURAL PERIODICAL. Agr. Hist. 2: 99–102.
(19) BEARD, CHARLES AUSTIN.
1915. ECONOMIC ORIGINS OF JEFFERSONIAN DEMOCRACY. 474 pp. New York.
(20) BEER, GEORGE LOUIS.
1907. BRITISH COLONIAL POLICY, 1754–1765. 327 pp. New York.
(21) ———
1908. THE ORIGINS OF THE BRITISH COLONIAL SYSTEM, 1578–1660. 438 pp. New York.
(22) ———
1912. THE OLD COLONIAL SYSTEM, 1660–1754. 2 v. New York.
(23) BIDWELL, PERCY WELLS.
1916. RURAL ECONOMY IN NEW ENGLAND AT THE BEGINNING OF THE NINETEENTH CENTURY. Conn. Acad. Arts and Sci. Trans. 20: 241–399, illus.
(24) ———
1921. THE AGRICULTURAL REVOLUTION IN NEW ENGLAND. Amer. Hist. Rev. 26: 683–702.
(25) ——— and FALCONER, JOHN I.
1925. HISTORY OF AGRICULTURE IN THE NORTHERN UNITED STATES, 1620–1860. Carnegie Inst. Wash., Pub. 358, 512 pp., illus.
(26) BOND, BEVERLY W., JR.
1919. THE QUIT-RENT SYSTEM IN THE AMERICAN COLONIES. 492 pp. New Haven.
(27) ———
1934. THE CIVILIZATION OF THE OLD NORTHWEST; A STUDY OF POLITICAL, SOCIAL, AND ECONOMIC DEVELOPMENT, 1788–1812. 543 pp. New York.
(28) BOWERS, CLAUDE G.
1925. JEFFERSON AND HAMILTON; THE STRUGGLE FOR DEMOCRACY IN AMERICA. 531 pp. Boston and New York.
(29) ———
1936. JEFFERSON IN POWER; THE DEATH STRUGGLE OF THE FEDERALISTS. 538 pp., illus. Boston.
(30) BRADFORD, WILLIAM.
1898. HISTORY OF PLYMOUTH PLANTATION. 555 pp., illus. Boston.
(31) BRANDES, E. W., and others.
1924. SUGAR. U. S. Dept. Agr. Yearbook 1923: 151–228, illus.
(32) BRIGGS, HAROLD E.
1940. FRONTIERS OF THE NORTHWEST; A HISTORY OF THE UPPER MISSOURI VALLEY. 629 pp., illus. New York.
(33) BRUCE, KATHLEEN.
1932. VIRGINIAN AGRICULTURAL DECLINE TO 1860: A FALLACY. Agr. Hist. 6: 3–13.
(34) BUCK, PAUL H.
1925. THE POOR WHITES OF THE ANTEBELLUM SOUTH. Amer. Hist. Rev. 31: 41–54.
(35) BUCK, SOLON JUSTUS.
1913. THE GRANGER MOVEMENT; A STUDY OF AGRICULTURAL ORGANIZATION AND ITS POLITICAL, ECONOMIC, AND SOCIAL MANIFESTATIONS, 1870–1880. 384 pp., illus. Cambridge.
(36) ———
1920. THE AGRARIAN CRUSADE; A CHRONICLE OF THE FARMER IN POLITICS. 215 pp. New Haven.
(37) BURNETT, EDMUND C.
1928. THE CONTINENTAL CONGRESS AND AGRICULTURAL SUPPLIES. Agr. Hist. 2: 111–128.
(38) CARLTON, FRANK T.
1910. AN AMERICAN UTOPIA. Quart. Jour. Econ. 24: 428–433.

(39) Carrier, Lyman.
1923. the beginnings of agriculture in america. 323 pp., illus. New York.

(40) ———
1937. the united states agricultural society, 1852–1860 . . . Agr. Hist. 11: 278–288.

(41) Carver, Thomas Nixon.
1911. principles of rural economics. 386 pp., illus. Boston, New York, etc.

(42) Chew, Arthur P.
1937. the response of government to agriculture; an account of the origin and development of the united states department of agriculture, on the occasion of its 75th anniversary. 108 pp. Washington, D. C.

(43) ———
1937. science serving agriculture. U. S. Dept. Agr. 43 pp., illus. Washington, D. C.

(44) Chinard, Gilbert.
1929. thomas jefferson, the apostle of americanism. 548 pp., illus. Boston.

(45) Church, Lillian.
1935. history of the plow. U. S. Bur. Agr. Engin. Inform. Ser. 48, 9 pp., illus.

(46) Clapham, John Harold.
1926–38. an economic history of modern britain. . . . 3 v., illus. Cambridge, England.

(47) Clark, Dan Elbert.
[1937.] the west in american history. 682 pp. New York.

(48) Clark, Neil M.
1937. john deere, he gave to the world the steel plow. 61 pp., illus. Moline, Ill.

(49) Clemen, Rudolf Alexander.
1923. the american livestock and meat industry. 872 pp., illus. New York.

(50) Cole, Arthur H.
1927. the american rice-growing industry. Quart. Jour. Econ. 41: 595–643.

(51) Commons, John Rogers, and others, editors.
1910. a documentary history of american industrial society. 11 v., illus. Cleveland, Ohio. See v. 7, pp. 29–37, 285–364; v. 8, pp. 21–78.

(52) Connor, L. G.
1921. a brief history of the sheep industry in the united states. Amer. Hist. Assoc. Ann. Rpt. (1918): 89–197, illus.

(53) Coon, S. J.
1930. influence of the gold camps on the economic development of western montana. Jour. Polit. Econ. 38: 580–599, illus.

(54) Craven, Avery.
1926. soil exhaustion as a factor in the agricultural history of virginia and maryland, 1606–1860. 179 pp. Urbana, Ill.

(55) ———
1928. the agricultural reformers of the ante-bellum south. Amer. Hist. Rev. 33: 302–314.

(56) ———
1932. edmund ruffin, southerner; a study in secession. 283 pp., illus. New York and London.

(57) Cutter, W. P.
1895. a pioneer in agricultural science. U. S. Dept. Agr. Yearbook 1895: 493–502.

(58) Dale, Edward Everett.
1930. the range cattle industry. 216 pp., illus. Norman, Okla.

(59) ———
1937. the cow country in transition. Miss. Val. Hist. Rev. 24: 3–20.

(60) DAY, CLIVE.
1925. HISTORY OF COMMERCE OF THE UNITED STATES. 394 pp. New York.
(61) DEXTER, HENRY MARTYN, AND DEXTER, MORTON.
1905. THE ENGLAND AND HOLLAND OF THE PILGRIM. 673 pp., illus. Boston.
(62) DICK, EVERETT.
1937. THE SOD-HOUSE FRONTIER, 1854–1890; A SOCIAL HISTORY OF THE NORTHERN PLAINS FROM THE CREATION OF KANSAS AND NEBRASKA TO THE ADMISSION OF THE DAKOTAS. 550 pp., illus. New York and London.
(63) DU BOIS, JAMES T., and MATHEWS, GERTRUDE SINGLETON.
1917. GALUSHA A. GROW: THE FATHER OF THE HOMESTEAD LAW. 305 pp. Boston.
(64) DUNBAR, SEYMOUR.
1915. A HISTORY OF TRAVEL IN AMERICA . . . 4 v., illus. Indianapolis.
(65) DUNHAM, HAROLD H.
1937. SOME CRUCIAL YEARS OF THE GENERAL LAND OFFICE, 1875–1890. Agr. Hist. 11: 117–141.
(66) EDWARDS, EVERETT E.
1930. HISTORICAL BACKGROUND OF THE PRESENT SITUATION IN SOUTHERN AGRICULTURE. South. Econ. Assoc. Proc. 3: 78–93.
(67) ———
1934. AMERICAN INDIAN CONTRIBUTIONS TO CIVILIZATION. Minn. Hist. 15: 225–272.
(68) ———
1935. THE NEED OF HISTORICAL MATERIALS FOR AGRICULTURAL RESEARCH. Agr. Hist. 9: 3–11.
(69) ———
1937. SOME SOURCES FOR NORTHWEST HISTORY; AGRICULTURAL PERIODICALS. Minn. Hist. 18: 407–414.
(70) ———
1938. T. L. HAECKER, THE FATHER OF DAIRYING IN MINNESOTA. Minn. Hist. 19: 148–161.
(71) ———
1939. AGRICULTURAL RECORDS; THEIR NATURE AND VALUE FOR RESEARCH. Agr. Hist. 13: 1–12.
(72) FAIRCHILD, DAVID.
1906. OUR PLANT IMMIGRANTS; AN ACCOUNT OF SOME OF THE RESULTS OF THE WORK OF THE OFFICE OF SEED AND PLANT INTRODUCTION OF THE DEPARTMENT OF AGRICULTURE AND OF SOME OF THE PROBLEMS IN PROCESS OF SOLUTION. Natl. Geog. Mag. 17: 179–201, illus.
(73) FARNUM, HENRY W.
1938. CHAPTERS IN THE HISTORY OF SOCIAL LEGISLATION IN THE UNITED STATES TO 1860. Carnegie Inst. Wash., Pub. 488, 496 pp.
(74) FAULKNER, HAROLD UNDERWOOD.
1931. FARM MACHINERY AND THE INDUSTRIAL REVOLUTION. Current Hist. 33: 872–876.
(75) ———
1938. AMERICAN ECONOMIC HISTORY. Ed. 4, 828 pp. New York.
(76) FAUST, ALBERT BERNHARDT.
1909. THE GERMAN ELEMENT IN THE UNITED STATES. 2 v. New York.
(77) FISH, CARL RUSSELL.
1927. THE RISE OF THE COMMON MAN. Hist. Amer. Life 6, 391 pp. New York.
(78) FLÜGEL, FELIX, AND FAULKNER, HAROLD U.
1929. READINGS IN THE ECONOMIC AND SOCIAL HISTORY OF THE UNITED STATES. 978 pp. New York and London.
(79) FORD, AMELIA CLEWLEY.
1910. COLONIAL PRECEDENTS OF OUR NATIONAL LAND SYSTEM AS IT EXISTED IN 1800. Wis. Univ. Bul. 352, Hist. Ser., v. 2, No. 2, 157 pp.

(80) Fossum, Paul R.
1930. EARLY MILLING IN THE CANNON RIVER VALLEY. Minn. Hist. 11: 271–282.
(81) Fussell, G. E.
1932. EARLY FARMING JOURNALS. Econ. Hist. Rev. 3: 417–422.
(82) ———
1933. SOCIAL AND AGRARIAN BACKGROUND OF THE PILGRIM FATHERS. Agr. Hist. 7: 183–202.
(83) ——— and Atwater, V. G. B.
1933. AGRICULTURE OF RURAL ENGLAND IN THE SEVENTEENTH CENTURY. Econ. Geog. 9: 379–394, illus.
(84) Gage, Charles E.
1937. HISTORICAL FACTORS AFFECTING AMERICAN TOBACCO TYPES AND USES AND THE EVOLUTION OF THE AUCTION MARKET. Agr. Hist. 11: 43–57.
(85) Ganoe, John T.
1937. THE DESERT LAND ACT IN OPERATION, 1877–1891. Agr. Hist. 11: 142–157.
(86) Garner, W. W., and others.
1923. HISTORY AND STATUS OF TOBACCO CULTURE. U. S. Dept. Agr. Yearbook 1922: 395–468, illus.
(87) Gates, Paul Wallace.
1936. THE HOMESTEAD LAW IN AN INCONGRUOUS LAND SYSTEM. Amer. Hist. Rev. 41: 652–681.
(88) Graham, Gerald S.
1938. THE GYPSUM TRADE OF THE MARITIME PROVINCES. Agr. Hist. 12: 209–223.
(89) Gray, Lewis Cecil.
1928. THE MARKET SURPLUS PROBLEMS OF COLONIAL TOBACCO. Agr. Hist. 2: 1–34.
(90) ———
1930. ECONOMIC EFFICIENCY AND COMPETITIVE ADVANTAGES OF SLAVERY UNDER THE PLANTATION SYSTEM. Agr. Hist. 4: 31–47.
(91) ———
1933. HISTORY OF AGRICULTURE IN THE SOUTHERN UNITED STATES TO 1860. Carnegie Inst. Wash., Pub. 430, 2 v., illus.
(92) Greathouse, Charles H.
1898. HISTORICAL SKETCH OF THE U. S. DEPARTMENT OF AGRICULTURE; ITS OBJECTS AND PRESENT ORGANIZATION. U. S. Dept. Agr., Div. Pub. Bul. 3, 74 pp., illus.
(93) Greene, Evarts B., and Harrington, Virginia D.
1932. AMERICAN POPULATION BEFORE THE FEDERAL CENSUS OF 1790. 228 pp. New York.
(94) Hacker, Louis M., and Kendrick, Benjamin B.
1939. THE UNITED STATES SINCE 1865. Ed. 3, 821 pp., illus. New York.
(95) Haney, L. H.
1908. A CONGRESSIONAL HISTORY OF RAILWAYS IN THE UNITED STATES TO 1850 . . . 273 pp., illus. Madison, Wis.
(96) Hansen, Marcus L.
1940. THE ATLANTIC MIGRATION, 1607–1860: A HISTORY OF THE CONTINUING SETTLEMENT OF THE UNITED STATES. Edited by Arthur Meier Schlesinger. 409 pp. Cambridge.
(97) Hayter, Earl W.
1939. BARBED WIRE FENCING—A PRAIRIE INVENTION. Agr. Hist. 13: 189–207.
(98) Heaton, Herbert.
1936. ECONOMIC HISTORY OF EUROPE. 775 pp., illus. New York.
(99) Heyward, Duncan C.
1937. SEED FROM MADAGASCAR. 256 pp., illus. Chapel Hill, N. C.
(100) Hibbard, B. H.
1904. THE HISTORY OF AGRICULTURE IN DANE COUNTY, WISCONSIN. 214 pp., illus. Madison.
(101) ———
1939. A HISTORY OF THE PUBLIC LAND POLICIES. 591 pp. New York.

(102) HICKS, JOHN D.
1931. THE POPULIST REVOLT; A HISTORY OF THE FARMERS' ALLIANCE AND THE PEOPLE'S PARTY. 473 pp., illus. Minneapolis.

(103) HOWARD, L. O.
1929. THE RISE OF APPLIED ENTOMOLOGY IN THE UNITED STATES. Agr. Hist. 3: 131–139.

(104) HUEBNER, GROVER G.
1924. AGRICULTURAL COMMERCE; THE ORGANIZATION OF AMERICAN COMMERCE IN AGRICULTURAL COMMODITIES. Rev. and enl. ed., 529 pp., illus. New York and London.

(105) HUTCHINSON, WILLIAM T.
1930–35. CYRUS HALL M'CORMICK. 2 v., illus. New York and London.

(106) ———
1935. THE REAPER INDUSTRY AND MIDWESTERN AGRICULTURE, 1855–75. *In* Essays in Honor of William E. Dodd, edited by Avery Craven, pp. 115–130. Chicago.

(107) ICKES, HAROLD L.
1940. NOT GUILTY! RICHARD A. BALLINGER—AN AMERICAN DREYFUS. Sat. Evening Post 212 (48): 9–11, 123–126, 128.

(108) ISE, JOHN.
1936. SOD AND STUBBLE; THE STORY OF A KANSAS HOMESTEAD. 326 pp. New York.

(109) JACOBSTEIN, MEYER.
1907. THE TOBACCO INDUSTRY IN THE UNITED STATES . . . 208 pp. New York.

(110) JAMESON, JOHN FRANKLIN.
1926. THE AMERICAN REVOLUTION CONSIDERED AS A SOCIAL MOVEMENT. 158 pp. Princeton.

(111) JENSEN, MERRILL.
1936. THE CESSION OF THE OLD NORTHWEST. Miss. Val. Hist. Rev. 23: 27–48.

(112) ———
1939. CREATION OF THE NATIONAL DOMAIN, 1781–1784. Miss. Val. Hist. Rev. 26: 323–342.

(113) JERNEGAN, MARCUS WILSON.
1931. LABORING AND DEPENDENT CLASSES IN COLONIAL AMERICA, 1607–1783; STUDIES OF THE ECONOMIC, EDUCATIONAL, AND SOCIAL SIGNIFICANCE OF SLAVES, SERVANTS, APPRENTICES, AND POOR FOLK. 256 pp. Chicago.

(114) JOHNSON, EMORY R., VAN METRE, T. W., HUEBNER, G. G., and HANCHETT, D. S.
1915. HISTORY OF DOMESTIC AND FOREIGN COMMERCE OF THE UNITED STATES. 2 v., illus. Washington, D. C. (Reprinted 1922.)

(115) KIRKLAND, EDWARD C.
1939. A HISTORY OF AMERICAN ECONOMIC LIFE. Rev. ed., 810 pp., illus. New York.

(116) KUHLMANN, CHARLES BYRON.
1929. THE DEVELOPMENT OF THE FLOUR-MILLING INDUSTRY IN THE UNITED STATES. 349 pp. Boston and New York.

(117) LARSON, C. W., and others.
1923. THE DAIRY INDUSTRY. U. S. Dept. Agr. Yearbook 1922: 281–394, illus.

(118) LEAVITT, CHARLES T.
1934. TRANSPORTATION AND THE LIVESTOCK INDUSTRY OF THE MIDDLE WEST TO 1860. Agr. Hist. 8: 20–33.

(119) LEIGHTY, C. E., WARBURTON, C. W., STINE, O. C., and BAKER, O. E.
1922. THE CORN CROP. U. S. Dept. Agr. Yearbook 1921: 161–226, illus.

(120) LEWTON, FREDERICK L.
1937. HISTORICAL NOTES ON THE COTTON GIN. Smithsn. Inst. Ann. Rpt. 1937: 549–563, illus.

(121) LOEHR, RODNEY C.
1937. THE INFLUENCE OF ENGLISH AGRICULTURE ON AMERICAN AGRICULTURE, 1775–1825. Agr. Hist. 11: 3–15.

(122) LORD, RUSSELL.
1938. BEHOLD OUR LAND. 310 pp., illus. Boston.
(123) ———
1938. TO HOLD THIS SOIL. U. S. Dept. Agr. Misc. Pub. 321, 122 pp., illus.
(124) MCILWAINE, SHIELDS.
1939. THE SOUTHERN POOR-WHITE, FROM LUBBERLAND TO TOBACCO ROAD. 274 pp. Norman, Okla.
(125) MCMASTER, JOHN BACH.
1883–1910. A HISTORY OF THE PEOPLE OF THE UNITED STATES, FROM THE REVOLUTION TO THE CIVIL WAR. 7 v. New York.
(126) MALIN, JAMES C.
1932. THE BACKGROUND OF THE FIRST BILLS TO ESTABLISH A BUREAU OF MARKETS, 1911–12. Agr. Hist. 6: 107–129.
(127) ———
1936. THE ADAPTATION OF THE AGRICULTURAL SYSTEM TO SUB-HUMID ENVIRONMENT. Agr. Hist. 10: 118–141.
(128) MATHEWS, LOIS KIMBALL.
1909. THE EXPANSION OF NEW ENGLAND. 303 pp. Boston.
(129) MAZYCK, WALTER H.
[1932.] GEORGE WASHINGTON AND THE NEGRO. 180 pp. Washington, D. C.
(130) MEYER, BALTHASAR HENRY, editor.
1917. HISTORY OF TRANSPORTATION IN THE UNITED STATES BEFORE 1860. 678 pp., illus. Washington, D. C.
(131) MILLER, JOHN C.
1936. SAM ADAMS: PIONEER IN PROPAGANDA. 437 pp. Boston.
(132) MILLER, MERRITT FINLEY.
1902. THE EVOLUTION OF REAPING MACHINES. U. S. Dept. Agr. Off. Expt. Stas. Bul. 103, 43 pp., illus.
(133) MORRIS, RICHARD B.
1927. PRIMOGENITURE AND ENTAILED ESTATES IN AMERICA. Columbia Law Rev. 27: 24–51.
(134) MUDGE, EUGENE TENBROECK.
1939. THE SOCIAL PHILSOPHY OF JOHN TAYLOR OF CAROLINE . . . 227 pp. New York.
(135) NEELY, WAYNE CALDWELL.
1935. THE AGRICULTURAL FAIR. 313 pp., illus. New York.
(136) NETTELS, CURTIS PUTNAM.
1934. THE MONEY SUPPLY OF THE AMERICAN COLONIES BEFORE 1720. Wis. Univ. Studies Social Sci. and Hist. 20, 300 pp.
(137) ———
1938. THE ROOTS OF AMERICAN CIVILIZATION; A HISTORY OF AMERICAN COLONIAL LIFE. 748 pp., illus. New York.
(138) NIXON, HERMAN CLARENCE.
1935. THE NEW SOUTH AND THE OLD CROP (1865–80). *In* Essays in Honor of William E. Dodd, edited by Avery Craven, pp. 320–334. Chicago.
(139) NOURSE, EDWIN G.
1924. AMERICAN AGRICULTURE AND THE EUROPEAN MARKET. 333 pp. New York and London.
(140) OSGOOD, ERNEST STAPLES.
1929. THE DAY OF THE CATTLEMAN. 283 pp., illus. Minneapolis.
(141) OWSLEY, FRANK L., and OWSLEY, HARRIET C.
1940. THE ECONOMIC BASIS OF SOCIETY IN THE LATE ANTE-BELLUM SOUTH. Jour. South. Hist. 6: 24–45.
(142) PAXSON, FREDERIC LOGAN.
1907. THE PACIFIC RAILROADS AND THE DISAPPEARANCE OF THE FRONTIER IN AMERICA. Amer. Hist. Assoc. Ann. Rpt. (1907) 1: 107–118, illus.
(143) ———
1924. HISTORY OF THE AMERICAN FRONTIER, 1763–1893. 598 pp., illus. Boston and New York.

(144) Pelzer, Louis.
1936. THE CATTLEMAN'S FRONTIER; A RECORD OF THE TRANS-MISSISSIPPI CATTLE INDUSTRY FROM OXEN TRAINS TO POOLING COMPANIES, 1850–1890. 351 pp., illus. Glendale, Calif.

(145) Phillips, Ulrich Bonnell.
1918. AMERICAN NEGRO SLAVERY. 529 pp. New York and London.

(146) ———
1928. THE CENTRAL THEME OF SOUTHERN HISTORY. Amer. Hist. Rev. 34: 30–43.

(147) ———
1929. LIFE AND LABOR IN THE OLD SOUTH. 375 pp., illus. Boston.

(148) Pirtle, Thomas Ross.
1926. HISTORY OF THE DAIRY INDUSTRY. 645 pp., illus. Chicago.

(149) Plumb, Charles Sumner.
1924. FELIX RENICK, PIONEER. Ohio Archaeol. and Hist. Quart. 33 3–66, illus.

(150) Pooley, William Vipond.
1908. SETTLEMENT OF ILLINOIS, 1830–1850. Wis. Univ. Bul. 220, ser. 5, v. 1, No. 4, 308 pp., illus.

(151) Pratt, Julius.
1925. EXPANSIONISTS OF 1812. 309 pp. New York.

(152) Purcell, Richard J.
1918. CONNECTICUT IN TRANSITION, 1775–1818. 471 pp. Washington, D. C.

(153) Riches, Naomi.
1937. THE AGRICULTURAL REVOLUTION IN NORFOLK. 194 pp., illus. Chapel Hill, N. C.

(154) Riegel, Robert E.
1930. AMERICA MOVES WEST. 595 pp. New York.

(155) Robbins, Roy M.
1931. PREEMPTION—A FRONTIER TRIUMPH. Miss. Val. Hist. Rev. 18: 331–349.

(156) ———
1933. HORACE GREELEY: LAND REFORM AND UNEMPLOYMENT, 1837–1862. Agr. Hist. 7: 18–41.

(157) ———
1939. THE PUBLIC DOMAIN IN THE ERA OF EXPLOITATION, 1862–1901. Agr. Hist. 13: 97–108.

(158) Robert, Joseph Clarke.
1933. RISE OF THE TOBACCO WAREHOUSE AUCTION SYSTEM IN VIRGINIA, 1800–1860. Agr. Hist. 7: 170–182.

(159) ———
1938. THE TOBACCO KINGDOM; PLANTATION, MARKET, AND FACTORY IN VIRGINIA AND NORTH CAROLINA, 1800–1860. 286 pp., illus. Durham, N. C.

(160) Rogin, Leo.
1931. THE INTRODUCTION OF FARM MACHINERY IN ITS RELATION TO THE PRODUCTIVITY OF LABOR IN THE AGRICULTURE OF THE UNITED STATES DURING THE NINETEENTH CENTURY. 260 pp., illus. Berkeley, Calif.

(161) Ross, Earle D.
1926. THE EVOLUTION OF THE AGRICULTURAL FAIR IN THE NORTHWEST. Iowa Jour. Hist. and Politics 24: 445–480.

(162) ———
1929. LINCOLN AND AGRICULTURE. Agr. Hist. 3: 51–66.

(163) ———
1933. HORACE GREELEY AND THE BEGINNINGS OF THE NEW AGRICULTURE. Agr. Hist. 7: 1–17.

(164) ———
1933. HORACE GREELEY AND THE WEST. Miss. Val. Hist. Rev. 20: 63–74.

(165) ———
1938. THE "FATHER" OF THE LAND-GRANT COLLEGE. Agr. Hist. 12: 151–186.

(166) Ryerson, Knowles A.
1933. history and significance of the foreign plant introduction work of the united states department of agriculture. Agr. Hist. 7: 110–128.

(167) Sanford, Albert H.
1916. the story of agriculture in the united states. 394 pp., illus. Boston, New York, and Chicago.

(168) Schell, Herbert S.
1931. drought and agriculture in eastern south dakota during the eighteen nineties. Agr. Hist. 5: 162–180.

(169) Schlesinger, Arthur Meier.
1922. new viewpoints in american history. 299 pp. New York.

(170) ———
1925. political and social history of the united states, 1829–1925. 576 pp. New York.

(171) ———
1940. the city in american history. Miss. Val. Hist. Rev. 27: 43–66.

(172) Schmidt, Louis Bernard.
1920. the westward movement of the wheat growing industry in the united states. Iowa Jour. Hist. and Politics 18: 396–412.

(173) ———
1921. the internal grain trade of the united states, 1860–1890. Iowa Jour. Hist. and Politics 19: 196–245.

(174) ———
1930. the agricultural revolution in the united states—1860–1930. Science 72: [585]–594.

(175) Shannon, Fred A.
1934. economic history of the people of the united states. 942 pp., illus. New York.

(176) Sherman, Caroline B.
1937. the legal basis of the marketing work of the united states department of agriculture. Agr. Hist. 11: 289–301.

(177) Shryock, Richard H.
1939. british versus german traditions in colonial agriculture. Miss. Val. Hist. Rev. 26: 39–54.

(178) ———
1939. the pennsylvania germans in american history. Pa. Mag. Hist. and Biog. 63: 261–281.

(179) Simms, Henry Harrison.
1932. life of john taylor; the story of a brilliant leader in the early virginia state rights school. 234 pp. Richmond.

(180) Sioussat, St. George L.
1918. andrew johnson and the early phases of the homestead bill. Miss. Val. Hist. Rev. 5: 253–287.

(181) Spinden, Herbert J.
1928. the population of ancient america. Geog. Rev. 18: 641–660, illus.

(182) ———
1928. thank the american indian . . . Sci. Amer. 138: 330–332, illus.

(183) Stephenson, George Malcolm.
1917. political history of the public lands, from 1840 to 1862, from preemption to homestead. 296 pp. Boston.

(184) Sutherland, Stella H.
1936. population distribution in colonial america. 353 pp., illus. New York.

(185) Treat, Payson Jackson.
1910. the national land system, 1785–1820. 426 pp., illus. New York.

(186) Trimble, William.
1921. historical aspects of the surplus food production of the united states, 1862–1902. Agr. Hist. Soc. Papers 1: 221–239.

(187) True, Alfred Charles.
1928. a history of agricultural extension work in the united states, 1785–1923. U. S. Dept. Agr. Misc. Pub. 15, 220 pp.

(188) TRUE, ALFRED CHARLES.
1929. A HISTORY OF AGRICULTURAL EDUCATION IN THE UNITED STATES, 1785–1925. U. S. Dept. Agr. Misc. Pub. 36, 436 pp., illus.
(189) TRUE, RODNEY H.
[1935.] SKETCH OF THE HISTORY OF THE PHILADELPHIA SOCIETY FOR PROMOTING AGRICULTURE. 52 pp. [Philadelphia.]
(190) TRYON, ROLLO M.
1917. HOUSEHOLD MANUFACTURES IN THE UNITED STATES, 1640–1860. A STUDY IN INDUSTRIAL HISTORY. 413 pp. Chicago.
(191) TURNER, FREDERICK JACKSON.
1906. RISE OF THE NEW WEST, 1819–1829. 366 pp., illus. New York.
(192) ———
1921. THE FRONTIER IN AMERICAN HISTORY. 375 pp. New York.
(193) ———
[1935.] THE UNITED STATES, 1830–1850 . . . 602 pp., illus., New York.
(194) UNITED STATES BUREAU OF AGRICULTURAL ECONOMICS.
1924. THE WHEAT SITUATION. U. S. Dept. Agr. Yearbook 1923: 95–150, illus.
(195) ———
1937. WASHINGTON, JEFFERSON, LINCOLN AND AGRICULTURE. 102 pp., illus. Washington, D. C.
(196) UNITED STATES BUREAU OF THE CENSUS.
1853. THE SEVENTH CENSUS OF THE UNITED STATES: 1850. 1022 pp. Washington, D. C.
(197) UNITED STATES CONGRESS.
1863. AN ACT TO ESTABLISH A DEPARTMENT OF AGRICULTURE. Stat. L., 37th Cong., 2d sess. (1862) 12: 387–388.
(198) ———
1892. AN ACT TO REPEAL TIMBER-CULTURE LAWS, AND FOR OTHER PURPOSES. Stat. L., 51st Cong., 2d sess. (1891) 26: 1095–1103.
(199) UNITED STATES DEPARTMENT OF AGRICULTURE.
1863. REPORT OF THE COMMISSIONER OF AGRICULTURE FOR THE YEAR 1862. 632 pp., illus. Washington, D. C.
(200) ———
1889. FIRST REPORT OF THE SECRETARY OF AGRICULTURE. 560 pp., illus. Washington, D. C.
(201) ———
1915. OUR FOREIGN TRADE IN FARM AND FOREST PRODUCTS. U. S. Dept. Agr. Bul. 296, 51 pp., illus.
(202) UNITED STATES FEDERAL FARM BOARD.
1932. STATISTICS OF FARMERS' SELLING AND BUYING ASSOCIATIONS, UNITED STATES, 1863–1931. U. S. Fed. Farm Bd. Bul. 9, 91 pp., illus.
(203) USHER, ABBOTT PAYSON.
1920. AN INTRODUCTION TO THE INDUSTRIAL HISTORY OF ENGLAND. 529 pp. Boston.
(204) VAN WAGENEN, JARED, JR.
1927. THE GOLDEN AGE OF HOMESPUN. N. Y. State Dept. Agr. and Markets Agr. Bul. 203, 95 pp., illus.
(205) WANLASS, WILLIAM L.
1920. THE UNITED STATES DEPARTMENT OF AGRICULTURE; A STUDY IN ADMINISTRATION. 131 pp. Baltimore.
(206) WEBB, WALTER PRESCOTT.
1931. THE GREAT PLAINS. 525 pp., illus. Boston.
(207) WELLINGTON, RAYNOR GREENLEAF
1914. THE POLITICAL AND SECTIONAL INFLUENCE OF THE PUBLIC LANDS, 1828–1842. 131 pp. Cambridge.
(208) WERTENBAKER, THOMAS JEFFERSON.
1922. THE PLANTERS OF COLONIAL VIRGINIA. 260 pp. Princeton.
(209) WIEST, EDWARD.
1923. AGRICULTURAL ORGANIZATION IN THE UNITED STATES. 618 pp., illus. Lexington, Ky.
(210) WILEY, B. I.
1939. SALIENT CHANGES IN SOUTHERN AGRICULTURE SINCE THE CIVIL WAR. Agr. Hist. 13: 65–76.

(211) WILSON, HAROLD F.
1935. THE RISE AND DECLINE OF THE SHEEP INDUSTRY IN NORTHERN NEW ENGLAND. Agr. Hist. 9: 12–40.

(212) ———
1936. THE HILL COUNTRY OF NORTHERN NEW ENGLAND; ITS SOCIAL AND ECONOMIC HISTORY, 1790–1830. Columbia Univ. Studies Hist. Amer. Agr. 3, 455 pp., illus. New York.

(213) WILSON, M. L.
1919. THE EVOLUTION OF MONTANA AGRICULTURE IN ITS EARLY PERIOD. Miss. Val. Hist. Assoc. Proc. (1917–18) 9: [429]–440.

(214) WILTSE, CHARLES MAURICE.
1935. THE JEFFERSONIAN TRADITION IN AMERICAN DEMOCRACY. 273 pp. Chapel Hill, N. C.

(215) WITTKE, CARL.
1940. WE WHO BUILT AMERICA; THE SAGA OF THE IMMIGRANT. 547 pp. New York.

(216) WOESTEMEYER, INA FAYE.
1939. THE WESTWARD MOVEMENT; A BOOK OF READINGS ON OUR CHANGING FRONTIERS. 500 pp. New York.

(217) WOODWARD, CARL RAYMOND.
1927. THE DEVELOPMENT OF AGRICULTURE IN NEW JERSEY, 1640–1880; A MONOGRAPHIC STUDY IN AGRICULTURAL HISTORY. N. J. Agr. Expt. Sta. Bul. 451, 321 pp., illus.

(218) WOODWARD, CARL R.
1929. AGRICULTURAL LEGISLATION IN COLONIAL NEW JERSEY. Agr. Hist. 3: 15–28.

(219) ZEICHNER, OSCAR.
1939. THE TRANSITION FROM SLAVE TO FREE AGRICULTURAL LABOR IN THE SOUTHERN STATES. Agr. Hist. 13: 22–32.

Agriculture in the World War Period

by A. B. Genung [1]

IN THE HISTORY of American agriculture the World War was a turning point. What happened to our agriculture during the war is widely known in a general way. Here is a carefully documented account that gives the story in more detail. It tells what the war did to our grain production, and to cotton, tobacco, hogs, cattle, dairy products, horses, sheep, poultry; what effect it had on prices, on the gross income of agriculture, on land values, on costs of production, and on the returns to farmers for their labor; and what its social effects were on the farm population. Finally, the author points out that "the alteration of the traditional financial and trade relationships between this country and Europe, which in the normal course might have spread itself over a span of two generations, was precipitated by the war within half a dozen years. Suddenly and under great stress, this country found itself compelled to reorient its entire farm economy." The war was the prelude to a new world.

THE PERIOD from about 1897 down to the World War was perhaps one of the best in our agricultural history. During that time commodity prices were slowly rising. Farming had emerged finally as a comparatively stable business, with gradually advancing land values, an improving physical plant, fairly tolerable conditions of tenure and

[1] A. B. Genung is Senior Agricultural Economist, Division of Economic Information, Bureau of Agricultural Economics.

debt, and a strengthened voice in national affairs. The major problems of that pre-war period were considered to be problems of production.

The production of an exportable surplus was then a cornerstone of our agricultural system. We were annually selling abroad something like 150 to 200 million bushels of wheat, 8 to 9 million bales of cotton, and well toward 1 billion pounds of pork, in addition to fairly large quantities of tobacco and fruit. In fact the export of agricultural products was the chief medium by which we met the service charges on our foreign obligations, for we were still a debtor Nation.

Government agricultural policy in those years fostered education and research calculated to make production more efficient. It had given some impetus to cooperative marketing, cheaper transportation, better credit facilities, and generally had helped to make a more favorable place for agriculture in the national economy. The country was committed to a protective tariff system throughout most of that time.

It was during that relatively tranquil period that the exploitation of virgin land resources had leveled off into a more intensive and conservative system, a system that involved also the adjustment of an age-old craft to the new order of machines and commercialization.

THE WAR A NEW AND DOMINANT FORCE

Then came the World War.

Suddenly the productive industries felt the impact of a force wholly new to that generation, a force so powerful that it could and did dominate the economy of this country and of much of the world. Almost overnight, as history is reckoned, production had to fit itself to an altered pattern of trade and consumption. Instead of developing through long, quiet years of efficient farming, gaged to fit the needs of a rapidly growing nation and a prosperous world market, agriculture had to be adapted to the pressures and the disruptions of war. Developments that normally would have been spread over generations were packed into half a dozen years.

That was what the war did to our agriculture, as a first consequence. It speeded it up, lifted it from its rational course of progress and forced it to an unnatural exertion in response to an abnormal demand. Under the stimulus of price and patriotism—finally of outright inflation—the farm business labored and expanded and provided the sinews. Then, in the aftermath, it was left high and dry with its output up and its prices down, its foreign market shrunken, its fixed charges a heavy burden. But that is a later story.

NATIONAL PURPOSE TO INCREASE FOOD PRODUCTION

The war period, for present purposes, must be considered as including the years 1914 through about 1920–21. Although the Armistice came in November 1918, the upward or expansion movement in agriculture did not culminate until 1920; some phases of it not until 1921.

National policies through that period were those inevitable in the emergency. The one objective was to win the war. Since certain foods, feeds, and fibers were vital, nearly all public action in regard to those things was calculated to increase the supply. Of course the rising cost of living became an issue among city people after a time, and the price policies of the Food Administration, for example, had to be fixed with due regard to that factor. But in the main the attitude and aim of official effort was to stimulate production.

Abundant evidence of this attitude as translated into public policy may be noted in the publications of the Committee on Public Information and the Food Administration, in the speeches of lawmakers, and in the administration of the wartime legislation.

A member of the Food Administration and of the War Trade Board in the spring of 1918 expressed the official spirit of American participation thus:

> Prior to our entrance into the war, the Allied peoples had suffered losses in resources and in men of which our people have no conception. No matter what sacrifices and losses the future may bring, it is not possible that our total relinquishments at the end of the war, in proportion to our resources and population, can equal those of the Allied peoples. . . . It is from every point of view the imperative duty, and ought to be esteemed the privilege, of the American people to assume our full share of the war burden. . . . Our efforts must be to hold the quantity of foodstuffs of the Allies to the highest point permitted by transportation facilities, and to make their diet in the qualitative sense as close to the normal as possible (*9*).[2]

Within the Department of Agriculture this expansion policy found expression in various ways, among them a rapid enlargement of the extension work which was then just beginning to make headway in the States. This work was put on a national basis in 1914 by passage of the Smith-Lever Act. The number of counties with agricultural agents jumped from 928 in 1914 to 2,435 in 1918, and the total extension staff from 2,601 in 1915 to 6,728 in 1918. The total appropriation for extension work rose from $3,597,235 in 1915 to $11,302,764 in 1918 and to nearly $17,000,000 in 1921. A special war-emergency appropriation of nearly $3,000,000 was made for extension work in August 1917. After the war, the number of counties with agents dropped to 2,043 by 1921, though it increased steadily in after years.

Before the World War the Allies—the United Kingdom, France, Belgium, and Italy—had leaned heavily on other countries for some of their indispensable food staples. The pre-war production of wheat, corn, oats, barley, and rye by these nations totaled about 1½ billion bushels a year; but their annual consumption of these cereals was nearly 2¼ billions.

In 1913 the Allies had imported 1½ billion pounds of animal fats. The dairy-fat supply normally came largely from Denmark, the Netherlands, Switzerland, Scandinavia, and Russia. The war cut off a considerable part of this supply by blockade or because of inability of the neutrals to get the feedstuffs wherewith to maintain their dairy output. Similar difficulties arose in respect to supplies of meat and sugar. In short the process of belt tightening began in western Europe almost immediately, and the food situation presently assumed a gravity equal to that of manpower and munitions.

Not only were Russia and the Baltic countries cut off, but the destruction of Allied shipping by submarines and mines had made the long haul from Australia and Argentina an unjustified risk as

[2] Italic numbers in parentheses refer to Literature Cited, p. 295.

compared with the haul from North America. In other words, it was to Canada and above all to the United States that the Allies looked, at first normally but in the end desperately, for wheat, meat, and fats as well as large quantities of other foods and feedstuffs.

Hostilities began on July 28, 1914, with the Austrian declaration of war upon Serbia. Russia entered the conflict on August 1, followed 2 days later by France, and on August 4 by England. The first shock instantly closed all the stock and commodity exchanges on this side of the Atlantic, this step being taken to prevent the dumping of foreign holdings here and general demoralization of our markets. The effect on the agricultural markets was momentarily depressing.

Soon after the outbreak of the war, however, England and France sent official representatives to the United States to handle the buying of supplies and began negotiating loans to supplement their balances already existing here. It is interesting to note that the Federal Reserve Board, as a result of an inquiry made September 1, 1914, reported American indebtedness to Europe maturing within the next few months as about 500 million dollars. The effect of the first war buying on our international trade—in fact what proved to be the historic reversal of our position from a debtor to a creditor nation—registered almost at once. The balance of trade had been running against us since April, and in August it was still over 19 million dollars against us. But in September the tide turned—the trade balance that month was 15 million dollars in our favor. In December 1914 it had climbed to 132 million in our favor and was rapidly increasing. Thus the vital war needs began to apply their powerful suction in American markets.

In order to convey a useful picture of the effects of the wartime demands upon our farm enterprises it is necessary to sketch what happened in certain individual lines of production. Not all lines were stimulated; some were depressed.

War is more harshly discriminating than peace. When peoples are fighting for existence they toss overboard the niceties of diet and of dress. The semiluxury foods—fresh fruits, certain vegetables, cream, lamb, and so on—are mostly dispensed with. Nations reach imperatively for bread, heavy meats, fats, and sugar. And always wool is needed for the soldiers.

WAR STIMULATION OF PRODUCTION

Wheat

Among our individual farm enterprises stimulated by the war, the growing of wheat received the first and by far the greatest impetus. In the 10 years before the war this country had harvested annually an average of about 48 million acres of wheat—about 30 million of winter and 18 million of spring wheat. The United States had been a wheat exporter ever since the founding of the country. The acreage and yield had increased steadily from the Civil War until about 1900. From that year to the outbreak of the World War, however, wheat acreage had shown some tendency to decline. Our exports of wheat likewise had dropped off considerably in the decade preceding the war. Nevertheless, we were, at the time the war broke out, one of the four chief wheat-exporting countries. Russia had been exporting about 165 million bushels a year, the United States some 107 million, Canada 94 million, and Argentina 85 million. Western Europe was and had been the great import market.

The war very soon closed the Dardenelles and bottled up the Russian wheat. It was this sudden choking off of the Russian supply that turned British eyes westward in an urgent search for more bread grain.

So the bidding for wheat began in American markets. By early 1915 the Chicago price had advanced more than 60 cents a bushel from the season's low point. Farmers were getting about $1.25 a bushel at interior markets. By May 1, 1915, wheat was bringing $1.40 a bushel.

The Economist, a London weekly, on January 9, 1915, tersely explained the rising prices to the British public as follows (*1, p. 49*):

> Not only are we at war, but Russia, our chief source of supply, is at war, and is unable, owing to the blockade of the Black Sea and the Baltic, to export her wheat crop—which, by the way, is not a good one. Then the Argentine harvest is reported to be suffering from bad weather. Two other big exporters are Australia and India. The wheat crop of the first has failed through drought, and the supplies from India are not overabundant, if we may judge from the fact that the Indian Government has, rightly or wrongly, put a restriction on exports.

By early 1915 the United States was exporting about 55 million dollars' worth of wheat a month—it was the export of wheat and to some extent of cotton that had turned the balance of trade so overwhelmingly in our favor. The wheat territory was responding to the pressure of war.

The area of wheat sown in the fall of 1914 was increased about 5 million acres and that in the spring of 1915 nearly 2 million acres over the previous sowings. More than 60 million acres were harvested, and the yield per acre was a record. The upshot was that 1915 was the year of our famous billion-bushel wheat crop—the largest ever grown before or since.

This huge crop, in a good year for wheat all over the world, brought a slump in price down to about the pre-war level, and the price remained low that winter and the following spring. Some 243 million bushels were exported from that crop.

Following the record crop and falling prices of the previous season, the acreage harvested in 1916 was reduced to 52 million and the crop to 636 million bushels, partly by a bad epidemic of black stem rust. The price advanced sharply that fall; growers could get $1.50 or more for good wheat. And by the spring of 1917 the price had soared to over $2.40 and farmers had swept their bins clean. Wheat now was valuable property. Incidentally, there was no little concern in the cities, by that time, about the high cost of flour and various other foods, a fact which had some effect presently in the creation of the Food Administration.

In the spring of 1917 the United States entered the war, and with its entry public policy was crystallized more definitely with respect to food supplies. The Food and Fuel Control Act of August 10, 1917, was one of the most drastic economic measures ever enacted into law in this country, up to that time. Briefly, it gave the President power to control the entire food supply, through provisions for licensing all handlers of food, fixing prices, punishing hoarding or the limiting of production, regulating trade practices, requisitioning supplies, operating manufacturing plants, railroads, etc., and the buying, selling, and storage of certain specified foodstuffs.

The Food Control Act guaranteed a minimum price of $2 a bushel for the wheat crop of 1918. Then on August 30 the President fixed a minimum price for the 1917 crop of $2.20 for No. 1 Northern at Chicago, with differentials for other grades and markets. Through the operations of the United States Grain Corporation this became the basic price for wheat. Then, also, to the incentive of price was added the urgent plea of patriotism. Food would win the war! Every form of educational propaganda that could be devised was employed to stimulate wheat acreage. But 1917 was a poor growing season; only 45 million acres were harvested. The crop was virtually the same size as the small one of the previous season—637 million bushels.

Then came the pinch in Europe.

> The most strenuous efforts had to be made during the winter and spring of 1917–18 to keep the Allied armies and civilians supplied with breadstuffs. No one will ever know the strain under which our own and Allied officials labored when, with practically a crop failure in this country, stocks of bread grains abroad fell below the danger point and the shortage and uncertainty of shipping rendered it doubtful if they could be replenished in time. February to April 1918, marked the crisis in the bread supply of the Allied nations. Conservation by the American people and close cooperation between officials made it possible to pass this turning-point which, otherwise, might have changed the history of the war (*8*).

Out of that small 1917 crop 133 million bushels were exported.

By an Executive order on June 21, 1918, the price of wheat was raised to $2.26 for No. 1 Northern spring and its equivalents at Chicago.

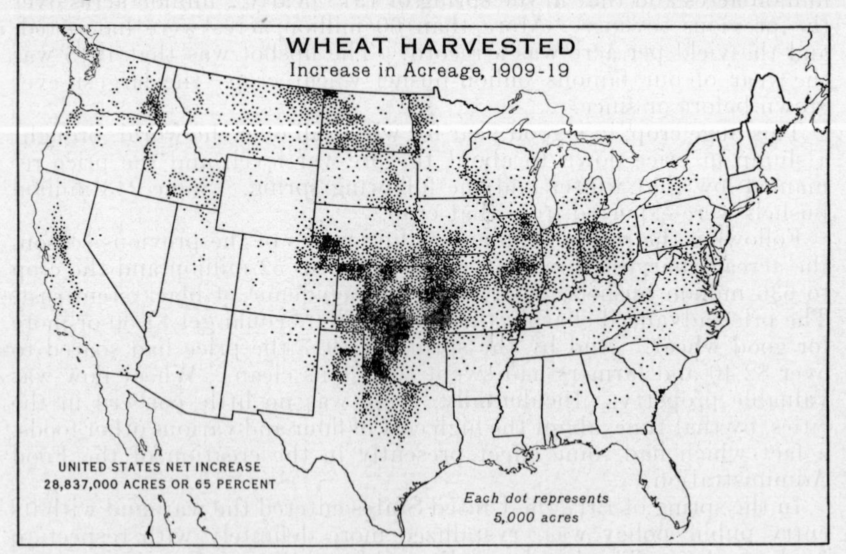

Figure 1.—Most of the increase in wheat acreage shown here between the 2 census years 1909 and 1919 occurred during the World War period. The heaviest increases in wheat acreage were in Nebraska, Kansas, and Oklahoma, but there were substantial increases also throughout the Corn Belt and in the spring wheat region.

The 1918 crop was a bountiful one. The harvested acreage had been stepped up to 59 millions, the crop totaled 921 million bushels, and from it 287 million bushels were exported. Most growers realized about $2 a bushel or slightly more.

By 1919 the war was over, but several countries were still calling urgently for wheat. The guaranteed price was still in effect when wheat was sown that year. From a record acreage, our farmers harvested a crop of 952 million bushels and sold it at $2 to $2.25 a bushel. Nearly 220 million bushels were exported.

To sum up the story of wheat expansion, the acreage rose from an average of 47 million for the period 1909–13 to 74 million in 1919, and the crop from 690 million bushels to 952 million. This was an increase of more than half in acreage and of 38 percent in production during the World War period (fig. 1). Of the 27-million-acre increase, nearly 22 million was winter wheat.

The expansion in wheat acreage was accomplished chiefly at the expense of other small grains, flaxseed, and corn and by plowing up grassland in the West.

The Secretary of Agriculture reported the situation as follows (*14*):

In the Corn Belt wheat increased 7 million acres and displaced 3 million acres of corn.

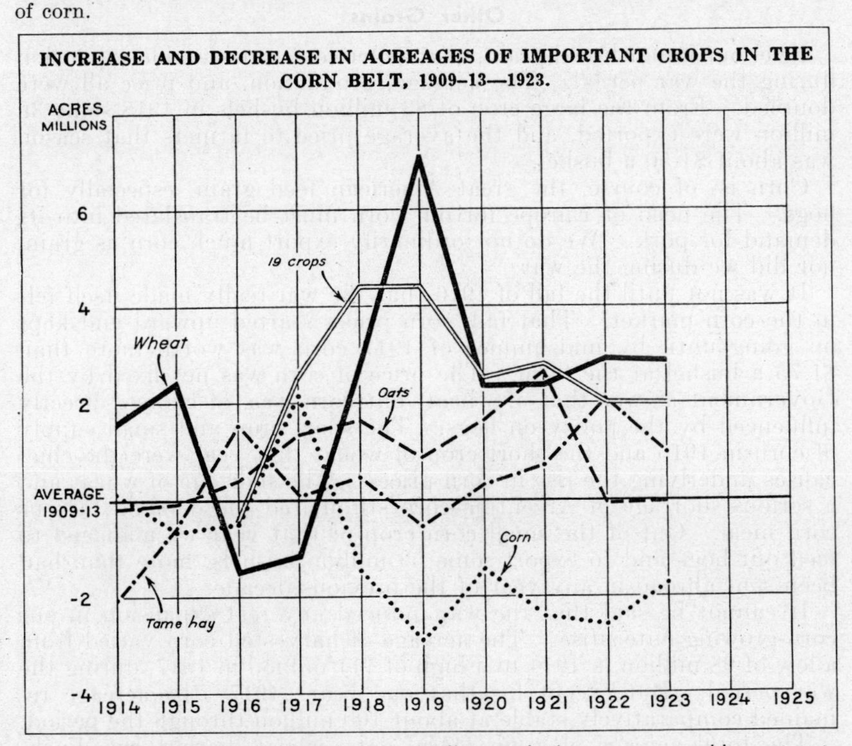

Figure 2.—The acreage of wheat decreased following the bumper crop and low prices in 1915. With the advance in prices in 1917, however, the acreage rose sharply. Acreage of the important crops of the Corn Belt, taken as a whole, increased somewhat over 4 million acres during the war period.

The largest addition to the winter wheat area was made in the Great Plains States of Nebraska, Kansas, Colorado, Oklahoma, and Texas. By 1919 the wheat acreage in these States had been expanded by over 13,450,000 acres. Corn was reduced 8,275,000 acres and better than 11 million acres of meadow and wild pasture land were plowed up and planted to crops.

The States of Minnesota, North Dakota, South Dakota, and Montana accounted for about 4,150,000 acres of the increase in spring wheat during the war. These States as a group at the same time materially enlarged their rye, corn, oats, and tame hay production and made important reductions only in the case of barley and flax. This crop expansion was brought about by plowing up some pastures and meadows in Minnesota and North and South Dakota, but more especially wild pasture lands in the semiarid sections of the western part of the Dakotas and in Montana.

The wheat area in the Pacific Northwest was enlarged to the extent of 1,250,000 acres, in considerable measure by decreasing the amount of summer fallow and by plowing up wild pasture lands, and only slightly through the replacement of other crops. Here again a substantial part of the additional acreage sown to wheat was semiarid land.

Such, in brief, was the wartime story of wheat. It was in the production of this crop probably more than any other that the greatest departures from the pre-war "normal" occurred. In turn, it was wheat that experienced some of the most acute difficulties in the realinement of supply and markets that grew out of the war (fig. 2).

Other Grains

Rye, our minor bread grain, also underwent considerable expansion during the war period. The acreage, production, and price all were doubled. From the large crop of 83 million bushels in 1918 some 36 million were exported, and the average price to farmers that season was about $1.50 a bushel.

Corn is, of course, the great American feed grain, especially for hogs. The need of Europe for our corn must be translated into its demand for pork. We do not ordinarily export much corn as grain, nor did we during the war.

It was not until the fall of 1916 that the war really made itself felt in the corn market. That fall, corn prices started upward and kept on going until by midsummer of 1917 corn was worth more than $1.75 a bushel at the farm. The price of corn was not fixed by the Government as was that of wheat, but corn was, of course, directly influenced by the policy on hogs. The short crop and small supply of corn in 1916 and the short crop of wheat that year were the chief causes underlying the rise in corn prices. The shortage of wheat and a serious shortage of Argentine corn stimulated the demand for our corn meal. Out of the small corn crop of that year we managed to feed our hogs and to export some 59 million bushels, more than had been sent abroad in any year of the previous decade.

It cannot be said that the war induced any real expansion in our corn-growing enterprise. The acreage of harvested corn varied from a low of 98 million in 1914 to a high of 111 million in 1917, during the war period. But except for that one year—1917—the acreage remained comparatively stable at about 100 million through the period.

The total acreage of grain (corn, oats, wheat, barley, rye, buckwheat, and rice) in the United States increased from approximately 203 million in 1914 to 227 million in 1919, or about 12 percent. Total production of those grains, however, increased less than 5 percent, and the output per capita of the population did not change significantly over the war period as a whole. After 1919 the acreage gradually dropped off.

Cotton and Tobacco

Although cotton is our greatest commercial and export crop, its production was not stimulated by actual war demand as was the production of wheat and pork.

It happened that the 1914 crop of cotton was the largest ever grown in this country up to that time—16 million bales. The outbreak of the war closed American cotton exchanges and demoralized the trade for a time. When the New York Cotton Exchange was reopened in mid-November the price had dropped 5½ cents a pound below late-July prices—that is, it had been cut nearly in half. Exports that autumn fell away to less than a fourth of those in the same months the year before. The South was filled with gloom, and many relief plans were set afoot—among them the "buy-a-bale" campaign.

Later on, in 1915, oversea trade picked up again, though of course the important German market was cut off. But the over-all effect of the war was to reduce world consumption of American cotton about 12 percent, on an average, below such consumption in the 3 years preceding the war, even though consumption in this country increased somewhat.[3]

In no other year during the war did the acreage of cotton again match the 36-million-acre figure of 1914. Whereas in the 5 years before the war our cotton exports averaged about 8½ million bales, exports during the war period averaged only a little over 6 million bales, or less than three-fourths as much.

Along toward 1917, however, the effects of industrial activity here, plus inflation and general rise in commodity prices, began to boost the price of cotton, together with those of other things, and for 3 years growers averaged more than 25 cents a pound for their cotton, the 1919 season's average price being 35 cents a pound. That was the year of the South's famous 2-billion-dollar cotton crop—never equaled before or since.

The stimulation to cotton prices thus came largely at the end of the war and more as a result of domestic business activity, general inflation, and moderately small crops than from actual war demand.

This development was one of the most interesting of a great war in relation to our main farm enterprises and one somewhat counter to the expectations of commentators voiced at the time the clouds were gathering in 1914. Indispensable as our cotton was, it did not take rank with the foodstuffs in the needs and demands of the Allies supplied by the United States.

The acreage and production of tobacco increased gradually during the war, although exports fell off. It was not until toward the close of the war that tobacco exports, prices, and production all soared to comparatively high levels. The expansion of acreage was from 1¼ million in 1914 to nearly 2 million in 1920.

One of the war outgrowths was a considerable rise in the consump-

[3] COOPER, MAURICE R. SOME EFFECTS OF THE WORLD WAR ON COTTON. U. S. Bur. Agr. Econ. [Rpt.] 15 pp. 1937. [Mimeographed.]

tion of smoking tobacco, particularly cigarettes. This is usually an incident of boom times, however induced, but soldiers are especially heavy smokers. The effect on tobacco prices was to raise them more than three times above the 10-cents-a-pound average that farmers were receiving before the war.

Livestock and Livestock Products

Among the livestock industries, hog production was the one naturally destined to feel the greatest stimulus from the war. The United States always had been a pork and lard exporter—in fact the leading exporting country for many years. During pre-war years we had been accustomed to ship abroad about 12 percent of our yearly production of pork and lard. The war ultimately doubled that percentage.

Thus, hog production, like wheat, already was sensitively geared to a foreign market, especially the British market. Two figures will suffice to indicate the call which that market made on our swine industry. In the 5 pre-war years our exports of pork and lard to the United Kingdom averaged about 450 million pounds; by 1918 we were shipping there over 1 billion pounds a year.

Hog production and prices usually follow a rather well defined cycle. When the war broke out in 1914 production was down, and prices were about $8 a hundredweight at the farms. It was not until 1916, however, that hog prices began their real rise. The average farm price began that year at $6.32, ended it at $8.76, and kept on going up. Still the number of hogs in the country was not large enough to satisfy the food authorities.

The Food Administration did not have capital enough to attempt any stabilization of the hog or pork market through commercial operations, as the Grain Corporation had done in wheat. What it did, therefore, was to set up a price yardstick and then maintain it by using the weight of Allied, Belgian Relief, Red Cross, and Army purchases and by control of the packers and of exports.

> The objects which it was desired to obtain by the Food Administration policy toward hogs were: (1) To increase the number of hogs in the country; (2) to increase the export of pork products to the Allies; (3) to stabilize prices so that producers could be assured of a reasonable return for their efforts; (4) to control the margin of profits to packers and distributors in order to protect consumers (*8, p. 53*).

After considering numerous recommendations of farmers' organizations and others relative to prices and to the corn-hog ratio, the Food Administration in November 1917 decided to put a peg under the price at about $15.50 for average droves of hogs.

> The first step is to stop the sudden break in prices paid for hogs at the central markets. These prices must become stable so that the farmer knows where he stands, and will feel justified in increasing hogs for next winter. The prices so far as we can affect them will not go below a minimum of about $15.50 per hundredweight for the average of the packers' droves on the Chicago market until further notice. . . .
>
> As to the hogs farrowed next spring, we will try to stabilize the price so that the farmer can count on getting, for each 100 pounds of hogs ready for market, 13 times the average cost per bushel of the corn fed into the hogs.[4]

The price averaged about $15 through the fall of 1917, and after

[4] Statement issued by the Meat Division of the U. S. Food Administration November 3, 1917.

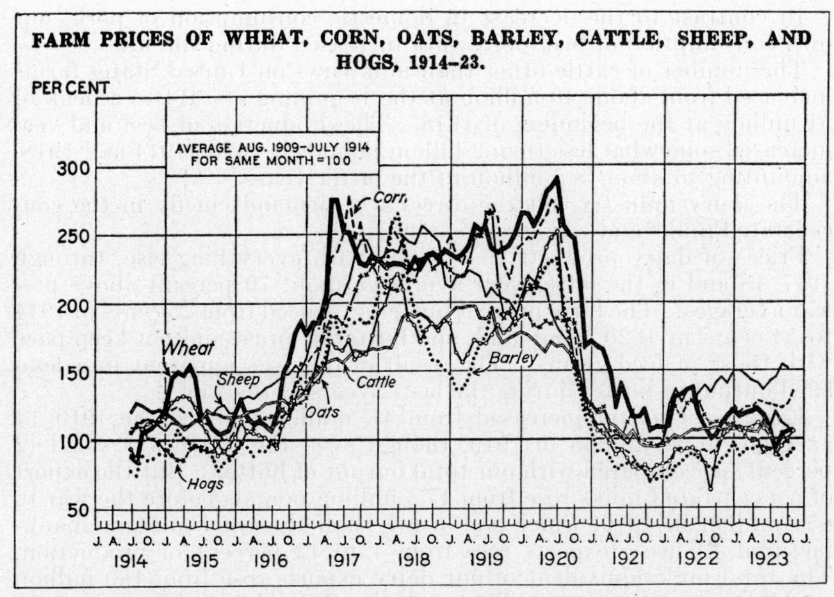

Figure 3.—Cattle prices did not rise so high as feed-grain prices during the World War. Hog prices, however, reached levels where the feeding of hogs was profitable during the latter years. Wheat was the market leader and more or less set the pace for other grain prices during the war period.

the Food Administration notice it did not go below the pegged figure. It went as high as $17.50 in September 1918 and to over $19 in the summer of 1919. Thereafter it slumped heavily until by 1921 the swine industry was among the first to encounter severe depression.

The response to these wartime prices and urgings was a considerable increase in pig production. From 53 million head of swine on farms at the beginning of 1914, the number jumped to nearly 57 million a year later; then, except for a recession during 1916, when there was a short corn crop, continued upward until it reached 64 million at the beginning of 1919.

Of all the livestock classes, hogs attained the highest wartime prices. Throughout the war hog prices were substantially higher than those of cattle, and during 1918 and 1919 they were higher than those of lambs most of the time. The same high prices that encouraged production also operated to reduce the consumption per capita of pork and lard in this country—a combination of circumstances which made possible the heavy exports to the Allies.

Prices received by farmers for beef cattle advanced from an average of $6.24 in 1914 to $9.56 in 1919; good beef-steer prices at Chicago nearly doubled, reaching $17.50 in 1919 (fig. 3).

The war raised our exports of beef from 150 million pounds in 1914 to 954 million in 1918. Our exports ordinarily were small as compared with those of Argentina, and the wartime increase here resulted from the shortage of shipping and the consequent difficulties in making the long haul from South America and Australia to Europe.

In contrast to the decrease in domestic consumption of pork, our own consumption of beef per capita increased during the war.

The number of cattle other than milk cows on United States farms increased from about 40 million at the beginning of 1914 to a peak of 51 million at the beginning of 1918. The production of beef and veal increased somewhat less than 2 billion pounds between 1914 and 1918, amounting to about 8.5 billion in the latter year.

The dairy industry felt the direct war demand chiefly in the concentrated milks and to a lesser extent in cheese.

Prices of dairy products rose, along with everything else, through 1917–18 and in the latter year averaged about 70 percent above pre-war averages. The farm price of butter advanced from 25 cents in 1914 to 54 cents in 1920. But milk and butterfat prices did not keep pace with those of feed grains. The result of this was apparent in a lessened output of butter during the last 2 years of the war.

Exports of butter increased from 4¼ million pounds, the 1910–14 average, to 34 million in 1919, though even the latter was small (2 percent) as compared with our total output of butter. But the export of concentrated milks rose from 17½ million pounds before the war to 853 million in 1919, which was nearly half the total amount manufactured. Cheese exports rose from 1 to 12 percent of production. The total milk equivalent of our dairy exports rose from 180 million pounds pre-war to 2,744 million in 1919. Domestic consumption was larger during the war than before.

The effect of the war stimulus on the dairy industry was to raise the number of milk cows on farms, between 1914 and 1919, from 19.8 million to 21.5 million and the total production of butter, cheese, and concentrated milks from 42 billion to somewhat over 45 billion pounds, milk equivalent.

One other class of livestock—horses—felt in rather mild form the pull of war needs, though with curiously little stimulus to production. Horses were among the first things the British and French agents started buying in this country. We exported nearly 1½ million horses and mules during the war period at an average export price of well over $200 a head. A large part of these were second-rate and surplus stock. City stables and western ranges alike were culled for passable animals heavy enough to haul guns and supply wagons. But there was no real stimulus to colt raising. The farm price of horses remained virtually unchanged and at a relatively low level.

The number of sheep in the country showed no expansion—in fact it declined somewhat during the war, although prices more than doubled.

The poultry industry was depressed rather than helped by wartime conditions, especially by the high grain prices. Although poultrymen were able to sell their eggs and fowls to a good domestic market most of the time, this was not one of the enterprises that felt the stimulus of European buying. On the contrary, from the first it encountered direct European competition for its raw materials of production—the grains, including wheat.

Summary of Wartime Expansion

Summing up the main items of wartime expansion in United States agriculture, we note:

The acreage of grains increased from 203 million to 227 million, or about 12 percent, and production from 253 billion pounds to 292 billion, although production varied with weather more than with acreage and the per capita output did not increase significantly.

The number of animal units, including poultry, on farms increased from 121 million to 140 million, or about 16 percent. (An "animal unit" as here used is the equivalent of a horse or cow in terms of feed consumption.)

The production of all meat rose from 14.1 billion pounds to 17.3 billion, or about 23 percent.

The total area of land in crops increased by about 40 million acres, or roughly 13 percent. For a year or two after the war our agricultural exports accounted for the products from over 80 million acres.

The Congressional Joint Commission of Agricultural Inquiry, making a comparison of crop values in terms of 1909 prices, concluded that of the total increase in value of crops between the census years 1909 and 1919, about 10.5 percent had been due to the larger quantity produced (*11, p. 42*).

INFLATION AND THE RISE IN PRICES

The greatest effort in production, as has already been indicated, was made after 1916. In the latter years of the war period, the financial and economic policies of all the Allied Governments reflected more and more the urgencies of the struggle. The financial policies had a direct bearing upon commodity prices and through them upon the agricultural situation. A long and costly war usually is financed by resort to inflation. The great European powers were driven to abandon gold during the World War, and virtually all currencies or credit structures were violently inflated, with a resulting general rise in all commodity prices.

Had the war ended in 1917, say, and without American participation, the agricultural story would have been quite different. It was this final inflationary episode, which got under way in 1917 and culminated in 1920, that keyed up our farm business so that it was vulnerable to the shock of deflation after the war.

There is an important distinction between prices that actually were high in that they were above the general price level and those that were merely higher than before the war. The fact that a price had advanced over the pre-war average was not so significant; but when it rose above the general price level, the effect in most cases was to stimulate production.

Prices of farm products rose until ultimately they were more than double the pre-war figures. As a group they lagged somewhat during the first 2 years of the war; then they were somewhat above prices of all commodities until the end of 1919, after which they followed the all-commodities price curve up to the peak in May 1920. On the downturn they fell earlier and faster than did commodities in general (fig. 4). Farm products as a whole had a moderately favorable unit exchange value, in terms of nonagricultural commodities, during the latter years of the war period.

Of course it is impossible by such curves as those in figure 4 to

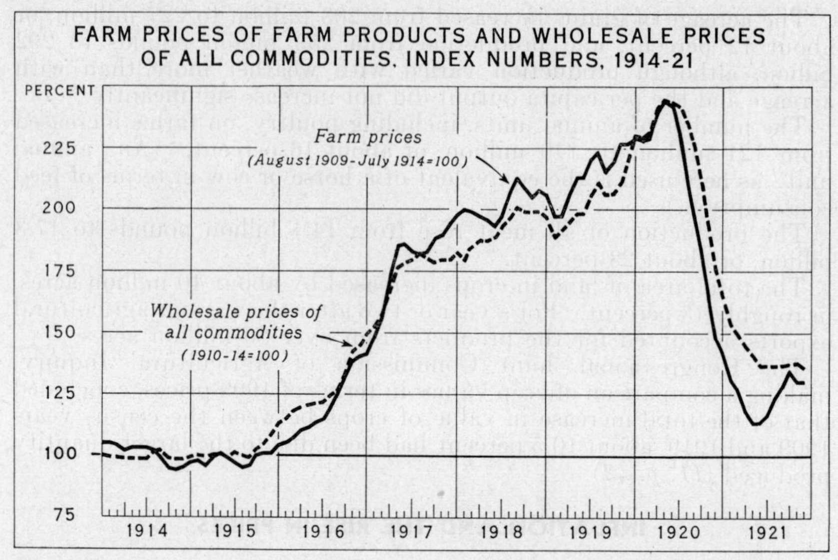

Figure 4.—Unit prices of farm products were at a slight disadvantage during the early years of the war period but moved up to a position of some advantage in relation to prices of all commodities during the latter years. They were among the first to fall after the peak reached in May 1920.

depict accurately the position of farmers in general. Some farmers were prosperous during the war, and some were not. Some products such as wool, cottonseed, wheat, tobacco, hogs, and beans rose to really "high" prices; and some, as horses, cattle, hay, onions, apples, eggs, and butter, stayed relatively "low." What must not be forgotten, however, is that the whole price level was much higher than before the war. Even prices that were below the general level in 1919 were, nevertheless, mostly far higher than prices of the same products before the war.

THE AGRICULTURAL BALANCE SHEET

The gross income from agricultural production in 1914 was approximately 7 billion dollars. The following year it increased only slightly, about a third of a billion. In 1916 it was estimated at 8.9 billion, in 1917 at 12.8 billion, in 1918 at 15.1 billion, and in 1919, the peak, at just short of 17 billion dollars. In 1920 the reaction set in, and gross income dropped to 13.5 billion dollars. With various ups and downs it declined finally to a low of somewhat over 5 billion dollars in 1932.

While income increased almost 150 percent, the current value of agricultural capital increased less than 65 percent, or from 47.8 billion dollars in 1914 to a high of 78.4 billion in 1920. Much has been said of the rise of land values in certain areas, notably in Iowa. A good clue to the relationship between land values and returns there may be seen in the figures on rented land. Taking that State as a whole, the average value of an acre of land rented for cash just about doubled between 1914 and 1920. The gross cash rent per acre nearly doubled. Taxes and upkeep doubled. The net rent increased about 57 percent (*7, p. 18*).

For the United States as a whole the average value per acre of farm real estate rose 70 percent between 1913 and the beginning of 1920. The latter represented the high point of the wartime period. Between 1916 and 1920 the rise was 60 percent. The average value of plowlands in the country rose from $58 an acre in 1916 to $90 an acre in 1920, or 55 percent.

It is perfectly true that agriculture experienced a substantial expansion of income and capital values. This is always the probable consequence of a marked rise in commodity prices—and prices during the World War climbed to heights not reached since the end of the Napoleonic Wars.

While gross income was rising, however, something was happening also on the expense side. The farmer's costs of production were mounting too. The wages of his hired help, prices of fertilizer, farm implements, and building and fencing materials, such charges as those for cotton ginning and for freight, and the omnipresent taxes and interest, all were treading closely on the heels of income.

The best estimates so far made indicate that the bill for hired help on farms, including board, rose from about 700 million dollars in 1914 to over 1,600 million dollars in 1920 (*13, p. 434*).

During the same interval the expenditure for fertilizer increased from 188 million dollars to 350 million; that for farm implements, including autos, trucks, tractors, and the cost of operation of the latter, from 328 million dollars to 1,150 million; that for cotton ginning, 56 million to 91 million. A good illustration of the two-edged character of the war prices is the case of feeds. Growers of grain, flax, cottonseed, and the like got high prices, but the livestock men had to pay proportionately for their feeds. The total feed bill rose from 431 million dollars in 1914 to 1,097 million in 1919.

The tax bill is always a first charge against the land. Taxes and interest are the two fixed charges that loom large in farmers' calculations even in the best of times. They have to be paid within certain time limits and in cash. The relation of commodity prices to those fixed charges—that is, the quantity of his produce required to pay them—is a vital matter to the farmer. The mounting weight of these charges during the war was significant, especially because of the situation after the war, when prices crashed and the swollen taxes and interest remained as huge burdens.

The tax bill on farm real estate alone increased from 222 million dollars in 1914 to 510 million in 1921—and went considerably above that figure within a few years (*13, p. 434*).

The National Industrial Conference Board estimated that the total tax bill paid by farmers—624 million dollars in 1913—had risen to 1,497 million in 1921 (*6, p. 29*).

Interest on farm mortgages was estimated as requiring the payment of 240 million dollars in 1914 and 545 million by 1921 (*13, p. 434*).

By 1921 freight rates stood at 211 percent of the 1914 figures in the Northeast, 169 in the West, and 156 percent in the far West (*2*).

The general situation was that while prices and gross income received by farmers somewhat more than doubled during the wartime period, their main items of production cost also doubled. In addition to this, farm families, like everyone else, had to pay their share of the increased cost of living.

The results of accounts kept on farms continuously through the war period, in different parts of the country, showed average net incomes increasing, but there were many farms in both the East and the West that failed to make current wages for the labor of the men who operated them.

For example, the average labor income, that is, the net income after deducting expenses and 5 percent interest on capital, reported on a group of 60 dairy farms in Wisconsin for the years 1913–17 was $408 per farm. For the high year 1917 it was $1,075 (*10*).

The average labor income on 33 New York dairy and general farms, covering the years 1914–20, was $1,241 a year. It was $453 in 1914, increased to $1,962 in 1917, and to a peak of $2,111 in 1919. It slumped in 1920, and in 1921 the farms showed a loss of $32 per farm.[5]

The average labor income on 100 Corn Belt farms in Indiana for the years 1914–19 was $743. In the peak year 1918 it was $1,421 (*4, p. 7*).

The average labor income on a group of about 50 farms in the hill country of southeastern Ohio for the years 1914–19, was $381. The top year was 1919, when the income was $784 (*3, p. 29; 12, p. 1305*).

Data prepared by W. I. King for the Congressional Joint Commission (*11, p. 56*), showed that from 1914 to 1918 the average annual earnings of the workers in agriculture increased from $321 to $590, those of persons engaged in mining from $650 to $1,280 per worker, those of persons in factories from $617 to $1,147 per worker, those of workers on railways from $723 to $1,394 per worker, and those of persons in all industries from $674 to $1,094 per worker.

From this it appears that the distribution of such economic rewards as were accountable to the war had not unduly favored the farmer. The farmers of the World War period had about three really profitable years, 1917–19. But neither their prices nor their profits were high as compared with those of the industrial community. They were sufficient to induce some expansion of plant and output, but it was inevitably an uneven, faulty expansion which threw out of gear no little of the favorable adjustment that had been achieved before the war. Moreover, any distortion of the settled pattern of production is more difficult to deal with in agriculture than in urban industry, because agriculture is a biological industry with a slow turn-over. It takes at least a year and usually several years to make adjustments in cropping systems and in herds and flocks.

CERTAIN SOCIAL EFFECTS OF THE WAR

It was not to be supposed that an economic disturbance as great as that occasioned by the war would fail to register its effects also in

[5] HARRIOTT, J. F., CRUIKSHANK, L. E., and GAUSS, JOHN. RESULTS OF FARM COST ACCOUNTS, 1932. N. Y. Agr. Col. (Cornell), Dept. Agr. Econ. and Farm Management Rpt., 50 pp. 1933. [Mimeographed.] See p. 5.

social changes. As the tension heightened in 1917, as the leaven of rising prices and wages worked within the farm business, many symptoms revealed themselves. Thousands of farmers near towns were persuaded to take factory jobs and leave their land to be worked by neighbors or by part-time effort. Many sons and even daughters did likewise. In many country schools sessions were shortened through the winter, and older children were called upon to help more than normally with farm work.

Then came the exodus of young men to enter the Army—a profoundly disturbing experience that required a readjustment of family labor to fill the gaps on hundreds of thousands of farms and in innumerable country activities. A generally unsettled state of mind permeated many communities and was reflected in considerable changing about by tenants and a wholesale movement of hired workers toward the highly paid factory jobs.

The extent to which the war unsettled the social equilibrium is revealed rather strikingly in the movement of population. Farm population just before the war had been about 32.3 million. A peak was reached probably in 1916, when about 32.5 million people lived on farms. But after that the number of farm people declined rapidly. As mentioned, the high wages in the cities drew large numbers of men away from the farms, especially in the Eastern, Central, and Southern States. An example is to be found in the movement of Negroes from southern farms to northern cities. Between 1910 and 1920 the census indicates that such migration included over 300,000 Negroes. Detroit showed an increase in Negro population of 611 percent; Cleveland, of 308 percent; Chicago, of 148 percent (*5, p. 34*).

Estimates made in the Bureau of Agricultural Economics indicate that about 1,100,000 men left the farms to join the armed forces; this was about one-fourth of the total number of men entering the military service of the United States during the war. Here, indeed, was the full impact of war making itself felt not only in economic but in striking social consequences.

By the beginning of 1919 the farm population had been reduced to 30.9 million by the migration to cities and to war.

Although the annual figures on wartime migration of population away from the farms are admittedly rather uncertain estimates, the most recent studies suggest that this net migration rose from about 400,000 in 1914 to a peak of about 1,350,000 in 1918; it had been almost as large in 1917 and was still large in 1919.[6] The 1918 figure includes over 500,000 men who left farms to join the armed forces, this being the net military migration after allowing for soldiers who returned to farms during that year.

With the demobilization of the Army the sequence of these social influences was reversed, a process that was heightened within a year or two by the industrial slump. It was the sudden reentrance into farm life of hundreds of thousands of young men, of the age to be marrying and wanting farms of their own, that undoubtedly aggravated the misery of the deflation period a little later. Thousands of

[6] GROVE, ERNEST W. FARM POPULATION, NONFARM POPULATION, AND NUMBER OF FARMS IN THE UNITED STATES, 1910–39 (PRELIMINARY). 39 pp., illus. *In* U. S. Bureau of Agricultural Economics in cooperation with the Agricultural Adjustment Administration and the Bureau of Home Economics, Income Parity for Agriculture, pt. 5, Population, Farms, and Farmers, sec. 1. 1939. [Multilithed.] See p. 27.

farms were bought by these young men, who went heavily in debt for property acquired at just about peak prices. Their misfortune was that they had arrived at maturity just in time to be caught in the disastrous web of circumstances spun by the war.

POLICIES AT THE CLOSE OF THE WAR

Governmental policies, not only in this country but in Europe, unquestionably played a large part in shaping the inflated situation that existed for about a year and half after the Armistice. All governments were under the necessity of raising huge loans for end-of-the-war and reconstruction financing. Huge credits were granted by the United States Government and banks to Europe. Frantic bidding went on for all kinds of materials, and it seemed in 1919 that the world never would catch up with the accumulated shortages.

The food ministeries of European countries bought even more wildly than did individual consumers. They bought such large quantities of many foods that they were unable to get rid of their hoards until the fall of 1921. In the summer of 1921 England dumped the last of her bacon on the German market. In September she still had on hand 80 million pounds of butter. In the winter of 1921, when sugar was practically unsalable in this country, Italy was still rationing sugar in order to get rid of her war-time hoards (*15*).

The building-up of the financial structure, in this country, into a towering pyramid of credit is described at length in the report of the Congressional Joint Commission of Agricultural Inquiry (*11*).

To the final halt called upon this process, the contraction of credit, the Commission ascribed primary responsibility for the crash of commodity prices and all the subsequent phenomena of acute depression.

In the United States every industry and every class of people were involved in the avalanche of descending prices. The turn in the tide from optimism, expansion, speculation, and extravagance to the reaction of deflation and depression occurred in the middle of 1920 and at about the time when the grain crop of the United States was beginning to go on the market. The prices of livestock and livestock products had already begun to decline, and these facts together, coupled with a failing export demand, were undoubtedly responsible for earlier and more rapid decline in the prices of agricultural products compared with the prices of other groups of commodities (*11, p. 13*).

It may be added that such has been the experience with every great inflation of modern times.

There can be no doubt that public and private policies adopted with respect to loans to Europe had a direct bearing for a time upon the status of that export market for our farm products after the war. While Europe was borrowing freely from us she continued buying also. When the flow of credit dried up, this foreign buying fell off. With the change in our position from a debtor to a creditor nation, our situation no longer meshed with the high tariff policy, which hindered Europe from paying us in goods. Of course other influences helped to close off the European market, notably the rise of nationalistic policies.

THE WAR AN ECONOMIC TURNING POINT

The loss of the European market for our wheat, pork, and cotton was one of the post-war developments that hit our agriculture not only vitally but with far greater suddenness than most such shifts. The alteration of the traditional financial and trade relationships between this country and Europe, which in the normal course might have spread itself over a span of two generations, precipitated by the war, took place within half a dozen years.

Moreover, the same forces which stimulated our agriculture had done the same in Canada, as well as in Argentina, Australia, New Zealand, and other Southern Hemisphere countries. Some of these were possessed of newer soils than we and also cheaper labor, so that to the depressing effect of our changed trade position was added the sharpened competition of these other agricultural producers.

Just as the war marked a turning point in our agricultural development, so did it likewise in public policy affecting agriculture. The end of the decade in 1919 closed the chapter, which had begun in the late nineties, of rising prices, expansion, and the whole pre-war progress of agriculture in a world of comparatively free enterprise. Suddenly and under great stress, this country found itself compelled to reorient its entire farm economy to fit the conditions of lost foreign markets, falling prices, and contraction, all complicated by the influences of an epochal change from horse to mechanical power, etc.

The world of abundance and of relatively free exchange had turned into one of low buying power, with international trade balked by a barricade of restrictions and political designs. Governmental policy here, as well as in other surplus-producing countries, had to be more or less completely redirected to meet the problems presented by a highly developed agriculture that had been thus thrust back upon itself.

LITERATURE CITED

(1) Anonymous.
1915. The high price of flour. Economist [London] 80 (3724): 49–50.

(2) Gabriel, Harry S.
1924. Freight rates. N. Y. Agr. Col. (Cornell) Farm Econ. No. 11, pp. 103–104.

(3) Hawthorne, H. W.
1919. Some points brought out by successive surveys of the same farms. Jour. Farm Econ. 1: 24–37.

(4) ——— and Dixon, H. M.
1924. Farm organization and management in Clinton County, Indiana. U. S. Dept. Agr. Bul. 1258, 68 pp., illus.

(5) Kennedy, Louise Venable.
1930. The negro peasant turns cityward; effects of recent migrations to northern centers. 271 pp., illus. New York and London.

(6) National Industrial Conference Board.
1923. Tax burdens and exemptions. Natl. Indus. Conf. Bd. Res. Rpt. 64, 159 pp., illus.

(7) Regan, M. M.
1939. The farm real estate situation, 1936–37, 1937–38, and 1938–39. U. S. Dept. Agr. Cir. 548, 42 pp., illus.

(8) Surface, Frank M.
1926. American pork production in the world war . . . 217 pp., illus. Chicago and New York.

(9) Taylor, Alonzo Englebert.
1918. War bread. 99 pp. New York.

(10) Taylor, H. C., and Mendum, S. W.
1919. War prices and farm profits. Wis. Agr. Expt. Sta. Bul. 300, 18 pp., illus.

(11) [UNITED STATES] CONGRESS, JOINT COMMISSION OF AGRICULTURAL INQUIRY.
1921. THE AGRICULTURAL CRISIS AND ITS CAUSES. Report of the Joint Commission of Agricultural Inquiry, pt. 1, 240 pp. (U. S. Cong. 67th, 1st sess., H. Rpt. 408.)

(12) UNITED STATES DEPARTMENT OF AGRICULTURE.
1926. FARM MANAGEMENT AND COST STATISTICS. U. S. Dept. Agr. Yearbook 1925 (Table 652): 1285–1311.

(13) ———
1938. AGRICULTURAL STATISTICS, 1938. 544 pp. Washington, D. C.

(14) WALLACE, HENRY C.
1923. THE WHEAT SITUATION. A report to the President. 126 pp., illus. Washington, D. C.

(15) WARREN, G. F., and PEARSON, F. A.
1924. THE AGRICULTURAL SITUATION, ECONOMIC EFFECTS OF FLUCTUATING PRICES. 306 pp., illus. New York.

The Development of Agricultural Policy Since the End of the World War

by CHESTER C. DAVIS [1]

THERE can be little doubt but that the past 20 years will be looked back upon as one of the most eventful and interesting periods in the whole of American agricultural history. It is too early as yet to appraise the events of this period, and the forces that shaped them, from an entirely detached historical viewpoint. The attempt, however, is worth making; and few people are as well equipped to make it, from the standpoint of long and intimate acquaintance with agricultural problems, as the author of this article. Here he tells the story of the increasing economic pressure upon farmers in the 1920's; the gradual spread of a powerful farm movement from the grass roots; the ideas back of the farm legislation in the latter part of the decade; the modifications in these ideas and their extension in the agricultural programs of the 1930's. It cannot be said, he concludes, that these laws have solved the farm problem. Presumably they will themselves be subject to change and displacement. But if experience in this field teaches anything, it is that a continuous thread runs through the evolution of agricultural policy notwithstanding its

[1] Chester C. Davis is a member of the Board of Governors of the Federal Reserve System.

inconsistencies and contradictions. The programs of the present become the foundations for the programs of the future.

DURING 1919 and the first half of 1920 the general expectation prevailed that an enormous demand for American goods and products of the farm would follow the removal of restrictions on consumption that war had imposed on the people of the world. Farmers and nonfarmers were slow to realize that an effective market is not created by the desires or needs of men or of nations but by their ability to pay with goods, services, gold, or credit.

Farmers of the United States had produced in abundance under the joint stimulus of patriotism and price; they continued the stride after the artificial market created by the war and the post-war spree of extravagant buying had faded away. The annual report of the Secretary of Agriculture for 1919 (*11*) [2] optimistically recited that "America during the war helped to save Europe and to preserve civilization by making available to the Allies, through increased production and conservation, large supplies of foodstuffs." The same report viewed the land problem from the standpoint of our capacity to expand still further the acreage tilled, pointing out that the cultivation of land still unused could increase the output of commodities by over 60 percent of the total.

Nevertheless a faint note of warning was discernible in the report. The Secretary raised a question (*11, p. 26*) as to "the bearing of the increasing prices of land and the resulting speculation on the progress of agriculture and the welfare of the farmer," and concluded (*11, pp. 28–29*):

> American agriculture should consolidate the gains already made; prepare for the period of competition which is to be expected with the return of normal world conditions, principally by increasing, through sound and economical methods, the productivity of areas already under cultivation; and utilize the services of the most experienced and judicious agricultural leaders in determining where, when, and how to bring into cultivation and develop public and private unused land.

In spite of the prevailing optimism, Secretary Houston recommended to the President that he call an agricultural conference at the earliest possible date because of changed conditons at home and abroad, existing uncertainties, and disturbed states of mind. When the conference was finally called, in January 1921, it was by another Secretary of Agriculture at the direction of another President, and it raised the curtain upon two decades of swift and radical change in agricultural policy, which is still unfolding as another general war overwhelms Europe.

AGRICULTURAL PRICES BROKE FIRST

Agricultural prices were the first to break in 1920. The July 1920 index of prices paid to producers was 10 points under the June index; the August index, 15 points below the July; and the September index, 15 points below the August. In contrast there was no noticeable drop in nonagricultural prices until near the end of the year. The blow struck the farmers at about the time the grain crop of the

[2] Italic numbers in parentheses refer to Literature Cited, p. 326.

United States was coming on the market. Within a few months every industry and producers of every class were swept along under the avalanche of descending prices. The boom market, which had endured while credits granted to Europe remained unexpended and while, at home, citizens were cashing bonds to buy goods, had come to an end.

The collapse of agricultural prices, particularly while the rigidity of nonagricultural prices and wages was creating a new and alarming disparity between farm income and costs, produced vehement protest from farmers everywhere. Existing farm organizations increased their membership, and new ones sprang into being. They exerted a pressure on lawmakers and administrators which, continuing through the years, has been primarily responsible for the unparalleled sweep of farm legislation from the early 1920's through 1938 and has carried the Federal Government into fields of farm aid undreamed of when the crisis of 1920 broke.

The quick violence of farm protest was due partly at least to the general unexpectedness of the price downturn. The apparent hunger of a world that had been strictly rationed for years had encouraged farmers in the belief that good markets for their crops would continue. The crops sold in 1920 had been produced at the highest costs ever known. Farmers had used credit freely in buying more land and equipment. They had set aside little as a surplus to offset losses in commodity prices. They saw no way to reduce production to match falling demand. Old debts must now be paid with products that brought sharply lower prices. The pressure for debt liquidation struck at a time when returns from crop sales were wholly inadequate to balance the debts incurred in producing them.

The ferment throughout the country during the last half of 1920 did not result in action at Washington. A Presidential campaign was under way. While demands for Government price fixing stirred farmer mass meetings, Washington talk was of higher tariffs, better farm credits, more loans to finance exports, and an improved legal status for cooperatives. The 1920 report of the Secretary of Agriculture pointed out that the year's crop had been the largest but one in the country's history and that the returns were inadequate and, while suggesting that no single solution could be found, insisted that big crops should not be allowed to impoverish the farmers who produced them.

JOINT COMMISSION OF AGRICULTURAL INQUIRY

Early in 1921 the new Congress created a Joint Commission of Agricultural Inquiry, the Senate acting on May 31, the House on June 7, and instructed the Commission to report its findings within 90 days (7). The Commission was directed to—

investigate and report to the Congress * * * upon the following subjects: (1) the causes of the present condition of agriculture; (2) the cause of the difference between the prices of agricultural products paid to the producer and the ultimate cost to the consumer; (3) the comparative condition of industries other than agriculture; (4) the relation of prices of commodities other than agriculture; (5) the banking and financial resources and credits of the country, especially as affecting agricultural credits; (6) the marketing and transportation facilities of the country.

The Commission was also directed to "include in its report recommendations for legislation which in its opinion will tend to remedy existing conditions" (*8, p. 3*) and to report "specifically * * * upon the limitations of the powers of Congress in enacting relief legislation."

The Commission completed its hearings and report by early fall, and delivered its findings on the causes of the agricultural crisis, with its recommendations, to Congress in early December.

In general the inquiry was broad and important, but its specific recommendations were limited and proved ineffectual when subsequently carried out. The farm groups at the time regarded them as inadequate to meet the conditions that were developing.

In attempting to arrive at the causes, the Commission studied changes in the purchasing power of the farmer's dollar, the relation of the prices of farm products to those of other commodities, and the physical output and the return to capital and labor in agriculture as compared with other industries.

It found that by May 1921 the purchasing power of the farmer's dollar was only 77 percent of its pre-war value. It reported that the prices of farm products had declined more rapidly and had fallen to a lower level than those of other commodities, although the physical output of agriculture had not kept pace with that of other industries, and that the return to farm capital and labor was relatively low.

The distress of agriculture was attributed primarily to the general business depression which began in 1920, although a failure of export demand was considered to be an important cause. The maintenance of unduly high freight rates, the lack of facilities for intermediate credit, and the need for an adequate and integrated warehouse system were also deemed contributing factors. Overproduction or overmarketing of farm products in 1920 was not adjudged to be an important cause of the subsequent price decline.

The Commission recommended granting preferred legal status to cooperative marketing associations, a system of intermediate credits for agriculture, improved warehousing facilities and supervision, reduction in freight rates on farm products, extension of the statistical, research, and foreign-service functions of the Department of Agriculture, better grades and standards for farm products, farm-to-market roads, and rural life improvement; and finally the Commission declared that renewal of confidence and prosperity was dependent on readjustment of commodity prices, which "cannot be brought about by legislative formulas but must be the result for the most part of the interplay of economic forces" (*8, p. 11*).

NATIONAL AGRICULTURAL CONFERENCE CALLED IN 1922

In the meantime, the War Finance Corporation was revived particularly to finance exports; an emergency tariff act, vetoed by President Wilson as one of his last official acts, was again passed and was signed by President Harding; the "farm bloc" was organized in Congress; the powers of the War Finance Corporation were broadened to enable it to make loans for agricultural rehabilitation, and its life was extended to 1924.

The National Agricultural Conference, called by Secretary of Agriculture Henry C. Wallace at the direction of President Harding, met in Washington January 23 to 27, 1922. Nearly 400 representatives of agricultural and related industries attended. Practically all of the notes that have been struck in subsequent agricultural policy were sounded in one way or another in that conference.

In his letter asking Secretary Wallace to call the conference, the President said (*9, p. 3*):

> It is unthinkable that with our vast areas, our unparalleled endowment of agricultural resources, our fertility of soil, our vast home market, and the great ability and resourcefulness of our farmers we should accept the status of a distinctly industrial Nation. Our destiny seems to require that we should be a well-rounded Nation with a high development of both industry and agriculture, supporting one another and prospering together. It must be, and I feel sure it is, the national wish and purpose to maintain our agriculture at the highest possible efficiency.

But the President clearly was not thinking in terms of a broad assumption of responsibility for agricultural policy by the Federal Government. In his opening address to the conference, he said (*9, p. 10*):

> It cannot be too strongly urged that the farmer must be ready to help himself. This conference would do most lasting good if it would find ways to impress the great mass of farmers to avail themselves of the best methods. By this I mean that, in the last analysis, legislation can do little more than give the farmer the chance to organize and help himself.

Secretary Wallace told the conference (*9, p. 13*) that "the agriculture of the Nation is in a bad state, and our entire business and industrial life is suffering in consequence."

The conference operated in 12 sections, each of which reported its recommendations, which, as incorporated in the final report, are too detailed and extensive for recapitulation here. One significant pronouncement on price adjustment suggested the slogan, "Equality for agriculture," which has resounded through every subsequent political campaign, and set prominently before the country for the first time the objective for which organized agriculture was to strive in the turbulent farm fights of succeeding decades. It was incorporated upon the insistence of a man who became an active leader of farm forces in their fight for farm equality—George N. Peek, later first Administrator of the Agricultural Adjustment Act. The paragraph reads (*9, p. 171*):

> Agriculture is necessary to the life of the Nation; and, whereas the prices of agricultural products are far below the cost of production, so far below that relatively they are the lowest in the history of our country; therefore, it is the sense of this committee that the Congress and the President of the United States should take such steps as will immediately reestablish a fair exchange value for all farm products with that of all other commodities.

The demand for equality for agriculture cropped out at several places in the conference report (*9, p. 137*):

> The conference declares that no revival of American business is possible until the farmer's dollar is restored to its normal purchasing power when expressed in the prices paid for the commodities which the farmer must purchase, and the conference further declares that by right the men engaged in the agricultural field are entitled to a larger return than they have heretofore received for the service they give society.

Adjustment of farm production to demand was stressed (*9, p. 137*):

The manufacturer has in the past quickly adjusted his production to price recessions while the farmer has not. When farm production is so large that the product cannot be sold for prices that will maintain a reasonable standard of living on the farms, the supply is too large. We recommend that the farmers and the farm organizations consider the problem of world supply and demand and make comprehensive plans for production programs so that they may be able "to advise their members as to the probable demand for staples, and to propose measures for proper limitation of acreage in particular crops," as pointed out by the President of the United States.

The conference report favored higher tariffs, more foreign credits to facilitate exports, an intermediate credit system for farmers, and recognition of farm cooperative-marketing associations and price stabilization through their operations, and made scores of other recommendations of varying importance.

Recommended for study were a system of crop insurance and the whole question of Government guaranty of agricultural prices.

THE SURPLUS-DISPOSAL PLAN IN EMBRYO

In the meantime, in December 1921, George N. Peek and Hugh S. Johnson, who were associates in the management of a farm implement company at Moline, Ill., had written and filed with the American Farm Bureau Federation their first brief, Equality for Agriculture (*3*), which set forth the principles and a plan of operation which were in general incorporated in the surplus-control bills which 2 years later became known by the names of their legislative sponsors, Senator Charles L. McNary, of Oregon, and Representative Gilbert N. Haugen, of Iowa.

While the National Agricultural Conference was holding the spotlight in Washington, an important series of conferences took place between Mr. Peek and General Johnson and Cabinet members and other officials. At their suggestion their plan was submitted first to a group of economists within and outside the Government and then to a group of industrial and financial leaders. The proponents of the plan remained in Washington until mid-February. When they left, their proposal was assured continued study by the interest of the Secretary of Agriculture and of Henry C. Taylor, who that year was to become the first chief of the Bureau of Agricultural Economics. The first drafts were prepared in the Department of Agriculture in 1923 under the direction of Charles J. Brand, who 10 years later became coadministrator of the Agricultural Adjustment Act. They emerged as the McNary-Haugen bills, which reached both Houses of Congress in January 1924.

The proposal is described by its authors in the following summary taken from Equality for Agriculture:

This is a plan to improve marketing of farm products, to insure a fair return from farm operations, to stabilize farm securities, to facilitate farm finance, and to secure equality for agriculture in the benefits of the protective tariff, by the following means:

Establish each year the fair exchange value on the domestic market of each principal crop, by computing a price which bears the same relation to the general price index as the average price of such crop for ten pre-war years bore to the average general price index for the same period. Protect this fair exchange value from world price by a tariff fluctuating with it and with world price.

Organize under Federal legislative charter a private corporation to maintain this value by buying carry-over from any such crop from farmers or associations of farmers at such value. Such corporation may sell for export exportable surplus at the world price, even if less than domestic price, and may sell for domestic consumption, any of its carry-over at not less than the exchange value. The process will result in little, if any, material interference with existing mechanism for supplying domestic consumption.

Purchases and losses by reason of sales to export or of downward fluctuations in such fair exchange value to be financed, viz:

From worst experienced years of price, production, and surplus, determine an empirical formula, which when applied to any future year, will compute a percentage of price per bushel or per pound, large enough to absorb any probable loss. This differential to be computed and announced in ample time before planting season to enable farmers to plan croppage with reference to existing supply.

By authority of a Federal statute, collect this percentage as a differential loan assessment on each pound or bushel when and as sold by the farmer. Issue scrip for such receipts, bearing interest on a retirable value to be fixed and announced when losses and expenses are determined.

Pass unabsorbed amounts in such fund to a farm-loan fund for reloan to appropriate banks and associations of farmers, at moderate interest, and on farmers' notes, for 1, 2, or 3 years, given for purchase of reproductive facilities.

In the first year, after a sufficient fund has accumulated to take care of annual agricultural loan requirements, the installment of scrip issued in the first year's operations is retired, and so on for each succeeding year's installment.

Wheat, cotton, corn and oats are tentatively proposed for the operation of this plan.

THE STAGE IS SET FOR FARM-RELIEF BATTLES

The Joint Commission of 1921 and the agricultural conference of 1922 helped set off the farm-relief campaigns which have continued almost without breathing space from that time to this. In the judgment of the more aggressive farm leaders the remedies proposed in the two reports were hopelessly inadequate to meet the conditions the reports recognized as existing.

Developments of later years reveal some surprising gaps and blind spots in these early post-war analyses of the farm problem. Commission and conference alike seemed unconscious of the clash between their demand that agricultural as well as industrial exports be restored and maintained and their insistence that this Nation vigorously pursue a policy of exclusion through higher and yet higher tariffs. Neither the conservative administration leaders nor the farm forces they called radical recognized that the volume of agricultural exports following the war and up to 1929 was financed in large part by extension of credit abroad—many of the loans not to be repaid.

It is less surprising that they failed to foresee the turn among the nations of the world toward autarchy, national self-sufficiency, and directed international trade, and that the consequence would be diminished export opportunities for the United States, a high-tariff, creditor Nation.

The full significance of the McNary-Haugen bills which were before Congress in varying forms from 1924 through 1928 does not end with the fact that the measures were twice put through Congress and twice vetoed. Their real importance lies in the fact that the continuous pressure for them made the Nation wholly conscious of its agricultural problem. Counterplans were put forward to sidetrack and substitute for the measures which the organized farm groups were demanding. Some of them were adopted, and their trial added to the experience and knowledge which has helped shape still later endeavors.

Early Alinement on Farm Relief

The line-up of forces on farm relief from 1923 to 1926 was discouraging from the point of view of those who favored aggressive action to restore farm prices to equality with costs. The cooperative marketing associations, which had developed along commodity lines into strength and prominence in the years following the war, were generally hostile. They were unconvinced that, given Federal recognition and support, they could not do the job themselves. The South as a whole was indifferent, partly because its chief farm organizations were the cotton, tobacco, and rice cooperatives and partly because of traditional opposition to increased Federal powers and to extension or recognition of the protective-tariff principle.

The East and the industrial centers were inherently opposed. Even when prominent industrialists recognized the importance to national prosperity of restored farm buying power, they were violently critical of any specific method proposed to that end.

Agricultural colleges and economists were as a whole indifferent to the problem. During the early years their leadership was negative and their attitude scoffing.

Outside of Congress and a small group close to the Secretary in the Department of Agriculture, official Washington was solidly opposed to any but the most orthodox Government moves to strengthen agriculture.

The spearhead of the movement for positive Government action from 1923 to 1926, therefore, was made up in the first stages by individuals and special groups; State units of general farm organizations were next to fall in line, and after them the national farm associations—the American Farm Bureau Federation, the Farmers' Union, and the Grange.

Generally through those years the farm forces were disposed to divide all over the field as to details of procedure. The cooperatives went their own way, with the exception of Northwest wheat associations, who favored the surplus-disposal plan. Some farm leaders were for outright Government guaranty of fixed prices. There were lively debates over the surplus problem—even over the question whether in fact any surplus of farm products existed. Many farm leaders contended that there could be no overproduction if marketing were properly organized.

Secretary Wallace, in his annual report for 1922 (*11, Yearbook 1922*), summed up the opposite view in saying:

> Some contend that there is no such thing as overproduction of farm products and cannot be as long as there are people in the world who suffer for food and clothing. On the same line of reasoning it can be argued that the production of automobiles will be inadequate until every man and woman and every boy and girl of high-school age owns one. There is overproduction, so far as the producer is concerned, whenever the quantity produced cannot be marketed at a price which will cover all production costs and leave the producer enough to tempt him to continue production.

Some Tariff Inconsistencies

Small voices were raised but scarcely heard when they questioned the wisdom of a tariff policy which excluded from this country the means by which foreign buyers could pay for our exports, while at the same time we demanded and expected that our exports would be maintained. Meanwhile the policy of raising tariffs swept on to its culmination in the Tariff Act of 1929 without effective protest either from the pros or the antis in the farm-relief fight.

Both sides failed to recognize the fact that continued exports through these years were made possible by the extension of credit to foreign nations and buyers. The total volume of new foreign issues floated in the United States from 1919 to 1929, inclusive, amounted to $8,172,000,000, while the net outward movement of long-term capital during the period exceeded $6,000,000,000. The heaviest flotations of new issues during these years were $1,201,000,000 worth in 1927 and $1,111,000,000 worth in 1928.

Even the farm proposals for a protected domestic consumption at parity with nonagricultural prices, independent of the world price for the surplus, depended for effective operation on the willingness and ability of the world market to take all the surplus the United States produced.

There was failure to recognize the effect of our change from a debtor to a creditor nation. Our status as a nation in another sense had also changed. We at last were at the end of the pioneering period. We now had a preempted continent—the last of the good free land had been taken up, and we were face to face with the problem of a maturing nation. No longer was there a frontier to act as shock absorber for dispossessed farmers and unemployed from industrial centers, with outside creditor nations ready to take our suplus production in payment on our debts to them.

The Farm Movement Spread by Regions

The persistence and growing strength of the farm-relief movement, from 1923 until the passage of the Agricultural Marketing (Federal Farm Board) Act in June 1929, is not explained wholly by index figures showing in national averages the purchasing power of farm crops in terms of other prices. The ratio of prices received to prices paid by farmers actually approached parity with the 1910–14 ratio in 1925, owing to the fall in nonagricultural prices at a time when farm prices were improving. But averages were misleading; they failed to reveal the local areas over which trouble was developing.

Distress did not strike all farm regions at the same time. It was most acutely felt first in the Spring Wheat Belt, and it was there that the first farm-relief movement caught on and incubated. The South had only three partly good years from 1919 to 1926, but nevertheless that region was slow to start thinking in terms of national action. The Corn Belt in 1921 and 1922 was not particularly interested when agitation for farm relief was running strong in Minnesota and westward. But when hog prices went back to pre-war levels in 1923, foreclosures and bankruptcies set in in earnest. The banks began to close. Land prices in Iowa in 1927 were 91 points below those of 1920.

The storm center began to shift from the Northwest to the Midwest about 1924.

THE DEPARTMENT'S PART

The influence of the Department of Agriculture in giving direction to the gathering farm-relief movement became clearly evident in the autumn of 1923. In October, Henry C. Taylor, Chief of the Bureau of Agricultural Economics, made a trip into the Dakotas, Montana, and the Pacific Northwest which gave him an opportunity to question most of the farm leaders of the region about the agricultural situation. Members of the groups which gathered to meet Dr. Taylor recall that he made no positive statements in support of any particular form of farm relief, but it was after his trip that the Northwest with singular unanimity started its drive for a Government export corporation to segregate and dispose of agricultural surpluses.

Secretary Henry C. Wallace first publicly referred to the export plan in an address to the Chicago Association of Commerce on November 14, 1923 (*12*). In this guarded endorsement, he said:

> Among all of the suggestions that have been made, the one which has been made by several people in this state and which has been considered at different times, seems to have more merit in it than anything else. It is simply this. In the case of those products of which we produce a large surplus, which must be exported, the government might well consider whether by setting up a government agency which would take that surplus and handle it in exactly the same way that many manufacturers have handled their surplus in times past, so that it would not be the government carrying the burden, but the producers of that crop, many who have given the matter consideration believe that of all the proposals suggested that offers the most hope.

On November 30, 1923, Secretary Wallace delivered to the President and published a report on The Wheat Situation (*13*), which provided the farm-relief forces of the Northwest with a wealth of ammunition which they were not slow to use. The report closed with these paragraphs:

> Inasmuch as the first step looking toward increasing the domestic prices requires the disposition of the surplus over and above domestic needs, and inasmuch as the facts presented in the foregoing pages indicate that the world production of wheat will probably be over-large for another year or so, the suggestion that the Government set up an export corporation to aid in the disposition of this surplus is worthy of the most careful consideration. Such a corporation necessarily would need rather broad powers. It would not be necessary that it should undertake to handle the entire crop, and it could probably carry on its activities in cooperation with existing private agencies. If it should be found necessary to arrange for the sale of the surplus exported at a price much lower than the domestic price, the loss so incurred would properly be distributed over the entire crop.
>
> The prime duty of such an export corporation would be to restore, so far as possible, the pre-war ratio between wheat, and other farm products of which we export a surplus, and other commodities. Its activities would therefore expand or contract according as the relative prices for farm products varied with other commodities, and it would cease to function as pre-war ratios become fairly well restored.

In December 1923 and throughout the winter so-called export corporation leagues sprang into being in the spring wheat States. Wheat growers' associations of the Northwest opened a militant campaign, and organizations of businessmen in cities and towns from Minnesota west pressed for action. In 1924 State farm organizations of the Corn Belt joined up, and the struggle was on in earnest.

CENTRAL IDEAS OF FARM-RELIEF PLANS

The agitation centered, first and foremost, around the general idea of equality for agriculture and the related idea of "a fair share of the national income." It also embodied the hope for security against bankruptcy prices and low and unstable income, drought and crop failure, and mortgage foreclosure and uncertain land tenure.

Prior to the appearance of the McNary-Haugen bill on the congressional scene, the Norris-Sinclair bill held the lead in farm support, although it had received no encouragement from the executive branch of the Government. Senator George W. Norris, of Nebraska, its chief sponsor, originally felt that the McNary-Haugen bill was an administration measure introduced to divert and divide farm support. He was strengthened in his conclusion by the fact that the original McNary-Haugen bill was drafted in the Department of Agriculture and had the quiet support of Henry C. Wallace, the Secretary of Agriculture, a fact which had much to do with the quick alinement of farm support back of it.

The Norris bill would have created a Government corporation empowered to buy or lease storage and processing facilities, and to buy, process, and sell farm products in raw or finished form. Its declared purpose was to eliminate as far as possible the commissions and charges between producer and consumer so as to increase the price to the former while decreasing the cost to the latter.

On their face, therefore, the provisions of the Norris bill promised to increase farm income by savings and short cuts which it was believed would be secured by substituting a Government agency for the private processors and middlemen. Its supporters read into the measure, however, the hope and expectation that the corporation would fix prices to farmers on a cost-of-production basis. The corporation was to be given $100,000,000 capital, with authority to sell tax-free bonds up to five times that amount.

In contrast, the McNary-Haugen bills proposed a minimum of interference with existing agencies and aimed only at the segregation and exportation of crop surpluses to bring domestic prices up to the "ratio" or fair-exchange level. It was proposed that operations should be made self-financing by collecting an "equalization fee" upon the first sale or the first processing of the commodity dealt with.

This plan was written into the original 1924 version of the McNary-Haugen measure and also into the vetoed bills of 1927 and 1928. The mechanism for implementing the plan varied considerably in the several bills, but at no time did the advocates abandon what they considered the essential ideas, (1) that the centralizing power of the Federal Government should be used to assist farmers to dispose of the surplus abroad and raise prices to the desired level in the domestic market, and (2) that the loss on the segregated exports was to be paid by the farmers themselves by means of an equalization fee.

The opposition centered its fire on the equalization fee, and assailed the proposal to bring about fair-exchange, or ratio, prices for export farm crops as "price fixing." They fought back against farmer charges that tariffs are ineffective on export crops. The supporters of the measures clung stubbornly to the principle of the equalization fee to enable the programs to pay their own way, but retreated temporarily from the fair-exchange-price principle and, instead, offered a bill in which the existing customs duties were made the measure of the price benefits to be secured by draining the surplus production off into export channels.

FARM-RELIEF PRESSURE FORCES COLLATERAL LEGISLATION

Under pressure of this general agitation, farm legislation advanced speedily along less controversial lines.

The Federal Government, always sympathetic to the idea of agricultural cooperation, moved to strengthen further the legal position of cooperatives with respect to the antitrust legislation by enacting the Capper-Volstead law of 1922.

Demand for further improvement in the credit structure had paralleled the fight for marketing reform. Specifically this was a demand for farm credit at rates comparable to those paid by businessmen and for the establishment of new banking institutions that could meet the peculiar credit needs of farmers. The Federal Farm Loan Act had been passed in 1916. Although this act greatly increased the availability of long-time farm-mortgage credit, it did not meet the needs of farmers for intermediate and short-time credit.

The Federal Intermediate Credit Act of 1923 provided for the establishment of 12 intermediate credit banks, to rediscount agricultural paper maturing within 3 years for banks and special lending agencies. This still did not fully meet the short-time credit needs of farmers. They had to wait another decade until the banks for cooperatives, the production credit corporations, and the production credit associations were set up or provided for in 1933 under the Farm Credit Administration.

To meet the growing unrest in the Northwest, the Norbeck-Burtness bill was introduced in late 1923, appropriating Federal funds with the general idea of turning spring wheat farmers into dairy production, and the President called the Northwest Agricultural Conference to meet in Washington in February 1924 to give it public support. The main body of the conference, which was made up chiefly of nonfarmers, endorsed the plan to spend money to diversify northwestern agriculture and recommended the establishment of the Agricultural Credit Co. to assist banks in the Northwest. Most of the farmer-members of the conference, however, united on a minority report endorsing surplus-control legislation along the lines of the McNary-Haugen bills, which had just reached Congress, and took their statement to the White House.

Action by the President about the same time to increase the tariff on wheat from 30 to 42 cents a bushel failed to lessen the pressure from the Wheat Belt, and the Haugen bill was brought to a vote in the House of Representatives in June 1924 and came within 36 votes of passage. In July the American Council of Agriculture was established at a big farm mass meeting in St. Paul to carry on the campaign for surplus-control legislation.

Special Organizations Play Important Part

The drive of the farm forces for a more clearly defined national agricultural policy brought into being from 1924 to 1928 a number of special organizations which cooperated with the general and long-established farm organizations and some of the cooperative marketing associations in support of particular bills. The American Council of Agriculture was the first of these to bring together a membership of cooperating organizations with national rather than regional scope. It was the center of leadership for the aggressive farm forces during 1924 and 1925. The national farm organizations sometimes joined in its statements and sometimes expressed their views independently.

The functions of the American Council of Agriculture in guiding the campaign for the McNary-Haugen bills passed to another special organization when the Executive Committee of Twenty-two was created early in 1926. This committee grew out of a conference of Governors of 11 Midwestern and Northwestern States which met at Des Moines, Iowa, in January 1926, on the call of the Governor of Iowa. Its activity ended when the second Presidential veto of the McNary-Haugen bill threw the issue into the 1928 political campaign.

The Corn Belt Committee of Farm Organizations was still another special body whose representatives were in Washington working closely with the Committee of Twenty-two during the years when the latter was active. But the American Council of Agriculture did most of the speaking for the proponents of farm relief from midsummer of 1924 until the early months of 1926.

Agricultural Conference of 1925 Draws Fire

With this prospect of continued activity on the farm front, President Coolidge in November 1924 called an agricultural conference which held hearings culminating in a series of reports filed in late January and early February 1925.

The conference report (*6*) failed to develop any program acceptable to the farm forces and served to spread the irritation that had become increasingly apparent. One of its proposals for a Federal cooperative marketing board with broad powers was defeated shortly thereafter in the House of Representatives.

Another section of the report (*6, p. 2*) directly attacked the pending proposals for handling exportable surpluses when it said:

> Any form of legislation or plan that tends toward a stimulation of production of any particular commodity for export will result in even further ill balance to our agriculture and, therefore, continued subjection of American farmers to competition with production based on lower standards of living abroad. There must, therefore, be established a balanced American agriculture by which production is kept in step with the demand of domestic markets and with only such foreign markets as may be profitable.

The conference failed to submit any blueprints for the establishment of the balanced agriculture it advocated. The fight went forward when the American Council of Agriculture filed its reply with Members of Congress, in which it declared (*10, p. 63*):

> No human agency can adjust acreage or number of these great commodities and, except by accident, arrive at, or anywhere near, the desired mark in production. No human agency should attempt to. The one attempting it would be

faced with the necessity of suggesting substitute crops to utilize the acres thus vacated. The difficulty of this is apparent. It is noteworthy that those ardent advocates who in 1923 would have turned the wheat farmers into commercial producers of butterfat, are now silent in the face of existing conditions in the dairy industry.

Even if it were possible for farmers through voluntary organization to make a nice adjustment of acreage to the estimated domestic demand, there is no possible way of forecasting to what extent drought and flood, hail and freeze, insects and disease—all these and others beyond the farmers' power to foresee and control—would thwart such calculations.

On the proposition that the task of handling the súrplus should be left to cooperative associations, the American Council had this to say (*10, p. 63*):

The great task is to deal with this normal surplus so as to preserve the home market for American producers at an American price that *does* equalize differences in production costs between farmers of this and competing countries. Those without experience in trying to accomplish this say: "Let the farmers organize cooperatively to do this thing." Undoubtedly, if this were practical, it would be the very remedy sought for. Co-operative organization has done great good for agriculture in this and other countries, and in years to come is destined to accomplish vastly more. The opportunity for co-operatives to demonstrate their worth by helping farmers secure a fair price for their products would be immensely increased if the question of the disposal of the surplus were itself disposed of otherwise. But to maintain a domestic price above world levels, and at the same time dispose of a substantial surplus at the world price, is a task which co-operative organizations of farmers alone cannot do, and which, if attempted by them, would destroy them.

The conference report had one direct effect on the form of the surplus-control legislation. Taking at face value the suggestion that cooperatives should handle the surplus problem, the bill was redrafted to provide that cooperative associations might organize to administer the export transactions with a particular commodity, backed by the equalization fee to spread the costs over all producers presumably benefited by the operation. While the modified bill failed to reach a vote in the Congress then in session, the changes may have accounted in part for the increased support the measure received from cooperative associations in 1926 and subsequent years.

South and West Unite

The year 1926 marked the union of the South with the West in backing the farm-relief program. The first conference with southern farm leaders took place in Memphis, Tenn., in March of that year, after which heads of southern commodity cooperatives, first cotton, then tobacco and rice, joined the western farm leaders in Washington.

These cooperative marketing associations, based on membership contracts and formed on commodity lines, were at that time the most active and influential of the southern farm organizations. Their influence in the national cooperative movement was great. As a result of their growing interest, midsummer conferences were held between proponents of the pending legislation and some of the nationally prominent sponsors of cooperative marketing, including former Governor Frank O. Lowden of Illinois.

A joint mass meeting of southern and western farmers in St. Louis in November, after the Haugen bill had met its second defeat in the House, issued a long declaration of principles. The section on surplus legislation said (*4*):

As a practical and immediate move to secure for agriculture a just and proper share of the national income and a position of equality with other industries in our national economy, we favor legislation that will enable farmers to control and manage excess supplies of crops at their own expense, so as to secure cost of production with a reasonable profit. We assert our conviction that such legislation must function through and foster cooperative marketing.

The tariff came in for critical attention at this convention. The declaration reads (*4*):

We recommend to farmers' organizations that they make a special study of the effects on agriculture of industrial tariffs and also of the effect of our change from debtor to creditor nation, and especially of its effects on the accumulation of our agricultural surpluses. Our "tariff primers" have taught us that the farmer would get his reward through the demand created by the high purchasing power of prosperous industrial classes. We demand that the farmer be given the opportunity to promote the national prosperity by his own increased purchasing power through increased prices.

Alternative Legislative Plans Appear

An alternative method for surplus disposal through use of customs debentures to subsidize exports reached Congress early in 1926. The general plan was developed by Charles L. Stewart, of the University of Illinois, and chiefly supported by the National Grange. It was essentially an export bounty which, instead of being paid in cash, was to be paid to exporters in the form of negotiable certificates (debentures) that could be used for paying import duties and hence would have a cash value. This increased buying power in the hands of exporters would enable them to bid more than the world price for exportable commodities. The increase above the world price was, of course, the objective of the plan.

The proposal that a Federal farm board be created to assist cooperatives to stabilize agriculture developed among opponents of the surplus-disposal programs and took several forms in 1927. The Curtis-Crisp bill, with administration support, gave it legislative status early in the year. The idea was endorsed in the report of the Business Men's Commission on Agriculture, which was one of two important committee pronouncements on agricultural policy published in late 1927 from quarters that until shortly before had been silent or negative on the farm question. The other report was presented by a special committee of the Association of Land Grant Colleges and Universities, also in November.

Important Committees Report on Agricultural Policy

The Business Men's Commission was sponsored and financed jointly by the National Industrial Conference Board and the United States Chamber of Commerce. A report of the former body on The Agricultural Problem in the United States had been published and given wide attention in 1926.

Referring to it as the administration plan, the Business Men's Commission endorsed the proposal for a Federal farm board to aid in the stabilization of prices and production in agriculture through advice to farmers on production and marketing and through a system of quasi-official stabilization corporations with power eventually to buy farm products at a price announced before the date of planting.

The commission condemned "legislative measures designed artificially to raise the domestic level of farm products above the world price level by export bounties, export debentures, or by agencies designed to dispose of surplus products abroad at a loss * * *" *(2)*. At the same time it asked, in effect, for a thoroughgoing revision downward of the tariff, starting with industrial rates, and then, when industry and agriculture reached approximately equal levels as to protection, to continue the reduction at equal rate, retaining adequate protection, however, on products the full domestic production of which is required by the country's long-run interests.

The report of the land-grant college special committee, like so many reports of the period, was strong on analysis and weak on remedy. It was important chiefly as a belated recognition by the agricultural colleges that a national agricultural problem did exist, and that they should be concerned with the development of a national policy to meet it. The discussion of the agricultural situation was revealing; of the tariff, straddling; and of the surplus problem, vague. "The movement toward stabilization and control," it concluded *(1)*, "may be hastened by favorable and sound types of legislation."

Progress of Farm Bills in Congress

Before these studies were undertaken, the effect of the union of farm forces back of export control legislation had been felt in Congress. The McNary-Haugen bill had passed both Senate and House, but had been vetoed by President Coolidge.

Early in 1928 a revised measure was introduced, dealing with all farm products instead of a limited number of basic commodities, and providing for operations similar to those proposed under stabilization corporations, with use of the equalization-fee plan only as a last resort if other moves failed to achieve the specified results. Again, both Senate and House passed the bill by substantial margins, and again the President returned it with his veto. On May 25 the Senate failed by 10 votes to muster sufficient strength to override the veto.

Agricultural policy commanded first-rank attention from the major political parties, but the threatened farm revolt against the administration failed to materialize in 1928. The farmer had been promised a general farm bill, and the Federal Farm Board was provided for in the Agricultural Marketing Act of 1929. He had also been promised higher tariffs, and he got them, too, in the Smoot-Hawley Act of the same year.

THE AGRICULTURAL MARKETING ACT OF 1929

The Agricultural Marketing Act of 1929 aimed to provide agriculture with a mechanism for the orderly production and marketing of farm products that would parallel the production and marketing mechanisms of other industries. The major provisions of the act were concerned with marketing, and the Federal Farm Board undertook to encourage cooperatives and stabilization corporations, provided the latter were established and owned by cooperatives. To unify the process of agricultural marketing with the support of loans, a 500-million-dollar revolving fund was put into the hands of the Board.

At the beginning of its operations, the Board viewed its principal function as the fostering of a system of cooperative marketing associations, but the drastic decline of agricultural prices which developed in the latter part of 1929 caused the Board to become increasingly concerned with the stabilization of the prices of agricultural commodities.

Notwithstanding many previous unsuccessful attempts to hold up prices by stabilization measures of storage and withholding, the Federal Farm Board through its subsidized stabilization corporations launched an ambitious attempt to support prices in this manner. Unfortunately, the period selected for the venture coincided with a world depression of unprecedented scope and severity. Operations might have been temporarily much more successful if, instead, they had coincided with severe droughts such as those experienced in 1934 and 1936.

The first efforts toward stabilization consisted of making loans to the cooperatives which would enable them to hold the commodities in storage until the market improved. This was followed by the setting up of stabilization corporations for wheat and cotton. These corporations took over most of the supplies that had been held by the cooperatives and in addition accumulated stocks by direct purchase in the market. Legally, these stabilization corporations were owned by the cooperatives, but the actual financing, operation, and risk-bearing were ultimately taken over by the Farm Board itself. The operations of the stabilization corporations resulted in heavy losses to the Board, which soon began to insist that gains in withholding supplies from the market could be realized only if production were held in line with actual market demand at home and abroad.

CONTINUED DEPRESSION FORCES FURTHER ACTION

Meanwhile foreign loans had practically ceased, and the export market shrank year by year. Renewed depression fell with cruel force on the American farmer.

Even at the peak of the business cycle in 1929, farm products could be exchanged for only 91 percent as much of other products, on the average, as they could have been exchanged for in the period before the war. By February 1933 the exchange value of farm products for industrial goods had fallen to 50 percent of the pre-war average. Their value in terms of taxes and interest was even less.

The disparity was present in the price of every farm product. It was most severe in the prices of export commodities, such as cotton, wheat, tobacco, and rice, where the disappearance or severe contraction of export demand had backed up great excess stocks of the commodities. It was also marked in hogs and hog products, the reduced export outlets for which had forced increased quantities into domestic consumption.

Gross farm income from the production of 1932 was less than half that of 1929, while fixed charges, including taxes and interest, were not proportionately lower. The Department of Agriculture estimated that the average farmer, after paying the expenses of production, rent, interest, and taxes, had only about $230 left out of his year's income. This gave him nothing as a return on his investment and much less than common-labor pay for his labor and management.

All the capital employed in agriculture had a value in January 1933 of only 38 billions of dollars as compared with 58 billions in 1929 and 79 billions in 1919, while farm debt remained virtually unchanged.

Credit was restricted and in many communities practically ceased to flow as thousands of country banks closed. Nearly 15,000 banks suspended operations during the 14 years 1920–33, involving total deposits of $8,500,000,000. Of these, 4,000 suspended in 1933, with total deposits of $3,600,000,000.

In the face of these conditions, it was obvious that further farm legislation would be enacted soon. It was only a question of what and when. During the winter of 1932–33 the agricultural committees of both Senate and House held hearings and produced bills, but the effort to enact them was less than wholehearted in view of the change in administration scheduled for March.

When the three national farm organizations were asked by the Senate committee to embody in a farm bill their ideas of what should be done, each brought its favorite remedy out of the past, and the result was a three-barreled measure combining the equalization-fee-surplus-disposal program of the Farm Bureau, the cost-of-production goal of the Farmers' Union, and the export-debenture plan of the Grange. The Secretary of Agriculture was to choose the method, or combination of methods, best calculated to work. This proposal did not command much congressional attention.

FORCES THAT SHAPED FIRST AGRICULTURAL ADJUSTMENT ACT

With mounting surpluses and stagnant markets staring farmers in the face, the argument for production control began to gain ground. Control legislation was freely discussed in 1932, and prototypes heralding the coming Agricultural Adjustment Act appeared in Congress during the winter of 1932–33.

Economists inside and outside the Department of Agriculture took a hand in shaping the Agricultural Adjustment Act of 1933. At the same time, responsible leaders of farm organizations had reached a stage of willingness to cooperate in trying to devise practical means to work for fair-exchange or "parity" prices through adjustment of the productive plant in line with probable future demand. The forces that had twice put the McNary-Haugen bill through Congress had been disorganized during the 4 years following 1928. Many of the leaders of that movement had experienced growing doubt whether, under existing and prospective world conditions, a sufficient foreign market could be found for an export surplus in the old proportions. This doubt became conviction when export outlets shrank with the termination of foreign loans by the United States.

All of the experience of the previous decade converged in the first Agricultural Adjustment Act and related measures.

The cooperatives had demonstrated to their own satisfaction that they could not hope to maintain and stabilize prices of the commodities for which they assumed responsibility so long as nonmembers shared in the benefits but escaped the costs assessed against members.

The interest of farmers in maintaining export outlets was recognized by provisions for disposal of excessive surpluses either abroad or in new uses at home.

The Federal Farm Board, which had operated with almost the complete support of organized agriculture, even of groups that had opposed its creation, had demonstrated the futility of attempting to control prices through storage and withholding without effective authority to control production.

Outlook Reports a Contributing Factor

Another important type of experience, of which nothing has yet been said, had originated in the Bureau of Agricultural Economics in the early 1920's and had continued with steady purpose since its beginning. That was the preparation and publication of outlook reports, covering all phases of farm production. In this work the Department drew heavily on the State agricultural colleges and experiment stations with their familiarity with local and regional conditions and problems.

The outlook reports aimed to promote efficient farming and balanced production. The Department had long lent its aid to the improvement of crops, livestock, and soils. The work got under way with the passage of the Morrill Act in 1862 providing for the establishment of the land-grant colleges. The research activities were intensified with the passage of the Hatch Act, in 1887, which provided for the establishment of the State agricultural experiment stations. Later on, in 1914 and 1917, with the passage of the Smith-Lever and Smith-Hughes Acts, machinery was provided for disseminating to the mass of farmers and farm youth the research findings and technical advances made in the experiment stations and research bureaus of the Department.

Beginning in 1922, the Department moved beyond the old boundary which had confined it merely to bringing the farmer improved techniques of production. The new step included the dissemination of economic information which would enable individual farmers to make adjustments in their acreage of crops and production of livestock in the light of prospective domestic and foreign demands. It was believed that farmers provided with such an outlook service could develop well-balanced systems of farming which would at least minimize, if not prevent, unprofitable agricultural surpluses and thereby stabilize income.

The objective of this program, obviously, was basically sound, but it depended entirely upon educational appeal as the motivating force. Even though they convinced farmers intellectually, the outlook reports failed to direct the economic behavior of many of the millions engaged in farming as individual units. The average farmer remained inclined to let the other fellow do the adjusting while he maintained or increased his production in his fight to meet expenses and interest payments. But the educational process started many farmers thinking about acreage allotments and quotas.

Domestic-Allotment Plan a Forerunner

An important contribution to the Agricultural Adjustment Act of 1933 was made by the domestic-allotment plan, which came to be widely discussed during the years in which the Federal Farm Board was gaining experience and disillusionment.

The domestic-allotment plan was proposed prominently after the export-debenture and equalization-fee plans had been set aside by the creation of the Federal Farm Board. The domestic-allotment plan recognized that these proposals would fail to work unless an export market existed that would take, at some price, all of the surplus of a crop above domestic requirements. It grew out of a doubt whether, under existing conditions, such large export outlets could be found. Therefore it sought to increase income directly for the domestic consumption, leaving the export surplus to take care of itself.

As originally conceived, it involved raising the price that farmers would receive on the domestically consumed portion of their export crops by limiting sales of such crops in the domestic market. The part of the crop which farmers could sell in the domestic market was called the domestic allotment, and they were to be given certificates covering that allotment. In order to move a commodity into domestic consumption, processors had to cover the quantities offered for sale with certificates purchased from farmers. The increased return on each farmer's domestic allotment was to result from the fact that he received not only the world price but also the proceeds from the sale of his certificates. No certificates were issued on production in excess of the domestic allotment, and on this quantity the farmers received only the prevailing world price. A somewhat different plan, incorporated in the Hope-Norbeck bills of 1932, eliminated the certificates and provided that cash-benefit payments realized from a processing tax and requiring limitation of production be made on the domestic allotment.

This plan, which developed through study and discussion by a small group of economists, aroused considerable interest in the winter of 1932–33 in both farm and nonagricultural circles. M. L. Wilson, recently Under Secretary of Agriculture, then an economist with the Montana State College, and John D. Black, professor of economics, Harvard University, developed the domestic-allotment plan with the aid of specialists on the staff of the Federal Farm Board and in the Department of Agriculture. Most of these men later became important figures in shaping programs under the Agricultural Adjustment Act.

The domestic-allotment plan definitely influenced the form of the agricultural adjustment legislation. Some of those who had worked on it participated in the discussions of farm legislation that took place following the election of 1932, before the new administration took office.

THE AGRICULTURAL ADJUSTMENT ACT OF 1933

In March 1933 the unofficial work carried on during the winter by informal groups matured into draftsmanship, with Members of Congress, farm leaders, Federal and independent economists, and executive officials all taking a hand.

The Agricultural Adjustment Act was passed in the spring of 1933. Under this act millions of farmers entered into contracts to reduce acreage in specified surplus crops in return for benefit payments, financed chiefly by processing taxes on the commodity concerned. In order to assure the success of the cotton adjustment program, cotton farmers were soon asking for marketing quotas with a penalty tax to force noncooperating producers into line. These requests led to the passage of the Bankhead Control Act, under the leadership of Senator John H. Bankhead, of Alabama.

This act imposed heavy taxes on the ginning of cotton, and at the same time provided participating cotton growers with tax-exemption certificates on their production allotments. This was soon followed by similar quota legislation for tobacco. Under the Kerr-Smith Tobacco Control Act, taxes were placed on the sale of tobacco, and participating tobacco growers were given tax-payment warrants on their production allotments.

The adjustment program was brought to a sharp halt by the Supreme Court decision in the Hoosac Mills case in January 1936, which held that the Agricultural Adjustment Act was unconstitutional in that it was a scheme for regulating and controlling agricultural production, whereas this power resided in the States and not in the Congress. The processing tax was also declared void because it was an inseparable part of the scheme for effecting production control. This decision, in turn, helped to determine the direction of the Soil Conservation and Domestic Allotment Act of 1936 and the Agricultural Adjustment Act of 1938. Under the conservation act an open or unilateral offer on the part of the Secretary replaced the contracts under the original adjustment program; conditional payments replaced benefit payments; direct appropriations replaced processing taxes; and the emphasis was shifted from acreage control toward soil conservation and upbuilding. Although it had obvious merits as an aid to better use of land, the Soil Conservation and Domestic Allotment Act was largely impotent as an aid to continued acreage control. The heavy production of wheat and cotton in 1937 was in part a testimony to that lack and intensified the problem faced by farmers and officials in 1938.

Farmers in general were dissatisfied both with the Supreme Court's narrow definition of the powers of the Federal Government to assist agriculture and with the ineffectiveness of the Soil Conservation and Domestic Allotment Act to implement acreage adjustments. So farm leaders took a more important hand in shaping the latest general agricultural law, the Agricultural Adjustment Act of 1938, than they had done with any of its predecessors that had become law.

PRECEDING EVENTS AND EXPERIENCE MOLD 1938 LEGISLATION

It is interesting to examine the extent to which this act and related measures represent a synthesis and culmination of earlier efforts. For this purpose the existing legislation may be considered under five major headings: (1) Soil conservation, good farm management, and balanced output; (2) loans, marketing quotas, and parity payments; (3) marketing agreements; (4) the diversion of surplus production into both domestic and foreign channels, and the development of new uses for agricultural products; and (5) crop insurance.

Soil Conservation, Good Farm Management, and Balanced Output

Maintenance of soil resources is a basic objective of the Agricultural Adjustment Act of 1938 and must be included in any farm program which hopes to bring enduring benefits to agriculture and to the Nation. The act of 1938 provides for payments to farmers who save and build up the soil. The supplemental income received for cooperation in the program enables them to check the inroads of soil erosion and hence take a necessary step in the application of the principles of good farm management to their enterprises. An important aim of the farmers' work under the present program is to keep the total acreage allotments at a level that will insure a normal supply of food and fiber for domestic consumption and export. This balance between depleting and nondepleting acreage tends not only to protect farmers against those erratic swings in production that have led to burdensome surpluses and ruinous prices but to guarantee consumers an ever-normal supply of essential farm products.

Under earlier programs the tendency was to work toward this objective through direct control of acreage. The experience of the Federal Farm Board led to this approach to the problem. As losses on commodities held by the stabilization corporations increased, the Board began to insist that gains could be made only if production were held in line with the requirements of orderly marketing. The shift from this approach following the Supreme Court's decisions of 1936 did not eliminate the necessity of working toward a balance between supplies of farm products, on the one hand, and domestic-consumption requirements and foreign demand on the other. On the contrary, it is only through such balance that the declared purposes of the present act—parity prices and parity incomes for producers and adequate and steady supplies of farm commodities at fair prices to consumers—may be attained.

These provisions emerge from the background of previous experience. The problem of soil erosion is one which has attracted the attention of farmers and agricultural experts since Revolutionary times. Since the latter part of the nineteenth century the State and Federal Governments have given attention to the problems of erosion control, and the results of this work eventually reached farmers through activities of the Extension Service. A most significant advance was made in 1930, when Congress authorized the establishment of 10 regional experiment stations whose work revealed the full seriousness of the problem and hastened the formulation of more effective measures for coping with it. Shortly afterward came the establishment of the Soil Erosion Service, first in the Department of the Interior and subsequently transferred to the Department of Agriculture, which inaugurated a program of soil-conservation demonstrations in cooperation with private landowners. The manifest importance of this work led to the passage of the Soil Conservation Act of 1935, which established the Soil Conservation Service. The work of this agency was closely integrated with that of the Agricultural Adjustment Administration, as the programs of the latter aimed not only to increase agricultural purchasing power through control of the production of basic crops but also to encourage adjustments from the chief soil-depleting crops to crops or uses which would conserve or improve the soil and check or prevent erosion.

The movement in this direction was given further impetus with the enactment of the Soil Conservation and Domestic Allotment Act of 1936, under which soil conservation became the primary concern of the Agricultural Adjustment Administration and farmers and ranchers received payments conditioned upon positive performance in improving and conserving farm and range land. The Agricultural Adjustment Act of 1938 embodies a reenactment of the Conservation Act of 1936, and the objective of soil conservation remains a major objective under the present program.

Loans, Marketing Quotas, and Parity Payments

A separate title of the 1938 act provides a series of supplemental measures which enable producers of corn, wheat, cotton, tobacco, and rice to obtain storage loans to put a floor under prices when these are threatened by a slump and to finance the holding of surplus supplies until they are needed. Furthermore, marketing quotas may be employed to buttress the price-supporting influences of the loans. Their effect is to limit the sales of a commodity during a marketing year when supplies are at excessive levels. Each farm is given a marketing quota, and penalties are prescribed for sales in excess of that quota. Quotas, however, may be introduced only after producers of a commodity, in a special referendum, have voted in favor of their use by at least a two-thirds majority. Finally, since the result of the loans and quotas may be to stabilize farm prices at levels still too low in the light of the goals of parity prices and income, the Secretary is authorized to make payments, insofar as funds are available, to producers of the five basic commodities, that together with their income from the sale of their crops, will bring them a return approximately equal to parity price on their normal production.

Here again, there are historical antecedents. The crop-loan idea became sufficiently widespread to furnish a basis for the Agricultural Marketing Act of 1929, which was administered by the Federal Farm Board. Through its revolving fund, the Board was authorized to facilitate orderly marketing through loans to farmer-owned cooperatives and stabilization corporations. Loans on corn, cotton, naval stores, and other commodities were important adjuncts to programs under the Agricultural Adjustment Act of 1933.

The marketing-quota device found partial precedent in the Bankhead and Kerr-Smith laws and is a logical accompaniment of acreage allotments and of the present policy of encouraging the storage of excess supplies.

The direct parity payments are clearly traceable to the post-war demands, as evidenced by the McNary-Haugen and domestic allotment movements, that agriculture be accorded parity prices and its fair share of the national income.

Various criteria for determining the level of price stabilization have been discussed for years in connection with farm legislation. These have included such standards as equivalent tariff protection, cost of production, parity price, and, more recently, parity income.

The criterion of tariff equivalence, which implies raising agricultural prices above the world-market level in about the same average proportion that the tariff has raised the prices of industrial products above the world-market level, has considerable justification on grounds of equity. It is not, however, very satisfactory. Industrial tariff rates are designed to check imports, and the rates necessary to do this do not necessarily constitute an accurate measure of the discrepancy between the positions of agriculture and industry.

Cost of production has a considerable amount of theoretical validity, but it is an unsatisfactory concept to use in practice. The experience of farm-management investigations and the studies of the Tariff Commission have indicated that the statistical determination of cost is exceedingly difficult and involves many arbitrary decisions, particularly with respect to the allocation of costs among different products produced on the same farm.

Parity price is easily calculated and easily understood, but the Department of Agriculture has pointed out that it is not always a reliable index of disparity between agriculture and industry. It assumes that over a period of time prices of all agricultural products will continue to bear the same relations to one another that they bore during the period selected as a base. In many instances the attainment of parity prices will bring undesirable results, such as impeding the normal consumption of farm products and even reducing the net income of producers below a fair level.

The Department of Agriculture has come to believe that parity income constitutes a more justifiable expression of the concept of agricultural-industrial balance than does parity price. The income concept was introduced into the Soil Conservation and Domestic Allotment Act of 1936, the purposes of which include the—

> reestablishment, at as rapid a rate as the Secretary of Agriculture determines to be practicable and in the general public interest, of the ratio between the purchasing power of the net income per person on farms and that of the income per person not on farms that prevailed during the 5-year period August 1909–July 1914, inclusive.

Unfortunately, the fact that incomes cannot be determined with the same statistical accuracy as prices greatly reduces the usefulness of the income criterion.

Consideration of all the proposed criteria raises the question whether the objectives of agricultural policy can be once and for all established by a simple exercise in arithmetic.

Marketing Agreements

Supplementing the provisions of the 1938 act aimed to prevent sudden surpluses from disrupting the farm-price structure, the Agricultural Marketing Agreement Act of 1937 enables farmers and distributors to establish permanent and rational marketing systems for entire crops and groups of crops. The basic device authorized by this act is the marketing agreement, the genesis of which is easily discerned. Like so many other devices, this idea crystallized during the McNary-Haugen period. The final version of the McNary-Haugen bill provided that surpluses in excess of the requirements for orderly marketing could be handled by marketing agreements between the then contemplated Federal Farm Board and farmers' cooperative associations or corporations established and controlled by cooperatives. The Agricultural Marketing Act of 1929 laid great emphasis upon orderly marketing and effective market organization but did not specifically provide for the use of marketing agreements.

The marketing-agreement idea was revived and made an integral part of the Agricultural Adjustment Act of 1933. The marketing-agreement provisions of the act permitted the organization of processors, distributors, and cooperatives into groups exercising centralized control over the marketing of agricultural products, and exempted such groups from antitrust laws. These provisions were supplemented by others granting the Secretary of Agriculture power to license distributors in order to eliminate unfair practices and to effectuate the general purposes of the act. Because of the doubt cast on the validity of the licensing provisions by the Panama Refining and Schechter decisions of the Supreme Court, orders of the Secretary were substituted for licenses in the 1935 amendments to the Agricultural Adjustment Act. The principal marketing-agreement provisions of this amended act were reenacted as the Marketing Agreement Act of 1937.

Surplus Diversion and New Uses

The Agricultural Adjustment Act of 1938 contains important provisions designed to widen the market for farm products. In the forefront are provisions authorizing the continuation of the Federal Surplus Commodities Corporation and the establishment of four regional laboratories to conduct research into and develop new uses and outlets for farm products. In addition, the Secretary of Agriculture is authorized to—

> use available funds to stimulate and widen the use of all farm commodities in the United States and to increase in every practical way the flow of such commodities and the products thereof into the markets of the world (*5*).

The idea of diverting farm surpluses into domestic channels antedated the present act, as evidenced by the congressional resolutions of 1932 directing the Farm Board to make available to the Red Cross up to 40,000,000 bushels of wheat and to distribute 45,000,000 bushels of wheat and 500,000 bales of cotton to distressed persons in the 1932 crop-failure areas.

The original Agricultural Adjustment Act authorized the Secretary to make use of available funds for the disposal of surplus agricultural products. This authority was greatly emphasized and extended by section 32 of the amending acts which provided that 30 percent of the receipts from import duties be segregated for use in surplus-removal operations.

Operations designed to increase domestic use of farm products by low-income consumers were carried out first by the Agricultural Adjustment Administration in conjunction with the Federal Surplus Relief Corporation, and since 1935 have been carried out by the Federal Surplus Commodities Corporation. As to new uses, the regional research laboratories represent the culmination of a line of activity in which the Department of Agriculture has long been engaged and to which both farm and industrial groups have given wholehearted support.

The provisions for encouragement of exports have a distinguished and obvious lineage in the equalization-fee plan which was a prominent feature of the McNary-Haugen bills and in the export-debenture plan of the late 1920's which was written into the proposed McKinley-

Adkins bill of 1926 and the Jones-Ketcham bill of 1928. Last of this line was the domestic-allotment plan, which was designed primarily to avoid the appearance of export dumping, which had been charged against both the equalization-fee and the export-debenture plans.

The history of the special provision enacted in 1935 that sets aside 30 percent of annual customs revenues to finance disposal of surplus at home and abroad illustrates clearly the influence of past events on present legislation. Representative Marvin Jones, of Texas, Chairman of the House Committee on Agriculture since 1933, was one of the early supporters of the export-debenture plan, which indirectly would have diverted customs revenues to pay bounties on agricultural exports. Chairman Jones conceived section 32 of the amending legislation as a direct way to accomplish the same purpose but broadened the purposes for which the funds could be used so as to include disposal of surpluses for relief and other domestic uses.

In many quarters consideration has recently been given to current proposals which would give the export-diversion idea a more prominent place in the present program than it now occupies. In some of their forms these proposals would virtually abandon other approaches, such as soil conservation and orderly marketing, in favor of a program of large-scale export diversion plus certain direct subsidies to farmers.

While under the present program large-scale attempts to stimulate exports have been made, notably with wheat and cotton and their products, it needs to be recognized that in view of existing world conditions this approach is less likely to attain desired results now than in earlier periods. With the progressive narrowing of world markets for agricultural products and with increasing supplies of competitive substitutes throughout the world, it seems impossible to increase our agricultural exports much above the recent level without causing sharp declines in price. Furthermore, many important countries to which we used to export in large volumes are engaged in a drive for agricultural self-sufficiency, and their strongly centralized governments are almost certain to resist effectively any influx of large supplies from abroad which would tend to make these countries more dependent upon outside sources of supply.

In presenting these new proposals, the proponents naturally give only the broad outlines, which possess a disarming appearance of simplicity, particularly when contrasted with the administrative detail necessary to carry out the present program. A more rigorous examination of such proposals reveals that without exception their effective operation requires detailed administration. For example, many of these plans call for the segregation of farmers' crops into two parts, one for export and one for domestic use. This means that quotas must be determined and enforced on the individual farms. Again, many of the plans imply the extensive regulation of all types of middlemen and processors in order to secure information as to the prices at which different portions of various crops are bought and sold. In any event, it is certain that proposals which involve the abandonment of vital parts of the current program should be carefully scrutinized to see whether or not they are really any simpler than the current program and whether their promise of greater gain for the farmer is a reality or only a mistaken hope.

Crop Insurance

The Agricultural Adjustment Act of 1938, under title V, cited as the Federal Crop Insurance Act, sets up the Federal Crop Insurance Corporation, an agency of and within the Department of Agriculture. This new agency has a capital stock of $100,000,000 and is empowered to write insurance against loss in wheat yields, commencing with crops planted for harvest in 1939. This new development has a background of its own. The hazards of farming have long been a subject of serious discussion, and in seeking modification it is but natural that the idea of insurance, applied so successfully to the elimination of other hazards, should be tried out in the field of agriculture.

As early as the latter part of the nineteenth century, private companies made an attempt to enter the field of all-risk crop insurance, and governments have been interested in the possibilities of crop insurance from an early date. The topic has been a matter of public interest in the United States since the early 1920's, and bills relating to crop insurance and resolutions calling for investigation of its possibilities have appeared frequently since that time. The immediate inspiration of the present law was the report of the President's Committee on Crop Insurance in December 1936, which proposed, among other things, that a crop-insurance plan for wheat, effective in 1938, be recommended to Congress.

SOME NEWER PROBLEMS

Even a brief history of agricultural policy since the end of the World War would be incomplete without some reference to three types of problems that have become increasingly prominent during the past decade. Approaches to a solution of these problems have been tentative and experimental, but there is a growing realization that they must be met.

One is the problem of tenancy. This is not a new problem. Ever since 1880, when the Census Bureau, under Francis A. Walker, first began to collect figures on farm tenancy, some attention has been given to the steady growth of tenancy at the expense of operator ownership. The trend did not become a matter of public concern, however, partly because other agricultural problems seemed more urgent and perhaps partly because farm tenants are not a homogeneous or articulate group. But during the last few years farm tenancy has received new emphasis as a factor in soil misuse. In addition, the fact that 42 percent of our farmers are now tenants, with the percentage as high as 70 in some States, seems to some people to be a sharp contradiction of the traditional American ideal of individual ownership.

The problem received prominent recognition through the appointment in 1936 of a Committee on Farm Tenancy, composed of citizens from various parts of the country. In 1937 Congress passed the Bankhead-Jones Farm Tenant Act, and under this act increasing sums have been appropriated each year to be loaned for the purchase of farms on a 40-year-mortgage basis. The administration of the fund, which is still small enough to be considered only experimental, is now in the hands of the Farm Security Administration. Meanwhile an attack on the tenancy problem is being made from another angle through the study, in several States, of local customs and laws relating to leases. The idea here is that many of the so-called evils of tenancy may be largely a matter of the conditions of tenure and that by an intelligent approach on the part of States and communities, these conditions can be made consistent with the welfare alike of tenants, landlords, and the soil.

The second problem is that of the large group of farmers who are on the fringe of commercial production or entirely outside it. This problem is possibly a belated backwash of the industrial revolution, finally having its full effect in agriculture.

Broadly speaking, three conditions prevented the appearance of a surplus farm population in the United States in the past. At first American farmers were largely self-sufficient. Next they were kept busy supplying the wherewithal for building up American industry, which was founded on farm exports. Then, when industry got into its stride, it was able for a time to absorb whatever surplus population there was on the farm.

One by one, these three conditions were reversed. The United States now has a highly commercialized agriculture which, like industry, is constantly undergoing technical improvement so that year by year fewer workers are needed to produce a given quantity of products. At the same time the domestic demand for many important food staples, unlike that for industrial products, is relatively inelastic; adequate industrial opportunities for the part of the farm population released from labor by improved techniques do not exist at present; and the rate of natural increase among rural people remains relatively high.

The net effect of these conditions is summed up in the fact that 50 percent of our farmers now produce 90 percent of our commercial agricultural products. The other 50 percent—which is more likely to grow than to be reduced—perforce constitutes a marginal and in part a surplus farm population. How are these people to make a livelihood?

The situation is not a theory but a hard fact. It is made worse by any adverse condition such as the recent widespread droughts. The marginal and surplus farmer is the rural counterpart of the unemployed city worker, and both would of course disappear if industry expanded enough to absorb them. Throwing the problem on industry's doorstep, however, does not alleviate the immediate plight of some millions of American citizens. On humanitarian grounds alone, their problem cannot be left unsolved. Aside from humanitarian grounds, there is the question of how healthy a society can remain if so large a number of its members have no apparent economic function and therefore no self-respecting way to gain a subsistence.

Obviously there is no simple or easy solution for this problem, which in fact is only one aspect of a much more complex situation. Too little has been done as yet to draw any very significant conclusions, though recognition of the problem as of major importance is itself significant. A limited attack has been made on the problem, first by the Federal Emergency Relief Administration, then by the Resettlement Administration, and today by the Farm Security Administration. This agency uses an individual-case-study method. The situation of each family with which it is concerned is studied individually, and an effort is made to give the family an adequate start toward self-sufficiency and a modest livelihood. This may involve resettlement of the subsistence-homestead type. The work proceeds on the theory that for the most part the rural unemployed are average folk, willing and able to make a living and that they can find a place for themselves if they can get the right kind of start. The Farm Security Administration has also attempted some cooperative projects, and it has started a promising program for medical care in rural areas.

The third problem has to do with the domestic consumption of farm surpluses. Orthodox methods for disposing of these surpluses have already been mentioned. An ingenious new method has recently been receiving considerable attention. This is the food-stamp plan being tried by the Federal Surplus Commodities Corporation as a possible way to overcome some of the shortcomings of distribution through ordinary relief channels. The food-stamp plan has three distinctive features. It attempts a systematic correlation of surplus production with actual need—for example, by getting certain foods to people whose diets are deficient. It operates through regular trade channels, making commercial dealers an integral part of the picture. And it apparently stimulates some additional buying of the surplus products beyond what the stamps themselves would provide.

All these aspects of the current farm problem are discussed at greater length elsewhere in this Yearbook. They are brought into the historical record here because, though relatively new, they indicate that under the drive of necessity there has been a significant broadening out of agricultural policy beyond the areas of price, export, and credit with which it has been traditionally concerned.

AGRICULTURAL POLICY; ITS MEANING AND EVOLUTION

A nation's agricultural policy is not set forth in a single law, or even in a system of laws dealing directly with current farm problems. It is expressed in a complexity of laws and attitudes which, in the importance of their influence on agriculture, shade off from direct measures like the Agricultural Adjustment Act through the almost infinite fields of taxation, tariffs, international trade, and labor, money, credit, and banking policy.

The combined indirect effect of policies in many of these other fields may be nearly as important, if not fully as important, in determining progress toward the goal—equality for agriculture—as are the direct approaches to the farm problem. A common tendency to ignore these related factors has been apparent in the oversimplification of most statements of what is called the farm problem.

Our own experience with farm legislation indicates that a nation never reaches the time when it can say its agricultural policy is fixed and complete. Evolution and change are nearly the only constant factors, partly because conditions at home and abroad which policy is required to meet are themselves constantly changing.

223761°—40——22

The intense effort and deep study of the business of farming in the United States, which so many individuals and groups have contributed during the two past decades, have produced the present system of agricultural laws and organizations, but it cannot be said they have solved the farm problems. Presumably these laws themselves will be subject to change and displacement. But if experience in this field teaches anything of value, it is that a continuous thread runs through the evolution of an agricultural policy notwithstanding the manifest inconsistencies and contradictions that appear in it. The programs of the present become the foundations for the programs of the future.

LITERATURE CITED

(1) Association of Land Grant Colleges and Universities, Special Committee.
1927. REPORT ON THE AGRICULTURAL SITUATION . . . AT THE 41ST ANNUAL CONVENTION, CHICAGO, ILL., NOVEMBER 15 TO 17, 1927. 40 pp. [n. p.]

(2) Business Men's Commission on Agriculture.
1927. THE CONDITION OF AGRICULTURE IN THE UNITED STATES AND MEASURES FOR ITS IMPROVEMENT . . . 273 pp., illus. New York and Washington.

(3) Peek, George N.
1922. EQUALITY FOR AGRICULTURE. 48 pp. Moline, Ill.

(4) St. Louis Conference on Agricultural Relief.
1927. DECLARATION OF PRINCIPLES, ADOPTED BY FARMER ORGANIZATION LEADERS OF SIX SOUTHERN AND SIX NORTHERN STATES IN CONFERENCE IN ST. LOUIS ON THE PROBLEMS OF AGRICULTURAL RELIEF. 6 pp.

(5) United States Agricultural Adjustment Administration.
1938. ANNOTATED COMPILATION OF THE SOIL CONSERVATION AND DOMESTIC ALLOTMENT ACT, AS AMENDED, AND ACTS RELATING THERETO (AS OF THE CLOSE OF THE THIRD SESSION OF SEVENTY-FIFTH CONGRESS JUNE 16, 1938). 73 pp. Washington, D. C.

(6) United States Congress, House Committee on Agriculture.
1925. AGRICULTURAL RELIEF. Hearings before the Committee on Agriculture . . U. S. Cong. 68th, 2d sess., Ser. CC, pt. 1.

(7) ——— Joint Commission on Agricultural Inquiry.
1921. THE AGRICULTURAL CRISIS AND ITS CAUSES. 240 pp., illus. (U. S. Cong. 67th, 1st sess., H. Rpt. 408, pt. 1.)

(8) ——— Joint Commission on Agricultural Inquiry.
1922. AGRICULTURAL INQUIRY. Hearings . . . under Senate Concurrent Resolution 4 . . v. 1, illus. (U. S. Cong. 67th, 1st sess., S. Con. Res. 4.)

(9) ——— National Agricultural Conference.
1922. REPORT ON NATIONAL AGRICULTURAL CONFERENCE . . . 210 pp. (U. S. Cong. 67th, 2d sess., H. Doc. 195.)

(10) ——— Senate Committee on Agriculture and Forestry and House Committee on Agriculture.
1925. MCNARY-HAUGEN BILL. Joint Hearings . . . on S. 4206 and H. R. 12127 . . . pt. i. 70 pp.

(11) United States Department of Agriculture.
1920–23. ANNUAL REPORTS OF THE SECRETARY. U. S. Dept. Agr. Yearbooks 1919, 1922.

(12) Wallace. Henry C.
1923. FARM AS BASIS OF NATIONAL LIFE. Speech before regular Association of Commerce meeting. Chicago Association of Commerce. 10 pp. Chicago.

(13) ———
1923. THE WHEAT SITUATION; A REPORT TO THE PRESIDENT. 126 pp Washington, D. C.

PART 2

Agriculture and the National Welfare

Agricultural Surpluses and Nutritional Deficits

by J. P. Cavin, Hazel K. Stiebeling, and Marius Farioletti [1]

WHAT IS a surplus from the economic standpoint? What three fundamental conditions cause surpluses of agricultural products, and how do the remedies differ in each case? How is it that a market surplus of a product can exist while at the same time there is a nutritional deficit of the same product? In what foods are we deficient when the nutritional needs of our people are all added up? How can the domestic market for agricultural products be expanded in the face of the declining rate of population growth? What is the significance of income distribution for the farmer's market? What long-time and what immediate policies are suggested by the relation of income levels to effective demand for farm products? What part does the now famous food-stamp plan play in these policies? These questions are here discussed by two economists and an expert in nutrition.

[1] J. P. Cavin is Senior Agricultural Economist, Division of Program Development and Coordination, Bureau of Agricultural Economics; Hazel K. Stiebeling is Senior Food Economist, Bureau of Home Economics; Marius Farioletti was formerly Agricultural Economist, Consumers' Counsel Division, Agricultural Adjustment Administration. The sections of the article headed "Surpluses and Deficits from the Standpoint of Nutritional Needs" and "Consumption Deficits and Food Selection" were contributed by H. K. Stiebeling; the sections "Increasing the National Income" and "The Problem of Income Distribution" are by Marius Farioletti; the rest of the article is by J. P. Cavin.

IT IS the fashion in much recent discussion of social and economic problems to catalog our national deficiencies of food, clothing, housing, health, etc., and to set over against them our actual or potential ability to eliminate these deficiencies. In the shadow of great stocks of cotton and wheat are placed the ill-clothed and ill-fed. Similarly, the army of the unemployed and the unused capacities of industrial plants are contrasted with our national needs in housing, transportation, and the whole array of economic goods of which so few ever have enough.

The result is the familiar paradox of scarcity in the midst of plenty; of the coexistence of surplus and shortage. Nowhere is the contrast more marked than between agricultural surpluses and nutritional deficits; nowhere does the remedy seem so simple and obvious—use the surplus crops or surplus acres to provide more and better food for those whose diets are below optimum.

WHAT IS A SURPLUS?

Unfortunately, this solution of the surplus problem is not as simple as appears at first glance. We need first to examine the meaning of the term "surplus." It is a vague term at best, rarely defined and loosely used by many persons, in many senses, and for many purposes.

In its widest popular sense, the term "surplus" is equivalent to the phrase "too much" or "too many." People complain of too much corn, too much cotton, too much wheat, too many workers, too many taxicabs.

In this sense the principal connotation of the term is economic. The taxi driver who complains that there are too many taxicabs means that there are too many relative to his ability to make a living. The cotton farmer means that there is more cotton available than can be sold at a price that will bring what he, or perhaps some economist, considers a fair or normal income.

How can we define a surplus so that the concept will be useful in programs of agricultural adjustment and consistent with efforts to advance the general welfare? A surplus is the amount by which supplies offered for sale are greater than the amount that will bring producers a normal income. By a normal income we mean one that brings comparable rewards to producers of like ability in both agriculture and industry over a period long enough to make adjustments to major changes in technology and demand, but excluding extreme peaks of boom and depression. Stated somewhat differently, it is an income obtainable during a period when the national income reflects the long-run productive ability of the Nation and when the different parts of the economy are in balance with one another.

Agricultural surpluses may be classed under three broad headings: (1) Those due to production outrunning demand; (2) those due to a decline in the consumption of a product; and (3) those due to a decline in general buying power or income.

A surplus of the first type—production outrunning demand—might arise from several causes, such as a much larger than average crop due to unusually good growing conditions, the introduction of improved methods of production, or an unusually large acreage planted because of miscalculation as to the course of prices or the size of competing supplies. Assuming that stocks carried over from the previous marketing year are at or above average, the result of any of the foregoing will be a supply that can be sold only at very unprofitable prices even when larger than average stocks are carried over to the next year. In some instances and in some degree the solution may lie in withholding part of the amount by which the total supply is above average entirely from the market and releasing it later on when conditions cause output to fall below average. This is the ever-normal-granary principle. However, if production continues to be so large that the stocks withheld from the market become larger than needed to offset any likely number of short crops, the only action that will restore the incomes of growers to normal will be a reduction of acreage and output.

A surplus of the second type—decline in the consumption of a product—may be illustrated by changes in the dietary habits of people. Thus in recent years the consumption of certain fruits, such as apples, has declined while the consumption of other fruits has increased. It becomes impossible for those who grow fruits affected by the down trend in consumption to continue their past average output and receive prices and income comparable to those of other fruit growers or of agricultural producers in general. Here again the only practicable solution is for the producers adversely affected to decrease their output and to regain their income position by the substitution in whole or in part of the production of other commodities, the consumption of which is increasing.

A surplus of the third type—one due to a general decline in buying power—may be illustrated by a business depression or by a decrease in the foreign demand for agricultural products brought on by policies of agricultural self-sufficiency in countries which formerly imported a large proportion of their normal requirements of food and fiber. The case of a decline in foreign demand unaccompanied by a business depression is analogous to a decline in the domestic consumption of specific commodities. It becomes impossible to obtain profitable prices on the usual volume of exports, and the only way out is for the producers of export goods to decrease their output, and for some of them to shift into the production of other agricultural products or move into nonagricultural occupations. The case of a business depression is somewhat different because normal incomes cannot be restored entirely by adjustments in the supply side. Industrial production drops, the national money income drops, and great numbers of people are thrown out of work. People in general have less money to spend, and agricultural producers find they cannot sell their output at prices comparable to those received when the factories were going full blast. Furthermore, even at the low prices, the normal rate of consumption of certain agricultural products, such as cotton, will decline and abnormal stocks will accumulate. Some progress toward the normal level of income can be made by reducing output, but such reduction will not by itself bring prices back to normal. It needs to be accompanied by the restoration of general business activity and general demand to their former level.

NORMAL PRODUCTION REQUIREMENTS

Can we measure normal production requirements and surpluses? We cannot do so with absolute precision, but calculations can be made that are sufficiently accurate to bring the problem into focus and to form the basis of action programs. One approach is to calculate normal supplies by using past averages of supplies adjusted for evident trends in consumption and demand. This has been used in determining acreage and production goals for basic crops under the Agricultural Adjustment Act of 1938. Normal supplies are calculated by adding together the requirements of normal domestic consumption, normal exports, and normal stocks. In the case of cotton, for example, a normal year's domestic consumption is the average annual quantity consumed in the United States "during the 10 marketing years immediately preceding the marketing year in which such consumption is determined, adjusted for current trends." A normal year's exports is similarly computed; while 40 percent of normal consumption and exports is taken as normal carry-over. For the year 1939–40, this yielded a normal-supply figure of approximately 18,200,000 bales of cotton. Given this norm, the amount by which actual production would cause actual supplies to exceed 18,200,000 bales would constitute surplus production.

Similarly we can calculate in terms of acreage a normal production level for our agricultural plant as a whole. Thus in order to give our present population an average per capita consumption of food and fiber equal to the level prevailing in the period of high demand, 1920–29, to supply probable export demand, and to provide average carry-over stocks, we need, at average yields, a harvested acreage of some 325 to 340 million acres. During the 5-year period 1928–32, our total harvested cropland averaged about 365 million acres. With normal growing conditions, improvements in the technique of agricultural production, and the absence of programs involving acreage adjustment or the diversion of soil-depleting acreages to soil-conserving uses, a return to this high level might easily take place. The 20 to 40 million surplus acres would be transformed into surplus products that would clog the markets and depress farm prices and incomes.

SURPLUSES AND DEFICITS FROM THE STANDPOINT OF NUTRITIONAL NEEDS

The present market surpluses of certain protective foods—dairy products, leafy vegetables, and vitamin-C-rich foods—are surpluses from the commercial standpoint but not from the standpoint of nutritional needs. These are the foods in which usual diets, and especially the diets of low-income groups, tend to be low as compared with diets that meet all-round nutritive needs. The diets of low-income groups tend to be lacking in these foods not only in the United States but apparently in all highly industrialized countries. In discussing the Englishman's food in the twentieth century, J. C. Drummond, a distinguished British biochemist, says: [2]

---

[2] DRUMMOND, J. C., and WILBRAHAM, ANNE. THE ENGLISHMAN'S FOOD; A HISTORY OF FIVE CENTURIES OF ENGLISH DIET. 574 pp., illus. London. 1939.

One thing is certain. A means must be found of bringing these essential foods within the reach of the poorest section of the community. How this is to be done is not yet apparent, but it is to be hoped that the problem will be faced in a frank and honest manner.

If the average consumption of protective foods by all families in this country could be raised to the level of those whose present diets may be rated "good" from the standpoint of nutrition, there would be large increases in national consumption. The figures would be approximately as follows: Milk, 20 percent; butter, 15; eggs, 35; tomatoes, citrus fruit, 70; leafy, green, and yellow vegetables, 100. These figures are not maximum, however, because many freely chosen "good" diets do not include nearly as much of the protective foods as many nutritionists believe they should include. For example, internationally recognized experts on nutrition recommend that we double our average consumption of dairy products. Nevertheless, to raise consumption even by the amounts indicated would imply fairly large increases in purchasing power.

At a still lower level, much more food would be consumed than at present if the diets of only the most needy families were raised to the point where average nutritive requirements would be covered, with little margin for safety. This level may be represented by the economical diet plan evolved by the Bureau of Home Economics.[3] If the consumption of the protective foods were increased only to this level among those families that are now consuming less than the quantities specified in the plan, the national increases in consumption would be approximately as follows: Milk, 10 percent; butter, 10; tomatoes, citrus fruit, 10; leafy, green, and yellow vegetables, 80.

Other diet plans suggested by the Bureau[4] for three higher levels of money expenditures for food show food choices that would insure higher than average nutritive returns for the expenditure. If each nonrelief family selected from among these diets the one that it could afford, the increases in consumption, assuming 1935–36 price levels and distribution of families by income, would amount to: Milk, 16 percent; butter, 26; tomatoes, citrus fruit, 8; leafy, green, and yellow vegetables, 80.

These figures indicate that there are deficiencies in the consumption of protective foods in this country. Depending on the criterion used, it would appear to be advantageous to the nutrition of our population if averages ranging from 10 to 100 percent higher than at present could be attained in dairy products, from 10 to 70 percent higher in tomatoes and citrus fruit, and from 80 to 100 percent higher in leafy, green, and yellow vegetables.

Deficits in consumption of foods are found chiefly, though not exclusively, among low-income groups—families on relief and the many nonrelief families whose incomes and living levels are low. It is true, of course, that farm families by producing a large share of their own protective foods enjoy certain advantages over their village and city neighbors. With favorable growing conditions and a willingness to invest the necessary land and energy in the project, even those at comparatively low economic levels can have an abundant and varied

---

[3] STIEBELING, HAZEL K., and CLARK, FAITH. PLANNING FOR GOOD NUTRITION. U. S. Dept. Agr. Yearbook 1939: 321–340, illus. 1939. See pp. 333 and 337.

[4] Described in the article cited in footnote 3.

food supply the year round. But this takes more capital and more planning ahead than many farm families can yet manage.

BALANCING SURPLUSES AND DEFICITS

From the standpoint of health, better diets could mean smaller outlays for illness, less loss of working time, greater physical efficiency, and longer, more productive life. With increased longevity, man would have need for all kinds of nutritious food over an extended number of years. For agriculture, better diets would mean increased production of fruits, succulent vegetables, butter, and milk, and hence more cows and more animal feed.

From a dietary standpoint the Nation urgently needs an increased consumption of protective foods that would require 8 to 10 million acres to produce. And if all could secure the "expensive good diet" now available to those who do not have to guard their food dollars too closely, we might need to utilize 30 to 40 million acres more than has been required for actual consumption in recent years. Given such increases, the chronic surplus problem of agriculture would vanish or be greatly reduced. The principal surplus problem would be one of temporary gluts of specific commodities.

The need for profitable outlets for agricultural products is so great that a quick response to any increase in effective demand seems assured. There can hardly be any doubt about the ability of agriculture to meet whatever changes in consumption are thus evidenced. As the final report of the Mixed Committee of the League of Nations on the relation of nutrition to health, agriculture, and economic policy stated, "The best proof that agriculture is able to adapt itself to the expansion in demand for the protective foods lies in the fact that it is already doing so."

It is difficult, however, to see how further burdens in the production of foods could be thrown upon agriculture without an assurance of a fair return, particularly when the bulk of the recommended consumption is in the relatively high-cost foods. To attempt to do so would be to force the cost of a general food subsidy on agriculture and further depress it in relation to the rest of the economy.

What Are the Remedies?

Large increases in consumption must come primarily from greater consumer efficiency, particularly better consumer knowledge of food needs; increased national income; better distribution of income; general lowering of prices paid by consumers; and perhaps some subsidizing by the Nation as a whole of the food consumption of certain underprivileged groups.

The lowering of prices in general involves increasing the efficiency of our entire productive and distributive mechanism and the elimination of laws and regulations which unduly favor the price interests of special producer groups as against the price interests of consumers in general.

Consumption Deficits and Food Selection

A better knowledge on the part of the public of nutritive values in relation to price, together with a keen appreciation of the importance of dietary adequacy to well-being could result in a higher proportion of good diets in this country than are found at present. As McLester put it in his presidential address to the American Medical Association in 1935:[5]

> In the past, science has conferred on those peoples who availed themselves of the new knowledge of infectious diseases better health and a greater average length of life. In the future it promises to those races who will take advantage of the newer knowledge of nutrition a larger stature, greater vigor, increased longevity, and a higher level of cultural attainment. To a measurable degree, man is now master of his own destiny where once he was subject only to the grim hand of Fate.

All of the answers in nutrition are not known to science, by any means. In fact the knowledge is still very fragmentary. Enough is known, however, to wipe out the great scourges of pellagra, beriberi, and scurvy, whenever the facts can be applied. Enough is known to rear children that on an average would be taller and straighter and more vigorous than their parents. But how can this knowledge be brought to people so they will be induced to accept it? Many public and private agencies are concerned with spreading the information about food values, nutritional needs, food buying, and food preparation so much needed by families. Hard at work at the task are schools and colleges the country over, classes of the Extension Service, club study groups, health centers, and clinics. By discussions, demonstrations, illustrated lectures, film strips, special pamphlets, articles in newspapers and in popular periodicals, and radio talks the new knowledge of good nutrition is being spread.

The same sum of money or the same amount of land and work can secure diets very different in nutritive value, depending on the combination of foods selected. Retail food prices are based primarily on costs of production and marketing and on the interplay of supply and demand rather than on the nutritive values of food. Many agencies, therefore, including the Bureau of Home Economics, have evolved broad patterns for food budgets suited to different economic levels or different types of home food-production programs.[6]

When money for food is limited, such plans suggest higher than average use of the less expensive dairy products, and also of grain products, especially the less highly refined forms. When more money can be spent for food these plans suggest higher than average consumption of fruits and succulent vegetables of all kinds, but especially of the green-colored and leafy vegetables, as well as of dairy products, eggs, and meats. Diet plans based on the relative costs of different classes of food as well as on food values and human needs can be stated in fairly general terms. As a result they can be adapted to markets in any part of the country or used as a basis for differing programs of food production for home use in any of the more important land use areas and still leave considerable room for catering to family tastes. Such material should be of help to families in villages and cities as well as on farms. Village and city families are faced with the problem of making the best possible use of the money available through wise food choices and the development of skill in food buying and prepara-

[5] McLester, James S. NUTRITION AND THE FUTURE OF MAN. Jour. Amer. Med. Assoc. 104:2144–2147. 1935.

[6] Carpenter, Rowena Schmidt, and Stiebeling, Hazel K. DIETS TO FIT THE FAMILY INCOME. 37 pp., illus. 1936. See also the 1939 Yearbook article cited in footnote 3, p. 333.

tion. Farm families have in addition the problem of effectively planning home production and conservation of food.

Since people tend to be rather slow to change their food habits even with intensive educational programs, it may be expected that dietary shifts due to education will be gradual. This will enable producers to adjust to them more readily. Perhaps agriculture will find that it can not only adapt itself to a slowly changing structure of demand but, by concentrating an increasing proportion of its productive resources on the protective foods, anticipate the movement somewhat and thus facilitate it.

Increasing the National Income

The educational approach to the problem of consumption deficits would have its greatest effect among people who can afford good diets but are choosing them unwisely from a nutritional standpoint. For them, better diets would not require an appreciable increase in total food consumption, but primarily some shift away from energy foods to protective foods.

But there are also large numbers of people who not only fail to choose their diets wisely but lack the means of purchasing the elements of a good diet. The problem here is not so much one of changing the composition of the diet as of making net additions to the existing level of food consumption. The most needed additions are usually among the protective foods, which generally are also the high-priced foods. For this group of people, measures affecting the level and distribution of income are of crucial importance in a solution of the problem of consumption deficits.

The possibilities of increasing consumption through factors affecting money income are of equal importance for the producers of agricultural commodities. They are especially important in view of the fact that recent changes in the rate of population growth indicate that the factor of an expanding population, which contributed so much to the enlargement of domestic demand for farm products in the past, can no longer be relied upon to absorb great quantities of such products. From 1920 to 1930 the absolute increase in our population was about 17,000,000. From 1930 to 1940 the increase is estimated as about 8,500,000, and by 1960 the population may have attained its maximum size.[7]

> It follows from analysis of the trend of the Nation's population that continued expansion of the domestic market for American goods and services must be sought through the increase of effective consumer demand, through increased productivity and broadened distribution of income rather than in the numerical increase of population.[8]

This statement holds equally well with regard to the problem of increasing the domestic consumption of agricultural products.[9]

There is no question but that an increasing total national income accompanied by increasing employment would effect an increased consumption of agricultural products. Fully employed workers pro-

---

[7] U. S. National Resources Committee. THE PROBLEMS OF A CHANGING POPULATION. 306 pp., illus. Washington. 1938. See pp. 21 and 24.

[8] See p. 8 of reference cited in footnote 7.

[9] Farioletti, Marius. THE PROBLEM OF INCOME AND ITS DISTRIBUTION. U. S. Dept. Agr. Yearbook 1939: 385–392. 1939.

vide larger and more profitable markets for agriculture than do the unemployed and the underemployed. The demand for the relatively higher priced protective foods would be increased, and predepression upward trends in the consumption of certain foods and toward more nutritive diets would be accelerated.

Large increases in total food consumption cannot be expected from expansion of the total national income. Our Nation consumed only 50 pounds more per person per year in the period 1925–29, when national income was increasing very rapidly, than in the period 1920–24. Such an increase, however, would be significant from the viewpoint of better nutrition and national health if it could be concentrated among the low-income groups and if it should consist of the varieties of food most important to dietary balance.

But if all consumer incomes increase proportionately, the total national income must be very large before consumers in the lower income third obtain really significant increases in purchasing power. A national income of about $90,000,000,000 to $100,000,000,000, as compared to an estimated national income of about $69,000,000,000 in 1939, would have to be obtained before full employment of the Nation's labor power could be approximated. The prospects for a $100,000,000,000 national income cannot be foreseen as a short-time goal.

The Problem of Income Distribution

The economic problem of distributing incomes more effectively is not a question of how to make all incomes equal. It is not a question of how to "soak" the rich. It is a question of what distribution of income will enable us to use our productive resources most effectively under a system of private property and production for profit.

The exact distribution of incomes which would be likely to induce and maintain maximum levels of production and consumption for a long period of time is unknown. However, it is reasonable to believe that the direction of change would be toward a narrowing of the range of all incomes along with relative increases in incomes below the average. This does not mean that the absolute levels of incomes above the average need be decreased.

The significance of changes in income distribution for consumers and producers of agricultural commodities is fairly clear. With a national income of a given size, significant relative increases in the money incomes of families ordinarily receiving less than $1,000—particularly those families receiving less than $750—would probably increase appreciably both the total expenditures for foodstuffs and the total consumption. The consumption of other agricultural products such as tobacco would also increase appreciably. This problem is worth exploring in some detail.

The potential market among the low-income groups in this country is very large. In 1935–36 about 42 percent of the Nation's families received incomes below $1,000 and got only 16 percent of the aggregate family income. About 27 percent of the families received incomes of less than $750 and got about 8 percent of the aggregate family income. Since the desire for consumption goods among these low-income families is known to be much greater than their ability to purchase, significant relative income increases would appreciably increase the rates of consumption for many goods and services. Furthermore, the volume of additional expenditures for goods and services might be a good deal larger than the income increases, because consumer credit for these low-income families would expand directly with their income increases, and no doubt they would make use of it.

A dollar increase in the purchasing power of low-income consumers is much more effective than a dollar increase in the total national income if the objective is to increase the domestic consumption of agricultural products. The income elasticity of food consumption for the low-income families under $500 and $500–$1,000 is very great as compared with the level of food consumption among families receiving $1,000–$1,500. If the food purchasing power of these two low-income groups could be increased significantly relative to the $1,000–$1,500 group, so that they could effectively demand the higher-income food-consumption pattern, substantial increases in the total consumption of many classes of foods could be expected. Among the foods most likely to show such increases are fresh and canned fruits and vegetables (also some of the dried products), milk and milk products, and meats, poultry, and eggs.

It is extremely difficult to alter the distribution of incomes, however, for it is imbedded in the complex of institutions and rights fundamental to our existing society. Thus alternative policies are resorted to in the public interest to offset some of the problems that apparently derive from the distribution of incomes. Social legislation designed to aid particular groups of low-income consumers is helpful if its economic effects do not tend to reduce the rates of employment and capital formation more than the Nation's ability to consume is increased.

When agriculture is effectively producing supplies of foodstuffs that cannot be sold profitably because potential consumers are unemployed or have a food purchasing power below the needs of adequate nutrition, it is probably more in accord with the long-time interest of the Nation and more economical to develop consumption-adjustment policies in addition to production adjustment rather than to use production adjustment alone. Policies designed to increase national income and the purchasing power of the lower income groups, together with measures designed to subsidize the food consumption in these groups, may be viewed as interrelated parts of a consumption-adjustment program.

Special Programs To Increase Consumption of Low-Income Groups

Measures for materially increasing the purchasing power of low-income groups are essentially of a long-time nature, as are those for increasing the over-all efficiency of the marketing structure.

Meanwhile special programs to improve the diets of low-income groups by various types of direct action have been devised. These involve subsidies of two main types: (1) The maintenance of special prices for commodities needed by the low-income groups, and (2) the free distribution of such commodities to these groups.

The first approach is illustrated by the efforts of communities to supply milk at reduced prices to children in schools, to nursing and expectant mothers, and to the unemployed.

It is important to note that this approach does not constitute such a marked departure from existing price arrangements as may at first appear and does not necessarily involve expenditures of public funds. Milk has long been sold under "classified" prices depending on whether it is to be used for fluid milk, for cream, for butter, or for other purposes. There is no reason why prices cannot also be classified on the basis of the consuming groups and of different services attached to different segments of the supply. Thus, while a small reduction in the general retail price of milk might not lead to an appreciable expansion of consumption, a somewhat larger reduction reflecting in part lessened processing and service applied to the low-income market where milk consumption is particularly inadequate might increase total consumption considerably and even increase the returns to producers over those obtained under the traditional pricing system. There are numerous other possibilities. Surplus pork, for example, might be ground into sausage and sold below average pork prices.

A similar plan involving Government expenditures would be to purchase surpluses of foods especially needed in the diets of low-income groups, reselling to certified families at prices below usual market levels. This would be analogous to an export subsidy program except that the surpluses would be disposed of within the country instead of abroad. Within a fairly wide limit, the foods thus sold would go to families who would not ordinarily be able to buy them at all or only in smaller quantities; hence such sales would not disrupt the regular channels of trade and would represent net additions to farmers' incomes.

The second approach is to distribute the surpluses without charge, the Government bearing the entire cost of the subsidy. Since 1935 there has been in operation a plan by which surplus farm products, purchased by the Federal Surplus Commodities Corporation, are distributed to families on relief or certified as needy through State welfare agencies. During the 4 years 1935–39 nearly 3 billion pounds of surplus foods have been distributed under this arrangement. These products have contributed to the nutrition of needy families, added new foods to the diet of many communities, and stimulated increased interest in a more varied diet on the part of nonrelief as well as relief families. Among the foods that have been distributed and the quantities thus saved are:

	Million pounds		*Million pounds*
Meats and fish	932	Cheese, dry skim milk, evaporated milk	133
Grain products	450	Butter, lard, other fats	104
Potatoes, sweetpotatoes	450	Sugar, and cane and sorgo sirups	26
Other vegetables	115	Eggs	14
Fruits	565		

In the past these supplies have been distributed to the needy families through central depots. Although this method of distribution markedly increased consumption among these families, there was complaint that the method was wasteful—that quantities received by families at one time often were larger than they could use without spoilage because of inadequate storage facilities, that there was no choice among the items that were available for distribution, and that the supplies were irregular.

A new way of distributing surplus foods is being tried experimentally in a considerable number of cities, towns, and counties. Instead of giving surplus commodities to States, counties, and cities to distribute, the Federal Government is giving food-order stamps to the families directly. The stamps, which are colored blue, can be taken to grocery stores, where they can be used to obtain surplus foods as additions to other family food supplies.

Two methods of distributing the surplus food-order stamps are being used. In most cities families at work on Work Projects Administration jobs and those who are receiving, or are certified as eligible to receive, public assistance in cash payments—old-age assistance, aid to dependent children, and aid to the blind—will be eligible to get the free blue surplus-food stamps if they buy orange-colored food-order stamps with part of their WPA or assistance payments. The orange stamps, good for the purchase of any food usually sold in a grocery store, may be bought at the rate of $1 to $1.50 a week per person for each member of the family. Their use is to insure that regular food purchases are kept up, so that food secured with the blue stamps will be in addition to and not in place of these regular purchases. One blue surplus-food stamp will be given free with each two orange stamps bought. For each dollar's worth of orange stamps bought, the family will receive 50 cents' worth of free blue stamps.

Families receiving grocery orders as part of direct public assistance are eligible to receive the free blue stamps without having to buy orange stamps. The grocery orders insure continuance of regular food purchases by this group.

The advantages of the stamp plan over the depot method of distribution are several. The usual channels of trade are used; families may choose for themselves which of the surplus commodities they will use, when, and in what quantity. This reduces waste. A longer list of commodities is available through the new plan, and the list changes from time to time. If the surplus of a product is used up, that product will be taken off the list. If the surplus of some other product piles up, that product will be added to the list. Official lists of surplus commodities that can be bought with blue stamps are sent to grocery stores and are posted there. The list as of August and September 1939 included butter, shell eggs, dry edible beans, dried prunes, wheat flour, and whole-wheat (graham) flour, corn meal, rice, cabbage, fresh peaches, fresh tomatoes, fresh green peas, onions (except green onions), and fresh pears.

NOT SIMPLE ARITHMETIC

The present situation is extremely complex. We obviously have great nutritional deficits which should be remedied in the interest of the national well-being. We also have surpluses in the sense that certain agricultural products are being produced in such quantities that they could not return normal incomes to producers even with a very high national income. In addition, we are operating at a level of national income considerably below that obtainable with our existing resources, which results in even lower prices and intensifies the depressing effects of the surpluses.

The solutions of these problems are by no means incompatible with each other. We can envision a situation in which the production of agricultural products, though kept within certain limits by an ever-normal-granary program, would be large enough to provide a high dietary standard for the country as a whole and, with national income at a very high level, could be sold at prices that would give agricultural producers an income comparable to that obtainable in other occupations.

Such a balance, though representing a vast improvement over the situation exising in recent years, would still leave large numbers of people with nutritional deficits. There would still be low-income groups lacking the means to buy the elements of a good diet; ignorance of dietary values and the art of spending money; and defects in the marketing structure tending to keep food costs up. Possible avenues of solution have been indicated but it should be remembered that they involve effort and study over a long period of time and large expenditures on the part of public agencies. The surplus-deficit problem is a real one, but its causes are deep-rooted and complex, and it is not open to solution by a simple exercise in addition and subtraction.

223761°—40——23

The Farmer's Stake in Greater Industrial Production

by Louis H. Bean [1]

IF THE national economic problem can be summed up in a single sentence, it can be said to be a problem of increasing industrial production in the United States to a point somewhere near our productive capacity. If that were done, not all farm problems but many of the worst of them would disappear. The author of this article sets out to show what increased industrial production would mean to agriculture and to outline briefly various current proposals for achieving it. These he groups in three classes: (1) Those for increasing purchasing power first, on the theory that increased production would be bound to follow. (2) Those for stimulating production first, on the ground that purchasing power would then increase more or less automatically. (3) Those that would combine the two approaches in a sort of middle-of-the-road program. Whatever is done, he believes that Government nowadays is bound to play an important role; but the amount of governmental action will vary inversely with the amount of cooperation of business and labor.

---

[1] Louis H. Bean is Counselor, Bureau of Agricultural Economics.

THE COMMUNITY of interest between farmers, city workers, and consumers persists as a vital reality in spite of the fact that the farm population now constitutes only 25 percent of the total instead of the 95 percent of 150 years ago.

On the farm fourth of the population the other three-fourths depends in many ways. For example, because of its relatively higher birth rate the farm population supplies the bulk of the annual increase in the total population. The products of our farms in 1929 furnished over 40 percent of the raw materials used by our factories and gave employment to 33 percent of our factory workers.[2] The railroads received 22 percent of their freight revenue and railroad labor received about the same proportion of its wage earnings from the transport of farm products. The fourth of the population living on farms is the largest economic group consuming the products of city labor and services, though it constitutes only about one-eighth instead of one-fourth of the national market. This disproportion is, of course, evidence of a much lower standard of living among farmers than among nonfarmers, measured in terms of material things, but it is also evidence of a great potential outlet for the products of our mines and factories if the purchasing power of the farm people were more nearly in line with their numerical ratio to the total population.

The dependence of farmers as a group on the welfare of laborers and consumers is much more obvious. For example, over 90 percent of the cash income from farm production is derived from the money income of consumers in the domestic market, the balance coming from the export markets. As consumers, typical wage earners' families spend 35 to 40 percent of their annual income for food and an additional 10 percent for clothing. Farmers get 40 to 50 percent of the average dollar spent for food in the retail markets, and urban workers probably receive in wages about 60 percent of what farmers spend for industrial products and services.

Because of this interdependence, farmers have a vital interest in any program or policy that will help to bring about full employment of the working population in the cities.

ECONOMIC REMEDIES, OLD AND NEW

In our shifting industrial conditions from decade to decade, various proposals have been made for attaining higher and more stable levels of industrial activity. Some of the proposals of the 1930's differ from those current in depression years of the 1920's and earlier decades in that they recognize a new set of relationships emerging between the United States and the rest of the world as well as between Government, business, labor, and agriculture in our own country.

In previous decades the Nation had the benefit of a rapidly growing city population, new frontiers, technological advances creating new industries, and expanding foreign markets. Remedies for depressions were sought solely on the basis of maintaining or restoring free competition and improving the prospects for profits. Thus in depression years wages were lowered in efforts to reduce production

[2] BEAN, L. H., and CHEW, A. P. ECONOMIC TRENDS AFFECTING AGRICULTURE. U. S. Dept. Agr. 46 pp., illus. 1933. See p. 11.

costs; prices of raw materials were allowed to fall low in relation to the prices of finished products; interest rates—the cost of credit—were lowered to reduce the cost of doing business and to stimulate the prices of industrial stocks and the flow of private savings into industrial ventures; and tariffs were raised to protect domestic industries against foreign competition.

In the early days after the 1929 collapse these indirect devices were again hopefully resorted to, but they no longer had their former apparent potency. This emphasized the fact that business and agriculture in the United States had new problems to deal with. As a matter of fact, Lord Macaulay in the 1850's and Woodrow Wilson in the 1890's had warned this country of the difficulties it would face once its physical frontiers were gone. Henry A. Wallace immediately after the World War warned us that because the war had made us a creditor instead of a debtor nation we would need to alter our foreign-trade policies so as to permit more foreign goods to enter in payment of debts to us and to pay for our agricultural exports, or else we would have to reduce our production of farm products for export. Others pointed to such factors as the increase in labor-saving machinery, the imminence of technological unemployment, and the greater instability in employment arising from increasingly large-scale corporate organization in the industries producing heavy machinery and other durable goods.

But the prosperity of the late 1920's, resulting from our willingness to lend money to other countries and the free use of credit for real estate and construction and finally for a vast speculative boom in industrial stocks, quieted these warnings. Their full significance was more clearly seen when in the early 1930's the usual indirect recovery devices failed to stem the deepening depression; when our financial institutions felt the full impact of the world-wide collapse in trade and in prices of commodities and securities; when foreign countries, also caught in the depression and becoming more and more nationalistic, erected trade barriers in self-protection.

Under these circumstances the indirect measures had to be supplemented by more direct measures for recovery. Among the latter those that predominated were concerned with increasing the purchasing power of consumers through Government activities in the belief that this would create a direct and immediate demand for more goods, which would result in more employment. Formerly production on the basis of past savings and bank credit had been relied on to create consumer purchasing power. But with private credit agencies unable to stimulate production and large corporations waiting for definite signs of increased demand before venturing to reemploy men and produce goods, Government was called upon to take the necessary steps.

Today, then, we have proposals for attaining full recovery and a higher standard of living that go beyond the older indirect ones. Some of them, like the pension programs, are efforts to increase purchasing power first as a stimulus to demand for goods. Some, at the opposite extreme, aim at increasing production and employment first as the basis for increased purchasing power. Others, like the "spend-lend" program proposed in Congress in 1939, are a combination of these two approaches.

It is doubtful that we shall adopt any single program for the next decade to the exclusion of others. In view of our complex economic system, we are more likely to pursue several of the basic programs already initiated and to perfect those aimed at (1) greater economic security for the aged and more purchasing power for the low-income groups, (2) greater stability in the flow of investments (private and governmental) into the production of durable goods, (3) greater stability in agricultural prices, and (4) the creation of new opportunities, including rural and urban public-works programs, for surplus farm labor and unemployed urban workers. As a means of raising the national standard of living, special efforts will be made to improve the economic and social conditions of the "lower third," which is made up chiefly of the noncommercial farm population and low-income wage workers. In these programs, Government will play an important role, the amount of direct governmental action varying, however, inversely with the degree of cooperation of business and labor.

LESSONS OF THE DEPRESSION

One of the results of the prolonged depression of the 1930's is a much clearer view of the incomes and living standards of the different groups of our population. It can also be seen more clearly which groups would have their living standards automatically raised by increased industrial activity and which ones are likely to remain stranded at the low-income levels unless Government, or Government in cooperation with private enterprise, provides the necessary opportunities for constructive work and better earnings.

Data from the consumer survey of the National Resources Committee [3] indicate broadly the living standards of the urban and rural population as measured by dollar income. One-third of all families and single individuals covered by this study had incomes of less than $780 during the year 1935–36. Forty percent of this low-income group were on farms, 20 percent in rural nonfarm communities, and 15 percent in small cities. The remaining 25 percent were in middle-sized and large cities. Divided according to occupations, 40 percent of all nonrelief families in the low-income group were engaged in farming, 39 percent were wage earners, and the remaining 21 percent were in clerical, business, professional, and other occupations. About half of the wage-earning group lived in rural nonfarm communities but undoubtedly derived some income from work on farms. Furthermore there are 20 to 25 percent more persons per family among the farm families in all income groups than among the nonfarm families.

It may therefore be concluded that about one-half of the lower third of the population with inadequate incomes is to be found among farm families. Among the nonrelief families 2.3 million farm families and another 2.3 million wage-earning families were in the third receiving incomes of less than $780 per family.

The majority of those receiving relief—1.5 million individuals and 4.5 million families, including 600,000 farm families—had incomes averaging only $182 per family. It is obvious that the chief need of

[3] [United States] National Resources Committee. Consumer incomes in the United States: their distribution in 1935–36. 104 pp., illus. Washington, D. C.

this group is an opportunity to work in nonagricultural occupations. For the 2.3 million urban families with incomes of less than $780, it may be said that they need more full-time work, or better wages, or both. If the heads of these urban families had had opportunities to produce industrial goods more abundantly and had been paid more adequately, commercial farmers would have had better domestic markets and would in turn have been able to purchase some of the greater industrial output. This, however, cannot be said equally for the 2.3 million nonrelief farm families and the 600,000 relief farm families, most of whom live on a subsistence basis and produce a very small proportion (probably less than 10 percent) of the total farm production that is marketed. It should be borne in mind that increased urban purchasing power has greater significance for commercial

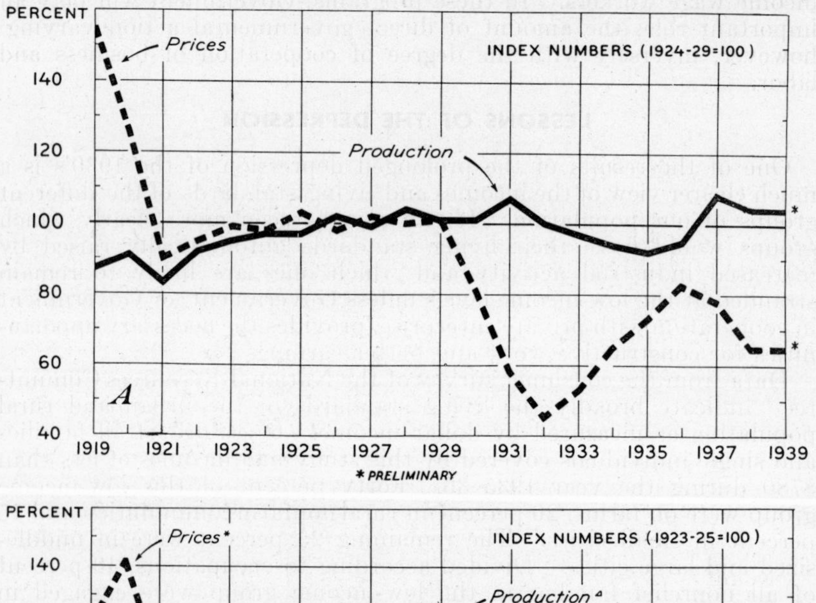

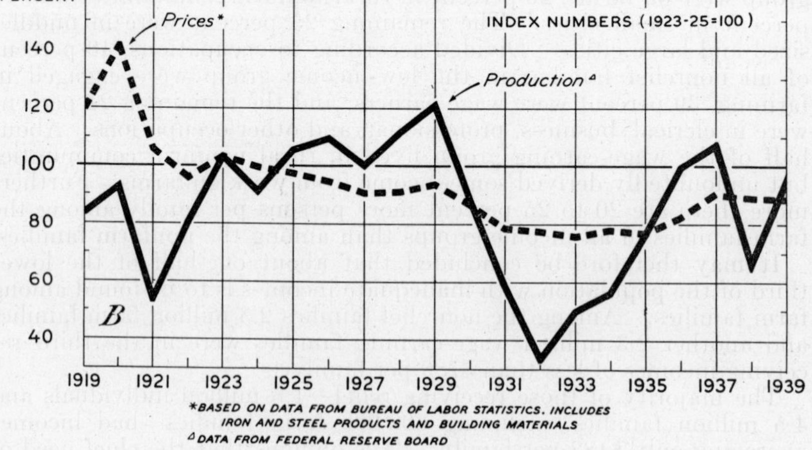

Figure 1.—*A,* Agricultural production and prices, United States, 1919–39; *B,* industrial production and prices of durable goods, 1919–39.

than for subsistence farmers. For the latter an improvement in living standards depends ultimately on nonfarming sources of income.

In 1935–36 farmers had an average yearly per capita income of $277, about half that of the nonfarm population ($539). While both of these averages represented substantial improvement over those of 1932, the year of lowest depression, they were substantially lower than those of 1929.

It is fairly clear that relatively low farm prices were largely responsible for the low farm income. Throughout the 1930's agricultural production in the aggregate did not depart greatly from the average of the 1920's (fig. 1, *A*). Prices were low, however, because of the low level of industrial production (fig. 1, *B*) as well as restricted foreign demand. During the years 1932–38 (including the partial recovery years, 1936–37) industrial activity averaged about 25 percent below that of 1929, whereas farm production (including that of the record drought years of 1934 and 1936) was on an average about equal to that of 1929.

It was this discrepancy between agricultural and industrial production plus declining foreign markets for farm products that gave rise to the efforts to raise agricultural prices to the level of industrial prices. The greatly reduced industrial production meant greatly reduced employment and general purchasing power. This in turn meant reduced prices for foods and clothing materials and thus lower prices to farmers. Furthermore, with reduced volume and fixed charges, costs per unit of industrial products increased, with the result that industrial prices were held up in relation to agricultural prices and the exchange value of farm products for industrial goods was reduced. The various agricultural programs that were adopted to bring about a more nearly normal relation between supplies of farm products and industrial production and between prices of farm products and industrial products are discussed elsewhere in this book.

INDUSTRIAL PRODUCTION CLOSELY LINKED WITH EMPLOYMENT AND NATIONAL INCOME

A simple illustration of the arithmetic of full industrial recovery is given in figure 2. Here are brought together three basic sets of data [4]—the total number of available workers in the nonfarm population, the total number of workers actually employed, and the course of industrial production from 1919 to 1939. It is clear that the total number of nonagricultural persons actually employed fluctuates with the volume of industrial activity and that the total number available for work rises year after year with the growth in population. In 1929 there were close to 38 million nonagricultural persons available for work, of whom over 36 million were actually working. By the end of 1939 industrial production had again reached the peak output of 1929, and the number of persons employed was about 35 million. Thus after 11 years it was possible to produce and service about the same volume of goods with fully a million fewer persons employed. This is only part of the evidence of technological progress, for in 1939

[4] BEAN, L. H. INDUSTRIAL UNEMPLOYMENT AND THE FARMER. U. S. Bur. Agr. Econ., Agr. Situation 23 (1): 9–13, illus.

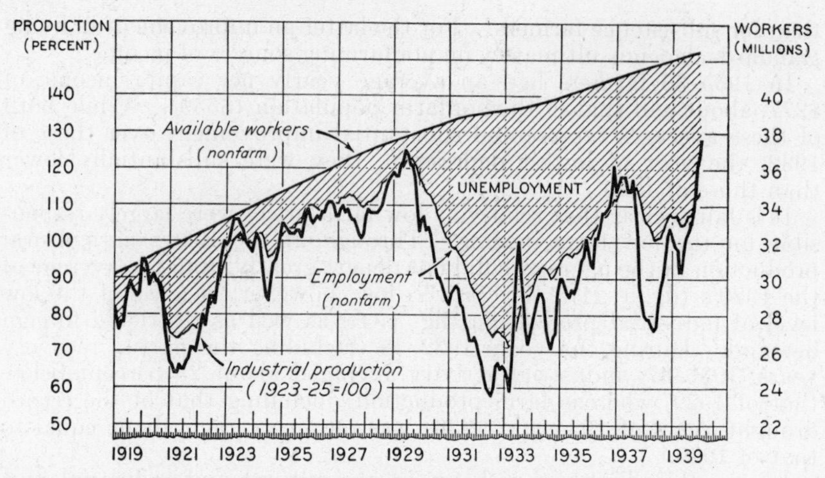

Figure 2.—Industrial production and industrial employment and unemployment in the United States, 1919–39; adjusted for seasonal variation.

millions of employed people were working considerably shorter hours per week than in 1929.

During that same 10-year interval the number of nonfarm persons available for work had increased by about 5 million (fig. 2) owing to population growth. But the prolonged depression of the 1930's, according to an unemployment survey in 1937, had brought into the labor market a large number of women, more than could be accounted for by the usual proportion of women workers to total population. With 35 million persons accounted for as employed at the end of 1939 and an estimated total of available workers of 42 to 44 million, the total of unemployed was estimated at 7 to 9 million, including those who would not be in the labor market if husbands or other members of the families were fully employed, those on relief work, and those who, as in 1929, would be unemployed because of ill health or for other reasons even with industrial activity at prosperity levels.

If "prosperity" for 1939 were to be interpreted in terms of full employment, it is clear from figure 2 that industrial production would have had to be about 25 percent greater than it was. What would this greater prosperity among workers and consumers have meant to farmers? To answer this question we need to translate full employment in terms of (1) population pressure on the farmers' standard of living arising from inadequate industrial production, (2) national income or consumer purchasing power, (3) foreign purchasing power for industrial and farm products, and (4) agricultural and industrial prices and wages.

BALANCE BETWEEN FARM AND NONFARM POPULATION UPSET

Inadequate industrial activity during the 1930's has had the effect of checking the movement of excess farm population to cities and stimulating back-to-the-land movements as relief for industrial unemployment. The result is a much greater pressure of farm population on the available farm income and living standards. On a substantial scale a back-to-the-land movement serves at best to give unemployed industrial workers a mere subsistence level of economic security. For industrialists, the back-to-the-land way of dealing with unemployment is hardly in keeping with their economic function of giving employment to both capital and labor as their contribution to economic welfare—unless they aim to create a new way of living which combines farming with industrial activity in such a way as to mean greater security with no lowering of living standards. For farmers whose relatively low living standards are in large part the result of too many persons sharing a given annual income from farm production, the back-to-the-land movement means, to some extent, both an increase in competition and a reduction in the urban demand for farm products.

The agricultural and nonagricultural working population share between them the task of providing the goods and services required by the total population. In a changing society like that of the United States, which is growing faster industrially than agriculturally, the proportion of those engaged on the land to those engaged in other production and services is a declining one; when the rate of decline alters materially it is evidence that something has gone wrong, that the usual adjustment between groups is not taking place. In the past there have been many instances, such as the depression years of the 1830's, the 1870's, and the 1890's, when over short periods the normal balance between the agricultural and nonagricultural working population was upset, but these upsets were temporary. Records over the past 100 years or more at 10-year intervals indicate that readjustments to approximately normal conditions were accomplished within each decade. But this has not been true of the decade of the 1930's.

Our total population has not increased as much during the 1930's as in earlier decades because of (1) a shutting off of immigration and (2) a reduced birth rate. The farm population reached its maximum before the World War and then declined in the 1920's as a result of cityward migration due to the relatively greater prosperity in the cities; but during the 1930's the total farm population was restored to its previous peak by the inability of the surplus farm population to find jobs in industry combined with the farmward migration of industrial workers and city families. The net result of this unbalance of population pressure is that the average standard of living of the farm population as a whole is about 20 percent lower than it would be if a normal proportion of the total population were living on the land and a normal proportion of the total working population were engaged in agriculture.

How Large Should Our Farm Population Be?

The question may be raised at this point as to when, in a country that has grown industrially as has the United States, the proportion of farm population to total population should cease to decline. It is, of course, obvious that it cannot continue to decline to the vanishing point. There is probably some optimum point of balance, taking economic, social, and other considerations into account, but what that point is is not known. In England industrialization and specialization went so far as to leave less than 10 percent of the working population engaged in agriculture. In France the proportion was stabilized at about 35 percent. What is the proper proportion for the United States?

A few figures will indicate the nature and magnitude of this basic pressure of population on the farmer's standard of living. Up to 1820 more than 90 percent of the working population was engaged in agriculture. With the rise of factory production and the growth of industrial-agricultural inventions, the proportion of the total working population engaged in agriculture began to decline and continued to do so persistently decade after decade (fig. 3). By 1900 only 42 percent of the working population was engaged in agriculture; by 1930, only 20 percent. This reduction represents an increase of about 60 percent in the nonfarm population, the farm population being about the same in 1930 as in 1900. It is important to note here that in 1930 the same number of people on the land as in 1900 cultivated more acres and, by using more machinery, more fertilizer, and improved methods of breeding and feeding, were able to supply the increased needs of the nonfarm population, which had grown about 60 percent in those 30 years. This may be taken as a rough measure of a 60-percent increase in efficiency in agriculture, keeping pace with increased efficiency in urban industries.

The United States was going the way of England up to 1930, for there was no evidence of a tapering-off in our rate of industrialization. A continuation of the pre-1930 tendency during the 1930's would have resulted in a smaller proportion of people living on farms and working in agricultural production than is the case. Between 1930 and 1940 the proportion of the population engaged in agriculture failed to decline for the first time in over 100 years. At the beginning of 1940 as large a proportion of the total population as in 1930 is still

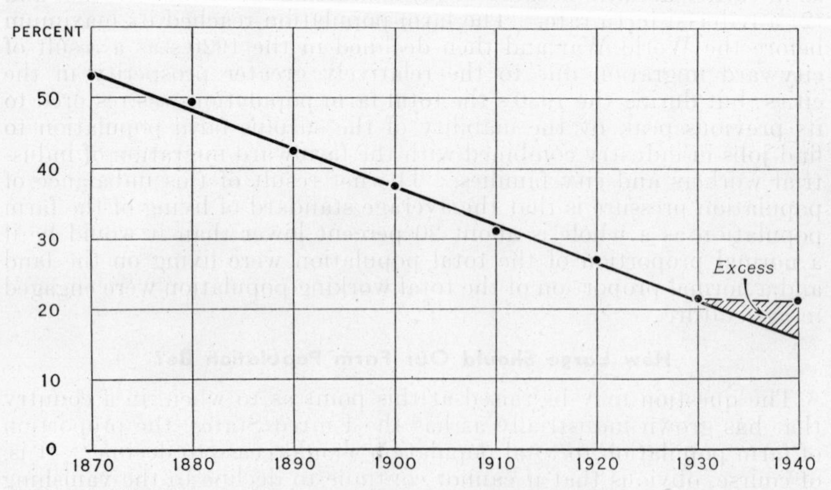

Figure 3.— Working population in agriculture—percentage of United States total of gainful workers 10 years of age and over.

on the land, and as large a proportion of the working population 10 years of age or over is engaged in agriculture. Had the trend of previous decades continued, instead of 21 percent there would have been only 16 percent on the land. During the 1930's there was no apparent diminution in the rate of technological progress in agriculture, and at the same time demand for export was reduced by an amount probably not equal to the increased domestic requirement of the larger nonfarm population. The net result is that there is now a larger working population on the land than is needed to maintain normal production for a growing total population.

Of the total population of the Nation—132,000,000 at the beginning of 1940—32,000,000 were living on farms. The total working population comprised about 54,500,000 people 10 years of age and over, of whom 11,500,000 were attached to agriculture. On the basis of the long-time trend in the proportion of the population in agriculture, these figures represent an excess of about 2,500,000 of working population and 3,500,000 others living on the land. This excess amounts to about 6,000,000 persons, or one-fifth of the total farm population, who under normal conditions would be living in towns and cities instead of on farms.

The distribution of gross income from farm production presented a problem in raising the living standards of farm people a generation or more ago just as it does today. In 1929, 20 percent of all farms were in the lowest gross-income brackets and produced only 3.4 percent of the total gross income, and half of all farms produced less than 16 percent. In 1899 also, half of all farms produced only about 16 percent of all gross income. At the other extreme, 20 percent of all farms produced 57.5 percent of gross farm income in 1929 and 56 percent in 1899.[5] This concentration is even more marked if we deal with cash income from marketing only instead of gross income (cash plus the value of goods produced for the farm home). It has been suggested that transferring the 20 percent of farm families with the lowest incomes to other occupations would raise the per capita farm income for the remaining farm population. Although the incomes of this 20 percent of farm families are such a small part of the total that they would add little to those of the other 80 percent, their transfer to other more gainful occupations would increase the ratio of consumers to persons on farms from 3 to 1 to 4 to 1, and the remaining farm population would gain from an increased demand and from increased industrial production of goods for the farm market.

In looking back on the 1930's a decade or two hence it may of course appear that the rate of industrialization began to taper off after 1930. At present, however, the failure of the rural-urban population ratio to decline after 1930 seems to be striking evidence of the fact that farmers and industrial workers face in these changing times domestic and foreign conditions that have not confronted them in any previous decade. Under normal conditions a slowing down of the rate of industrialization might be expected when technological advances in agriculture were no longer keeping pace with those of industry and the increase in total population required an equivalent increase in the

[5] The 1929 estimates were derived by O. E. Baker, of the Bureau of Agricultural Economics, from the 1929 Census of Agriculture. The 1899 estimates were derived by the writer from the 1899 Census of Agriculture.

farm proportion to supply the additional domestic food and fiber requirements. But the cessation of the decline in the proportion of farm population in the 1930's was due to (1) the lack of industrial employment and of nonfarm opportunities for surplus farm labor and (2) the slowing-down of the rate of population growth in the cities—which in turn was due to a reduction in the birth rate and a purposeful shutting off of immigration.

A restoration of industrial activity to the levels called for by the trend of the first quarter of this century would provide major relief to population pressure on the land and on rural living standards.

THE FARMER'S STAKE IN INCREASED INDUSTRIAL ACTIVITY

More industrial production means more income for all, but not necessarily a larger share for farmers.

Industrial production about one-fourth greater than that at the end of 1939 would produce practically full employment, open some opportunities for surplus farm population in nonfarming industries, and, by creating a larger national income, expand the total of consumer expenditures for food, clothing, and industrial products made from agricultural raw materials. It would also to some extent expand foreign purchasing power for our products.

The gross monetary value to the farming population of such an increase in industrial activity can be readily visualized from the following basic over-all relationships:

By the end of 1939 the national income, measured in terms of goods and services produced, was equivalent to an annual total of about 70 billion dollars, as compared with 83 billion in 1929 and 40 billion in 1932. With prices lower in 1939 than in 1929, this was practically equal to the 1929 real income, but the national standard of living, on

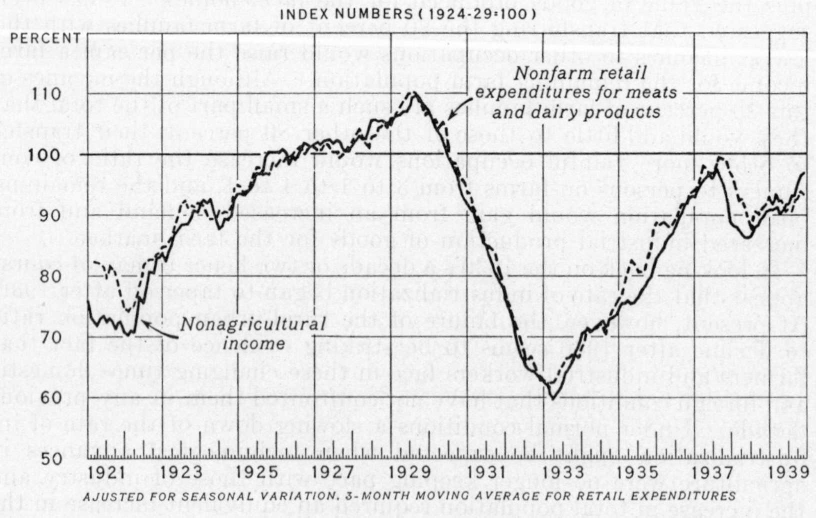

Figure 4.—Nonagricultural income and retail expenditures for meats and dairy products, United States, 1921–39.

a per capita basis, was lower than in 1929 to the extent of the 8-percent increase in total population during that decade. A further increase of about 25 percent in industrial production, with prices generally unchanged, would lift the national income from the present 70-billion-dollar level to over 90 billion. The farmer's interest in this greater national income or general purchasing power springs from the fact that during the decade of the 1930's retail expenditures for food have closely paralleled the ups and downs of total consumer purchasing power (fig. 4).

Total retail expenditures for food have averaged close to 20 percent of that part of the national income received by nonfarm consumers. This suggests that if our economic groups and their patterns of expenditures remain as they are, about 4 billion dollars more would be spent by consumers for food with a 90-billion-dollar national income than with one of 70 billion dollars. Under these circumstances, farmers who in 1939 got 40 percent of the consumer's dollar would get something over 1.5 billion dollars more for their sales of food products in the domestic markets.

What the total receipts of farmers from food and nonfood products might be with a 90-billion-dollar national income may be judged from the fact that in 1929, when the national income from production and services was 83 billion dollars, cash income from the sale of farm products amounted to 11.2 billion, and in 1939 when the national income approximated 70 billion dollars, cash income from the sale of farm products amounted to 7.7 billion. On the basis of the 1929 relationship, farmers would have about 2.5 billion dollars more, and on the basis of the 1939 relationship they would have about 2 billion dollars more if the national income were 90 instead of 70 billion. The 1929 ratio would be more likely to prevail if foreign markets for farm products were restored to their 1929 magnitude.

Increased industrial activity and greater consumer purchasing power would help restore the farmer's foreign markets. With the greater volume of industrial activity required to support a 90-billion-dollar national income, imports from foreign countries would be expanded, partly because we need certain raw materials from foreign sources in our industrial activity and partly because the increased purchasing power would stimulate a greater effective demand for consumption goods from abroad. During the 15 years before the World War, imports (including duties) amounted to about 6.5 to 7 percent of the value of our domestic production. During the 1920's that proportion was somewhat smaller—more nearly 6 percent; and during the 1930's it has averaged less than 5 percent. This basic dependence of imports on the volume and value of domestic industrial activity is shown in figure 5, in which imports of competitive agricultural products are contrasted with the value of farm and industrial production. The relatively greater increase in imports in 1935 and1937 springs from the effects of the 1934 and 1936 record-breaking droughts. Otherwise imports of both farm and nonfarm products go up and down with industrial activity. A rise in the value of our domestic production of about 20 billion dollars accompanying a 20-billion-dollar rise in the national income would mean an increase in imports of about 1 billion dollars.

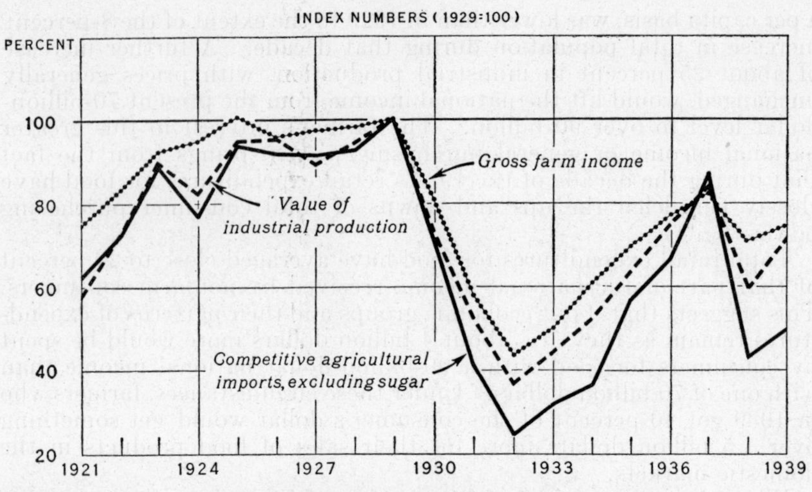

Figure 5.—Imports of competitive agricultural products, value of industrial production and gross farm income, 1921–39.

It may be noted from table 1 that the aggregate value of domestic production tends to approximate the aggregate of national income produced.

Table 1.—Value of domestic production and imports, 1900–1938 [1]

Year	Aggregate value of domestic production	Imports for consumption including duties paid	Ratio of imports to value of production	Year	Aggregate value of domestic production	Imports for consumption including duties paid	Ratio of imports to value of production
	Million dollars	*Million dollars*			*Million dollars*	*Million dollars*	
1900	15, 163	1, 060	7. 0	1929	78, 976	4, 924	6. 2
1905	20, 534	1, 345	6. 6	1930	61, 996	3, 576	5. 8
1910	27, 721	1, 874	6. 8	1935	51, 424	2, 396	4. 7
1915	34, 828	1, 975	5. 7	1937	69, 073	3, 480	5. 0
1920	92, 480	5, 428	5. 9	1938	57, 810	2, 251	3. 9
1925	71, 868	4, 728	6. 6				

[1] Data from U. S. Dept. Commerce, Survey of Current Business, 56 pp., Sept. 1939. See p. 11.

How much of such an increase in imports, which is the equivalent of an increase in foreign buying power for American goods, would be used for purchasing our surplus farm products? At present about one-fourth of our total exports are agricultural. If imports were to be stimulated by greater industrial activity to the extent of a billion dollars, farmers could expect to share to the extent of about 25 percent of the increased foreign purchasing power this would represent.

These gains to farmers in general from increased domestic and foreign purchasing power, resulting from an increase in industrial production and in the national income, would of course be very substantial, especially if prices of industrial goods and services purchased by farmers were not increased or were allowed to decline.

The extent of the gains might be affected, however, by declining export demand, by technological changes affecting domestic demand, and by an increasing share of the consumer's dollar going for distribution.

During the 1920's, particularly after 1925, as the Nation advanced toward the higher living standards of 1929, part of the farming population failed to keep pace. The national income, as represented by income received by all individuals, advanced about 10 billion dollars between 1925 and 1929, but the increased income from livestock products, which responded to the rising national income, was offset by a declining income from crops, with the result that the total farm income changed very little—from 10.9 billion in 1925 to 11.2 billion in 1929. This failure of income from crops to keep pace with other income was due chiefly to (1) declining foreign demand for our surplus export crops as Europe returned to its pre-war production stride and foreign competition increased, and (2) a declining demand for feed crops due to the increasing displacement of horses by agricultural machinery. Again during the latter part of the 1930's these factors appear to have modified the effect of industrial activity and the national income on farm income, for after 1936 the proportion of farm income to the national income declined somewhat.

The Disparity Between Farm Income and Nonfarm Income

The extent to which the favorable effects of more industrial production may be modified by shifts in demand and also by increases in distribution and production costs is indicated by the fact that ever since the World War there has been a lack of balance between the incomes of people living on farms and of those living in cities. If the per capita farm income available for family living just before the World War is compared with the per capita income of the nonfarm population (parity income) and both are traced through their major shifts during the war and post-war years and the 1930's, the following maladjustments may be found: During the war years farm income per capita, after allowing for business expenses, rose relatively more than did the average per capita nonfarm income (table 2). By 1919 farm income per capita had risen to 260 percent of that of 1910–14; nonfarm income per capita reached only 163 percent. But farmers have paid for this brief period of relative advantage with relative shortages

Table 2.—Farm and nonfarm per capita income and farm wage rates

[1910–14=100]

Year	Per capita income		Farm wage rates	Year	Per capita income		Farm wage rates
	Farm	Nonfarm			Farm	Nonfarm	
	Percent	*Percent*	*Percent*		*Percent*	*Percent*	*Percent*
1910–14	100	100	100	1929	161	197	180
1913	101	105	103	1932	41	121	96
1914	101	102	101	1933	62	112	85
1915	107	104	103	1934	88	126	95
1916	130	118	113	1935	108	133	103
1917	198	134	141	1936	121	149	111
1918	234	153	177	1937	129	162	126
1919	260	163	207	1938	109	150	124
1921	97	160	155	1939	104	155	122

in income ever since. In 1921 farm income dropped to 97 percent of the pre-war figure, while nonfarm income remained at 160. During the following recovery period agriculture lagged. By 1929 nonfarm income had risen to 197 percent and farm income to 161 percent of their respective pre-war averages. The contrast during the 1930's was even more marked, for farm income available for family living in 1932 fell to 41 percent of the pre-war figure and nonfarm income only to 121 percent. In other words, in 1932, after paying production expenses, farmers had only about one-third the income required for parity with nonfarm income.[6]

Heroic measures in the form of agricultural, industrial, social, and monetary programs after 1932 helped restore nonfarm income for the years 1937–39 to 155 percent of the pre-war average and farm income to about 115 percent. A large part of this disparity may be explained by relatively higher distribution and production costs for agricultural products. In 1939 costs of goods used in agricultural production were 145 percent of those of 1913, and costs of distribution of farm products 157 percent.

The problem of raising the 1939 income from farm production to parity was a problem involving about 2.4 billion dollars of additional farm income. After deducting about 3.9 billion dollars' worth of business expenditures, chiefly in the nature of cash outlays, farmers as a group had about 4.5 billion dollars available for family living. On a per capita basis, this was equal to 64 percent of the per capita income available for the nonfarm population, on the basis of 1910–14 income. An additional income of 2.4 billion dollars without increased business expenditures would have brought per capita income from farm production into parity with nonfarm income. Part of this discrepancy, to the extent of 807 million dollars, was made up by Government payments.

The income relation between farmers and the rest of the population by the end of the 1930's may be summarized as follows: Farm income per capita was only a little better than before the war, nonfarm income about 60 percent better—a disparity not accounted for by differences in relative living costs. Farm income was short by about 2.4 billion dollars annually of being on a par with nonfarm income, and about one-third of that discrepancy was being made up by Government payments for cooperating in soil conservation, crop adjustment, loan, and other programs.

A substantial part of this income disparity can be looked upon as a matter of price disparity. By the end of 1939 prices of farm products were relatively lower than industrial prices and had a purchasing power of only about 80 percent of that of the pre-war years. Looked at as a price problem, the welfare of farmers could be substantially increased either by a rise in farm prices of about 25 percent, provided it could be obtained without a reduction in consumption, or by a lowering of prices for the industrial goods purchased by farmers of about 20 percent, provided the latter could be obtained without a reduction in the wage earnings of industrial workers.

These basic interrelations between prices, wages, and consumption

[6] In this comparison possible differences in relative levels of farm and nonfarm living costs have not been taken into account, for no adequate comparable measures are as yet available.

are also involved in the fact that farmers received in 1939 a smaller share of the consumer's dollar than formerly. As a result of more services supplied to consumers, relatively higher processing and distribution costs, and higher wage rates paid by all agencies engaged in transportation, handling, processing, wholesaling, and retailing, farmers in 1939 received only 40 percent of the consumer's dollar paid for a given quantity of foods as compared with over 50 percent in 1913. As a matter of arithmetic, it would seem that there would be a substantial gain to farmers if by a lowering of industrial wages they now received their pre-war share of the consumer's food dollar; but this can hardly be accomplished without lowering the purchasing power of all those engaged in the processing and handling of farm products. Such a reduction in the wages of those handling and processing farm products would need to be compensated by an increase in the volume of consumption and of employment in the distributive occupations, to obtain which it would be necessary to increase the purchasing power of the low-income groups whose consumption of food and clothing is inadequate.

As a general rule farmers are more interested in adequate annual wage earnings for industrial workers than in relatively high wage rates with low annual earnings. Similarly, industrial workers are more interested in an adequate annual farm income than in relatively high farm prices and low annual income. Farmers, however, do have a vital stake in improving the wage levels of the many underpaid industrial workers, if for no other reason than that for each hundred-dollar increase in their income low-income workers would spend a much larger proportion for food than would those with larger incomes.

Prospects for Industrial Expansion

It is clear from the facts presented so far that the welfare of the unemployed and low-income groups of the urban population depends on more industrial production, more jobs, better wages, and greater security of employment and earnings.

The welfare of farmers, as we have seen, is intimately bound up with that of the rest of the Nation. But to a greater degree than is the case with city workers, the farmer's welfare and his ability to regain, and perhaps to increase, his former per capita share of the national income depend on more than a restoration of industrial activity and full urban employment. Even with a general rise in living standards based on increased industrial activity, a higher national income, and improved wage earnings among the low-income groups in industry, farmers would still need to make sure that consumption of food and clothing among low-income groups increased enough to more than offset the reduction in foreign demand and in the domestic demand for feed crops due to increased use of motor power. They would still need new opportunities in nonfarming occupations as an outlet for the surplus farm population created by the relatively higher birth rate in rural areas and by the continued reduction in man-hours of labor required for normal agricultural production. It is because of these basic facts underlying the agricultural problem that Government is of necessity becoming more and more involved in programs for the improvement of the farmer's standard of living.

223761°—40——24

Proposals for Industrial and Agricultural Recovery

Every major depression brings a multitude of proposals for recovery and for raising the standard of living. Some involve new utopian forms of social organization, but most involve modifications of the present system rather than new departures. Some of the latter proposals will be briefly examined here. Even the most conservative today do not propose a complete abolition of governmental action; the argument centers on the degree and the kind of action.

The proposals and experiments emerging out of the depression of the 1930's for making the capitalistic system function better fall into three broad classifications: (1) Those that have to do with increasing purchasing power as a means of stimulating the production of goods; (2) those concerned with increasing the production of goods as a means of creating purchasing power; (3) those that would directly or indirectly stimulate purchasing power or the production of goods or both by manipulating specific elements in our complex economy.

The agricultural programs that have been adopted are chiefly in the third class. They fall into two broad groups—those that are aimed at helping the farmers who produce the bulk of farm products sold commercially, and those that aim to improve the production and living standards of submarginal and subsistence farmers. These programs are discussed elsewhere in the present volume.

For industrial recovery, full employment, and greater economic security within the framework of the present system, there are almost as many proposals as there are notions as to the causes of poverty and depressions.

Old-age pension schemes may be taken as a good example of proposals to raise living standards through creating purchasing power. They have their origin in the fact that a growing proportion of our population is 60 years of age or over. Obviously if all those over this age had a steady income in the form of a monthly pension and spent that income currently, the demand for goods and services would be enormously increased. The outstanding difficulty with the extreme pension proposals is that they involve huge sums to be provided by sales taxes or by the issuance of special pension money to be redeemed by the purchase of stamps. With about 13 million persons over 60 years of age, a monthly payment of $200, or a yearly total of $2,400, would mean a total annual payment to the aged of about 30 billion dollars. A monthly payment of $100 would mean a total of 15 billion dollars. If these sums are considered as additions to the 1939 national income, which was about 70 billion dollars, they would represent an additional 40 percent and 20 percent, respectively. The issuance of new money in this amount without a simultaneous expansion of industrial and agricultural production would bring about a disturbing price inflation and would undoubtedly lead to a great deal of Government control and direction of our economic activities. On the other hand, the collection of the amount in taxes on transactions of all sorts could have the effect of putting many concerns out of business, reducing both employment and purchasing power in general. Old-age pensions are undoubtedly going to be a more important element in our economic system. The basic principle involved, however, is that the young may look forward to old age with a greater degree of economic security and plan their lives so as to utilize their talents more effectively in work and in cultural development. Progress in that direction will depend upon our ability to increase the national income and to devise such taxation for old-age pensions as will also sustain production, employment, and the national income.

Proposals Emphasizing Increased Production

In juxtaposition to schemes for increasing purchasing power are the proposals for increasing production first. These involve economic planning and concerted action on the part of all industries to produce all the goods and services required by consumers with prices, wages, and profits so adjusted as to make for a full distribution and consumption of what is produced.

Proposals of this sort are based on such considerations as the following: (1) That purchasing power and national income are created by productive activity, which means payments for wages, for materials, and for services of various sorts; (2) that an individual firm or industry faced with declining demand tends to keep its prices up, reduces production in line with declining demand, and discharges its employees so as to keep losses at a minimum; (3) that concerted cooperative action to maintain output in line with agreed-upon normal volumes, if undertaken by all members of an industry and by all interrelated industries, would automatically prevent a decline in demand and permit wages and profits to be maintained and prices to be lowered in line with decreased costs per unit; (4) that such inducements and devices as loans and guaranties against losses and governmental aid in distributing surpluses to low-income groups ought to be applied in industry just as they have been in agriculture; and (5) that the concerted action by individual industries under the National Industrial Recovery Act of 1933 would have been effective if it had provided directly for increased production and for interindustry planning and cooperation, instead of merely dealing with price and wage policies without regard to volume of production and employment.

The first of these considerations is of course generally true, except for the qualification that behind much of our industrial activity is the use of credit and savings. This will be touched on later.

The second consideration is also generally true; but it should be noted that relative inflexibility of industrial prices (and other costs such as wages and transportation rates) has given rise to antitrust and antimonopoly activity on the part of the Department of Justice and to other proposals for making prices flexible in the interest of greater employment.

It has been argued that if industrial prices were made as flexible as agricultural prices, the exchange value of farm products would be greater and that this would stimulate increased consumption of industrial goods and diminish the magnitude of depressions. This argument is also used with respect to relatively stable and high wage rates, freight rates, and other costs that do not yield to the impact of depressions. It is undoubtedly true that in any given situation the distribution of the Nation's purchasing power is determined in large measure by prices and costs and that in years of depression a low consumption of industrial products is associated with relatively high prices, and a relatively large or sustained consumption of farm products is associated with low prices. But this does not necessarily mean that lowering industrial prices, especially during a period of sharp recession, would bring increased consumption; or that preventing agricultural prices from declining would reduce the consumption of farm products. Experience shows that by and large farmers press upon the markets a fairly stable volume of production and that prices fall during depression because of reduced employment in other industries. In the case of industrial products, there is little experience with general price declines. Where such declines have taken place in industrial raw materials used in the production of durable goods (for example, copper used in automobiles), they have generally not been effective in stimulating increased sales of the finished product. The volume of sales of the finished product is often affected much more by the money income of consumers than by price, and certainly much more than by the price of raw materials.

Still another difficulty with the suggestion that industrial prices be made more flexible in periods of business recession is the reasonable certainty that greater flexibility might temporarily have just the opposite effect from that desired. It might actually intensify the recession, because demand might cease altogether as manufacturers and consumers waited for the completion of the price decline. This fear was actually entertained during 1930–32 by those who finally sponsored the creation of Code Authorities under the National Industrial Recovery Act as a measure to stop price competition and wage reductions. During the late 1930's it was generally agreed in the construction industry that lower construction costs would favor increased volume; yet the prospect of reduced material costs or reduced financing costs was feared as a possible deterrent to the slow but welcome progress then under way.

This view, that reducing industrial prices would add very little to increased sales and employment and that losses instead of profits would result to individual firms, was recently ably argued before the Temporary National Economic Committee by the United States Steel Corporation; and one of the logical corollaries of that argument, the need for economic planning, was pointed out by another witness,[7] as follows:

> * * * Throughout their analysis the steel corporation has claimed that changes in steel prices have little or no effect on the demand of the final consumer for the products finally made from steel. This result follows, they claim, since the price of steel makes up such a relatively small fraction of the cost of finished automobiles, houses, tractors, locomotives, watches, and other products. A parallel argument is made by lumbermen in explaining why reduced lumber prices would not increase the sale of houses, by members of building unions in explaining why reduced per-hour wage rates for bricklayers and carpenters would not increase the sale of houses, and by farmers in explaining why reduced wheat prices do not increase the sale of bread. No doubt as the steel industry is now organized, and as the activity legally permitted corporations in this country is now circumscribed, there is no way by which changes in steel prices can be coordinated with changes in other prices. (It might be pointed out in this connection, however, that the antitrust laws are solely directed against combinations in *restraint* of trade, and that so far as I am aware, there has never been any case to test whether combina-

[7] Statement by Mordecai Ezekiel to Temporary National Economic Committee, January 24, 1940, on Studies on the Demand for Steel, filed by the U. S. Steel Corporation.

tions for the *expansion* of trade would be similarly illegal.) As business organizations now operate, however, it is no doubt true that there is no existing means by which reductions in steel prices could be brought about concurrently with reductions in cement prices, lumber prices, freight rates, automobiles, furniture, houses, and perhaps even in wage rates per hour (though not incomes per year) of workers engaged in some of the more highly paid trades such as steel fitters, carpenters, and bricklayers. It is perfectly obvious that if some means could be found by which concerted reductions could be made in the prices of many products at the same time, the additions of these savings all down the line would produce a very much greater reduction in price of the final finished product than would be possible if only a single industry made the change in price. In periods of great economic contraction such as that which occurred in 1930–32 or again in late 1937 and 1938, it should be possible for such concerted reductions in price to be accompanied by concerted expansions in output. The steel corporation itself has shown that such an increase from low to high output would greatly reduce the cost of product per ton produced.

Many discussions of the possibility of concerted action by industrial units have seemed to assume that only if Government took over the ownership of the industries themselves through public ownership or socialism, or took over control of the production of corporations through some form of fascism, would it be possible to bring about any such concerted action as that outlined above. There are, however, other possible techniques by which a democratic government may find ways to cooperate with industrial producers in assisting them to develop concerted programs of production and price change without involving either of these extreme forms of action. Certainly in agriculture the farms of this country are still owned by individual farmers, and the programs of farm production are worked out democratically with the participation and approval of individual farmers. Yet at the same time the producers of the major export crops have been afforded through the Agricultural Adjustment Acts and associated programs a means of taking concerted action with respect to the acreage and price of their major crops without involving either socialism or fascism. The fact that it has been possible to work out democratic procedures and carry through concerted action in the field of agriculture may suggest that parallel democratic procedures could be developed in the field of industry; and through these democratic procedures production might be increased, prices reduced, and employment raised on a larger scale than individual industries have been able to establish and maintain during recent years. Certainly the testimony of the United States Steel Corporation that it would never pay them to reduce prices would suggest that private corporations, if they continue to operate in the next few years with the same philosophy as has controlled their operations in recent years, will never find ways to solve the large and continuing unemployment. And yet, if private enterprise is to survive, business must find a way under private enterprise to solve the problem of unemployment and to provide a continuing rise in the standard of living—more goods to consume for each day's work.

In concluding this statement I would like to indicate that I am quite aware of the fact that no way has yet been developed and put into action by which the officers of the steel corporation or any of the great corporations similarly situated could take such concerted action to reduce prices and increase production in many industries concurrently as that which has just been suggested above. I would also like to indicate that the problem is a much larger one than the problem of prices and production alone. Expansion in production and employment can be continued and maintained only if the buying power made available to the workers is increased rapidly enough to assure that consumer demand increases in proper proportion to the increase in output, so that further increases in production and further expansions in plant can be stimulated and called into action. The problem of devising any such program so as to secure a proper proportioning of the changes in prices, wages, production, employment, investment, and expansion in plant and equipment, is much more intricate and extended than can be discussed at this point.[8]

Even the most ardent proponents of concerted programs of economic planning or industrial expansion realize that we do not now have the basis for putting a full program into effect. Such a program

[8] For a full discussion of an industrial-expansion proposal see EZEKIEL, MORDECAI. JOBS FOR ALL THROUGH INDUSTRIAL EXPANSION. 299 pp., illus. New York and London. 1939.

calls for effective organizations of labor, management, and consumers in individual industries, and these do not now exist. It calls for cooperation between industrialists, farmers, railroads, bankers, distributors, and the Government. It calls for detailed knowledge as to the demand for a multitude of products, many of them of constantly changing character, quality, durability, and utility. It calls for democratic and therefore time-consuming procedures in setting up plans with much detail as to volume, prices, wages, profits, and the disposal of surpluses if plans go wrong.

In view of these and many other difficulties, proponents of such a program would limit its application to a few basic interrelated industries and gradually develop the planning and administrative arts involved. At the same time, these proponents argue that if we are ever to have industrial production at an abundant level and maintain it on an even course of expansion, we should resort to some comprehensive program of planning to make full use of our capital, labor, material, and managerial resources. They cite as evidence of this need the depression of 1937–38, which came at a time when many indirect, incomplete programs had brought higher wage rates per hour than ever before, nearly parity prices for farm products, the exercise of monetary control by the Federal Reserve Board, and a number of other so-called favorable factors.

A Middle Way

Finally, a third group argues that our economic system is so complex and diverse that it cannot be lifted automatically to a level of abundance for all by any over-all plan involving either stimulated purchasing power or the democratic planning of output by organized and publicly guided groups of business, labor, and agriculture. This group suggests a number of ideas in the nature of a compromise between the two broad over-all approaches.

For a convenient summary of these proposals we may again resort to testimony presented to the Temporary National Economic Committee. According to Alvin Hansen, of Harvard University, who testified before the Committee May 16, 1939, the starting point is an analysis of our recent booms and depressions in terms of the flow of savings and of new investment in productive equipment. The stream of income and purchasing power consists of two elements, namely, purchases of consumption goods and services and purchases of capital equipment. That the size of the national income depends upon or is related to these two types of expenditure is clearly seen in figures 6 and 7. There has been a very close correspondence between changes in the total of expenditures by producers and consumers for new durable goods and changes in the national income throughout the 1920's and 1930's. The relationship is such that for most of the 20-year period an increase of 1 billion dollars in these expenditures has been accompanied by an increase of 2 to 2½ billion dollars in national income. The lower volume of expenditures in 1937 than in 1929 is due primarily to the smaller expenditure by consumers for housing and by producers for plant construction.

These expenditures for new durable goods, it is argued, come from savings on the part of individuals and of businesses; and an economy

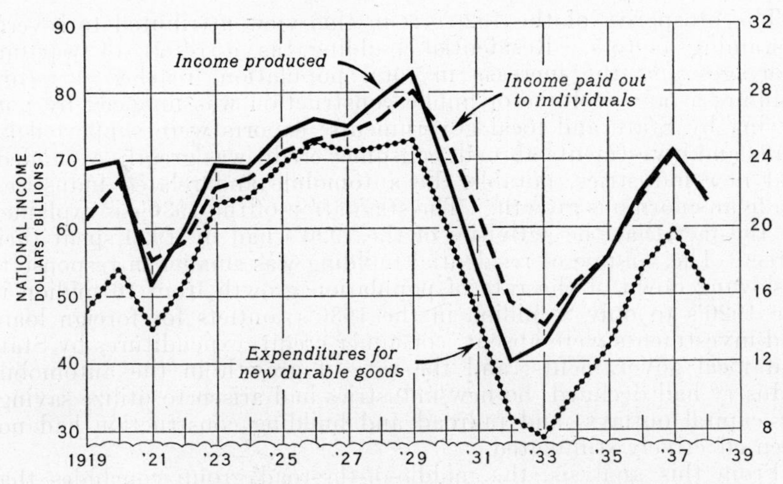

Figure 6.—The national income and expenditures for new durable goods.

like ours, in which savings in the form of individual accounts and of allowances for depreciation and depletion amount to several billion dollars a year, can avoid declines in income and employment only through the continuous development of new outlets for expenditures on industrial plant and equipment and on public and private construction. The flow of private investment requires technological progress, new industries and resources, and population growth. If these conditions do not exist or do not call forth a volume of capital expenditures equal to the new savings and the savings set aside for depreciation and depletion, total consumer purchasing power is inadequate to sustain current production, and the resulting unemployment brings on additional curtailment in consumption.

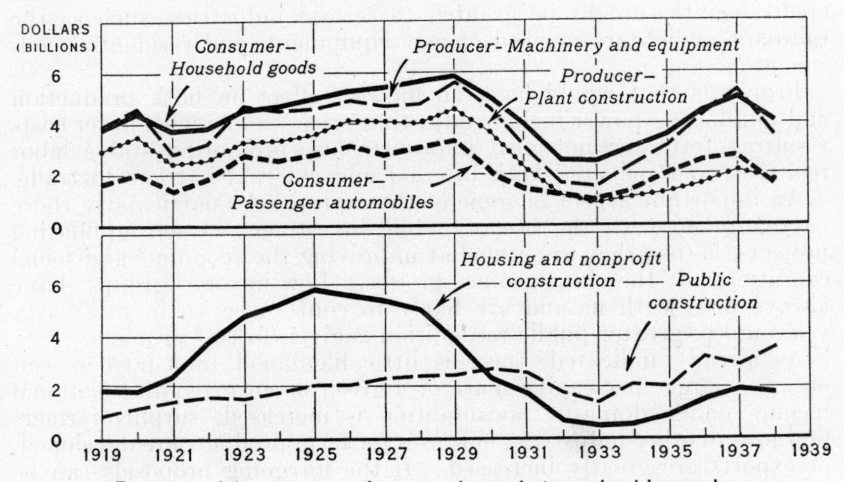

Figure 7.—Major items in the expenditures for new durable goods.

The prosperity of the 1920's is in this view attributed to several sustaining factors. Residential building, as a result of wartime shortages and the increase in total population, reached a record volume; a large volume of public construction was financed by borrowing by State and local governments; exports were supported by loans and investments abroad; consumer credit was greatly expanded; and new industries, notably the automobile and related industries, made an enormous growth. The stagnation of the 1930's is explained by the fact that the activities of the 1920's had by 1929 spent their force. The volume of residential building was smaller in response to a slowing down of the rate of population growth from 16 million in the 1920's to only 8 million in the 1930's; outlets for foreign loans and investments were absent; consumer credit, expenditures by State and local governments, and the rate of growth in the automobile industry had declined; no new industries had arisen to utilize savings for capital outlays; and railroad and building construction had not been effectively stimulated.

From this analysis, the middle-of-the-road group concludes that full employment now depends upon devising more certain means of using savings by (1) stimulating private capital outlays, (2) increasing public investment, and (3) expanding community consumption as a supplement to private consumption. For the purpose of creating purchasing power and absorbing savings, it is proposed that old-age benefits be liberalized, that the Federal Government make contributions from tax revenues supplementing old-age benefits based on individual contributions, and that consumption taxes be reduced and income taxes raised. It is further proposed that the flow of purchasing power be stimulated by increased Government investments in self-liquidating projects and in the conservation and increased efficiency of our human resources. This would include various local services, public health, public recreation, low-cost housing, and low-cost food.

To stimulate production as a source of purchasing power, it is proposed to encourage private investment. Among other methods, credit facilities might be granted to certain industries, such as the railroads, which are in need of new equipment, and residential construction.

Proposals that would have an indirect effect on both production and purchasing power include adjusting prices in line with lower costs resulting from technological improvements, promoting stable labor relations, and reducing both internal and external barriers to trade.

An important aspect of some of these proposals, particularly those having to do with the use of public investment in self-liquidating projects, is that they are aimed at improving the economic and social condition of the low-income groups. Low-income groups have always been with us and are likely to continue even in prosperity years unless greater public recognition is given to this problem.

As already indicated, there is little likelihood that farmers can obtain a larger per capita share of a given or an expanding national income unless domestic consumption is increased, surplus farmers find jobs in other industries, new uses for farm products are developed, or exports are greatly increased. If the foregoing proposals can be effectively developed on a substantial scale, they hold real promise of achieving the first two of these possibilities. They would not only serve to raise the average national living standard by substantially raising the present standard of the lowest third of the population, but they would make possible the development of rural works programs that would provide new opportunities for that part of the working population which is being displaced by technological advances in both farming and nonfarming industries.

Those who argue that the Federal Government will need to play an important role in stimulating private investment and supplementing it with public investment point also to the need for modernizing the Federal budgetary system. They say that the basic problem is to separate operating expenditures from capital expenditures, as is done by all businesses and by some European Governments, including those of Sweden and Denmark. When large corporations borrow huge sums from the public for plant expansion and equipment, they charge only annual interest and amortization against the current year's income; the investment is carried as a capital account. It is proposed that the Federal Government follow a similar practice in the case of long-time investments. Some of the investments would be of a self-liquidating sort, bringing annual income that would in time liquidate the investment. Others would be for such things as necessary buildings, parks, and recreational and health facilities that would not yield an annual return. But if interest and amortization on these public investments were met annually through taxation or other means, and other current operating expenses were met by current income, it is argued that the Federal budget would be balanced in exactly the same way as the accounts of a going concern with a long-time capital structure are kept in balance.

The 1940's begin with war raging in Europe and Asia and the course of economic and social progress for every country, including the United States, greatly obscured. But we are entitled to place a great deal of confidence in our ability to raise the national standard of living and to have it more effectively distributed if we continue to be concerned with the economic and social problems of those who now lack effective purchasing power; to improve the taxing and credit devices available to the Federal Government, using them where necessary to supplement and encourage private enterprise; and to do everything possible to utilize our vast productive capacity.

The City Man's Stake in the Land

by ARTHUR P. CHEW [1]

THE AUTHOR of this article attempts a comprehensive survey that will make plain the city man's interest in agricultural problems—an interest that he holds to be vital and many-sided though often unrealized. "The urban stake in the land," he concludes, "is not just in preserving the soil and maintaining its fertility. It includes less tangible elements, which affect the entire rural-urban balance. . . . But any approach would require rural-urban cooperation. . . . The agricultural problem is not a separate thing, walled off entirely from matters of urban concern and of such a nature that the city dweller can tackle it or leave it alone. He cannot detach himself from it. He has a vital interest in the distribution of the people on the land, in the relationship they have to it, in the use they make of it, and in the amount and distribution of the resulting farm income. This interest involves him inevitably in important land use responsibilities."

WHAT TO DO with our land is fully as important to the city man as it is to the farmer. Modern conditions, however, tend to hide this fact. Occupations have become so specialized that people forget the dependence of one occupation upon another and forget also the basic fact that all occupations rest upon the land. This forgetfulness may have serious and even tragic results. It may provoke conflicts between town and country, and it may even change suddenly

[1] Arthur P. Chew is Special Agricultural Writer, Office of Information.

into land-grabbing imperialism. History affords many examples. Nations that waste their land often covet new lands abroad. Care for the national heritage, in which every citizen has a part, is protection against land hunger. Nothing is more important to the general welfare; for passionate land hunger can cause revolutions and wars. In the United States land hunger, at any rate on a national scale, is not imminent. But there are things we can do to keep it in the distance.

Fifty or a hundred years ago the city man's interest in the land of the United States was evident to him constantly. It was a highly personal interest. It struck him chiefly in the fact that westward migration, free land, and the spread of agriculture into a virgin continent gave everyone an agricultural opportunity. Greeley packed the idea into a watchword—Go West, young man, go West. Everyone knew what Greeley meant. Everyone could get a farm or could start some business with roots in expanding agriculture. All aspects of the ensuing progress had their start in farming. Stay-at-homes as well as westward migrants knew it well. Indeed, the stay-at-homes profited equally with the migrants, since the development of the continent developed all parts of the national economy. Like the soldier with "a marshal's baton in his knapsack," the citizen kept a plow in his toolshed and dreamed of acquiring land.

But with the closing of the frontier the dream evaporated. In proportion as it became more difficult for the city dweller to become a landowner, he lost his sense of participation in the national heritage. Actually, though not in the old personal sense, his stake in this heritage became more important. It came to light in an increasing aimlessness of migration; in the crowding of rural people into urban occupations; in increased taxation for the relief of rural distress; in flood hazards aggravated by improper farming, grazing, and lumbering; in the pressure of agricultural surpluses on the market; in the consequent disturbance of the rural-urban balance; and finally in the progressive misuse and depletion of the soil.

Superficially the urban interest in our land concerns mainly the food supply and the availability of suitable areas for forests, wildlife refuges, and parks. For these requirements our land supply is ample. It is sufficient, with proper care, to provide food and raw materials for our probable maximum population, to produce agricultural commodities for a considerably increased farm export trade, and to leave enough land for a large extension of forests, wildlife refuges, and recreation areas. In another sense, however, we have an acute land shortage. Millions of people who want land cannot get it. The paradox is a problem of national concern. In short, we have pressure of population on the land supply. City people feel it equally with rural people.

In other countries where this problem exists, depopulation or political expansion—that is, the acquisition of more territory elsewhere—are the only solutions. The United States has another and better possibility. Through wise land management it can make the land it has sufficient not only from a national food and fiber standpoint but from the standpoint of rural human needs. This is a problem in population adjustment as well as in the allocation of different lands to different uses. It is perhaps our most important national problem. This country has a chance to live at home, on a standard far higher than the present one, with town and country in a permanently good adjustment. The problem involves the use and simultaneously the conservation of resources, and it is at once urban and rural.

RURAL AND URBAN ATTITUDES TOWARD THE LAND

In talking to farmers about the land, and particularly about the top of it, or the soil, one takes certain things for granted. It seems unnecessary, for example, to emphasize the stake of the farmers in soil conservation. Who knows the worth of the soil better than the farmers? Soil is their principal means of production; it is mainly what they buy when they buy land. Naturally, they do not want it to vanish, and proof that it is vanishing alarms them at once. Soils men have demonstrated, to be sure, that soil may be washing or blowing where it appears to be safe. Farmers who do not know what is taking place may act as if they did not care what happens to the soil; but of course they do care. When they know it is in danger and know also that preventive measures can be applied, they are ready to act.

Some farmers who realize what is happening are unable to stop it because the necessary action would oblige them temporarily to wait for a part of their income, and they cannot wait. It would oblige them, in other words, to invest more than they can spare in soil conservation. Their failure to act, however, should not be called indifference. Farmers who own soil, who know that it needs protection, and who have the means to protect it will generally do so. In wider aspects of land utilization, such as the allocation of different lands to different uses and the bearing of crop distribution on farm income, the farmers' interest is strong and vocal.

It is different with the nonfarm interest in the land. Nowadays this interest is largely unrealized. Where it is conscious, it takes the form chiefly of concern about the purely physical aspects of land utilization, such as forest gutting, hillside gullying, or soil blowing. These things are mere surface indications of the urban stake in the land, which includes the causes as well as the effects of land use maladjustments. Soil erosion, the symptom most prominent in urban thinking about the land, is often an effect rather than the cause of low farm incomes and rural poverty. It may yield more readily to social and economic measures than to exclusively physical procedures. In the South, for example, the attack on erosion must generally begin with rural rehabilitation and tenure reform, and must fit crop diversification, terracing, strip cropping, and other physical improvements into an improved social and economic framework. City people are not generally aware of these things.

This we can tell from the fact that they favor expenditures for soil conservation in the narrow sense more than they favor expenditures for farm-income stabilization or for aid to the rural poor. Actually, farm-income improvement and rural rehabilitation are direct means of land use improvement and therefore of soil conservation. There is no isolated problem of soil conservation. There is a broad problem of the relationship of the man to the land, in which city dweller and farmer have a joint concern and which has many impacts on urban life. Expenditures earmarked for soil conservation are not more important from the standpoint of urban welfare than other expenditures for the improvement of the agricultural land use system. All the necessary expenditures rank equally in this respect.

Primarily the interest in the land of the city dweller today comes from his dependence on it for foodstuffs and raw materials, and on his need of the farmer as a buyer of city goods. But rural-urban trade is only the foundation of the urban interest in the land. It carries a lofty superstructure, the stability of which is vital to everyone because it involves our entire economy.

There is no free or cheap land any more—no beckoning West to draw labor from the towns. No longer can great masses turn from industry to agriculture for a livelihood. There is no more room for mass migration. As a matter of fact, the balance of migration is toward the cities even in periods of urban depression. On a net basis it is the cities that are absorbing rural unemployed rather than vice versa. In the first 5 depression years of the 1930's, the annual net migration from farms to cities averaged 119,600. In the period 1935–38 the annual net cityward migration was 331,000. In short, the land supply is not today an adequate safety valve for the unemployed, even with subsistence farming and part-time farming on the increase.

Evolution of Our Land Policy

It will help us to see the relationship of the land to our whole national economy if we glance at the origin and evolution of our national land policy. In the nineteenth century the Federal Government gave away more than one-quarter of the available farm land and practically gave away immense areas of forest and grazing land. The idea was to fill the States with homes, to build up communities, and to establish an enduring civilization by giving the ownership of the soil in small tracts to the operating occupants. This was the declared object of the homestead acts. The national land policy, in combination with railroad building, mechanical invention, and a keen overseas demand for agricultural products, built up our agricultural industry.

To a considerable extent, however, it failed to accomplish its primary purpose—fulfilling the dream of a land of family-owned farms. In the fourth decade of the twentieth century more than 42 percent of the farm families were tenants; resources that had seemed limitless proved insufficient. Specifically, the policy ignored important regional differences, gave occupants the right to abuse the land, allowed immense areas to come into the possession of speculators, and utterly failed to conserve timber, soil, and water. In a word it caused premature and in fact needless pressure of population on resources. Among the associated ill effects, two are of special concern to the nonfarm community: (1) The rise of the agricultural surplus problem, with its attendant soil wastage and rural poverty; and (2) the creation of an army of landless rural folk—a rural proletariat that tends in various ways to drag down urban living standards.

Our early land policy should not be blamed for everything that ails the land today. On the contrary, the policy was natural and indeed inevitable for its time. In part, moreover, it fulfilled its objectives. Notably, it developed the agricultural industry and established owner operation widely. That it would become self-defeating in the end could hardly have been foreseen. Formerly our ratio of population to resources was extremely low, and the idea that population growth would eventually drive a wedge between ownership and operation and cause dangerous soil wastage was almost inconceivable. Land scarcity is the final lot of all expanding populations; but in the United States the prospect seemed only to concern remote posterity. The boldest did not foresee that population growth would be more rapid here than anywhere else in the world. It required 200 years for the pioneers to clear their way to the prairies; yet by the end of the nineteenth century practically all the good arable land was in crops. Nor did anyone realize that the market for our agricultural products would one day unexpectedly contract. Hence the early land policy outlived its usefulness and ultimately produced effects the opposite of those intended. It wasted the land, oversupplied the markets, caused an alarming growth of tenancy, and tended to weaken the industrial and commercial superstructure.

Rural and Urban Problems Interrelated

Today our land use system separates farm operation from farm ownership, drives country people into city jobs or city bread lines, generates waves of aimless rural migration, dangerously depletes the soil, lowers the quality of the rural personnel in many areas, necessitates broad programs for rural rehabilitation, worsens the flood hazard, hampers efforts to lower the cost of producing farm commodities, and fosters types of farming that burden the national Treasury with expenditures for surplus control. On such foundations it is impossible to build a strong national economy. The old saying that agriculture and industry have their ups and downs together should have a revised version. Decay of the land through land use maladjustments means the decay of the whole economy.

Certain urban groups appear sometimes to prosper independently of agriculture. Wage rates in some industries, for example, are higher now than they were in 1929. Farm depression has not stood in the way. But the total income of industrial workers is lower than it was in 1929 and the number of unemployed much greater. Moreover, the improved bargaining power of certain wage groups is a result partly of the extent to which the Government makes payments to the unemployed, both urban and rural, and consequently takes them off the labor market. It is the result partly, in other words, of the extent to which economic conditions in town and country have forced a redistribution of the national income. Temporary islets of prosperity in a sea of depression are no proof at all that urban groups can afford to ignore the condition of agriculture. On the contrary, such islets should remind us that the sea may rise and cover them also.

There is abundant proof that broadly speaking urban and rural incomes rise and fall together. One item is the parallel movement of farm income and factory pay rolls (*1; 2, p. 13*).[2] These indexes of the country's condition have long moved in unison. Indeed, they have been remarkably similar in their totals. Factory wages paid in the predepression period 1924–29 aggregated $11,000,000,000 to $12,000,000,000 annually. In the same period the annual gross farm income averaged about an equal sum. In 1932 the factory wages fell to about $5,000,000,000 and the gross farm income likewise. Both totals rose in 1937 to about $10,000,000,000.

Needless to say, the important thing about these figures is not the approximate correspondence of the totals. That is more or less accidental. Factory pay rolls are only a part of the urban income; the total, of course, includes profits and other investment returns. On the other hand, the gross farm income has to cover interest, taxes, and the expenses of farm production. The important fact about these urban- and rural-income figures is the fact that they fluctuate not independently but in an evident interrelationship, as a result undoubtedly of reciprocal forces that bind agriculture and industry together inseparably. Among the forces that depress the farm income, and consequently the urban income, is our gravely maladjusted land use system.

THE LESSON OF THE MIGRATIONS

Events point the moral sometimes. There was a connection, for example, between erosion in the Dust Bowl and the recent desperate migration to the Pacific slope, which gave rise to staggering new problems for towns and cities. Erosion was not the only cause of this wholesale uprooting of people from the land; perhaps it was not even the main cause. Many things contributed to the disaster, among them the shrinkage of our export markets, the displacement of manpower by tractors, the discovery in a series of drought years that farm readjustment was overdue in the Great Plains, and the cumulative pressure of farm depression and farm debt. Visible erosion, however, with unprecedented duststorms, brought matters to a head and showed that much farm abandonment or farm consolidation or crop shifting was unavoidable. The consequent migration, unlike the earlier migrations, saw no pot of gold at the end of the rainbow but only continued poverty and unemployment. It burdened relief rolls, depressed wage rates, created problems of housing and sanitation, complicated the tasks of school authorities, necessitated increased taxation for police and fire protection, and caused ill feeling between migrants and residents. Every Californian realized at once that he had an interest in the land use situation and that the Great Divide cannot divide rural from urban problems.

More commonly rural poverty affects urban life in ways less obvious, often at points remote from its source. In the years between 1920 and 1930 migration was heavy from farms in the Cotton Belt, in the southern Appalachian and Ozark mountain areas, and in the Lakes States cut-over region. In fact the migration from these areas amounted to 20 percent or more of the rural population present there at the beginning of the period. Some of the migrants went to

[2] Italic numbers in parentheses refer to Literature Cited, p. 382.

nearby towns; but many of them went to distant towns. Some 167 manufacturing cities received three-fourths of the overflow.

Cityward migration is not bad in itself; indeed, it is normally the means of building up our cities. About 40 percent of the new workers in cities between 1920 and 1930 came from the farms. Between 1910 and 1930 the number of persons living elsewhere than on farms increased by nearly 33,000,000, and the farms contributed 12,000,000 (net) of the increase by migration (*8*).

But cityward migration from areas of rural poverty, where standards of living and of education are very low, tends to increase urban costs rather than urban wealth. It lengthens the relief rolls. Migrants from rural problem areas sometimes take the position formerly occupied in cities by immigrants from low-standard regions of Europe. Like their forerunners, they are difficult to assimilate (*8*). It is urban economy to help rehabilitate them "in place" on the land, which then they may not have to quit in such large numbers. Moreover, those that do go to town will be better able to cope with their new environment.

URBAN INTEREST IN RURAL LIVING STANDARDS

Cities that receive the rural migrants have obviously an interest in the standards of living that prevail in the areas from which the migrants come. It is important that the migrants shall be good material. That is unlikely if they migrate from areas of poor health, poor housing, and poor education. In 1930 about 4,000,000 of the 30,000,000 people who had been born in the South were no longer living there. Many that had dwelt in rural slums had gone to urban slums and had become a charge on city budgets (*7*). Comparatively few were adequately prepared for city life. Educational levels are low in the rural parts of the Southern States; local authorities cannot raise enough money. Throughout the country, indeed, rural education is a difficult problem. Farm people are responsible for the care and education of some 31 percent of the Nation's children; yet farm income is only 9 percent of the national income. Shortage of educational opportunity results inevitably in many rural areas and leaves potential migrants ill-equipped for any jobs above the level of common labor. The basic remedy is more farm income, an investment that yields an urban as well as a rural dividend.

City people have to concern themselves with land and population adjustments whether the cityward migration is large or small. In the former case they have to provide for the rural surplus population in urban occupations or otherwise. In the latter case they have to help finance its retention on the land. Some 2,000,000 young people who otherwise would have gone to the cities remained on the farms in the depression years of the 1930's, though their presence on the land was commercially unnecessary. Inevitably the fact imposed charges on the cities, since it aggravated the farm surplus problem and necessitated subsidies for so-called noncommercial farming. Hence the urban stake is considerable, not only in soil conservation, but in tenant-purchase operations, rural rehabilitation, better land-leasing methods, farm-income support, and other measures that improve the relationship of rural people to the land.

URBAN ASPECTS OF FARM TENANCY

Farm tenancy is a problem that on the surface appears to be wholly rural. Yet it is profoundly urban as well. As population grows—and ours is still growing—farm tenancy increases necessarily. More people want farms than can buy farms. Farm tenancy can be the path to farm ownership; it is a normal rung in the tenure ladder. But when it increases too rapidly, as it has done in recent years, it is the path to serfdom for large numbers of tenants; possibly indeed to worse than serfdom, since serfdom at least did not detach the peasant wholly from the soil, whereas excessive tenancy does. It crowds the tenure ladder so that many must drop off and become wage hands either on the farms or in the cities.

Underlying all forms of land utilization, in all societies, is the tenure system. Are the cultivators of the soil bondmen or free? That is the basic question. There is little efficiency in a slave society—indeed none by modern standards—because slaves cannot benefit much from increased productivity. In feudal societies, with serfs bound to particular tracts and yet not wholly without tenure rights, the chances for relative efficiency are better. This country never had feudalism; perhaps that is why the South reverted to the slave economy. Elsewhere than in the South, and eventually there also, the dominant principle came to be that of fee-simple ownership, with proprietors free to work the land themselves, to hire the necessary labor power, or to enter into agreements with tenants.

Gradually at first, and then more and more rapildy, owner operation gave way to tenant operation. In the half century from 1880 to 1930 the number of farm tenants more than doubled, and the proportion of tenants to owners on each 1,000 farms increased 138 percent. Moreover, the number of farmers with only nominal farm ownership increased, as may be seen from the fact that in 1930 the total farm-mortgage debt represented about 22 percent of the value of all farms as compared with only 10 percent in 1910. Since 1930, through repayment, refunding operations, and foreclosures, the absolute amount of the farm-mortgage debt has declined. Nevertheless, it still takes more of the farm income than it took before the war. Without stable and continuous land tenure, farmers have small incentive to care for the soil or to develop good forms of economic and social life. Causes of this condition, means of checking the trend and of lessening the bad effects, and the penalties of letting things drift are national problems.

Farm land rented in 1935 constituted more than 45 percent of all the farm land in the country, as compared with only 31 percent in 1900. We can get an inkling of one cause of the increase from the fact that from 1930 to 1937 about 5,500,000 farms in the United States changed hands, about 1,500,000 of them as a result of foreclosures, forced sales, tax sales, or bankruptcy proceedings. Farmers were losing their equities en masse (fig. 1). In 1890, farmers as a whole had a 69-percent equity in their land. This steadily decreased decade by decade until in 1930 they had only a 52-percent equity. In some States in 1930 farmers had only a 30-percent equity in their land, and in many States their average equity was 40 percent or less. Many farm-

223761°—40——25

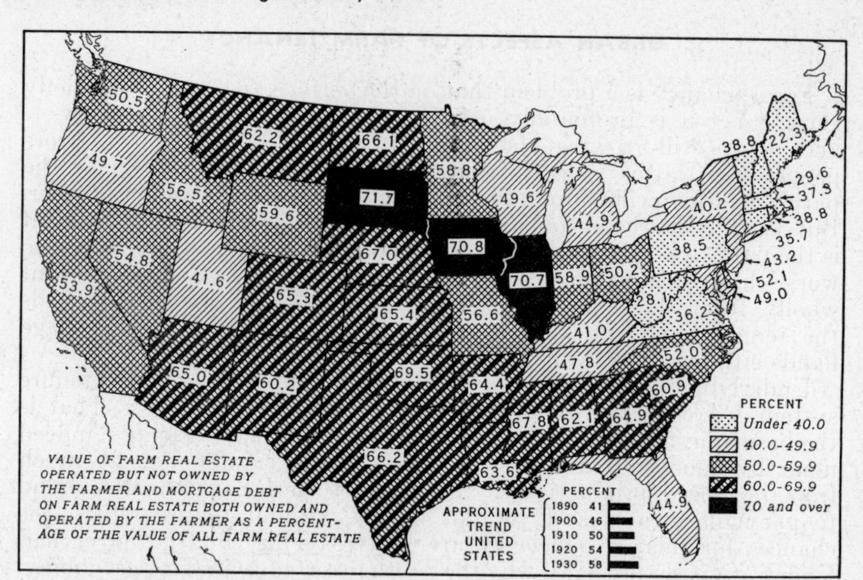

Figure 1.—Percentage of the value of farm real estate not belonging to the farm operator, 1930.

ers were becoming propertyless, with damage to the land, to the family-farm system, and to investment and employment conditions throughout the country.

Excessive farm tenancy and difficulties in rising to ownership heighten job competition and also injure the land. And the consumer pays. Soil erosion, which costs the United States perhaps billions annually in reduced yields, abandoned acres, and lost fertility, is generally worse under tenancy than under owner operation. The reasons are well known. Tenants cannot take long views; they cannot plan ahead; they must get the largest current return, regardless of the effect on the soil, in which of course they have no property stake. Therefore tenancy helps to raise the cost of living.

Consumers may not notice the effect from year to year—they may never link rising food prices to soil losses; but the connection will be there. Farm prices are at present too low. But there is a difference between price advances caused by soil losses and price advances that reflect suitable crop adjustments or increased urban buying power. In the latter case the national wealth increases; in the former it declines. Consumers get something back when they help to raise the farm income by rational means. They get no return whatever for underwriting soil erosion. Nor does the farmer benefit, for his costs go up.

The urban interest in the control of soil erosion, and therefore in the improvement of farm-tenure conditions, rests on the fact that the soil nourishes the whole economy. Our historical land use methods involve appalling soil losses. Already, destructive farming and grazing have ruined or impoverished more than 100,000,000 acres of good cropland and impaired an additional 200,000,000 acres. In some degree erosion has affected more than half the land surface of the country. Not all erosion is bad; on the contrary, some of it increases soil productivity. Of the detrimental erosion, moreover, the degree of severity varies greatly from one area to another. Seriously harmful erosion makes for economic maladjustments between town and country and may show up eventually in impaired living standards and even in weakened national defenses. Bad farm-tenure conditions rank high among the causes.

Rampant farm tenancy poisons urban life in other ways. It distributes farm income badly, and the example spreads to the cities. The connection is plain. After the country divides its total income into the urban part and the rural part, the subdivision of the rural part is in order—in other words the apportionment of it among landlords and tenants and mortgagors and mortgagees. With excessive tenancy, the "lower third" in agriculture comes off badly. The demand for farms among would-be renters causes rents to rise; many States have reported advances in the last few years. This means additional farm distress.

More than 600,000 needy farm families, mostly tenant families, have asked and received financial aid from the Farm Security Administration. Almost as many more need help but cannot be reached with present funds. Very low incomes in the bottom group in agriculture tend to mean correspondingly low incomes for the bottom group in the towns and cities, as a result of the continual interchange of rural and urban population. Moreover, excessive farm tenancy, with increasing rural instability, depreciates urban as well as rural investments and involves a gravitation of farm ownership into city hands. This is bad for all concerned as absentee management is costly and often inefficient.[3]

Absenteeism Harmful to Cities

Superficially, the decline of farm ownership by farmers, since it implies an increase in farm ownership by nonfarmers, may seem to strengthen the latter group. In recent years, however, the increase in the urban ownership of farms has accompanied a decline in the urban income from agriculture. The return from farm property is the important thing, rather than the precise location of the title deeds. Rent is harder to collect than interest. Hence mortgagees who become owners may get less as farm proprietors than they got previously as creditors. There is no point in exaggerating the possibly bad effect on farm earning power of the shift of farm ownership to nonfarmers. Among the other causes of declining farm income, such as the shrinkage in exports and the increase of domestic unemployment, it is minor. Indeed, the drop in owner operation of farms is far more largely an effect than a cause of declines in farm earnings. Larger earnings would lower the foreclosure rate. It is evident, nevertheless, that whatever reduces the farmer's equity in the land may also reduce the value of the other claims upon the agricultural income.

This can be read in the story of farm land values. In 1920, immediately before the first post-war depression, farm-land values for the

[3] Absentee management should not be confused with large-scale or corporation farming, which in certain areas, notably in California, appears to succeed.

country as a whole were 70 percent higher than in the pre-war period 1912–14. Undoubtedly from the standpoint of real farm earning power they were too high. Then came a sharp drop, which continued less sharply until 1933. The decline between 1920 and 1930 was about 32 percent. Forced selling of agricultural land increased considerably after 1921; it became drastic after 1929, with the absentee interest mounting proportionately. "Where one farm a year was taken out of the hands of its owner involuntarily in the pre-World War period 1910–14, about six were taken away each year in the period 1930–34" (*3*). During these years, however, absentees did not find their newly acquired properties profitable. On the contrary, in an immense majority of cases, they discovered that foreclosure proceedings were generally a losing business.

After 1933 farm-land values recovered gradually—at the rate of about 4 percent until 1937. Farm incomes likewise rose in this period, largely in consequence of Federal farm programs. There was a decline in forced sales. In 1938 the number of forced sales was about 69 percent less than in 1933, and the number of farm bankruptcies was about 70 percent less. In the fiscal year 1939 farm bankruptcies were at their lowest point in almost two decades.[4] This meant, of course, that farmers were making their payments to creditors more regularly. They were transferring an increased farm income to the nonfarm claimants on the agricultural earnings instead of transferring their property. Moreover, farmers maintained their payments to creditors and had more income to spend themselves. The principle involved here is of vital significance to the urban group. It shows that the ratio between the cityward movement of farm income and the cityward movement of title to farm property tends to be inverse, and that from an income standpoint farming is most remunerative to nonfarmers when owner operation declines least.

Farm Tenure Reform Aids Operator Ownership

Paradoxically, one way to check the drift of farm ownership from the country to the town is to improve the farm leasing system and make tenancy a better way of life. Here again the urban benefit can be in dollars and cents as well as in a better urban-rural balance. One reason is obvious. Farm tenants under a leasing system that obviates excessive annual moving and gives them incentives to farm better and take better care of the land will be better able to meet their rentals and to buy farms when the opportunity comes.

There is a still more important way in which better tenancy conditions can make for more rather than less owner operation. Satisfied tenants need not rush into the farm real estate market at the first opportunity; they need not trample over one another to bid up the price of land. As a result, those among them who do enter into land-purchase contracts will get better terms. More of them will win through to complete farm ownership. Depressions will cause fewer farm foreclosures.

Farm-tenancy reform will diminish the competition and increase the number of winners in the race for farm ownership. It will bring

[4] United States Bureau of Agricultural Economics. farmer bankruptcies in 1939 lowest in 18 years. 6 pp. 1940. [Mimeographed.]

about an actual increase in genuine owner operation rather than merely an increase in the number of farm mortgages. There is equal benefit to nonfarmers and farmers, because both groups lose when farms that have been sold to the operators do not stay sold.

APPROACH OF LAND SCARCITY

The broadest aspect in which the urban stake in the land appears has been mentioned already, in connection with the closing of the frontier. Our economy is changing from one of land abundance to one of land shortage. This seems anomalous, in view of the well-known superabundance of farm production and the fact that our ratio of population to resources is still comparatively low. Growth of population, however, involves necessarily an increase in what may be termed land hunger, even if the Nation's food requirements can be met by using only part of the available land supply. County agricultural planning committees everywhere bear witness to this fact. In all parts of the country they report a conflict between the desirable uses of the land from an economic or physical standpoint and the land requirements of the resident population. There is more than enough land to supply the commercial market but not enough to provide farms for all who want farms. Needless to say, the number of such people increases in times of depression and urban unemployment.

Land planning by the county committees runs up against a general obstacle—too many farmers in relation to the opportunity for making a living from farming. Worn-out farms indicate the need for conservation measures, such as the diversion of cropland to grass or trees. Adjustment of production to the market leans in the same direction; it calls for the diversion of acreage from soil-depleting to soil-conserving crops, an operation that tends to lessen both the number of farms and the number of necessary farm workers. In Parke County, Ind., for example, 78 farmers drew up a land use planning map (*5*). On taking stock of the county's resources and pondering what to do about tax delinquency, soil erosion, and crop adjustment, they came to the startling conclusion that only 112,000 of the county's 280,000 farm acres should remain in crops. Naturally this raised the question of what to do with the surplus farmers. This is a crucial human problem. As yet, the committee has not discovered the answer.

In trying to decide what should be done with the land for the sake of the soil or to suit production to demand, the county committees find they have delineated another problem. They have earmarked a certain percentage of the county population which ought not to be in farming or ought to be in farming elsewhere. Usually, however, there is no "elsewhere" for these people (*6*). The land supply is insufficient. With the frontier closed and all the good land taken up, we do not have land enough even for all the rural folk who want to farm, not to speak of land-minded urban people. It could be argued, of course, that the land shortage is apparent rather than real; that the true name for it is lack of employment. Men do not usually want land primarily for its own sake, but rather for the income that can be derived from it. If an equivalent income can be obtained in city jobs, population will not press on the land supply. Actually, however, urban jobs are not sufficiently available. As a result, the land supply will not accommodate all the people who have no employment elsewhere, though it suffices amply for commercial farm production.

Urban Repercussions of Rural Unemployment

Nonfarmers have to act with regard to this apparent land shortage; they have to contribute funds for dealing with it. Needless to say, the money for farm relief, rural rehabilitation, and land rehabilitation comes largely from the nonfarm community. Failure to see that land shortage is really employment shortage, the remedy for which must be chiefly urban, may heavily increase the costs. Suppose, for example, that the cities try to push the urban unemployed onto the land, instead of providing city jobs for the rural jobless. The result inevitably would be increased expense and decreased efficiency in farm relief, and this would lead to increased taxation.

Our national agricultural policy would be relatively inexpensive if it had simply to facilitate adjusted, efficient, and conservational production. But it has to promote another and very different end besides; it has to provide for large numbers of rural people whose presence in agriculture is commercially unnecessary. Hence the program embodies certain conflicts, which are not the fault of the program planning, but which necessarily complicate the program and make it more expensive. The best and perhaps ultimately the cheapest way to dissolve the army of the rural landless is to provide industrial employment.

Certain of the farm programs help farmers to withhold surplus acres and surplus manpower from production. Simultaneously other farm programs help the landless to get farms; they encourage so-called subsistence farming, which necessarily at the same time produces something, even though it may be very little, for the market. It is absolutely necessary to move at once in these opposite directions. With markets as they are at present, commercial agriculture cannot run full blast. Yet the limitation of it reduces rural employment. Along with Federal assistance to commercial farmers, therefore, the Government must help an increasing number of noncommercial land occupiers. Essentially, this means it must help them to produce. Whatever resolves the contradiction and promotes commercial crop adjustment along with aid to the rural poor cuts down the cost of farm relief. Among the means available, none can compare with the revival of industrial employment. Ultimately, this may come cheaper to the urban community than programs for keeping more people in agriculture than ought to be there.

Agriculture as an Economic Shock Absorber

In depression, agriculture functions as a shock absorber. It does so mainly in two ways, each of them compulsory. (1) It takes price cuts, because crop adjustment with surpluses on hand is slow and difficult; (2) it carries many people on the land for whom no remunerative work can be provided there or elsewhere. In other words, it provides consumers' goods at less than cost and shoulders more than its share of the relief load. In these shock-absorption powers the urban community has a large if unacknowledged interest. It cannot afford, however, to abuse them; that would be like killing the goose that lays the golden egg. Hence, the urban community must not let the farm-price structure collapse entirely or regard the land as a wholly sufficient refuge for rural and urban unemployment.

The urban community has not made these mistakes. On the contrary, it has approved and aided both the commercial and the noncommercial programs for farm relief—both the programs for maintaining farm income and farm prices and the efforts of the Government to make the land a better home for the rural poor. In addition it has provided relief in the cities for the urban unemployed. Ultimately, however, the question will arise of supporting rural policy with more adequate urban policy, especially in what affects the rural unemployed. Primarily this is an urban problem, since urban industry can expand indefinitely whereas a considerable part of agricultural production is ultimately limited by the capacity of the human stomach. Inescapably, the burden of caring for the rural unemployed is largely on urban people, whether these rural people stay on the land or migrate to the cities. Employment is better than relief.

It may be useful to illustrate the problem with some vital statistics. On the basis of the current life-expectance rates, the increase between 1935 and 1955 in the total population of working age, that is to say in the number of people between 18 and 65, will be about 14,500,000. There will, of course, be considerable migration to the cities. Let us suppose, however, that there is none. In that event, the growth in the working-age population will be: 3,000,000 in cities; 4,000,000 in rural nonfarm areas; and nearly 7,500,000 farms.

But there is too much manpower on commercial farms already. Our farm production for all requirements could be maintained and increased without drawing at all on the labor of these 7,500,000 people. They could be idle; the rest of the farm population would be entirely capable of doing all the necessary farm work. Evidence of this is the fact that as long ago as 1929 the more productive half of all the farms produced about 85 percent of the value of agricultural production. These more productive farms, without ceasing to produce for export, could expand their output for domestic comsumption.

Let us put the matter in a different way. In 1930 the average American farm worker produced 150 percent more than his predecessor of 1870. Normal requirements, for both domestic and foreign sale, can be met today with about 1,600,000 fewer workers on farms than were on farms in 1929. Limitation of our farm output to the amount just sufficient to satisfy the commercial demand would deprive about 3,500,000 rural workers of their jobs. These facts take on increased significance when we recall that the farm proportion of the total population decreased from more than 50 percent to less than 25 percent between 1870 and 1930. In other words, exclusive emphasis on purely commercial farm production, with manpower employed in its highest efficiency, would throw an enormous burden of additional unemployment on the cities. Successful handling of the problem necessarily involves a sharing of the costs and benefits between town and country.

OTHER RELATIONSHIPS BETWEEN CITY AND COUNTRY

There is also a tremendous urban interest in rural land for urban uses. Urban or nonfarm uses of the land are very important. Large numbers of city people use rural land for residence purposes, and consequently participate in rural land-use planning. The urban interest in part-time farming is substantial and growing. Part-time farming is important in every State in the Union. In some States half or more than half the farms are part-time farms. Such farms, though less numerous than the rural residences of urban people, account for a larger acreage. Most part-time farms depend directly on nearby cities; the occupants have city jobs and work on their small farms in their spare time. Some part-time farmers work in other purely rural occupations. City people with part-time farms, who have connections in the city and roots in the soil, develop a dual viewpoint which helps to obviate conflicts between urban and rural people.

City populations have a big interest in the use and development of rural lands for recreation and are the chief users of rural recreation areas. In the use of land flood-control measures, the urban interest is greater than the rural interest. Millions of city people, among them practically all who live on the banks of large rivers, know that the flood problem is their problem. Flood damage commonly extends far beyond the flooded areas. Such results as loss of income through shut-down plants, loss of employment, interference with power, light, and heat services, and injury to highways, bridges, and railroads involve whole regions. Loss from sickness and epidemics, dislocation of nearby agricultural markets and sources of supply, and damage to property values may spread widely beyond the areas of merely physical damage. Land treatment for erosion control and flood control yields both tangible and intangible benefits, in which urban people share.

One of the most costly consequences of unchecked water run-off and soil erosion is stream siltation. This is of course very largely an urban problem. Siltation destroys important engineering works; it fills reservoirs and levels stream beds so that levees become less effective. Annual silt damage has never been reckoned comprehensively in dollars and cents, but it represents an enormous charge, much of which falls on urban taxpayers. There is only one economical and practical method of dealing with the silting problem, namely, control of erosion on the watersheds.

City dwellers have a big interest in rural tax conditions. Widespread rural tax delinquency, the result of low farm prices and harmful land use methods, depresses urban as well as rural land values and complicates the fiscal problems of township, city, county, and State governments. Naturally it adds to the burdens of nondelinquent taxpayers, both urban and rural.

Examples could be multiplied of the urban interest in rural land use programs. One of the most interesting, because it shows the many-sidedness of the urban-rural interdependence, concerns the bearing of the programs on sales of urban goods to rural people. It might be supposed that fertilizer sales would be greatest where the soil is most depleted. On the contrary, in areas where farmers use commercial fertilizer, the better farms are the better prospects for the fertilizer salesman. Extreme soil depletion leads to a decreased demand for fertilizer, to less efficient farming generally, and eventually to farm abandonment. Fertilizer applications, particularly in the South, are lower on the poor than on the better farms. Also, they are lower in years of poor than in years of good farm income. Thus the low cotton prices of 1914, 1920, 1926, 1930, and 1931 brought a sharp drop in the use of fertilizer in the years immediately following.

Good land, protected against erosion and maintained in fertility, favors sales of machinery and the prompt payment of machinery bills. Science and invention have allowed the farmer to specialize in the biology of agriculture and turned over the mechanics of the job to the factory, with the result that the industrialist has become literally the farmer's working partner. As such he has a permanent interest in the soil that agriculture uses, and in the income that the farmer earns.

THE LAND PROBLEM ONE ASPECT OF THE ECONOMIC PROBLEM

In short the urban stake in the land is not just in preserving the soil and maintaining its fertility. It includes less tangible elements, which affect the entire rural-urban balance. Among them, as we have noted, are the reciprocal influence of farm and nonfarm incomes, the bearing of rural unemployment on rural employment, and the tendency of declining operator ownership to cause widespread social maladjustment. National welfare requires a well-distributed national income. That is impossible if wide disparities exist between farm and nonfarm prices and if more and more farmers lose their farms. City people help themselves when they help farmers to counteract the forces that drive them from their farms. Not by taking the soil away from the farmers, but by returning it to them, can the soil be made secure.

There is one way, and one way only, to increase the urban stake in the land. It requires a delicate rural-urban adjustment, which will make farm and nonfarm production increase simultaneously in the right proportions. This will mean an increase, equitably shared, in the entire national income. Agriculture can get its due share of the national income only through an approach to abundance. There must be an increase in both farm and factory production but at different rates, since the farm production is relatively high already. Only thus can surplus goods and surplus labor be absorbed. Perhaps the approach should be indirect, through measures to raise the domestic level of consumption. More industrial production would follow. But any approach would require rural-urban cooperation.

Moreover, the cooperation must be planned. It cannot be entirely automatic. There are two main requirements: (1) Concerted effort to decrease the production of unwanted farm surpluses, and simultaneously to increase the production of soil-conserving crops; and (2) decreased infiltration of idle labor and capital, both urban and rural, into lands that should not be farmed, overgrazed, or logged. The best remedy for the overproduction of the surplus crops, such as cotton and wheat, is an improved domestic market for other farm products. The best remedy for compulsory submarginal farming and for other exploitive land uses is practically the same thing, namely, more industrial employment.

Higher consumption per capita and more nonfarm employment are cures for the ailments both of the agricultural land and of the agricultural people. They are cures for urban ailments, too. Eventually, they will give us a streamlined agriculture which will produce adequately for all requirements without waste of land or labor.

The agricultural problem is not a separate thing, walled off entirely from matters of urban concern and of such a nature that the city dweller can tackle it or leave it alone. He cannot detach himself from it. He has a vital interest in the distribution of the people on the land, in the relationship they have to it, in the use they make of it, and in the amount and distribution of the resulting farm income. This interest involves him inevitably in important land use responsibilities.

LITERATURE CITED

(1) Bean, Louis H.
1930. POST-WAR INTERRELATIONS BETWEEN AGRICULTURE AND BUSINESS IN THE UNITED STATES. Internatl. Conf. Agr. Economists Proc. 2: 178–197, illus.

(2) Bean, Louis H., and Chew, Arthur P.
1933. ECONOMIC TRENDS AFFECTING AGRICULTURE. July 1933. U. S. Dept. Agr. 46 pp., illus.

(3) Bjornsen, E. Hjalmar.
1940. FARM DEBT AND FARM FORECLOSURE. U. S. Bur. Agr. Econ., Agr. Situation 24 (2): 18–21, illus.

(4) Eakin, Henry M.
1936. THE SILTING OF RESERVOIRS. (Revised by Carl B. Brown, 1939.) U. S. Dept. Agr. Tech. Bul. 524, 168 pp., illus.

(5) Hadley, N. S.
1940. 78 FARMERS MAKE A MAP. U. S. Bur. Agr. Econ., Land Policy Rev. 3 (1): 15–21, illus.

(6) Johnstone, Paul H.
1939. SOMEWHERE ELSE. U. S. Bur. Agr. Econ., Land Policy Rev. 2 (6): 1–9.

(7) Leybourne, Grace G.
1937. URBAN ADJUSTMENTS OF MIGRANTS FROM THE SOUTHERN APPALACHIAN PLATEAUS. Soc. Forces 16: 238–246, illus.

(8) Lively, C. E., and Taeuber, Conrad.
1939. RURAL MIGRATION IN THE UNITED STATES. U. S. Works Prog. Admin., Div. Res., Res. Monog. 19, 192 pp., illus.

PART 3

The Farmer's Problems Today and the Efforts to Solve Them

Agriculture Today: An Appraisal of the Agricultural Problem

by O. V. Wells [1]

THIS SECTION of the Yearbook consists of a group of articles that discuss one by one the major problems of present-day agriculture in the United States. The following article is intended as an introduction that will set these details in their proper perspective. The author first surveys the current economic and social situation of farmers in the United States, endeavoring especially to bring out the trends that have apparently been occurring over the past two decades, and the problems they pose. Then he tries to discover the main factors or forces, both within and outside of our national boundaries, that have caused these trends and problems. Finally he indicates the principal current lines of attack on the problems. These lines of attack, he believes, can be best understood if they are considered as making up three main streams of action.

ACCORDING to a recent historian, "if intelligence is to be gauged in political programs, the conditions of life which gave them origin must first be known" (*7*).[2] An effort has been made in earlier articles in Part 1 of this Yearbook to trace the response of Government to the needs and demands of farmers and farm people in this country

[1] O. V. Wells is Head Agricultural Economist, in charge Division of Program Development and Coordination, Bureau of Agricultural Economics.
[2] Italic numbers in parentheses refer to Literature Cited, p. 396.

from 1776 through 1939. But we also need to approach the agricultural problem from the analytical angle—to describe each of its elements, and to endeavor to agree on the lines of attack that seem most reasonable in view of the economic setting of the problem, relevant scientific knowledge, and the current state of political thought.

The following section of the Yearbook, then, is devoted to an analysis of the need for agricultural reforms and adjustments and of lines of action that are evolving to meet these needs. This article, which is intended to serve as an introduction to the discussions, will consider the current economic position of American agriculture and the standards of living of farm people; will outline some of the causes or forces that have helped to create the current situation; and will indicate in a general way the several lines of action or methods of attack that are being developed.

CURRENT TRENDS IN AGRICULTURE

American agriculture today is an exceedingly complex structure. It accounts directly for the labor and living of almost one-quarter of our population and supplies almost all of the raw food materials and fibers that are used to sustain and clothe the whole population. What happens to agriculture is of vital importance not only to farmers and rural people but also to the entire Nation; and conversely, farmers and rural people are necessarily interested in the course of business and commerce and in the foreign policy of the Nation.

Because of the wide diversification within agriculture and the close interrelation between agriculture and other elements of the national economy, it is extremely difficult to summarize the economic status of agriculture as a whole or of the agricultural as opposed to the nonagricultural group. Such a summary is worth attempting, however. For this purpose the indexes of agricultural and nonagricultural prices—that is, prices received and prices paid by farmers—are most commonly used. They are charted in figure 1. Statistics summar-

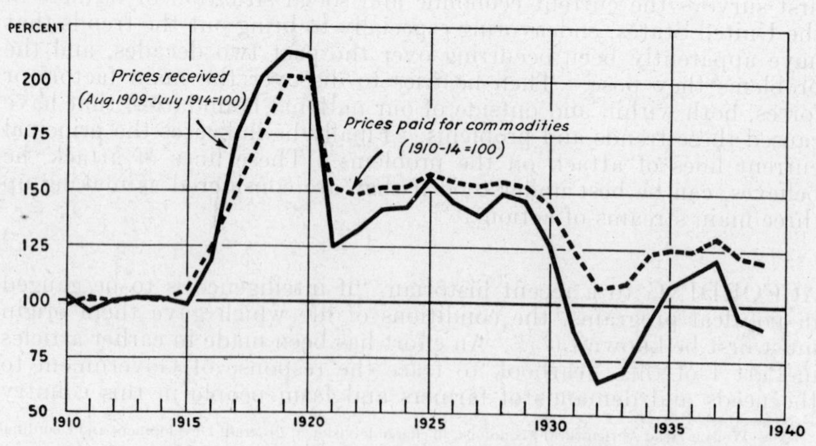

Figure 1.—Prices received and prices paid by farmers, index numbers, 1910–39

izing these data and showing the accompanying changes in gross and net farm income are given in table 1.

Attention is called to two facts brought out in figure 1. First, agricultural and nonagricultural prices have tended to rise and fall together, as would be expected considering the interrelationship to which attention has already been called. And second, in the depression that began in the fall of 1920 agricultural prices fell first, fell farthest, and stayed down longer than nonagricultural prices; this pattern was repeated in the great depression that was ushered in by the stock-market crash in the fall of 1929 and again in the recession that started in the summer of 1937.

Table 1.—Selected statistics related to agriculture, 1910–14 to 1935–39

Period	Index of prices received [1]	Index of prices paid[1]		Index of farm production [3]	Farm income [4]		Farm population	
		Goods	Goods and services [2]		Gross	Net for living	Total	Proportion of national
					Million dollars	*Million dollars*	*Thousands*	*Percent*
1910–14	100	100	100				32, 197	34. 1
1915–19	161	151	151				32, 002	31. 6
1920–24	151	161	172				31, 415	28. 8
1925–29	147	155	168	100	12, 630	7, 634	30, 405	25. 9
1930–34	88	122	132	99	7, 508	3, 705	31, 020	24. 9
1935–39	106	124	129	100	9, 630	5, 720	31, 843	24. 7

1 Bureau of Agricultural Economics, 1910–14=100.
2 Service charges include wages, taxes, and interest.
3 Bureau of Agricultural Economics, 1925–29=100.
4 Includes food and supplies produced and used on the farm. U. S. Government payments included, 1933–39.

It was, in fact, this recurrent relative weakness that led farmers and their representatives to the conclusion that agricultural prices and income were unduly depressed and that an increasing degree of agricultural organization and Government aid was necessary if farmers were to obtain a "fair share" of the national income or if agricultural prices were to be raised toward a "parity level."

Admittedly, the parity price or income concept around which so much of the agricultural controversy has centered is open to some criticism. Agricultural commodities are not themselves a homogeneous group, and the prices of some commodities have averaged higher than those of others in relation to the parity level. Again, adequate data on income obtained from work off the farm are not available. Finally, it is always difficult to maintain the prices of two or more groups of commodities at the same relative level in a dynamic world.

But the effect of agricultural prices and incomes on rural progress and standards of living is more meaningful than the comparison of agricultural and nonagricultural prices as such. Are farm people doing well? Are rural standards of living at a reasonably desirable level? Are farm people progressing toward a more secure or a higher standard of living?

It is possible to get an idea of how well farm people generally are getting along from certain estimates relating to the size and distribution of agricultural incomes in 1935–36. It has been estimated that in that year slightly over 600,000 farm families received some form of direct relief and the incomes of the other 6,000,000-odd farm families were distributed as shown in table 2.

Table 2.—Distribution of nonrelief farm families by income levels, 1935–36 [1]

Income level (dollars)	Families	Proportion of all families	Cumulative percentage of total	Income level (dollars)	Families	Proportion of all families	Cumulative percentage of total
	Number	*Percent*	*Percent*		*Number*	*Percent*	*Percent*
Under 250	232,040	3.8	3.8	1,000 to 1,500	1,394,821	22.6	74.9
250 to 500	858,963	13.9	17.7	1,500 to 2,000	730,811	11.8	86.7
500 to 750	1,108,400	18.0	35.7	2,000 to 2,500	340,645	5.6	92.3
750 to 1,000	1,027,044	16.6	52.3	2,500 and over	473,834	7.7	100.0

[1] Arranged from data in Consumer Incomes in the United States, Their Distribution in 1935–36 (*10*).

Assuming that 85 percent of the relief families receive less than $500, these data indicate that approximately 1,600,000 families, or almost one-quarter of all farm families, have incomes of less than $500 a family, and that about 40 percent of all farm families have incomes under $750. What does this mean?

Although adequate information is not available, it seems reasonable to assume that the greater portion of the farm families with incomes under $750 often cannot afford the minimum material necessities for the maintenance of vigorous physical health, are sometimes unable to avail themselves of ordinary legal rights and privileges, and often find themselves unable to share in the basic nonmaterial aspects of our American culture or civilization. That is, such data as are available indicate that an income of about $750 is needed to supply the minimum physical and cultural requirements, at the prices prevailing in 1936, for the typical farm family of two adults and three children (*5*).

There is, then, a substantial degree of rural poverty in the United States, regardless of the particular statistical measure used. But it may be argued that there is also a substantial degree of urban poverty and unemployment. The question is whether farmers as a class have as good a standard of living as the average American.

Attempting to describe or compare standards of living is always difficult, but there are certain indices to which attention may be called. To begin with, the 25 percent of the American people who live on farms are producing almost one-third of the children in the United States. What kind of medical care is available in rural areas? And how are these children educated?

In rural areas and small towns, the medical facilities, measured in terms of number and character of doctors, dentists, and nurses and the hospital space in relation to population, are in general definitely inferior to facilities available in larger towns and cities. In 1939 the rural areas and the towns of 2,500 people or less had 48 percent of the population but only 31 percent of the doctors, while cities of over 100,000 people had 30 percent of the population and 44 percent of the doctors (*3*). In addition, rural physicians are older and as a rule perhaps less well trained than those in the cities, and dentists, nurses, and hospital facilities are still more unevenly distributed (*2*). Finally, only about one-fourth of the 2,500 rural or semirural counties have organized health departments capable of effectively applying modern methods of disease prevention and control (*1*).

The story is the same when education is considered. With about 31 percent of all children 5 to 17 years old, farmers receive about 9 percent of the national income; and almost 13.5 percent of these school-age children are on farms in the Southeastern States, which have only about 2.25 percent of the national income (*11*). Even allowing for the fact that considerable numbers of farm children attend town schools, the effect of this income disparity is apparent. Approximately one-half the school population is enrolled in rural schools. These rural schools usually have a shorter term than urban schools; they have less than half the property value per pupil of urban schools; they are staffed by teachers whose annual salaries are less than half those of their better-prepared colleagues; and they can offer only a meager curriculum compared with that of the urban schools (*8*).

Comparisons also show that rural housing conditions are inferior to those existing in cities, although some improvement is being made through the increased use of modern equipment. Farmhouses are on an average older than city houses, are less likely to be constructed of fireproof materials, and are far less well equipped. About 8.5 percent of all farmhouses, for example, have flush toilets as compared with 85 percent of all urban dwellings; about 30 percent of the farm homes have water in the house, including 8 percent with piped cold water and 14 percent with hand pumps in the house, as compared with 95 percent of urban homes with running water; and about 25 percent of the farmhouses have electricity for lighting as compared with more than 95 percent of urban homes with modern lighting equipment.[3] Only in the case of the radio is there an approach to equality. Slightly less than 70 percent of the farm families reported ownership of radios on January 1, 1938, as compared with somewhat over 90 percent of the urban families.

Automobiles and trucks are often needed in connection with farm operations, as well as to give farm families the access to service, trading, and amusement centers that is usually provided by buses and streetcars for the urban population. Statistics for automobiles on farms are not available, but in 1930 there were 193 motor vehicles registered per 1,000 persons in all unincorporated areas as compared with 250 vehicles per 1,000 persons in all incorporated towns and cities (*6*). Apparently farmers own relatively fewer automobiles and trucks than nonfarmers, and it is easily observed that farm roads are as a rule much inferior to the streets and intercity highways on which most urban motor vehicles are operated.

Farm families tend to have somewhat better diets than village or city families owing to the use of such home-grown protective foods as fresh fruit, green vegetables, eggs, and milk (*9*). But even here there is still much to be desired, and there are wide areas in the South, the Appalachian region, and the Great Plains where substantial dietary improvement is needed, as it is also among certain rural classes

[3] ENGLE, N. H. HOUSING CONDITIONS IN THE UNITED STATES. U. S. Bur. Foreign and Dom. Com. 78 pp., illus. 1937. [Processed.]

such as the migratory farm workers on the Pacific coast. A survey of the South in 1937 indicated that an additional 6,000,000 acres of cropland and 9,000,000 acres of pasture could well have been devoted to the production of additional home-grown food for farm-family consumption.[4]

Answers to the following questions should furnish another index or measure of the returns accruing to farmers. Are farm people satisfied with current standards of living? Are farm returns or is farming as a way of life sufficiently attractive to induce farmers to maintain the productive capacity of the Nation's farm land? In part the answer is found in the sustained fight for remedial agricultural legislation which has been under way since 1920, but there are other indices that also need to be considered.

The net migration of approximately 6,000,000 people from farms to urban centers during the decade 1920–30; the resumption of this net outward movement in 1933; its continuance at an average level of 250,000 to 350,000 people annually despite the high level of urban unemployment; and the concern over the 2,000,000 young people currently "backed up" on farms—all of these facts indicate a continuing population pressure in rural areas (*4*). Usually this pressure has been relieved by the migration of farm people, especially the young people, to the cities and towns and industrial or commercial employment. That the outward migration has been greatest from those rural areas where standards of living were usually the lowest indicates that the way of life as it now exists in these areas is often unsatisfactory. It also gives additional weight to the argument for improved rural medical and educational facilities if these migrating farm people are to be equipped to adapt themselves to a new environment.

Finally, the pressure of an excess population and the continuance of exploitive methods of crop and livestock production are taking their toll from the land itself. Farmers often fail to maintain the productive capacity of their farms; and altogether it is estimated that about 3 percent of the Nation's land has already been essentially destroyed for tillage, that another 12 percent is severely eroded, and that an additional 41 percent is moderately eroded. Of the more than 400 million acres of land currently classed as cropland, approximately 61 percent is either subject to erosion under current cropping practices or is of such poor quality as not to yield a satisfactory return at any reasonable price level. Erosion and overcropping or overgrazing are accounting for the loss of millions of tons of plant nutrients each year, and it is estimated that three-fourths of this annual loss could be prevented were farmers willing and able to apply the conservation measures needed (*12*).

FORCES AFFECTING THE AGRICULTURAL SITUATION

All of these indices lead to the question, Why have farm prices and standards of living continued for two decades at such relatively low

---

[4] STEANSON, OSCAR, and LANGSFORD, E. L. FOOD, FEED, AND SOUTHERN FARMS; A STUDY OF PRODUCTION IN RELATION TO FARM NEEDS IN THE SOUTH. U. S. Bur. Agr. Econ. Farm Mangt. Rpt. 1, 25 pp. 1939. [Mimeographed.]

levels? What are the social and economic forces behind the observed fact?

Farmers, editors, and social scientists generally have been advancing explanations ever since the sharp break in agricultural prices in the fall of 1920. Though no definitive analysis has yet been made, there is increasing agreement on a considerable number of the factors that have tended to create or maintain the current agricultural situation. Fundamentally, the situation is the result of pressure of an "overexuberant" production on a stable or already well-supplied market.

To begin with, the foreign market for our agricultural products has declined. The farmers of the United States have traditionally relied upon the export market, especially that of Europe, to absorb their agricultural surpluses. True, the export market was declining prior to the World War, but domestic population was rapidly increasing, the foreign demand was revived by the war, and exports were maintained at a high level in the reconstruction period following, or until about 1925.

But in recent years the foreign outlet has accounted for only about half the volume of exports recorded in the period 1920–24. There are several causes for this decline in export demand. The United States was changing from a debtor to a creditor nation at the same time that American farmers were making surplus profits as a result of the World War. But at the close of the war we failed to make arrangements that would allow the foreign debts to be paid. Instead, we joined with the other nations of the world in raising tariffs in an effort to wall out foreign goods and protect the domestic market. United States farmers have also been faced with increasing competition in such export markets as remained open. Canada, Australia, Brazil, and Argentina, especially, increased agricultural production and pressed their products on the foreign market.

At the same time that the foreign market was declining, millions of work animals were being displaced in the United States by automobiles, trucks, and tractors, so that the domestic demand for feedstuffs was being materially curtailed. Altogether the number of horses and mules in cities and on farms declined by about 13,500,000 head from 1914 to 1939, and this decline shifted over 40,000,000 acres of good farm land from feed crops to production for the commercial market.

A third factor in bringing about a disappointing demand is found in the fact that the requirements for food and fiber for domestic consumption are being stabilized. Both anti-immigration laws and a declining birth rate have operated to restrict population growth, and the average per capita consumption of food has been relatively stable since the World War. True, population is still increasing in the United States and will continue to increase for some time, but the rate of increase is steadily declining, and it now appears that population can be expected to reach a stable level about 1960.

Over against these factors making for a stable or declining demand for agricultural products a number of factors have been actively working toward increasing agricultural production. For one thing, agriculture is organized in terms of individual or small-scale operations, and it is almost always seemingly to the advantage of each individual farmer to produce as much as possible for market since his production alone cannot appreciably affect the prices he receives. Farming is also an enterprise in which the returns from the land, the operating equipment, and the labor usually accrue to the same individual, so that most farmers find it impossible to reduce costs during a period of depression, as do some industrial operators, by refusing to pay rent or by forcing labor out of employment. These two conditions, combined with a continuing pressure of population on the land, tend to force agricultural production upward when prices are favorable and to make it difficult to obtain any substantial downward adjustment.

The increasing efficiency of agricultural production brought about by advances in technology is another important factor. During and following the World War, the development of large-scale machinery allowed a considerable acreage of new land to be brought under cultivation, especially in the Great Plains; and since 1919 the effect of a continuous stream of technological improvements has been felt. Among the current advances in this field is the development of the small, rubber-tired, general-purpose tractor, which seems to be so well adapted to the family-size farm as to mean that the number of work animals will continue to decline. Another advance is the development of hybrid seed corn, which will apparently increase corn production somewhere between 150 and 250 million bushels above what would have been expected if the old open-pollination method had been continued. Other examples can easily be cited.

The development during the last decade of an industrial situation in which available labor has far outrun opportunities for employment has forced a very large number of rural young people to remain on the farm. Thus the agricultural population has increased at the same time that agricultural prices and the demand for agricultural products have been sharply reduced. This restriction of opportunities has limited the cityward migration of the excess rural population and made it increasingly necessary to consider the problems of the lower one-fourth or one-third of the farm group. It has broken down the fiction that every hard-working young farmer could expect eventually to own a well-equipped family-size farm and has forcibly emphasized the fact that every effort must be made to develop new approaches or new ways of life within agriculture itself.

Another factor in the current situation is the relative inflexibility of marketing costs, which throws the greater part of the burden of a decline in food or fiber prices on the farm group. Agricultural marketing costs are chiefly influenced by wage rates, freight and transportation rates, and the operating efficiency of the marketing system itself. All of these factors are relatively stable, with the result that marketing charges absorb most of the consumers' expenditures for agricultural goods in years when prices are extremely low. Thus farmers and agricultural workers are continually engaged in efforts to reduce freight rates, to regulate commodity speculation, and to increase marketing efficiency by any means that appear practical.

The steady growth of farm tenancy in the United States also influences rural standards of living and affects the land itself. Slightly over 42 percent of all farms were tenant-operated in 1935, and another

10 percent were operated by owners who rented additional land. It must also be remembered that the mortgage debt on a great many farms is so heavy that hundreds of thousands of farm families are maintaining only the semblance of farm ownership. Tenancy itself, of course, is not necessarily an evil; but the fact remains that the steady growth of tenancy in the United States is accompanied by a growth in the number of farm families who are faced with serious problems of insecurity, have unstable occupancy of the farms they operate, and cannot afford to be much concerned with the problem of soil conservation.

Finally, one of the most important factors in the agricultural situation—and the one that is perhaps least often recognized—is the increasing urbanization of rural standards of living and the insistence of farm people that they be allowed to enjoy the same modern conveniences as the rest of the population. A number of forces have contributed to this attitude. The off-the-farm experience gained by young farmers during the World War, the increasing commercialization of agriculture, the radio, the movies, the automobile, and the consolidated school have all raised questions in the minds of farm people about the value of agriculture as a way of life when that way involves greater sacrifices of leisure, recreation, and social status than are demanded of any other sizable group in the Nation. As a result, the current agricultural situation is affected not only by agricultural surpluses and an uncertain market situation but also by the desires and demands of the farm people themselves for a better life. This in itself is a strong stimulus to the development of a more effective agricultural program.

HOW THE PROBLEMS ARE BEING ATTACKED

With the forces that have just been noted in mind, we may consider the several activities that are being developed in an effort to obtain agricultural relief and adjustment.

These activities include efforts to obtain acreage adjustments, to regulate agricultural marketings, to stabilize annual supplies, to insure crop production, to put a floor under prices through the use of commodity loans, to obtain soil conservation, to encourage farm forestry, to rehabilitate distressed farm families, to adjust the rural tax structure, to develop a more adequate farm credit system, to subsidize exports, to encourage increased consumption of food among relief clients, to develop new uses for agricultural products, and to reduce marketing costs. They also include the efforts of farmers and their representatives to appraise agricultural problems and plan ahead.

Although these activities cover a wide and varied field, they all tend to fit into a general framework or to fall into three general streams of action: (1) Activities designed to increase incomes to farmers producing commodities for sale on a commercial basis; (2) activities designed to increase incomes or improve living conditions among such classes as migrant laborers, sharecroppers, subsistence farmers, and victims of drought and flood; and (3) activities designed to encourage better land use and more efficient farm management.

Since the sharp fall in agricultural income following the World

War, special attention has been concentrated on the search for devices to maintain adequate prices and incomes for farmers producing the basic agricultural commodities—corn, cotton, tobacco, wheat, fruits, vegetables, dairy products, and meat. The economic basis for this search is found in the existence of some 25 to 50 million acres of surplus cropland and in the fact that one-third to one-half of the farm population is inadequately employed.

The working out of this line of attack led to the development of the so-called ever-normal granary program outlined in the Agricultural Adjustment Act of 1938. This act provides for acreage allotments financed by conditional grants or benefit payments as a means of adjusting agricultural production, commodity loans as a means of stabilizing agricultural prices, and marketing quotas for use in years when supplies seem to be excessively high. Farmers have also asked for some form of adjustment payments to offset the effect of industrial tariffs and to maintain farm incomes somewhere nearer the parity level. The Agricultural Adjustment Act of 1938 provided for such price-adjustment payments, and Congress appropriated considerable sums for such payments in both 1938 and 1939.

Another activity in this field is the development of marketing agreements and orders and other efforts to improve the general efficiency of the agricultural marketing system. Marketing agreements are used chiefly in connection with the marketing of fruits, vegetables, and fluid milk. These devices offer a means of regulating marketings, including the manner in which supplies are divided among different markets or split up among the several forms in which a particular commodity may be marketed. Other activities designed to improve the marketing system include grading and standardization work and efforts to reduce interstate trade barriers, to reorganize terminal market facilities, to reduce freight rates, and to regulate commodity speculation. Cooperative marketing associations, of course, are another device which many farmers are using to improve their marketing situation.

Attention is also being directed toward increasing market demand. Such efforts include the development of the surplus-purchase and relief-distribution program and the food-stamp program under the Federal Surplus Commodities Corporation; the encouragement of research to find new uses for farm products, including the establishment of four regional laboratories for the carrying on of such research; and a wide variety of devices to hold or regain the foreign market for agricultural products, ranging from efforts to increase and standardize the staple length of cotton to direct subsidies for the export of cotton and wheat.

The development of a more nearly adequate credit system for farmers is another activity that has been under way since the World War. As a result, farmers are now in a much better position than at any time in the past to obtain credit through Federal land banks, the Intermediate and Production Credit Associations, the Banks for Cooperatives, and, since 1933, the Commodity Credit Corporation.

A second stream of activities has been developed in an effort to meet the needs and demands of the disadvantaged classes in the agricultural group, including migrant farm laborers, sharecroppers, farmers on submarginal or drought-stricken lands, farmers on too-small farms, rural people without adequate employment, and the increasing number of rural young people who are being dammed up or forced back on the land. With few exceptions, specific attention was not focused upon the problems in this field until about 1933 or 1934.

The rural-rehabilitation program, emergency loans and grants, farm-debt adjustments, the tenant-purchase program, medical and community-service cooperatives, the financing of water facilities in drought areas, camps for migrant farm workers, and allied activities of the Farm Security Administration are addressed primarily to the problems of this class in the farm population. In addition, considerable sums have been expended each year since 1929 in connection with feed and seed loans and flood relief.

The subsistence-homesteads experiment and the efforts of the Resettlement Administration to find new patterns of agricultural organization or settlement also belong in this field, and settlements established by these agencies are being continued under the direction of the Farm Security Administration. Several agencies, including some State governments, are interested in devising better forms of lease agreements and in securing their general adoption in areas where tenant-landlord relations need to be improved. Another experiment that seems to be especially sucessful is the program of the Rural Electrification Administration. At the time this agency went to work in 1935 only 11 percent of the rural homes were electrified. Within the short space of 4 years this has been increased to approximately 25 percent.

A third stream of activities is directed toward obtaining changes in land use or methods of farming needed in order to insure soil and water conservation and to obtain efficient production. This field has long been a subject of research and discussion. It continues to occupy the attention of farmers and agricultural workers, since the need for good land use and increased efficiency is generally recognized, even though it is also realized that increased efficiency will accentuate some of the other problems with which agriculture is currently faced.

Activities in this field include research and extension work directed toward the development of better plants and animals, new practices that will increase production per acre of land or per head of livestock, and new methods of doing farm work that will reduce the amount of labor required. Another attack on this problem is the acquisition and operation of forest and submarginal farm land by public agencies, where these lands are of such a character that private operation is inadvisable or inefficient.

Soil conservation is receiving increased attention. Most of the work in this field also has been done since 1933. Current activities include the effort to stabilize the acreage of soil-depleting crops under the agricultural conservation program; activity on the part of the State agricultural colleges; and the work of the Soil Conservation Service, especially created to encourage conservation through research, demonstration, and cooperation with soil conservation districts, which are being organized under enabling acts passed in 36 States prior to January 1, 1940. The value of forest conservation has long been recognized in the United States, and increasing attention is being given to the need for encouraging selective cutting and other desirable forest practices on privately owned timberland and for developing an adequate farm-forestry program. A wide field of activity is also open to county and State governments in the field of tax revision and the handling of tax-delinquent land.

In conclusion it should be emphasized that though any well-rounded agricultural program must stress those things that farmers can do to help themselves, farmers also realize that sustained agricultural prosperity cannot be attained unless it is accompanied by sustained general prosperity for the entire Nation. Farmers can do much to improve their economic and social status by their own efforts, but as long as the chief source of farm income is the sale of farm products for consumption by people who are not farmers, efforts to increase and stabilize the incomes of nonagricultural consumers are as important as any efforts that can be made in the agricultural field itself. In a broad sense, there is one problem, not two. This is the reason that farmers are and always have been interested in the commercial and industrial policies of the Nation as these affect both the prices of the goods farmers buy and those of the goods they sell.

* * * * * * *

This article was prepared shortly after the outbreak of the European war in September 1939. An effort has been made to outline the existing agricultural situation in the belief that this will supply a better basis for understanding the following discussions, which endeavor to analyze each of the many elements here briefly mentioned. The outbreak of the war introduces a new factor into the problem and emphasizes one of the essential elements of the situation with which agriculture is always faced. Farmers live in a changing world, and one of the outstanding characteristics of the current situation is the fact that the forces at work are changing so rapidly that new problems are developing even as old problems are being solved.

LITERATURE CITED

(1) American Medical Association, Bureau of Medical Economics.
1937. RURAL MEDICAL SERVICE. 80 pp. Chicago. (Reprinted from organization section of the Journal of the American Medical Association.)

(2) Brunner, Edmund de S., and Lorge, Irving.
1937. RURAL TRENDS IN DEPRESSION YEARS; A SURVEY OF VILLAGE CENTERED AGRICULTURAL COMMUNITIES, 1930–36. 387 pp. New York.

(3) Davis, Michael M.
1936. PROBLEMS AND ISSUES OF MEDICAL SERVICE. 37 pp. Chicago, The Julius Rosenwald Fund.

(4) Lively, C. E., and Taeuber, Conrad.
1939. RURAL MIGRATION IN THE UNITED STATES. U. S. Works Prog. Admin., Div. Res., Res. Monog. 19, 192 pp., illus. Washington, D. C.

(5) Maddox, James G.
1939. SUGGESTIONS FOR A NATIONAL PROGRAM OF RURAL REHABILITATION AND RELIEF. Jour. Farm Econ. 21 (4): 881–896.

(6) Paddock, Robert H., and Rodgers, Roe P.
1939. PRELIMINARY RESULTS OF ROAD USE STUDIES. U. S. Dept. Agr., Public Roads 20 (3): 45–54, 62–63, illus.

(7) PHILLIPS, U. B.
1929. LIFE AND LABOR IN THE OLD SOUTH. 375 pp., illus. Boston.
(8) SMITH, PAYSON; WRIGHT, FRANK W., and associates.
1939. EDUCATION IN THE 48 STATES. (U. S.) Advisory Comm. on Ed., Staff Study 1, 199 pp.
(9) STIEBELING, HAZEL K., and COONS, CALLIE MAE.
1939. PRESENT-DAY DIETS IN THE UNITED STATES. U. S. Dept. Agr. Yearbook 1939: 296–320, illus.
(10) [UNITED STATES] NATIONAL RESOURCES COMMITTEE.
1938. CONSUMER INCOMES IN THE UNITED STATES: THEIR DISTRIBUTION IN 1935–36. 104 pp., illus. Washington, D. C.
(11) ———
1938. PROBLEMS OF A CHANGING POPULATION. 306 pp., illus. Washington, D. C.
(12) UTZ, E. J., and KELLOG, CHARLES E.
1938. THE NATURE AND EXTENT OF SOIL LOSSES. U. S. Dept. Agr. Yearbook 1938: 84–96, illus.

Our Major Land Use Problems and Suggested Lines of Action

by L. C. Gray [1]

HERE is a comprehensive discussion of problems of land use in their broadest setting—the economic and social backgrounds, the desirable objectives, the constitutional framework within which policies must be shaped, the development of land use policy since 1862, and our present land-tenure and submarginal-land problems. The author thus puts one of the major dilemmas of today: "If our industrial economy could be so reshaped as to afford adequate and dependable employment for the surplus rural population, land-settlement policy could be aimed at achieving and maintaining a population balance that would assure a comfortable standard of living from commerical farming. If adequate outlets into industrial employment cannot be provided, a land-settlement program will have to be developed in the direction of a more nearly self-sufficient economy for a larger number of families than could maintain an adequate living standard under commercial farming." Among future needs, he lays special emphasis on an adequate small-holdings program, better landlord-tenant relationships, and closer integration of land use policies.

ECONOMIC AND SOCIAL SETTING OF NATIONAL LAND PROBLEMS

THE LAND problems and policies of a nation depend partly on the physical characteristics of the land itself, but even more on the stage

[1] L. C. Gray is Assistant Chief, Bureau of Agricultural Economics.

of economic development, customary or legal institutions, and prevailing national attitudes of the people.

Population Density and Degree of Industrialization

A most significant factor in determining the character of the land problems for a nation, or even for a major regional subdivision, is density of population in relation to the degree of industrialization. Where the economy is predominantly industrial a much larger population can be maintained without excessive pressure on agricultural land resources, especially if industrial products are exchanged for foreign agricultural products.

The United States has advanced beyond the stage of population density in which land policies to attract population need be employed. A high degree of industrial and commercial development has prevented population pressure from becoming as excessive as it is in densely peopled agricultural countries, such as Java, Barbadoes, or Puerto Rico; and at the same time our population density has not reached that of densely peopled industrial countries which must depend largely on importations of agricultural products. In the main we are agriculturally self-contained, except for certain tropical products.

So long as we retain restrictive immigration policies our population does not appear likely to reach the extreme densities that characterize some of the western European countries, for our birth rate has been falling for nearly a century. Indeed, it has recently been estimated that our population may become approximately stationary within a few decades at a level that would mean a density of little more than 50 persons per square mile, or about one-fourteenth that of Belgium, less than one-eighth that of Germany, and about one-fourth that of France. Even if we continue agriculturally self-contained, a density of 50 per square mile will not represent a serious pressure on our agricultural land resources, provided we employ sound policies of land utilization and tenure.

Agriculture and Industry Ill-Balanced

Incongruous as it may appear in the light of the foregoing statements, many of our most serious rural problems emerge from the fact that too large a proportion of our population is endeavoring to make a living in commerical farming. This has come about because of diminution of foreign outlets for our agricultural staples, failure of industry to absorb the annual increase of rural population, and introduction of labor-saving farm equipment. The ill balance of agriculture and industry is especially serious because of its fluctuating character and the instability this introduces into rural life. In times of industrial prosperity rural population is drawn into the cities. In depression large and burdensome numbers return to rural areas for support. These conditions reflect rural overpopulation in the sense that the market will not absorb agricultural products at prices that will return a money income adequate to maintain a suitable standard of living for those whose livelihood depends mainly on the land. This does not mean overpopulation in the absolute sense in which general population density has been discussed. However acute the economic problems of our agriculture, we are really one of the most fortunate nations of the world in the opulent relationship of present and prospective population to available agricultural land. Nevertheless, we cannot afford a wasteful utilization or an uneconomical and socially unjustified distribution of land resources among those who use them.

Regional Overpopulation

Even the superabundant production of our farms comes mainly from only a small proportion of them, for it has been estimated that half the value of the products that reach the market is produced by less than 11 percent of the farms. A large proportion of the remaining farm families are employed primarily in production for family use, with at best the incidental production of small quantities for sale. Such families are most numerous in the southern Appalachians, the Ozarks, northern hill areas, and cut-over areas, and are found sporadically in other parts of the country. In part, their mode of life is a traditional survival of frontier modes of life and work preserved through isolation; in part, it reflects a regionally redundant population in relation to available agricultural land resources, intensified by high birth rates and local inadequacy of industrial employment.

In certain other regions there is redundancy of agricultural population because of the necessity of changing from a relatively intensive to a relatively extensive type of farm economy. In the Great Plains and intermountain regions, for example, ill-advised homestead policies attracted a population unduly large in view of the necessity of shifting from grain growing to livestock or combination farming. In the South serious soil depletion, partial loss of foreign markets for cotton, substitution of machinery for human labor, and the apparent necessity of shifting to types of land use requiring much less labor per unit of land have steadily increased the surplus rural population unable to find adequate employment.

The relative national and regional overpopulation of the countryside, intensified in some areas by protracted drought, has resulted in uprooting large numbers of families from the soil and setting them adrift as migratory tenants and laborers moving hither and yon looking for casual employment. Many farm families who remain on the soil are faced with difficult economic conditions and lowered standards of living.

General National Objectives in Shaping Land Policies

Land policies, as well as other types of policy, must be shaped with reference to the broad ideals and objectives of the Nation. The United States has long been characterized by the concept that the primary purpose of the Nation and its Government is to promote the welfare of its citizens as individuals, in contrast with the prevailing ideology of certain other nations that the welfare of their citizens must be subordinated to the enhancement of the greatness, power, and prestige of the state. Pursuit of the latter objective may induce a policy of achieving a maximum population, as Italy and Germany have attempted to do in spite of an already overcrowded condition, in the interest of military power. On the other hand, although the United States is far less densely populated, its declining birth rate is generally viewed without serious concern, and even with some satisfaction, because of its significance in the maintenance of high living standards.

The trend of land policies depends also on the political and economic system, which determines whether national objectives are to be achieved by individual enterprise and private property in land and other production goods or by public initiative and the collectivization of goods. Under the assumption of continued private ownership, land-policy problems take the form largely of how to overcome the abuses, from a social point of view, of private landownership while retaining its advantages. Policies concerning regulation of land use, zoning, adjustment of relations of landlords and tenants, regulation of land settlement, and taxation, which emerge for consideration, either would not be required or would take different forms under public ownership.

From the beginning, the people of the United States have emphasized private enterprise and private ownership of land with a minimum of governmental interference. This, then, is our starting point for the consideration of land problems and policies, and we shall consider them within the general framework of our characteristic institutions.

CONSTITUTIONAL ASPECTS OF THE DEVELOPMENT OF LAND POLICY

The student of land policies must always be aware of the constitutional provisions that restrict the extent of interference with individual rights, limit substitution of public ownership for individual ownership, or define the scope of the powers of the various branches of government.[2]

Nature of Private Ownership of Land

Landownership is a bundle of rights, including the right to use (or abuse), improve, or dispose of the land owned. The owner may grant or dispose of one or more of his rights, retaining title to the remainder; for instance he may grant an easement, dispose of his subsurface mineral rights, or grant to a tenant the right to use the land for a period.

The rights of ownership by private individuals, however, are limited by certain governmental rights, but in many respects these are ill-defined. The principal ones are a limited right of taxation; the right to acquire land by eminent domain for clearly authorized public purposes, paying therefor its fair value; and the police power—that is, the right and obligation of government to provide for and safeguard the health, safety, and morals of its citizens and a still vaguer obligation to provide for the general welfare.

In the frontier stages of national development, land was so abundant that there were few ways in which the interests of the general public appeared to be injured by the use or disposition of privately owned land. Therefore few restrictions were imposed. In popular opinion, in custom, and in the attitudes of legislatures and courts, landownership acquired a degree of absolutism which still puts the burden of proof on the public agency that would seek to restrict the employment of the rights of ownership.

[2] For a fuller discussion see The Soil and the Law, U. S. Dept. Agr. Yearbook 1938, pp. 298–318.

As our economic and social life have become more and more complex the broad public interest has been found to be increasingly affected by the unrestrained exercise of individual or corporate property rights in land. There is a growing opinion that land is vested with a paramount public interest, that private landownership is granted by society rather than being an inherent individual right, and that when it comes into direct conflict with the general welfare either it must be restrained or the land must be converted, with due compensation, into public property.

Certain Limitations on the Powers of the Federal Government and the States

The Federal Constitution, as interpreted by the courts, defines the jurisdiction of the Federal Government, leaving to the States the remaining jurisdiction. No regulatory power over privately owned land is specifically granted to the Federal Government. Such powers as it may exercise must be derived from the powers to raise and expend revenue and regulate commerce and from other powers incidental to these. The Federal Government enjoys very broad powers over the lands it owns.

Both the Federal Constitution and the constitutions of various States, as interpreted by the courts, impose restrictions on the powers which the respective agencies may exercise over privately owned land. Some of the principal types of restrictions may be summarized as follows:

1. The provision that prohibits depriving persons of "liberty or property without due process of law" has been especially potent in limiting the so-called police power. The latter concept is still ill-defined, particularly in its application to land, and has been extended but slowly, opposed at every step by the safeguards embodied in the "due process" clause.

2. From the due process concept has been derived the principle that State expenditures must be confined to clearly authorized public purposes. The constitutions of various States also include a number of specific restrictions on State expenditures.

3. Derived from the general philosophy of our system of threefold governmental structure—legislative, executive, and judicial—and specifically embodied in the constitutions of certain States is the doctrine that Congress or a State legislature may not delegate its authority to administrative agencies.

4. The provision in the fourteenth amendment to the Federal Constitution that no State may deny to any person within its jurisdiction the "equal protection of the laws" is interpreted to permit reasonable classification of persons and property provided there is uniformity of treatment within the class.

5. Interstate compacts are subject to approval by the Federal Government.

In summary, it will be apparent that the power of either Federal or State Government to remedy serious social disadvantages in the use, tenure, and disposition of privately owned land is not very explicit and may be extended only by convincing legislatures and courts that the social welfare in particular situations is so paramount that the individual rights protected by a constitution may be justifiably subordinated.

THE DEVELOPMENT OF NATIONAL LAND POLICIES

From the beginning of the Federal Government the conviction prevailed that the progress and prosperity of the Nation would best be promoted by private landownership and therefore that the public domain should be rapidly distributed into private ownership. During the next hundred years this principle predominated in national land policies.

Until 1862 virtually all disposal of the public land to individuals was by sale, except for the limited granting of land as an inducement to or reward for military service. In the sale of land there was no restriction as to the amount that might be acquired except the ability of the purchaser to pay for it. Gradually interest in promoting and facilitating settlement gained headway against the originally predominant concern with making the public lands a source of revenue. Lowered minimum prices and reductions in the minimum size of purchasable units, together, for a time, with credit on the purchase price, made it easier for settlers to buy land. By a series of temporary and limited acts, and finally by a general act in 1841, squatters were excepted from the auction system and protected from loss of their homes by recognition of a preemption right to purchase for $1.25 an acre 160 acres on which they had settled and made improvements.

The year 1862 marked the beginning of the second epoch of Federal land policy. It witnessed abandonment of military bounties—hitherto largely a source of benefit to speculators, a decrease in auction sales, and the adoption of the homestead principle of granting land virtually free in limited quantities on condition of occupancy for a certain period and the making of improvements. The principle was gradually modified by shortening the required period of residence, with special exemptions for soldiers or veterans; by increasing the maximum acreage obtainable, in partial recognition of the special agricultural conditions of semiarid areas; and by providing special conditions for acquiring homesteads in national forests, with access to needful timber and stone, and for encouraging protective timber planting. All these provisions were designed in theory to aid or facilitate actual settlement.

Unfortunately the selling of the public domain continued to parallel the homestead system until sale as an important method of disposition was abandoned in 1891, and even the homestead policy was modified to permit commutation of part of the required period of occupancy by money payment. In fact throughout most of the three decades after 1862 it continued to be easy for speculators to acquire choice lands in large blocks, frequently to the exclusion of homesteaders, who were forced to purchase at advanced prices.

Hundreds of millions of acres were transferred to the ownership of States and corporations through the swampland grants, grants in aid of education, and grants to subsidize the construction of wagon roads, canals, and railways. Since such grants were for the most part without condition as to use and subsequent dispositon of the land, in effect the Federal Government to this extent resigned its power to direct the course of land use and settlement. Generally the States and corporations concerned sold their land holdings unconditionally, usually at advanced prices, although a number of States in the West have followed a leasing policy.

The year 1891 may be considered the beginning of a third epoch in national land policy, for it marked abandonment not only of sales policies, but also of the general idea that the public lands should be put into private ownership as rapidly as possible. The President was authorized in that year to reserve lands in the public domain covered with timber or brush; and during the next decade and a half nearly 195,000,000 acres were reserved. This was a significant manifestation of the growing recognition of the social importance of land. Later it was followed by measures providing for Federal purchase of land for forests and wildlife refuges.

Although homestead policies continued to operate for nearly half a century after 1891, they soon ceased to have constructive significance because of virtual exhaustion of public land suitable for arable farming. In fact they came to have a nuisance character, enticing hapless pioneers into the occupancy of lands hopelessly unadapted to arable farming, frequently to the detriment of the range interests.

Recent years have seen the beginning of a fourth epoch in national land policy. In addition to increased emphasis on policies for forest and wildlife conservation, there have been attempts to overcome certain social disadvantages that accompanied private landownership. Since a number of these new attempts are discussed in detail elsewhere in this Yearbook, the remainder of this article is confined to consideration of the elements requisite for a well-rounded land policy.

In the light of the present perspective, the shortcomings of the extreme laissez faire policies of the nineteenth century are apparent, though the historical inevitability of these policies must be recognized. Most of the present-day problems of land use and tenure, viewed from the standpoint of agriculture, are traceable to these shortcomings. In considering the various groups of problems one by one, we shall have occasion to take stock of what is being done about them. It will be apparent, moreover, that they are interrelated.

LAND-TENURE PROBLEMS AND POLICIES

There can be little doubt that an essential aim of American land policy in the past has been the establishment of family-size farms owned by those who operate them. Yet the means adopted have fallen far short of realizing this objective.

Freedom of Disposition

In large measure this failure grows out of the almost unlimited freedom of disposition of property in land that developed in this country. After title passed into private ownership, there were no restrictions on the right of the owner to dispose of the land whenever, however, and to whom he might desire, although a body of State law developed to determine the direction of ownership in case the owner died intestate.

Advocates of freedom of disposition argued, with some truth, that it had the advantages of elasticity and readiness of adjustment to changing conditions, individual and social, and that under it each individual was free to acquire and continue to own the size and type of farm unit he was best adapted to handle. This conclusion rests on the hypothesis that the majority of individuals will act continuously in their own interest and that the individual interest coincides with the social or public interest. In practice this does not always prove to be true. Hence a number of socially undesirable results have followed from complete freedom of disposition of landed property.

Land Speculation

Since a large proportion of the land granted in the prehomestead period and a considerable part of that granted between 1862 and 1891 was not limited by the ability or intention of the grantee to use it, extensive land speculation developed. Land passed from one speculator to another until finally it came into the hands of those willing to put it to use, either directly or through tenants, but usually at an advanced price. Fortunately, failure to limit grants to a size suitable for an operating unit did not result directly, as a general rule, in the creation of large landed estates rented to tenants, such as developed in England and certain continental countries. The preoccupation of the original receivers of large grants with speculation and the predominant concern of large capitalists with investment in the rapidly rising industrial system prevented such a result except in a relatively few instances.

The most serious form of land speculation developed subsequently from the freedom of disposition, which permitted farms and farm land to be bought and sold, or mortgaged, in the open market. This process is not carried on by professional speculators only. To a considerable extent farmers themselves are motivated by the desire for a speculative profit from land. Indeed, purchase has become a principal means whereby farmers may acquire ownership of land whether their primary purpose is farm operation or a subsequent profit from resale.

Thus freedom of disposition has been a principal factor in causing agriculture and interdependent businesses to incur the hazards of fluctuating values of farm real estate, which constitutes about five-sixths of the farm investment. The inflationary influence of the World War resulted in an intense wave of land speculation. Thousands of farmers, amazed by the sudden advance of real estate values, sold their farms and then found it necessary to pay still more to acquire other farms. Many bought far beyond their operating requirements or, encouraged by paper profits, indulged in other forms of extravagance, largely on credit. Mortgage indebtedness increased enormously. Then a long period of decreasing real estate values set in during which much of the security supporting the huge debt structure was gradually washed away. Foreclosures and delinquency increased notably, and much farm real estate passed into the ownership of creditor agencies.

The outbreak of another great war carries the possibility of another speculative orgy, and it is well to consider methods of avoiding it and its unhappy consequences.

It may be hoped that rigorous steps will be taken to prevent credit from becoming again a stimulant and vehicle of land speculation. Undoubtedly an important instrument of prevention lies in farm credit and banking policy. It has been suggested that the imposition of heavy State taxes on profits from resale within a limited period would be an effective deterrent and that the Federal stamp tax on legal documents representing the transfer or encumbrance of real estate might be modified to accomplish a similar purpose. It is possible, too, that the capital gains and surtax provisions of the Federal income tax might have a deterrent effect.

A still more unfortunate consequence of the freedom of disposition which characterizes our system of farm ownership is manifested in the instability of farm tenancy, itself largely a result of freedom of disposition by landowners. Even for owner-operators the ever-present possibility of disposition by sale causes management and improvement policies to be of a more transitory character than they otherwise would be.

Some of the land reformers of the 1850's who were urging adoption of the homestead policy foresaw that the granting of land without restrictions on subsequent disposition, even in limited quantities and on condition of 5 years' occupancy, would result in tenancy and speculation instead of realizing their ideal of family-size farms occupied by home-owning farmers. They therefore proposed that homesteads be alienable by neither sale nor foreclosure but only by exchange, as a farmer might trade a work horse for a riding horse.

The proposal was not adopted, but in the light of later developments there may be reason to regret that it was not approved then, or what would have been better yet, put into effect at the very beginning. Some of our most serious farm-land problems, which now must be dealt with by less drastic but also less effective measures, might thereby have been avoided. Such a far-reaching change now would be revolutionary. It is of interest, however, that in certain projects of the Farm Security Administration restrictions on the right of disposition, looking mainly to preventing speculation and unwarranted subdivision, have been included in contracts for purchase of farms from the Federal Government.

Tenancy and Land-Tenure Policies

In 1935 about three-sevenths of the land in farms was rented either by tenants and croppers or by "owners additional." For better or worse, therefore, that proportion of our farm land was under the immediate control or management of persons who did not own it, except insofar as landlords supervised the management of the land rented.

Assuming private landownership and freedom of disposition, tenancy of the right type may have certain advantages from the standpoint of the tenant himself. Tenancy may afford a means of obtaining the use of a farm without having to invest in land the funds needed to provide operating capital, and particularly without having to incur the hazards of large mortgage indebtedness. If for any reason the farmer is uncertain how long he will remain in a particular location or if he doubts the desirability of a particular farm, tenancy affords him a temporary arrangement or an opportunity to become thoroughly acquainted with the farm before purchasing it. If he is inexperienced, tenancy may provide a period of apprenticeship under an experienced landlord.

For those who have become owners and who, for one reason or another, do not desire to, or cannot, operate their holdings directly, renting to a tenant may provide a convenient alternative.

Not all the poverty, ignorance, ill-health, poor standards of living, lack of social contacts, and even wasteful use of soil frequently found to characterize tenant families are attributable to tenancy as a form of land tenure. On the contrary, poverty, ignorance, inefficiency, and other disabilities may compel people to be tenants. But tenancy may intensify these conditions and be contributory to their development. Whether this is true depends very largely on the type of tenancy—that is, on the relationship between landlords and tenants. Though there are numerous cases and considerable areas where these relationships are reasonably wholesome, by and large the types of farm tenancy prevailing in the United States are probably the worst in the civilized world.

This is due largely to the character of landownership. For a large proportion of the landlords, ownership or intent of ownership of a particular farm may be quite transitory. The landlord may not be a farmer but one who has acquired a farm through inheritance, for speculative purposes, or by foreclosure of a mortgage and expects to sell at the earliest opportunity. Even with intent to continue as owner he may be compelled through financial reverses to sell the farm. Thus for a large proportion of the landlord class there is no continuity of relationship with particular farms, and there is a disinclination to develop a long-time program for farm improvement or a long contract with tenants.

Consequently, the tenant's outlook is uncertain, and this influences his management plans and his attitude toward making improvements or maintaining existing improvements as well as conserving the soil. The difficulty is intensified by the fact that relatively few tenant contracts provide for compensation to the tenant, on termination of his period of occupancy, for improvements made by him. Lacking such provisions by contract or by statute, the common law awards the improvements—even those subject to removal, if they are attached to the land—to the landlord. Another serious consequence of uncertain tenure is a natural disinclination on the part of many tenants to identify themselves with the social life or concern themselves with the welfare and progress of the communities in which they live.

Although an improvement in land-tenure policies alone could not be expected fully to stabilize American farm life or to change habits of exploitation into habits of conservation, policies making for security of tenure can contribute largely toward such ends.

There has long been a large body of opinion favorable to measures to facilitate acquisition of farms by tenant families. The objective would have to be achieved by purchase, and safeguards would have to be employed to insure that ownership would continue in the hands of operating farmers; otherwise we should merely repeat the results of the homestead system, which soon produced widespread tenancy.

The most widely prevalent idea has been to make easy credit available to tenants. It is not always a benefit to a farmer, however, to exchange an obligation to pay rent for an obligation to pay interest. Until a substantial part of the principal is paid, permanence of tenure may be no more assured, particularly under private credit, than under a rental arrangement. For reasons already mentioned, many farmers find a favorable tenant contract with a good landlord preferable to assumption of a heavy mortgage indebtedness.

On the other hand, many tenant farmers are capable of responsible ownership and would be benefited by purchasing under suitable conditions. An important segment of a sound land policy, therefore, is a credit system adapted to the needs of this class. After many years of delay, during which atrocious systems of private mortgage credit prevailed, our Government has evolved policies of public credit better adapted to the requirements of tenants endeavoring to become farm owners—first, the farm land banks (see Agricultural Credit, p. 740) and more recently the Bankhead-Jones Farm Tenant Act of 1937.

The latter marks a distinct advance, embodying advantages not hitherto available. Among these are (1) a rate of interest as low as 3 percent, (2) a very small down payment, (3) 40 years for repayment, on the amortization plan (not an entirely new policy), (4) local committees of experienced farmers to assist in selecting the farm and the purchaser, (5) authority for the Government to require proper care of land and improvements, (6) prohibition against a second mortgage, and (7) the withholding of title for 5 years to prevent speculative sale.

Funds have not yet been made available by Congress to permit expanding the policy sufficiently to exert a significant influence on our tenant problems, and adequate safeguards against subsequent speculation and development of tenancy have not been adopted. These defects will probably be removed in time.

Various other measures have been proposed to check the increase of farm tenancy, recently estimated at about 40,000 farms a year. One proposal is partial exemption of owner-operated farms from taxation, favorably considered in a number of States. A wider extension of the credit facilities of the farm-loan system has probably aided some operating owners to avoid slipping back into tenancy. The rehabilitation program of the Farm Security Administration has supplied a combination of credit and technical guidance to numerous tenants too poor and too technically incompetent as yet to look forward to early purchase of a farm, even under the Bankhead-Jones Act. Some of them gradually build up to the stage where they are prepared to climb onto the higher rung of the ladder. Measures to prevent excessive speculation would remove an important cause of the reversion of farmers from ownership to tenancy.

Parallel in importance with policies that seek to convert tenants into owners or prevent reversion from ownership to tenancy are measures aimed at improving the character of the relationship of tenants and landlords.

The British have developed, through many decades, a body of practical legislation and administrative arrangements providing for (1) compensation at the expiration of their contracts for improvements made by tenants, (2) compensation to the tenant for unwarranted and arbitrary termination of the agreement by the landlord or even for refusal to renew it, and (3) compensation to landlords for waste committed by tenants.

In this country, certain constitutional difficulties and established attitudes in public opinion and in the courts tend to impede the fullest development of these lines of policy. Nevertheless, initial legislation pointing in some of these directions is being sympathetically considered in several States.

An important gap in existing land policy is the lack of an adequate small-holdings program, such as has been developed in a number of other countries. A large class of potential tenants and owners of small holdings now drift about aimlessly looking for casual and precarious employment, who for reasons of general social welfare should be rooted in the soil. In the main they are people of farming experience and background and would prefer country life if they could have a dependable foothold. The credit provisions of the Bankhead-Jones Act could probably be adapted to meet this need, except that in many areas there is need for subdivision of large holdings and the construction of necessary buildings.

Range Problems

The range problems of the West are distinctive, as compared with pasture problems elsewhere, largely because of the extensive areas of public domain and State-owned land involved. Until the passage of the Taylor Grazing Act in 1933, the remaining public domain—about 165,000,000 acres—was a grazing common. Anyone was free to use it with no restrictions except those imposed by customary rights more or less supported by public opinion, legislation, and the courts. Since the public domain was widely interspersed with privately owned and State-owned land and since Federal statutes prohibited fencing Federal land, the greater part of the area was unfenced. Inevitable consequences were a continual scramble to get as much grass as possible, serious impairment of range resources, deterioration of herds, and intensified financial instability due to lack of provision for feed reserves for unusually dry years.

The Taylor Grazing Act was a notable legislative departure from the previous policy—or lack of policy—in that it authorized temporary withdrawal of public domain from homestead entry and provided for the formation of districts within which public domain is leased to stockmen under regulations looking to range conservation, formulated and applied by the stockmen themselves subject to Federal supervision.

In order to achieve greater control, conservation, and stabilization on the extensive areas of privately owned land interspersed with the public domain, stockmen have formed cooperative grazing districts, in some cases under special legislative authorization, to lease the privately owned land and regulate its distribution and use.

Size of Holdings

In many cases holdings are too small for economical operation under the type of farming required. This is especially serious in the western Great Plains. The ill-advised application of homestead policies to this territory divided the land into small units of 320 or 640 acres, where operating units of several sections are requisite. Ownership is in the hands of widely scattered absentee owners, many of whom have a wholly incorrect idea of the rental or sale value that could be sustained under a range economy. It is therefore extremely difficult for ranchmen to effect a consolidation of these scattered units.

Representatives of the United States Department of Agriculture have been trying to arrange 10-year leases between existing owners and farm operators needing larger holdings; but leases sufficiently long and on suitable rental terms are difficult to obtain, since a large proportion of the land is held for early resale.

Under the so-called submarginal land program, to be discussed, large areas have been repurchased by the Federal Government during the last few years, with a view to creating operating units of adequate size and thereby repairing the damage wrought by homestead policies in that section.

The situation in the Great Plains is paralleled in many parts of the South, not because of the homestead system but because of the necessity of replacing the cotton economy with a more extensive type of farming.

THE SUBMARGINAL LAND PROBLEM

Numerous farm families, estimated at 500,000, are on land so poor that it will not maintain a decent standard of living. The situation is due partly to original mistakes in the selection of land and partly to subsequent deterioration through soil depletion and the cutting of timber. Frequently, also, the operating unit is of insufficient size.

In hilly or mountainous areas, such as the southern Appalachians, moreover, a large proportion of the population is accustomed to a scanty self-sufficing economy, and it is doubtful whether any but the younger people could adjust themselves successfully to a commercial type of farming. The problem is further aggravated by the high rate of natural increase of population and insufficient emigration.

Where the problem presents these characteristics it is probable that solutions will have to take the direction largely of helping these families to improve a self-sufficing economy through the application of intelligence and cooperation. Their labor resources might be employed to achieve better houses and household equipment, a more rational diet, and greater cleanliness and sanitation and to develop forms of recreation that can be accomplished through collaboration of neighbors.

Where natural resources are hopelessly insufficient, even for a self-sufficing economy, resettlement of families should be associated with Government purchase of their land and its employment for forests, parks, wildlife refuges, and other public services. The public purchase of submarginal land on a wider scale is justified in many areas where families handicapped by inadequate natural resources or holdings of inadequate size are of a type capable of adjusting themselves readily to a new environment. Hitherto, however, the Federal program aimed at these objectives has not been supplemented by an adequate program of resettlement.

An important objective in the public purchase program is an improvement of the general pattern of population distribution in sparsely occupied areas, in the interest of eliminating unnecessary public expenditures for roads, schools, electric power lines, and other public services.

A program of Federal purchase of land aimed primarily at these objectives was carried on for several years following 1934 through the employment of relief funds, and over 9,000,000 acres, mostly of farm land, was acquired and improved for use as forests, recreation areas, game refuges, ranges, and other purposes. Under title III of the Bankhead-Jones Farm Tenant Act, Congress authorized the expenditure of $50,000,000 over a 3-year period for these purposes, but only about one-third of that amount has been appropriated.

Tax Delinquency

Closely related to the problems just discussed is extensive tax delinquency, a result partly of widespread economic distress in rural areas, especially those characterized by inadequate natural resources and unduly small holdings, and partly of the unwillingness of large timber owners to continue tax payments after cutting the timber. As a consequence of tax delinquency local governments are seriously embarrassed financially, large areas remain unused or underused, and land titles fall into confusion.

In virtually all of the States tax-delinquency legislation has been based on the theory that tax-delinquent land should be resold. A usual practice is to offer tax certificates for sale, subject to redemption by the owner during a period of several years. In case of failure to sell, the county or other unit of government bids in the certificate. In case of failure to redeem, the county, State, or other governmental unit may take title. In many cases, however, existing laws do not permit the public agency to obtain a clear title, and there is no adequate policy for administration of the land even if title is obtained. Yet much of the tax-delinquent land is better adapted to public administration than to private utilization, and there is little private demand for the tax certificates except as a temporary investment or for the purpose of still further wrecking the land by cutting remaining odds and ends of timber.

More realistic procedures, based on adequate land classification, are needed to distinguish the areas adapted to private utilization from those on which public administration would be in the public interest. Tax-delinquency legislation should facilitate the passage of title of the latter class of areas into public ownership, and public purchase should be employed to facilitate the blocking of scattered units of tax-delinquent land reverting to public ownership.

Prevention of Socially Undesirable Settlement

Occupancy of submarginal lands, tax delinquency, and socially costly patterns of occupancy are due to lack of a program of guidance and direction of land settlement in the public interest.

State legislation was long concerned with attracting settlers through the activities of State immigration departments, with little regard to methods or results. In recent years legislation in some States has been aimed at affording settlers a measure of protection against misrepresentation by unscrupulous land salesmen, by establishing State real estate boards and passing of blue-sky laws. One State, Wisconsin, has undertaken to apply zoning laws to prevent scattering occupancy that increases the expense of providing local public services. To some extent it is possible to employ State or Federal subventions for roads or schools to a similar end. Some of the Western States have endeavored to prevent issuance of irrigation bonds for enterprises technically or economically unsound. Administration of public credit could also be so directed as to discourage occupancy of land incapable of yielding a reasonable standard of living.

These various restrictive or preventive measures, however, will be adequate only if they can be based on an effective classification of land, and merely restrictive measures are likely to prove less effective than a positive public program for guiding land settlement and shaping its character from the standpoint of individual and general welfare. Various experiments in this direction have been made by certain States and by the Federal Farm Security Administration. So far, however, no comprehensive program has been established.

Land-settlement policy, as well as other agricultural policies, is at present handicapped by the poor balance between rural and urban population mentioned earlier. If our industrial economy could be so reshaped as to afford adequate and dependable employment for the surplus rural population, land-settlement policy could be aimed at achieving and maintaining a population balance that would assure a comfortable standard of living from commerical farming. If adequate outlets into industrial employment cannot be provided, a land-settlement program will have to be developed in the direction of a more nearly self-sufficient economy for a larger number of families than could maintain an adequate living standard under commercial farming. An early determination of the outlook and a shaping of settlement policies is accordingly highly desirable.

Reclamation

A similar uncertainty affects judgment as to reclamation, through irrigation or drainage, at public expense or by public subsidies. If agriculture is to be predominantly commercial and to suffer from restricted markets, additional reclamation at public expense will present a different problem from that if there is to be a redundant population that must be supported under a self-sufficing economy, with no good land available that can be spared from commercial agriculture.

After trying various expedients to encourage reclamation of public land by private enterprise, the Federal Government embarked in 1902 on a policy of subsidized reclamation. The program has met with certain financial difficulties, but it has not been on a very large scale in relation to the agriculture of the Nation as a whole, and it has created a number of agricultural oases in the midst of extensive arid areas.

Another recently developed phase of irrigation policy has been aimed at facilitating irrigation of small units of land on existing farms and ranches, in order to stabilize the farm economy by providing a supplementary source of feed or by enabling farmers to raise a more diversified supply of food for family use. One such policy is the Water Facilities Act of 1937, under which the Department of Agriculture is authorized to facilitate construction on private lands of inexpensive water facilities, such as wells, pumps, small reservoirs, and diversion dams. Recently funds were appropriated to enable the Department of the Interior to construct small reservoirs.

Soil Conservation

Abuses under private landownership in the United States have resulted in extensive impairment of soil resources. It has been estimated that over 50,000,000 acres of cropland has been essentially destroyed, that more than three-fourths of the original surface soil has been lost on 282,000,000 acres of all types of land, with considerable losses on other large areas, and that 75 percent of the cropland areas of the United States reported by the 1935 census are in need of conservation practices.

Until the Soil Erosion Service—which later became the Soil Conservation Service—was established in 1933, there were no public policies for dealing with these menacing problems. A comprehensive program was then inaugurated to determine the most feasible technical methods, to awaken the general public to the seriousness of the problem, and particularly to stimulate farmers to adopt measures to check soil depletion and to repair its ravages.

To the latter end, small watersheds, ranging from 8,000 to 200,000 acres but typically about 25,000 acres, were selected to demonstrate the value of soil conservation practices to farmers and the aggregate results for the watershed as a whole in reducing damage from floods or siltation. The Soil Conservation Service entered into a 5-year cooperative contract with each farmer willing to have the program developed on his farm. Generally, the farmer agreed to supply a considerable part of the requisite man and team labor. The drawbacks of this method are its relative slowness and costliness and a lack of certainty as to the extent and permanence of its influence.

During the last 2 years there has been a shift in the method of attack from action by bureaus of the Government in cooperation with individual farmers to control and direction by groups of farmers themselves organized in specially created conservation districts, with the planning and technical assistance of the Soil Conservation Service. The original individual cooperative projects are being carried out, but the emphasis has changed to the district approach. Soil conservation districts are created under general enabling acts, which have been passed by the legislatures of all but a few States. As an organized governmental unit, the district has wide powers for promotion, education, and cooperation, with the consent of the land occupiers affected, and under the police power can pass ordinances compelling action, subject, however, to a majority referendum vote of the land occupiers. Thus far principal emphasis has been placed on the educational and cooperative, rather than on the compulsory, functions.

To a large degree, however, some of the most serious obstacles to conservation of the soil and timber resources are not overcome by the types of conservation policies thus far described. These obstacles include cost-price relationships, which cause many of the necessary conservation measures to be unprofitable to the individual operator; differences in the individual and the public interest in evaluating goods and income in the remote future; forms of land tenure that prevent the operator from having an economic interest in conservation; sizes of farm units too small to permit the type of husbandry that will promote conservation; and lack of capital.

In recognition of these economic obstacles the Conservation and Domestic Allotment Act, which succeeded the original Agricultural Adjustment Act, provides a system of subsidies to stimulate the adoption of certain practices considered favorable to soil and range conservation.

Flood Control

The problem of soil wastage is intimately bound up with the problem of flood control. Inadequate soil cover, lack of moisture-absorbing soil structure, and the cultivation of steep slopes make for rapid run-off and increase the momentum of water movement, intensifying its destructiveness to the soil itself as well as causing damage in other ways. Accumulations of soil materials in stream channels, resulting from erosion, tend to fill reservoirs with silt and to prevent streams from carrying off abnormal volumes of water.

Until recently flood-control policy has been confined to the engineering work of the War Department in constructing levees, diversion channels, and storage reservoirs, and in channel straightening, mostly on the lower courses of major streams. By the Flood Control Act of 1936 and supplementary legislation the Department of Agriculture was authorized to engage in what has come to be known popularly as "upstream engineering." This takes the form of various land use measures, supplemented by minor engineering works, to retard the flow of water into and through the innumerable small tributary streams and thereby prevent or lessen the aggregation of floodwater in destructive volume.

Farm Forestry

About 185,500,000 acres of woodland, nearly 30 percent of the total forest area of the continental United States, is included within the boundaries of farms. In extensive areas these important resources have been very wastefully used, partly through ignorance of methods of forest management and partly because of economic pressure on farmers for the realization of immediate income. In recognition of the important public interest involved, the Cooperative Farm Forestry Act passed in 1937 aims to provide a comprehensive program of assistance to farmers in making more effective use of their woodlands and conserving their timber. The act strengthens and extends arrangements for supplying farmers with technical information and with seedlings and other planting stock and for direct cooperation with farmers. An appropriation of $2,500,000 annually is authorized for this purpose.

LAND POLICIES OF THE IMMEDIATE FUTURE

The task of the immediate future consists mainly in further development along the main lines of advance already established, with modification of detail in the light of experience, improvement of machinery and methods of administration, and amplification of the scope of some of the measures. It will be desirable also to fill some of the gaps indicated in this article, such as the lack of an adequate small-holdings program and of suitable arrangements for improving the landlord-tenant relationship. Especially is it important to effect a closer integration of the various policies. This is being accomplished in part through local and regional planning and through various other measures.

The Challenge of Conservation

by Bushrod W. Allin and Ellery A. Foster[1]

"WE DREAMED a great dream, of freedom and abundance," say the authors of this article; and they proceed to tell what that American dream was. Many things in this dream have come to pass, but many other things have not; they tell why and in what ways so much of our rich heritage has been wasted. Then they ask what needs to be done, and they sum up the needs in a few brief statements that constitute the challenge of conservation. That challenge is not to abandon the dream but to stick to it. The fight has merely shifted to new frontiers, and we can win it if we have a tough-minded realization of what those new frontiers are. This article is essentially a contribution to an American credo.

NORTH AMERICA has seen a swift and spectacular wasting of resources on a grand scale, particularly in the last 50 years. The western range lands have been ravaged and gullied as a result of overgrazing. Rivers have been contaminated by the dumping of filth until they are no longer habitable for fish or useful for recreation or fit for domestic water supply. Torrents of water rushing off stripped

[1] Bushrod W. Allin is Principal Agricultural Economist and Ellery A. Foster is Senior Agricultural Economist, Division of State and Local Planning, Bureau of Agricultural Economics.

hillsides have intensified the savagery of floods, destroying property and lives and choking stream channels and costly reservoirs with sediment. "Inexhaustible" forests vanished before the combined onslaughts of ax and fire. Forest fires, burning uncontrolled, wiped out not only forests, but towns and human lives as well. The land itself in many sections suffered a fate similar to that of the forest, and ghost farms, like ghost towns, mark regions where the exploitation was fiercest (fig. 1). Less important than these, but indicative, is the fact that the passenger pigeon was exploited to extinction, the American bison to near extinction.

CAUSES OF EXPLOITATION

What forces caused this exploitation—this waste—in contrast with more thrifty policies that might have been pursued? The answer is not simple.

One of the chief reasons our ancestors left Europe was to find freedom. They desired to escape the oppression of the Old World. One of the restraining influences there was the necessity for conserving the natural resources. Conservation therefore seemed to be one of the distasteful restrictions of liberty that the colonists were trying to escape. To top it off, the abundance of resources that the early settlers found, together with glowing reports of still more plentiful resources to the west, made it easy to develop the legend of inexhaustibility which early arose to condone exploitation. At the same time, this legend was a convenient excuse for not allowing money making to be hampered by conservation, an excuse for ignoring the Old World necessity of husbanding the resources out of which money can be made. Even this situation was not simple, however. Undoubtedly the great need

Figure 1.—"Ghost farms" as well as ghost lumber towns mark the path of exploitation.

throughout the early days was to develop and use the natural resources of the country. Few, if any, foresaw that they would be developed with a speed unparalleled in history, so that there was real danger of going too far. Even so, the greatest destruction took place after many people well knew what was happening. There was much mention of soil exhaustion and the necessity for both building the soil and turning it to more scientific uses in the early reports of the commissioners of patents and agriculture, but soil conservation was then visualized as an individual, not as a national, problem.

Mortgages, tenancy, absentee ownership of farms have been among the major forces causing exploitation in more recent times. They have tended to put extra pressures on the land to produce more. At the same time, thay have tended to discourage conservation and to make it economically difficult for the farmer to put anything back to maintain soil fertility. As evidence, the value of tenant-operated farms showed a greater proportionate decline from 1930 to 1935 than that of owner-operated farms.

Absentee financial control is one of the outstanding devices through which economic forces have encouraged exploitation. For example, in a forest region, if the local people, including the landowners, could vote on how the forests were to be handled, they probably would insist in many cases upon sustained-yield operations under which local timber industries could have permanent life. The creditors of the forest owners, however, particularly if they live at a distance, are frequently more interested in liquidating their investments than in developing permanent industries in rural sections. In fact, as long as absentee private owners and creditors have complete control, forest destruction will probably be a common practice where there is timber to be exploited.

The demands of modern war have been a primary force encouraging exploitation. Extensive plowing of the western plains for wheat growing was a direct result of the 1914–18 war. The consequences were felt even on the eastern seaboard, where dust from the Great Plains hung in the air like a pall in the drought periods of 1933 and 1935. War made its impact felt on many soils besides those of the Great Plains and on many resources besides soils. Under war conditions, the temptation was even greater than in peacetime to "mine" the soil—to take as much from it as possible without putting anything back. Steep hillsides were plowed, and the rains were allowed to wash the topsoil away. War demands hastened the cutting out of many hardwood lumber operations in West Virginia and adjacent mountain regions, and greatly accelerated the movement of the industry into the last great hardwood reserves, those in the Mississippi Delta.

Conditions after the World War brought new economic forces that encouraged exploitation and strengthened old destructive forces. Failing markets for farm produce resulted in economic pressure on the individual farmer to keep on mining the soil. As more and more farmers became tenants, the pressure on the soil resources became greater; the man who did the farming no longer had an owner's interest, and the land often had to support two families where it had formerly supported one. Not only increased tenancy but also more and heavier mortgages encouraged exploitive farming. Widespread destructive cutting of southern second-growth timber was a direct result of the post-war crisis in cotton. When cotton slumped from 20 cents to 6 cents, the farmers turned to the forest lands that make up 60 percent or more of the area of most Southern States, where the second growth had started to bring the timber back. They went to work logging trees that in many cases had not yet grown big enough either to make good lumber or to yield decent returns to operators or employees, most of whom were farmers.

Abundant resources and freedom to exploit them naturally led Yankee ingenuity to find ways to exploit more efficiently. Thus, technology has played a part. For example, logging methods became more efficient in getting the timber out of the forest; but at the same time they became more destructive of the forest itself.

In this new country of ours, government—which in older countries was the chief force on the side of conservation— for more than a hundred years has simply acted in accord with the dominant attitudes of the people. Americans not only disliked anything that smacked of regimentation; they also felt that the best way for government to encourage growth of the new country was to give private initiative the freest possible hand in developing and using natural resources.

Not only were valuable resources given away to private interests with no strings attached, but even publicly owned or controlled lands have been subject to fierce exploitation. Farm lands, publicly owned or controlled through various agencies or institutions, have usually been, and to a large degree still are, managed with little or no more regard for conservation than the average privately owned farm. As late as 1933 vast areas of western range lands—Government-owned—were open to free public use for stock grazing with no regulation whatever. Although the giving of natural resources to private individuals with no restrictions on use or exploitation was the chief means by which Government aided and abetted waste, yet some of the worst exploitation has been on these range lands, which remained in public ownership but over which practically no conservation control was exercised, either public or private. As another example, the vast public domain of Alaska has been given virtually no protection and even today is still ravaged by fires which at one sweep burn millions of acres, damaging the soil and destroying timber, forage, and wildlife.[2]

WHAT IS CONSERVATION?

Conservation is a very old idea. Centuries before America was discovered, Chinese scholars wrote comprehensively and understandingly of it. Yet China has been one of the most backward nations in practicing conservation.

Despite the predominance of the exploitive philosophy, even in the early days individual Americans realized the evils of exploitation. George Washington was conscious of the bad results of soil erosion,

[2] In contrast with the range lands, the Alaskan public domain, and publicly owned or controlled farm lands, the national forests have been under conservation management since as early as 1891 in the States and 1892 in Alaska. The former cases represent the old policy of the U. S. Government in conservation, and the national forests the new policy, which was not adopted all at once but which has found its place gradually, spreading from one program and one agency to another.

and he not only wrote about it but developed methods for checking it on his lands in Virginia. Here, as in China, the problem has not been lack of scientific knowledge of what to do so much as difficulty in getting the principles of conservation accepted and the simple effective conservation measures practiced.

To understand conservation, it is helpful first to recall that in a real sense the basic wealth of a nation consists of its natural resources—soils, waters, minerals, forests, range lands, and wildlife. In its broadest meaning, conservation deals with the preservation and development of all forms of public values; but in the usual sense it deals with natural resources, and it is so treated here.

From the standpoint of conservation, natural resources are divided into two main groups. One of these comprises the resources that under good management produce a growth or an increase, renew themselves, or can be maintained indefinitely as a continuing source of new wealth. Soils, forests, range lands, wildlife, and to some extent water resources are in this category. The other group includes the resources that are depleted or used up by use, even under the best management. Iron, coal, oil, and other mineral resources are in this category. These categories represent, respectively, the fields of agricultural conservation and mineral conservation. The objectives and the methods in these two fields are quite different. Agricultural conservation aims primarily to preserve and in some cases to build up the wealth that produces the growth. Mineral conservation aims primarily to husband and to prevent the waste of resources that inevitably dwindle with use. In general, public interest in conservation has encompassed both of these fields, often without distinguishing between them.

The viewpoint is too often encountered that conservation means essentially giving up or foregoing something today in order to have it tomorrow. In other words, the belief is widespread that conservation must be expensive in terms of present income—that it always looks entirely to the future. This is an inaccurate view. Conservation does not necessarily mean using less today. It does mean wasting less. It is a matter of husbandry, or good management practices. Good conservation practices frequently are no more costly to apply than destructive ones. Sometimes they cost less.

It frequently does cost something to shift from wasteful or destructive practices to conservative ones, but the cost of doing this cannot be measured solely in relation to direct money returns, as private investors ordinarily reckon such costs. Nor can it be compared with complete accuracy to such expenditures as those for schools, police, and highways, which are a continuing source of expense. Rather, the cost of shifting from exploitation to conservation is a special sort of cost that a well-organized society should need to stand but once.

Another view sometimes advanced is that agricultural conservation may add to the problem of adjusting agricultural production to effective demand. It is pointed out, for example, that by conserving and building up soil fertility, a greater productive capacity will result than if exploitive methods were followed. It is sometimes asked, also, whether forest conservation might not result in such an abundance of timber that stumpage prices would decline to less than the costs of growing it. Such things could happen, but in determining the best way to meet these problems it is necessary to recognize that the world is not static, but changing. Effective demand in the future may be much greater than at present, if for no other reason than that potential demand is now much greater. Certainly it would seem that we should look forward to the possibility of increasing effective demand and that it is the direst folly to continue the waste and destruction of natural resources merely because of the possibility that conservation might result in a greater product than markets will absorb at present prices and incomes.

There is no incompatibility between conservation and year-to-year control over the extent of use of the total productive capacity. For example, limits could be placed at any time on the acreage to be used for particular farm crops. A similar limit might be placed on the amount of timber to be cut from the forest. In this way, reasonable control might be exercised over prices. Through allocation of quotas, a fair distribution might be made of the total market opportunity.

But to rely on a scarcity of basic resources as a means of controlling current production is to create difficulty or delay in increasing production in response to expanding markets, if not to prevent such increase. Would this not be a defeatist or negative policy, inconsistent with the hopes and aspirations of a democratic society?

Conservation in a democracy means wise use of resources for the greatest good of the greatest number in the long run. This objective means that conservation must be concerned with more than the physical condition of natural resources themselves. It means relating the management of resources to the welfare and betterment of the people as a whole.

Beginnings of the Conservation Movement

As the disastrous effects of exploitation began to appear in more and more places, a strong sentiment developed among civic-minded people to stop such destruction and waste, even though it meant sacrificing some of their precious American liberty. The people of the United States gradually awoke to the need for conservation.

Active public interest in conservation was first rewarded in 1871, when growing concern over the decline of fisheries resulted in the creation of the office of United States Commissioner of Fish and Fisheries. A memorial of the American Association for the Advancement of Science 2 years later started the movement that led ultimately to the establishment of the Forest Service.[3]

Subsequent milestones, each marking the beginning of a particular phase of conservation, were: Creation of the Division of Economic Ornithology and Mammalogy (1886), which later became the Bureau of Biological Survey; the act of Congress empowering the President to proclaim public lands as forest reserves (1891); the changing of the forest reserves into "national forests" (1905), with a change of policy from "no use" to "wise use"; the beginning of the soil survey (1899); an act to protect Alaskan fisheries (1906); establishment of the Inland Waterways Commission (1907); creation of a mining technology

[3] TRYON, F. G. CONSERVATION. In Encyclopaedia of the Social Sciences v. 2 (v. 3–4 of orig. ed.), pp. 227–230. 1937.

223761°—40——28

branch in the United States Geological Survey (1907), which later became the Bureau of Mines; and the organization of the National Conservation Commission (1908). In large degree the purposes of the agencies set up in this period were informational and investigative.

From 1908 to the 1930's the principal advances in conservation were in the assembling and arranging of the facts that finally began driving home to citizens of the United States the truths that this country's resources are not inexhaustible and that, owing to a more violent climate and more unstable natural conditions, conservation is even more necessary here than in Europe.

During this same period, modest beginnings were made in 1911 in the Federal purchase of lands for national forests in the eastern United States, and in 1920 Congress passed the Mineral Leasing Act and the Federal Water Power Act.

While these events were taking place in the Federal Government, many States were organizing conservation agencies to deal with game and fish, with State-owned lands, with drainage and waters, with State forests and parks. For the most part, little was done by local agencies of government, the responsibility being left primarily with the State and Federal Governments.

Up to the last decade the large-scale conservation accomplishments were in the national forests and the public parks, and in cooperative forest-fire protection. Some of the States attempted conservation of wildlife, with varying degrees of success, but little public effort had been made to encourage conservation of soil, and even the public range lands were still being fiercely exploited.

Aside from work done in the western national forests, scientific forestry was being applied only to the dregs of forests, where attempts were made to nurture the little growth left as the aftermath of destructive logging instead of preventing devastation before it happened. While substantial progress was made in protecting private as well as public forests from insects, diseases, and fire, much of the forest land still does not even have fire protection, and practically nothing has been done to protect private forests from unwise cutting. Virtually nothing has yet been accomplished to correlate the American timber industry with the growth of American forests. In one locality logging operations take everything, including small trees that should be allowed to grow for many years. In other stands, timber worth logging and ripe for the ax dies and rots in the woods.

CONSERVATION AS A NEW FRONTIER

Apparently economic and social crises were necessary before a majority of American statesmen and other leaders would seriously consider conservation as a field for action rather than mere talk and study. The crisis of 1929, deepening into the near-calamity of 1932 and 1933, spurred Americans, individually and through colleges, research agencies, and Government, to make a searching study to find out what was wrong.

As Americans have traditionally depended upon the frontier in time of economic crisis, these searchers for a solution of more modern problems looked for new frontiers—frontiers for idle men and idle money. Students of the depression—layman as well as scientist—found that the frontier of new land was gone. They found westward migrants of the depression surging against the Pacific coast and eddying back, still drifting, in misery, want, and insecurity. Most investigators found once-fertile lands, their fertility washed or blown away, where the people either clung on in poverty or drifted away to relief rolls in the towns or to live as vagrants on the highways.

Others found the timber gone in regions where humming sawmills once meant payrolls and prosperity. There they found the people idle, and the stripped lands idle too. They found destructive logging that was taking everything from the woods—capital and all, spelling the doom of timber towns; and lumbering operations in young, half-grown forests that yielded only a pittance to the farmer loggers (fig. 2). At the same time, they found other timber that was ready for logging going to waste in the woods.

They looked then to industry. With many factories idle or partly idle, the thoughtful have asked, Why build more factories until we are able to distribute the products of those we already have?

As a result of this searching, many people, inwardly even though they may not have expressed it, apparently came to a conclusion which might be stated as follows:

We dreamed a great dream, of freedom and abundance.

We solved the problem of production with a technology such as the world had never seen. We made machines our slaves to do the work. We did it in freedom to exploit the stored resources of a rich continent, resources which fed the machines and fed, clothed, and housed us.

Now we are faced with other problems.

One of them we share with the entire world. That is the problem of learning

Figure 2.—Lumbering operations in young, half-grown forests yield only a pittance to the farmer loggers because the trees are too small for economic logging.

to produce for peace and not for war, for the improvement of life and not for its destruction.

Closely linked with this problem of producing for peace is the problem of distribution. We have to learn to distribute what is produced for peace—to keep money circulating—so that factories will not be blighted with idleness and people with want and insecurity until they are desperate enough to accept war.

Inextricably related to these two problems is that of conservation—of conserving the resource foundations under farms and factories, under life itself. For too long we condoned exploitation in the name of liberty and with the excuse that it was necessary to develop the country. Today conservation offers us a new frontier for investing idle money and idle labor to underwrite production and defense, to renew the American dream.

The increasing interest in conservation is not due alone, however, to a new economic understanding. Much of the interest arises from an improved understanding of less tangible values. This is popularly characterized by the longing of many present-day Americans to restore the "old swimmin' hole" of their boyhood, so that their sons can thrill to joys their fathers knew. The longing is, of course, for more than swimming holes. It is the need of a people who love the outdoors to get away from factories and offices, away from farms and towns, and go where they can swim, picnic, hike, ride, boat, fish, ski, hunt—in short, where they can play. They want playgrounds where the whole family can play, each to his liking; playgrounds where, for example, there are swings and sand boxes and a wading pool for the children, a place where mother can read or visit in the shade, and a stream where dad can go fishing. People are turning to conservation to preserve one of the basic American liberties, that of access to open country for recreation, including hunting and fishing (fig. 3).

Even the combination of a new economic understanding with the desire for outdoor recreation does not fully account for the increased interest in conservation. Many people have become interested

Figure 3.—Conservation enables sons to thrill to joys their fathers knew.

Figure 4.—Conservation means preserving the soil—the foundation under our farms and under our industries. Contour tillage and strip cropping help to do this.

through seeing what happens to the quality of human beings when the land washes away or when the forest is cut over and sawmills shut down. They have learned that "land is life," not only in an absolute sense, but also in a relative sense. Productive land can mean a better life. When soils wash or blow away or when their fertility is sapped by improper cropping, poor land is left. Liberty to exploit indiscriminately has its sequel in liberty to starve. When people settle on land that is poor they are doomed to a poor life.

The poverty, misery, ignorance, and disease of populations long stranded where the soil is inherently poor or where the sawmills once were and where the land is not fit or not needed for farming have shocked many people into becoming interested in conservation. These people are interested primarily in building up and conserving human qualities. They see conservation—wise use—of soil, of forest, of range lands as a fruitful means to humanitarian ends.

Does all this mean that we as a Nation have at last come to look upon our land as a place in which to settle down and live instead of just to camp long enough to skim off the cream of the resources and then move on? We have already settled the frontiers of new land. Today we have to build our new frontiers on the foundations of the old. Through conservation, we may yet make the American dream of freedom and abundance come true. But without conservation—conservation wisely and vigorously applied, not merely talked and written about—we may wake up some bleak dawn to find ourselves indeed a poor nation, our chances for permanent abundance vanished or seriously impaired.

RECENT STEPS IN CONSERVATION

This realization of the need for conservation has already resulted in action on a vast scale. The Soil Conservation Service (created as the Soil Erosion Service in 1933) and the agricultural adjustment program, through emphasis on conservation, are designed to get action in applying soil-conservation measures to American farms (fig. 4). The Taylor Grazing Act of 1933 was an action measure to bring the public range lands at last under responsible control and conservation. Expanded public acquisition of forest and submarginal farm lands has been a preface to action in restoring their resources and in meeting the new demands for outdoor recreation. In varying degrees it has also helped to relocate farmers who had been waging a hopeless struggle on poor land. The Civilian Conservation Corps and programs have put thousands to work in conservation.

Out of our experience with these programs, we have learned that conservation can be practiced without impairing our liberties. In fact, we have learned that to safeguard abundance is to insure liberty.

PROBLEMS NEEDING SOLUTION

The job of shifting from exploitive methods to conservation methods can now be said to be fairly begun. But we should not make the mistake of considering what has been done as more than a beginning. In fact, widespread action has not even been started in one of the greatest fields for conservation—on private forest lands. Many other difficult problems remain to be solved. The more important ones in the agricultural field—farming and forestry—are:

How to get soil conservation applied in a reasonable time on all the farms and range lands that need it.

How to improve the conditions of people living on poor lands and in isolated locations and to prevent further settlement there.

How to solve the problems of private and tax-delinquent forest lands: To protect them adequately from fires, insects, and diseases; to stop destructive timber cutting and at the same time prevent waste of good timber that now dies and rots in the woods; to rebuild forests on millions of stripped acres; to develop and open up nonfarm forest lands for recreation and other public purposes along with timber production.

How to extend shelterbelt plantings, which make farming and farm life better in the prairie regions.

How to divide conservation responsibility between Federal, State, and local Governments and private citizens in the most effective way to get the work done.

How to finance our investments in conservation so they can be treated as such and not as current expenses that threaten us with bankruptcy.

How, if we must supply the demands of war—which too often in the past have been met by unrestrained exploitation—to see that it is done with the highest regard for the laws of conservation.

How to do all these things democratically, with a minimum of restraint on individual liberties.

Altogether, these problems make a huge task, but no greater than some the United States has successfully tackled in other fields.

FARMERS IN CONSERVATION

The farmer not only feeds the world. He is at the same time custodian of its greatest resource—the farm land—and to a considerable extent of the timber and range lands as well. For these reasons, the farmer is a key figure in conservation. In fact the farmer has such a large share of the conservation job that it is only fair for the rest of the people to help him do it, as they are doing through payments for conservation practices under the Agricultural Adjustment Administration, through soil conservation demonstration projects, through aids to farm forestry, and in other ways.

Today the farmer is in an especially responsible position, not only in relation to the conservation of farm lands but of nonfarm lands as well. In many counties farmers' agricultural planning committees have already mapped out, according to their best judgment, the parts of the county which should be used for something besides farming; the areas which should be used for farming; and the questionable areas which should be given further study. In many counties the nonfarming areas make up a very large part of the land.

Figure 5.—A farmers' township committee planning the use of tax-abandoned, cut-over lands in Wilma Township, Pine County, Minn. (Photo courtesy Minnesota Department of Conservation.)

As the farmer committees go on with their work, they find that the way these nonfarming areas are handled has much to do not only with conservation, but also with how well the farmer gets along. For example, in the forest regions, the farmers' taxes are lighter if there are timber industries to share the burden and if settlement in forest regions is not too scattered. Forests, even those not part of the farms, often are an important source of winter income for farmers. In many sections, forest fires endanger the farms as well as the timber. Irrigation water frequently depends on mountain forests. Nonfarm range lands provide seasonal forage for farm livestock. Local forests in good condition mean low-cost farm lumber and the saving of freight costs. Farmers, as much as any other group, are interested in using wild lands for recreation, especially for hunting.

These relationships between nonfarm lands and the farmer's welfare can be improved chiefly through solving conservation problems. Farmers' agricultural planning committees are taking an interest in planning for rural land use and for agricultural conservation as a whole, not merely for land in farms. For example, they plan the zoning of nonfarm lands against certain types of use so as to save on road, school, and other costs (fig. 5). They are striving to develop constructive programs for tax-delinquent lands. They seek means of handling large forest holdings as well as farm woodlands in ways that will perpetuate and build up local timber industries as sources of taxes, employment, and low-cost farm lumber. In these and other phases of action, farmers are playing an important role in putting agricultural conservation into effect on the land.

Our Soil Can Be Saved

by H. H. Bennett[1]

SOIL CONSERVATION is one of the major problems on which farmers have concentrated a good deal of attention in recent years. Here is a brief summary of the status of our farm soils, followed by a compact account of the principal steps that have been taken to arrest and reverse the trend toward disastrous erosion and loss of soil fertility. The author tells us that the practical results of the joint efforts of farmers and public agencies are already visible. Slowly the patterns of land use are changing. The careful fitting together of the various public programs authorized by the Congress and the States is responsible for much of the gain. But soil conservation cannot be divorced from the general problem of farm income, and in fact the farmer is gradually becoming more aware of the deep interrelationship of all his problems.

THE FORCES OF SOIL DEPLETION

EXAMINED in the light of scientific knowledge, soil depletion is no simple process. It can result from the extraction of chemical elements from the soil, from the break-down of soil structure, or from the actual removal of topsoil. Crops gradually remove the elements

[1] H. H. Bennett is Chief of the Soil Conservation Service.

of fertility from the soil; methods of tillage and rotation have an important effect upon soil structure; and erosion by wind or water removes the entire body of the soil.

The readiness with which the depleting processes start to work and the absence in the past of adequate measures to check those processes have resulted in a rapid and serious change in the fertility and productivity of much of the soil of this country. Farmers and other land users are becoming increasingly conscious of these changes. Thousands of them are faced with a serious condition of soil depletion throughout a major part of the cultivated area of this Nation. It is even more important to recognize that they are also faced with a destructive process of soil depletion, under the influence of which present conditions, however bad, will inevitably become worse. The problem, therefore, is not merely to remedy a condition of soils that is already bad, but to forestall a far more serious impoverishment by checking the forces that are wastefully and needlessly devastating the soils.

Soil Erosion

Soil erosion is the most easily recognized and most readily measured of the soil-depleting forces. Deepening gullies, such as the awesome chasms that break the earth in many parts of the southern Piedmont (fig. 1) and the dust storms sweeping from the surface of the Great Plains, have served to focus public attention on the erosion problem.

Figure 1.—The gullies of Stewart County, Ga., are noted for their enormous size and depth. More than 100,000 acres are affected by gullies 50 to 200 feet deep.

Surveys of the United States indicate that some 50,000,000 acres of once good cropland has been ruined for further cultivation, while another acreage of equal proportions has been badly damaged. This land in all equals the area of the three great Corn Belt States of Ohio, Illinois, and Iowa. In view of this widespread destruction already accomplished, it is significant to note that approximately 75 percent of our total cropland is now subject to soil erosion and therefore threatened with eventual extreme depletion.

Although figures on the destruction of our farm lands through erosion are stupendous, they do not reveal the full significance of the erosion problem to the individual farmer. Reports from localities where detailed surveys of erosion conditions have been made tell the story in more specific terms. In Winona County, Minn., for example—an area located in one of the more fertile farming regions of the United States—land has been classified according to its suitability for cultivation and the conservation practices that are necessary in order to maintain fertility. It was revealed that of the 218,716 acres of cropland in the area surveyed, 42,352 acres, or slightly less than 20 percent, was either so badly eroded, or subject to such severe erosion, that it could no longer be used for cultivation except at prohibitive costs. To balance this loss, there were about 40,000 acres of land now in pasture or woods that could be satisfactorily used for crops. Therefore, even under the most favorable conditions of land use—if all land were used for the most productive purpose to which it is suited—some decrease in crop acreage would be necessary.

A further difficulty is encountered in the fact that the land suited to cultivation is not distributed among the individual farms in equal proportion to the land that should be taken out of crops. A considerable net shrinkage in the land available for crop cultivation in the Winona County area therefore appears inevitable if the processes of soil erosion are to be checked and resources maintained at their present level of productivity or better.

Similar conclusions have been reached as a result of detailed surveys of erosion conditions and land use in other parts of the United States—areas where the degree of erosion is characteristic of relatively large and economically important regions. If American farmers are to prevent further deterioration of soil through erosion, some of the land now in crops must be shifted to pasture or be reforested. This need is recognized in one of the basic principles of the soil conservation program: a more efficient use of all farm-land resources is in many cases essential in order to maintain the individual farmer's income in the face of a considerably decreased crop acreage.

Other Causes of Depletion

Although soil erosion is the most serious and damaging process whereby productivity is being drained from American soils, it is by no means the only one. Cropping annually takes from the soils of the United States thousands of tons of chemical matter needed for plant nutrition. Leaching away of the soluble chemicals from the soil is also an important factor in the depletion of soil productivity.[2]

[2] A more detailed technical discussion of the nature and extent of soil losses from various causes is to be found in Soils and Men, Yearbook of Agriculture 1938.

No thoroughly accurate measurement of these losses of valuable chemicals from the soil is available, but the best possibe estimates indicate that approximately 12,600,000 tons of nitrogen, 15,200,000 tons of potassium, 1,200,000 tons of phosphorus, and 255,000,000 tons of organic matter are taken from the soils of the United States every year by crops, grazing, and leaching.

The Decline of Soil Productivity

One of the most important measurements of the decline in soil productivity is expressed in terms of crop yields. During the last 75 years tremendous improvements have been made in the science of crop production. Chemical fertilizers have been developed and applied in greatly increased amounts. Agronomists have devised better crop rotations and methods of farm management. Plants and seeds have been adapted to the varying conditions of climate and soil. This and other related work should have resulted in a tremendous increase in crop yields; some experts have estimated that acre yields for our major crops should have increased by 40 to 60 percent in the last half century.[3]

But the disconcerting fact is that crop yields have not in fact increased in accordance with scientific progress. In Ohio, for example, the average yields of corn per acre for the State were about the same in 1920–29 as they were in the decade 1870–79. Yet the average use of fertilizer per acre on Ohio farms increased 340 percent from 1890 to 1929. This and similar illustrations point to the conclusion that the steady depletion of soil fertility has often, and perhaps generally, offset advances in the science of agricultural production.

Where crop yields have been maintained in the face of declining soil fertility, it has meant increasing costs of production for a large proportion of the farmers. Records showing the tremendously increased use of artificial fertilizer during the last 50 years indicate one way in which this increased cost has come about. That hundreds of thousands of farmers have been forced below the margin of profitable operation and have necessarily abandoned their lands is another fact bearing out this point. At the present time the Bureau of Agricultural Economics estimates that there are between 500,000 and 600,000 farmers occupying land that is submarginal for crop production at any reasonably probable price level. Although a good portion of this land was originally of such poor character as to be unsuited to cultivation, much of it has been brought to its present unproductive condition by erosion and exhaustion of the soil.

COMBATING SOIL EROSION ON A NATIONAL SCALE

Because of its primary importance as a soil-depleting process, efforts to conserve fertility have centered about the control of soil erosion. It should be strongly emphasized, however, that erosion control as such cannot be considered separately from other factors that contribute to good farm management. As erosion is only one cause of soil depletion, so is erosion control only one means of conserving soil fertility. The best agronomic practices play their part in a soil conservation program

[3] SALTER, R. M., LEWIS, R. D., and SLIPHER, J. A. OUR HERITAGE—THE SOIL. Ohio Agr. Col. Ext. Bul. 175, 20 pp. 1936.

along with the measures aimed directly at preventing soil washing or blowing. Terracing, contour cultivation, and other control measures are intimately linked to the plan of crop rotation and to the assignment of land to its best use. A soil conservation program for any given farm, therefore, involves the treatment of the land according to its adaptabilities, and coordinates into a single tool for soil defense all the necessary protective measures of agronomy, engineering, and farm management.

The fact that soil conservation has become one of the major goals of American agriculture is due primarily to the fact that farmers themselves have awakened to the need for protecting the productivity of their lands and are taking a leading part in the work. One of the best indications of this important fact is shown by the trend of the soil conservation program in the 6 years it has been under way.

Starting in 1933, soil conservation activities of the Federal Government were first focused upon a series of demonstration projects in each major type-of-farming area. All farmers within a given watershed were given an opportunity to enter into a 5-year cooperative agreement. During this time technicians of the Soil Conservation Service surveyed each farm, laid out a system of conservation management, and aided the farmer in applying the new techniques of land use. Through these projects and similar work done in connection with Civilian Conservation Corps camps, and by the cooperative educational work of the agricultural extension services, an understanding of the value of soil conservation was developed among farmers of almost every State.

Today the picture has changed considerably. The Government no longer needs to carry the idea of soil conservation to farmers, for the farmers themselves are now taking the initiative in conservation work. Of particular significance has been the speed with which soil conservation districts have been organized. These local public agencies are established under State laws by majority vote of land users in a given area and are governed by a board of supervisors consisting primarily of locally elected farmers. Soil conservation districts are public bodies with which the Federal and State Governments can enter into cooperative agreements to provide technical help in surveying soil conservation problems and to work out methods for the better use of the land. In the case of soil conservation districts the Soil Conservation Service is cooperating not with individual farmers, as in the demonstration projects, but with locally organized groups of farmers who, on their own initiative, are working out solutions to their soil conservation problems.

Laws providing for the establishment of soil conservation districts have been enacted in 38 States. Under these laws, 314 districts have been organized; they embrace a total area of some 190,000,000 acres, while an equally large acreage is covered by districts in process of organization.

Land covered by intensive soil conservation work for which the Soil Conservation Service has helped formulate plans now amounts to approximately 48,269,000 acres. But approximately 26,000,000 acres of that total consists of large tracts of range land and public lands used chiefly for grazing. Of the 300,000,000 acres of cropland in the United States that are affected by soil erosion, only a small part, therefore, has

Figure 2.—A strip rotation of small grain alternated with a row crop in South Carolina. The small grain will be followed next year by lespedeza.

at this time been effectively placed under conservation management.

What goes on in these areas is more significant than their extent. For each farm signed up under cooperative agreement, a complete plan is worked out by the farmer and technicians of the Soil Conservation Service. Basic to this plan is a revised system of land use. Surveys of soil types, slopes, and erosion conditions determine what land is suited to crop cultivation, what to pasture, and which areas should be devoted to woodland or wildlife cover in order to prevent further soil depletion. On the basis of the improved land use, a plan of crop management and rotation is developed (fig. 2). This in turn is closely interwoven with soil-conserving practices that may include terrace construction, strip cropping, pasture contour furrowing, reforestation, and shifting of some cropland to improved pasture. Generally, the revised farms show a net decrease in crop acreage, although the farmer's income is usually maintained, if not increased, by virtue of better management. Gradually these areas are being blanketed with complete protection against erosion and with improved farming methods that protect the permanent productivity of the soil.

In the demonstration projects the farmer provides the labor and materials, while the Soil Conservation Service offers technical help in running contour lines, constructing waterways, establishing grass or forest cover, and other related tasks. Payments received by the farmer under the Agricultural Adjustment Administration program and rehabilitation loans of the Farm Security Administration often are the means whereby the farmer meets the cost of some of these improvements.

In the case of the soil conservation district, the Service draws up a memorandum of agreement with the district and agrees upon a plan of work in the execution of which the Service will provide specified help, such as technical supervision, the loan of heavy machinery, and at times the labor of a C. C. C. camp. The district, rather than the Service, then executes cooperative agreements with the individual farmers. By working with the soil conservation districts, the Service is able to avoid considerable administrative and organizational work and to concentrate its efforts on the technical problems encountered in planning and executing a local soil conservation program. In the course of its work, the district frequently calls upon State and other Federal agencies for help in accomplishing the objectives set forth in its work plan, and thereby serves as a focal point for the effective coordination of State and Federal action programs.

The extent to which soil conservation districts have been organized is significant evidence that farmers are recognizing the social responsibility involved in the erosion problem. There are other indications of the growing collaboration of neighbors and communities in this work when faced with the necessity for group effort. In the vicinity of Temple, Tex., an area of some 30,000 acres has been put under complete conservation management, every farm being covered by the cooperative agreement and operated in accordance with a conservation plan of management. One of the outstanding features of the work in this area is the construction of a series of terraces that wind their way over parts of six different farms. To accomplish the mutually desired end of adequate soil conservation, the owners of these farms have virtually obliterated their boundary lines insofar as the operation of the farms is concerned. When men can meet the challenge of soil depletion with such realism and practical cooperation, it augurs well for the future of the conservation program.

Pitfalls and Errors

It would be a fallacy, however, to imply that the problem of interpreting and putting into effect a Nation-wide program of planned land use has become a fait accompli. Considerable progress has been made, and soil conservation practices are in effect on tens of thousands of acres of farm land, but on a great many of the Nation's 7,000,000 farms, land is still being farmed in a way injurious to the farmer, the community, the State, and the country.

The difficulties of making the program universal are closely tied up with the character, psychology, and innate conservatism of the American farmer. These frequently manifest themselves in a reluctance to change or to adopt new methods. For example, in the Corn Belt—on land that should be countour-farmed—some farmers still judge the skill of their hands by the straightness of their corn rows.

But the most difficult problem the Soil Conservation Service has had to face has been that of the farmer, often eager and willing to cooperate, who is in definite need of individual instruction and attention in carrying out soil conservation practices on his farm. The Service has neither the equipment nor the personnel to take care of the individual needs of all the Nation's farms. Demonstration farms, demonstration areas, and conservation districts remain the first line of advance toward modern methods of soil conservation.

A third problem has arisen out of the popular misconception that soil conservation farming methods invariably result in lowered farm income. This belief has undoubtedly kept a substantial number of farmers from adopting conservation practices. Yet all the evidence to date indicates that on thousands of farms the introduction of conservation measures and improved farm management will at least maintain, and possibly increase, farm income. The advantages of conservation farming with respect to crop yields have been particularly apparent in the Great Plains, where the presence or absence of water is so decisive in determining the quantity and quality of crops.

In addition, it must be readily admitted that the Soil Conservation Service has made a number of mistakes in the past in carrying forward its share of the soil conservation program. Undoubtedly other mistakes will be made in the future; that is only human. But the number is decreasing and will continue to decrease with experience and progress in research. A great many currently unknown quantities need to be defined, and a number of theories and beliefs need to be subjected to the cold light of scientific investigation. The permanency of soil conservation advances will depend to a considerable degree on the thoroughness and scope of research in the months and years ahead.

ACCOMPLISHMENTS

Meantime, while the Soil Conservation Service has been carrying on intensive control work in cooperation with local groups of farmers and the State extension services, the Agricultural Adjustment Administration has been executing a more widespread but less intensive program. During 1937, under the Agricultural Conservation Act, 3,743,904 farmers were given benefit payments for soil-conserving practices. Some of these farmers, located in soil conservation project areas or districts, used these payments for improvements recommended in the complete farm plan developed with the aid of the Soil Conservation Service. Others, not in those areas, carried out one or more individual practices, such as planting soil-conserving crops, constructing terraces, and restricting grazing on pasture.

The practical results of the joint efforts of farmers and public agencies to conserve the soil resources from further depletion are already visible. Slowly the patterns of land use are changing in accordance with the dictates of conservation. Plow lines are curving around the contours where formerly they cut stiffly up hill and down. Terraces and grassed waterways are carrying safely to the streams waters which formerly rushed seaward with a load of priceless silt from the fields of cotton and corn. Strips of close-growing crops alternating with row crops (fig. 2) are checking erosion, forming the basis of improved rotation plans, and preventing the wind from tearing up the surface of cultivated fields.

One of the most striking examples of a successful effort to stop soil depletion that had reached tragic proportions is the so-called Dust Bowl in the southern Great Plains. In 1935 and 1936 more than 6 million acres of land in this area was subject to severe wind erosion, the consequences of which were dramatized throughout the country in reports of duststorms, abandoned farms, devastated crops, and homeless refugee farm people. Surveys in 1939 revealed that less than 1 million acres was still subject to severe blowing; and this represented largely the outlying fringe of the Dust Bowl area. Increased rainfall, as compared with that of the extreme drought years, was of course a major factor in this restoration of the land to productive use. But conservation practices enabled farmers to utilize the small rainfall as never before, and therefore results were far out of proportion to the actual increase in precipitation, which even during the last few years has been below the long-time average. Planting of cover crops, careful attention to soil moisture before wheat is planted, and the use of strip and contour cultivation have effectively checked soil blowing (figs. 3 and 4). Contour furrowing and basin listing have caught and held the precious rainfall on the croplands and pastures, making it yield the utmost benefit.

The practical advantage of these conservation methods is illustrated by two farms near Hereford, Tex., situated across the road from each other and having practically identical soil and rainfall conditions. One farm, on which no soil- and moisture-conserving practices had been applied, produced 4½ bushels of wheat to the acre in 1938 and 15

Figure 3.—Snow is retained behind furrows plowed on the contour. This method also prevents flooding and assures equal distribution of rain water.

223761°—40——29

Figure 4.—Restoring an overgrazed simiarid range by contour furrowing. These furrows for holding moisture were installed on an Idaho range with the help of C.C.C. labor.

in 1939. On the farm where soil and moisture had been carefully conserved, 23 bushels to the acre were produced in 1938 and 36 in 1939.

The careful fitting together of the various public programs authorized by the Congress and the States has been responsible for much of the gain made in the soil conservation work. Within the responsibilities of the Soil Conservation Service itself lie opportunities to tackle the land use problem on a broad front. The erosion-control work provides the means of protecting soil fertility on lands capable of successful operation as farms or ranches. Added impetus is given this program with private landowners by the water-facilities program under the Pope-Jones Act and the farm-foresty program provided for in the Norris-Doxey Act. The former program, confined to the 17 Western States wherein semiarid conditions exist, enables farmers to obtain help in building stock tanks, dams, water-spreading devices, small irrigation works, and other water developments. These water improvements are being made only on the basis of complete farm plans which indicate how the new structures can most successfully contribute to the productive use and conservation of the entire farm or ranch unit. Projects under the farm-forestry program now being initiated will help the farmer make the most practical use of those areas of his farm that are primarily suited to trees. Plans for farm-forestry developments on individual farms will also be integrated with the complete farm plan for conservation and wise land use.

Some lands, however, are so badly depleted, or were originally so unfertile, that further cultivation of them is impractical regardless of what steps are taken to check erosion. Abandonment of the lands offers no solution to this problem, for the erosion once started is more than likely to continue, particularly in the semiarid regions where wind blowing constitutes the major menace. To cope with such conditions, the Soil Conservation Service is able to purchase submarginal lands and to develop the acquired tracts for nonarable uses, such as grazing.

Approximately 11,000,000 acres of land has now been acquired under the submarginal land program and converted into pastures, ranges, forests, wildlife preserves, and public recreation areas. Much of this formerly submarginal land has been leased to stockmen or farmers living in the purchase areas, which has enabled them to shift to a less intensive type of farming, featuring pasture and livestock in place of cash crops. The land-purchase activities have thus contributed to conservation farming over far greater areas than the acreage to which the Government has actually taken title.

A similar result has been obtained through a special program of cooperation between the Farm Security Administration and the Soil Conservation Service. Rehabilitation loans issued by the former agency have been used to enable farmers on small dry-land farms in the Great Plains to lease additional land and adopt a type of farming—livestock production—better suited to natural conditions. Soil Conservation Service technicians have cooperated in planning farm operations for the enlarged tracts, in order to insure that the productivity of the land is permanently protected.

THE OUTLOOK FOR SOIL CONSERVATION

With realistic recognition of the gains that have been made, we must also take cognizance of the unsolved problems and difficulties that still remain to be overcome before the forces of soil depletion are really checked on American farm lands. The outstanding achievement may perhaps be said to be the conclusive demonstration that soil conservation is practical for the United States, and that this Nation need not see its lands and rural people impoverished as those of other countries have been. In actual accomplishment—in terms of acres under control or of farms placed under conservation management—we have only made a beginning.

Many of the most difficult problems are economic. For example, we have the insecure farm tenant, who, moving to a new farm every 3 years on an average, does not stay in one place long enough to make a conservation program profitable, but on the contrary is under pressure to extract everything he can from his temporary farm. There is the problem of the surplus farm population in areas where soil depletion has already rendered a high proportion of the land unfit for cultivation. Today we have no new free lands to which these people can turn; yet the longer they remain on their rapidly eroding and exhausted acres, the faster the day of eventual failure and ruin approaches. Soil conservation cannot, moreover, be divorced from the general problem of farm income, for whether he be tenant or owner the farmer who is under heavy financial burdens sees no way out of his hand-to-mouth existence with its cruel, slow death to the soil.

The solution of these problems extends far beyond the techniques of soil management. In tackling them the farmer is gradually becoming more aware of the deep interrelationship of all his problems. What he faces is essentially the need of eliminating throughout the structure of his farming system those forces that are contributing to the depletion of his soil, and of building an agriculture that will stand the most severe test of time in safeguarding soil fertility.

The New Range Outlook

by W. R. Chapline, F. G. Renner, and Raymond Price [1]

NOT ONLY farm soils but the range resources of the West have deteriorated until the grazing capacity of the range today is little more than half what it was originally. But a new outlook is now developing, and these authors tell the story of the change. They point out that the complex range pattern, with its multiplicity of overlapping problems, has necessitated several programs the success of which is of vital concern to farmers and stockmen. The interests of farmers and public agencies have been coordinated in the new outlook, and the future looks hopeful.

PARTLY from increasing interest in conservation, but mostly from sheer necessity, a new range outlook is developing. There is a greater appreciation of the intrinsic value and importance to the national welfare of that vast area of land, largely in the West, which supports varying amounts of native grasses and other plants and is most successfully used for livestock grazing, watershed protection, a home for wildlife, and recreational and other uses.

By far the most significant element in the new outlook is the interest of farmers and stockmen in the restoration and better management of the range. Many stockmen, alone or in cooperation with

[1] W. R. Chapline is Chief, Division of Range Research, Forest Service; F. G. Renner is Chief, Division of Range Conservation, Soil Conservation Service; and Raymond Price is Senior Forest Ecologist, Forest Service.

the Federal Government, have reduced their herds to a safe number to maintain the grazing capacity of their ranges, are already handling the grazing on their lands closely in accordance with the best-known range practices, or are interested in gaining greater knowledge of sound management.

CHANGES CAUSING THE NEW OUTLOOK

Of first importance in this new outlook is the dwindling of the once open range. Except for a few rudimentary beginnings of settlement, less than a century ago the territory lying between the Mississippi River and the Pacific coast was a far-flung expanse of prairie, plain, desert, and mountain highlands—a great natural virgin range. The realization that this "great American desert" was a potential source of wealth created a tide of westward expansion. Migrating people moved steadily into this area from the East and the South seeking forage, timber, minerals, croplands, and homes. The coming of the railroads extended this expansion and aided in the settlement of the West. Today, inroads have been made on every part of the western range. Much of the tall-grass prairie of the Midwest, for example, is now devoted to agricultural crops. Lands have not only been taken for crops but also for cities, roads, and other uses in the rapid process of settlement.

The total area of range land in the West today is 728 million acres—about 119 million acres less than it was a century ago, but still nearly 40 percent of the continental land area of the United States. This is not of course in a single open tract. It consists of desert and plain, mountain and plateau, and semidesert areas interspersed with valleys and tablelands. The mountainous forested range lands are largely within the national forests and the more arid lands chiefly within the grazing districts. The remainder consists of tracts of all sizes, many of which are intermingled with croplands and form a mosaic of lands in private, county, State, and Federal ownership.

This intermingling of range and cropland is a second major factor in the new outlook. Grazing on the western range, once independent and almost wholly pastoral, is now an integral part of western agriculture. The growing of livestock on the range, their production on fenced pastures, and crop production are merely different phases of agriculture. Croplands now produce 35 percent of the feed for livestock in the range territory; the balance still comes from range land. On much of the range, livestock production would be very difficult and precarious if crops did not furnish the feed needed to carry the livestock through the winter. Range and ranch are now inseparable. Western agriculture, a 13-billion-dollar enterprise, is in large part a complex of interdependent crop farming and grazing of range land.

The lowered production of the remaining range, resulting from the run-down condition of the basic resource—the forage, with the soil on which it grows—constitutes a third major factor in the new range outlook. In an effort to obtain a living and some profit, to which they are justly entitled, stockmen have attempted to graze too many livestock. Until the last few years, lack of control of the unreserved public domain tempted many stockmen to overuse this range and their own intermingled holdings in order to discourage others from attempting to come in on an already fully stocked area. Moreover, prolonged periods of dry years, with the extremely severe droughts of 1934 and 1936, sapped the vitality of forage already heavily burdened by too-close grazing. While many range holdings have been maintained in satisfactory condition through wise use and some have been restored, in general the whole character of the range has changed. As a whole the capacity of the range for livestock production is 52 percent less now than when it was in virgin condition (*7*).[2]

A large percentage of the range land to the west of the Rocky Mountains is in public ownership of one sort or another, but east of the Rockies the larger part of the range is in private holdings. The more level topography and generally better soils of the eastern part, coupled with rainfall that is better than the average for the whole range area, have rendered it less susceptible to damage through overuse than range farther west. But despite these natural advantages, the vegetation in general is only about half as thick as it was when first used for pasturage. Where once 2 acres was enough on which to graze a cow for a month, now nearly 4 acres is required. A widespread replacement of the native palatable and nutritious plants by unpalatable, less nutritious, and even noxious plants has accompanied this waning of the forage. The hardy short grasses have to varying degree given way to weeds and shrubs of lower value. In eastern Colorado, for example, Russian-thistle, snakeweed, and cactus are now growing in the presence of the better but greatly weakened grass cover. In the Plains the greatest deterioration has come from cultivation followed by abandonment, but the deposition of soil blown from adjacent abandoned or unwisely plowed fields has caused further deterioration of the plant cover on many acres of uncultivated range.

The greater and more widespread deterioration of the forage cover west of the Rockies largely reflects the generally poorer growing conditions and the previous lack of grazing control on the former open, unreserved public domain. In 1935 average deterioration here was estimated to be more than 65 percent. The value of the low-lying, more arid, and naturally scantily vegetated salt-desert shrub type of the Southwest has been reduced on an average by 71 percent. Here, where vegetation, soil, and climate are in delicate balance, the past quarter of a century of drought, intensified by overuse, has had drastic results. On a large part of the semidesert winter range in Utah and Nevada, Russian-thistle has come in after the destruction of the more valuable grasses and palatable shrubs. Private range has also suffered. The foothills surrounding the great central valley of California, for example, which once supported nutritious perennial grasses, now are taken over by introduced annuals—less nutritious plants that dry up early and make sustained livestock production uncertain and more costly. The higher ranges in this western region have deteriorated somewhat less.

Loss in forage cover of the western range has been accompanied by an inevitable soil deterioration (*7*). Destruction or severe weakening and thinning of the highly valuable native plants has resulted in the

[2] Italic numbers in parentheses refer to Literature Cited, p. 457.

loss of an effective soil-protective cover. This loss of a desirable plant cover to break the force of heavy rains and check run-off means also a reduction in the mantle of litter and loose porous topsoil, which sifts and filters run-off waters, and in adequate plant-binding roots and humus, which hold the soil and facilitate maximum percolation and absorption of water. Thus, as a result of deterioration of the plant cover, the fertile productive topsoil over much of the range has been washed away, increasing the difficulties of restoring range and watershed values.

The magnitude of these losses becomes evident when it is realized that four-fifths of the important water-producing, life-giving area of the West is made up of range land. No less than 589 million acres of range is eroding, and of this eroding area three-fifths is contributing silt in disturbing quantities to major western streams, impairing their value for irrigation, power, and municipal water supplies. Devastating floods, spilling muck and debris over highly valuable croplands and ruining homes in their wake, are now common where once they seldom occurred.

Recognition of the serious effects of drought on forage production is another major consideration in the new outlook on the range. Over most of the range area annual precipitation is under 15 inches—less than one-third that in the East. Moreover, rainfall in the West in most years is below average, in 1 to 4 years out of every 10 being more than 25 percent below, causing a drought condition which seriously hampers forage production. These facts serve to emphasize the extremely close relationship between range-forage production and rainfall. Dry years, and the resulting reduced forage production, occur with such frequency that sustained economic use of the range requires conservative stocking to avoid livestock losses and permanent injury to the forage.

A serious handicap in the effective and profitable use of range land is the large acreage of submarginal land and land of high public value now in the hands of private owners. Attempts at dry farming have clearly failed on 15 million acres or more, leading to tax delinquency, farm abandonment, excessive relief rolls, and a long train of other social and economic ills. Other range lands, low or uncertain in forage productivity, excessively depleted, and slow of recovery, are being held in private ownership with difficulty because of high original cost, undue investments in improvements, and taxes. Many of these lands have been taken over by banks, insurance companies, or other nonresidents. Seldon is such land given the control that will prevent excessive use and deterioration. In addition, on a large area of range land having high public value for watershed protection, private owners cannot afford the cost of restoration and other measures necessary to assure adequate protection to public improvements, farms, and towns lying lower down on the drainage system.

PROGRAMS RELATING TO RANGE LAND

The problems relating to the use and conservation of range land are many, complex, and varied. They apply to so vast an area and are so far reaching in their implications that no single measure can correct the situation. A commendable start has been made toward the solution of the problems, but it may be many years before the necessary remedial measures are fully attained. The following summary of the major problems relating to the range will furnish a background for appraising progress now being made and yet to be accomplished:

1. Stopping further deterioration of soil and forage and starting the rebuilding process on the 500 million acres or more of range land still deteriorating.

2. Relieving private owners of 125 million acres of submarginal lands and lands of high watershed and other public values; and otherwise overcoming maladjustments, building up sound economic private and public units, and effectuating a well-balanced integration of crop and range land for use by domestic livestock, correlated with the conservation of watershed, forest, wildlife, and other range-land uses and services.

3. Improving administration of the 350 million acres of public lands so as to facilitate their more rapid restoration and greater service to stockmen-farmers and to related community interests.

4. Alleviating the serious handicaps to sustained production under which the owners of the 375 million acres in private ownership now operate in order to insure greater social and economic security for the population.

5. Obtaining and making available for application information that will aid the effective and economical restoration of depleted ranges and production of livestock and assure conservation and wise use of the range resource for public betterment.

Each of the several programs now in operation strikes at one or more aspects of these problems. Research aims to obtain the information needed by stockmen and farmers in managing their ranches and also to establish the factual basis on which public agencies can formulate plans for their policies and programs of action. The range extension program brings such information to farmers and stockmen and through demonstrations of improved methods and practices seeks to help the farmer to better his range conditions and management practices (fig. 1). The soil conservation program applies to both privately owned and public ranges. Either directly or under cooperative arrangements, the Department of Agriculture is furnishing advice, labor, and other assistance in bringing about management and soil conservation practices that will aid in bettering conditions, overcoming soil erosion, and giving better watershed protection. The range-conservation program under the Soil Conservation and Domestic Allotment Act relates directly to privately owned range lands and those State and county lands under direct control of private owners. The national-forest and grazing-districts programs apply primarily to range lands in public ownership, but both aim to coordinate use of these public lands with the management and use of range lands held in private ownership.

Research

The key to maintenance of the range, with all its direct and indirect social and economic benefits, is the restoration and correct use of the range forage and the soil on which it grows. Thus, the premise upon

Figure 1.—Because better animals produce more meat and calves, and therefore greater monetary returns, than those of lower grade in proportion to the amount of forage consumed, careful distribution and handling of livestock is essential to good range management.

which range programs are built is the development of basic principles and practices of better management.

Fundamental to such development is knowledge concerning the forage values and growth requirements of range plants, the most effective and profitable methods for the use of the range, and possibilities for rehabilitating deteriorated areas. In cooperation with other Federal and State agencies, the Department of Agriculture is engaged in a broad program of research, dealing with the fundamental aspects and interrelations of soils, climate, vegetation, and animal life in the range area.

The forest Service, in forest and range experiment stations in the several regions of the West, has research centers for the study of interrelations of soils, climate, vegetation, and plant and animal life. The Forest Service, through forest and range experiment stations in the several regions of the West, has research centers for the study of range management, artificial revegetation, values and uses of range plants (fig. 2), and watershed management of range lands. As a result of explorations in foreign countries, the Bureau of Plant Industry is introducing new plants and, through plant breeding and selection, is developing improved strains suitable for the range. The Soil Conservation Service is obtaining information on methods for collecting seed of native species and for mass production of seed and plants for revegetation in soil-erosion control, and is studying other means of erosion control on pastures. The Bureau of Animal Industry is conducting studies of livestock husbandry.

On the basis of the results of these research projects along many lines, and in the light of the new outlook on the use of range land, principles and practices have been evolved that will go far toward remedying present conditions.

Stocking the range in accordance with its true grazing capacity is of prime importance. This means stocking year after year with the number of animals each range unit will support each season without injury to the range, to tree growth, or to the watershed and without unwarranted interference with game, recreation, or other land services. The vital significance of such stocking is realized in drought years when forage production is low. If stocking is based on the amount of forage produced in the better years, drought exacts a heavy toll. Because of shortage of feed, there are losses by starvation, the livestock able to exist are in poor condition, costly supplemental feeding is required, and finally sales at ruinous prices may be necessary. But of more far-reaching importance is the deterioration of the range resulting from overuse. Stocking must be conservative in all years to insure forage for livestock with a minimum of supplemental feeding in years of drought. In most instances this requires stocking at a rate that will utilize not more than 80 percent of the average forage production. During over 20 years of this type of stocking on an experimental area in the Southwest, the grazing capacity of the range doubled, the calf crop increased 50 percent, and death losses were only one-fifth to one-third of those on adjacent overgrazed ranges. Moreover, under such management a return of more than 8 percent was realized on an investment of $69 per cow during an 11-year period (*2*).

Figure 2.—Recording the density of vegetation on sagebrush-wheatgrass range in southern Idaho grazed by sheep in spring and fall. Range research furnishes the basis for sound use, restoration, and management of range lands.

Other basic principles of better range management include stocking the range with the class of livestock for which it is best suited, grazing the ranges during the proper season so as to make the best use of the forage and allow the forage plants to grow and reproduce, and distributing the livestock so as to utilize the forage evenly and avoid concentration.

High mountain ranges where winter snow accumulates cannot be grazed except during the summer, after the vegetation has developed sufficiently for the forage to be utilized without damage to the plants or the range. On these ranges the soil is too wet and the forage supply is insufficient to permit grazing during the early period of plant growth. It is particularly essential that the grazing of these ranges be moderate during the fall period when the important perennial forage grasses are storing foods for growth the following year (*4*). On foothills and the edges of valleys growth starts earlier in the spring and often takes place again in the fall; consequently it is best to use these ranges for spring and fall grazing. It is best to use other lower foothill and valley ranges, where snowfall is light and is usually the only permanent source of water supply in winter, when snow is present.

Where climate and topography permit yearlong grazing, ranges should be stocked at a sufficiently low rate to prevent damage, especially during the growth periods. Certain range types, however, should be used during the growing season; for example, because of its turf-forming characteristics, tobosa grass in southern New Mexico withstands grazing unusually well during the growing season and is of greatest value while green and tender. Using these latter types during the growing season permits grazing on other types less able to withstand grazing at that time to be deferred until the vegetation has made full growth.

A system that is being widely used, particularly on seasonal ranges, is deferred and rotation grazing. In its simplest form this means dividing the range into three to five units of approximately equal grazing capacity and deferring grazing on the units in rotation until the grass and seed crop have matured. By the use of this system the perennial grasses that reproduce chiefly by seed are able to mature a seed crop every few years. After the seed is matured, grazing aids in planting it through trampling by livestock.

Where ranges are so badly deteriorated that better range-management practices alone cannot effect early rehabilitation, grazing must be temporarily suspended and artificial revegetation measures applied. Research indicates that range areas with reasonably good soil and moisture conditions can be restored to productivity by planting seed of adaptable forage species (*6*). For example, sowing smooth bromegrass on plowed furrows spaced 4 feet apart, followed by brushing with a brush drag, has improved the grazing capacity of deteriorated oakbrush range in central Utah by as much as 900 percent (*5*). Tests indicate that land in Montana formerly plowed and now abandoned, lying waste, and eroding can be restored as valuable range by drill planting of crested wheatgrass and several other species. Also new and improved strains of range grasses are being developed that are especially adapted to particular range sites.

A necessary part of these better management practices is the construction of needed range improvements—building of fences, development of watering places and salt grounds, eradication of poisonous plants.

On ranches where such improved practices and other results of research have been applied they have hastened restoration of depleted ranges, facilitated livestock production, and helped to stabilize the ranch operation. Tests in Montana have demonstrated that conservative grazing increased calf production by 50 pounds or more per breeding cow. The cost for range forage and feed alone was 1.5 cents less per pound of weaning calf weight on range pastures conservatively grazed than on similar pastures overgrazed 25 percent (*3*). Similarly, in southern Idaho it was found that the condition and yield of range sheep fluctuates in accordance with general range conditions, which in turn are related to management practices (*1*).

The quest for fundamental information, which will undoubtedly furnish the basis for great advances in range management and artificial revegetation, has only begun.

Extension

In range extension work the effort is to disseminate information concerning better range management and other ranch practices for direct application on individual holdings. Research results and principles are presented in a practical form to owners, users, and managers of range lands, and test demonstrations of desirable practices adapted to local conditions are conducted.

This program is largely carried out by county agents and State extension specialists of the Extension Service, working in cooperation with stockmen and ranchers. Extension workers schooled in crop production and animal husbandry practices have helped the farmer and stockman in hay production, herd improvement, care of sick animals, and feeding practices. The campaign for better sires has greatly improved the quality of range livestock during the last 20 years. This improvement in quality has resulted in reduction in the number necessary for profit and thus has somewhat relieved overstocking on the range. Through 4–H Club and similar rural activities future farmers and stockmen are becoming better acquainted with the important range-forage plants and their possibilities. County agents have also been a major factor in facilitating the handling of the range conservation program of the Agricultural Adjustment Administration.

Many of the principles of better range management developed by research are not yet widely known, but their application should greatly aid in improving the economic condition of most ranch operators. An increase in the extension personnel trained in range management would immeasurably broaden the possibilities of better management of the range. Such men could also aid livestock owners in formulating management plans for private holdings. Dissemination and local application of the latest research results on revegetating the range, stocking to safeguard against drought losses, the best-known methods of handling stock, and keeping records of operation costs would aid not only in furthering better range-management practices but in coordinating range and livestock production with other western and national agricultural pursuits.

Soil Conservation

The effects of drought and heavy stocking in much of the western range area have been accentuated in recent years by severe wind and dust storms, which have swept much of the grass and other cover off thousands of acres along the eastern border of the area. In some instances ranges have recovered to a remarkable extent. But in limited areas much of the better soil has been removed and replaced by "blow dirt" and the original forage plants have largely given way to Russian-thistles.

Wind erosion is a more serious problem where cultivated lands intermingled with the range have been permitted to erode. An attack on this problem requires a systematic community approach.

Land-Utilization Projects

One aspect of the Soil Conservation Service program involves changing or modifying, by means of public purchase, existing patterns of land occupancy and utilization that cause rural poverty and misuse of the soil.

The change is effected by taking lands not primarily suited for cultivation out of crop production and restoring them to native forage cover. By carefully selecting the tracts to be purchased and allowing only restricted grazing, it is possible to bring about control of grazing on all privately owned range used in connection with the project area. In addition to 9,102,237 acres purchased, approximately 4,200,000 acres have been approved for acquisition under the Bankhead-Jones Farm Tenant Act, which authorized the present program.

The lands purchased are developed for grazing use, with their relationship to the entire community taken into consideration. Fencing, stock tanks, wells, pasture contouring (fig. 3), seeding of eroded and submarginal cultivated lands to range grasses, and many other range and pasture improvements are carried out.

During the time the lands are being purchased and developed, the

Figure 3.—Contour furrowing on range land conserves moisture and checks run-off and erosion. The increased moisture restores the vigor of the plants, which results in increased seed production and volume of feed.

operators who are to remain in the area are given temporary-use agreements which entitle them to use the optioned land under protective restrictions. These agreements involve no fees until title to the land is vested in the United States. The ultimate objectives are (1) to provide for the restoration of the land resources of the area and (2) to bring about the proper utilization of the available resources, at the same time furnishing the maximum number of families with an improved means of living.

Achievement of the first of these objectives is fairly simple. On many of the older projects there is already ample evidence that conservation of the soil is being accomplished.

The second objective presents many complex and difficult problems. At the inception of a land-utilization project the units are studied to determine how each operator can best be helped to set up an operation that will provide a more adequate income. Difficulty is frequently encountered in obtaining enough land or the right parcels of land to enable the operator to effect a complete adjustment from the old to the new pattern of use. Changes are being accomplished, however, and the condition of all operators, as well as that of the communities as a whole, is being improved.

In allocating land use privileges two methods are followed. In some cases the individual operator is allotted a certain amount of purchased land to be fenced and operated together with his own as an independent unit. In others, the project lands are leased to an association of operators, which in turn allocates the grazing privileges to its members. In this case the Federal lands are used in common. In either case, the need of the individual for grazing privileges to balance his private holdings is the basis for allocation.

One of the most important range problems in connection with proper land use, especially on the Plains, arises from the fact that many ranches there are too small for adequate support of a family. Many hundreds of these small units are now abandoned, yield no return to the owner, and are idle or subject to exploitation and misuse by speculative grazing interests. In many of the localities devoted to mixed farming and grazing, ranches were used for crop production during favorable periods, but under the extended drought conditions of recent years crop production has been unsatisfactory. Moreover, study of long-time weather records and of soil conditions indicates that grazing is the most satisfactory permanent land use for much of this area. This means that larger acreages are required to sustain a family-size unit. In order to provide ranches of sufficient size, agreements have been developed under which financial assistance from the Farm Security Administration enables operators to lease or purchase the additional land and livestock needed. A complete program of conservation practices is then developed by the Soil Conservation Service in cooperation with Farm Security representatives and the operator. Proper grazing is always an integral part of this plan, and, where necessary, mechanical means to increase forage production on range lands are included. Any land retained in cultivation is operated under proper conservation practices and is used principally for supplemental forage production.

Soil Conservation Demonstration Areas

In the range territory as a whole, soil conservation demonstration areas have been centered in localities most severely damaged by wind and water erosion. In the Plains States such areas usually have a high percentage of cultivated land. These mixed farming and ranching operations vary from farms with only a small acreage of native range to ranches with 2,000 or more acres of grazing land. The latter may have from a few to several hundred acres of cropland, all of which may be used for additional forage production.

On the larger ranch units, restriction of stocking to the grazing capacity and use of grazing rotations are the greatest aids in improving the range. These are usually supplemented by fencing and water development to effect better control and distribution of the livestock, and by such mechanical structures as contour furrows and water spreaders. Most of these ranches have materially reduced the number of livestock from that carried in former years.

In establishing demonstration areas the problem of conservation has been approached from the standpoint of the economic needs and requirements of the whole community. Complete surveys of each ranch are made, taking all physical factors into account and considering each individual farm as a distinct unit. Practices are recommended that will provide land stability and at the same time maintain the ranch income at the highest possible level.

In critical areas in the Plains a good grass cover to prevent blowing is vital, and this emphasizes the importance of conservative stocking and the use of supplemental soil-stabilization practices to maintain the maximum cover. On areas of mixed farming and grazing, the most desirable practice is the maintenance of livestock to utilize not only the range forage but also the feed crops produced. On many areas the amount of range is not sufficient to provide for rotation grazing, and there is not enough grass to maintain the herds through the normal grazing season. Under these conditions it is often difficult to maintain the animals in a satisfactory condition and at the same time afford adequate protection to the range.

One of the most effective means of accomplishing this is to include cultivated pastures in the ranch plan. It is often necessary to use temporary pasture or annual crops for this purpose. In the southern Plains region, for example, Sudan grass has been used a great deal for supplemental pasture. This crop furnishes pasture during the summer months and enables the rancher to let his native range recuperate from approximately June 15 to September 15. This is the season of greatest growth for the most valuable native grasses on the Plains, when they are able to increase their vitality and productivity and develop a cover that will prevent erosion. In certain areas, the use of wheat or rye for winter grazing has long been practiced, and in some instances these crops are grazed during the spring and early summer rather than harvested. This practice protects the early growth of native grass and supplies forage at a time when there is little else available for livestock.

On many range areas, contour furrows or ridges of various types have proved to be of considerable value in retaining moisture and preventing soil losses. Maximum benefits can be attained only if the mechanical treatment is accompanied by proper grazing practices.

Such soil and moisture conservation practices as brush and rock-detention dams and stream-bottom fencing for the creation of a vegetative shore line and the prevention of bank cutting, serve not only to distribute the water evenly over watersheds, thereby creating an even, well-distributed vegetative cover, but also hold back the vegetative litter and silt.

The result is increased soil fertility, the prevention of erosion, and better conditions for growth of vegetation; farmers along the valleys gain by a more even and continuous flow of comparatively clear water for irrigation and domestic uses; and the users of the range lands have a greater and more dependable supply of forage. Further down the watercourses, where large irrigation and power projects are served through the great storage dams, the life of these dams is perpetuated because the silt and debris from the watersheds above are held back.

All of these conservative land-management practices tend to set up permanent and economically sound communities throughout the entire drainage basin.

Range Conservation in the Agricultural Adjustment Program

The range-conservation program of the Agricultural Adjustment Administration, inaugurated in 1936 under the Domestic Allotment Act, is an important step in the interest of well-managed and productive private range lands. The purpose is to assist and encourage ranchers to restore their range lands and maintain them in the most highly productive state. The program was formulated on the basis of the recommendations of stockmen themselves, and on the best information available from the Department's several bureaus dealing with range-land use, from State agricultural colleges and experiment stations, and from other sources. Encouragement in carrying out the objective is offered in the form of payments authorized under the act. Such payments are conditioned upon the adoption of betterment practices designed to establish or maintain a good stand of grass or other desirable forage plants, to arrest soil erosion, and to bring about effective use of the forage resource of the individual ranch.

The range-building practices authorized include:

1. Reseeding of range lands by (a) natural reseeding by deferred grazing of lands that have suffered depletion but still have a fairly well distributed remnant of native grass sod; (b) artificial reseeding of lands on which the native sod has been destroyed by plowing and the only or principal growth consists of weeds, or on which depletion has occurred to such an extent that there are no longer sufficient numbers of the better forage plants to reseed the area naturally; (c) artificial sodding of perennial sod grasses such as grama or buffalo, which cannot be successfully established by seeding but which spread by stolons or root shoots.

2. Erosion and run-off control on ranges which are in need of mechanical aid. Practices recommended include contour furrowing or subsoiling and the construction of spreader dams and terraces.

3. Water developments for livestock on range lands inadequately watered and where additional water will permit better distribution

223761°—40——30

of livestock and more equal utilization of the forage crop. Practices include construction of earthen tanks or reservoirs, concrete or rubble masonry dams, and wells, and the development of natural watering places.

4. The conservation of forage values of range lands through the elimination of noxious and undesirable plants.

These lands are administered through the cooperative efforts of State and county committeemen elected by neighboring ranchers within the counties, aided by the Extension Service and qualified range technicians.

During the 3 years that the program has been in operation much has been accomplished. In the western division, for example, which includes States west of the Mississippi excepting Oklahoma, Texas, South Dakota, and Nebraska, natural reseeding of range land by deferred grazing was applied on over 19,500,000 acres; 258,000 acres of range land were artificially reseeded; 23,037 springs or seeps were developed, and 3,865 wells were dug; 130,442 acres of land were contour-listed, furrowed, or subsoiled; and over 4,000 linear feet of spreader terraces were constructed. In this region more than 14,000 ranchers participated in the 1938 program, which embraced an area of approximately 90,000,000 acres of range land and 500,000 acres of mountain-meadowland—an important step toward the attainment of better use of the range resource.

National-Forest Program

The national-forest range program aims to provide a sustained forage supply and watershed cover on the 80 million acres of range land within the national forests in the West that is usable for grazing and, through wise use of these lands, to serve the highest possible public good. In allocating grazing privileges in pursuance of this objective, the Forest Service gives preference to the resident home builder to aid him to build up an economic agricultural enterprise capable of satisfactorily supporting a home. By correlating and managing the national-forest range with adjacent range and croplands, stockmen and farmer-stockmen are better able to round out effective yearlong operations and maintain them on a more permanent basis. Although no vested rights are allowed to accrue, qualified permittees are safeguarded in the use of these ranges to the fullest extent consistent with sound range-management principles. Nominal fees for the use of these public properties are collected, partly as a means of offsetting the cost of their protection and improvement.

In the use of these ranges general grazing-management plans are prepared for each forest and ranger district, the basic planning unit being each range allotment used by the individual livestock owner or group of owners. In drafting these plans a complete appraisal or inventory of all the resources of the land is made. Each resource problem is analyzed, objectives are set up, and ways and means are provided in the plan for the attainment of the objectives. The numbers and class of livestock to graze, the proper season and degree of use, including opening and closing dates of grazing, and the system of grazing and handling the livestock on the range are provided for in accordance with the best-known management practices.

The plans, insofar as practical, are worked out by the Forest Service with the users of the range and their livestock associations, thus definitely fostering cooperation with the users individually and collectively. These associations, which number over 750, elect advisory boards to represent the stockmen in drafting proposed recommendations for use of the range. In addition, other groups such as community, city, county, or State organizations interested in watershed protection, recreation, wildlife, and other range-land uses join with the livestock owners in considering plans for the administration of the national-forest ranges.

In addition to the grazing for domestic livestock, national-forest ranges furnish grazing for all or part of the year to 1,841,000 big-game animals and to countless numbers of small-game animals and birds. By proper management, livestock and big game can occupy the same range on many millions of acres. Moreover, nearly half of the total national-forest area is not grazed by domestic stock and furnishes in varying degree an extensive food and cover resource for wildlife. Within the national forests are over 36,500,000 acres in 661 refuges and sanctuaries of different kinds. Included in these are more than 3,500,000 acres in the West closed especially for big game.

Today, after nearly 35 years of management with a conservation objective, the national-forest ranges are being used to advantage by 1,500,000 cattle and horses and 5,500,000 sheep and goats owned by nearly 25,000 paying permittees with 14,000 additional settlers allowed free use for their few head of domestic stock.

At this date there are in place more than 16,500 miles of fence, 5,500 miles of stock driveways, and over 10,250 water-development units as aids in facilitating the best use of the range.

Through range-management and conservation practices, much of this range has rapidly improved. Other parts, badly deteriorated at the time of reservation for national-forest purposes, have been slow to recover, the rate of recovery depending in part on the degree of deterioration of the soil and vegetation. Generally, where the fertile topsoil and a remnant of the valuable native plant cover remained, restoration of the range has progressed satisfactorily under proper grazing use. The badly depleted areas, through controlled grazing, by seeding to palatable grasses and other plants, and by certain engineering measures, are being restored in order to afford desirable watershed protection and satisfactory sustained forage production. As a whole the national forests, through this program of use based on better range and watershed management, have improved about 20 percent in productivity during the last 35 years.

Grazing-District Program

Provisions enacted in 1934, and amended in 1936, for the regulation and control of grazing on the then remaining unreserved and unappropriated public domain marked an important step toward the conservation and wise use of these ranges. Approximately 134 million acres of these lands, located in 10 States west of the Plains, are now incorporated in 52 grazing districts administered under the Taylor Grazing Act by the Grazing Service of the Department of the Interior.

The objectives of administration under this act are to protect, improve, and develop these public grazing lands; to regulate occupancy and use of them by livestock so as to promote the greatest public benefit through prudent management; and to bring about proper correlation with private lands. These objectives are being met through a program of construction of range improvements, range surveys and classification, and the control of grazing and other use through a system of licenses and permits. The program has been developed upon a cooperative basis with Federal and State agencies, the Civilian Conservation Corps, and the stockmen who are the principal users.

Under the range-surveys unit, approximately 65,000,000 acres of range have been surveyed and 10,248 dependent properties appraised.

The range-improvement program has consisted mainly of water development; soil-erosion control; reseeding; stock-trail, truck-trail, and bridge construction; fire protection and suppression; and the control of rodents, insects, poisonous plants, and predatory animals. The program calls for the early issuance of permits for grazing the lands. Last year, grazing licenses and permits were issued to 19,342 stockmen owning 11,032,642 head of livestock.

The program also includes consolidation of land ownership by exchanges with States, railroad companies, and individuals; the coordination of range use through agreement and through local stockmen's associations; and cooperative plans for the joint administration of repurchased areas within grazing districts.

During the 5 years of administration approximately 10 million acres in grazing districts have been set aside for wildlife use. In addition, provisions have been made in each grazing district for wildlife in common with livestock. The districts have been subdivided into units and allotments to facilitate range management and to promote unity of interest, and fences have been constructed to facilitate the control and handling of livestock on the range.

COORDINATING THE NEW OUTLOOK

The complex range pattern, with its multiplicity of interrelated, overlapping problems, has given rise to the several programs described, each endeavoring to render service in the new range outlook. The success of these programs is of vital concern to the farmers and stockmen directly and indirectly involved. The private owner of range lands and livestock will obtain the maximum of help in meeting his problems through that form of public leadership which strives to create conditions under which self-help can be most effective. The stockman is equally concerned with the administration of publicly owned range lands and their effective coordination with his own land, since the handling of public lands has a direct bearing on his welfare. This relationship extends beyond private range lands and livestock to private croplands and the entire agricultural system.

The Department of Agriculture has endeavored to meet this responsibility for coordination through the close integration and correlation of the several programs for which it is directly responsible. With the coordinated interest of farmers and public agencies in the new range outlook, the prospect for better conservation and wiser use of the Nation's range resource looks hopeful.

LITERATURE CITED

(1) CRADDOCK, G. W., and FORSLING, C. L.
1938. THE INFLUENCE OF CLIMATE AND GRAZING ON SPRING-FALL SHEEP RANGE IN SOUTHERN IDAHO. U. S. Dept. Agr. Tech. Bul. 600, 43 pp., illus.

(2) CULLEY, MATT J.
1937. AN ECONOMIC STUDY OF CATTLE BUSINESS ON A SOUTHWESTERN SEMIDESERT RANGE. U. S. Dept. Agr. Cir. 448, 24 pp., illus.

(3) HURTT, L. C.
1935. OVERGRAZING INCREASES PRODUCTION COSTS. Amer. Hereford Jour. 26 (9): 58, 60–61, illus.

(4) MCCARTY, EDWARD C.
1938. THE RELATION OF GROWTH TO THE VARYING CARBOHYDRATE CONTENT IN MOUNTAIN BROME. U. S. Dept. Agr. Tech. Bul. 598, 24 pp., illus.

(5) PRICE, RAYMOND.
1938. ARTIFICIAL RESEEDING ON OAK-BRUSH RANGE IN CENTRAL UTAH. U. S. Dept. Agr. Cir. 458, 19 pp., illus.

(6) STEWART, GEORGE, WALKER, R. H., and PRICE, RAYMOND.
1939. RESEEDING RANGE LANDS OF THE INTERMOUNTAIN REGION. U. S. Dept. Agr. Farmers' Bul. 1823, 25 pp., illus.

(7) UNITED STATES FOREST SERVICE.
1936. THE WESTERN RANGE . . . 620 pp., illus. (U. S. Cong. 74th, 2d sess., S. Doc. 199.)

Forest-Resource Conservation

by R. E. Marsh and William H. Gibbons [1]

TO MANAGE our forest lands as a public trust and to make the best possible use of the vast resources of public and private forests is a problem that has captured the imagination of many men. Here is a clear-cut picture of the forestry situation in the United States, beginning with the extent, the distribution, and the uses of forest lands, the ownership pattern and its effects, and an appraisal of present and potential timber resources and national requirements for timber. Forestry people are compelled to think far ahead. The authors of this article outline a long-time program the benefits of which would be far-reaching and fundamental. It means making the fullest use of the land consistent with economic practicability. It means "an adequate supply of timber and timber products to meet domestic needs, together with a substantial exportable surplus. As a basis for countless private forest activities and industries, it would provide, in whole or in part, the economic foundation for thousands of communities."

FOREST-RESOURCE conservation offers one important means of maintaining a balanced rural economic and social structure in the parts of the country which will grow timber, through utilizing all the

[1] R. E. Marsh is Acting Chief and William H. Gibbons is Senior Forester, Division of Forest Economics, Forest Service. In the compilation of this article reports and unpublished manuscripts by many members of the Forest Service have been drawn upon. Where authoritative data on forest conditions such as those so far furnished by the Forest Survey have been available, they have been used. Where such data were not available, the best approximations possible, which are believed to be substantially near the truth, have been made.

land productively for the purposes for which it is best suited, maintaining private industries in perpetuity, and holding a reasonable part of the population in the country in a healthy, diversified rural life.

THE FOREST-LAND RESOURCE

The forest-land resource, including associated range, marsh, and water, is an empire in area and should be no less in opportunity.

One-third of the land area of the continental United States exclusive of Alaska, or 630 million acres, is forest land. This is half again as much as our farm-crop land. It exceeds the combined area of France, Germany (before Munich), Italy, Norway, Sweden, Belgium, the Netherlands, and the British Isles.

Nearly three-fifths is east of the Plains in the area which contains over four-fifths of our people (fig. 1). The South has one-third (table 1). The ratio of forest to the total land area varies from 5 percent in the Plains to more than 50 percent in the Northeast and

Table 1.—Forest-land areas of the United States, by broad classes and regions, 1938

Region	Total forest land	Commercial forest land [1]	Noncommercial forest land		
			Total	Withdrawn from timber use [2]	Chiefly valuable for purposes other than timber [3]
	1,000 acres	*1,000 acres*	*1,000 acres*	*1,000 acres*	*1,000 acres*
Northeastern	62, 148	59, 376	2, 772	2, 691	81
Central	29, 328	29, 231	97	97	
Lake	55, 634	52, 395	3, 239	(4)	3, 239
South	210, 609	202, 531	8, 078	1, 285	6, 793
Columbia River Basin	99, 514	73, 842	25, 672	2, 145	23, 527
California	48, 159	13, 655	34, 504	1, 567	32, 937
South Rocky Mountain	102, 576	30, 653	71, 923	3, 077	68, 846
Plains	22, 190	14	22, 176	16	22, 160
Total	630, 158	461, 697	168, 461	10, 878	157, 583

[1] Land capable of producing timber of commercial quantity and quality available for commercial use.
[2] Commercially valuable land in parks, preserves, etc.
[3] Includes the oak-cedar breaks of Texas and Oklahoma, mesquite and piñon-juniper in the West, chaparral in southern California, remote and inaccessible alpine ranges, and other areas which appear to be permanently out of the commercial timber-producing class because of low productivity or extreme inaccessibility. Much of the area has an important value in protecting the watersheds of navigable streams, preventing or reducing soil erosion, protecting wildlife, providing game cover, etc.
[4] About 2,500,000 acres included in commercial forest land.

South. Significantly, the existing forest land is mainly land which cannot be used economically for any other purpose.

Future shifts between forest and other forms of agriculture, by whatever means decided, seem likely to be localized, compensatory, and relatively small. Keen competition for large areas of forest land seems improbable. On the other hand, the United States has scores of millions of acres where the soil has been so badly damaged by cultivation and erosion that it is submarginal for farming. On much of this the forest is creeping back. Some day these lands may again be needed for cultivation; meanwhile, there may be no better or cheaper means for rebuilding them than restoration to forests.

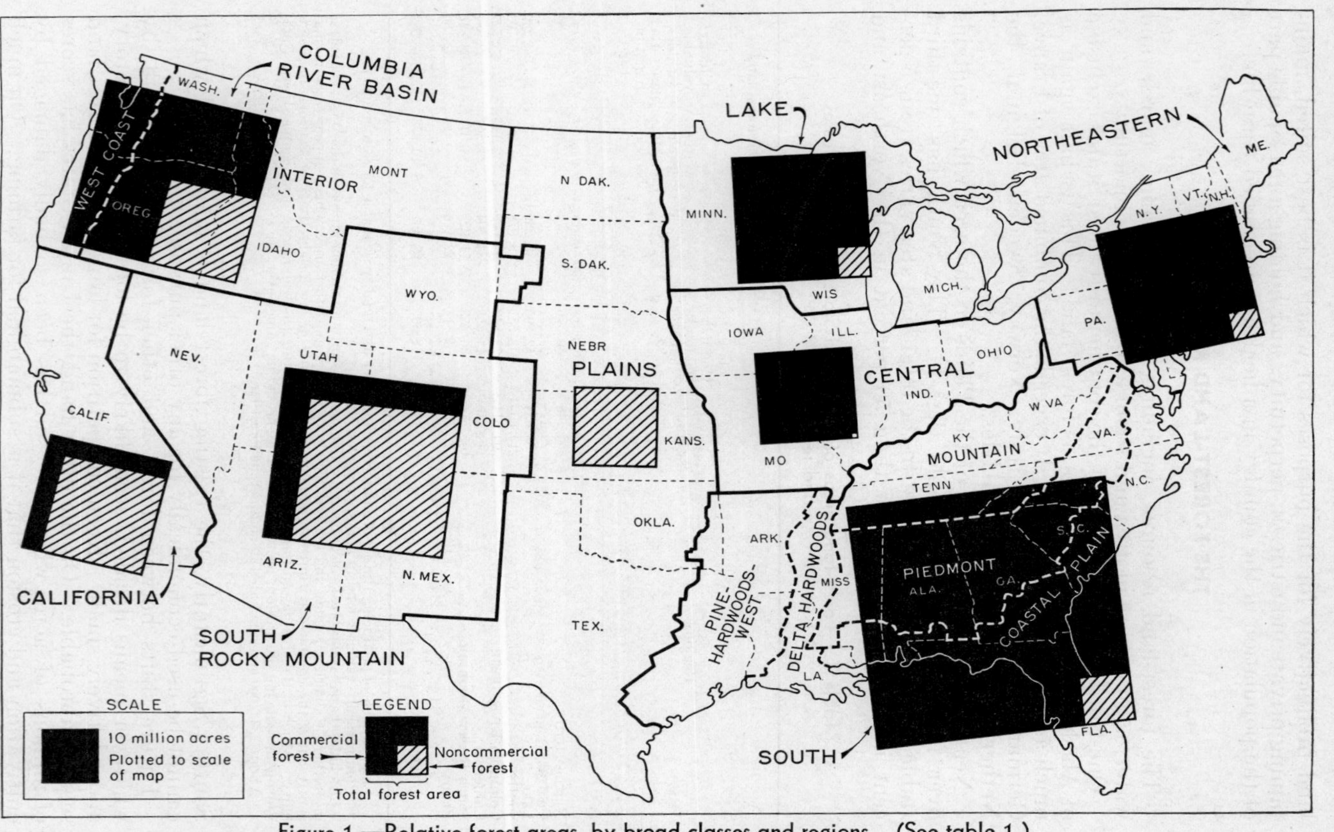

Figure 1.—Relative forest areas, by broad classes and regions. (See table 1.)

In general, we have enough forest land to meet all national needs in abundance. But making this land an economic asset rather than a liability depends upon the successful application of forestry. And forestry means the management of land not only for the sustained production of timber but also for the permanent assurance of other products and benefits.

Forest Land a Multiple-Use Resource

Too often we think of forest land in terms of timber only. But in fact, when used for forestry, forest land serves at least five major purposes, each of which constitutes a large and essential phase of our national life. These major purposes, or uses, are: (1) Timber production, (2) watershed services, (3) recreation, (4) support of wildlife, and (5) forage production.

With few exceptions, major uses need not be mutually exclusive; on the contrary, millions of acres can be used for two or more of them simultaneously. This unique multiple-use quality of forest land is one of its greatest assets.

The nature and extent of the multiple-use quality may be seen in the acreages that can be used for different purposes:

(1) Commercial timber crops can be grown on some 462 million acres.

(2) Nearly three-fourths of all forest land exerts a major or moderate influence on watersheds. Fully half exerts a major influence. The latter includes the steep slopes of the Rockies, Sierras, Appalachians, and other mountain ranges of the West and East, which are the main sources of most major streams; erosible soils like those of the Piedmont and the high bluffs along the Mississippi; and other areas like the Ouachita section of the Ozarks, where stream-flow or run-off conditions are critical.

(3) More than half of the forest area, mainly in the West and South, is grazed by domestic livestock.

(4) Practically the entire area is suitable for wildlife.

(5) Eleven million acres of land naturally suitable for timber use has so far been set aside exclusively for scenic purposes and recreation, in the form of parks, monuments, and other reservations. Much of the rest can also be used for recreation.

A surprisingly large area may be used very effectively for all five purposes. On other areas certain major uses will be restricted or excluded. No one factor exerts a greater influence on the use made of forest land than the character of ownership. But regardless of ownership, everywhere some correlation and adjustment are necessary to insure optimum multiple use and benefits. Forest-land management that is satisfactory from the standpoint of public interest will accomplish this.

Timber Use

Timber growing is the most tangible economic use to which forest land may be put. Furthermore, timber can be grown almost anywhere that land is available and with less cultural effort than any other land crop. No other crop has greater flexibility as to time of harvesting, or even remotely approaches timber in the accumulation of the basic plant materials, cellulose and lignin.

American economy has long been characterized by a high rate of wood consumption. Within the memory of men now living, a wealth of virgin timber was ready at hand and practically free for the taking. The United States now uses about a third of the lumber, more than half the paper, and nearly two-fifths of the wood in all forms consumed in the world.

Ample timber supplies are essential to our national wealth and well-being. Wood is an exceedingly adaptable material for thousands of products. It is used just as it comes from the forest, with only crude shaping—fuel wood, poles, posts, house logs. It is used in a further-processed form—sawed lumber, veneer, shingles, flooring, barrel staves. It is the principal material for innumerable fabricated products—boxes, furniture, woodenware, musical instruments. It appears in a great and constantly increasing variety of chemical products—pulp, paper rayon and other textile fibers, cellophane, acetone, alcohol, plastics. And the full possibilities of wood have not been touched—how to use it most effectively; how to treat it for resistance to decay, insect attacks, and fire; and, finally, how to transform it into other materials.

Wood is the basis of an enormous number and variety of industries. Lumbering is one of our great industries. Forest industries in 1929 employed about 1¼ million persons and produced commodities valued at about 5 billion dollars. This does not include people engaged in forest administration, protection, planting, and dependent trades and services.

The use of forest land for growing timber thus not only furnishes essential consumption goods but supports industries and communities, supplies tonnage for railroads and international trade, and is the basis of many thousands of service jobs.

Fortunately our 462 million acres of commercial forest land is ample under proper management to supply our future timber needs, with a margin for export. This acreage, however, includes not only land bearing timber stands that could be utilized under the 1929 market and operating conditions, for example, but also other land on which present or future timber stands can be economically utilized only under more favorable but reasonably conceivable future conditions. Obviously our commercial forest-land acreage cannot be considered stable. It will vary with the play of economic forces and changing social customs and usages.

Commercial forest land occurs in significant amount in all regions except the Plains (fig. 1). The South, with 203 million acres, is far in the lead. Next is the Columbia River Basin, with 74 million acres, including the Douglas fir belt of western Oregon and Washington (table 2).

But these lands and their timber have not been managed according to the principles of good forestry. Timber depletion, followed by migration or cessation of forest industries, consequent wrecking of communities, and a whole train of economic and social ills, has been the usual practice. Most of the cut-over areas are only partly productive. Far too often growing stocks are characterized by large areas of inferior species and low-quality stands of more valuable species.

Table 2.—Commercial forest area of the United States, by character of growth and region, 1938

Region	Total		Saw-timber areas [1]			Cordwood areas [2]	Fair to satisfactory restocking areas [3]	Poor to nonrestocking areas [4]
			Total	Old growth	Second growth			
	1,000 acres	*Percent*	*1,000 acres*	*1,000 acres*	*1,000 acres*	*1,000 acres*	*1,000 acres*	*1,000 acres*
Northeastern	59, 376	13	21, 154	8, 002	13, 152	15, 361	14, 702	8, 159
Central	29, 231	6	9, 680	367	9, 313	8, 660	5, 204	5, 687
Lake	52, 395	11	7, 123	3, 586	3, 537	10, 831	13, 442	20, 999
South:								
Coastal Plain	62, 534	14	27, 899	9, 430	18, 469	8, 992	9, 752	15, 891
Piedmont	49, 372	11	27, 614	4, 958	22, 656	11, 428	6, 428	3, 902
Mountain	38, 408	8	10, 850	2, 538	8, 312	18, 295	7, 303	1, 960
Delta	12, 324	3	8, 573	3, 346	5, 227	1, 987	582	1, 182
Pine, hardwoods, west	39, 893	8	21, 758	4, 856	16, 902	7, 259	5, 049	5, 827
Total	202, 531	44	96, 694	25, 128	71, 566	47, 961	29, 114	28, 762
Columbia River Basin:								
West coast	25, 790	6	14, 203	10, 987	3, 216	4, 392	2, 812	4, 383
Interior	48, 052	10	29, 903	26, 219	3, 684	7, 575	5, 711	4, 863
Total	73, 842	16	44, 106	37, 206	6, 900	11, 967	8, 523	9, 246
California	13, 655	3	11, 417	8, 653	2, 764	148	155	1, 935
South Rocky Mountain	30, 653	7	22, 683	17, 889	4, 794	5, 859	161	1, 950
Plains	14	([5])	5	1	4	4	5	
Total	461, 697	100	212, 862	100, 832	112, 030	100, 791	71, 306	76, 738

[1] Includes areas characterized by timber large enough for sawlogs (lumber) in accordance with the practice of the region regardless of its actual use. Old-growth areas bear uncut or lightly cut stands of mature saw timber; second-growth areas support predominately immature saw timber which has come in following removal of the old timber by cutting or other causes. This means: For the South, at least 600 board feet per acre in trees 9 inches diameter breast high and larger of pine and cypress and 13 inches and larger of hardwoods (of the 96,694 thousand acres of saw timber it is estimated 22 million acres bear less than 1,500 board feet per acre); Lake, 2,000 board feet per acre in both hardwood and softwood trees 9 inches and larger; Columbia River Basin, interior, 3,000 board feet per acre for pine and 4,000 board feet for fir trees 11 and 13 inches and larger, respectively, and for West coast, 5,000 board feet per acre in trees 15 inches and larger for softwoods.

[2] Cordwood areas bear stands characterized by timber too small for sawlog production but large enough for cordwood regardless of whether the stand is cut for this use or held for saw timber. Does not include noncommercial woodland even though subject to some cutting.

[3] Fair to satisfactory restocking areas include lands on which at least 40 percent of the growing space is fully occupied by commercial species predominately below cordwood size.

[4] Poor to nonrestocking areas include lands with less than 40 percent of the growing space fully occupied by commercial species predominately below cordwood size.

[5] Less than 0.005 percent.

A major problem is the 77 million acres of largely idle land, much of which should be planted with trees—especially in the Lake States, the South, the Northeast, and the Columbia River Basin. Building up the inferior second-growth saw-timber stands into satisfactory growing stocks is another major problem in the East.

Assurance of abundant and continuous supplies of wood at low prices will be a potent factor in encouraging development of new uses and greater consumption. But perhaps the most important result of forest management will be the establishment of permanent private industries for extracting and processing timber products. No longer will these industries have to follow a retreating timber supply or be handicapped by heavy transportation costs in acquiring raw materials. They can locate at convenient points throughout or near forested areas and will constitute nuclei around which community activities will develop.

Watershed Services

The beneficial effects of forest cover in regulating stream flow and preventing erosion may well represent greater values than the timber crop. Indeed, in many areas the "water crop" alone justifies maintenance of the forest.

With the destruction of the forest cover, floods seem to be increasing in frequency and destructiveness. Despite mounting expenditures for engineering control works, average annual flood losses in recent years have exceeded 110 million dollars. Single floods sometimes are calamities. The Mississippi flood of 1927 cost 246 lives and some 300 million dollars.

Forests do not prevent floods, but through retarding run-off and thus reducing flood peaks, they do reduce the destructiveness of floods. Forested lands exercise such a favorable influence in regulating stream flow and minimizing floods that no effective plan for flood control can ignore them.

The destruction of forests is a major factor in causing erosion on a large scale. In regions where forests once held and built up the soil, 10 percent of the land area is seriously and 40 percent moderately eroded; that means soil deterioration on 485 million acres. And not only does erosion deplete the fertility of the land, but irregular and uncertain stream flow and deposits of silt and sand can largely destroy the value of the huge investments that have been made in dams, levees, and channel improvements. With a growing recognition of the extent of the erosion evil, reforestation as a control measure is being employed more widely each year.

The function of forest cover in keeping the water of springs, streams, and reservoirs clear and pure for domestic use is universally recognized. Providing an adequate supply of clear, pure water has become a vast and expensive problem for many cities. Investments in municipal waterworks already run into billions of dollars. Dependable supplies of clear water are equally essential to western irrigation agriculture, which produced a 900-million-dollar crop in 1929 and represents an investment of perhaps 5 or 6 billion dollars. The importance of clear and permanent streams to fish and to recreation generally is perhaps not so widely appreciated.

Half of the forest area exercises a major influence on watersheds; almost a quarter more, a moderate influence. The rest exercises only a slight protective influence. Most of the latter area is comparatively level land, swamp and overflow land, or land having deep sandy soils, where run-off and erosion problems are not serious.

Unfortunately, large areas of protection-forest land are not exercising as much influence as they might because of the present condition of the forest cover. A satisfactory forestry program would call for something approaching the full influence of the forest on practically every major stream and on most minor streams having a flood menace or used or available for municipal water supplies, irrigation, power, and navigation.

Little forest land need be withheld from timber or other use for the sake of the protective function. Among the exceptions are a few tracts protecting municipal watersheds. In general, when managed under practices that are satisfactory for timber production, forest land will sufficiently fulfill its protective and other functions at the same time. Of course, timberlands are not the only concern. Large areas covered with inferior tree growth or brush have high value for protection of water and soil. Like that of the timberlands, their protective value is quickly impaired by fire and overgrazing.

Recreational Use

Recreation is a tremendously important forest-land use. More nearly than any other setting for outdoor recreation, the forest meets all the needs for relaxation, for play, and for aesthetic enjoyment—from simple picnicking and sightseeing to prolonged wilderness camping and the spiritual and inspirational stimuli afforded by "cutting all bonds of habit and drifting into the timeless continuity of the primeval."

Practically all forest land has some recreational value. Some has such exceptional recreational value that it should be withdrawn from timber and grazing use. This includes areas of superlative scenic value, wilderness areas, wooded strips along highways, campgrounds, land needed for forest-home sites, and areas to satisfy intensive needs near large population centers.

Eleven million acres of forest land have already been withdrawn from timber production for recreational use. This acreage may eventually be doubled or even trebled. It cannot be too strongly emphasized, however, that the recreational needs of vast numbers of people may be satisfied by lands which are also being used for timber production.

Wildlife Production

Forest lands furnish the environment for many classes of game, fur bearers, and other wildlife. Most forest land is capable of producing wildlife having social or economic value.

Wildlife held its own with uncivilized man, but civilized man has destroyed its habitat and hunted it unceasingly for food and fur and sport until numbers have dwindled and species vanished. It has become increasingly dependent on the forest for food and shelter.

Encouraging progress has been made in forest-wildlife conservation. The steady downward trend of nearly 300 years has been reversed in recent years; and, with increasing knowledge, the why and the how of management are better understood. Yet, except in a few areas and in a few States, the existing wildlife population is far below what forest lands and waters can support in balance with other uses.

By use or misuse of forests and waters man upsets the balance of nature. Wildlife management and forest management, effectively integrated, can create and maintain a new balance. The protection of forest land from fire and the application of desirable silvicultural measures in using the timber contribute to the welfare of wildlife.

Forage Production

About 342 million acres of forest land—chiefly in the Western, Southern, and Central States—is grazed by domestic livestock. This grazing furnishes a current return to many landowners, aids generally in fire protection, and helps to make forests accessible with roads and trails.

The 160 million acres of western forest range brings income to thousands of stockmen, benefits other phases of western agriculture, and contributes substantially to our national meat, wool, and leather supply. Upon the luscious feed of this high-mountain summer range, stockmen depend largely for the weight or quality gains of their livestock. About half of the western-range livestock products, valued at some 400 million dollars in 1935, are produced on forest and woodland range.

The western forest range is badly depleted, however. Its actual grazing capacity is now about 2 million livestock units. By management and other forms of public and private action, it can be restored to support 3 million.

In the South, a large part of the 12 million cattle and 11 million hogs graze at least part of the time on the 125 million acres of forest range. This range is virtually a grazing common and makes negligible returns to timberland owners. Promiscuous burning, which is done to "green up the feed," is injurious to the forest.

In the Central region (fig. 1) 21 million acres of commercial forest land is in farm woodland, of which three-fourths is grazed. But the forest-grown forage is so poor that little more than shade for livestock is obtained. Furthermore, unregulated grazing practically prevents timber production and seriously reduces watershed benefits. Exclusion of livestock from these woodlands, except under restrictions that will prevent damage to the forest, will not reduce stock production and can be a major factor in restoring the forest and thereby increasing farm income.

Other Forest Products

Numerous other forest products furnish employment and contribute to the national income. Many are susceptible of further development. Naval stores—turpentine and rosin—from southern longleaf and slash pines are normally valued at about 40 million dollars a year. The naval stores industry is an important factor in the economic life of the South. So far as permanence of timber supply is concerned, its future seems assured. Naval stores production is about double domestic consumption. A permanent industry of present or greater size will be a great advantage to forestry in the Southeast. It will help to keep productive large areas of land not adapted to other forms of agriculture, and it will give employment to tens of thousands of people.

Wood and bark for tanning, edible nuts, maple sugar and sirup, Christmas greens, and many other products are derived from our forests.

THE INFLUENCE OF OWNERSHIP ON PROVIDENT FOREST-LAND USE

Ownership has exercised a variable but dominating influence on all of the uses and benefits of forest land. Some of the most baffling problems have grown directly out of forest ownership.

Some of the main facts of ownership in the continental United States, exclusive of Alaska, are shown in table 3. Each class and form of ownership or control has its own inherent advantages and limitations, and objectives of owners within the same class vary widely. The ownership pattern in many places is so complex that it constitutes a serious handicap to forest management.

Table 3.—Ownership of forest land in the continental United States, exclusive of Alaska

Ownership class	Total	Commercial	Noncommercial	Ownership class	Total	Commercial	Noncommercial
	Million acres	*Million acres*	*Million acres*	Public—Continued.	*Million acres*	*Million acres*	*Million acres*
Private:				National parks and monuments.	6.5		6.5
Farm woodland	185.5	138.8	46.7	Public domain	24.0	4.7	19.3
Industrial and other	248.3	202.1	46.2	National forests	122.0	81.5	40.5
Total	433.8	340.9	92.9	Other Federal	5.0	4.2	.8
Public:				Total	196.3	120.8	75.5
Community	7.8	7.1	.7				
State	19.0	16.9	2.1	All classes	630.1	461.7	168.4
Indian reservations	12.0	6.4	5.6				

The primary object of most private ownership is direct financial returns. In the long run, private forest-land management must be economically sound from the standpoint of financial returns to the owner. Timber is the product that offers the highest returns and accordingly the greatest incentive to private ownership.

The manifold watershed services do not ordinarily afford revenue to the private owner, nor does most of the recreational use of the forest. Yet these nonrevenue-producing uses are of great concern to the public generally, as is also the management of the timber, forage, and wildlife resources on a sustained-yield basis.

During the settlement of this country the exploitation of the supposedly inexhaustible forests took the form of rapid liquidation with a view to quick profits. More recently it is coming to be realized that our future supply of forest products and services depends on sustained management of the resource. This and a growing realization of the financial soundness of continuous yields are being reflected in better land management by some owners. But in varying degree private owners will disregard or minimize public interests. On a substantial acreage this will be so serious that public ownership will be necessary.

Public ownership—Federal, State, or local—differs from private ownership in objectives, stability, and financial ability. Public forests, generally speaking, represent a recognition of the difficulties experienced by private owners in coping with the many perplexing problems involved in the practice of forestry. Public ownership, often accompanied by restrictions on private forest-land management, has long been accepted in many countries as a major safeguard against the impairment of the sustained productivity and economic values of forest resources.

Under public ownership, timber, forage, and wildlife uses can be placed on a sustained basis. Special areas may be dedicated as needed to any one of the major uses as the paramount one. Full correlation can be effected between all uses and services. The potentialities of multiple use can be fully realized.

Under public ownership, the protection to watershed services afforded by good vegetative cover may more readily be supplemented by upstream engineering measures. Nearly two-thirds of our forest area having an important influence on watersheds is in private ownership, where both incentive for protection and assurance of continuity are least. Public forests necessarily provide for watershed protection as a primary objective.

Under public ownership, forest recreational uses will be fostered, which is unlikely under private ownership.

Under public ownership, wildlife conservation is greatly simplified. Publicly owned forests offer one of the best opportunities for wildlife production and are increasingly important for public hunting and fishing grounds as access to private lands is gradually shut off. In private forests, except for limited areas from which the public is excluded, the financial incentive to produce wildlife crops is lacking.

Public and private owners share the responsibility for some of the worst forest-range depletion. Both can be credited with some of the best range management.

Private Ownership

Of our 630 million acres of forest land, 434 million is in private ownership. In almost every respect this area is our most critical forest problem.

The portion available for and capable of growing commercial timber includes 341 million acres (table 3). It comprises three-fourths of the commercial forest. It contains nearly three-fifths of the remaining saw timber and furnishes more than 95 percent of the timber cut. It includes most of the best and more accessible land and possibly nine-tenths of the potential timber-growing capacity of the entire country. Together with the 93 million acres of noncommercial forest land, it contains nearly two-thirds of the important watershed areas.

Farm Woodlands

Nearly one-third of the commercial forest land, or 139 million acres, is farm woodland, 95 percent being east of the Plains.

Mostly in small tracts, albeit integral parts of some 3,500,000 farms, farm woodlands constitute a distinctive type of forest-land ownership and one well adapted to keeping forest land permanently productive (table 4). Ownership is fairly stable. Costs of ownership and management are relatively small. Management usually requires only part of the farmer's time. But the income-producing potentialities of timber crops have seldom been fully appreciated, and because of this the farm forest has probably received less positive effort and more abuse than any other major farm crop, with the possible exception of natural pastures.

Unfortunately, farm-forest owners have labored under serious handicaps, such, for example, as: Lack of bargaining power; poorly equipped and haphazardly run manufacturing plants that fairly mangle the product and reduce returns; less aid and encouragement through research and extension than for any other large farm crop. Hard pressed for cash, without knowledge of values or silvicultural requirements, and without an urge for good forest management,

Table 4.—Ownership of commercial forest areas of the United States, by regions, 1938

Region	All areas	Federally owned or managed				State, county, and municipal	Private		
		Total	National forest	Indian reservation	Other		Total	Farm woodland	Industrial and other
	1,000 acres	*1,000 acres*	*1,000 acres*	*1,000 acres*	*1,000 acres*	*1,000 acres*	*1,000 acres*	*1,000 acres*	*1,000 acres*
Northeastern	59, 376	1, 529	1, 307	--------	222	3, 493	54, 354	17, 083	37, 271
Central	29, 231	1, 440	1, 329	--------	111	250	27, 541	20, 364	7, 177
Lake	52, 395	6, 818	5, 522	771	525	14, 039	31, 538	15, 060	16, 478
South:									
Coastal Plain	62, 534	2, 881	2, 296	--------	585	641	59, 012	18, 673	40, 339
Piedmont	49, 372	2, 301	1, 799	--------	502	791	46, 280	31, 059	15, 221
Mountain	38, 408	4, 212	3, 861	43	308	133	34, 063	18, 805	15, 258
Delta	12, 324	14	14	--------	--------	105	12, 205	3, 596	8, 609
Pine, hardwoods, west	39, 893	3, 500	3, 388	1	111	26	36, 367	11, 483	24, 884
Total	202, 531	12, 908	11, 358	44	1, 506	1, 696	187, 927	83, 616	104, 311
Columbia River Basin:									
West coast	25, 790	9, 888	7, 329	220	2, 339	1, 653	14, 249	1, 599	12, 650
Interior	48, 052	32, 192	27, 506	3, 182	1, 504	2, 400	13, 460	668	12, 792
Total	73, 842	42, 080	34, 835	3, 402	3, 843	4, 053	27, 709	2, 267	25, 442
California	13, 655	6, 811	6, 696	115	--------	45	6, 799	326	6, 473
South Rocky Mountain	30, 653	25, 120	20, 418	2, 052	2, 650	492	5, 041	96	4, 945
Plains	14	14	14	--------	--------	--------	--------	--------	--------
Total	461, 697	96, 720	81, 479	6, 384	8, 857	24, 068	340, 909	138, 812	202. 097

farmers have commonly accepted lump-sum prices for their timber holdings, which have then been cut without any restrictions whatever.

Nevertheless, farm forestry has made measurable headway in recent years. All told, about 41 million acres of farm forests have been put under some form of management—1.6 million under intensive sustained yield management; 9.7 million under extensive sustained-yield management; and 30 million under extensive management without sustained-yield. But some 20 million acres are still to be restocked, and possibly 75 million acres of deteriorated forests must be rehabilitated if production is to be increased to a reasonable level. About 45 million acres of this is now without organized fire protection.

Industrial and Other Nonfarm Ownership

Hardly anybody would minimize the problems involved in the farm woodlands; yet the 202 million acres of commercial forest land in industrial and other nonfarm private holdings, 80 percent of which is east of the Plains (table 4), is probably the crux of the forest problem.

This 202 million acres—which comprises more than two-fifths of our total commercial forest land and from which comes the great bulk of our more important timber products—is owned by land, lumber, pulp and paper, and mining companies, railroads, and miscellaneous agencies and individuals. About one-third of this, or some 70 million acres, is in comparatively large holdings—300 holdings of 50,000 or more acres each make up almost 50 million acres; 50

223761°—40——31

owners, holding 200,000 acres or more, account for nearly 25 million acres. There are, however, hundreds of thousands of small tracts held by absentee owners. This is highly significant, for sizable holdings, financial ability, and stability of ownership facilitate the continuity of policy necessary for sustained timber management.

As everybody knows, industrial owners have generally followed the policy of liquidating the timber resource—the opposite of sustained timber management. Even now many if not most owners question whether forestry is for them.

No one with understanding questions that private owners face some disconcerting problems and uncertainties in embarking upon forestry programs. For example:

(1) Fire, insects, and disease continue to take or threaten to take a heavy toll of timber values.

(2) The per capita consumption of wood, particularly of lumber, has declined, and other materials have cut greatly into former demands for wood.

(3) Industrial holdings have generally been acquired for liquidation, rarely for sustained management. The resulting ownership pattern in many instances constitutes a serious handicap to forest management, and one that can be rectified only with difficulty.

(4) Many owners, large and small, are unable to incur the expenditures required by forestry, particularly where deteriorated lands must be rehabilitated and where returns must be deferred. Thus there is pressure to continue what has been aptly described as a cut-out-and-get-out policy—to dispose of the land in one way or another as soon as possibilities for immediate revenue are exhausted. Millions of acres of cut-over land has been sold for farming or allowed to go tax delinquent. Much of that sold for farming turned out to be submarginal for that use.

Nevertheless, recently—particularly during the last decade—there has been a striking change for the better in the management of industrial holdings. Distinct gains have come through fire protection organized with Federal and State cooperation, the influence of the short-lived National Recovery Administration code, the example of the national forests, research and extension by the Federal and State Governments, and the impact of the conservation movement generally. At the same time, great credit is due those owners who in spite of handicaps are pioneering in the timber-growing enterprise.

The best information available on the status of forest practices on industrial and other nonfarm commercial land indicates that some 29 million acres is under some form of management—4 million under intensive sustained-yield management; 7.5 million under extensive sustained-yield management; and 17 million under extensive management without sustained yield.

Obviously there is still a long way to go: 37 million acres, or nearly 20 percent of the industrial and other nonfarm acreage, is not under any form of management although restocking poorly or not at all; 137 million is unmanaged but at least partly productive. Some 60 million acres of this needs, but is still without, fire protection. On millions of acres, no one knows just how many, now bearing second-growth saw timber, cordwood, or younger stands, the forest must be rehabilitated, the growing stock built up, the composition improved.

Public Ownership

Of the 196 million acres of forest land in public ownership, or nearly one-third of our forest land, the great bulk—170 million acres—is owned or managed by the Federal Government (table 3).

The West and the East afford a pronounced contrast in the proportion of forest land in public ownership. This, of course, is largely because the national forests, which contain 122 million acres of forest land, were established in the West mainly by Presidential decrees or acts of Congress applied to large areas of public domain, much of which contained virgin forests.

Community Forests

A very old form of public forest, and one more likely than other more distant public forests to give the individual citizen a feeling of personal proprietorship, is the community forest, owned by a county, a city, a town, a hospital, a school, etc.

This class of forests includes some 8 million acres. More than 1,000 of these forests, aggregating 3 million acres, are under administration and development. Our tens of thousands of incorporated and unincorporated communities have a great opportunity for a sizable expansion in both the number and area of community forests. Such forests can yield wood and timber for community use, protect water supplies, and afford opportunities for recreation. Sale of surplus timber may also bring in a cash revenue. The management of the forests to produce these goods and benefits will furnish opportunities for income and employment to local citizens.

State Forests and Parks

Each of the States owns some forest land; all together own about 19 million acres. About 11 million acres are designated as State forests and parks. About 90 percent of this area is in 10 States—New York, Pennsylvania, Minnesota, Michigan, Montana, Idaho, Washington, New Mexico, Wisconsin, and Massachusetts. The remaining 8 million acres is in game refuges and in scattered tax-reverted areas and remnants of Federal grants. Most of the scattered tracts are protected against fire, and from some the timber is being sold, with or without cutting restrictions.

The policies of the several States with respect to State forests and parks are conspicuously diverse. Practically the entire area is protected against fire and trespass. More than half of the area has been developed intensively for recreation; among the leaders in this activity are Connecticut, Indiana, Massachusetts, New Hampshire, New York, Ohio, Pennsylvania, and Vermont. On more than half of the State forest area timber management ranges downward from intensive cultural operations and controlled cutting, with Arizona, Connecticut, Idaho, New Jersey, New Mexico, Pennsylvania, and Vermont among the more progressive States. About 60,000 acres were planted in 1938, mostly in Indiana, Michigan, New York, New Jersey, Pennsylvania, Washington, and Wisconsin. Management and protection have been materially expanded and intensified through grants of Civilian Conservation Corps, Works Progress Administration, and other emergency labor.

The possibilities for State forests have hardly been scratched in most States. The South, with fully one-third of all our forest land, has only 3 percent of the State forests and parks.

Federal Ownership Other Than National Forests

Uncle Sam's forested lands are in more than one basket, although most of the federally owned or controlled acreage is in the national forests (table 3).

Public domain.—The remaining public domain of the Western States contains about 24 million acres of forest land; about one-fifth with commercial timber, much with range values, and nearly all important for watershed protection. Management is limited to the areas recently included in grazing districts. Even fire prevention has been lacking or at best sporadic.

Indian forests.—In the Indian reservations are forests aggregating 12 million acres—about one-half commercial—which are managed for the benefit of their Indian owners by the Department of the Interior. Management, which in general has kept pace with that of the national forests, calls for maximum returns consistent with sustained yield and watershed protection.

National parks.—In the national parks, under the Department of the Interior's administration, are roughly 5 million acres of forest. Reserved for scenic and recreational purposes, and given the maximum protection against fire, insects, and disease, these stands also afford watershed benefits. Under wildlife protection, the parks are important game refuges.

Miscellaneous Federal ownership.—In such holdings as the Oregon and California and Coos Bay road lands in Oregon, the national monuments, the wildlife refuges, and the farm-resettlement purchases, the Federal Government has almost 7 million acres of forested land. All of these areas are under management, and some are intensively developed for recreational use or wildlife.

National Forests

Although the national-forest enterprise is still largely confined to the Rocky Mountain and Pacific Coast States, national forests or purchase units are located in 40 States, Alaska, and Puerto Rico.

The net area of the national forests, exclusive of Alaska and Puerto Rico, is 156 million acres; about 122 million is forest, the remainder intermingled grass and alpine country. Private and other interior holdings total 52 million acres.

The national forests, administered by the Department of Agriculture, represent the first large-scale trial in the United States of public ownership and administration of a great natural resource. They also represent the first large-scale land classification in the country. Their withdrawal has kept a large area of submarginal land out of cultivation and has retained under public control millions of acres that are submarginal for any private ownership. Their establishment was a major factor in reversing the traditional Federal policy of disposing of all public land, regardless of its character, for "development."

Despite the difficulty of placing almost one-twelfth of the land area of the United States under administration in a pioneer undertaking, the national-forest enterprise has been at least fairly successful. This is evidenced in many ways, but not least in the change in public opinion from bitter opposition, mainly western, to Nation-wide approval and a demand in most States for more national forests.

The national forests are being built up through intensive, carefully planned protection, by planting, and by timber-stand improvement. All cutting is controlled. Varying in intensity with the demand for timber, management plans cover practically the entire timber area. Local communities and privately owned industries dependent on the cutting and manufacture of the timber from the national forests are stable, in contrast to many communities engaged in the liquidation of privately owned timber. Of the 81.5 million acres of commercial forest land in the national forests, 3.4 million acres is under intensive sustained-yield management; 33.3 million acres is under extensive sustained-yield management; and 3.5 million acres is under extensive management without sustained yield. Additional land at least partially productive, protected against fire, and with management assured as the cutting of the timber becomes possible, amounts to 35.9 million acres; and 5.4 million acres is unproductive, largely as a result of fires before or since the land was incorporated in national forests.

Fire protection, controlled cutting, planting, and range management have materially improved watershed services, particularly in the West but increasingly in the East. Significantly almost all major and most minor western rivers and many of the most important eastern rivers head in the national forests.

The 81 million acres of range land in the western national forests has been built up steadily under management plans which now cover nearly the entire area. The demand for this range exceeds the supply, although present use aids 25,000 pay permittees and several thousand owners who graze a few head of "exempt" stock in the forests.

Large wildlife reservoirs, the national forests afford an unsurpassed opportunity to work out the new concept of wildlife management integrated with that of timber, range, and other resources. Big game has increased 150 percent since 1924—and other wildlife, including fish, correspondingly—without having reached excess numbers except locally.

Forest recreation is the most concrete and direct service which the national forests can render to millions of people. Out of the 32 million visitors to the national forests in 1937, over 12 million stopped to enjoy one or more forms of forest recreation. With requisite facilities and administration, this use could be greatly increased.

But great as are these and other accomplishments, the building up of the national-forest resource has been too slow. Much too small an area is under intensive timber management. Forest ranges are too far below full productivity. Wildlife management has lagged, and recreational facilities fall far short of meeting the requirements of the people who are or should be using the national forests. In watershed protection efforts have been confined too largely to ordinary protection, and special supplemental provisions needed for fully satisfactory protection are largely lacking. Acquisition of land has proceeded at a snail's pace.

Among the reasons for this situation are: The remoteness and inaccessibility of much of the area; the rather widespread public opposition in the early years; the serious handicap of private and other interior holdings which, at the extreme, have made satisfactory administration impossible; lack of technical knowledge; inadequate legislation; and insufficient funds.

PRESENT AND POTENTIAL TIMBER RESOURCES

It remains to deal with the timber on the 462 million acres classed as commercial forest land. The volume, character, location, ownership, economic availability, rate of cut or destruction, and rate of growth of the stand of timber influence the determination of whether positive measures are needed to put the forests on a satisfactory basis, and if so, what measures.

Volume and Location of Present Timber Supplies

Saw Timber

Of the broad classes of timber, saw timber is in greatest demand and is the most important. It is preferred for most timber products, being required for lumber, cross ties, veneer, and similar sawed or sliced products.

The total supply of saw timber is about 1,760 billion board feet. Nearly three-fourths of it, or 1,260 billion feet, is old growth (table 5).

The old-growth saw timber—characteristically 200 to 300 years old and often older—still dominates the market, although the cut of second growth is increasing.

The supply of second-growth saw timber is far too small to insure a sustained output following the cutting of the old growth. Moreover, second growth is characteristically cut long before it reaches physical or financial maturity.

Softwood saw timber comprises nearly 1,500 billion board feet, or 85 percent of the total. Douglas fir, with 490 billion feet, 80 percent of which is in Oregon and Washington, is far in the lead. Ponderosa pine, widely distributed through the West, is second, with 225 billion. Then come the southern yellow pines, western "true" firs, and western hemlock, with 197, 122, and 116 billion board feet, respectively. The once large supply of northern white pine in the Lake States, highly prized as a standard wood for millwork, boxes and crates, novelties, and patterns, has been so depleted that it now comprises less than 1 percent of the country's softwood.

Hardwoods make up only 15 percent (271 billion feet) of the saw-timber stand, yet contribute 28 percent of the saw-timber cut. Oak leads with 84 billion feet. The hardwood stand is practically confined to the East, with two-thirds south of the Ohio and Potomac Rivers. Depletion, especially in the more valuable species, has progressed further than in softwoods.

Because of the steady progress of liquidation from one region to another, the remaining saw timber is not well distributed geographically in relation to the commercial forest land. The East, with three-fourths of the land, has less than one-third of the saw timber. West-

Table 5.—Stand of saw timber in the United States, by character of growth and region, 1938 [1]

Region	Total saw timber		Softwoods			Hardwoods		
			Total	Old growth	Second growth	Total	Old growth	Second growth
	Million bd. ft.	*Percent*	*Million bd. ft.*	*Million bd. ft.*	*Million bd. ft.*	*Million bd. ft.*	*Million bd. ft.*	*Million bd. ft.*
Northeastern [2]	84,025	4.8	41,056	19,121	21,935	42,969	10,490	32,479
Central [2]	14,301	.8	369	121	248	13,932	1,382	12,550
Lake [3]	57,616	3.3	20,881	11,773	9,108	36,735	20,449	16,286
South:								
Coastal Plain	117,774	6.7	82,105	27,331	54,774	35,669	22,465	13,204
Piedmont	108,987	6.2	70,197	11,864	58,333	38,790	14,160	24,630
Mountain	45,390	2.6	7,940	2,900	5,040	37,450	13,830	23,620
Delta	33,004	1.8	2,849	1,168	1,681	30,155	14,988	15,167
Pine, hardwoods, west	81,415	4.6	51,541	11,537	40,004	29,874	13,183	16,691
Total [3]	386,570	21.9	214,632	54,800	159,832	171,938	78,626	93,312
Columbia River Basin:								
West coast	602,249	34.1	597,594	484,907	112,687	4,655	-------	4,655
Interior	280,383	15.9	280,082	264,135	15,947	301	-------	301
Total [3]	882,632	50.0	877,676	749,042	128,634	4,956	-------	4,956
California [2]	213,480	12.1	213,480	206,520	6,960	-------	-------	-------
South Rocky Mountain [2]	124,992	7.1	124,991	114,794	10,197	1	1	-------
Plains [2]	35	([4])	35	15	20	-------	-------	-------
Total	1,763,651	100.0	1,493,120	1,156,186	336,934	270,531	110,948	159,583

[1] Includes trees large enough for lumber, cross ties, veneer, and similar sawed or sliced products in accordance with the cutting practice of the region concerned. Minimum sizes are: South, softwoods, 9 inches diameter breast high, hardwoods, 13 inches; Lake, 9 inches, both softwoods and hardwoods; Columbia River Basin, interior, pine and fir, 11 and 13 inches, respectively; and west coast, softwoods, 15 inches. Old growth comprises mature saw timber, most of which is the remainder of the uncut or lightly cut original stands. Second growth comprises immature saw timber much of which is barely of sawlog size.

[2] Includes saw timber on saw-timber areas only.

[3] Includes saw timber on cordwood and restocking areas as well as on saw-timber areas. The saw timber on the saw-timber areas of the Lake region amounts to 46,143 million feet, 16,796 million of softwoods and 29,347 million of hardwoods; and in the Columbia River Basin region it totals 847,280 million feet, 842,333 million softwoods and 4,947 million hardwoods. In the South the saw timber on areas supporting 1,500 board feet or more per acre totals 346,785 million feet, 191,474 million of softwoods and 155,311 million of hardwoods.

[4] Less than 0.05 percent.

ern Oregon and Washington, with only 6 percent of the land, have over one-third of the saw timber and two-fifths of the old-growth saw timber. Nearly nine-tenths of the old-growth saw timber is in Rocky Mountain and Pacific Coast States.

Although about two-thirds of the saw-timber cut comes from the East, perhaps half of the great store of virgin timber in the West is economically available to the East. Under orderly utilization this western supply would be of great value in helping to tide over the interval which must elapse before the East can be put on a satisfactory timber-growing basis. But the pressure to liquidate is so great that most western operators are throwing their stumpage on the market with little regard to sustained-yield requirements. The consequent depressed market conditions render systematic timber growing more difficult for eastern owners.

Cordwood

There are some 2,455 million cords of wood in trees 5 inches in diameter up to saw-timber size, and in tops and limbs of saw-timber trees. The volume of the small trees is about 1,850 million cords, or about two-fifths of that of the saw timber.

Except for the tops and limbs of saw-timber trees, which should be utilized up to the measure of feasible and economical woods practice, the great bulk of the cordwood is hardly available for cutting. On the contrary, under good forestry practice, cordwood-size trees would ordinarily be regarded as growing stock to grow into saw timber for more valuable products. The cutting of such trees should be limited to thinning or other stand-improvement work, or to stands managed primarily for such products as fence posts, pulpwood, and fuel wood. Two-thirds of the cordwood-tree volume is in the East, where there are large areas of young second-growth timber. From the standpoint of real forestry, the present cordwood growing stocks are generally unsatisfactory in quantity and quality.

Total Volume of Timber

The total stand of timber is 519 billion cubic feet, including 364 billion feet in saw-timber trees and 155 billion in cordwood trees (table 6). The West, with 26 percent of the commercial forest land, has 57 percent of the total timber. The per acre volumes of 495 and 680 cubic feet in the Lake States and South might be compared with the 760 in Sweden, a country where forests are under systematic management. The higher potential capacity of the United States forest lands calls for larger growing stocks here than in Sweden, in order to maintain a sustained output commensurate with the timber-producing capacity of the land.

Table 6.—Total stand of softwoods and hardwoods in the United States, by type of material and region, 1938

Region	All trees			Saw-timber trees [1]			Cordwood trees		
	Total	Softwood	Hardwood	Total	Softwood	Hardwood	Total	Softwood	Hardwood
	Million cu. ft.	*Million cu. ft.*	*Million cu. ft.*	*Million cu. ft.*	*Million cu. ft.*	*Million cu. ft.*	*Million cu. ft.*	*Million cu. ft.*	*Million cu. ft.*
Northeastern	47, 901	12, 915	34, 986	16, 733	7, 408	9, 325	31, 168	5, 507	25, 661
Central	12, 001	419	11, 582	3, 198	66	3, 132	8, 803	353	8, 450
Lake	25, 809	8, 970	16, 839	15, 737	5, 201	10, 536	10, 072	3, 769	6, 303
South:									
Coastal plain	39, 256	23, 457	15, 799	26, 510	17, 486	9, 024	12, 746	5, 971	6, 775
Piedmont	38, 562	20, 108	18, 454	24, 006	14, 116	9, 890	14, 556	5, 992	8, 564
Mountain	19, 991	3, 240	16, 751	10, 637	1, 620	9, 017	9, 354	1, 620	7, 734
Delta	11, 697	918	10, 779	8, 762	669	8, 093	2, 935	249	2, 686
Pine, hardwoods, west	28, 508	14, 446	14, 062	18, 210	10, 550	7, 660	10, 298	3, 896	6, 402
Total	138, 014	62, 169	75, 845	88, 125	44, 441	43, 684	49, 889	17, 728	32, 161
Columbia River Basin:									
West coast	125, 088	122, 446	2, 642	106, 888	106, 121	767	18, 200	16, 325	1, 875
Interior	71, 991	71, 710	281	47, 393	47, 331	62	24, 598	24, 379	219
Total	197, 079	194, 156	2, 923	154, 281	153, 452	829	42, 798	40, 704	2, 094
California	62, 582	62, 582		60, 538	60, 538		2, 044	2, 044	
South Rocky Mountain	35, 677	35, 653	24	25, 798	25, 798		9, 879	9, 855	24
Plains	12	12		7	7		5	5	
Total	519, 075	376, 876	142, 199	364, 417	296, 911	67, 506	154, 658	79, 965	74, 693

[1] Includes tops and limbs (tops only in softwoods as well as portion of tree suitable for sawlogs.

Ownership of Timber Supplies

The character of ownership of the timber as well as of the land is a primary factor in our forest situation. It largely influences the time and rapidity of cutting, and the organization of operations for sustained yield. It influences the measures taken before, during, and after cutting to insure the establishment, development, and protection of new stands. By no means least, it affects the consideration given to dependent industries and communities.

Ownership of saw timber is of special importance. The national requirements for forest products will best be met if programs of forestry are based on saw timber as the major object of management and if sufficiently long rotations are used to produce timber of considerable size and relatively high quality. This has been the experience of every country where forest management has been substituted for forest liquidation.

Table 7 shows how the saw timber is distributed among the various classes of owners. Public agencies own or control about 737 billion board feet, or 42 percent, of the supply. This includes a large proportion of the relatively inaccessible timber in the West. Only 31 billion feet of the publicly owned or managed saw timber is in the East. This in itself emphasizes the desirability of considering a greatly expanded program of public ownership in the East. In the nature of the case, public ownership is comparatively free from pressure for immediate financial returns. It is far better adapted than

Table 7.—Ownership of stands of saw timber in the United States, by regions, 1938

Region	Total	Federally owned or managed				State, county, and municipal	Private		
		Total	National forest	Indian reservation	Other		Total	Farm woodland	Industrial and other
	Million bd. ft.	*Million bd. ft.*	*Million bd. ft.*	*Million bd. ft.*	*Million bd. ft.*	*Million bd. ft.*	*Million bd. ft.*	*Million bd. ft.*	*Million bd. ft.*
Northeastern	84,025	1,667	1,617		50	1,283	81,075	19,972	61,103
Central	14,301	368	312		56	163	13,770	10,059	3,711
Lake	57,616	5,255	3,875	1,139	241	5,662	46,699	13,851	32,848
South:									
Coastal Plain	114,242	2,587	1,883		704	570	111,085	37,016	74,069
Piedmont	112,602	3,315	2,868		447	400	108,887	70,400	38,487
Mountain	44,797	5,464	4,938	160	366	226	39,107	21,450	17,657
Delta	34,302	162	162			25	34,115	8,471	25,644
Pine, hardwoods, west	80,627	3,703	3,651	2	50	49	76,875	23,792	53,083
Total	386,570	15,231	13,502	162	1,567	1,270	370,069	161,129	208,940
Columbia River Basin:									
West coast	602,249	269,059	208,035	5,052	55,972	33,180	300,010	11,914	288,096
Interior	280,383	182,012	152,584	23,652	5,776	15,887	82,484	1,634	80,850
Total	882,632	451,071	360,619	28,704	61,748	49,067	382,494	13,548	368,946
California	213,480	88,346	85,449	2,897		775	124,359	2,800	121,559
South Rocky Mountain	124,992	115,352	100,280	6,983	8,089	1,409	8,231	124	8,107
Plains	35	35	35						
Total	1,763,651	677,325	565,689	39,885	71,751	59,629	1,026,697	221,483	805,214

private ownership to correlation of management for sustained timber production with other uses.

There are 221 billion board feet of saw timber in farm woodlands, mostly east of the Plains. Relatively accessible and of better-than-average timber-growing capacity, the farm woods include 30 percent of the forest land but only 13 percent of the saw timber. Although the conditions are generally favorable for sustained timber production on farm woodlands, the small average volume of the growing stocks indicates that satisfactory timber management has not been attained.

Industrial and other nonfarm owners hold the largest acreage of forest land and the largest volume of saw timber. On an average, their land is potentially more productive and their timber more accessible than that in public ownership. They supply two-thirds of the national saw-timber cut. Less than one-fifth of their land but 60 percent of their timber is in the West. The motivating force of immediate financial returns is reflected in the prevalent lack of sustained-yield management, in the large acreage without satisfactory fire protection, and in the abandonment of millions of acres.

Availability of Timber Stand

The timber-stand statistics presented above should not be interpreted as measuring the quantity of timber available for cutting. From this standpoint the gross figures should be reduced, for two reasons.

(1) Most of the cordwood and younger saw timber should be retained as growing stock. Growing stock, together with the land, makes up the forest capital upon which sustained yield or forest "interest" must be based.

(2) An appreciable portion of the timber is economically unavailable—cannot be cut profitably—because of size and quality, proportion of inferior species, logging difficulties, remoteness from established transportation, market conditions, or other reasons.

Economic Availability of Saw Timber

It is estimated that about two-thirds of the saw timber in the United States could be cut profitably, by reasonably efficient operators, under present operating and market conditions.

In the West, where much of the saw timber is high up in the mountains, about half is economically available now. Improvements in logging and milling practices, combined with changing economic conditions, will undoubtedly push back the limits of economic availability, but considerable volumes may never be utilized.

Possibly 90 percent of the saw timber in the East is economically available. Most of the eastern timber is much closer to markets than the bulk of the western timber. In fact, in practically all regions east of the Plains, inferior quality, rather than inaccessibility, is the most serious obstacle to profitable utilization.

Veneer Logs

Timber suitable for the production of high-grade veneers is becoming increasingly scarce. In the North, some veneer logs are obtained from second-growth stands, but large hardwood logs practically clear of defects, from which high-grade veneers are customarily produced, are obtained mainly from old-growth stands. Inevitably, therefore, the hardwood veneer industry has turned to the South for much of its raw material, imposing a heavy drain on the best-quality timber of that region.

The West leads in the production of softwood veneers. The large, old-growth timber of the West is especially well adapted to this use. Douglas fir leads all other softwoods for veneers and is second only to red gum in total quantity consumed.

Pulpwood

There is an enormous supply of timber that would yield satisfactory pulp, especially in the Pacific Northwest and the South; all told, it is several hundred times the annual pulpwood cut. But only a small part of the supply of species now used in pulp and paper manufacture is available for this use, or at least as available as some of the foreign supplies. We import as much pulpwood, or its equivalent in wood pulp and paper, as we cut in our own forests. The manufacture of pulp involves many complex technical and economic problems. With technical progress, and with sound forestry, there will be opportunities for greatly expanding the use for the pulp of the southern pines and of the Douglas fir, "true" firs, and hemlock of the far West.

Forest Drain and Timber Growth

Any sound appraisal of forest-resource conservation will take account of forest drain—the volume of material removed from the forests annually by cutting and that killed or destroyed by fire, insects, disease, and other destructive agencies. Also of fundamental significance are the volume of annual growth and the relation between drain and growth.

Forest Drain

In 1936, a year in which economic activity was still considerably below the predepression level, the total drain on our timber supply was 13.5 billion cubic feet (table 8). Seventy percent of this, equivalent to 47.8 billion board feet, was saw timber. And saw timber includes the oldest timber of highest quality—the cream of the forest.

Cutting accounted for 85 percent of the total drain, and 89 percent of the saw-timber drain; destructive agencies for the rest. The included fire losses, however, are not a full measure of the damage to the forest caused by fire; for example, they do not take account of the destruction of young growth on millions of acres, or of the depreciation in the productive capacity of the forest soil.

Lumber, manufactured mostly from old growth, accounts for 58 percent of the saw-timber drain. Fuel wood was second, with 13 percent. Pulpwood, hewed ties, fence posts, veneer logs, mine timbers, cooperage stock, shingles, poles, piling, and miscellaneous products made up 18 percent. Loss by fire, insects, disease, windfall, etc., accounted for 11 percent.

The ratios of drain to hardwood stand, both of saw timber and of total volume, were about twice the corresponding ratios for softwood. The problem of adequate hardwood supplies is more acute.

Table 8.—Timber removed from commercial forests of the United States by cutting and by destructive agencies, 1936

TIMBER CUT FOR COMMODITIES

Item	All timber [1]			Saw-timber trees [2]			Cordwood trees [3]		
	Total	Softwood wood	Hard-wood	Total	Soft-wood	Hard-wood	Total	Soft-wood	Hard-wood
	1,000 cu. ft.	*1,000 cu. ft.*	*1,000 cu. ft.*	*1,000 bd. ft.*	*1,000 bd. ft.*	*1,000 bd. ft.*	*Cords*	*Cords*	*Cords*
Lumber	5, 367, 585	3, 997, 846	1, 369, 739	27,702,415	22,016,083	5, 686, 332	218, 422	150, 908	67, 514
Fuel wood	3, 619, 482	1, 219, 241	2, 400, 241	6, 400, 401	3, 121, 767	3, 278, 634	25,551,196	6, 495, 647	19,055,549
Pulpwood	705, 924	638, 026	67, 898	2, 252, 147	2, 107, 802	144, 345	2, 519, 165	2, 196, 496	322, 669
Hewed ties	354, 189	182, 611	171, 578	1, 491, 753	885, 461	606, 292	92, 300	37, 000	55, 300
Fence posts	327, 060	131, 434	195, 626	628, 576	252, 354	376, 222	2, 113, 031	964, 527	1, 148, 504
Veneer logs	252, 443	71, 472	180, 971	1, 190, 415	412, 733	777, 682	7, 747	181	7, 566
Mine timbers (round)	161, 016	47, 264	113, 752	151, 102	77, 693	73, 409	1, 147, 749	272, 921	874, 828
Cooperage stock	149, 447	61, 169	88, 278	704, 346	333, 603	370, 743	7, 010		7, 010
Shingles	108, 658	107, 600	1, 058	492, 590	489, 271	3, 319	12, 157	11, 086	1, 071
Other	354, 203	153, 379	200, 824	1, 429, 629	710, 516	719, 113	543, 258	159, 950	383, 308
Total	11,400,007	6, 610, 042	4, 789, 965	42,443,374	30,407,283	12,036,091	32,212,035	10,288,716	21,923,319
TIMBER REMOVED BY DESTRUCTIVE AGENCIES									
Fire	861, 608	588, 595	273, 013	1, 390, 373	1, 195, 796	194, 577	6, 678, 064	4, 137, 164	2, 540, 900
Insects, disease, etc	1, 201, 141	861, 706	339, 435	3, 973, 930	3, 570, 783	403, 147	4, 801, 810	2, 079, 911	2, 721, 899
Total	2, 062, 749	1, 450, 301	612, 448	5, 364, 303	4, 766, 579	597, 724	11,479,874	6, 217, 075	5, 262, 799
Aggregate	13,462,756	8, 060, 343	5, 402, 413	47,807,677	35,173,862	12,633,815	43,691,909	16,505,791	27,186,118

[1] Includes saw-timber and cordwood trees. The volumes, necessarily shown in cubic feet, include the tops (cordwood size and larger) of the softwood saw-timber trees and the tops and limbs of the hardwood saw-timber trees. Bark is not included.

[2] Includes only timber of saw-timber size. The volumes, in board feet, are equivalent to the lumber which could have been sawed from such trees.

[3] Includes only the merchantable volume, in cords, of trees below saw-timber size, from saw-timber, cordwood, and restocking areas.

The outstanding importance of the South as a source of timber supply is emphasized by the fact that it accounts for one-half of the Nation's forest drain. The Douglas fir belt of western Oregon and Washington follows, with about one-fifth.

Current Timber Growth

With the old-growth timber of the East practically exhausted and with the accessible supply in the West diminishing rapidly, the amount, character, and geographic distribution of current timber growth assume primary significance. Information regarding growth in many regions is inadequate, so that it is impossible to make more than a fairly good estimate of growth for the country as a whole.

The total current growth is estimated at 11.3 billion cubic feet; saw-timber growth at 32 billion board feet, two-thirds of which is softwood. Nearly two-thirds of the saw-timber growth is in the South, principally in pine forests.

But not all of the growth really counts. Little commercial significance can be attached to the growth on economically unavailable stands. Then there is the matter of species or quality; for example, in the Lake States, the rapidly growing aspen—a short-lived species used only in limited quantities—accounts for about one-third of the total growth. Probably not more than 9.6 billion cubic feet, including 27.5 billion board feet of saw timber, can be considered as effective growth.

Relation of Current Growth to Drain

Although current growth approaches current drain more closely than it has since man began extensive use, the situation is actually less favorable than the growth-drain comparisons of table 9 indicate. Not all of the growth is effective. Cutting, for the most part, takes the better trees, while most of the growth is in inferior species or small, low-quality trees. Much of the drain is concentrated locally, and forest industries continue to cut out and close down, with a disastrous aftermath of unemployment, wrecked communities, and stranded populations.

Table 9.—Current annual growth and drain, 1936

Region	Combined saw timber and cordwood			Saw timber			
	Growth	Drain	Ratio, drain to growth (growth=1)	Growth	Drain	Ratio, drain to growth (growth=1)	Saw timber cut for lumber
	Million cu. ft.	*Million cu. ft.*		*Million bd. ft.*	*Million bd. ft.*		*Million bd. ft.*
Northeastern	1,260	1,370	1.1	2,625	2,468	0.9	978
Central	568	907	1.6	978	1,781	1.8	469
Lake	979	983	1.0	1,850	2,420	1.3	1,307
South:							
Coastal Plain	1,626	1,691	1.0	5,645	6,705	1.2	3,532
Piedmont	2,143	1,812	.8	6,841	6,550	1.0	4,128
Mountain	893	1,487	1.7	1,810	3,908	2.2	1,723
Delta	478	573	1.2	1,278	1,846	1.4	964
Pine, hardwoods, west	1,355	1,126	.8	4,829	4,633	1.0	2,930
Total	6,495	6,689	1.0	20,403	23,642	1.2	13,277
Columbia River Basin:							
West coast	917	1,833	2.0	2,739	9,550	3.5	6,772
Interior	717	1,016	1.4	2,508	4,714	1.9	2,831
Total	1,634	2,849	1.7	5,247	14,264	2.7	9,603
California	155	501	3.2	414	2,649	6.4	1,647
South Rocky Mountain	196	164	.8	516	584	1.1	422
Plains							
All regions	11,287	13,463	1.2	32,033	47,808	1.5	27,703

The high ratios of drain to growth in the West are less significant than they would otherwise be because of the large quantities of virgin timber which permit a certain excess of cutting. It appears, however, that the present stand of economically available timber is less than the regulated growing stock necessary to sustain the current rate of saw-timber utilization.

The saw-timber stands in the East have only about two-thirds of the volume needed to sustain the current annual saw-timber drain. The all-timber volume needs to be increased even more.

Timber Requirements

No one can say with assurance just how much wood we shall use at any future time—even within the next decade, not to mention 50 or 100 years hence. Equally indeterminate is the amount of timber that we shall supply to other countries. Yet a sound program of forestry must aim to anticipate future domestic requirements and foreign demands with some degree of probability.

Among the factors that will influence the amount of timber we can consume or dispose of is the timber supply itself. An abundance of timber of the desired character and quality, available at low cost, would make for larger consumption; competition from other materials would be reduced, as wood would tend to replace more costly and less accessible materials. On the other hand, scarcity, poor quality, and high prices would make for less consumption. This is one reason why utilization of the great quantity of inferior materials now present in our forests constitutes a serious problem.

Another important factor is the ability of people to purchase. For example, bringing the average quality of the buildings on the 3 million farms in the South to a decent level will depend in large measure on the ability of the farmers to purchase lumber. Higher standards of living and greater prosperity would unquestionably make for greater consumption of timber.

There are also great possibilities for developing new uses and products, particularly through chemical processes. Although wood is by no means a stranger in the chemical-utilization field, it is still largely used, except for shaping by manufacture, in substantially the form in which nature produces it. But even so, many of our present uses of wood have developed during this century. Equally revolutionary changes in wood utilization may be expected in the future, with resultant increase in consumption, although certain present uses may decline.

Then there is every reason why the United States should play a larger part than heretofore in world timber markets. The trend of wood consumption in all the principal countries except the United States has been upward for a century. Meanwhile, most countries have arrived at a point where there is little opportunity to increase their present timber yield on a sustained basis. World markets may therefore take larger volumes of American timber, provided it is available and priced within the purchasing reach of foreign consumers.

Finally, the amount of American timber consumed will be influenced by the efficiency and aggressiveness with which all avenues for the utilization of wood are expanded. It is reasonable to believe that modern scientific methods applied to promoting the use of forest products, whether in present forms or as something entirely different, would increase consumption just as has been the case with other materials.

Table 10 summarizes what is believed to be a reasonable judgment of possible future consumption, markets, and other forest drain, looking ahead several decades.

Although domestic consumption has declined markedly from the peak of 45 billion board feet in 1906, we are still large users of lumber. Despite the development and steady promotion of other building materials, more than four-fifths of our dwellings are of all-wood construction, and stone, brick, tile, and concrete houses ordinarily also

Table 10.—Estimated future annual drain on American forests

Use or drain	Saw timber	All timber	Use or drain	Saw timber	All timber
	Million bd. ft.	*Million cu. ft.*		*Million bd. ft.*	*Million cu. ft.*
Domestic consumption:			Margin for new uses, for export, and for a safety factor	12,000	3,800
Lumber	30,000	6,000			
Fuel wood (70 million cords)	7,000	5,170			
Pulpwood (25 million cords)	7,000	2,500	Total estimated cut	63,000	19,400
Miscellaneous present uses	7,000	1,930	Losses, fire, insects, disease, etc	5,000	2,000
Total	51,000	15,600	All agencies	68,000	21,400

contain large quantities of lumber. Much lumber will be needed to construct and maintain really satisfactory rural and urban housing. A careful analysis of trends and other factors indicates a probable need of 30 billion board feet annually for the next 10 years. For the longer pull, an equal rate of consumption appears reasonable.

With the development of farm forestry and improved wood-burning stoves an upward trend in the use of fuel wood may be expected. Present annual consumption is some 60 million cords.

Ultimate self-sufficiency in pulpwood and a continuing upward trend in paper consumption will necessitate a large increase over our present annual 8 million cords of domestic pulpwood.

The margin indicated for new uses and export and as a measure of safety is considered reasonable in laying out a constructive program of forestry. Although it may seem large, one must remember that not all of the timber that is grown has to be cut; that in publicly owned forests the maintenance of forest cover, to protect watersheds and assure other benefits, usually takes precedence over timber use and that many decades will be required to put our forests in condition to yield permanently 21.4 billion cubic feet a year.

A Plan of Timber Management

The sustained-yield objective proposed in the preceding paragraphs is greatly in excess of current growth. Evidently a substantial advance in forestry is requisite to attain that objective. This is necessary also if full use, consistent with economic practicability, is to be made of our commercial forest land. It is also clear that intensive management of all commercial forest land would eventually produce timber in excess of any economic needs that now appear probable.

Any practical concept of management designed to bring ultimate yields into harmony with probable requirements must recognize that the intensity of management on a given tract will be influenced by many economic and physical factors. Lands characterized by good site, favorable ownership, proximity to consuming centers, and the like, will be managed intensively. The poor and remote sites may justify little more than protection. An intermediate category will be adapted to an extensive form of management.

A plan of management which would bring ultimate timber yields and requirements into balance is summarized in table 11. This plan, which is of course somewhat theoretical, recognizes the need for flexibility, takes account of regional conditions and opportunities, and would ultimately provide a sustained annual yield of 21.4 billion cubic feet, including 68 billion board feet of saw timber.

Table 11.—A suggested plan of management to bring timber yields and requirements into balance

Type of management	Area	Total annual yield
	Million acres	*Million cubic feet*
Intensive forestry [1]	100.0	8,400
Extensive forestry [2]	311.7	13,000
Simple protection	50.0	[3] 0
Total	461.7	21,400

[1] Management under a long-term plan based on high standards of cutting practice, cultural measures, planting when necessary, and protection, so that the quantity and quality of the yield approach the productive capacity of the land.

[2] Involves, in addition to adequate fire protection, such cutting practices and cultural measures as are necessary to maintain growth in sufficient quantity for commercial utilization.

[3] None of the estimated 370 million cubic feet of growth is considered to be economically available.

To attain such an objective in 75 years would require an increase under intensive forestry of more than a million acres a year. It would mean a great expansion in the area under extensive forestry. The growing stock in the East would have to be built up to twice the present available stand. In the West the remaining timber would have to be carefully husbanded to facilitate the conversion of the western forests to a sustained-yield basis.

Such a plan would have far-reaching and fundamental benefits. It calls for the fullest use of the land consistent with economic practicability, and it would provide an adequate supply of timber and timber products to meet domestic needs, together with a substantial exportable surplus. As a basis for countless private forest activities and industries, it would provide, in whole or in part, the economic foundation for thousands of communities.

THE ACTION PROGRAM REQUIRED

Space permits only a sketch of the program required to restore and maintain the forest resource, and that largely of the aid which the public in its own interest might well give to private owners. In general, a program to be adequate must provide the action needed to achieve two major purposes:

(1) To stop forest liquidation and to create and maintain a real forest economy with human welfare its goal, by putting our forest land permanently to work producing in abundance all the products and services of which it is capable.

(2) To enable our people to utilize abundantly the timber and other products and services of the forest. Existing utilization reflects bare subsistence levels for many of our people, not reasonable standards of living. There are great opportunities for expansion in our use of these products and services if they can be made available at low cost and if our people generally have the requisite purchasing power.

Private Forests

The safeguarding of existing stands in the East and their development into adequate growing stock is the most urgently needed measure. Generally speaking, a forest property upon which stands are already established, even though inadequately, can be developed into a regulated sustained-yield enterprise at less expense and more quickly than can one upon which stands are largely lacking.

This does not minimize the necessity of providing for an adequate planting program for areas not likely to restock naturally; for the development of adequate protection against fire, insects, and disease; and for the control of cutting in the western regions, to facilitate the conversion of those forests to an adequate sustained-yield basis.

Obtaining products other than lumber just as far as practical from improvement or salvage cuttings would help to build up the growing stock. The yield of usable growth could also be increased by careful selection of the stands to be cut and of the trees to be cut within those stands, where partial cutting methods can be applied. Those stands and trees should be cut which offer no prospect of making a good rate of growth in volume or value, and those should be left which promise to increase rapidly in volume or value in the near future. Wherever possible, a good stand of thrifty young and middle-aged trees should be left on cut-over lands. Through various silvicultural operations it would be possible to increase the proportion of fast-growing or otherwise desirable species and more nearly to maintain that density of stand which is most favorable to rapid growth of timber.

There is general agreement that Government must play a larger part than heretofore in effectuating a forestry program, because of the size, diversity, and complexity of the problems and the obstacles which must be overcome. Existing and proposed policies and measures boil down to three major forms of public action:

(1) Public cooperation, in many forms.

(2) Public regulation.

(3) Public acquisition, by the Federal Government, States, and communities.

From a long-run point of view, many eminent authorities believe that nothing less than all three forms of action, going forward concurrently, will really fill the bill. There can be little question that each has strong and weak points, while together they seemingly cover all essential requirements.

Public Cooperation

Public cooperation on private forest land may be furnished by the Federal Government directly or through the States, by the States, or by smaller political subdivisions. Its essence is the removal of inherent or man-made handicaps insurmountable by private owners, and its justification is the public welfare.

The "right" of private enterprise to make its own decisions is not ordinarily impaired by public cooperation. In fact, private owners favor cooperation, if for no other reason than that most of its forms carry financial aid, and the cooperation is voluntary on their part.

Public cooperation has already taken several forms. All of these

223761°—40——32

should be continued, most of them on a broader scale, and several further measures are needed.

Protection against fire.—Adequate protection against fire is one basic requirement. Federal aid on private and State lands began with the Weeks law of 1911 and was expanded greatly by the Clarke-McNary Act of 1924, which established three cardinal principles for cooperation:

(1) Aid to go only to States that provide a protection system by legislation.

(2) Funds granted not to exceed combined State and accredited private expenditures.

(3) Cooperation to be handled through appropriate State officials.

In the fiscal year 1939, the Federal Government cooperated with 40 States and Hawaii in providing fire protection; some 269 million acres are now under protection. Only about 1 percent of the protected area was burned during the calendar year 1938, and losses were about $7,180,000; about 20 percent of the 144 million acres without protection was burned over, with an estimated loss of $28,800,000.

Organized protection should be provided for the unprotected 144 million acres, almost three-fourths of which is in the South. On much of the area already protected the protection should be intensified.

Protection against forest insects and diseases.—Protection against insects and diseases should be given greater emphasis. Losses caused by these agencies exceed those from fire. The outstanding need is for a Nation-wide organization to discover incipient epidemics by frequent surveys and to fight them while small.

Forest and forest-products research.—Obviously, if private and public owners alike could have sound technical knowledge on how to handle forest resources, and authoritative information on the production, use, and marketing of forest products, they could do a much better job.

Only a few of the large corporations and industrial associations are financially able to conduct research on the broad scale that is necessary for solving many forest problems. For the 3.5 million farm-woodland owners and most of the 1 million or more industrial and other nonfarm owners, it is out of the question. Public agencies will have to do the job for private owners as well as for themselves.

The Federal forest research organization includes a Nation-wide system of forest experiment stations and the Forest Products Laboratory. By far the greater part of the forest research carried on up to now has been done by the Federal Government. There is a large opportunity for the States and other agencies to expand their work in this field, particularly on State and local problems.

Forestry extension.—Although extension work in forestry with both farmers and industrial owners has been under way for years, it is still on an entirely inadequate basis. This is the more remarkable because effective forestry extension—and to be effective it must be supported by adequate research—can go to the heart of the problems of private ownership. The big job of forestry extension is to change the thinking of private owners, to make them want to grow timber, and to show them how to do it. This work will have to be greatly expanded if Federal and State efforts are to measure up to the needs of the forestry-extension job.

Utilization extension.—Promotion of the use of forest products should be a major feature of any well-rounded national program of forestry. Of course, no one means can be depended on exclusively to insure markets. Demonstration of and instruction in new or improved methods of processing and using forest products can, however, perform much the same function in this field that forestry extension proper can in the field of timber growing. But in spite of the clear need for it, there has never been adequate provision for publicly supported utilization extension.

Benefit payments to farmers.—Fuller recognition of improved forest practices in benefit payments under the agricultural conservation program would tend to stimulate farm forestry. This would also help farmers to increase their income, particularly those with appreciable areas of land submarginal for cultivation but suitable for forests, and those in the problem areas of forest regions who have so far received the least aid although needing it most.

Forest planting—Unless the public gives a further lift, private ownership is likely to be slow in doing its 25-million-acre planting job. Federal aid is now limited to farms. Planting on industrial and other nonfarm holdings might be stimulated by Federal aid in furnishing low-cost seed and planting stock in much greater quantities than is now supplied solely by the States.

Cooperatives.—Through pooling their forest resources and efforts in cooperative associations, many small owners might in time largely work out their own salvation. But to furnish essential advice and leadership, continuing extension and research effort and perhaps additional Federal legislation will be required.

Forest credits.—Federally sponsored large-volume credits may be the key to good forest practice by many private owners.

Forest fire insurance.—Forest fire insurance would provide relative freedom from one serious financial uncertainty for private owners, yet such insurance is lacking in this country.

Forest taxation.—Although there is no panacea for the tax problem, equitable State and local forest taxation can remove a real though exaggerated handicap. Contrary to popular opinion, the numerous State tax-exemption and yield-tax laws so far passed have been almost universally ineffective.

Public Regulation

Public regulation, the second form of concurrent action on private forest lands, probably offers the greatest hope of stopping promptly the destruction of old-growth and second-growth forests. Advocates of public regulation point out that:

(1) Regulation is essential because of the inadequacies of both public cooperation and public acquisition.

(2) Regulation will assure a private quid pro quo for public expenditures in most forms of cooperation. The lands of a private owner may be protected against fire, insects, and diseases by public cooperation, but without some form of control he can nullify all by destructive cutting.

(3) Regulation would not go beyond flexible minimum forest-practice requirements needed to keep private lands fairly productive.

(4) Regulation protects private owners who recognize social

obligations inherent in good forest-land management from those who might otherwise continue ruthless liquidation.

(5) Regulation is not a new exercise of sovereignty. Nearly every country that has a real forestry program exercises some degree of control over the handling of private forests.

(6) Regulation is not wholly new and untried even in the United States. Although it is largely limited to fire-protection controls, four States already have regulatory laws going beyond fire protection.

Public Acquisition

Where private forestry will not pay its way, or where private owners cannot or will not function in the conservation of the forest resource, public acquisition is the only sure solution. More specifically, the public should acquire forest land needed to accomplish the following:

(1) To insure the beneficial effects of the forest in regulating run-off and minimizing floods and in controlling erosion.

(2) To safeguard the economic life of dependent communities and regions by furnishing maximum continuous opportunities for privately owned industries and for gainful employment in growing, harvesting, processing, and using timber.

(3) To create a permanent forest economy in forest regions where no sound economy has ever existed.

(4) To unscramble private-ownership patterns built up for liquidation and so complex as to make satisfactory forest-resource conservation impossible.

(5) To insure the restoration of wrecked or devastated forests.

(6) To consolidate existing public forests and purchase units, the administration of which in the public interest is now often thwarted by private or other interior holdings of key timber, range, recreational tracts, or water facilities.

Investigations by the Forest Service indicate that about one-third of the forest land in private ownership could advantageously be taken into public ownership—by communities, the States, or the Federal Government—in order to give the greatest assurance that the resource will be restored and handled in the public interest.

Public Forests

All public lands now held or hereafter acquired should be made outstanding examples of good management and public service. Given the necessary legislation and appropriations, it will be possible to put all the public forest resources under much more intensive management than has heretofore been possible and to build them up to a much higher level of productivity. The public forests should be made in fact as well as in theory the basis for a real forest economy with all that such an economy implies in public service. The beneficial effects should extend far beyond their boundaries.

Farm-Management Problems in an Era of Change

by Sherman E. Johnson [1]

WHEN ALL is said and done, most farm problems get down to the one problem that worries the farmer most—how can he manage his farm so as to make a livelihood? This article analyzes the nature of the farm business from a broad standpoint and shows the types of adjustment open to farmers who have to meet economic difficulties. Much attention is given to adjustments required for sheer business survival, since this has been the acute problem during much of the past decade. National agricultural policy is brought into the picture because so many farmers have found that their own individual efforts are not enough to enable them to cope with modern conditions. Finally, the author considers the agricultural situation region by region and indicates some of the adjustments in farm management that are possible or needed in each region.

MANY of the important farm-management problems that face farmers today differ from region to region, and with the type of farming within each region. Some are not of recent origin—for instance, the erosion problem and the low-income situation in the South. Most of them, however, have their roots in the expansion of the farm production plant to meet wartime and boomtime demands for farm

[1] Sherman E. Johnson is Head Agricultural Economist, in charge Division of Farm Management and Costs, Bureau of Agricultural Economics.

products. Once production was built up to a high level, the low prices resulting from the shrinkage of both domestic and foreign demand brought a train of maladjustments that have become apparent in the form of farm foreclosures, tax delinquency, and other evidences of distress. These are manifestations of the painful and wholly inadequate results of individual efforts to contract agricultural output. The public action programs instituted in recent years are long-delayed recognition that more than individual action is necessary to cope with some of the maladjustments and defects that have appeared in our agricultural economy under the stress and strain of national and world events in the post-war period.

Other forces have operated in one or more regions of the country to accentuate the maladjustments caused by the low incomes resulting from the shrinkage in demand for agricultural products. Serious droughts have occurred in one or more regions every year from 1930 to 1936. Rapid adoption of power farming in the 1920's released for production of market crops much land that formerly was used for producing feed for work animals. Reduction in labor requirements incident to mechanization has displaced large numbers of hired workers and many farm operators and their families. Inadequate care of the farms and growing destruction by wind and water erosion have become increasingly evident in many areas.

THE INFLEXIBLE NATURE OF THE FARMING BUSINESS

The nature of the farming business is such that once new land has been brought into production and new investments have been made in buildings and equipment, it is difficult under any circumstances to contract production in response to lower prices. Historically, such adjustments have never before been necessary for the entire country because expanding markets have kept pace with increases in production, except for short periods. Some areas in certain regions, such as the Northeast, have suffered from the competition of newer, more productive areas, but over a period of years adjustment has been accomplished through abandonment of the poorer lands and a shift in types of farming in the better areas to supply nearby markets with bulky and perishable products.

Adjustment through the process of land abandonment is feasible, however, only when employment opportunities are open in other occupations. With millions of unemployed persons in the cities, even with farm income as low as it was in 1932, farming represented the only available opportunity for those on farms.

The farmer acting as an individual cannot influence the forces external to his own business, including the price of his product. Consequently, his management problem as an individual is one of utilizing the productive resources at his command in such a way that he will receive the highest possible return from his investment and for the work that he and his family do. Extreme pressure for income under depression conditions may dictate action on some farms that leads to such results as soil depletion or deterioration of farm buildings. Although such action may represent the best adjustment the farm family can make in the circumstances, it still leaves them with very inadequate returns and may be quite contrary to the larger social interest. Public action is then necessary to deal adequately with such a situation.

PROBLEMS FACED BY FARMERS

At any one time the farm business as a going concern is the result of past commitments based on prevailing or expected cost and price relationships. But if the expected relationships do not materialize, the farmer may be faced with one or more of the following adjustment problems:

(1) Whether changes should be made in the organization of the business in order to increase farm income. These might involve changes both in kinds and proportions of the crop and livestock enterprises.

(2) Whether changes should be made in operating practices in one or more crop or livestock enterprises.

(3) Whether changes will have to be made in farm organization or operation, or both, in order to meet certain pressing financial obligations. (This is the problem of business survival.)

(4) Whether he or members of his family should seek outside employment part of the time.

(5) Whether he should stay in the business or sell out to go into another occupation or perhaps to retire.

The first problem involves questions pertaining to the organization of the farm business that have been given much attention in farm-management studies. If the changes do not require new investments in land, buildings, equipment, and livestock, the problem is one of balancing the additional outlay that would be involved against the increases in income that might be expected from the change. The question of the relative risk involved in the two plans must also be considered. If new investments are called for in the projected plan, provision must be made for both interest and depreciation on these. The cost of this new investment then becomes a factor of resistance to the change. If the additional labor required exceeds the available family labor the questions of cost and availability of hired labor must be considered. Even if the additional labor can be furnished by the family, the question should be raised whether the net income to them is worth the required sacrifice of leisure. Often this choice involves the loss of educational opportunties for the children and perhaps overwork for certain members of the family.

The second problem, changes in operating practices, often involves only changes in variable costs, such as feeding dairy cows more purchased feed. Then the difference in cash outlay can be balanced directly against the difference in income. But perhaps more often the change involves investment in equipment, such as a tractor, in which case interest and depreciation enter in and furnish resistance to the change. The question of changes in operating practices will be taken up later in connection with the effects of technological development on farm-management problems.

But suppose the farmer finds that adjustments of types 1 and 2 would be profitable in his business; he may still be prevented from making the shift if it involves new investments for which he cannot obtain the necessary funds. This raises adjustment problem 3, concerning changes necessitated by pressing financial obligations. It is evident that sometimes changes otherwise desirable may be prevented by financial difficulties, or the situation may dictate a wholly new set of adjustments. The question of business survival then becomes the greatest management problem.

Adjustments Necessary for Business Survival

In working out the adjustments necessary for business survival, it is important that the farmer have clearly in mind the nature of his cost problem as it is conditioned by the fixed nature of some farm investments and by the lack of alternative uses for some of his land, buildings, and equipment. Most important of all is the presence or lack of alternative employment for the farm family.

The statement is often made that a large proportion of the farming costs are fixed in the sense that they cannot be readily reduced by curtailing output when prices fall. Fixed costs, as contrasted with variable costs, have their origins in the fact that the productive life of land, buildings, and some equipment and livestock exceeds the production period; also predetermined-payment contracts for the use of land and buildings and sometimes for livestock and equipment are entered into in advance of the production period.

The different cost items can usually be classified as follows:

Fixed costs:
- (1) Rent for land and buildings.
- (2) Interest on investment in equipment and livestock.
- (3) Obsolescence and that part of the depreciation on buildings, machinery, and livestock which does not vary with their use.
- (4) Insurance on buildings, equipment, and livestock.
- (5) Taxes on real estate and personal property.
- (6) Wages for the operator and other family labor.

Variable costs:
- (1) Current supplies, such as seed and fertilizer.
- (2) Hired labor and other services.
- (3) Current repairs and replacements, which vary with the use of buildings and equipment.

It is obvious that once commitments have been made on a given farm, the items enumerated as fixed costs in the above list will not vary proportionately with the quantity of output and that therefore a large proportion of the costs cannot be avoided by reducing production. How, then, does a farmer meet a situation with prices that do not cover the costs of production as they are listed above? The answer is that some of these costs are postponable in the sense that the operator can stay in the business for a time without meeting them. It will be noted that the fixed costs include rent for land and buildings, interest and depreciation, and wages for the operator and other family labor employed on the farm. If the farmer owns the land and is fortunate enough to be free of debt, he will have no cash outlay for land rent and interest. Depreciation does not constitute a current cash expense, and the operator and his family may have to take much less than prevailing wages as their return for the time they have worked on the farm.

If prices continue to drop and the land is suited for other uses that promise higher returns, the farmer may shift to other lines of production. But in a general depression the prices of other products may be equally low, and perhaps there are no openings in other occupations.

The farmer may then find that landlords and creditors will compromise on rent and interest payments, depreciation can be postponed, insurance dropped, and taxes go delinquent for a time. When circumstances necessitating such postponements arise, the variable costs and a minimum living for the farm family perhaps constitute the only costs that must be met in order that production be maintained.

There is little information available on how the farmer adjusts his costs in a depression period. Even where accounts have been kept the different items have not been segregated to show the timing and the extent of reduction in the various items as the depression deepens. Information is available on the cash outlay for both family living and farm operations on a small group of farms in the wheat area of central South Dakota for the period 1930–38.[2] In this area the financial pressure caused by a combination of drought and depression was probably as extreme as anywhere in the country. On the other hand, the farms in the group in question were among the larger and more successful in the area. Greater adjustment in expenses was therefore possible. The information serves as an illustration of how costs are adjusted under financial pressure but should not be considered characteristic in detail of the adjustments that were made elsewhere.

Total cash outlay for both family living and farm operations dropped in 1933 to a low point of 48 percent of the level in 1930. Family living expenses reached their low point in 1934 at 56 percent of their 1930 level. Current operating expenses were at their low point in 1933 when they averaged 63 percent of their 1930 level. They increased in 1934–36 because of the need for purchased feed to tide over the drought. Hired labor was reduced to 5 percent of its 1930 level at its low point in 1934. Expenditures for repairs were at their low point in 1934 when they were 15 percent of the 1930 level, but they increased to 62 percent in 1935, indicating that if operations are to go on, equipment and buildings must be maintained at least on a minimum basis.

On this group of farms the expenses for rent, interest, and taxes were listed as the amount accrued for the given year rather than the amount actually paid; hence information is not available regarding the actual adjustment made in these items. However, even the contract obligations for these items were reduced considerably in this area in the years following 1930. On the basis of available information on delinquency in interest, rent, and tax payments in this area, it seems probable that these items went unpaid on most of these farms in the years 1932–34 and perhaps also in 1936.

It is obvious that the problem of business survival has been of foremost importance to farmers of this area as well as many other areas in recent years. The question then arises, how are adjustments for business survival likely to affect the intensity of operations and hence the volume of output on a given farm? This would seem to depend upon a balancing of additional expenses (the expenses that will increase with output) against the probable returns for additional product; also on whether opportunities exist for increasing the output; and perhaps on the stage in the struggle for survival—that is, whether the attempt to maintain the business seems worth while.

[2] Unpublished information collected by the South Dakota Agricultural Experiment Station, cooperating with the Bureau of Agricultural Economics in the first 3 years of the period.

Many farmers find it possible to increase output in a depression period by applying more labor and by using their equipment more intensively. The additional labor is furnished by the farmer and his family and is not considered by them as additional expense. The Corn Belt farmer, for instance, may forget about a soil-saving rotation and plant a larger percentage of his land to corn, if he has the necessary equipment and if longer hours of work on the part of the farm family will meet the additional labor requirements. Such action partly accounts for the increase in corn acreage in the Corn Belt between 1929 and 1932.[3] During the recent depression a common method of increasing the intensity of operations on Corn Belt farms was to increase the size of the dairy enterprise. When this involves a shift to milking the cows formerly used exclusively for beef production, almost the only additional resource used is the labor of the farm family; they will be obliged to work longer hours doing chores.

Under such conditions the volume of output from a given farm unit is very likely to increase. It seems evident, however, that whether it does so in a given case depends on the type of farming followed and on the nature of the individual farmer's cost situation, as well as on how low the price of the product falls in relation to the additional expenses. For instance, if the farmer owns his land and has no indebtedness he may find it advisable to seek the "storm cellar" for the period of the depression. In other words, he may actually reduce his volume of output. In taking this action he may not receive the largest possible net cash returns for a time, but he may realize that they can be obtained only if he and his family work harder, and at the sacrifice of soil maintenance and at a greater cost of building and equipment depreciation, both of which must be made up some time in the future. He may decide that the value of the additional income at the present time is not worth this sacrifice. Thus he is in a position where he can afford to take the long-term view and consider other costs in addition to those that vary with output.

But even the farmer who is hard-pressed financially may find that his land and his type of farming require large cash expenses for labor, feed, and fertilizer if he is to increase his output. Balancing this increase in cash expenses against the additional income, he may find that he cannot increase his return above expenses by increasing his output. Moreover, the price of the product may fall so low in relation to cash expenses that the farmer in this situation may be forced to reduce his output.

This approach in analyzing the individual farmer's adjustment problem when he is under pressing financial obligations should throw some light on a question about which there has been much previous discussion, namely, whether there is more exploitation of soil resources in a period of relatively low prices for agricultural products than in a period of high prices.[4] It seems probable that in a period of very high relative prices, such as those during the World War, nearly all farmers

---

[3] BUREAU OF AGRICULTURAL ECONOMICS, DIVISION OF FARM MANAGEMENT AND COSTS. ACCOMPLISHMENTS OF THE A. A. A. PROGRAM TOWARDS THE LONG-TIME OBJECTIVE OF A BALANCED AGRICULTURE. Unpublished manuscript. 1938.

[4] JESNESS, O. B. AGRICULTURAL ADJUSTMENT IN RELATION TO GRAIN AND DAIRY PRODUCTION. *In* American Institute of Cooperation, American Cooperation, 1936, pp. 722–731. Washington, D. C. 1936.

would find it profitable to increase the volume of production. Expansion into new, and perhaps poorer, land areas could also be expected in such a period, whereas depression conditions would lead to increase of output by only a part of the producers—those struggling for business survival. A larger group, of course, would be likely to neglect established crop rotations and the use of commercial fertilizer. Perhaps a more serious problem in depression is the unrecompensed depreciation of buildings and equipment.

INDIVIDUAL ADJUSTMENT AND SOCIAL VALUES

It is evident from the foregoing that some of the adjustments individual farmers may make, especially in the interest of business survival, may be quite contrary to the larger social interest; and when the total effects of such adjustments are considered they are often detrimental to farmers as a group. Public action is therefore needed to assist farmers to adjust their business during a depression in such a way that the larger social interest is better served, and so that farmers themselves may obtain increased incomes without expanding production beyond the absorptive power of the market and at the expense of soil depletion, building maintenance, and, worst of all, the education and health of growing children.

While public assistance to farmers has been instituted along many lines in recent years, one of the vital needs today is a better integration of public action with the needs of the individual farm. We need answers, area by area, to some of the following problems: (1) What kinds of public programs are needed to assist farmers in meeting the problems in a given area? (2) If present programs do not fill this need, what changes or modifications would be necessary to accomplish the purpose? (3) What changes can be made in program application to accomplish more readily the objectives sought? (4) How can farmers best adjust themselves to the requirements for participation? (5) How are present and contemplated programs likely to affect given sizes and types of farms in specific locations? (6) What will be the probable magnitude of change in farming as a result of a given program? All these questions involve farm-management problems. Adequate answers are of vital importance to both farmers and program administrators.

Two factors of importance in both prosperity and depression are conservation and the effects of technical progress. As it appears to the farmer, the question of soil conservation is largely one of balancing present income against expected income in the future, unless the uncertainty of his tenure prevents him from counting on future income. In the public interest it may often be desirable to prevent the soil depletion that results from extreme need for present income on the part of individual farmers. The social group is better able to strike a balance in favor of future income than is the individual.

It has been previously mentioned that technological developments have been one of the important causes of at least temporary distress to many farm groups. This situation arises from a divergence of individual and social interest, at least in the transition period. From a broader social standpoint, all technical progress is desirable that results in the production of new products needed by society or a reduction of effort in the production of old products. The divergence of interest arises when the new processses are adopted without providing alternative employment for those who are displaced, either directly by the new practice or as a result of pressure from lower prices caused by increased volume of production. Whenever practices are adopted that result in the lowering of labor requirements for production the change usually results in less demand for hired labor, although on farms where nearly all the work is done by family labor the change may only relieve the physical burden of farm work.

At any given time there is a wide disparity in adoption of any improved practice. In some of the Eastern States, within relatively short distances one can see small grain being harvested with a cradle, a grain binder, and a combine harvester. On the farm where grain is now harvested with a cradle the adoption of a newer method would not necessarily increase the income to the farm family. It would depend on the nature of the farming costs on this farm. If the grain is now harvested by family labor that could find no employment otherwise or if the field is so small that a harvesting machine would represent a disproportionate investment, the income would not be increased. However, it cannot be overemphasized that hand labor competing with more efficient machine methods on other farms and in other areas will bring very low returns for the effort expended, and both the individuals concerned and society as a whole would benefit if more productive employment could be found.

The introduction of new practices elsewhere will decrease the incomes of those who cannot adopt them only when the price of the product is lowered by an increased volume resulting from such adoption. Increased production from a given area of land is inherent in many biological developments, as hybrid corn; but increased production from mechanical developments is not likely to be very important in the future because there is little new land to be brought into production. The urge to increase the volume of a given product, therefore, encounters competition from other products for the use of the land, or raises the question of the possibility of more intensive cultivation of the same area. But even though the price of the product is not lowered by increased supplies, the income disparity between the groups that adopt the new practices and those that continue with the old will widen if the new development results in actual cost reductions. There is an offsetting factor, however, in that substituting machinery for labor usually increases the proportion of cash costs and therefore increases the price risks in farming.

REGIONAL PROBLEMS AND SUGGESTIONS FOR IMPROVEMENTS

We turn now to a regional consideration of farm-management problems. Differences in the timing and the severity of the impact of depression, drought, and the other major forces that have affected farming in the different regions in recent years can be observed from the information supplied by farmers on the financial results from their businesses for each year since 1922.[5]

The year-to-year changes in the average net returns to the farm family and the farm investment on the farms reporting this information since 1922 or 1923 are shown in figure 1 on an index basis.[6] In the following discussion the changes in returns during this period are compared by groups of States representing the North, the South, and the West. Some of the causes for the present situation in each region are analyzed and some steps in adjustment are suggested.

The North Atlantic Region

According to figure 1, the returns in the North Atlantic States did not drop nearly as rapidly during the depression as in the Lake States and the Corn Belt, nor did they reach as extreme a low point. This relative stability in returns in the Northeast needs to be related to the situation in the World War boom period. As compared with those of the pre-war period, 1910–14, farm prices did not rise as high in the war boom in the North Atlantic region as in the other two regions. But they stayed about 20 points higher during the 1920's, and they did not drop so low during the depression as in the areas more closely tied to the export market. This evidence would indicate that farm returns in the North Atlantic States were on a relatively high level in the 1920's as compared with that of the pre-war period, and that therefore the less precipitous drop in the depression is even more significant.

The conclusion seems justified that the region as a whole shows considerable stability in farm prices and farm income. There are, of course, great variations from year to year in certain specialized types of farming—potato growing, for instance. But for dairy products, poultry, and even some of the fruit and vegetable crops, the large nearby markets serve as a stabilizer of prices and income. Moreover, the climatic environment of this region as compared with those of some others involves less risk in crop production; hence there is less year-to-year variation in the quantities of products marketed.

When the land resources of the North Atlantic region are compared with those of the other two regions, it is realized that the North Atlantic is an older region and that in many sections soils of rather low natural fertility have been depleted by constant cropping. To rebuild or even to maintain them at their present levels of productivity involves cash outlay.

If we consider the problems in this region by types of farming we realize that in spite of past stabilities in prices and income there are many groups of farmers that today are facing severe competition from other areas and are wondering whether they can remain in the business under such competitive strain. To approach this question intelligently we need to analyze how inter-area competition takes place

[5] For some regions since 1923. Information obtained by mail questionnaire from farm operators and compiled by S. W. Mendum in the Bureau of Agricultural Economics. While this sample may not be strictly representative of farming in each region, it is believed to reflect quite adequately the year-to-year changes. The States included in each region are as follows: North Atlantic—all States east of Ohio and north of Maryland and West Virginia; Great Lakes States—Minnesota, Wisconsin, and Michigan; Corn Belt—Iowa, Missouri, Illinois, Indiana, and Ohio; South Atlantic—the Atlantic Seaboard States from Maryland south, and including West Virginia. South Central—Kentucky, Tennessee, Alabama, Mississippi, Louisiana, Arkansas, Oklahoma, and Texas. Great Plains States—North Dakota, South Dakota, Nebraska, and Kansas; Mountain States—Montana, Wyoming, Colorado, New Mexico, Arizona, Utah, Idaho; Pacific States—Washington, Oregon, and California.

[6] The average dollar returns for the base period 1924–29 are taken as 100. The computed returns, or net results, do not include the value of farm products produced on the farm and consumed in the household, nor do they include income from sources other than the farm business.

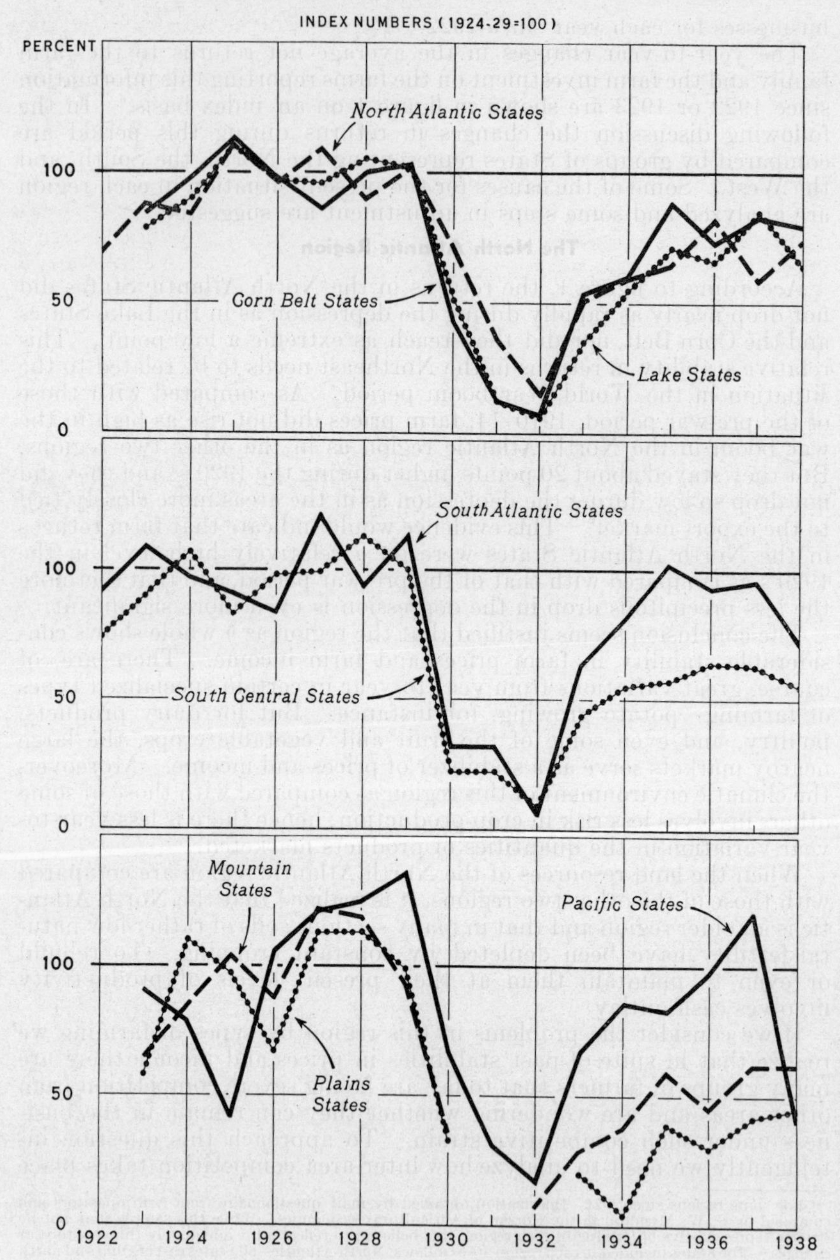

Figure 1.—The returns from farming in eight major regions in 1922–38 were individually computed from reports of farmers. As shown here, they represent the cash receipts of the farm business reduced by the cash outlay, with net increase in inventory value of farm personal property added or net decrease deducted. Net income from sources other than the farm business has not been included. The States included in the special groups are as follows: Corn Belt States: Iowa, Missouri, Illinois, Indiana, and Ohio; Lake States:

and also the relative permanence of some of the advantages and disadvantages of competitive areas.

During the last 100 years this region has shifted from grain farming, wool production, and self-sufficing diversified farming to intensive production of dairy products, poultry, and fruits and vegetables. Part of this shift was forced by competition from the newer areas, but fortunately for this region the growing industrial population at the same time created new nearby markets for the more bulky and perishable products. Growing industries also furnished alternative employment for those who could not readily adapt their farming to the new situation.

The real pinch in inter-area competition occurs when outside competition makes present farming unprofitable and when no other alternatives are available. What happens then, of course, is that the fixed costs cannot be met and the farmers with heavy indebtedness find their mortgages foreclosed. Eventually the pressure will be transferred from farm income to land values. If the land-value structure is high enough to absorb the shock, the agriculture of the area may again be prosperous even after such a readjustment. In the meantime, however, many farmers are crowded to the wall, and some of the poorer farms are abandoned.

It may be worth while to refer again to the old principle that if two or more areas are producing a product for the same market their total costs of production tend to be equal unless there is serious maladjustment in production. Thus the advantages of more productive soil or nearness to market (and therefore lower transportation costs) tend to become capitalized in land values. Other less permanent advantages may also be capitalized. If then for some reason a part of such advantages is lost, the readjustment takes place first through lower farm incomes, but eventually land values are adjusted to the new income expectancy, and costs in the different producing areas again approach equality, that is, with land rent included.

In the North Atlantic region the onward pressure of competition seems to have left some eddies in which farmers are still operating on a self-sufficing basis and obtaining relatively low family incomes. This group constitutes an urgent problem today because industrial opportunities have not developed to attract the younger generation to the same extent as in the 1920's.

In contrast with the self-sufficing group, extremely specialized commercial farms have been encouraged by the nearby markets. There is, of course, a great diversity in farming types even within small areas. A type-of-farming pattern on a map may look like anything but specialization, but when the detailed set-up of a dairy farm, a poultry farm, an orchard, or vegetable business in this region is examined a high degree of specialization will be found as compared with middlewestern farming systems.

Minnesota, Wisconsin, and Michigan; Plains States: North Dakota, South Dakota, Nebraska, and Kansas. The other groups are those used in the censuses. Net losses were shown by those reporting from the Mountain States in 1931 and from the Plains States in 1932, mostly because of reductions in inventories in those years. Index numbers for 1924–29 are taken as 100 percent.

The existence of an extraordinary amount of specialization as a general phenomenon has a very close relation to the problems of organization and operation that confront farmers in this region today. The poultry industry, for example, has developed close to the urban markets along the Atlantic seaboard and has benefited from a period of relatively low grain prices. It has been influenced tremendously by a remarkable development of scientific knowledge about breeding, feeding, and control of disease. Some of these developments came earliest in some of the eastern experiment stations—and the eastern poultrymen took advantage of the possibilities more rapidly than their competitors in the Midwest. One cannot be certain, however, that the resulting difference in comparative advantage is permanent. To retain this advantage means that leadership in new technical and economic developments must be held in this region.

This much one can say about the poultryman's position from now on, however. His feed costs are likely to be relatively higher than formerly, and it is therefore more important than ever for him to keep abreast of current scientific developments. Probably the most efficient use of labor and equipment represents a problem which would deserve study on many poultry farms. It is possible that correction of maladjustments of this character would offset loss of advantage in other directions.

In dairying, the outstanding change, and the greatest problem from the farm-management angle, is related to the adoption of soil-improvement practices. Encouraged by the agricultural conservation program, dairymen are apparently stepping up the normal rate of adoption of these practices. In other words, the conservation program seems to be hastening a desirable adjustment. Increased use of lime and fertilizer is bound to affect hay and pasture yields. What are the implications of this? Will it mean too much milk? Will farmers really adjust their rations to take advantage of the home-produced feed? Some farm accounts indicate that dairymen are too slow to adjust their purchases of grain when more roughage is available.

A companion problem is the probable effect of the Agricultural Adjustment Administration program on dairy production in the Midwest and on supplies of grain feeds which the farmer in the Northeast has to buy. Preliminary studies indicate that the A.A.A. program by itself will not greatly increase dairy production in the Midwest. In fact, dairying in the Corn Belt increases more rapidly in depression periods—when corn, hogs, and beef cattle are selling at distress prices. Potentially the Corn Belt is a formidable competitor in dairy production, but this competition will not become a reality as long as corn, hogs, and beef cattle are more profitable enterprises. Greater competition may be expected from the Lake States because of lack of alternatives there. Some increase in the price of concentrate feed can be met by reductions in purchases because of the increased production of hay and pasture already mentioned.

The vegetable growers are confronted with numerous farm problems in connection with changing market demands and competition from other areas. In this field it seems important to study the special demands of the given market and, if possible, to discover outlets for products which either from a seasonal or a quality standpoint can best be supplied by a given producing area. The same need for staying ahead of the competitive procession appears here as in poultry production. Both are very specialized commercial enterprises. Developments in the quick freezing of fruits and vegetables will probably intensify competition for vegetable growers who are depending for their advantage on nearness to market.

Increased mechanization on vegetable farms involves larger and larger investments in the business. These, of course, are made in the first instance in the hope of increasing incomes, but if they involve the use of borrowed money they also increase the risks of the enterprise and leave the operator vulnerable when rapid changes take place in market demand and prices. On the other hand, a mechanized large-scale enterprise may be the only type that can successfully meet competition from other areas. If so, this type of farming is likely to shift to producers who can afford to carry such risks.

Conditions in the apple industry, particularly on the marketing and price side, have been undergoing rapid changes. Varieties that formerly commanded premiums have experienced lower prices when supplies increased. It is possible that many orchardmen with moderate-sized orchards, who have earned a good living from specialized apple production, will find it necessary to add some other enterprise, such as dairying or poultry, in order to have a paying combination in the future.

The possibilities of combining forest enterprises with farming in this region need to be fully explored. At present we lack adequate information regarding expected production on a sustained-yield basis, in regard to potential markets, and therefore as to the returns that can be expected. It seems probable that farm forestry can compete successfully with other uses for additional acreages of some of the poorest lands, but perhaps even more important is better care and utilization of the land now in farm woods.

The Lake States

Net returns in the Lake States fell more rapidly and farther during the depression than in the North Atlantic region (fig. 1). In this respect they paralleled the situation in the Corn Belt. Moreover, the returns also indicate slower and relatively less recovery up to 1938 in the Lake States than in either of the other two regions.

This result is probably influenced largely by the returns from manufactured dairy products, which constitute a large part of the income from farms in this region. Nearby metropolitan markets are important outlets for farm products, especially in Michigan and parts of Wisconsin. However, they are not of sufficient size in relation to the agriculture of the region to exert the stabilizing influence on income that was noted in the North Atlantic region.

The land resources in the Lake States vary from the fertile Corn Belt soils in the southern part (these areas really consitute a part of the Corn Belt) to much less productive soils in many areas of the so-called cut-over lands. Looking to the future, it probably will be necessary to use rather large amounts of commercial fertilizer to

223761°—40——33

maintain production in many areas. This will constitute an additional expense in production that so far has been necessary only to a minor extent.

The farming areas in this region that are too far north to compete in corn production and are not adjacent to special markets have very few alternatives to dairy farming as the major source of income. Hence they are mainly dependent on the long-term price outlook for manufactured dairy products. Increased dairy production in other areas, unless it is offset by increased demand, therefore constitutes the greatest threat to farm income in this region. One means of adjusting to such a situation would be through changes in the farming systems that would result in less purchased feed—feeding dairy cows relatively more roughage and pasture and less of the concentrates. Such an adjustment would utilize more effectively the natural advantages of this region. However, the shift should be accompanied by a definite improvement in the quality of the roughage, or considerable losses in milk production are likely to result.

Even then, the new adjustment is likely to involve less intensive operations and lower incomes on many farms that are already too small to return satisfactory incomes to the farm family. Agricultural conservation programs emphasizing the use of lime and fertilizer to build up stands of high-quality legumes and pastures can assist materially in the adjustment. Greater emphasis on the direct contributions of the farm to family living is highly desirable. In some of the cut-over areas this aspect is extremely important, as is also working out some means of combining farming and forestry. In this region there is the same need for information regarding production and income expectancy from forest enterprises as in the North Atlantic region.

The Corn Belt

Farming in the Corn Belt States consists predominantly of production of corn and of meat animals for the market. A more self-sufficing type of farming is carried on in the southern parts of these States, and production for nearby markets is important in some areas, but, on the whole, the changes in net returns for this region that are shown in figure 1 reflect the relative prosperity of farmers dependent on corn, hogs, and cattle for their incomes.

With the use of motorized equipment the typical Corn Belt farm is a highly commercialized business, requiring a large investment in land, livestock, and machinery. The level of land values is so high that many farmers find it difficult to own their land, and those who do frequently carry a large indebtedness. With high fixed costs resulting from the heavy investment, the farming business is especially vulnerable in a depression period. Consequently, farm foreclosures in recent years have concentrated much farm ownership in the hands of former creditors. This has accentuated the growing problem of supervised farming. Many of the managerial decisions formerly made by farm operators are now made by farm supervisors employed by the new landowners. Since the farms are constantly held for resale and because there is need for a simple type of lease which assures the landlords of their share of returns, it is frequently not possible to make desirable long-term adjustments in farming on such land.

This recent acceleration of supervised farming is but one phase of a growing separation of certain management functions from the farm operator in commercial farming areas. It has taken place in three principal directions: (1) Through the landlord-tenant relationship; (2) through the debtor-creditor relationship; and (3) through the public action programs. The management functions assumed by the public programs represent the injection of society's interest into the management of our agricultural resources. In the Corn Belt such programs are being sponsored largely by the Agricultural Adjustment Administration, the Farm Security Administration, and the Soil Conservation Service.

Of major influence in Corn Belt agriculture is the impact of technological developments such as hybrid seed corn, the rubber-tired tractor, and the new-type corn pickers. Will they mean even larger and more strictly commercialized farms? If so, what other employment opportunities are open for the displaced population? Will farming be further stratified into highly commercial and subsistence groups? The recent introduction of small tractors and "baby" combines indicates a tendency to adapt machines to existing sizes of farms, but a larger investment is still required than on the old family farm, and fewer workers are needed. Much remains to be done in this region to take advantage of new developments without inflicting undue hardships on the groups in the farm population that are adversely affected by the change.

The South

The two southern regions are considered together because the situation in both is so intimately related to returns from cotton. In both regions there are important areas of self-sufficing farming; also tobacco, sugarcane, rice, and fruit and vegetable production are important in some areas; and wheat growing and ranching are major activities in western Oklahoma and Texas. Nevertheless, cotton dominates the situation in southern agriculture. Cotton production constitutes a highly commercialized enterprise on both the large plantations and the small farms where it is grown.

The outstanding problem in the South is the low average income per farm family. Starting on a very low base, reductions in returns, such as those indicated for the two southern regions in figure 1, endanger the health and the morale of the population. The fact that relatively greater recovery in farm returns has been made in the South Atlantic States than in the South Central region, as indicated in figure 1, is due to some extent to a long-continued drought period in the western part of the South Central region.[7]

The low farm-family income is intimately related to the high ratio of population to productive land resources that has developed because of the need for hand labor in cotton production. As compared with 83 acres of cropland per farm in Iowa, Illinois, and Indiana, the eastern cotton States (Louisiana, Arkansas, Mississippi, Tennessee, Alabama, Georgia, South Carolina, and North Carolina) in 1934 averaged 30 acres of harvested cropland. This amounts to about 5 acres per capita of farm population. During the 14-year period

[7] There is also some evidence of a downward change in the size of the farms reporting from this region.

1924–37 the estimated gross farm income per capita of farm population, including receipts from cash sales, the value of commodities consumed in farm households, and agricultural adjustment payments, averaged $162 in these States as compared with $381 in the remainder of the United States.[8]

In periods of high cotton prices the relative returns for the use of land in alternative enterprises favored specialization in cotton, and the resulting income in those years provided somewhat more adequately for the farm population. However, the high percentages of land in cotton and in corn for mule feed developed a soil-erosion problem that has increased in seriousness in recent years. With lower incomes from cotton and no alternative employment for the farm population, the pressing need for cash income makes it extremely difficult to establish a type of farming that will maintain soil resources. The smaller the farm, and therefore the more inadequate the present production base, the more difficult it is to effect the adjustment. Soil conservation requires the use of winter cover crops and the retention of part of the land in grass and other close-growing crops. To establish such a rotation requires cash outlay, and the immediate cash returns are likely to be less than for cotton. Thus the extreme pressure for cash income furnishes an effective resistance to change.

Payments under the agricultural adjustment programs have made possible some adjustments in the direction of conservation. The cotton-reduction program also has permitted the use of some former cotton land for the production of badly needed farm food and feed. Greater attention to the contribution of the farm to family living is highly desirable as a first line of defense against the low-income situation.

A further upsetting factor in the South at the present time is the rapid progress of mechanization in the more level farming areas. While the mechanical cotton picker is not yet perfected, most of the tillage and dusting operations can be mechanized. The introduction of the small tractor and complementary equipment may hasten this adjustment considerably.

The forces of mechanization operate in the direction of labor displacement. The need for conservation dictates less intensive farming (a smaller proportion of tilled crops) and therefore also encourages labor displacement. More power and equipment are needed to handle soil-conserving crops. Thus a combination of forces, the greatest of which is the low income from cotton, is exerting pressure on the old established economy. The displaced labor is casting about for other employment opportunities. As long as none are available, the displaced laborers must necessarily stay in their present locations even on a greatly reduced income basis.

Ultimately the solution of the problem of low farm incomes in the South probably lies in employment outside of agriculture, which may be combined with part-time farming or at least with rural living. In the transition period, however, certain defense measures must be developed. Among these are the increased attention to farm food and

---

[8] THIBODEAUX, B. H. FACTORS OF ECONOMIC IMPORTANCE IN SOUTHERN AGRICULTURE. Address at County Agents' Short Course in Agricultural Economics, Camp Grant-Walker, Pollock, La., Sept. 18, 1939. U. S. Bur. Agr. Econ. 17 pp., illus. 1939. [Mimeographed.]

feed needs, already mentioned;[9] exploring the possible contribution of forest enterprises; and finding other cash enterprises that will serve as possible alternatives to cotton. Most of all, however, a program is needed that will enable a part of the farm population to find nonfarm employment.

The Great Plains

While the States comprising the Plains region in figure 1 actually include only a part of the Great Plains, the agriculture of these States is chiefly influenced by what has become known as the Great Plains problem. The origin of that problem is a conjuncture of drought and depression, the economic effects of which are plainly evident in the relative net returns shown in figure 1. In this region Government payments of various kinds have constituted virtually the only income received by many farmers in several of the years since 1930.

The drought cycle has been so severe that many people have raised the question whether any type or size of farm can be found that will permit a farm family to survive the prolonged drought periods on a self-supporting basis. It seems likely that the higher-risk farming areas of the region should be shifted back to the less intensive grazing use. The temptation to plow up such areas in the wet cycles necessitates instituting some control over their use. Public ownership may be the only feasible control in some instances.

Even in some of the better areas a means will have to be developed for maintaining the organic matter in the soil, thus preventing soil blowing. Perhaps this can best be achieved by seeding perennial grasses on a considerable part of the present crop acreage and then leaving the land in grass over a period of years and plowing it for crops only as rapidly as an equivalent acreage is seeded back to grass. A combination wheat-and-grass farming of that type requires the addition of livestock to utilize the grass and therefore raises the problem of feed supplies in dry years. While herds can be sold down to basic foundation stock, a minimum feed reserve of some kind is necessary. Public purchase of small areas of the poorer lands and setting them aside as public grazing grounds available largely for drought emergency use may help for the summer season. Winter feed can be carried over on the farm for one season but not so successfully for a longer period. Crop insurance gives promise of stabilizing materially the income from wheat. Perhaps crop insurance for feed crops, with losses payable in kind, could be utilized to spread feed-crop risks over a wider area.

Wherever irrigation development is feasible it should be carried out in a way that will permit an integrated use of irrigated and nonirrigated farming land along with the grazing land. Such integration would be most desirable on a farm-unit basis, but where this is not possible integration on an area basis should be planned in order that irrigated land may be used as a winter-feed base for livestock.

The natural forces influencing Great Plains agriculture are so powerful that here, more than anywhere else, public action seems necessary

---

[9] STEANSON, OSCAR, and LANGSFORD, E. L. FOOD, FEED, AND SOUTHERN FARMS; A STUDY OF PRODUCTION IN RELATION TO FARM NEEDS IN THE SOUTH. U. S. Bur. Agr. Econ. Farm Mangt. Rpt. 1, 25 pp. 1939. [Mimeographed.]

to assist in effecting the adjustments that are needed to stabilize the agriculture of the region. Among such measures are the development of supplemental irrigation, public land purchase, crop insurance, and assistance in establishing the types and sizes of farms that seem to have the greatest promise of withstanding the climatic hazards.

The Mountain and Pacific Regions

The Mountain and Pacific regions are considered together because in both problems associated with ranching and irrigation are of primary importance. The Mountain States show the combined effects of the drought and depression (fig. 1) in the same way as the Plains States. As previously mentioned, the Plains farming problem is important also in Montana, Wyoming, Colorado, and New Mexico. Moreover, the more strictly ranching areas of these States suffered from the same drought cycle.

If the ranching areas are to maintain their most important resource—grass—an effective conservation program must be instituted. Since there is no alternative to a grazing use of the land, conservation can mean only less intensive use—fewer cattle and sheep on the range. There is perhaps some possibility of increasing carrying capacity by developing more accessible water supplies, by rodent control, by rotation grazing, and by certain other means; but with all such improvements in mind, stabilization of agriculture in ranching areas requires adjustment of livestock to the numbers that the range can permanently support. Such adjustment at times will involve considerable sacrifices of present income in the interest of permanent agriculture—greater sacrifices perhaps than ranchers who are hard pressed for funds can be expected to carry out without public assistance. It may also involve losses on investment in fixed plant. Since much of the grazing land in the West is in public ownership, an important problem is to develop policies for its use by ranchers on a conservation basis. (See The New Range Outlook, p. 441.)

The need for integrating to the fullest possible extent the use of irrigated areas with surrounding nonirrigated and range lands has already been mentioned. However, many irrigation projects have developed important cash crops for outside markets; of these, sugar beets, fruits, and vegetables are the most important. How to meet the necessarily high water costs in relation to prices received for these products constitutes the most important problem on these projects. The situation is most acute in the apple areas, because apple prices have been extremely low and competition for western apple growers is likely to be severe in the years to come. Shifting to other types of farming involves tremendous losses of investment. Developments in the quick freezing of fruits and vegetables may increase the competition in these crops for the areas that now possess seasonal climatic advantages.

In view of the temporarily saturated market for fruits and vegetables and also for sugar beets, the settlers on the new irrigation developments are forced to plan systems of farming involving the production of the more staple farm products and of food and feed for home use. Settlement on these newer projects needs to be planned carefully to avoid some of the past mistakes in irrigation development. These are traceable largely to overoptimism regarding the income possibilities of the land when used for specialized commercial crops, but also to failure to recognize the probable additional costs that must be incurred for land leveling, and later for drainage.

The large concentration of migrants from the Plains and the South creates an additional problem in the Pacific States. It is essential that these families be given opportunities for settlement in the new areas. They will require much financial and supervisory assistance in order to gain a foothold in their new environment. The possibilities of developing farm homes for migrant settlers in the cut-over areas of the Pacific region need to be carefully explored.

SOME NATIONAL AND SOCIAL CONSIDERATIONS

What will be the national effects of the adjustments that seem desirable on a regional basis? These effects need to be appraised and suggestions for both individual and public programs of adjustment need to be modified to fit into a framework of national agricultural policy. The most important information needed as background for such an appraisal is that regarding the prospects for industrial recovery. This would make possible estimates of the probable improvement in market outlets for farm products, and of how large a population must earn a living on farms during the next few years.

If employment opportunities outside of agriculture are likely to remain closed to the agricultural population in the next decade, a realistic approach to farm-management problems, regionally and nationally, necessitates seeking ways and means to improve incomes for the farmers now living in an area, and also preparing a part of the population for other opportunites whenever they appear. Types of adjustments in farming must be considered from the standpoint of attaining the greatest security and stability of income for the total population in an area, as well as higher returns for the individual operator. For the time being, this may mean a compromise with the most efficient farming from the individual point of view in order to provide the best available opportunity for farmers who would otherwise be displaced and for agricultural labor.

If a relatively large population must earn a living on farms, major consideration must be given to questions of improving efficiency and increasing incomes on small farms. How can operators of small farms take advantage of technical progress and compete with the larger units in a way that will yield more satisfactory incomes to the farm family than such farmers are now receiving? Stated in another way, what assistance can be rendered to the half of American farmers that produces only 10 percent of the output that reaches the market? The answer is not likely to be labor-saving machinery, unless the overhead expense for its use can be somehow reduced and the labor thus saved used elsewhere to add to the returns of the farm family. Increased production for home use is a first line of defense and perhaps a partial answer in some instances, but some cash income must be had to purchase the goods which cannot be provided by direct home production in our modern economy.

Perhaps there are some lessons to be learned from the European countries in connection with this problem. No doubt we need to consider the possibilities of integrating commerical and noncommercial farming to the end that the former provides a part of the employment and income for the latter. But there are probably even greater possibilities of integrating the operation of small farms with some nonfarm employment. The isolated self-sufficing farming areas will find this type of adjustment most difficult.

National agricultural policy and programs can be shaped in the direction of increasing the domestic-market outlets for the farm products that are most desirable from the standpoint of the welfare of the consuming population, and adjustments in farming can be promoted that will gear into such a policy. This type of approach is likely to provide a satisfactory living for more people on farms and at the same time promote better living for low-income nonfarm people. That is, if it is deemed nationally desirable from a dietary standpoint to increase the consumption of dairy, poultry, fruit, and vegetable products, these are the very products that require relatively large amounts of labor, and therefore provide work for more farm people. They are also quite well suited to production on relatively small farms.

Encouragement of such adjustments might go hand in hand with shifts away from the staple crops of cotton, corn, and wheat. The adoption of such a program would of course require adequate safeguards to the incomes of present producers of these products, especially in the transition period.

It is evident that measures for improving the present farming situation involve a well-integrated combination of individual adjustment and public action, with the public-action programs furnishing a favorable setting for the adjustments that farmers can make on their own farms.

The Influence of Technical Progress on Agricultural Production

by R. S. KIFER, B. H. HURT, and ALBERT A. THORNBROUGH [1]

IN THE complex changes that have affected modern agriculture, technical progress has played a large part. Perhaps it is even the warp of the fabric; certainly it has enormously influenced the whole modern economy. It would be easy to write about the wonders of modern technology, and it would also be easy to curse them as responsible for most of our ills. This article does neither. It attempts a sober appraisal, point by point, of the influence of changes in farm power and equipment, plant and animal breeding, fertilizers, animal feeding, disease control—not only the changes in the past but those in prospect in the near future. These changes affect the whole of our agriculture—methods of production, quantities produced, the manpower needed in farming, capital requirements, size of farm units, the organization of the farm, operating costs, conditions of tenure. It is not too much to say that our destiny will depend to no small extent on our understanding of these factors and our ability to direct them for the service of all our people. The article is based on information prepared for an interbureau committee on technological developments in agriculture.

[1] R. S. Kifer is Senior Agricultural Economist, B. H. Hurt is Associate Agricultural Economist, and Albert A. Thornbrough is Agricultura Economist, Bureau of Agricultural Economics.

TECHNICAL change has had a predominating influence on the progress of civilization during the last 200 years. The invention and perfecting of automatic or partly automatic machines and their increasing use have relieved many of the production processes of their former dependence on human labor. But the effects have not been due solely to an increase in the output per man. Changes in methods of production, growing efficiency in methods of distribution, and the introduction of new products to fill new demands have created an economic world fundamentally different from that of our own colonial times. The products that we buy and use today are as different from those of the earlier period as are the ways in which we make and obtain them. The change goes on at an accelerated rate, and it is the general belief that the future will bring changes still more striking than those of the past.

Technological development has changed the problems of agriculture as much as it has changed the methods of production. A century ago the future supplies of food and fiber for the world were a matter of grave concern. Today, with the world population approximately doubled, the problems created by excess production in agriculture are more troublesome, in the United States at least, than are those arising from scarcity. The problem of employment for the people is more significant for the present than that of increasing the production of food.

The transition from a self-sufficing agriculture, in which the farmer produced not only his own food but also much of his clothing and equipment, to the present specialized commercial type of production is the result of a combination of developments within agriculture and economic forces outside it. The development of the railroads and accompanying improvements in transportation and communication created new outlets for farm products from the interior regions of the United States. New equipment and new methods of production transformed agriculture from a primitive to a highly complex industry. The cotton gin, horse power, the steel plow, the reaper, and the threshing machine initiated a change that is now accelerated by the tractor and associated equipment such as the combine harvester, the corn picker, and multirow tillage equipment. Before agriculture has been able to adjust itself to these changes, a mechanical cotton picker, beet lifter, or cane stripper may be forcing new adjustments between labor, capital, and production on farms.

Increased production per unit of land has followed the development of new, better adapted, or more productive varieties of crops. The increased use of fertilizers and improved rotations and tillage practices still further increase the potential production of food and fiber. Improved breeds of livestock and a widespread knowledge of superior methods of feeding and care lead to more effective use of crops in the production of livestock and livestock products. All of these new developments promote efficiency in production and are directed toward the ideal of obtaining more products either from the effort expended or from capital expenditure made.

The aggregate influence of these developments in the United States may be readily grasped if we consider the decrease in the proportion of people now engaged in agriculture and the increase in the production of those employed. The proportion of workers engaged in agriculture decreased from one-half of all workers in 1870 to one-fifth of all workers in 1930. During the same period the average agricultural production per capita in the United States increased 22 percent.[2] Thus those engaged in agriculture in the United States not only have been supplying food and fiber to more people but have actually increased the average amount of agricultural products per capita of total population.

Because social and economic adjustments are initiated by technical change, agriculture is faced with the necessity of further adjustments. With present techniques, production of most farm products exceeds the quantities that domestic and foreign demand will absorb without depressed prices and lower farm income. It is true, also, that known techniques and practices are not utilized fully. As the known practices come into general use and as new developments are made available, increases in production may be expected. The release of workers in agriculture as the result of the introduction of labor-saving equipment and the inability of these displaced workers to find employment in industry pose a serious labor-replacement problem. Thus technical developments that increase the production of farm products or that tend to displace workers in agriculture may lead to important economic and social maladjustments.

Presumably the adoption of a new process gives some immediate advantage to the individual using it. Why, then, with all the technical developments in agriculture in recent years, has the income of farmers been decreasing? Probably some farmers in some sections have benefited from technical change, but the influence of increased production on prices may have depressed incomes of farmers not in a position to use the improvements. The effect on price may have offset any decrease in cost or increase in production even for those farmers using the new methods. Thus a sequence of developments may have been set up which runs contrary to the objectives of agricultural policy. An understanding of the effects of technical progress may provide a basis for directing the use of new developments in such a way as to fully utilize their benefits and to minimize their disadvantages. Technological developments add to the material well-being of society in the long run, but the pains of adjustment and transition may be acute, especially under the conditions existing today.

Directly and indirectly technological progress affects agricultural production in many ways. The directions and degrees of influence are almost as diverse as the developments themselves. In order to be incorporated into the production organization, particular developments must make some contribution by way of (1) increased volume of production, (2) improved quality of product, (3) lower cost per unit of product, or (4) less fatigue and less tedium in connection with farm labor. The effectiveness of any one process may depend largely on the contribution of complementary processes. The value of an innovation may be derived indirectly from its contribution to other related developments; that is, the contribution that a new process can

[2] EZEKIEL, MORDECAI. POPULATION AND UNEMPLOYMENT. Amer. Acad. Polit. and Social Sci. 188: 230–242, illus. 1936.

make to efficient production depends in a large measure on the stage of development of related processes and on the relative prices of labor, equipment, and the resulting product. The influence of the tractor is not solely that of a more effective power unit. Its value depends in part upon combining the added power with machinery capable of doing work not feasible with horses.

The flow of technological improvements with their incentive to adjustments in farming is only one of the forces that make agriculture a dynamic rather than a static industry. Changes in the economic situation, the growth and disappearance of markets resulting from shifts in population, the growth or decline of competing areas, the introduction of competing products, and changes in the consuming habits of customers may likewise induce changes in the organization and volume of production in agriculture.

Besides their direct influence, economic factors may also have a marked influence on the rapidity with which technical changes are adopted and hence may speed up or retard the adjustment to new techniques or processes. The fact that there is a lapse of time between the development of a process, its adoption into general use, and the actual making of adjustments to it permits some appraisal of the probable consequences of technical improvement and makes possible the development of programs to facilitate change. Many of the potentially important technological developments are not yet in use but have progressed so far in the experimental stage that some judgment of their economic use and limitations can be made.

FARM POWER AND EQUIPMENT

The change from horses to tractors for farm work, trucks for hauling, and automobiles for travel has speeded up the rate with which work is done and has increased the capacity of the labor force on farms. A natural adjustment to this greater capacity of labor is to increase the size of the business unit and to reduce the use of extra labor on the typical family farm. Moreover, greater power and recent improvements in machine design make possible better seedbed preparation and more thorough tillage. Improved harvesting equipment has reduced losses in harvesting and thus contributes to increased production from a given area. When equipment and land area are properly balanced, these gains are sometimes achieved with little or no addition to the investment in working capital for a given land area.

Changes in Farm Power

Probably no other group of developments has influenced agriculture so much as those related to mechanical power and the equipment that such power brought into common use. The National Research Project of the Works Progress Administration estimated that in 1935 the tractor, motortruck, and automobile saved in agriculture or shifted to industry labor equal to that of 345,000 persons for 1 year.[3] The number of horses, mules, and colts on farms decreased from 26,500,000 in 1915 to 15,182,000 in 1939. This decrease of work

[3] McKibben, Eugene G., and Griffin, Austin R. Changes in farm power and equipment; tractors, trucks, and automobiles. [U. S.] Works Progress Admin. Natl. Res. Project Rpt. A–9, 114 pp., illus. 1938. [Processed.]

stock in the face of expanding crop production was a direct result of the use of tractors, trucks, and automobiles. It seems likely that the trend to less labor and fewer horses will continue.

The tractor, by bringing more drawbar power to particular operations, has made possible operation at higher speeds and use of equipment of greater working width than is feasible with horses. Larger or more effective equipment can be used for ordinary farm operations. The belt pulley on the tractor provided a mobile source of power for work previously done with a stationary engine. The power take-off, transmitting power from the tractor, increased the efficiency and dependability of such harvesting equipment as mowers, grain and corn binders, small combine harvesters, corn pickers, and field ensilage cutters.

From the heavy, cumbersome tractor, limited to heavy-draft field work and certain types of belt work, the trend in tractor development has been to lighter tractors of higher speeds, adapted to a greater variety of uses. Further modifications in tractor design may be expected, and the production of a small tractor at low cost is a possibility. Developments in agriculture in the immediate future, however, are most likely to result from (1) increased use of general-purpose tractors, (2) increased use of small tractors on the smaller farms, and (3) equipping tractors with rubber tires.

According to recent estimates there are something like 1,600,000 tractors in use in the United States.[4] This is almost double the number reported by the census in 1930 and indicates an increase of 746,000 tractors during a 9-year period.

Three-fourths of all tractors sold in the United States in 1937 were general-purpose tractors, and as the all-purpose type has dominated sales since 1935, it is probable that 50 percent of the tractors now on farms are of this type. The proportion of tractors equipped with rubber-tired wheels is increasing (fig. 1).

Tractors are used in all areas, but the highest degree of mechanization has been reached in the small-grain-producing areas, in the Corn Belt, and in specialized areas such as the dairy, truck, and orchard areas of the Eastern and Western States. In the Southern and Eastern States small farms and low incomes have not favored the use of tractors; mechanical power is used, however, in certain areas on large farms and for specialized production. The small all-purpose tractor will probably increase the rate of mechanization in the areas where farms are small, and large numbers of workers and work stock may be displaced.

The small tractor is also adapted to the small farms of the North Central States. Here it may offset the tendency to combine and enlarge family-operated farms. Continued mechanization would displace more work stock and encourage larger farms in some areas where the units are now small. In the small-grain areas, which are more fully mechanized than others, the small tractor may displace horses for work on small farms. Adjustments of size of farm to power equipment, which have been under way for some time, will probably continue.

---

[4] ANONYMOUS. DISTRIBUTION OF TRACTORS ON U. S. FARMS BY STATES, COUNTIES. Implement and Tractor 54 (14): 41. 1939.

Figure 1.—Tractors equipped with rubber tires have a wider range of usefulness and a longer working life, yet cost less to operate and repair than those not so equipped. Their increased use in the past few years has been revolutionary in the farm machinery field.

Probably the most rapid single development in the field of farm power and machinery in recent years is the adaptation to and use of rubber tires on agricultural tractors and field machinery. This development has not only expanded the sphere of usefulness of tractors but also reduced tractor operating costs. With fuel consumption per acre reduced about 10 percent on rubber-tired tractors as compared with those with steel wheels, repair bills reduced as much, and the life of the machine extended, the cost of doing farm work with tractors should be less now than it was with the best type of equipment available a few years ago.

Eventually the total investment for farm power may also be reduced. With a small outlay for trailers to use with the higher-speed rubber-tired tractors it may be possible, in some areas, to dispense with motortrucks. Field-to-field movement of the tractor and tractor equipment will also be facilitated by the use of rubber tires.

Tillage and Seeding Equipment

The trend in the development of tillage implements during the last 5 years has been toward lighter, more flexible machines that can be used successfully in connection with light and easily maneuverable tractors. Trends in development have also been influenced in the last few years by recognition of the erosion problem and modification of tillage practices to control rather than to increase erosion. Tractors equipped with power-lift mechanisms and mounted implements such as plows, cultivators, drills, and planters will facilitate the adoption of conservation practices on the rougher land areas of the eastern part of the United States. The development of implements for the steeper slopes will make operations on rolling and hilly land less disadvantageous as compared with operations on level land.

Recent developments in planting machinery are largely concerned with tractor-operated planters, features to permit the use of new planting methods, and the combining of tillage, fertilizer-distributing, and planting equipment in single units. Advantages of reducing man labor and insuring timely operations during critical periods are gained by combining in one operation some phases of the preparation of the seedbed, the distribution of fertilizer, and the planting of the seed. Such combinations have been accomplished with various classes of horse-drawn machines, but with tractors sufficient power is available for the use of heavy tools and for satisfactory simultaneous operation of several kinds of equipment.

Changes in fertilizer-placement devices by means of which the fertilizer is placed more advantageously for the growth of the seed or plant may have considerable economic importance.

Harvesting Equipment

Developments have been more rapid in harvesting equipment than in other types of machinery. The new machinery has reduced the need for seasonal harvest labor, and many farmers use such equipment to avoid the problems associated with hiring seasonal labor as well as to take advantage of lower harvesting costs.

Of recent developments in harvesting equipment, the grain combine is probably the most important, and the manufacture of new types of combines adapted to harvesting grass, seeds, and soybeans, as well as small grains, has increased their use. In 1939 about 110,000 combines were in use.[5] In 1920 less than 5 percent of the wheat crop was harvested with combines; in 1938 approximately 50 percent of the crop was "combined."

Of the approximately 92 million acres of corn harvested in the United States in 1938, about 90 percent was harvested for grain. About 13 percent of this acreage was harvested with mechanical pickers (fig. 2). Since about 100 acres of corn is the minimum for which a farmer can operate a picker economically, expansion of the mechanical pickers is limited. If the design of the corn picker could be simplified so that its cost could be reduced, its use would be greatly expanded. In view of the rapid development during the last few years of machines for so-called family-size farms, a simplified, low-cost picker is a possibility, and this would remove one incentive to concentrate corn acreage on large farms.

The windrow pick-up baler is an example of a group of machines that bring about marked changes in methods for a particular type of farm work, but which, because of their limited adaptation, have a minor influence on production as a whole. Where they are used, pick-up balers effect a considerable reduction in labor requirements for haying, but at present their influence on the general farm-labor

[5] For reference see footnote 4, p. 513.

Figure 2.—This new automatic corn picker was developed at the Agricultural Byproducts Laboratory of the United States Department of Agriculture at Ames, Iowa.

situation is slight. Their use will probably not be sufficiently extended to cause much change, at least in the near future. Other machines of this class are the field ensilage harvester and the hay drier.

Although over 800 patents have been taken out on cotton harvesters and much attention has been given to their development, the stripper type of cotton harvester is the only one that is considered beyond the experimental stage. The stripper, which removes the entire boll from the plant, has been used to a limited extent in the Southwest, where climatic conditions and the type of plant growth favor this method of harvesting. The mechanical cotton picker, several of which are now being developed although none is yet in regular production, is intended for use on the higher grades of cotton produced in the South Central States.

In general the quality of mechanically picked cotton is lower than that of cotton hand-picked under similar conditions. This is due in part to leaves and bits of trash that become entangled in the lint and to stains caused by the green leaves. Spinning tests show that machine-picked cotton is more "wasty" than similar hand-picked lots, especially in the case of cotton picked early, when the leaves are greener and more likely to stain the lint.

The beet harvester, like the cotton picker, has not yet reached a stage of development where it can compete with labor at current wage rates. It may, however, have an important influence on sugar-beet production in the future. The labor peaks in growing sugar beets occur when the plants are blocked and thinned and when the beets are harvested.

Equipment and methods for blocking and thinning beets are being developed. A harvester that lifts and tops the beets and separates the tops and roots into piles has been developed and has performed fairly well under some conditions; but under other conditions, particularly where there is a considerable variation in the size of the beets and in the height of the crowns from the ground, the performance of the machine has been unsatisfactory. The development of an improved lifting and topping machine within the next few years, however, is a possibility.

Improvements in pumps and power for irrigation have made feasible an extension of pumping in some pump-irrigation areas. Although the development or expansion of irrigation has important consequences in a particular locality, total production in the United States is not likely to be affected. Changes in pump equipment in wells already in use affect farm operations only to a minor degree. Deep-well pumps with semiopen impellers, for instance, appear to be replacing other deep-well types, particularly where wells yield water containing much sand. The advantage is primarily that of making operation more dependable and reducing the necessity for frequent repairs. More significant are the portable sprinkling irrigation systems used to supplement rainfall, to supplement surface irrigation where the distribution of water is uneven, and to water land where gravity systems are not practicable. The use of these systems is increasing, although no estimate of the rate of increase is available. The most important use is to supply water to crops of high value in areas where irrigation is not regularly practiced. In this way the production of crops sensitive to variations in moisture conditions can be stabilized, and the quality, particularly of small fruits and vegetables, can be improved.

CROP PRODUCTION

The combined influence of the multitude of recent developments in the field of crop production and farm practices may be as significant as developments in equipment and power, or even more significant.

223761°—40——34

Figure 3.—Plant breeders control diseases of tobacco, as of other plants, by breeding disease-resistant strains. The anthers of a tobacco flower are removed to prevent self-pollination preliminary to cross-breeding the susceptible cultivated plant with a wild species immune to the deadly blue mold.

Plant breeders develop superior varieties of crops adapted to local conditions and resistant to disease and insect pests (fig. 3). Advances in this field may more than offset the gradual decline of fertility in continuously cropped soils.

An outstanding example of crop improvement is hybrid corn, which in the course of 7 years has replaced open-pollinated varieties on a major portion of the corn acreage in the Corn Belt and on about 25 percent of the national acreage. The greater vigor of the hybrids and their resistance to lodging, plant diseases, and insects increase acre yields by 10 to 20 percent in the Corn Belt, where they are adapted to prevailing conditions. It is estimated that, because of the use of hybrid seed, corn production in 1938 was nearly 100,000,000 bushels greater than it would have been had open-pollinated seed been used on all the corn acreage; further increases when known hybrids are put into use may be twice as great. The possibilities of hybrid vigor are not fully measured by this estimate, for the development of hybrids adapted to the Southern and Eastern States may bring increases in production in these areas also. As the areas capable of the highest production receive the greatest benefits from hybrid corn and as costs do not increase in proportion to the increase in yields, a tendency to concentrate production in the better areas may be expected. Moreover, because of their resistance to lodging, the hybrids are particularly well adapted to the use of a mechanical picker, and this combination of advantages from two technical developments increases the advantage of both to growers in areas where they can be used.

If there is no control over corn acreage, the combined inducement of higher yields and lower production costs for hybrid corn is likely to increase production in commercial areas, with the probable result that supplies of corn will be so great that they can be absorbed only at lower prices. As most of our corn is marketed through livestock, the consequence of such a development would be lower prices not only to those benefiting from the improved techniques but also to producers in areas where hybrids are not adapted.

Progress in breeding other plants that are as important to other areas as corn is to the Corn Belt is helping to increase or stabilize the Nation's food supplies.

Thatcher wheat, introduced as late as 1934, is resistant to the stem rust that cut spring wheat yields in 1916, 1935, and 1937, and it gives promise of greatly reducing crop injury from this disease. Probably more important for the future, however, are the tests now under way to produce varieties of wheat resistant to other types of rust and to other diseases. The gradual improvement of wheat varieties has enabled farmers to maintain yields in spite of declining soil fertility and increasing damage from weeds, insects, and plant diseases; and it has permitted an extension of production into areas of high risks and low average yields.

Early-maturing varieties of grain sorghum adapted to the western parts of Nebraska and South Dakota may so stabilize feed production there that some farming risks from drought will be removed.

The introduction of Punjab flax in California and the development of cold-resistant varieties for the Southern States may increase flax acreage, make it possible to replace part of the cotton acreage with flax, and reduce the need for imported flaxseed.

Strains of sugar beets resistant to curly top have removed one danger for western beet producers. Recently developed varieties of beets superior to the European varieties promise to eliminate the risks connected with beet production in the humid areas, but no immediate increase of sugar production per acre is anticipated. One factor limiting sugar production is the assignment of quotas. A removal of quotas with no change in prices would probably result in an increased domestic production.

Soybean production, which has increased rapidly and reached a new high acreage level in 1939, will probably expand somewhat further. The increase will probably be largely in the Corn Belt States pending the development of seed varieties suitable for other sections. Although the 1939 acreage would produce sufficient soybeans to meet the current demand, a prospective decline in the need for oats and the displacement of low-yielding hays by alfalfa would permit some further expansion in acreage.

Improvement of cotton varieties by increasing the length of staple may strengthen the export position of United States cotton. In 1938, 13 percent of the United States production was grown in single-variety cotton communities. In combination with selection of superior varieties, better production methods, and more careful grading, the one-variety communities should decrease the proportion of cotton of less than 1 inch in staple length. The primary result might be to narrow the price differentials for different staple lengths. All factors combined might result in an increase of cotton yields, however, for production is related closely to use of fertilizers, but it seems unlikely that either production or prices will be immediately affected.

FERTILIZERS AND SOIL AMENDMENTS

Recent developments in fertilizers and fertilizer use are concerned with concentrated fertilizers and the correction of soil deficiencies in the so-called minor elements. The increased use of inorganic materials as sources of nitrogen and the use of double or triple phosphates and higher-grade potash salts increased the plant-food content of commercial fertilizers from 13.4 percent in 1880 to about 16 percent in 1925 and to 18.1 percent in 1934. The use of concentrated fertilizers is slowly increasing. In some areas lower handling and transportation charges per unit of plant food are important to an increased use of fertilizers.

The use of magnesium in correcting sand drown of tobacco, of manganese sulfate in curing chlorosis of tomatoes, and of zinc sulfate in combating pecan rosette, little leaf of peaches, and similar diseases illustrates what is occurring with an increasing number of elements that are now used to control nutritional deficiency diseases of plants. As experience more accurately defines the soil regions deficient in particular elements and the crops affected, the use of these "minor" elements will continue to increase. The effect on production may be more important locally than nationally, and no measure of the potential influence of this development can be made.

The consumption of fertilizers in the next few years is likely to be influenced more by farm prices and farm incomes than by developments in fertilizer manufacturing.

CONSERVATION PRACTICES

The immediate effects of conservation practices are of less importance than are their long-time consequences. The broad program of measures designed to retard soil erosion and to slow down the rate of depletion of fertility could hardly be expected to have an appreciable influence on total crop production within the next decade. Soil depletion and its correction are tied closely to farm practices, local customs, prices of farm products, and conditions of land tenure. A conservation program must make use of a wide variety of corrective measures and adapt them to local conditions. Consequently, information on the rate of introduction of even well-recognized practices and on the benefits from recently introduced practices is difficult to obtain.

Although the immediate effects of conservation practices on crop yields are less important than the lasting benefits to crop production, certain practices, especially the selection of better land for crop production and the use of cover and soil-improvement crops, may increase acre yields.

Shifting low-producing land from crop production and concentrating grain crops on the more fertile land of a farm increases average acre yields without an increase of total production. This aspect of the conservation program permits farmers to eliminate from crop production, or to shift to soil-improvement crops, areas on which yields and profits are low.

Such practices as terracing, strip cropping, contour farming, and, to a large extent, crop rotation enable a farmer to slow down the rate of soil depletion on his farm. They would, in time, increase crop production.

Cover and soil-improvement crops, on the other hand, have caused considerable increases in yields of the crops following them. Their use has been made an important part of the agricultural conservation program in the Southern States. In 1937 nearly 10,000,000 acres were in crops planted for cover and soil improvement. The acreage of these crops was more than double that of 1928–32. Without doubt the increased use of soil-improving crops has contributed to the higher yields in recent years in the Southern States. Moreover, the cumulative effect of green-manure and cover crops may be still more important. Increases in yields per acre of 70 percent for corn and 25 percent for cotton have resulted when green-manure crops were plowed under.

ANIMAL BREEDING AND FEEDING

Important current developments in the field of livestock production are progeny testing, artificial insemination, correction of nutritional deficiencies, and disease control.

Progeny testing enables breeders to locate sires capable of transmitting high producing ability to their offspring (fig. 4). Production and breeding records on 2½ percent of the dairy cows in the United

Figure 4.—Milk-producing ability of cows has been greatly increased by selection of sires capable of transmitting this capacity to their offspring. These 16 daughters of a proved sire produce more milk than their mothers.

States furnish a basis for selecting a limited number of proved dairy sires. The ultimate effect should be a gradual increase in the productive capacity of dairy animals, but because selection itself is a slow process and the transmission of superiority requires time, the improvement will not lead to maladjustment in production. Progeny testing has been limited so far to dairy animals and poultry, although it has been shown that beef cattle, hogs, and sheep can be improved by the same process. Production of meat and other animal products is not likely to be affected by it in the near future.

Cross-breeding of beef cattle, hogs, and sheep has been practiced for a number of years. Probably 20 percent of the cattle in the Gulf coast region have some Brahma breeding, and the percentage is increasing. Cross-breeding of swine is still largely experimental, although 60 percent of the hogs marketed in Chicago in 1938 and 65 percent of those marketed from Iowa were of mixed breeding. A cross-breeding program would have greater advantages for large than for small herds, since with the latter the cost of maintaining breeding stock would offset the advantages of crossing. Under experimental conditions crossbred hogs required 5 percent less time to reach maturity and 5 percent less feed to produce better carcasses than did standard-bred hogs.

Cross-breeding of sheep to produce good-quality mutton lambs from high-producing ewes of wool types is practiced on about 10 percent of range sheep. Relative values of mutton and wool have increased the practice in recent years, but it is not likely to affect production in the range area.

Cross-breeding of poultry has been more effective in broiler production than in other aspects of the industry. Although crossbred stock will probably replace standard stock for specialized broiler production, it is not likely to have a marked effect on the total output of poultry and eggs.

Artificial insemination of dairy cows should give wide distribution to the advantages of progeny testing. Seventeen breeding associations controlling 15,000 cows now practice artificial insemination. The results should be a reduction in the number of males, elimination of the sire as a factor in spreading disease, and improvement in the genetic make-up of herds. Improvements would take place gradually, however, and adjustments could be made as needed. Artificial insemination is feasible for all classes of livestock, but a practical application has been made only in dairy cattle breeding.

Recent developments in feeding have been concerned largely with vitamins and minerals. The correction of deficiencies of minerals such as iodine, calcium, phosphorous, iron, copper, and cobalt has been influential in eliminating some difficulties in livestock production in certain areas. A notable instance is the use of manganese to eliminate perosis in broilers produced in batteries. Determination of mineral and vitamin deficiencies in rations requires study of local feeding conditions. One result of the recognition of these deficiencies, in poultry production particularly, will be an increased use of standardized commercial feeds that contain the necessary elements.

Changes in beef and dairy cattle rations are to be expected with variations in supplies and prices of roughages and concentrates.

In some areas a minor shift to feeding less concentrates has probably increased the use of forage.

Forage Production

The acreage of pasture in the United States seems to have increased somewhat since 1930. The total acreage of tame hay has changed very little, an increase in the Southern States being offset by a decrease in the Western States. Alfalfa acreage increased in the North Central States, and that of lespedeza increased particularly in the southern portions of the North Central States. The most important shift has been from clover and timothy to higher-yielding legume hays. This shift to high-producing hay crops, together with the application of lime and phosphate, has increased yields per acre. A shift to higher-yielding hay seems to have been made in the Northeast and the North Central and East Central States. The shift in the Southern and Western States seems to have been to lower-yielding hays. For the country as a whole the influence of the shifts would probably be to increase hay production.

The influence on production of the change in total acreage and in kinds of hay varies among regions. In the North Central States the decrease in hay acreage between 1928–32 and 1938 just about offset the increase in the proportion of high-yielding types of hay, so that total production there as well as in the Northeast has not changed. Increases in hay production amounting to 46 percent in the South and 18 percent in the East Central States may be expected from an increased acreage and changes in kinds of hay which took place between 1928–32 and 1938. Decreases in the acreage of alfalfa in the Western States were sufficient to reduce hay production about 12 percent. If these shifts in acreage of hay represent permanent changes, an increase in livestock numbers will probably take place in the Southern States. In the East Central States the trend toward less use of concentrates and greater use of forage will probably continue. Insofar as the decrease in hay production in the Western States represents a loss of alfalfa because of drought, a recovery of acreage may be expected, and there should be little influence on livestock production.

Disease Control and Sanitation

A more widespread knowledge and application of measures to control animal diseases and insects injurious to animals should reduce death losses and, by increasing the proportion of thrifty animals, increase the efficiency with which livestock and livestock products are produced.

Although no campaigns on the scale of those carried out in the past against hog cholera, bovine tuberculosis, or tick fever are in prospect, general improvement in control measures may be expected.

The bovine-tuberculosis-eradication program has been extended to nearly all counties in the United States. As a result the disease has been practically eliminated. While the program was under way, demands for replacement stock in areas being tested amounted to about 300,000 head annually. This demand for animals has ceased. Moreover, only a negligible number of slaughtered animals are now condemned because of tubercular infection. The decrease has been gradual since 1917 and therefore will have no appreciable influence on the output of meat.

Testing for Bang's disease and condemnation of infected cows are now largely responsible for the demand for replacement animals. The continuation of this demand, which was for about 175,000 animals in 1938, depends on the continuation of the Bang's disease program.

Infectious equine encephalomyelitis has caused severe losses of horses and mules in recent years. Approximately 200,000 cases and 40,000 deaths were reported in 1938. Improved preventive and control measures should reduce losses in the future.

Improved methods of treatment for internal parasites (fig. 5) and such diseases as hog cholera, mastitis in dairy cows, pullorum disease and range paralysis in chickens, and blackhead in turkeys will tend to reduce occasional losses from outbreaks of these diseases and should increase the output of products not only per animal but also per unit of feed and of labor. Cyanide poisoning of livestock in areas where sorghums, Sudan grass, and Johnson grass are used for feed should be reduced either by treatment of affected animals or through breeding sorghums with low hydrocyanic acid content.

The combined influences of these and other developments in the control of diseases and injurious insects cannot be measured, but as more effective measures are devised and as methods of sanitation,

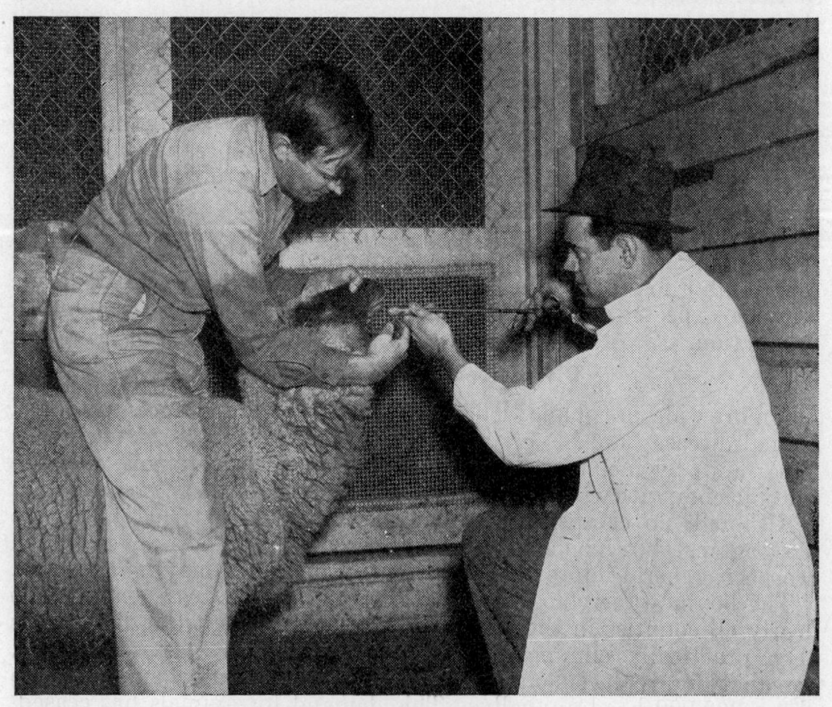

Figure 5.—It takes a big dose of phenothiazine—1 full ounce—to remove worms from sheep. Department zoologists, who discovered the value of this new drug as a livestock medicine, use a balling gun to administer a capsule of it to an infested sheep.

prevention, and treatment become more widely known and practiced, the output of livestock products should be increased. Education regarding control measures is particularly important in regions where parasites have seriously affected livestock enterprises, as in the South and Southeast.

Changes in the volume of production of livestock are more likely to result from changes in supplies of feed available than from changes in production methods. Developments in methods may, however, be essential to successful livestock production in areas like the Southeast, where larger quantities of feed are becoming available.

EFFECTS ON PRODUCTION

The preceding discussion of developments most likely to affect agricultural production leads to the conclusion that technical improvements will tend to increase the volume of farm products for sale. Any attempt to estimate probable increases would have to be in simple terms and cover only the major commodities most likely to be affected. Not only will adjustments in actual production on farms be made in the light of the advantages of technical improvements, but they will also be conditioned by changes in agricultural programs and in the relative prices of different commodities. Moreover, the economic situation at any given time may either advance or retard the use of new methods so that estimates of increased production cannot be given definite time limits.

The influence of mechanization on the output of the farm is made primarily by replacing work stock with machinery and thus adding salable crops or livestock products as a result of using for commercial production land that was needed for the production of horse feed. Assuming that there are no changes in present crop acreages, an additional 500,000 tractors on farms could easily release for other uses land now producing 70,000,000 bushels of grain and 2,500,000 tons of hay. One possible adjustment would be a diversion to other crops of the acreage in corn, oats, or hay for horse feed. With favorable prices the acreage of cotton in the South could be increased; otherwise a shift might be made to other possible cash crops. Such crops as sweetpotatoes for starch and other vegetable crops may be suggested; however, the only major shift in sight is in the Corn Belt, where land in corn or oats may and probably will be shifted to soybeans. In the Eastern States some acreage might be shifted to hay, but as the area is deficient in grain production such a shift would probably not be extensive.

Increases in production due to conservation practices are those immediate returns in crop yields which result from the use of cover and green-manure crops. If in the Southern States the soil-improving crops now being grown were to be turned under and followed by corn or cotton, the production of corn and cotton would be increased. Whether such a program as this is carried out will depend on the availability of power and equipment for turning under the soil-improving crop.

Estimates of increased crop yields due to improved varieties may be limited to the supposition that hybrid corn will occupy the major portion of corn acreage in the Corn Belt and that the increased production on farms will correspond to that under experimental conditions. On that basis, corn production in the Corn Belt could be increased 100,000,000 bushels a year. The subject of improved varieties of small grains is too large a one to consider here in detail, but progress in developing varieties suited to particular conditions and resistant to plant disease promises to eliminate hazards in production and may, as in the case of flax in the Southern States, open new areas for production. Thatcher wheat, for instance, is expected to increase the production of hard spring wheat by reducing damage from stem-rust epidemics.

As already noted, expansion of soybean acreage in the Corn Belt will probably continue. The ultimate acreage will depend on the relative returns from soybeans as compared with those from corn and hogs. A reduction of the acreage in oats and a shift from other hay crops to alfalfa will make room for some expansion of soybean acreage.

Considered by areas, the increases in crop production for which new outlets must be found seem likely to be largest in the corn and livestock areas of the North Central States; yet significant changes may be expected in the Southern States. Mechanization and a shift from horses to tractors provide the basis for crop increases in all areas. Hybrid corn in the Corn Belt and conservation practices in the Southern States should increase production. Unless the cropping systems are altered because of a decreased demand for certain crops and unless there is a shift to cotton in the Southern States or to cash grains in the North Central States, the primary influence of increased crop production would be to increase livestock production rather than to make more crops available for market.

A further reduction of 1,500,000 in the number of horses would make available for cattle and sheep nearly 4 percent of the average annual hay production for the period 1927–36, which would amount to an increase of approximately 5.5 percent of the hay used by cattle and sheep. One influence of the conservation program is to increase acreages of hay and pasture crops. This increase, plus the effects of pasture-improvement programs, should encourage the production of roughage-consuming animals. If, as seems likely in most areas, the production of roughage can be adjusted to the need for it, the influence of crops on livestock production would be in proportion to the probable increases in grains.

Technical developments in animal production and marketing should remove some of the difficulties of raising livestock in the Southern States. There seems to be no reason, however, to expect developments that would change present regional advantages in livestock production. Differences in methods of handling livestock result in some differences in feed requirements for production. If the excess of feed crops were to be used by different kinds of livestock in the same proportion as feed was used in the different regions in 1928–32, livestock production would be increased in all areas.

A large increase in livestock production would be made possible in the South Atlantic and South Central States by the combined influence of mechanization and conservation practices. Prospective increases of available feed would permit an increase of nearly 25 percent in livestock production. An expansion of the hog enterprise to a point at which byproducts became an inadequate source of feed might result in increased grain requirements per 100 pounds of pork. Some changes might be made in feed requirements for other livestock. However, it has been estimated that an increase in livestock numbers amounting to 31 percent for milk cows, 136 percent for other cattle, 31 percent for hogs, and 54 percent for chickens over the numbers on farms in 1937 would be needed to provide sufficient livestock products to meet even minimum diet requirements [6] for the farm population in these regions.

If livestock could be distributed according to population it would seem unlikely, therefore, that production in the Southern States will increase to such an extent that large quantities of livestock products will be placed on the market. A need for cash income and a concentration of livestock on a small proportion of the farms would lead to some increased sales of livestock and livestock products. A need for cash income might bring about a shift from feed crops to cotton or some other cash crop unless such a shift were prevented by restrictions on the acreages in these crops.

An increase of livestock production in other areas would probably result in a greater quantity of products for market and significant increases in the production of dairy products, meat, and eggs might be anticipated. This increase in areas outside the Southern States would add to the quantities of livestock products placed on the market, which in time might amount to an annual output approximately 5 percent greater than the 1938 production.

EFFECTS ON MANPOWER NEEDED IN AGRICULTURE

The saving in the time required for farm work resulting from the use of tractors, tractor equipment, motortrucks, and electrical equipment has reduced the need for workers, particularly in some sections. The trend toward reduction in the number of workers in agriculture seems likely to continue for the next decade at approximately the rate of decline in the last 10 years. If it does continue at this rate, displacement of 350,000 to 400,000 workers will probably take place unless (1) wage rates are lowered to the point where a shift to the use of equipment is retarded and workers lacking alternative employment outside of agriculture are retained on farms; (2) agricultural production is increased to such an extent that workers can be profitably employed regardless of the extent of mechanization; or (3) individuals displaced in areas of commercial production are established in noncommercial areas or on subsistence units in commercial areas. Unless planned direction is given to developments, some adjustments will probably be made along all three lines, and, as in the past decade, many displaced workers will be thrown on relief rolls or will join the stream of migrants in search of work.

In the North Central and Eastern States an increase in the quantity of feed for livestock, if it resulted in an increase in livestock production, would in a measure offset the saving in labor and might

[6] STEANSON, OSCAR, and LANGSFORD, E. L. FOOD, FEED, AND SOUTHERN FARMS; A STUDY OF PRODUCTION IN RELATION TO FARM NEEDS IN THE SOUTH. U. S. Bur. Agr. Econ. Farm Mangt. Rpt. 1, 25 pp. 1939. [Mimeographed.]

even increase labor requirements in some areas now mechanized. It seems likely, however, that there will be a gradual trend toward a clearer differentiation of commercial and subsistence farming and less demand for seasonal hired labor.

A shift in the power used on farms and in the type of farm organization in the Southern States would probably release a large number of agricultural workers, and a shift to livestock and crops requiring less labor than cotton would not increase the need for labor. Consequently, the displacement of labor by machinery may be more serious in the South than in other areas.

CAPITAL REQUIREMENTS IN AGRICULTURE

Substitution of mechanical power and equipment for hand labor will tend to increase the capital invested in the farm plant. Changes in equipment are unlikely to affect total investments, however, for in 1930 the value of land and buildings made up 84 percent of the value of farm property. Machinery represented only 5.8 percent of the total valuation. Moreover, since motortrucks, tractors, and automobiles reduce the number of horses and displace horse equipment, they do not increase farm investment in proportion to their cost. The investment in tractors and equipment on a 950-acre mechanized cotton plantation would be approximately the same as the investment in animals and equipment for operating with mules.[7] On small farms mechanization would probably increase the investment to some extent, depending on the number of work animals displaced.

Mechanization in the North Central States apparently increased the investment in equipment and power. On farms of 135–174 crop acres on which horses were used, the investment in animals and equipment in 1937 averaged $1,640; on farms of the same size on which general-purpose tractors were used, the investment averaged $2,192. As these figures are based on current values, part of the difference may be accounted for by the tendency to have newer and more expensive equipment on farms using tractors, and by the likelihood that some horse-drawn equipment was still carried in the inventory.[8]

Although mechanization of farms will require some increase of investment in working capital, the increase is not likely to be more than 25 or 30 percent greater than that required for nonmotorized farms. In any case it would represent a small proportion of the total investment in the agricultural plant.

More important than the actual increase in the investment in equipment for the ordinary farm is the fact that a given set of machines is most economical with a certain acreage. With less acreage, the cost of machinery is relatively higher. At the same time, the small-scale operator must invest in a complete set of machines for a certain operation, since the equipment cannot be divided. This may retard some beginners unless they receive aid to finance purchases.

New varieties of crops and new cropping practices require little or no additional investment, although such items as structures for soil conservation may necessitate an outlay for rented equipment or for

---

[7] LANGSFORD, E. L., and THIBODEAUX, B. H. PLANTATION ORGANIZATION AND OPERATION IN THE YAZOO-MISSISSIPPI DELTA AREA. U.S. Dept. Agr. Tech. Bul. 682, 92 pp., illus. 1939.

[8] GOODSELL, WYLIE D. COST AND UTILIZATION OF POWER AND LABOR ON IOWA FARMS. Iowa Agr. Expt. Sta. Res. Bul. 258, pp. 317–363, illus. 1939. See pp. 344 and 361.

construction. Such outlays would be in the nature of permanent investments.

If livestock numbers are increased, the farm investment in animals other than work stock would be increased and some additional outlay for buildings and equipment would be needed on some farms.

The evidence at hand points to increased capital needs for agriculture, of not more, however, than 25 percent of the working capital and 5 percent of the total investment. Whatever increase is made in the size of commercial farms would increase the required investment per farm, and this would make it more difficult for a farm laborer to acquire sufficient capital to begin tenant operations. On the other hand, the establishment of subsistence farms with smaller capital requirements would tend to prevent a large increase in the average investment per farm for the country as a whole.

SIZE OF FARM UNITS AND FARM ORGANIZATION

Developments related to farm power and equipment seem most likely to affect the number of crop acres in a farm unit. Farms have changed in size through inheritance, sale of land, and from other causes; but the tractor- and power-operated equipment have made an increase in size possible, and in fact have initiated pressure in that direction for the simple reason that tractors can do more work in a given time than horses. When a farmer buys a tractor for a farm too small to utilize it effectively, he will probably want to increase his crop acreage, and in many cases he will find the means to do it.

Adjustments to mechanization occur slowly. There are still adjustments to be made in response to the mechanization that has occurred in the past, and adjustments to future mechanization can be expected. Statistical analyses of changes in the average size of farms in the United States have been inconclusive. Average figures have been obtained by including all types of farms, and reductions as well as increases in size of farms. Thus opposing tendencies cancel each other. It seems quite probable that separating from the mechanized farms the small nonmechanized farms belonging to the self-sufficing, part-time, and sharecropper groups would show that there has been an increase in the size of mechanized farm units.

The appearance of the small tractor in the last year or so introduces a new factor. The somewhat lower costs of purchase and operation of this small machine as compared with those for the larger tractor will tend to bring further mechanization onto the smaller farms. The small tractor may have a tendency to "freeze" the size of the newly mechanized small farms. On the assumption that the small tractor will fit into the small-farm organization economically, there would be less pressure to increase the size of the farm holding beyond the working capacity of the tractor. Increased holdings would soon require more power, and any increase in size would therefore be made from other motives than the pressure of mechanization alone.

The introduction of the small tractor into the Corn Belt should help the small farmer to survive and would therefore aid in checking consolidation of small farms. The small tractor will probably have very little effect in the small-grain States. In the North Atlantic

States it would probably extend mechanization with little effect on the size of holdings.

In the plantation areas of the South the increasing use of tractors, with the accompanying changes in farm organization, is displacing many sharecroppers. This does not, however, represent any real change in the size of holdings; it merely reflects the extension of operations by the owner or large leaser to a greater portion or to the whole of the plantation. In other than plantation areas it appears probable that mechanization will tend to increase the actual size of farms, although the change will be made very slowly.

It is to be expected that the agricultural adjustment programs, the change in emphasis in the various livestock and crop enterprises, and the increasing use of mechanical power will give rise to further changes in the organization of farms. Some changes in kinds of specialization characteristic of various regions might easily follow. For example, the development of more drought-resistant and earlier maturing grain sorghums adapted to areas of Nebraska and South Dakota may increase the production of livestock, replacing cash-grain production. The further development of the quick-freezing process appears likely to diminish the advantage of specialized production of fresh small fruits and vegetables in areas that rely upon the off-season demands of the northern markets. The Pacific Northwest is looking toward the production for quick freezing of small fruits, peas, lima beans, brussels sprouts, and other products. Any shift in production northward and any reduction in the market for fresh vegetables, particularly during the winter, will intensify the economic problems of the rural South.

EFFECTS ON FARM COSTS

In general, technological developments are adopted and utilized because it is hoped that the expected returns will exceed the costs. It is true, however, that some equipment will be adopted because of its greater convenience, and that the farmer may be willing to incur an increase in cost or suffer a decrease in net income to obtain the convenience. The extent to which income can be sacrificed has definite limits, of course, for such a sacrifice carried to an extreme would lead to insolvency.

Although a technological development may lower the cost per unit of product, a change in the nature of the costs incurred may be highly effective during periods of economic adversity in creating pressures upon the cash income of a farm. Those farmers who have mechanized their operations usually have increased the relative importance of their cash operating costs. Mechanization also usually increases the total investment in equipment somewhat over that required for doing work with horses.

The cash expenses required for gasoline, oil, grease, and repairs in the operation of tractors and motor vehicles cannot be deferred during periods when prices and cash income are low or when the weather has reduced cash income. The small farmers and plantation operators who mechanize will find themselves more dependent upon commercial farming, and dependence on the market renders them more susceptible to financial difficulties during adverse periods.

During these periods the farmer who uses horses is in a relatively favorable position because much of the operating cost can be furnished by the farm itself in the form of feed and pasture.

During periods of low income, farmers using or planning to increase their use of fertilizers will adjust their purchases by reducing the amount per acre, by decreasing the acreage fertilized and put into production, or by foregoing any fertilization until more favorable conditions return. The fact that the prices of fertilizers and of tractor supplies are less variable than the prices of agricultural products tends during depression periods to intensify the financial difficulties of farmers using them.

TENURE AND TECHNOLOGY

Technological developments in agricultural production are placing some barriers in the path of those seeking farm ownership. Any development that increases the investment required makes it more difficult to acquire ownership. Any development that tends to displace farm operators and laborers adds to the ranks of those who are trying to obtain a foothold at the lower levels.

The investment required for mechanization is small compared to the total farm investment. The appearance of smaller power units and equipment with lower first costs, the growth of a used-tractor market, and provisions for financing have aided the farmer in acquiring mechanical equipment. Nevertheless, the burden of the investment becomes proportionately greater at lower income levels. It is also more difficult for individuals at these levels to obtain credit to buy equipment.

Efforts to enlarge the acreage operated have adverse effects upon individuals in the weaker tenure groups. Larger units mean that a smaller number of operators are actively engaged in production. The displacement of farm operators through the consolidation of farms adds to the number seeking farms. The present surplus of prospective tenants, resulting from both technological displacement and the backing up of farm population, increases competition for farms and leads ultimately to higher rental rates. This competition has already altered the straight third-and-fourth-share rent system in the cotton areas of Texas.[9] Tenants are being charged for pasture formerly provided without cost; cash rents are exacted for dwellings and for land used to grow feed crops. It seems reasonable to expect that this competition for farms will be prevalent in the South as mechanization progresses. Another possible development may be the migration of surplus tenants from southern areas into other areas where they will compete with resident tenants for land.

The change in tenure relationships will probably be most striking in the South. Mechanization enables a plantation operator to dispense with sharecroppers by doing more work with his tractor and tractor equipment and by hiring the necessary labor. Such sharecroppers have the alternatives of competing for other tracts of land or of accepting the income that can be derived from wage work.

[9] HAMILTON, C. HORACE. THE SOCIAL EFFECTS OF RECENT TRENDS IN THE MECHANIZATION OF AGRICULTURE. Rural Sociol. 4 (1): [3]-25. 1939. See p. 9.

Technological developments in agriculture seem to widen the differences in income between wage laborers or sharecroppers and owner-operators or the more well-to-do tenants.

COMMERCIAL AND NONCOMMERCIAL FARMING

The less productive half of the farms reported by the census in 1930 sold only 11 percent of the farm products entering commercial channels in 1929.[10] Not all of those farms are noncommercial, for many sharecroppers and small farmers who produced less than $1,000 worth of products depended almost entirely upon their cash income for the necessities of life.

Although distinctions between commercial, self-sufficing, and part-time farms must be made arbitrarily on the basis of certain ranges of farm incomes, it is convenient to divide farm operators according to their dependence for a living on the income derived from the sale of farm products. A self-sufficing farmer may obtain most of his living from his own farm products. A part-time farmer attempts to supplement his farm income with nonfarm earnings. A commercial farmer may use more of his own products for the family than a low-income operator produces altogether; yet his total sales of products may be large in comparison with the amounts used on the farm.

If a large number of sharecroppers are released from agriculture in the South they may have no opportunity to engage in commercial farming as tenants. Their opportunities are limited to subsistence farming, part-time farming, wage labor, or relief. Although the list of jobs available to part-time farmers is extremely varied, it is doubtful that part-time employment offers much possibility of relieving the expected displacement. Further, migrants leaving the cities for rural areas for the purposes of residence and small-scale farming would offer competition to displaced sharecroppers.

It would seem, on the whole, that under current conditions of industrial unemployment, insufficient demand for a number of farm products, and a surplus agricultural population, mechanization will tend to increase subsistence farming wherever there is a possibility of establishing such farm units.

An increase in subsistence farming as well as in the mechanization of commercial farming would indicate that one part of the farm population is becoming more dependent upon industry and the national economy as a whole, while the other part, to the extent that it actually becomes self-sufficient, is gradually becoming less dependent on other economic groups. Commercial agriculture is so organized that it must sell to other groups in order to carry on production. Mechanization and other developments that have increased the dependence of farmers on cash income have also increased their vulnerability to changes in the economic system.

---

[10] BAKER, O. E. A GRAPHIC SUMMARY OF THE NUMBER, SIZE, AND TYPE OF FARM, AND VALUE OF PRODUCTS (BASED LARGELY ON THE CENSUS OF 1930 AND 1935). U. S. Dept. Agr. Misc. Pub. 266, 76 pp., illus. See p. 68.

The Place of Forests in the Farm Economy

by Burt P. Kirkland [1]

A PREVIOUS article dealt with the problem of large forest areas in private and public ownership. But there is another kind of forest that is a more direct part of the farmer's resources—farm woodlands. About 18 percent of all land in farms is woodland, and on some farms 60 percent of the land is in forest. The author of this article shows that most of this woodland is actually or potentially valuable if it is managed properly. For example, instead of getting building material from a thousand or more miles away, the farmer can grow it for himself. He can also market forest products. In certain favorable situations, the whole farm can become what is called a "forest farm," devoted almost entirely to timber growing. Local forests also offer an excellent field for cooperative management and the cooperative marketing and use of timber products by farm communities. The author indicates briefly how some of these things can be done.

FOR nearly three centuries American farmers depended directly on the farm woodlands and other nearby forests for the greater share of their fuel and building materials. Other products of the forest lands, such as game and fish, were important for food, and some animals supplied fur and leather for clothing. During most of this era the farm was generally looked upon as the family home to be

[1] Burt P. Kirkland is Principal Forest Economist, Division of Forest Economics, Forest Service.

223761°—40——35

improved and conserved in every possible way. Although large areas of forest had to be destroyed in clearing land in the forest regions, it was an almost universal practice to reserve part of the forest on each farm unit as a permanent source of needed materials.

The highly adverse position of the farm as a commercial enterprise has during the last 50 years compelled the farmer to draw on every possible asset to maintain his commercial position. One result has been that in most woodlands assets have been destroyed that normally should have been held for the most urgent family emergencies. At the same time the capacity of the woodlands for growing high-quality material has been impaired.

When the farmer looks beyond farm boundaries for sources of employment and for needed forest materials he is too apt to find that the forests of his community outside of farm ownership have become even more deteriorated than his own woodlands.

With the shrinkage in the foreign markets for agricultural produce and unfavorable prices in domestic markets, public and private agricultural agencies and farmers themselves have had to reexamine the farm and the rural community for sources of farm-family support. In the aggregate, it is found that 185 million acres, or about 18 percent of all land in farms, is occupied by woodlands, of which about 139 million acres is estimated to be actually or potentially valuable for commercial timber production. The relative area of farm woodlands in the United States as compared with the areas of other privately owned forests and of publicly owned forests is shown in figure 1. Enormous farm areas in nonforested regions contain no woodlands. In many forested regions 60 percent or more of the farm area is in forest. These forest lands are generally of better quality than the average of larger forest properties.

Besides the farm woodlands, virtually all the forests within easy reach of the farm or of the farm community should normally have a

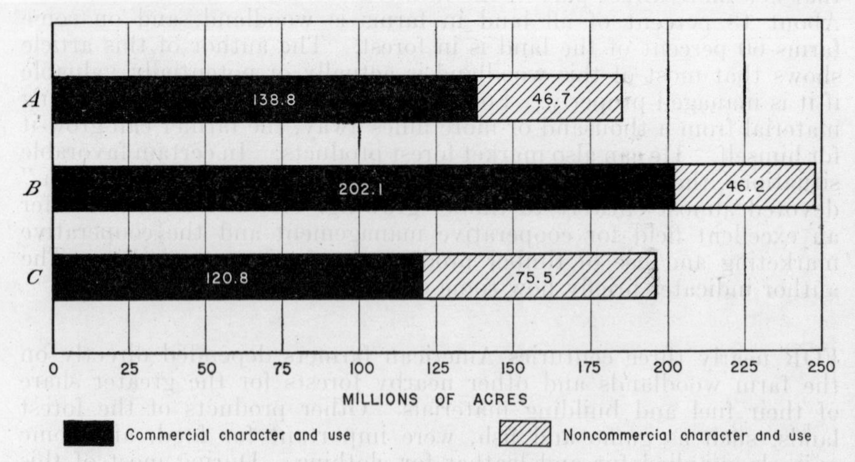

Figure 1.—Division of the 630.1 million acres of forest land in the United States by ownership: *A*, Farm woodlands, 185.5 million acres; *B*, other private ownership, 248.3 million acres; C, public ownership, 196.3 million acres.

favorable influence on the farm economy. The total area of such forests is unknown. If we should estimate that all forests within 10 miles of any farm home in a settled community are potential sources of forest products easily available to the farm, or of employment, it is highly probable that more than 150 million acres of nonfarm forests are thus closely interwoven with the farm and related rural economy.

The importance of the farm woodlands in the farm economy was long obscured by the abundant timber supplies and by the labor opportunities available in these other nearby forests. Lumber and other forest products, generally sold to farmers direct by the manufacturer and subject to low transportation costs, were cheap. This accounted for the spacious farm buildings built in most rural regions over 50 years ago. In many regions the farmer must now look 1,000 to 3,000 miles away for a source of these materials, and he pays freight charges far greater than the cost of growing as good timber on his farm or in other nearby forests. For these reasons the farm economy is vitally influenced by the management both of the farm woodlands and of other local forests. If the farm woodlands normally hold the primary interest of the farmer, other local forests should be a close second.

Owing, therefore, to the continuous demands of farmers on farm woodlands and other local forests for fuel, materials for shelter, and other essentials of living; to the contribution of nonfarm forest properties to local taxes; to opportunities for forest employment and to many other benefits from the forest, both the farm woodlands and other local forests deserve the continuous interest and participation of farmers in measures to improve management practices.

The subject can be developed with more clarity by discussing separately the principal ownership classes of forests found under typical conditions in rural communities. These classes of ownership are the farm woodlands (integral parts of the average farm enterprise), privately owned nonfarm forests, and public forests of various types. Of these the farm woodlands are economically capable of the most intensive management. Of the other local forests separate consideration needs to be given those that are expected to remain on the tax rolls in some form of private ownership and those now or eventually to be in public ownership.

THE FARM WOODLAND

Despite the seriously deteriorated condition of most farm woodlands, which produce no more than one-third to one-half of the volume of wood they are capable of producing and are worth a far smaller fraction of their potential value, their contribution to farm income and to farm living is very significant. The largest volume of wood withdrawn from farm woodlands is used directly on the farms, chiefly as fuel wood and posts. Nevertheless, farm woodlands produce nearly one-fourth of the sawlog supply of the United States. In farm value, forest crops rank tenth among all farm crops. In addition, there are the game, fish, and recreation values of farm forests and the large contribution well-cared-for woodlands make to the aesthetic values and to other values inherent in a well-balanced enterprise.

Special Position of Farm-Woodland Products in the Rural Economy

The utilization of American forests remote from settlement is accompanied by great waste. This is because industrial wood forms no more than 60 percent of the stem and branch volume of softwoods or 40 percent of the volume of hardwoods. Exceptions occur, as where industry uses cordwood materials such as pulpwood and distillation wood. In all large continuous forest areas wood fit only for fuel is so plentiful that most of it cannot be used. This is a serious detriment to clean logging operations and to economical utilization of poorer trees. At existing market prices it does not pay to transport low-grade fuel wood from these areas to population centers.

In most farm-woodland regions the situation is different or can be organized on a different basis. The proximity of the farm family and of rural village families to the woodland nearly always makes wood an economical fuel for at least part of the domestic and industrial requirements of each community. The relative inconvenience of preparing and burning wood fuel in many cases can be overcome by mechanizing the preparation of the fuel and improving the fuel-burning equipment. Other uses of small or low-grade trees needing removal according to sound silvicultural practices include posts and poles. Sawdust and planer shavings from primary wood-manufacturing plants are also useful for bedding animals and for other farm needs.

In addition to these well-known uses of wood there are potential uses that may become of the utmost importance. It is well known, for example, that ethyl alcohol can readily be made from wood by converting the cellulose to sugar, which in turn is converted to alcohol by fermentation and later distilled. Methyl alcohol has, of course, long been a commercial product of the distillation of wood. It has been demonstrated in Europe, both experimentally and by practical operation, that by means of a suitable gas producer installed on motor vehicles small blocks of air-dried wood or wood charcoal can be used as a motor fuel. The forests, therefore, constitute an alternative source of motor fuel as oil resources become depleted.

The utility of all these products in the rural economy insures that whenever good forest practices can be coupled with good community organization, complete utilization of the yield from well-managed forests can be made a reality. This situation can rarely be duplicated outside of well-settled areas and is therefore special to communities well provided with farm woodland or with other close-by or intermingled forest areas.

Another important feature of the contribution of the farm woodland to the rural economy is the high quality and value of wood of the better species commonly found in farm woodlands. These valuable woods include black cherry, sugar maple, and various species of oak. Although these special values apply to only a small percentage (5 to 20 percent) of the total volumes and can often be realized only by effective processes of refinement as yet lacking in many communities, it is noteworthy that unlike most farm products today they can be exchanged on a parity basis for other products in national markets. Unfortunately many farm woodlands have been stripped of mature timber of this class, and many years will be required to put their growing stock in condition to yield regular supplies of high-quality material.

In between these products of high exchange value and the large mass of products such as fuel and sawdust that can be used only on the farm or in nearby villages, both hardwoods and softwoods may, if properly handled, yield a substantial volume of rough and planed construction lumber and some other products of intermediate value. This wood is suitable for use as basic building material and for a number of other uses throughout rural communities. Produced at the wages prevailing within each community, it can be equitably exchanged for other products among farmers and other rural dwellers.

These multiple uses of the various grades of material create a unique variety of values from the farm-woodland resource. Some of these values are realizable solely through the labor of the farmer himself in creating products for his own use; other products created by further labor of the farmer or his employees are equitably exchangeable within the rural economy; and under some circumstances still other products become available that are capable of refinement to a state of high exchange value in national markets. The farm woodland thus provides fuel and materials for shelter and even contributes to food and clothing, so that a larger percentage of its products than of any other major farm crop, except products of the farm garden, is finally consumed on the farm or in the farm community. The wheat or cotton grower must ship out 80 percent or more of his product. The corn grower sells his corn mostly through livestock production. Their products are thus subject to all the vicissitudes of Nation-wide and even world-wide economic maladjustments. The farmer and the rural community need not suspend use of farm-woodland products because of such maladjustments. They may, indeed, increase use under adverse conditions.

Rehabilitation and proper management of farm woodlands is for the reasons just given a vital element in the security of the farm family and of the rural community. Further development of rural community organization may be necessary, however, to realize these possibilities to the full.

The Farm Woodland as an Element in the Farm Investment

Besides, the production of fuel and timber used in farm structures and operations lends balance to the farm enterprise and gives partial insurance against fluctuations in markets for other farm products. When the major farm products cannot be exchanged on favorable terms for all of the varied means of subsistence not produced on the farm, the forest produces several of the necessary items at home without the need for external exchanges. Balance within the farm enterprise lends value to the farm investment.

Except for localities where small farms are used intensively, as in some Pacific coast fruit districts and elsewhere, only a part of the average farm is in intensive use for crops or improved pasture. A considerable part is generally unimproved pasture of low yield, and a considerable area may be wasteland, entirely unused. In forest regions, wastelands and areas in partial use should generally be converted from open land to timber—the only crop that with little annual labor keeps on adding to value at a compound interest rate of 2 to 5 percent. Wherever the more valuable species of trees are found, large, well-grown timber is a readily salable asset, and a good stand of such timber is a "savings account" of high value and safety.

Although reduced in many cases to marginal value as a resource, the farm woodland that still contains merchantable-sized trees can, if intelligently handled, reward the labor required for rehabilitation more directly and more liberally than most other kinds of rehabilitation on the farm. This is true for two reasons. (1) The multiple uses of wood, already noted, nearly always permit a choice of use where some value can be produced. (2) Until the time for harvesting, probably no form of production is carried on so largely by nature, almost unaided, year in and year out. Given well-selected trees with proper growing space adjusted by occasional removal of trees that can be spared from the stand, production goes on at a compound-interest rate, with volume growth closely proportionate to the volume of merchantable trees (those 6 inches or more in diameter) and also contributed to by the younger growth on hand.

In addition to rehabilitating woodlands already containing merchantable timber, it is nearly always important to recognize the value of young growth that has come up on cut-over areas, abandoned fields, and pastures. Thousands of farms also contain land exhausted by cropping, damaged by erosion, or otherwise lying waste, which for various reasons cannot or should not be restored to crop or pasture use. Immediate financial returns cannot be expected on such areas, but skillful afforestation will place them in condition to accumulate value at a low compound-interest rate equivalent usually to 2 to 4 percent. From the age of 25 to 30 years on, these young stands will produce enough poles, posts, and cordwood to pay for their care.

Although farm woodlands connected with permanent family homesteads generally received good care in the days before farming was dominated by the commercial point of view, techniques of management were by no means developed to the full possibilities. Conservatism in cutting often preserved trees beyond their useful growing period and reduced possible yields. Regenerating areas generally were neglected, and developing young stands missed the frequent and judicious thinnings that they should have had.

With the existing deteriorated condition of most farm woodlands the need for improved techniques is many times multiplied. Recovery of productive capacity is an exceedingly slow process except where proper methods make more rapid progress possible. But improved techniques cannot be expected to come into use spontaneously. Sufficiently well supported public efforts to permit personal contacts of some local forest organization with every farm-woodland owner desiring help in introducing improved practices will be necessary. In many cases, trained men should be sent to mark the trees for cutting, as is done by the Swedish forestry boards.

How this work should be organized is still an open question, but it is certain that a minimum of 1 man per county will be necessary. To raise the efficiency and volume of work per forested acre to Swedish standards would require 5 to 10 men per county. It is clear therefore that efforts so far made bear little relation to needs.

THE FOREST FARM

Particularly in forest regions east of the Great Plains large areas of hilly, stony, sandy, or otherwise infertile soils lie within, or once lay within, farm units that under the economic conditions of an earlier time were quite successful. With the opening to market, by railroads, waterways, and highways, of the entire area of the United States, production of staples tended to gravitate to the more favorable areas, leaving agriculture depressed in the poorer land areas. Farm abandonment is common in some, while in others settlement continues although incomes and standards of living are low.

Where forest occupies much of the land and where land values have reached a low ebb there is opportunity through consolidation to create farm units large enough to depend on forest products as the primary source of cash income. Five hundred acres or more may be required for a family-size unit. Although large compared with most eastern farms, this is smaller than the family unit in western grazing areas. This type of forest farm is already developing in the Naval Stores Belt, primarily because of the ease with which naval stores production can be organized to yield annual income. When the simplicity of organizing timber production for annual income is equally well understood and suitable outlets have been established for other forest products, thousands of opportunities should be seized to build up forest farms.

The essence of good management on such areas is to cut lightly every 3 to 5 years in all stands 30 years or more old or in stands of mixed ages. If the farm has 500 acres and each acre is to be cut over every 5 years, then 100 acres should be cut over annually, removing about the equivalent of 5 years' growth, except in young or depleted stands where 20 percent or more of the growth should be added to the growing stock. By this simple procedure annual yield is assured. One great advantage of the forest crop over crops requiring complete annual harvest is the facility with which timber can be stored in the living tree from low-price periods to those of higher prices.

A peculiarity in which forest farming differs from most farm enterprises is that the crop of live timber performs a dual role—it is at one time the principal capital of the enterprise, while at another time the same volume unit becomes a commodity for use or sale. The difficulty most frequently facing sound forestry practice, especially in pioneer countries or where land use is not stabilized as between the forest crops and other uses, is premature cutting of trees that should be left for further growth.

The forest farmer should not neglect to utilize some of his more fertile land for vegetables, grain, hay, and other crops needed on the self-sustaining farm, nor to reserve sufficient pasture for livestock. No more than 5 to 20 percent of the total farm area need be kept for these purposes. Effective utilization of the crop and pasture area is essential to hold down operating and family-living costs.

The forest farmer needs intelligence and physical stamina to succeed. Management of the forest by men able to direct the enterprise and perform much of the labor is devoid of the heavy supervisory costs that are unavoidable in larger enterprises. The incentive of personal interest added to these qualities usually insures much lower produc-

Figure 2.—Farmstead near Cooperstown, N. Y., surrounded by well-cultivated fields In the background on the right is woodland capable of immediate profitable management. On the left, an extensive area, partly of abandoned orchard, lies waste, though it would support a highly productive forest.

tion costs and higher acreage returns for the operator than could otherwise be obtained. This organization of forest production is especially adaptable to large areas of forests in regions with mild climate, such as the South and the Pacific Northwest, but it also fits the situation in other regions where settled areas border on extensive forest areas. It may be by far the cheapest method of restoring over-exploited forests. Activity in this direction will unquestionably develop at a slow rate because of the absence of men with knowledge combined with some capital. Temperamental and mental attitudes are involved as well as the necessity of overcoming social attitudes growing out of speculative and other bad ownership practices. The educational measures discussed elsewhere must be well advanced before much progress can be made.

The labor requirement on the woodland portion of the forest farm may be estimated at not far from 1 day an acre a year. This is to cover all cultural operations and harvesting of logs, poles, posts, cordwood, or other products, including transportation to a central yard on the farm or to a roadside. It may or may not include delivery to a shipping point or manufacturing plant, or to rural consumers. The more of these functions that are performed by the forest farmer himself, the higher his labor income will be per acre of forest. From the cost standpoint the labor can usually be performed more cheaply by the forest farmer or his own employees than by others.

This approach to the problem of land submarginal for crops and pasture can assist in keeping all the land of a community on the tax rolls and increase community productivity in a field noncompetitive with staple food and fiber crops (figs. 2 and 3). As in the case of woodland on smaller farms, local sales of products from forest farms should become important in many communities. These products are acceptable in exchange for foods, forage, or other products, and for services. Over-all efficiency of the community is enhanced by a balanced internal economy; but external sales should not be neglected.

NEEDS OF INDIVIDUAL FARMERS NOT OWNING WOODLAND AND OF RURAL COMMUNITIES

Numerous communities in the West and considerable areas east of the Great Plains are organized into farm units too small for woodland to be significant in the farm enterprise. Many of these small farms are heavy users of forest products. Thus it has been estimated that the average acre of productive apple orchard in the Wenatchee Valley of Washington needs the annual growth of 10 to 15 acres of nearby ponderosa pine forest to supply boxboards and other lumber requirements of the apple grower. Under other conditions, such as those in the Missouri Ozarks and parts of the Appalachian region, small landowners on poor land cannot usefully employ their labor on the farm longer than during the crop season of 4 to 6 months. The part-time employment which the general distribution of forests makes possible is needed. Even where farms are larger, winter work is often light, and forest employment may give needed additional income. In other cases, some members of the farm family need outside employment.

Throughout central Europe people living in hilly country are well

Figure 3.—Farm lands near Cooperstown, N. Y. About one-third is cultivated land and pasture, one-third is merchantable woodland capable of immediate productive management, and one-third is now unproductive though suitable for forestation.

housed and fed because of a successful combination of intensive forestry with agriculture. This is facilitated by the intermingling of farm and forest lands. Part of the forest is individually owned, but some is often in communal or State ownership.

Where communities have extensive forests besides farm woodland and where forest employment and forest products from outside the farm holding are needed, it is very important that the nonfarm forests be organized to give the maximum benefits in each community. This can be done either under continued private ownership or under some form of public ownership. In neither case have methods been devised in the United States that obtain all possible benefits from these larger forest holdings.

MANAGEMENT OF NONFARM PRIVATELY OWNED FORESTS IN THE FARM COMMUNITY

It is not possible to speak so definitely of the future management of the great body of privately owned forest lands outside of farm ownership (fig. 1). This subject is discussed in the article on Forest-Resource Conservation, p. 458.

Good management for these nonfarm forests requires (1) stabilization of ownership, (2) rebuilding the timber stands to their former productivity, (3) providing patterns of taxation and ownership tenure that will eliminate economic pressure for excessive exploitation, (4) providing for community benefits from nearby forests, and (5) utilizing employment possibilities.

The great problem is to create an ownership pattern, owner and community attitudes, and organization for active use of the forest and forest products that will insure steady advance toward immediate and long-term objectives of forest management.

The county planning committees fostered and participated in by the Department of Agriculture are concerned with solving these problems and establishing such degrees of social control as will minimize future losses from mismanagement of resources. Other Federal, State, and local agencies are working to the same end. With such large areas involved, there is room for many types of ownership and management. The forests may be controlled, for example, by industry, estates, country clubs, or game and fishing clubs. From the community viewpoint, forms of ownership that permit broad participation and free access by the people of the community are most desirable.

In the past the relation of these important resources to community welfare was more or less accidental. No important community organization gave consideration to the means of obtaining maximum benefits from them. Sometimes they were exploited by casual or transient labor with no close ties to the community chiefly concerned and very little to any other. In other cases beneficial employment and business relationships existed, but short-sighted and ill-informed exploitation of the timber led to rapid deterioration. A decade of depression has taught us that ill-considered and wasteful exploitation of resources brings an unfavorable economic reaction to the communities concerned.

It is evident that a basic problem is to change the management policies from too diverse individualistic viewpoints to a community point of view. In other words, there is involved not only permanence of the forest resource but its management in such a manner as to diffuse widely the benefits from it, in the interest of "the greatest good of the greatest number in the long run" (the objective of Forest Service management). Cooperative management, discussed on pages 545-546, may often be the answer.

Utilizing Employment Possibilities

Management of these forests should be organized with special reference to creating a maximum of rural employment. Forest work will never be comparable to the spectacular exploitation of a virgin oil field, where a few weeks' labor by a few men may bring in a well flowing hundreds of barrels a day. Naturally the yield to both labor and capital in the latter case is high, but it is temporary when measured by the life of nations. In contrast, forest restoration and use can yield only slow and modest returns, but forests can be made to yield returns continuously through periods centuries long.

The prevailing local rate of rural wages generally makes forest work economically feasible. Higher wages, where socially necessary, must usually be subsidized from other sources. Two classes of work in the forest may be distinguished and treated somewhat differently in employment policies: (1) Removal of the forest products and cultural operations to maintain growth and (2) construction of permanent improvements, such as roads.

Most important is the work of utilizing the products of the forest. The major cultural tool in forest management is a continuous process of selection of trees, some for removal and some for further growth. The great bulk of the work in the forest is in utilization and maintenance. In well-settled localities this work continually yields the variety of products mentioned under The Farm Woodland (p. 536) and rewards reasonably the money and labor expended. Unlike farm-woodland management, the accomplishment of this work in extensive areas devoted almost exclusively to forest use requires centralized organization of some type, regular wage payments, sales of products, etc.

The second class of work in extensive forests consists of the construction of permanent improvements, of which roads are usually the most important. The average weight of the product per acre per year in forests is greater than that produced in annual crop and livestock operations. More roadway is therefore required per unit of area than in average farming areas. Unlike the farm woodlands, which can depend largely on public roads for access and for transportation of products, extensive forest areas under unified management must nearly always be provided with road systems at the expense of the forest owners. Although it is a complete illusion to expect road-construction costs to be less as a result of conversion of land from annual crop and livestock production to forest use, the cost may shift from taxpayers' to other shoulders. Other forest improvements include providing limited building facilities and in some cases fences, water developments, and other minor items. In addition to these depreciable capital investments, considerable work in regeneration and care of young stands may properly be capitalized.

It should be noted that while the current work of utilization should yield returns sufficient to employ labor on a self-sustaining basis, many of the forest improvements, especially in depleted areas, fall in the category of things needed for permanent preservation of our national domain. Yet moderate development of these facilities falls well within the field of private investment, expecially if fostered by suitable credit institutions which enable proprietors to carry on operations beyond their own capital resources. Roads and other developments should sometimes be built more substantially and permanently than is possible if they are to be liquidated within the periods appropriate to private finance. With the aid of public subsidies such work may well be done to utilize otherwise idle labor in times of depression. Considerable recovery on these public investments will accrue through taxation of future income. Public subsidies for these types of work are common in most European countries. Suitable organization standards to assure continuity of the forest enterprise must be prerequisite to such public aid.

PUBLIC FORESTS—FEDERAL, STATE, AND COMMUNITY

The systematic development of opportunities for rural populations to obtain fuel and other products and to utilize their own labor, especially outside of crop seasons, in national, State, and commercial forests has not gone far as yet. Although forest products are now used freely in many rural districts, large opportunities for their further and more effective use remain. In some national-forest areas definite plans have been perfected to provide a certain amount of stable employment to local residents.

A good example of intensive coordination between a national-forest program and adjacent farm areas is found in the Chippewa National Forest in Minnesota. The needs of each agricultural community in or near the forest were investigated to determine how much forest area and forest work need be allotted to each community to bring the community income to reasonable standards. The required forest work consists partly of sustained-yield utilization of timber and partly of investments for the future, such as forest planting and the creation of transportation and other forest improvements.[2] In the United States where forest land is abundant, national forests may often be partly devoted to common grazing ground under an orderly charge permit system.

State and community forests are being built up with similar aims. Vast opportunities still remain for perfecting all forms of public-forest management. Public forests are just beginning to be developed as the stabilizing factor in supplying forest industries with raw material. Public forests should be managed with as much regard for local community interests as has already been recommended for privately managed lands. In addition they have to serve broad State and Federal interests.

[2] KNUTSON, CLARENCE E. THE APPLICATION OF A LAND UTILIZATION PROGRAM TO THE CHIPPEWA NATIONAL FOREST. Jour. Forestry 37: 738-740. 1939.

COOPERATIVE ORGANIZATIONS

The educational and other public assistance mentioned in this article, though confined to traditional channels, may show the way to more productive handling of the farm woodlands and similarly situated forests so far as concerns measures that can be taken in the forest itself. But these measures may not in themselves increase the actual utility of the woodlands for the farmer or for the community to the full extent that is possible. The average farmer can no more afford to own the necessary manufacturing equipment to prepare timber for higher-grade uses on the farm or for marketing than he can afford to own a flour mill. Likewise it is often inexpedient or financially impossible for other owners to provide adequate facilities. United action is thus essential.

In those communities where diverse wood-using industries exist and where grades of lumber needed locally are sold at reasonable prices, additional facilities for processing and marketing farm-woodland and other local forest products may not be urgently needed. In many if not the majority of communities either the primary wood-utilization plants are extremely antiquated or none exist. Full economic use of products from farm and other local forests must in numerous places await the construction of modern plants. One such plant, a pioneering development, is shown in figure 4.

Because improvement of forest stands always requires removal of various materials, the problem of providing adequate facilities for manufacturing is complicated. Where the convenience of the manufacturer is the sole criterion for the needed facilities, forest utilization is apt to assume an unbalanced character. Facilities need to be designed with special reference to utilizing what needs to be cut for the good of the forest. This complete reversal of the usual point of

Figure 4.—Plant of the Otsego Forest Products Cooperative Association, Cooperstown, N. Y. This is a pioneer effort still in the experimental stage, designed to prepare hardwood timber suitable for the general market for sale at full value and to saw and plane local hemlock and pine for use on farms and in the community. Fuel wood, sawdust, and other byproducts are also available to farmers.

view will increasingly demand procedure in accord with sound technical advice and direct control by farmers and other forest owners through cooperative organization.

The farm-woodland cooperative has another special function because so large a percentage of forest products must be used within the community. It provides a place of business and continuous service for exchanges of products among members and for diffusing production and use of forest products throughout the local community. By means of it, positive action can be taken to increase the use of forest products, especially in creating better constructed and better heated rural buildings.

In addition to these special needs that may be met by cooperative organization, the recognized functions of cooperation in the general agricultural field hold with full force. There is very special need for grading and refinement of products before sale; for improved bargaining power; for control of plants and of sales by farmers; for ownership by farmers of capital stock as one form of savings to equalize standards of living over long periods; and for realizing the educational values that are inherent in cooperative effort of any kind on an important community job.

The requirement that the farm-woodland cooperative shall look out for all the forest interests of members, from production of timber to its processing and distribution, places exceptionally heavy burdens on the management. For that reason it demands exceptional abilities and training.

There seems little doubt that the forest cooperative movement will grow in future. In addition to attending to strictly farm-woodland management, processing, and marketing problems, the local cooperative may well assume ownership or managing custody of other local forests.

It has been proposed that local cooperatives should be set up in each community having such forest areas, to take title to the lands and apply unified management and that under certain circumstances public subsidies shall be given. Cooperative management seems logically to offer a good method of introducing a community viewpoint and creating an increased measure of local responsibility for these areas. It appears unnecessary, however, to insist upon complete surrender of title of all forest lands to the cooperative. A form of management contract could readily be devised which would be fair to all owners, unify management policy, increase income from sales of products, and provide for steady improvement in each holding by more effective utilization of normal biological forces. Complete acquisition by the cooperative would be desirable in those cases where existing owners are disregarding community needs or have no further interest in their holdings.

Ownership of some forest land by a cooperative drawing its supplies mostly from small owners would tend to stabilize its source of raw materials. The forest owned by the association would provide materials at times when farmers and others failed to supply sufficient volume. Many pulp companies and lumber companies hold title to forest lands for this purpose. Publicly owned forests may provide this basic raw material supply in some cases.

CONSERVATION OF SOIL AND WATER

The measures described for forest management are also highly effective in conserving soils not needed for crop and pasture. The same principle holds for nonfarm forest land. As nearly all labor intelligently applied in the forest is either immediately or eventually rewarded directly by commodity production, costs chargeable to soil conservation are almost nil. The ungrazed and unburned forest is nearly 100 percent efficient in preventing erosion. Under some climatic conditions and with certain species of trees, certain soil types deteriorate by transference of mineral constituents between soil horizons, but this deteriorating action is slow and can usually be prevented by proper mixtures of species and proper silvicultural management.

The foregoing facts justify the broad generalization that vast areas of well-managed farm woodlands, besides being essential to the well-being of the average farmer in humid regions, constitute a safe guardian for a great national reserve of farm soils not now needed for crop or pasture use but available in case of future need. These soils are generally of secondary quality and would not be profitable in commercial farming at present. Exceptions occur in bottom-land and swamp areas where soils are rich but the cost of improving them for agricultural use is excessive and not now justified.

In the same way, any soils in the humid region not in farms can be conserved at very low cost under forest management until such time as more urgent needs may have to be met.

WORK OF THE PUBLIC AGENCIES

Through several of its agencies the Department of Agriculture has long been interested in educating farm woodland owners to protect all forests from fire, insects, and diseases and otherwise to foster good management practices on farm woodlands and other forests. A brief review of the work of the Department to further these ends is given in approximately the order in which the work was initiated by the various agencies.

Forest Service

For more than 40 years the Forest Service has included farm forestry within its field of activity. Limited financial resources have compelled restriction of its work mainly to publication and a limited number of studies in farm woodlands. Extension foresters of the Forest Service cooperate with the Extension Service of the Department and with State extension foresters by providing information and in other ways.

Under the Weeks law of 1911 and the Clarke-McNary law of 1924, the Secretary of Agriculture, through the Forest Service, has cooperated with the States and through them with private and other agencies within the States in protecting the forests from fire. Under section 4 of the latter act the Secretary of Agriculture is also authorized to cooperate with the various States in the procurement, production, and distribution of forest-tree seeds and plants for the purpose of establishing forests upon denuded or nonforested lands on farms.

Through the interest of the President and the use of emergency relief funds the Forest Service initiated the Prairie States Forestry project, designed to provide protective forest belts on large numbers of farms in the Plains States. That work has been successfully carried on at variable rates since 1935. About 10,950 miles of successful strips of trees have been established. Although planned for protective purposes, these belts will eventually furnish considerable supplies of posts, fuel wood, and other farm timber.

Still more recently the Forest Service has been charged with the responsibility of studying forestry cooperative methods and experimental development of forest cooperatives in New Hampshire and New York. This approach to farm-woodland and other rural forest problems has already been discussed.

In the whole national field of forestry the Forest Service has charge of about 175,000,000 acres of national forests, of forest research at 12 forest experiment stations and the Forest Products Laboratory at Madison, Wis., and, in general, is charged with the duty of fostering good-management practices in all the forests of the Nation. In its management of the national forests multiple use is an important principle.

Other Department Agencies

For many years the Bureau of Plant Industry has carried on experiments at the Northern Great Plains Experiment Station at Mandan, N. Dak., to determine the species and varieties of trees and shrubs best adapted to planting under the adverse conditions of the Plains. Also for many years the Division of Forest Pathology has carried on scientific investigations of fungus diseases affecting forest trees. In recent years considerable sums have been made available to this division for fighting the more serious fungus attacks, such as those of white pine blister rust and Dutch elm disease.

Insects are among the most serious enemies of forest trees. Extensive investigations have been carried on by the Bureau of Entomology and Plant Quarantine to identify and classify forest insects; to ascertain their distribution and habits; and, on the basis of this knowledge, to determine the most effective methods of control. The Bureau also guards against the introduction of foreign insect pests.

Since July 1, 1925, the Extension Service has had funds for distribution to the States under terms similar to those under which other agricultural extension funds are distributed. Under this program 40 States now employ extension foresters, some of whom have several assistants. In a very few instances county extension foresters have been provided under this program.

Because the funds available have been limited, forestry extension work has consisted mostly of publications, addresses, and demonstration areas. Nothing approaching the activity of the Swedish forestry boards has been possible.

For several years the Farm Credit Administration has appraised farm woodlands as part of the mortgage-credit base for farms. Loan value has been based on permanent productivity of the woodlands rather than on their liquidating value.

The interest of the Agricultural Adjustment Administration in conservation and in reducing areas planted to certain soil-depleting crops has led in some areas to payments for forest planting and to a limited degree for other forest practices. For example, in the

1939 agricultural conservation program in the northeast region the following schedule of payments was in effect:

Northeast region

A. All States.
   1. Planting forest trees, $7.50 per acre, 1,000 trees per acre.
   2. Forest improvement, $3 per acre to develop 100 trees per acre.
B. Maine, Vermont, New Hampshire, Massachusetts, Rhode Island, New York, Pennsylvania.
   3. Fencing livestock out of farm wood lots, $0.375 per acre. Payment will not be made for more than 2 acres for each animal unit normally grazed.
C. All of Rhode Island and New Hampshire and parts of Maine, Massachusetts, Connecticut, Vermont, and New York.
   4. Woodland rehabilitation on hurricane-devastated woodlands, $4 per acre.

Heretofore woodland areas have not been included in the acreage against which the maximum soil conservation payment on a given farm is calculated. It has been suggested that a separate base should be set up for the forest land on each farm. The 1940 agricultural conservation program provides a special allowance of $30 for forest planting in some regions. This can be earned without interfering with payments for conservation practices on cultivated and pasture lands. It is probable that forestry policies of the Agricultural Adjustment Administration will undergo further development during the next few years.

The Soil Conservation Service, first organized in 1933, has used a new approach to conservation problems. This consists of active use of a project method through which intensive work is done in selected demonstration areas and, more recently, in soil conservation districts set up under State law. The work includes close contact with landowners, cooperative agreements designed to encourage activity on their part, and the furnishing of labor on farms through the Civilian Conservation Corps, Work Projects Administration, and other available sources of manpower. The primary purpose of soil conservation is served in part through forest planting and care of existing woodlands.

During the fiscal year 1940 funds specifically for farm forestry have become available through the Cooperative Farm Forestry Act. The Soil Conservation Service has major responsibility in the administration of the funds appropriated under this act. This work is only in the initial stages, and several years may elapse before policies reach a settled condition.

The Farm Security Administration, concerned primarily with low-income farmers, has an opportunity to encourage clients in intelligent use of farm-woodland holdings. It is natural that supervision of crop, livestock, and home economics practices rather than forestry have so far been of paramount importance.

In addition to its work on farms, the Farm Security Administration has financed through loans three large forest cooperative enterprises located in northern New Hampshire, at Cooperstown, N. Y., and in the Tygart Valley, W. Va. These have been on part-time or full-time operation for only a short while. Conclusive data on operating results must await several years' further operating experience. It is desirable to expand this experimental eooperative program into certain other areas.

As the primary planning agency of the Department of Agriculture, the Bureau of Agricultural Economics is concerned with woodland areas of farms, with the problem of retiring submarginal areas from farm use, with the relation of farm areas to more or less extensive forest areas, and with many other general problems concerning forests.

It should be clear from the foregoing that the work of several agencies of this Department must continue to impinge on farm forestry problems and on other forest problems in farming regions. Good management of farm woodlands and other forests of agricultural regions is so important and so closely related to many activities of the Department that it is impossible to concentrate all forestry contacts in one agency. This diversification has the great advantage of bringing many points of view to bear. Correlation of these activities and integration with State programs have been provided for in the recent reorganization of the Department. Out of this should in time come a sound composite view of the place of forestry in the farm economy.

Cooperating State Agencies

Cooperation with the States follows the Federal pattern in that responsibilities are divided. The State foresters, State extension foresters, and, in some States, forest schools occupy spheres partly well defined and partly overlapping. In several ways relations have been established between the Department of Agriculture and these agencies.

The Need of Unified Local Aid in Farm and Other Forest Management

It seems clear that all of the public agencies that operate in the field of forestry have more or less important functions that cannot be discontinued without adverse results.

On the other hand, direct adoption of sound forest practices by farmers and other forest owners is proceeding at a slow pace, partly because contacts with any of the agencies mentioned are relatively few. As a consequence, existing knowledge both of the economic and social need for sound practices and of what constitutes such practices is not being rapidly assimilated or put into effect by owners of forest land.

All of the modern European countries counting on private forest ownership as an effective means of obtaining maximum social benefits from substantial portions of their forest land have devised means of maintaining direct local contacts with forest owners. The methods developed over a period of many years in Sweden and adopted more recently in Finland are instructive. These consist in setting up local forest boards in every Province (about equivalent to our county), which carry out provisions of the laws affecting private forests. This is done in Sweden by maintaining close contacts with forest owners and by assistance in the management of private forests. Assistance is given to owners in marking over 75 percent of the timber to be cut in annual fellings.

Until equally effective educational aids and other assistance to local forest management are devised in this country, progress must continue to be very slow despite the numerous agencies working at these problems, mostly from the top.

Acreage Allotments, Marketing Quotas, and Commodity Loans as Means of Agricultural Adjustment

by J. B. HUTSON [1]

IN GENERAL, the author points out, there are two types of economic adjustment open to farmers acting as a group. One is to regulate the marketing of crops already produced; the other is to adjust production itself to the effective market demand. Only after the first method proved to be inadequate to meet severe economic conditions did farmers in the United States turn to the second. In brief compass, this article gives a picture of three main elements in the adjustment program currently being used by producers of the principal agricultural commodities. It describes the operation of acreage allotments and the payments that accompany them; marketing quotas—an emergency measure for use when excessive supplies accumulate; and commodity loans, which are used to stabilize supplies and prices of certain products.

[1] J. B. Hutson is Assistant Administrator, Agricultural Adjustment Administration.

THE NEED for adjustment of agricultural production in the United States is the result of a number of national and international production and trade factors that have been effective for the last quarter of a century, as well as of the increasing necessity for soil conservation.

Until a few years ago farmers could find markets for all they could produce, and little consideration was given to any adjustments in agricultural production. The foreign market was almost unlimited. But the situation has radically changed.

The United States has been a creditor nation since the end of the World War in 1918. Foreign trade has diminished, with a consequent loss of foreign markets to United States farmers. The farmers' problem has been aggravated by the increased mechanization of agriculture, which has facilitated an extension of farming to areas that formerly did not yield a sufficient return to justify cultivation. The result of these and other factors has been the accumulation of surpluses which has dramatized the need for adjustment in the production of certain crops.

With a growing realization of the need for some adjustment in agriculture, differing views arose as to how this adjustment was to be accomplished. In general there are two possible approaches to the problem: (1) Orderly marketing and (2) acreage adjustment. Under the first, necessary remedial measures are taken after a crop has been produced; the second aims at preventing the production of surpluses.

Since unlimited production had always been the rule, it was only natural that orderly marketing proposals were considered first in the United States. This method in various forms was also adopted in a number of foreign countries with respect to such commodities as rubber, coffee, and sugar.

In the United States the attempt to obtain adjustment through marketing regulation was evidenced in the 1920's by such farm-relief efforts as the McNary-Haugen bills and by the establishment of the Federal Farm Board. During the 1930's, in addition to the program for expansion of markets and the conservation of our agricultural resources, programs were developed for production adjustment through limitation of the acreage of major crops, particularly of those crops that in the past had depended to a relatively large degree on the export market.

The programs of the Agricultural Adjustment Administration have been developed primarily in terms of acreage. Marketing quotas have been used in some instances but in the process of administration are in most cases ultimately expressed in terms of acreage. Use is made of orderly marketing mechanisms, but in connection with acreage measures and not as substitutes for them.

ACREAGE ALLOTMENTS

More than half the short-time fluctuations in the production of the important farm crops are due to changes in acreage. In order to encourage more uniform crop acreages and to keep national supplies, including reserve supplies, in line with demand, acreage allotments are determined for important crops and groups of crops under the agricultural conservation program.

Acreage allotments have been determined individually for cotton, corn, wheat, rice, tobacco, potatoes, and peanuts in most years since 1933. An allotment is determined for all other soil-depleting crops as a group.

Acceptance of the acreage allotments is voluntary. Payments are made to producers whose plantings do not exceed the allotted acreage for each crop as an inducement to make the adjustments. These payments are based on the normal yield of the allotted acreage in each case. The funds available for these payments are divided among the producers of the different commodities in accordance with the following formula in the Agricultural Adjustment Act of 1938:

> In allocating funds among the commodities the Secretary shall take into consideration and give equal weight to (1) the average acreages planted to the various commodities (including rotation pasture), for the 10 years 1928 to 1937, adjusted for abnormal weather and other conditions, including acreage diverted from production under the agricultural adjustment and soil conservation programs; (2) the value at parity prices of the production from the allotted acreages of the various commodities for the year with respect to which the payment is made; (3) the average acreage planted to the various commodities during the 10 years 1928 to 1937, including the acreage diverted from production under the agricultural adjustment and soil conservation programs, in excess of the allotted acreage for the year with respect to which the payment is made; and (4) the value based on average prices for the preceding 10 years of the production of the excess acreage determined under item (3).

Obviously the proportion of the funds for the different commodities varies from year to year with changes in crop acreages. In general the proportion of the funds available to the producers of a particular commodity increases with a reduction and decreases with an increase in the acreage allotment.

The Agricultural Adjustment Act of 1938 in addition to a specific authorization of funds for the agricultural conservation program authorizes parity payments to producers of corn, wheat, cotton, rice, and tobacco, if and when appropriations are made therefor. Any funds appropriated for parity payments, unless otherwise specified by law, are apportioned among the producers of these commodities whose plantings do not exceed allotted acreages in proportion to the amount by which each commodity fails to reach parity income. The payments thus have an influence on the acreage planted.

The first step in the acreage-allotment procedure is the determination of national allotments for the different commodities or groups of commodities. These allotments are then apportioned among States, counties, and farms. The national acreage allotments for cotton, corn, wheat, and rice are determined in accordance with formulas in the Agricultural Adjustment Act of 1938, which provide for an acreage that with normal yields will result in a total supply somewhat in excess of normal supplies. The excess supplies serve as reserves to be drawn upon when yields are adversely affected by unfavorable weather.

The national acreage allotment is in most cases divided among States and counties on the basis of a 5- or 10-year average acreage adjusted for trends and abnormal conditions. Different bases are used for different commodities in apportioning the county acreage allotments among farms but, in general, history, type of farming, and available land, labor, and equipment are important factors.

The county acreage allotment for cotton is divided among farms on the basis of the tillable cropland available for growing cotton, with certain provisions for minimum acreages for small farms and for farms that have had large acreages in the past. In the case of corn in the commercial area, the county allotments are apportioned among farms on the basis of history and the kind and amount of land available for growing corn. For most other commodities the historical acreage is used, adjusted either in accordance with a definite formula or with the judgment of the local committee for type of farming, crop-rotation practices, and land, labor, and equipment available for producing the commodity.

The dividing of the allotments among individual farmers has been the cause of many irritations. In general, these were due to (1) inadequate and inaccurate data or (2) the fact that the changes in farming operations of the individual were more rapid than the formulas in the program provided for. The problem of inadequate data has been fairly well solved by the information that has gradually been accumulated under the agricultural adjustment programs. The other problem has been partially met through adjustments, but in a program that is Nation-wide in extent it is inevitable that the provisions will not fit every farm perfectly.

If the planted acreage is to approximate the national allotment, it is necessary that a large majority of the producers participate in the program. In the case of wheat in 1939, with approximately 70 percent of the growers participating in the program, the acreage planted in the entire country was nearly 10 percent in excess of the acreage allotted. With 95 percent of the cotton growers participating, the acreage planted to cotton in the entire country was slightly less than the national allotment. Approximately three-fourths of the producers of corn in the commercial area participated in the program, and the planted acreage was within 2 percent of the national allotment for the commercial area.

Thus it appears that it would be possible through the acreage-allotment and payment procedure to influence greatly the acreages of the different commodities planted. Obviously the amount of funds available for payment is an important factor in determining the proportion of the farmers participating in the program.

MARKETING QUOTAS

As has been stated, different methods of adjustment are most effective for different crops. Under the Agricultural Adjustment Administration farmers have accumulated considerable experience in the use of marketing quotas for certain crops, particularly cotton and tobacco, while for other crops marketing quotas have not been used although there is authority for quotas for wheat, corn, and rice under stipulated conditions.

The marketing quota is essentially a mechanism for allocating to producers shares in the total market for a commodity on either a quantity or an acreage basis. The marketing quota seeks to limit the amount of a commodity coming upon the market during a given period. Penalties are levied on marketings in excess of the quotas.

The effectiveness of a marketing quota depends largely upon the type of crop to which it is applied. A quota is most effective for those crops that must pass through definite processes or channels before consumption. Compliance with the quota can be checked readily at the point of processing or handling. In the agricultural adjustment programs this has been done for cotton at the gins and for tobacco at the tobacco markets.

Enforcement of marketing quotas presents a different and more difficult problem, however, in the case of commodities that may be used for livestock feed on farms or disposed of through other channels not susceptible to checking. This possibility of bootlegging commodities has been one of the principal arguments against various price-fixing proposals. Those who have opposed price fixing have had serious doubts as to the ability to maintain a check on the marketings of the commodity. Wheat and corn are two of the major commodities that would present these difficulties if marketed under quotas.

The differences in the applicability of quotas have been reflected in the actual operation of the A. A. A. programs. Under the original Agricultural Adjustment Act of 1933, steps were taken to supplement the voluntary provisions for production adjustment with the compulsory features of the Bankhead Cotton Act and the Kerr Tobacco Act of 1934. These acts provided national marketing quotas for the respective crops, with growers receiving tax-exempt marketing certificates or warrants for their pro rata share of the national quotas. Amounts marketed in excess of these quotas were subject to penalty taxes. The purpose of these taxes was to prevent noncooperating producers from offsetting the adjustments made by cooperating producers. With these measures supplementing the voluntary features of the original act substantial adjustments were made in cotton and tobacco acreage. However, these acts were based primarily upon the principle of production control, and after the Supreme Court decision of January 6, 1936, which held the production-control features of the A. A. A. unconstitutional in the Hoosac Mills case, the Bankhead and Kerr Acts were repealed, along with the Warren Potato Control Act, which was just then being placed in operation for the 1936 potato crop.

In the interim between the decision in the Hoosac Mills case and the Agricultural Adjustment Act of 1938, no marketing-quota provisions were available for the major crops. Cotton production increased materially in this period, particularly in 1937. Tobacco supplies had already been fairly well adjusted, so that tobacco surpluses did not accumulate as did surpluses of cotton.

The marketing-quota principle is an integral part of the Agricultural Adjustment Act of 1938. The use of quotas under this act, however, is based directly upon the right of Congress to regulate interstate and foreign commerce and not on production control. The Agricultural Adjustment Act of 1938 specifies in detail the conditions under which quotas may be used, sets up formulas for computing and allocating the quotas, and further restricts their use by the provision that before any quota can become effective it must have been approved by a two-thirds majority of the producers of the commodity concerned voting in a referendum on the specific question (fig. 1).

Marketing quotas, as provided for in the Agricultural Adjustment

Figure 1.—Top, A South Carolina farmer considers how to vote in the referendum on cotton marketing quotas. Lower, An Arkansas farmer marks his ballot.

Act of 1938, are considered as supplemental to the acreage-allotment provisions of the act, to be used more or less as emergency measures when excessive supplies accumulate. The act defines normal supplies on the basis of previous consumption and exports, and directs the Secretary of Agriculture to proclaim marketing quotas when the supplies of fixed major commodities exceed normal by more than the following stated percentages: For cotton, when the supply is over 107 percent of normal; for wheat, 135 percent; for corn and rice, 110 percent; and for tobacco, 105 percent. After a quota is proclaimed a referendum is held on the question of making the quota effective. Corn quotas apply only to producers in the commercial corn-producing areas. Penalties for marketing in excess of the quotas are also fixed in the act.

Thus far the marketing-quota mechanism has been a means of making the acreage adjustment part of the program for cotton and tobacco apply to the noncooperator and to keep him from expanding his production at the expense of the cooperator who has adjusted his acreage by seeding within acreage allotments. This use of the marketing quota is made possible through different methods specified in the act for the application of quotas. For cotton, tobacco, and rice, the act provides that the quotas be proclaimed before, not after, the crop is planted. Then, if quotas are approved in a referendum, they are translated into acreage equivalents, and compliance with quotas on the part of individual farmers consists of marketing only the production from the acreage equivalent of the marketing quotas. For the three crops mentioned the quotas are a definite part of the adjustment mechanism.

For wheat and corn, however, the application of marketing quotas under the act would be more in the nature of an emergency measure to handle the marketing of a crop already produced when supplies were excessively large because of especially good yields, large plantings by noncooperators, or for other reasons. For these crops the quotas would not be proclaimed until after the crop had been planted and the yield could be estimated. In these cases the quotas are intended to act directly as a means of promoting an orderly flow of the product to market. The quotas would affect adjustment indirectly through causing farmers to hold back excess supplies in one year and thus encourage then to grow less in the succeeding year.

No marketing quotas have been proclaimed for wheat or corn. Enforcement of compliance with quotas presents much more difficult problems with these crops than with tobacco and cotton because of the difficulty, already pointed out, of checking the use of wheat and corn.

The experience of the cotton and tobacco farmers indicates the effectiveness of the quota mechanism. Cotton acreage, which in 1932 had been about 35 million, was adjusted to 26 to 27 million under the first Agricultural Adjustment Administration programs but increased to 30 million acres in 1936 and more than 33 million in 1937. Since 1938, cotton farmers have voted for marketing quotas, and the acreage was held to approximately 24 million in 1938 and in 1939. Tobacco farmers voted for marketing quotas for 1938, but they failed to approve marketing quotas for 1939, even though the tobacco-supply situation was such that quotas were proclaimed. In 1939, in the absence of quotas, tobacco farmers grew a record crop of flue-cured tobacco and large supplies of other types, and prices were adversely affected. When the producers were given the opportunity they approved marketing quotas for 1940.

As was pointed out, marketing quotas for these two crops can be administered fairly satisfactorily because of the nature of the crops. Also, cotton and tobacco farmers during several years have accumulated considerable experience in the use of the quotas. Producers of such crops as wheat or corn would have to gain this experience before marketing quotas for these crops would be as effective.

The administration of the marketing quotas has been accompanied by its own problems, of which the principal one has been to get quotas established sufficiently ahead of planting time so that farmers could make definite crop plans. As the program has developed there has been more opportunity to plan ahead and meet this difficulty. Marketing quotas also bring the problem of enforcement, but as the quotas are made effective only after the approval of at least two-thirds of the producers voting in a referendum, enforcement is limited to relatively few individual cases.

Like acreage allotments, marketing quotas have been accompanied by payments to cooperators. With a large majority of producers receiving payments in connection with acreage allotments, which are identical with the marketing-quota requirements, it is not possible to determine precisely the relative effectiveness of each method. The noncooperator, however, receives no payments; so for him the quota is the principal factor in his individual adjustment. The fact that quotas limit noncooperators to the same basis as cooperating producers undoubtedly causes some producers to cooperate who might not otherwise do so.

Necessary acreage adjustments could conceivably be brought about solely through marketing quotas for those crops to which the quota method is well adapted. To the extent to which this could be done, payments for keeping crop acreages in line with needs could be reduced.

COMMODITY LOANS

The A.A.A. farm program seeks to provide for a stable and continuous flow of farm products to market at prices fair to both producers and consumers. The experiences of the drought years, 1934 and 1936, contributed to a greater realization of the need for larger reserve supplies of major food and feed crops. The present farm program provides for these larger reserves. Such reserves will depress prices unless provision is made for maintaining them rather than putting them on the market. Consequently commodity loans have become a definite part of what is known as the Ever-Normal Granary program. The Agricultural Adjustment Act of 1938 anticipated this use of commodity loans by providing for mandatory loans on specified commodities, with minimum rates set at 52 percent of the parity price of the commodity. To the extent that prices fall below these stipulated levels the loans maintain values above market prices.

Experiences in this country in the early 1930's and similar experiences in foreign countries have led to a general realization of the need for having a definite plan for liquidation in mind when loans are made, if heavy losses are to be avoided. For most commodities this means that provision must be made for bringing production into line with needs during the following year or period. In the case of a few commodities, where a substantial increase in consumption can be brought about, the excess supplies may be used for relief purposes. However, in most cases provision will need to be made to move the excess supplies into regular trade channels. The problems encountered in this connection vary with the characteristics of the different commodities and will be discussed under each commodity.

The Agricultural Adjustment Act of 1938 authorized loans on any agricultural commodity, including dairy products, and specifically directed the Commodity Credit Corporation to make loans on cotton, corn, and wheat under supply and price conditions laid down in the act itself. In addition to stipulating rates at which these loans should be made, the act provided that there should be variations and adjustments in these rates on the basis of variations in the grades and qualities of the commodities which were security for the loans.

Amounts, terms, and conditions of loans offered to producers of agricultural commodities other than cotton, wheat, and corn are determined by the Secretary of Agriculture with the approval of the Commodity Credit Corporation and of the President. No loans on cotton, corn, wheat, or rice may be offered to producers during a marketing year in which supplies of any of these commodities have reached levels at which the application of a marketing quota is authorized under the act, if a referendum on such a marketing quota has resulted in an unfavorable vote of the producers and the quota has thereby been rendered inoperative. This provision is designed to protect the value of the commodity which constitutes the security for the Government loan, since unregulated and burdensome marketing would tend to force down the price of the commodity.

Wheat

The Commodity Credit Corporation is directed to offer loans to wheat producers under conditions defined in the Agricultural Adjustment Act of 1938. Under title III, the loans are to be offered to cooperators in the agricultural conservation program who hold their wheat plantings within the acreage allotments established for their farms on terms different from those offered to noncooperating producers.

Loans are to be offered to cooperating producers: (1) In any marketing year beginning in a calendar year in which the farm price of wheat on June 15 (or thereafter during the marketing year) goes to less than 52 percent of the parity price; or (2) in any marketing year in which the July crop estimate for wheat indicates a crop in excess of a normal year's domestic requirements and exports. Rates of such loans are to be not less than 52 percent and not more than 75 percent of the parity price of wheat on July 1, the beginning of the marketing year.

Loans are to be offered to noncooperating producers only in years when marketing quotas for wheat are in effect, and then only on so much of their crop as, under the marketing quota, would be subject to a penalty if marketed. The rate of loans to noncooperators is to be not more than 60 percent of the rate to cooperators in the conservation program.

Wheat can be stored and kept for relatively long periods. Unless prices advance substantially above parity there will be little substitution of other commodities for wheat. Consequently the principal problem in making loans on wheat is that encountered in regulating the production of the wheat crop. In effect this means that if funds are available for keeping the production of wheat in line with needs, or if some other method of getting control is available, there is no occasion for any substantial loss on loans made on wheat.

The certificate plan has been suggested as a means of keeping the production of wheat in line with needs. Under this plan the producer would receive certificates equivalent to his share of the commodity needed for domestic consumption. A fixed price would be established for the certificates on the basis of the difference between the farm price and the parity price, perhaps with minimum and maximum levels. The certificates then would be purchased directly or indirectly by the persons who make the first sale or importation of articles manufactured from the commodity. They would purchase certificates in an amount equal to the quantity of the commodity used in the manufactured articles. Producers would receive the regular market price for their entire production, but in addition to this they would receive through the certificates an extra return on their share of the domestic market. It is probable that through the certificate plan and loans the income of wheat growers could be kept near parity with but little cost to the Treasury.

Corn

The Agricultural Adjustment Act lays down in detail the conditions for offering loans on corn. Different conditions apply to producers who comply with the allotment prescribed by the act for the commercial corn area and to producers who do not. For producers outside the commercial corn-producing area, eligibility for loans is conditioned upon not exceeding the soil-depleting allotment established under the Soil Conservation and Domestic Allotment Act.

To cooperating producers within the commercial corn-producing area, loans are to be offered: (1) During any marketing year beginning in a calendar year in which the November crop estimate indicates a crop in excess of a normal year's domestic requirements and exports; or (2) in any marketing year when on November 15, or thereafter, the farm price of corn goes below 75 percent of the parity price.

These loans are to be offered at rates determined by national supply and price factors, as follows:

At 75 percent of the parity price if the November crop estimate does not exceed a normal year's domestic consumption and exports but the farm price of corn is below 75 percent of the parity price on November 15 or at any time thereafter during that marketing year.

At 70 percent of parity price if the November estimate exceeds the normal year's requirements by not more than 10 percent.

At 65 percent of parity price if the estimate exceeds the normal year's requirements by more than 10 and not more than 15 percent.

At 60 percent of parity price if the estimate exceeds the normal year's requirements by more than 15 and not more than 20 percent.

At 55 percent of parity price if the estimate exceeds the normal year's requirements by more than 20 and not more than 25 percent.

At 52 percent of parity price if the estimate exceeds the normal year's requirements by more than 25 percent.

Loans are to be made to noncooperating corn growers in the commercial area only in years when a marketing quota is in effect for corn, on only that portion of their crop which the marketing quota requires shall be stored, and at only 60 percent of the rates for cooperating producers.

Loans are to be offered to corn growers outside the commercial area who are cooperating in the conservation program at 75 percent of the rates for cooperators within the area. Marketing quotas for corn do not apply outside the commercial area.

Like wheat, corn also can be easily stored. But unlike wheat, corn is largely a feed crop for which other feed crops can be easily substituted. Consequently when loans are made on corn, not only the production of corn but also that of other feed grains must be kept in line with needs.

Generally it seems that until marketing quotas are proved to be administratively practical for corn, corn loans are a reasonable risk only if funds are available in a sufficient amount to keep the production of both corn and other feed grains in line with trade needs.

Cotton

Provisions of the act of 1938 with regard to loans to cotton producers distinguish between growers complying with the acreage allotments set up by the act and those not complying. It directs that loans shall be offered to cooperators during any marketing year in which the average price of ⅞-inch Middling cotton on the 10 designated spot markets goes below 52 percent of the parity price. The rates of these loans are to be not less than 52 and not more than 75 percent of the parity price of August 1, the beginning of the marketing year for cotton.

Cotton growers who are not complying with the acreage allotments set up by the act are to be eligible for loans only in years when cotton marketing quotas are in effect, and then only on that portion of their crop which cannot be marketed except under the penalty provided for by the marketing quota and at rates equal to 60 percent of the rates offered to cooperators.

Cotton can be easily stored. Also, it has been demonstrated that the cotton acreage can be regulated through marketing quotas. However, about half the cotton crop is exported. If loans are made above the world price, provision must be made for a loss on that portion of the crop exported. Also, rayon and other fibers compete with cotton, and if cotton prices are advanced too much it is probable that these competing fibers will displace some cotton in the domestic market.

At present the cotton problem is complicated by a legislative restriction. No loan cotton can be sold for less than the amount loaned on it plus carrying charges and any payments made to producers in connection with it. The effect of this is to restrict greatly the sale of loan cotton. If this restriction were revised or modified, it would appear that loans could be made on cotton moderately above the world price with only moderate losses.

Tobacco

For several years governmental lending agencies have made loans to producers of the fire-cured types of tobacco through the cooperative marketing associations. In most years the loan rates have been above the prices that would have prevailed without the loans.

Before the production-adjustment program the cooperative marketing associations accumulated relatively large supplies of these types of tobacco. Even after the production-adjustment programs were effective, difficulties were encountered in moving these holdings into trade channels. About two-thirds of the fire-cured crop is normally exported. The grade and moisture-content requirements vary from country to country. It was impossible for a single agency to anticipate the requirements of all of the different foreign countries. Eventually that portion of these holdings which could not be moved into regular trade channels was diverted to byproduct uses.

During the 1939 marketing season loans were made on flue-cured tobacco. The 1939 crop was about 40 percent above the current level of world consumption, and in the midst of the marketing season buyers for the British trade withdrew from the market because of difficulties in getting exchange. Normally about one-third of the crop is sold for the British trade, and practically all of the production of some grades is normally used by the British. British manufacturers normally keep about a 2-year supply on hand, and it is expected that the British trade will again be in the market when present supplies are used up. Obviously it is necessary that the portion of the crop normally used by the British trade be graded, redried, and prized (packaged) to meet the British trade requirements if it is to be used eventually by British manufacturers; consequently loans were arranged through the established agencies which have in recent years handled the purchases for the British trade.

Under the loan arrangement that was worked out, these agencies make purchases of the tobacco in the usual manner for the account of the Commodity Credit Corporation. The agencies paid about 7 percent of the total cost of the tobacco, including buying, grading, prizing, and carrying charges, for which they obtained an option for the purchase of the tobacco if exchange becomes available before June 30, 1941.

This arrangement has two advantages: (1) It tends to insure that the tobacco will be handled in such a way that it can be used by the manufacturers who normally use it if exchange becomes available; and (2) the investment made by the trade will tend to insure its cooperation in eventually moving the tobacco into regular channels.

The acreage of tobacco can be regulated through marketing quotas, and surplus stocks of tobacco can be stored for long periods. Both of these conditions tend to facilitate the operation of loan programs without danger of large losses. As is the case with cotton, however, a large part of the production of some types of tobacco normally is exported in competition with tobacco produced in other countries. Consequently, loans above the level of export prices will result in losses. However, special arrangements with exporters, such as those under the 1939 flue-cured tobacco loans, and the availability of byproduct outlets serve to reduce the possibility of such losses.

Other Commodities

The Commodity Credit Corporation from time to time makes loans on commodities for which the production-adjustment features of the program are not available. Loans have been made on raisins, hops, butter, prunes, wool, dates, and pecans. In most cases difficulties have been experienced in moving some of the supplies accumulated under these loans into trade channels. Some of these supplies that have not been taken by the trade have been moved into relief channels and some diverted to byproduct uses.

THE PLACE OF PAYMENTS IN ADJUSTMENT

The payments made to farmers have been of two kinds: (1) The agricultural conservation payment, and (2) the price-adjustment or parity payment. The funds for these two types of payments are appropriated separately and the basis for each is different. While these payments do help induce compliance with the program, their broader purpose is to promote soil conservation and to maintain and improve the income of producers.

The soil Conservation and Domestic Allotment Act of 1936 authorized annual appropriations of not more than $500,000,000 for payments for carrying out the purposes of that act. To accomplish these purposes the planting of crops under acreage allotments is essential. The payments make up in part to farmers the sacrifice in income involved in producing on fewer acres. Also, the carrying out of specific soil-building practices requires some cash outlay on the part of the farmer, and the payments are intended to defray in part the cost of these practices. In general, the conservation payments are compensation to the farmers for doing things in the national interest which the farmer would be unable or less able to do alone.

A large part of the benefit of conservation payments is indirect—that is, through the successful operation of the program which the payments make possible. With a successful program farmers get better prices for their products than they otherwise would.

The price-adjustment payments are not authorized in any specific amount, but the Agricultural Adjustment Act of 1938 provided that these payments might be made to producers when funds were made available for the purpose. These payments are primarily of a subsidy nature and, when funds are available, are made to producers of specified crops when the farm prices of those commodities are at particularly low levels. These direct payments to producers are provided in order to bring the return to the producer closer to parity.

Both the conservation and the parity payments are an actual addition to farm income, but in total these payments are less important than the indirect benefits. In the 4 years 1936 to 1939, inclusive, the average annual national farm cash income was $8,552,000,000, while for the same period Government payments averaged $486,000,-000 per year, or 5.7 percent of the national average farm cash income.

HOW THE A.A.A. PROGRAMS ARE ADMINISTERED

The programs of the Agricultural Adjustment Administration are administered through the decentralized farmer-committeemen organization which has been established since the beginning of the Administration.

The local administration of the A.A.A. farm programs is in the hands of community, county, and State committees of farmers.

All cooperating farmers are members of county agricultural conservation associations, and community committees are elected annually from local members of these associations. Such committees are limited to three members. Among their duties are such matters as preparing, checking, and approving forms used in connection with the programs; recommending acreage allotments and soil-building goals for farms in the community; assisting in checking performance, as a preliminary step in the granting of payments and loans; and helping county committees and extension agents in the educational work of the programs.

As of July 1, 1939, there were 3,021 county agricultural conservation associations in the Nation as a whole, comprising about the same number of county committees and approximately 24,056 community committees.

County committees of three farmer members are elected by county delegates chosen by the community farmers at the same time the community committees are elected. The county committee elects a secretary, who may be the county agent; in case the county agent is not elected, he becomes an ex officio member of the committee without power to vote.

The county committees review forms and other documents filed in the county in connection with the programs; apportion county acreage allotments among individual farmers in accordance with standards fixed by the act; fix soil-building goals; supervise preparation of applications for payments and loans; and perform general county administrative work. Members of these committees and of community committees are paid on a per diem basis for time actually spent in discharge of their duties, and administrative costs are pooled with those of the community committees and prorated among the cooperating producers in the county.

The State committees are composed of farmers, except for the State director of extension, who is always a member. The farmer members, usually four in number, are appointed by the Secretary of Agriculture, upon recommendation of the Agricultural Adjustment Administrator, who generally consults with the State extension director and officials of the principal farm organizations before making his recommendations.

The State committees are in direct contact with the A.A.A. in Washington. They are in general administrative charge of the program in the State. Within the framework of law and of national A.A.A. policy and keeping always in close touch with county and community sentiment, the State committees determine State policies and direct the application of the programs in the State. Their work, in part, is to review county recommendations for acreage allotments and soil-building goals; to hear appeals from decisions of county committees; to advise the regional director on general policy within the State; to outline soil-building and range-building practices; and to recommend changes in the programs, as well as to assist in the development of new programs.

There are more than 80,000 active community, county, and State committeemen. Including alternate committee members, the entire decentralized organization consists of more than 125,000 committeemen actively engaged in or available for the administration of the various phases of the program.

The relation of the county agricultural conservation committee to one part of the A.A.A. program, the wheat loan, is illustrated by the procedure necessary for a farmer to obtain a loan on wheat. The principal steps are as follows:

The farmer applies to his county office for a loan. After determining from the records that the farmer is eligible for a loan through cooperation in the farm program, the county committee has the farmer's bins inspected (if the loan is on wheat stored on the farm) to see that storage requirements are met, and samples of the farmer's wheat are sent to the State office for testing for grade. On the basis of the reports from the field inspector who inspects the farmer's bins and the quantity of his stored wheat and from the State office on the quality of the wheat, the county office completes forms which the producer can present to a bank or other lending agency and obtain his loan. In the case of an application for a loan on wheat in commercial storage, a warehouse receipt from an eligible warehouse makes the bin inspection unnecessary.

223761°—40——37

The Meaning of Foreign Trade for Agriculture

by ARTHUR P. CHEW [1]

THE AUTHOR of this article deals with basic considerations in foreign trade. He argues that the foreign-trade situation determines the fundamental nature of the agricultural problem in the United States and that it is now more rather than less significant than formerly. From a broad historical and economic analysis he concludes that no creditor nation can indefinitely maintain a favorable trade balance to get rid of its surplus production. The ultimate consumption-production balance must be domestic, and domestic consumption must be stepped up when an unfavorable trade balance appears. But this does not mean resorting to a self-sufficient economy. On the contrary, he argues, maintaining the international exchange of goods at a high level in itself makes for increased domestic consumption and general prosperity.

BROADLY, American agriculture has three main possibilities, each of which turns on foreign trade. The first is that it will regain its foreign market, through trade agreements and improved international relations. Then it will have to make only small long-time adjustments. The second is that it will not regain its foreign market. In that event, if the home demand remains unchanged, agriculture will have to retire an enormous acreage permanently. The third possibility assumes that

[1] Arthur P. Chew is Special Agricultural Writer, Office of Information.

agriculture will get substantial compensation for the decline of the foreign demand in the shape of an increased domestic market, along with some resultant favorable influence on its export position. This will require action to increase the national income, through increased industrial production, and to increase the purchasing power of the low-income groups. It will involve some changes in the crop pattern; but the total foreign trade may be larger ultimately since the country will more readily take imports for exports.

Each of these three possibilities involves changes in our foreign-trade policy. Revival of the former market requires virtually world-wide abandonment of trade restrictions and implies that the United States will make its full share of the concessions. Permanent loss of foreign trade, on the other hand, will still leave American agriculture under world-market influences; for tariff protection cannot be effective unless domestic agricultural production drops to the point of shortage. In drought years, foreign competition would leap over the tariff. With domestic buying power raised to offset the decline of foreign buying power, as the third possibility requires, exports will be relatively less important. Nevertheless, they may actually increase in total volume, because the country will be in a better position to take imports in exchange. Any course on which we can embark, in short, will be a reorientation to foreign trade.

On what we do about foreign trade depend the answers to a host of other agricultural problems, such as the alteration of the crop pattern, the adjustment of commercial to noncommercial farming, the ratio between farm and nonfarm population, and the adjustment of agriculture to the rest of the economic system. It is impossible to allocate different lands to different uses, to conserve the soil efficiently, and to improve land-tenure conditions without reference to foreign trade. In short, the foreign-trade problem influences the entire farm economy. Indirectly, it dominates the production of crops consumed at home as well as that of the crops grown largely for export.

Some persons believe, because the percentage of our farm production exported is now only 5 or 6 as compared with 16 in 1934 and 14 or 15 before the World War, that the farm export problem is becoming less significant. Actually, it is becoming more significant. There is even an inverse relationship between the volume and the importance of our farm export trade under present conditions. The smaller the volume, the greater becomes the need for agricultural readjustments. Our agricultural industry grew up largely for trade with Europe; it depends vitally on the export market to absorb its surpluses and to maintain the level of its prices in the domestic market. American agriculture is still an integral part of the world economy, and this affects everything it does.

THE FOREIGN-TRADE SITUATION POSES THE FARM PROBLEM

That we can hide behind the tariff, turn to price fixing, and rely on Government aid for limited farm export trade is conceivable. Nevertheless, that too is a response to the world situation, and not an avoidance of it. Even a diminishing farm export trade, if it depends on price fixing at home and subsidies in the world market, is a determining factor in our agricultural life. Our governmental policy looks primarily, through reciprocal agreements, toward the restoration of relatively free international trade. It resorts only with profound reluctance to price control and subsidies. It stands ready to drop these things in favor of world agreements arrived at in international commodity conferences. Nevertheless, even if this hope fails and the solution proves eventually to be mainly a domestic one, it will still be true that the foreign trade situation posed the problem and dictated the response.

Farmers saw their problem in terms of foreign trade early in the 1920's, during the agitation for the McNary-Haugen plan. They saw it truly. Then as now the weakest spot in the agricultural situation was too large production for export. Farmers wanted to separate the home market from the world market. They urged that supplies for export should be segregated and sold abroad under conditions that would allow domestic prices to rise behind the tariff. The proposal involved a fundamental readjustment to foreign trade.

In one form or another, this proposal has had a part in everything that has been done since in our agricultural policy. It rested on a sound if crude analysis. Essentially, the problem today is the same as it was in the 1920's. We see it now, of course, in terms far more complex. Now it appears to us as part of the world struggle toward a new economy with so-called autarchy or economic nationalism in conflict with economic internationalism. Essentially, the issue is world unity versus national unity as the basis of the rural-urban balance.

Foreign trade will not be hereafter what it has been in the past. It will not be an answer to the problem of the surplus, since it will not carry away a net surplus of the national production of all products above the national consumption of all products. It will tend to be reciprocal, with exports quickly offset by imports. Reciprocal international trade, with goods and services brought in to offset goods and services sent out, leaves the consumption-production balance unchanged. It alters only the form of the surplus. True, the new form of the goods and services may be in better demand than the old; it may correspond better to actual prevailing wants. But if the people have insufficient buying power, part of the supply will constitute an economic surplus still. Liquidation of the surplus then becomes a domestic problem. This is the thesis of the present article.

POLITICS A FACTOR IN FOREIGN TRADE

It should be borne in mind that foreign trade is always a problem in politics as well as in economics. Indeed the very theory of it rests on political foundations; it has to do with commerce across as distinguished from commerce within national frontiers. Hence whatever changes the frontiers changes the trade. Other things being equal, an increase in the number of political sovereignties within a given area means an increase in the proportion of its international to its domestic commerce. Conversely, a decrease in the number of political units means a corresponding decrease in the exports and imports. Changes brought about in that way in the volume of the trade across frontiers may or may not be useful in an economic sense. They may simply reflect an alteration in the number of customhouses and be negative from the standpoint of human welfare.

Current diplomatic and military operations in Europe, for example, may greatly increase or greatly decrease the number of independent political units there. In the event of an increase in the number of Europe's national frontiers, more goods will have to pay tariffs, and international trade will show an apparent gain. If on the other hand the number of political units declines, the areas of relatively free trade will expand, and customs collections may partly give place to excise taxes. More of Europe's trade will be theoretically domestic. It goes without saying that the new ratio between domestic and foreign trade will not be the measure of any real economic change that may have taken place. Light on that problem will have to be sought in other directions; in the extent, for example, to which the frontier changes have or have not favored technology and good relations between town and country. Mere substitutions of foreign for domestic trade or vice versa are worthless. What finally counts is the total production and consumption.

In the political economy of international trade the entire world today is in conflict between two opposite principles. One is the principle of force, which through annexations, protectorates, and dictated spheres of influence essays to make more and more of the trade of certain nations essentially domestic in character. It projects their political influence beyond their borders, so that what were formerly exports are no longer truly exports, and what were formerly foreign investments are henceforth on a parity with investments in the homelands. The opposing principle, of course, is that of agreement. This principle, though it has never yet been supreme, has progressively until recent times substituted mutual for one-sided advantage as the basis of trade among peoples. Setbacks notwithstanding, it seems destined ultimately to triumph; for the essence of trade is equality of exchange. Trade that is mutually advantageous has no need of force; it grows and prospers through comparative advantage. Meantime, nevertheless, the political aspects of international trade are dominant, and they will always be influential. In foreign trade economics cannot be divorced from politics.

HISTORICAL DEVELOPMENT OF AMERICAN FARM EXPORTS

Let us glance at the historical development of our agricultural export trade. In the early years of the Republic, our farmers produced cereals and meats chiefly for home consumption. Farms were largely self-sufficing. More than 90 percent of the population, indeed, was rural. Trade with Europe did not become important until well along in the nineteenth century. Then, however, it developed rapidly, as a consequence of the industrial revolution and of mass migration to the West.

The age of machinery, which started in England toward the end of the eighteenth century, led to industrial specialization in the Old World and to agricultural specialization in the New. Europe was the workshop; the United States was the breadbasket and the leading

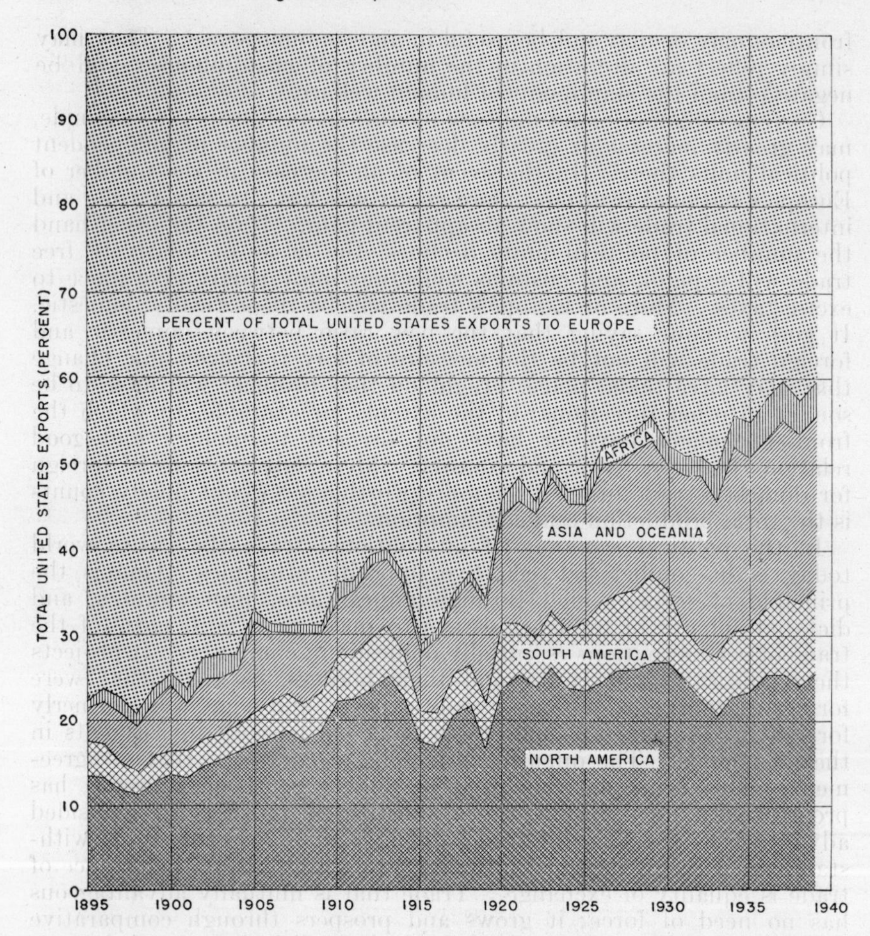

Figure 1.—Declining relative importance of Europe as outlet for United States exports. In the last 50 years the relative importance of Europe as an outlet for the exports of the United States has declined from about 80 to about 40 percent. In the first 9 months of 1939, Europe took about 41 percent. In 1915 and 1916, during the World War, Europe took about 70 percent of our exports, as compared with about 60 percent in the year before the war. The percentage dropped off again after the war to a point which was almost in line with the pre-war trend. In fact, by 1929 the percentage of our exports taken by Europe was 45, or exactly what projection of the pre-war trend would have indicated. The continents that have compensated for the decline in the relative importance of Europe are North America (chiefly Canada), Africa, South America, and Asia. Countries in the Asiatic group have risen most in relative importance. In the first 9 months of 1939, for example, Asia and Oceania took about 20 percent of our exports, as compared with only 4 percent in 1895.

source of fibers. Four-fifths of our exports between 1830 and 1860 were farm products, with cotton, tobacco, cereals, and meat products constituting the bulk of the merchandise. In this period trans-Atlantic commerce was ideally reciprocal. In return for our grains, meats, fibers, and tobacco Europe sent us tools, textiles, metals, glassware, earthenware, and most articles of comfort and luxury.

Eventually, however, Europe sent to us not merely finished industrial goods but means of industrial production. The industrial revolution crossed the ocean. Manufacturing took root here, and our imports of finished goods declined. Our imports of machinery, of steel for railroad building, and of capital goods in general, increased; also, our imports of raw materials for manufacturing. Soon after the Civil War we began to export manufactured goods in moderate quantities. Thereafter, nonfarm goods formed an increasing proportion of our export trade. This change, though gradual, was of revolutionary significance—it implied that we were becoming less dependent on European industry, and it gave our trade with Europe something of a one-sided character. As a matter of fact, we began, shortly after the Civil War, to have a considerable excess of exports over imports.

For several decades the farm share of the export trade, though it declined in proportion to the total, increased tremendously in volume. Not counting forest products, our agricultural exports rose from about $297,000,000 in value in 1870 to more than $840,000,000 in 1900. The peak year was 1898. Up to that time our cereals, livestock products, cotton, and tobacco found an almost insatiable European market. Indeed, our exports of these things went almost exclusively to Europe (fig. 1).[2] Europe had loaned us a great deal of money. Consequently, our goods went to Europe without need for us to receive immediately an equivalent in kind. In large measure we had received payment in advance. Eventually, nevertheless, the increasingly one-sided character of the trade brought about a change in its volume.

The turn of the century brought a decline in our farm exports. By 1910 the outbound commerce, except in cotton, tobacco, and fruit, was down in volume nearly to the level of the 1880's. This was a consequence of the increasing difficulty which Europe experienced in sending goods to us. Our imports of Europe's manufactured goods, for example, dropped to only about 30 percent of the total imports, as compared with more than 60 percent in 1860. On the other hand, our imports of raw materials for manufacture trebled, and the source of these products was largely non-European (fig. 2). Europe, though still vitally important to us as a market, was less important to us as a source of supplies.

Because its trade with us had grown unbalanced, Europe was turning elsewhere for agricultural products—to Canada, Argentina, and Russia for grains; to Argentina for meat; and to Australia and New Zealand for sheep and dairy products. Indeed some European countries, though not yet Great Britain, were hearkening to the demands of their farmers for tariff protection against the United

[2] Figures 1 and 2 have been adapted from the following publication: BEAN, L. H. OUR CHANGED FOREIGN TRADE. U. S. Bur. Agr. Econ., Agricultural Situation 24 (3): 17–20, illus.

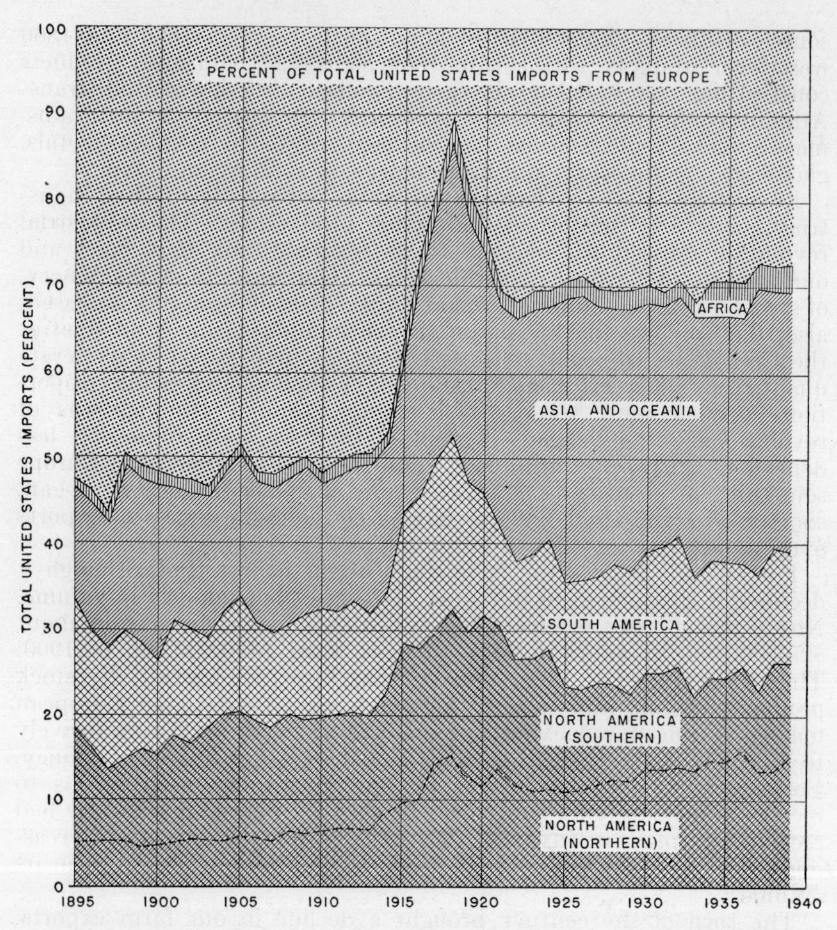

Figure 2.—Declining relative importance of Europe as source of United States imports. In our imports as in our exports the relative importance of Europe has declined. In 1895, for example, Europe supplied 52 percent of our imports. In 1939 it supplied only 28 percent. The drop came somewhat abruptly, rather than gradually as did the drop in our exports to Europe. Up to the outbreak of the World War Europe was still supplying close to 50 percent of our total imports. The World War reduced that to about 10 percent in 1918. After the war there was some recovery. In the period 1921 to 1938 our imports from Europe were about 30 percent of our total imports. Since 1936 the percentage has been about 28 percent. Canada, Asia, and Oceania have taken up the relative decline. Before 1914 Asia and Oceania sent us about 15 percent of our total imports. Since 1924 they have sent us about 29 percent. Before the war the contribution of North America (chiefly Canada) was about 7 percent. Since 1930 it has been about 14 percent.

States and other agricultural exporting countries. Germany, France, and several other countries raised their agricultural tariffs. Economic nationalism was coming. The hemispheric specialization, with its basis here in tremendous agricultural capacity and in Europe in a tremendous growth of industry and population, was breaking down.

Reverse Trend During the World War Only Temporary

As is well known, the World War reversed the slump in our agricultural exports. Wartime expansion in this country brought into cultivation 20,000,000 additional acres of wheat, and 5,000,000 additional acres of rye. It increased cattle and hog numbers by more than 20 percent, brought about gains nearly as large in a number of other basic foodstuffs, and caused expansion in our tobacco production. By 1918 our farm-commodity exports, including cotton, had reached a point 45 percent above the pre-war level. Our farm exports in 1919 amounted to nearly 20 percent of our total farm production.

But the change was only temporary. The expansion rested on precarious foundations, chiefly loans extended by the United States to the importing countries. In the late 1920's, when the lending policy broke down, our farm exports declined. In 1937 they were the lowest in 60 years. Essentially, our wartime growth of farm exports was a mere interlude. Post-war conditions revived and accelerated the pre-war trend toward declining agricultural exports.

Probably our agricultural export trade would have declined only very slowly had the war not intervened. Europe could have got supplies here for a long time, even without sending us anything in exchange. It had ample purchasing power on deposit. The war depleted its dollar exchange and plunged it into debt to us. Our excess of exports over imports before the war represented chiefly payments of interest and principal on borrowed capital. Interest payments alone required more than $200,000,000 annually. After the war, we became on balance a creditor country. Other nations owed us more than $500,000,000 annually on interest account alone. Eventually the interest due us annually rose to more than $1,000,000,000 until repudiations and defaults reduced it. It was impossible to maintain a large favorable balance of trade based only on additional credits.

Exports of foodstuffs were the first to decline. Exports of meats and cereals slumped sharply from year to year; in the fiscal year 1935 exports of cured pork dropped to 22 percent and exports of lard to 48 percent of the pre-war average. Our cotton exports, after an upturn for a number of years, dropped likewise, and in 1938–39 amounted to only 3,500,000 bales. In the 1938–39 decline, however, our cotton-loan policy was a factor. Between 1932 and 1939 the production of foreign cottons increased nearly 45 percent, and Europe's takings of foreign cotton increased almost proportionately. In the middle 1930's the total farm exports were only slightly more than half the pre-war volume. The United States had lost its former place in world trade as supplier of basic foodstuffs.

Prominent as both cause and effect was a movement in western Europe toward agricultural self-sufficiency. Wheat and wheat-flour production in Europe jumped from 1,100,000,000 bushels in 1922 to 1,500,000,000 bushels in 1932. The world's imports of wheat and wheat flour declined from an average of 819,000,000 bushels in 1927 to only 426,000,000 bushels in 1934. World imports of beef and veal products declined 33 percent between 1928 and 1933, and similar declines took place in world imports of live cattle, dairy products, and other staples. Accompanying these changes were drastic restrictions on international trade—tariffs, embargoes, quotas, and exchange limitations. Underlying these things, however, was a progressive decline in the earlier hemispheric reciprocity. In many countries whose foreign trade declined sharply after 1921, internal production increased after 1929 or fell only moderately below the 1929 level. Our own foreign trade declined with no offsetting increase in our internal production, which indeed also declined tremendously.

EARLY INTERPRETATIONS MISTAKEN

Theory that developed with the early reciprocity misconceived it. In what was dynamic, changing, and essentially temporary, the theory assumed an automatic and permanent balance. International division of labor between industrial countries and agricultural countries, it held, would continue forever and produce endless progress. Our own population increased tenfold and our wealth proportionately. Europe's population increased from about 200,000,000 in 1800 to more than 500,000,000 in 1900, and at the same time its standard of living rose. But the method had limitations. It made the industrial countries more dependent on food imports and yet nursed the agricultural countries along toward industrial independence. The original reciprocity could not endure. Trade among the nations came to rest more and more on other foundations—chiefly on credits and capital loans.

One reason was that our reciprocal trade with Europe in the nineteenth century did not put the whole of our economic system into the world economy; it put only part of it there—the agricultural part. In industry it fostered an opposite trend, of which protection was the guiding principle. Manufacturing grew up behind the tariff, on a price level relatively much higher than that of agriculture. It had a greater price differential in its favor throughout the nineteenth century than it has today. Agriculture had free or cheap farm land, with the prospect of increasing land values; hence the distribution of advantages may not have been grossly uneven. Agriculture's involvement in and industry's exemption from world competition was bound, however, to create a problem eventually. When industry too developed an export trade, the import difficulty arrived.

In the beginning of the industrial revolution no one could have imagined such a development. Agriculture and industry were then very primitive. Farmers knew nothing of mineral fertilizers and very little of plant and animal breeding. Farm production per man or per acre seemed fixed by nature. Population, especially in Europe, seemed likely always to press upon the food supply. Europe's agriculture improved materially. Deliverance from the food difficulty came chiefly, however, through industry. Railroads and steamships carried Europe's factory products abroad and brought foodstuffs back. Trade fed the growing populations—the exchange of manufactured goods for foods. Trade solved the population problem for decades. But when the trade tended to get out of balance, through the spread of industrialism to agricultural countries, it became evident that this crude international division of labor, with industry emphasized in Europe and agriculture elsewhere, had actually been unstable from the very start, though it had had a long inning.

Perhaps we can state the general principle. In countries with limited agricultural resources, the law of diminishing returns is highly authoritative. It limits the domestic food supply and tends to keep the populations small. Industry provides an escape, though industry cannot expand indefinitely. Industrial labor and capital can be employed, however, long after agriculture has passed the point of diminishing returns. Factory output can be increased tremendously by mass production. Population growth may therefore continue, provided only that factory goods can be exchanged for foods. Industry can grow if it has buttresses in agriculture abroad. But this requirement is often difficult to satisfy. As industry expands and needs a conversely disproportionate development of agriculture elsewhere, it has fewer agricultural areas to balance it off. Nevertheless, the relationship can endure under the proper conditions for a long time; as long, in fact, as the agricultural buttresses retain their simple agricultural character.

Apparently the broadest basis for foreign trade will always be the exchange of factory goods for foodstuffs and raw materials. (There is room for a considerable reciprocal exchange of industrial products of different kinds, costs, or qualities; but the basis for trade of this sort is convenience rather than sheer necessity.) Modern industrial countries, however, have difficulty in getting adequate farm supports abroad. Fewer can do so, moreover, as the agricultural countries too become industrialized and have less need for industrial imports. This throws the industrial countries back on their domestic agriculture, which will now be far too small. Not choice but necessity controls them, though the procedure means lowered standards of living. World unity between agriculture and industry then reverts to an aggregation of local or national urban-rural balances, with tariff barriers and all-round loss of comparative advantage as usual though not necessary features, and with desperate imperialism as one alternative. "Fighting for trade" is a term that has a very literal meaning

There is a fatal paradox. Although industrialism stimulates population growth in certain countries beyond the supporting power of the national agriculture and makes the people vitally dependent on foreign trade, it simultaneously nurses industry in the agricultural countries. In short, the process first creates and then destroys an international division of labor and with it a certain kind of international trade. Then the swollen populations face decline. They cannot return, without decimation, to primitive self-containment; their domestic resources are insufficient. In many countries, for example Great Britain, Belgium, the Netherlands, and Germany, self-sufficiency is impossible. Not even kitchen gardens could be provided there for everyone; not to speak of farms to produce enough cereals, meats, dairy products, and fibers. Attempts on the part of these countries to establish more nearly a domestic balance between industry and agriculture, though natural in the circumstances, are merely projects of despair.

This would promise well for renewed trade between western Europe and North America but for the fact that it takes two to make a deal. Only reciprocal wants can nourish a permanent international trade. And, broadly speaking, we do not want what Europe can supply, or at any rate not to the extent that we did formerly. In trying to make itself as nearly self-sufficient as possible, western Europe does not expect to prosper. Ultimately, it hopes instead to establish trade relationships with countries that need its products. Even that can merely postpone the difficulty, which must recur. Overdeveloped European industry cannot balance itself indefinitely with nonindustrial countries. The supply of these countries will give out. Postponements of the crisis should not be despised, since posterity may know better how to deal with it. Manifestly, however, the answer is not a permanent division of labor between industrial and agricultural countries. No such arrangement can possibly be permanent.

PERMANENT BASIS OF INTERNATIONAL TRADE

The permanent basis of international trade is comparative advantage. Certain comparative advantages, such as those of climate and geography, are often practically permanent; for example, those of growing rubber in the Tropics and wheat in the temperate zones. Other comparative advantages may be great at one time and small at another, as we can see from the fact that Europe has lost its superiority in manufacturing. Our own preeminence in some industries, such as the mass production of automobiles, may not be permanent. Large unified markets may be developed elsewhere, and we have no monopoly of engineering. Invention and discovery may develop new types of comparative advantage. In addition to the natural advantages of soil and climate, there are innumerable acquired advantages of skill and knowledge, which international trade can strengthen and perpetuate. It by no means follows, just because the nations are no longer predominantly industrial or agricultural, that they cannot trade with one another at all. Yet the world-wide diffusion of similar industrial skills obviously tends to diminish the opportunity.

Possibilities exist, to be sure, for the international interchange of even industrial products, not to mention the products of agriculture. Trade between Great Britain and Germany, for example, was large both before and after the war. Yet both are industrial countries dependent mainly on the exchange of factory goods for foodstuffs and raw materials. Countries with similar technologies have different aptitudes, training, tradition, and social organization, as a result of which their costs of production may vary. American typewriters, British textiles, Swiss watches, and French lace are familiar examples. Such international trade, however, involves reciprocity. It stands apart, moreover, from the great problem of balancing agriculture with industry, and apart from the problem of countries like the United States that want to export farm products but not to import factory goods. There will not be room anywhere indefinitely for large favorable balances of trade. Only reciprocal international trade can be truly permanent. Countries that wish to export must also import.

In discussing so complex a matter as foreign trade, it is difficult to avoid oversimplification. There are very few clear-cut dichotomies, with one thing set off against its opposite. It has been shown, for example, that the early trade between the New and the Old Worlds, with its basis in hemispheric specialization, tended to be reciprocal. Actually it was never merely a simple and immediate interchange of goods and services, but also an affair of loans and credit. Deferred payment was a factor. With its industrial surplus western Europe bought goods and services from the United States and also a stake in our economic development. It lent to this hemisphere a part of its production annually, in the expectation of receiving it back eventually with interest. It became part owner of American farms, factories, mines, and railroads.

In consequence certain European countries, notably Great Britain and France, developed favorable balances of trade; they had an excess of merchandise exports over imports until nearly the middle of the nineteenth century. Other European countries had favorable trade balances until much later. In this way they became creditor countries; western Europe preceded the United States in this status by nearly a century. Inevitably, however, as the American development proceeded and provided payments of principal and interest on the capital previously borrowed, the merchandise balance turned in our favor, and Europe on the other hand began to have trouble in disposing of its goods. The proof was the rise there of unemployment, which is the industrial expression of the surplus problem, long before the corresponding agricultural difficulty developed here. In recent years we have had unemployment, too, in both town and country. But the fact that Europe had it before we did was a reflection partly of the trans-Atlantic balance of trade. Unfavorable trade balances, which usually involve unemployment, are a sign that consumption should be stepped up domestically.

Favorable trade balances have at least provisional utility. They take care of surpluses and allow production to run above consumption domestically. Temporarily this condition, the first cause of which is foreign lending or the exportation of capital, satisfies a number of requirements. It carries surpluses away from the surplus countries, helps along the development of backward countries, and diffuses science and techniques throughout the world. Moreover, it enables surplus countries to get out of economic crises without redistributing their national income. Obviously, if the commodity surplus can be exported, it need not be consumed domestically, and the national distribution of income may remain substantially unchanged.

Surpluses of exports over imports, with the exportation of capital as the operating mechanism, often have yet another function; they stimulate outward movements of labor also, and relieve the pressure on the labor market. The world migrations of the nineteenth century and the resulting development of virgin continents were a response to investment opportunities. Capital and labor emigrated from their native lands together. But the favorable trade balances that the double movement created at first changed over later into unfavorable trade balances and left the problem of balancing consumption with production domestically more difficult than if it had been tackled in the beginning.

Sometimes debtor nations temporarily have favorable trade balances. Our own pre-war experience is an example; but as payment proceeds, the favorable balance declines. It can be restored only by replacing the payment of debt with a grant of credits. Hence, by its very nature, the favorable trade balance is only a temporary device for balancing consumption with production. The ultimate consumption-production balance must be domestic.

Many countries are still industrially undeveloped. It is to these that the industrially mature ones will prefer to turn for foodstuffs and raw materials, and also for favorable trade balances. In that way they can kill two birds with one stone. They can satisfy their wants and get rid of their surpluses. This is not simply an affair of equal exchange. Factory surpluses in the developed countries represent more than just enough purchasing power for necessary imports. The excess can be used in foreign investment. Eventually, however, capital exports to the undeveloped countries must diminish. The first form is the exportation of finished goods; but the second and final form is the exportation of means of production—of machinery and sometimes of entire branch factories. This phase of the one-sided trade movement is necessarily the declining phase, since it raises the backward countries to industrial maturity.

Even if political or other conditions protract the surplus-deficit relationship, the reciprocity fails eventually. For example, India served England well for decades both as a source of agricultural raw materials and as a market for processed goods. Cotton and other crops went from India to Great Britain; Lancashire textiles and other commodities went back and supplanted the products of the Indian native industries. Though Indian agriculture benefited temporarily, India became excessively ruralized, since its handicrafts decayed without being replaced by machine industries.[3] In recent years the rural population of India has been about 73 percent of the total population, as compared with 66 percent in 1901 and 58 percent in 1881. The resulting excessive pressure of population on the land, accompanied by extreme rural poverty, may have been as detrimental to the British commercial interest as would have been the rapid development of Indian manufacturing. Now Great Britain is fostering Indian industry.

The dependence of Indian agriculture on foreign industries is a cause of profound unrest. It has given rise to the Gandhi movement for the revival of village industries, and simultaneously to native industrialism and to demands for Indian autonomy in tariff making. In its own fashion, without using the slogan, India moves toward economic nationalism—in other words, toward some kind of approximately domestic rural-urban balance. On the basis of excessive agricultural specialization, it can exist no longer. The symptoms are overcrowded, inefficient agriculture on the one hand and lack of urban employment on the other.

In consequence India seethes with nationalism both political and

[3] LADEJINSKY, W. AGRICULTURAL PROBLEMS OF INDIA. U. S. Dept. Agr., Off. Foreign Agr. Relations, Foreign Agr. 3 (8): 321–346, illus. 1939. [Processed.]

economic. It wants native industries, not merely as a basis for increased domestic trade, but as a means of alleviating pressure of population on the land and at the same time of modernizing its agricultural technique. One-sided economic development indefinitely is impossible for India, just as it was for the United States. Probably it no longer benefits even England and the other industrial countries that supply the Indian market, since the overgrowth of the Indian rural population has reduced per capita buying power to the vanishing point.

BIOLOGY GOES ALONG WITH ECONOMICS IN FOREIGN TRADE

In the exportation of capital for the creation of favorable balances of trade, there is biology as well as economics. Regarded as merely a source of profit, the exportation of capital often seems inept. It may involve immense financial loss. Usually, however, it facilitates a desirable outward movement of labor as well. Capital and labor leave home as partners under the steady pressure of their growth, which would otherwise expose them to low interest and low wages, and leave them in slavery to the owners of natural resources. Ricardo, with Malthus' law of population as his starting point,[4] declared that population growth combined with rents, royalties, and other charges for the use of land would steadily increase the disparity between earned and unearned increment. This doctrine seemed impregnable. Nevertheless, interest and wages rose in the country of its origin, social conditions improved there, and the pressure of population on subsistence declined.

Labor and capital in Great Britain did not refute the Ricardian thesis. They simply got around it. Specifically, through joint emigration, they escaped from the local land monopoly into rich and cheap resources throughout the world. They went together to the United States, to Canada, to Africa, to India, to Australia, to South America, and to the Orient. Each block of capital took with it, directly or indirectly, a certain number of executives, technicians, and laborers, and the double movement benefited stay-at-home capital and labor also. Soon it had its counterpart in a dozen countries where capital and labor were superabundant, and as a result the industrial system developed offshoots throughout the world.

Theoretically, the potential field for this kind of thing is still enormous. The continent of Africa has scarcely been touched. Comforts and satisfactions of western life are almost entirely lacking in China and are by no means abundant in the Soviet Union. Much development can take place even in Canada, Mexico, Central America, South Amer-

[4] David Ricardo (1772–1823) was an English political economist, chiefly famous for his theory of distribution, which deals with the division of the produce of the land and labor of a country among the several classes that take part in production. An important element in the theory is that economic rent is the return imputable to land for its production contribution. Ricardo defines economic rent as measuring the excess of the value of the product of a given amount of capital and labor on good land and the value of the product of the same amount of capital and labor employed on marginal or no-rent land or at the intensive margin of cultivation. Thomas Robert Malthus (1766–1834), English political economist, published in 1789 the first edition of his Essay on the Principle of Population as It Affects the Future Improvement of Society. In this he declared that population increases in a geometrical, food in an arithmetical, ratio, so that population unless checked by war, pestilence, or famine tends to increase faster than subsistence. In later editions Malthus dropped the mathematical formula and retained only the general idea that the growth of population tends always to press upon the food supply.

ica, India, and in the Middle East. The field is still almost virgin.[5] Yet the competition for entrance into it is bitter. There are more contestants than prizes; the demand for "spheres of influence" far exceeds the supply. In consequence there is a general tendency to enter them by force. Force goes with exported capital and labor as guarantor and guardian. Within a country, if the laws are favorable, capital and labor can move about under the prompting solely of the principle of comparative advantage. It may take force besides in the international sphere.

Moreover, as soon as the exported capital and labor become productive, and generate the inevitable return flow of goods and services, the search for deficit areas recommences. It ends in a vain struggle for perpetual favorable balances of trade—for a condition in which exports may always exceed imports. The struggle is vain for a very simple reason. Favorable trade balances represent a lost investment unless they change in due season into unfavorable balances. Even when a nation extends its power or its boundaries to cover the investment, it must take back some day an equivalent in imports. Many countries had unfavorable balances of trade before the World War, precisely because they had previously had favorable balances. Though they strove to reverse the tide, they could not. All countries try to keep their trade balances favorable or to hold their unfavorable balances down, because the alternative is economic stagnation or redistribution of wealth. None has yet proved that exports can continue without imports.

IMPLICATIONS OF OUR CREDITOR POSITION

Foreign lending by the United States has produced an impasse already. It irks us that our debtors decline to pay; but we do not make a way for them to pay. We do not receive their goods with open arms. When goods come in anyway, in spite of tariffs, and threaten us with an unfavorable balance of trade, we talk about embargoes and quotas, entirely in the conventional manner. Our reciprocal trade program lags mainly because the country objects to imports. Farmers and manufacturers alike insist on protection against foreign competition. Each group may favor lower tariffs on what it does not produce itself; but the result is a stalemate. Though it is a creditor nation, the United States lacks a creditor psychology. With surpluses constantly produced at home, it wonders how it can receive surpluses from abroad. No one knows the answer. The dilemma involves a painful choice. Either we must let the goods come in and make shift to consume them domestically; or we must keep them out and struggle to maintain a favorable balance of trade.

Obviously, when powerful and productive nations want to have favorable balances of trade simultaneously, an impossible situation exists. They cannot just swap surpluses, particularly of similar things. Even the exchange of dissimilar goods alters merely the form of the difficulty, without changing the net surplus position. The basic trouble is the tendency of production to outrun consumption. Rationalization, or the rationing of an insufficient market, is a misnamed and

[5] HOBSON, C. K. THE EXPORT OF CAPITAL. 290 pp. 1914. London.

ineffective remedy, a temporary expedient. Industry tries it through trusts, cartels, and other trade agreements; agriculture through cooperative marketing, acreage restrictions, marketing quotas, and import controls. Such action can diminish surpluses of goods only by creating surpluses of labor and capital. It is not a true solution of the surplus problem. Swinging from overproduction to underemployment in industry and to drastic crop limitation in agriculture is ultimately futile. The only final remedy is increased consumption.

In the depression after 1929 the share of the United States in a much reduced volume of international trade declined more than that of almost any other country. In 1934 our share was only 9.8 percent of the total, as compared with 13.8 percent in 1929. Agriculture suffered much more than industry. The agricultural porportion of the total domestic exports dropped to 26.5 percent in 1938 as compared with 38 percent in 1927. With production power far beyond the effective buying power of the home population, we had nowhere to put our surplus. We had not developed a domestic outlet for it, or seriously contemplated doing so, and our favorable balance of trade was falling.

The immediate cause was the virtual cessation of our foreign lending. Yet even if we had resumed such lending, the action would merely have postponed the decline of the favorable trade balance. Lending implies subsequent receiving; and in international trade both operations influence the movement of goods. Countries that lend money abroad should remember that real repayment is always in goods and services and that the only way for a creditor country not to have an unfavorable trade balance eventually is to make no collections whatsoever. Only by forgiving its debtors can a creditor country keep its trade balance on the favorable side.

This country's position is unusual. It has surplus production power in industry as well as in agriculture. In some years before the World War our exports of nonagricultural goods ran close to a billion dollars. Potentially, indeed, the surplus problem is chiefly industrial if we may judge by our unemployment totals. True, agriculture more commonly has large unsold stocks of goods. Proportionately, for the time being, it is more dependent on foreign outlets. Nevertheless, both of the two great branches of production have more production power than the domestic market can employ at present, and the unused capacity is larger in the cities than on the farms. Hence, if we rely to any extent on foreign lending to carry away the surplus, it will raise questions as to the goods we should take as final payment.

Two big reasons justify taking mainly industrial imports. (1) Consumption per capita can be more easily increased on the industrial than on the agricultural side; and (2) the receipt of nonfarm imports is necessary to sustain our farm exports, and consequently to preserve our comparative farm advantages. It suffices to mention cotton. Without a foreign market for cotton the South would be prostrate; there is no cash crop for the domestic market into which the South could shift its entire export acreage. And we cannot export cotton without importing something else. Taking imports for exports, however, raises another question. How are we going to get the imports consumed, on top of our domestic production?

223761°—40——38

There can be no evasion of the problem. Foreign countries that take our exports can pay us in only three ways: (1) By shipping gold to us; (2) by borrowing money in this country; and (3) by selling goods and services to the United States. As a permanent device we can dismiss the first method, because the world's gold reserves outside the United States are insufficient and because we do not want more gold. As to foreign lending by the United States, the obstacles are many. Moreover, this way of financing exports merely defers the necessity to take imports for exports. Taking goods and services from foreign countries is the only final way. Moreover, it is the best way, since it keeps us in foreign trade and allows our production to continue in the established ways without loss of comparative advantage.

Manifestly, however, the incoming goods must either displace domestic products or be consumed domestically in addition to the normal domestic supply. This is the fundamental challenge. In the first case, with domestic goods displaced, the imports will cause unemployment. In the second case, through price changes or otherwise, they will alter the distribution of the Nation's real income. These, however, are not obstacles; they are merely conditions. Hereafter, production for foreign consumption will increasingly involve letting foreigners produce an equivalent for consumption here. Therefore we must raise the domestic level of consumption. Industry and agriculture cannot remain at cross-purposes. Neither can push its own interest exclusively; each must recognize that the period of exports without imports is drawing to a close.

The issue is not world trade versus self-containment. Essentially, it is whether or not we shall recognize now or later that the favorable balance of trade must tend to disappear and that our international trade, whether it be large or small, must be approximately equal and reciprocal. It is obviously possible to have either a large or a small amount of reciprocal international trade—to have the import and export total either high or low. Our problem is to decide which is the better course, and it is not a difficult problem. It is better to maintain our foreign trade on a high level.

With foreign trade maintained reciprocally on a high level, our comparative advantages will be retained. Foreign trade on a high level of exports and imports is entirely feasible and desirable. It is the desirable alternative, especially for agriculture, to the old system of disproportionately one-way trade. The negative of self-containment, it excludes also the basis on which our export trade has depended heretofore. It sacrifices what has been the supreme significance of our foreign trade in the past—namely, its power to keep our production running above our domestic consumption. Reciprocal international trade keeps only the benefits of international specialization and comparative advantage. These, however, are very substantial benefits.

Into a prosperous United States selected goods can be imported liberally. That we know from what happened before the depression. In the calendar year 1929, during the greater part of which business was active in the United States, we imported merchandise to the value of $4,399,000,000. Our exports exceeded this figure by only $842,000,000. It is evident that for the great bulk of our exports we took payment in imports, and no one complained. In the ensuing depression imports and exports declined together. In 1932, for example, the merchandise imports totaled only $1,323,000,000; but the exports were down also—to $1,612,000,000. Buying less abroad did not give us proportionately more business at home.

Such facts do not necessarily prove that the decline or disappearance of our favorable balance of trade would raise no problem. Between 1901 and 1913 our annual excess of exports over imports averaged in the neighborhood of half a billion dollars, and during the World War it jumped to the billions. It is impossible to deny that the absence of a favorable balance involves either less production or more consumption domestically, and adjustment to either position is difficult. Nevertheless the figures above cited show clearly that liberal imports not only do not prevent business activity but actually are one of the usual conditions. It may prove easier than we think to absorb domestically our surpluses or their import equivalent.

INTERDEPENDENCE OF FOREIGN AND DOMESTIC COMMERCE

The increased domestic consumption need not and indeed should not be only or mainly of goods domestically produced. It can advance as well, and indeed better, through international trade whereby the different countries can retain and develop their comparative advantages. There is no need whatever, merely because imports for the most part must balance exports, to turn away from foreign trade and to make every country do without or produce inefficiently what it could readily bring in.

Action to raise the consumption of the masses through a more equitable distribution of income enhances the opportunity for more liberal trade conditions throughout the world. It is not an alternative but a complementary means of improving the balance between consumption and production. The consumption level can be raised higher on a basis of world trade than on a basis of relative self-containment.

Practically, the cure for the problem of the surplus, which we have sought hitherto in various methods for stimulating export trade, is not wholly in foreign trade at all or wholly in domestic readjustments, with increased consumption per capita. It requires sound policies in both fields. With buying power efficiently distributed, the foreign-trade situation will improve. Largely of itself it will become an affair of reciprocal imports. With higher incomes the people of the United States will be able to consume more of the farm surpluses. Some cotton may be left over, and some wheat, tobacco, and fruit. For these crops there may be an increased foreign demand. In the absence of an entirely adequate foreign market the growers can turn partly to the production of something else—something wanted at home. There is a large potential demand for dairy products, fruits, and vegetables. It is better to satisfy that than to insist on exports without imports.

Specifically, the problem calls in the domestic field for a narrowing of the margin between consumption and production and in the sphere of foreign trade for a continuous effort to realize the benefits of international differences in the kinds, costs, and qualities of production. Full employment available at good wages is the basic requirement. With that accomplished it will not be a calamity any longer that agriculture and industry do not complement one another on a hemispheric basis as they did formerly. New types of international trade, based on new types of comparative advantage, will develop in a world economy.

Our imports of industrial raw materials and of semimanufactures and luxury goods will increase. Foreign buying power for our agricultural and other surpluses will be larger; simultaneously the domestic market for farm products will expand. So long as it exists and thrives it will matter little whether our export trade is predominantly agricultural or predominantly industrial. In either case it will facilitate distribution—which is all that counts. Sales will increase both at home and abroad and costs of production will go down.

This is the formula of prosperity. Along with increased production and consumption domestically will go increased foreign trade, and the increased foreign trade in turn will enhance the domestic prosperity. Trade among the nations will then be a means of facilitating consumption everywhere rather than simply of shifting goods from surplus to deficit areas. It is entirely feasible, through the coordinate development of rational domestic and rational foreign-trade policies, to solve the problem of the surplus and at the same time materially to increase the wealth of nations.

Reciprocal Trade Agreements— A New Method of Tariff Making

by L. A. Wheeler [1]

IT IS inconceivable, says the author of this article, that the nations of the modern world, including the United States, will adopt a policy of free trade. The trend in recent years has been in the opposite direction. Tariffs there will be. The question then is what method of tariff making is the most advantageous for the United States, and more specifically, for American agriculture? The author holds that reciprocal trade agreements should be considered as a method of tariff making that is alternative to the older method based on the process commonly called logrolling. After briefly reviewing the historical significance of the tariff to farmers in the United States, he contends that the reciprocal-trade-agreement method of tariff making, while perhaps not all that is necessary for the most effective conduct of commercial policy, is better suited to present-day conditions, including those in agriculture, than the old method. This is a subject on which there has been much controversy, and the author frankly takes one side of the argument.

[1] L. A. Wheeler is Director, Office of Foreign Agricultural Relations.

IN JUNE 1934 Congress passed an amendment to the Tariff Act of 1930 which has since become popularly known as the Reciprocal Trade Agreements Act. The primary purpose of the act was to contribute to economic recovery in the United States by opening the channels of international trade. Specifically, this was to be accomplished through trade agreements between the United States and individual countries, in connection with which the President was authorized to make concessions to foreign countries, chiefly in the form of reductions in import duties on foreign products to the extent of 50 percent below the rates established in the Tariff Act of 1930.

This act has been in operation for 6 years. Altogether 22 agreements have been negotiated, 2 of which were with Canada. At the present time (March 1940) 20 are in effect. Approximately 60 percent of the total foreign trade of the United States is with the countries with which we have these agreements.

In the trade agreements numerous concessions have been made by the United States in the form of reductions in import duties. It has been estimated roughly that these reductions have resulted in a decrease in the average import duties on dutiable products from over 50 percent to less than 40 percent, ad valorem.[2] At the same time the United States has obtained numerous concessions from foreign countries in the form of improved treatment of American export products, either through reductions in import duties or in expansion of the quantities of particular products permitted entry from the United States.

The purpose of this article is to examine one aspect only of the reciprocal-trade-agreements program—its use as a method of tariff making in the United States from the point of view of the American farmer. No attempt is made here to examine in detail the concessions granted by the United States in the form of duty reductions on agricultural products. Nor is any analysis made of the concessions obtained by the United States in the form of reduced trade barriers affecting our agricultural exports.

Historically the tariff policy has been one of the major political issues in the United States. But it has been debated largely from the point of view of its effect on our manufacturing industries. It was not until the Tariff Acts of 1922 and 1930 that any particular emphasis was placed on the role of the tariff in protecting agriculture.

The tariff policy of the United States is of interest to agriculture chiefly from three points of view. (1) Import duties tend to restrict imports generally and thus restrict the amount of dollar exchange available to foreigners to purchase surplus agricultural products. (2) Such duties restrict imports of manufactured products and thus tend to raise the prices of things that farmers buy. (3) Duties restrict imports of agricultural products and thus, to the extent that they are effective, tend to raise the prices of those agricultural products not on a surplus basis in the United States. It is well understood, of course, that under ordinary conditions import duties on products such as cotton and wheat, of which exportable surpluses are produced, are of no value from a price-raising point of view, since such products have to be sold on a world-market basis regardless of what the United States import duty may be. The reason for this is that the surplus

[2] Computed by dividing total calculated duties collected by the total value of dutiable imports.

must be sold at world-market prices, which, in the absence of governmental intervention in fixing prices internally, will also apply to the quantities sold in the domestic market.

THE SIGNIFICANCE OF THE TARIFF TO THE FARMER

In approaching this discussion of reciprocal trade agreements as a method of tariff making, it may be useful to examine the relative importance of the tariff to the farmer from these several points of view during the period preceding the World War of 1914–18 and the period since the end of that war.

Before the World War

During the three decades prior to 1914, the United States was a debtor country—that is, we owed more to foreign countries than foreign countries owed us. Under these circumstances, it was necessary that we maintain what is popularly termed a "favorable" balance of trade—an excess of exports of merchandise over imports of merchandise—in order that we might have the means to make payments on our foreign debt, both capital and interest.

At first sight this really fundamental fact seems to have little bearing on the question of the effect of the tariff on agriculture. Actually it has had a very direct bearing. We had to export more than we imported. And the tariff, by restricting imports, helped to increase the excess of exports over imports. To put the matter another way, the fact that the tariff restricted imports during this pre-war period was of no great consequence from the standpoint of foreign purchasing power for our agricultural products, since, under the circumstances then existing, foreign countries, or more specifically, the western European countries importing agricultural products, had an adequate supply of dollar exchange to pay for their imports from us in spite of the fact that we restricted our imports from them through our tariff policy. This was true largely because, during this period, the amount of dollar exchange available to foreigners was augmented by our payments on our debts.

But looked at from the point of view of the effect of the tariff on the prices of things farmers had to buy, the situation was quite different. In the pre-war period the United States had not developed to its industrial maturity. In fact one of the outstanding arguments for the tariff was that it aided "infant" industries. During those years farmers bought, or would have liked to buy, many goods that were produced more cheaply abroad than in this country. The tariff prevented such goods from being sold in the United States at these low prices and thus penalized the farmer, who, generally speaking, was selling on the world market and buying on the domestic market.

From the third point of view—the effect of the tariff on prices of things farmers produced and sold—it is apparent that our tariff policy was of relatively little importance prior to 1914. Since colonial times American agriculture had been organized primarily on an export basis—that is to say, most of the important agricultural products were produced in excess of domestic requirements, and it was necessary to dispose of this surplus abroad. There were, of course, certain exceptions, the most important of which was wool. The United States has never produced any significant surplus of wool, and therefore the tariff has usually been effective in maintaining domestic prices above world prices. Whether this has been advantageous to American farmers in general is, of course, another question. In the case of sugar also the tariff has been effective, but in pre-war years even more than recently the number of farmers producing sugar was insignificant as compared with the total number of farmers. And all farmers consume sugar. Furthermore, before the war transportation facilities were not such as to permit a ready flow of some of the more perishable agricultural products which now enter in large volume into international trade, as, for instance, fruits and vegetables, dairy products, and meat. Even though we may not have had a surplus of some of these products, lack of transportation facilities was a more important factor in protecting domestic interests than our tariff policy.

It is evident, therefore, that in the pre-war years the one aspect of the tariff that was of particular interest to the farmer was the increase in the prices of things that farmers had to buy. The tariff gave little protection to the farmer as a producer, and there was no question of reducing foreign purchasing power for our agricultural export products through the tariff.

Since the World War

What has been the situation in the post-war years? First of all, the war changed the United States from a debtor to a creditor country. Instead of our owing large sums of money to foreign countries, foreign countries owed large sums to us. In this kind of situation it was necessary that our imports of goods and services exceed our exports in order to provide foreigners with the means of making payments on their debts. From this point of view a trend toward lower tariffs was clearly indicated. What actually happened was that the tariffs were increased, first in the Emergency Tariff Act of 1921, then in the Fordney-McCumber Act of 1922, and finally in the Smoot-Hawley Act of 1930. Partly for this reason foreigners did not get a sufficient supply of dollar exchange through exports to us to pay for imports from us and also to make payments on their debts. Nevertheless, during the 1920's our exports continued to expand. This was because large foreign loans by American citizens provided foreign countries with the necessary dollar exchange to balance the discrepancy between our exports to them and their exports to us. During the 1930's our export balance continued, although both our exports and our imports were on a much lower level. The principal factor sustaining foreign purchasing power since 1930 has been the purchase by the United States of huge quantities of gold.

In short, the change in the debtor-creditor status of the United States made it much more important than before the World War that imports be increased in order to provide foreigners with the means of paying for our export products and also to make payments on their debts. But the tariff policy of the United States during the greater part of the post-war period so far has worked in the opposite direction. The substantial disadvantage of the high-tariff policy to agriculture from this point of view was, however, obscured during the 1920's by the large flow of funds abroad in the form of loans.

What about the effect of the tariff on the farmer as a consumer during the post-war years? In general the high-tariff policy continued of course to operate to the disadvantage of the farmer as a consumer, just as it had in pre-war years. But there was a substantial difference in the degree of disadvantage. It is probably safe to say that the tariff has been less burdensome to the farmer as a consumer since the end of the World War, largely because many of our industries have increased their efficiency to a point at least equal to that of similar industries abroad. Some of them, such as the automobile industry, have surpassed foreign producers in efficiency of production. There are, of course, numerous examples of more or less monopolistic industries which, behind the protection of a high tariff wall, are in a position to demand higher prices than could otherwise be obtained. But those industries—and there are many of them—in which the technique of mass production has put the United States on an export basis are able to sell and, in many cases, do sell their products at prices below those of foreign industries. These include a great many of the staple items needed by the farmer, such as hardware, automobiles, tractors, and the like.

As a matter of fact, during the post-war decades it is probable that most farmers, as consumers, have been hurt more by the tariff on agricultural products such as sugar and wool than by the tariff on manufactured goods. In general, the effect of the tariff in boosting prices of things farmers have to buy has become less important than it was during all of the nineteenth century and the first decade of the twentieth, during which American industry was growing toward maturity.

Protection Against Foreign Agricultural Products

It remains to examine the significance of the tariff in protecting domestic agriculture against foreign competition. There continue to be, as in the pre-war years, relatively few agricultural products that are in a position to be benefited directly and significantly by import duties. But the list is longer than in our earlier history. The prime examples of effectively protected agricultural industries continue to be sugar and wool. To these flaxseed may be added. In a sort of border zone are three of the major agricultural industries of the United States—beef production, dairying, and poultry production. If no protection whatever were afforded to these particular industries it is conceivable that the imports from particularly favored foreign sources of supply would increase in some years to an extent that would be measurably disadvantageous from the point of view of our domestic producers.

The beef-cattle industry, for instance, has not been producing any surplus for export since the end of the World War. In fact in years of reasonable prosperity beef production in the United States falls below our potential requirements. Without any protection whatever against imports, in the form of either import duties or sanitary embargoes, there doubtless would be, in such years, a considerable importation of cattle from Canada and Mexico and of chilled beef from Argentina; possibly as much as 15 percent of our consumption would be imported.

In the case of the dairy industry, there seems to be little reason to doubt that in the absence of any protection there would be, particularly on a seasonal basis, rather large importations of butter from New Zealand and Denmark. Even now we import considerable cheese, although most of it is of foreign types.

The poultry industry is less subject to potential competition from abroad than either the dairy or the beef-cattle industry. Canada is the principal potential source of imports of both poultry and eggs, although in the event of free trade it is altogether likely that the United States would ship a great many more of these products to Canada than Canada would ship to us. In fact turkeys from Argentina are about the only poultry item that might be imported to the serious inconvenience of domestic producers; and even in that case it is doubtful in view of the increasingly efficient production of turkeys in the United States, whether Argentine imports would offer any considerable threat. There has been, it is true, long-continued agitation against imported dried and frozen eggs from China on the ground that such imports injure the American poultry industry. It is noteworthy, however, that the years in which dried-egg imports have been largest have been the years in which our poultry industry has been most prosperous.

Whatever might be the significance of imports under a free-trade system, the fact stands out that the prices received by producers in all these borderline industries are dominated by two factors: (1) The amount of domestic production, and (2) the level of consumer demand in the United States. It seems fairly clear that this would continue to be the case even though no duties whatever were assessed on imports of these products. Imports would be considerably larger than they are now when business conditions were good or when our supplies were short. They would be small in years when business conditions were poor or domestic supplies were large.

Probably the principal increase in foreign competition in the agricultural sphere since pre-war days is in tropical vegetable oils. Imports of these products for both edible and nonedible uses have increased enormously. It is probable, in fact it is practically certain, that the free entry of these products would result in a further increase in imports. To what extent such increased imports would affect the welfare of American farmers, it is extremely difficult to say and certainly beyond the scope of this article to explore.

Additional examples of increased foreign competition of somewhat localized character might be mentioned—for instance, in such commodities as winter vegetables from Cuba and Mexico. In fact, in the whole field of fruits and vegetables, foreign competition might be expected to be considerably keener than it was before the war in the event of free entry into the American market, largely because of the enormous improvement in transportation facilities for such products.

In addition to these examples of more or less direct competition, numerous instances have been brought forward of the indirect competition of substitute products the elimination of which would permit a substantial expansion of domestic production of products for similar use. An outstanding example frequently given is tropical starches, such as tapioca. It is probably true that complete elimination of imports of such starches would permit an expansion in production in the United States of substitute products, such as corn, potato, and sweetpotato starches. It is quite unlikely, however, that this expansion would redound to the benefit of producers in any significant way, since the complete substitution of domestic for tropical starch would require only a very small percentage of our products suitable for starch making.

Summing up, it may be concluded that from the point of view of the farmer as a consumer of nonagricultural products the tariff policy of the United States is of somewhat less significance than in pre-war years. On the other hand, from the standpoint of the producer of the agricultural surplus products such as cotton, wheat, hogs, tobacco, and many kinds of fruit, a high-tariff policy is a greater handicap than formerly, since in a creditor country it is essential that imports be greatly increased if exports are to be maintained. Finally it appears that insofar as he produces the deficit or self-sufficient products, the American farmer is in a position to receive more effective protection than during the era of agricultural expansion of the nineteenth century.

Numerous references have been made to what might happen in the event that import duties were abolished on particular agricultural products. Actually, complete free entry is outside the realm of possibility. The choice must be between different degrees of protection for both agriculture and industry rather than between protection and free trade. It is quite inconceivable, for instance, that any Congress would pass a tariff act with duties as low as those in the Underwood tariff of 1913, in which a great many agricultural products were on the free list. This being the case, the question arises as to how best to bring about changes in import duties in the interest of the country as a whole, and particularly in the interest of the farmer.

THE OLD METHOD OF TARIFF MAKING

Until the passage of the Trade Agreements Act of 1934 the historic method of tariff making in the United States was a complete revision of the tariff approximately every 10 years. Under this practice a tariff bill would be considered first by the Ways and Means Committee of the House of Representatives, when opportunity would be given for interested parties to present their views. The Ways and Means Committee would then report the tariff bill to the House, and after long debate and many revisions it would be passed and sent to the Senate, which, in turn, would refer it to the Senate Finance Committee. The Finance Committee would then go through much the same procedure as had the Ways and Means Committee. After further changes in rates of duty and general provisions by the Finance Committee, the bill would be reported on the floor of the Senate. Another more or less prolonged debate would take place in the Senate, and additional changes would be made. Finally the bill as it passed the Senate and the bill as it passed the House would be referred to a joint conference committee to iron out discrepancies. After the conference committee had agreed upon it, it would once more be submitted to the Senate and the House for final approval before being sent to the President, who would decide whether to approve or disapprove the measure as a whole.

The net result of this kind of procedure was, of course, something considerably short of a "scientific" tariff. In general the tariff rates on particular products were arrived at through a complicated process of compromises and deals. The ultimate result was likely to be heavily weighted on the side of the interests of the protected industries as compared with the interests of consumers and of the producers of our export products. In fact the system permitted export interests little opportunity to make their views heard. One of the best examples of the farmer's getting outtraded in this tariff-making process was the case of hides and shoes in the Tariff Act of 1930. In the course of the passage of that act it is said that agricultural support for a tariff on shoes was obtained on the basis of putting a tariff on hides, which were formerly on the free list. But the tariff on hides was put at 10 percent ad valorem and that on shoes at 20 percent. And the 20-percent tariff on shoes was largely effective, while the tariff on hides had very little effect on the prices livestock producers received for their cattle.

It is true that in the Tariff Acts of 1922 and 1930 a gesture toward greater flexibility and change in the rates of duty embodied in a general tariff act was provided in the so-called flexible provision (sec. 332 of the Tariff Act of 1930). This section provides for investigations by the Tariff Commission of differences in costs of production at home and abroad and gives the President authority to increase or reduce tariff rates by as much as 50 percent on the basis of such findings.

As a matter of fact, however, relatively few cases were investigated in comparison with the total number of items in a tariff bill. And in most cases where action was taken the duties were increased. There is good reason to suspect that the principal element of flexibility lay in the possibility, under the difference-in-cost formula, of making the facts fit the conclusion rather than the conclusion fit the facts. However that may be, the fact remains that the principle of adjusting tariffs according to differences in costs of production is impracticable. It is impossible to say just what the difference in cost of production actually is. There are, first of all, great differences in quality which an average difference cannot by the nature of things take into account. There are also great differences between the products and costs of individual producers within the United States and also within particular foreign countries. But in the case of agricultural products, further difficulty results from the fact that the cost of production in a particular year is determined to a very marked extent by the yields obtained. And the yields are, of course, determined to a large extent by weather conditions. Taking corn as an example, the costs of production per bushel during the years of extraordinary drought in the United States, 1934 and 1936, were far above those in, say, 1937, when the weather was favorable and yields generally were high. So far as the tariff is concerned, it might well be argued, and in fact it was argued by many farmers who had to buy corn for feed in the drought years, that the duty should be reduced or eliminated. But according to the cost-of-production formula, the duty should have been increased in those years.

Differences in cost of production should of course be taken into account in tariff adjustments, but to rely upon such differences to the exclusion of other considerations must inevitably lead to absurd results.

TARIFF MAKING UNDER THE TRADE-AGREEMENTS PROGRAM

That the reciprocal trade-agreements program is, among other things, a new method of tariff making is attested by the fact that reductions have been made in the duties on articles in 420 paragraphs out of a total of about 730 paragraphs in the Tariff Act of 1930, or almost 60 percent. Furthermore, a considerable number of duties have been "bound"—that is, guaranteed against increase—and an additional number have been bound on the free list. Up to the present time no increases in duties have been made under the Trade Agreements Act.

Under the trade-agreements program the procedure has been as follows: First the Department of State announces the intention to negotiate a trade agreement with a particular country; in recent years it has announced also the commodities on which the United States may grant concessions in connection with such an agreement. Next, public hearings are held by an interdepartmental committee known as the Committee for Reciprocity Information, made up of representatives from the Departments of State, the Treasury, Agriculture, and Commerce and the United States Tariff Commission. At these hearings representatives of domestic producers advance arguments against duty reductions on particular products, while representatives of import interests advance arguments in favor of duty reductions. Representatives of export industries are also present and indicate concessions they would like to see obtained from foreign countries on their particular products.

The information developed in these hearings, together with all available information on the subject in the various Government departments, is carefully reviewed by a special interdepartmental subcommittee (known as a country committee because it handles the detailed work relating to an agreement with a particular country), established to work on the agreement in question. This subcommittee reports its findings to the interdepartmental Trade Agreements Committee, which is also made up of representatives of the Departments of State, the Treasury, Agriculture, and Commerce, and of the United States Tariff Commission, under the chairmanship of the Department of State. The Trade Agreements Committee considers in detail the recommendations of the country committee and, with such changes as may seem appropriate, passes its recommendations along to the Secretary of State and the President. These recommendations include not only concessions that are desired from the foreign country in question but also definite suggestions as to the extent to which the United States might without serious injury to domestic industries make concessions in return. All of this procedure is gone through before the negotiations actually start. In the course of the negotiations any questions that arise are sent back to the Trade Agreements Committee for consideration and are passed on to the Secretary of State and the President for final approval or rejection.

This, in brief, is the mechanism of the trade-agreements program. What are its advantages over the historic method?

There are four major points in which it has greater flexibility: (1) It gives an opportunity for careful and detailed consideration of the economic aspects of each individual case upon which duty reductions may be proposed. (2) It provides for subclassifications of particular products, so that the great bulk of classes in which domestic products predominate can be excluded from the duty reduction, which may apply only to the particular kinds and classes of articles in which the foreign country in question is primarily interested. (3) Duties may be reduced on a seasonal basis, that is, only during those months of the year in which domestic production is nonexistent or very small; this, of course, applies primarily to agricultural products. (4) Reductions may be applied on specifically limited quantities. The last, as an outstanding development in tariff making under the reciprocal trade-agreements program, deserves special mention.

Under this practice, in cases where it seems likely that if the duty were reduced imports might increase greatly, to the distinct disadvantage of American producers, the procedure of limiting the quantity on which the duty reduction will apply has been adopted. An outstanding example of such procedure is found in the duty reduction on cattle in the trade agreement with Canada. In the first place the duty reduction applies only to certain classes of cattle, namely, (1) those weighing over 700 pounds, (2) dairy cows, and (3) calves. In the second place, except for dairy cows, the reductions apply only to specified quantities. And in the third place, in the case of the heavy cattle in which competition is most important, the reduction applies to only a certain number of cattle in each quarter of the year. By this means it was possible to grant to Canada a concession on cattle which permitted a substantial increase in her exports to the United States and at the same time assured the domestic producers against a flood of imports. In the case of the heavy cattle, for instance, the duty reduction applied to a quantity representing only 1½ percent of our annual slaughter of cattle and calves.

But perhaps the principal advantage of the trade-agreements method of tariff making over the older method lies in the fact that it takes into account directly the interests of our export industries. It would, of course, be possible, if it were politically feasible, to have a general revision of the tariff act in which duties were generally reduced as compared with those in the preceding act. As a matter of fact, such a revision has been made on a few occasions in our history, although the general tendency has been upward rather than downward. But even if import duties were reduced, which would be an advantage from the standpoint of foreign purchasing power, there would be no assurance whatever that foreign restrictions on our export products would also be relaxed. Under the trade-agreements method reductions in foreign restrictions are definitely assured, since it is on the basis of such reductions that concessions in the form of duty reductions are made by the United States.

One additional argument may be advanced in favor of the trade-agreements approach, namely that it puts the Government of the United States on a more equal footing with other countries in the field of international trade. The days of nineteenth-century laissez faire have passed. Since the beginning of the World War, governments everywhere have taken increasingly direct control in matters of foreign trade. By this it is meant that in practically all foreign countries important in international trade the executive branch has authority quickly to change import duties, establish import quotas, and otherwise control foreign trade, and this authority is exercised. It is important in this situation that the executive branch of the Government of the United States be empowered to act quickly and effectively in meeting particular situations brought about by such actions of foreign governments. The authority to conclude reciprocal trade agreements may not be all that is necessary but it does add greatly to the bargaining power of the United States in meeting particular situations.

Methods of Increasing Agricultural Exports

by H. B. Boyd [1]

"OUR AGRICULTURE is still geared to a large export trade," the author of this article points out, "and our surpluses consist largely of the excess over our domestic needs which formerly could be sold abroad. Either these surpluses must again move in large volume into foreign markets or agriculture must be adjusted to the domestic market"—an adjustment that could be made, he argues, only with great difficulty. Supplementing the previous article in the Yearbook which discussed the trade-agreements approach to foreign trade, this article attempts to explore briefly all the other possibilities, from straight barter to the use of export subsidies. Pros and cons are discussed in each case, and the difficulties facing any effort to increase agricultural exports under present conditions are frankly recognized by the author.

THE RESTORATION and improvement of export markets for products of our farms is necessary for the continuance of the existing organization of American agriculture. The adjustments which have been made since the close of the World War, though of considerable magnitude, have not brought agriculture into a stabilized relationship with outlets available at present. The further adjustments which would be necessary if agriculture were to be restricted entirely

[1] H. B. Boyd is Director of the Division of Special Programs, Agricultural Adjustment Administration.

to the domestic market, even if domestic purchasing power were considerably raised and the entire domestic market reserved for domestic products, could be accomplished only at great loss in real national income and with untold human suffering.

THE GROWTH AND DECLINE OF OUR AGRICULTURAL EXPORT TRADE

The export trade of the United States in agricultural products first developed during a period of comparatively free competition. Coincident with the opening of the fertile lands of our Middle West Great Britain repealed her corn laws, making free a large and discriminating market. Continental European markets, while not uniformly free, were open to American products. Our fertile new soils and favorable climate, supplemented later by large-scale production methods and more efficient farm machinery, gave us a great advantage in the production of many agricultural commodities. These products found a ready sale, and we could well afford to specialize in their production and buy from other countries those things which we could not produce to the best advantage. Under these conditions of relatively free trade and specialization, our foreign trade in agricultural products at the end of the nineteenth century had reached a volume never previously attained by any country of the world.

By supplying the foreign demand for cotton, wheat, beef, butter, cheese, and pork products, the United States repaid its debts to Europe and became the richest nation in the world. Then came the World War boom with inflated prices and soaring land values, followed by the inevitable collapse. In the 1920's, trade was maintained by foreign loans, which apparently will never be repaid. Finally, in the last decade we have discovered that the frontier has moved to other countries. We have keen competition in exports, and barriers to trade in importing countries are far greater than before the World War.

OBSTACLES TO THE REVIVAL OF EXPORTS

Our agriculture is still geared to a large export trade, and our surpluses consist largely of the excess over our domestic needs which formerly could be sold abroad. Either these surpluses must again move in large volume into foreign markets, or agriculture must be adjusted to the domestic market. There are two obstacles to the revival of exports: (1) Competition from other sources of supply and (2) barriers to trade in consuming countries. As to the first, we can have no just complaint against the agricultural development of countries with resources similar to our own, but there is great opportunity to improve world trade in a number of agricultural commodities by cooperative action of all countries concerned through special international agreements. As to the barriers to trade in consuming countries, we do have reason to complain, although we ourselves have raised trade barriers which are unnecessarily high. Agriculture would benefit from mutual action with other countries to bring about a lowering of these barriers to foreign trade.

Import duties as first imposed were intended simply as an easily

233761°—40——39

collected source of revenue and not as a device for controlling imports from foreign countries.

The use of an import duty as a protective tariff usually started as an aid to new industries in their developmental stages, with the expectation that such protection would become unnecessary when the new industry was fully established. In practice, however, protective tariffs tend to become permanent. They are defended as being necessary to achieve national self-sufficiency in a world in which there is war or danger of war, to moderate the effects of rapidly changing technological conditions, and to protect against "cheap foreign labor" and low production costs in foreign countries. In more recent years, many nations have also imposed quotas, exchange controls, and embargoes as additional means of protecting home industries against foreign competition. Such measures tend to prevent the most effective specialization, whereby each country would produce those commodities it could produce to the best advantage and exchange them for the specialized products of other countries.

Prior to the World War our own tariffs were low in comparison with those of more recent years. Although consumers objected to tariffs on the ground that they frequently aided monopolies and increased living costs, there was comparatively little criticism on the basis that tariffs reduced foreign purchasing power for American agricultural products. At that time the United States as a debtor nation was sending large amounts of money abroad as interest and repayments on debts and as interest and dividends on stocks and bonds of domestic corporations owned abroad. Moreover, recent immigrants were sending large remittances back home. By the end of the World War, however, these supplements to foreign purchasing power had diminished greatly, and after the war our increased tariffs further restricted foreign purchasing power for American goods. During the decade of the 1920's, the effect of these losses in foreign purchasing power was hidden or temporarily offset by huge loans and investments and American tourist expenditures abroad.

After the tourist trade fell off and we reduced our foreign loans and investments, it was not long before a disproportionate part of the world's gold had flowed into the United States in order to maintain a balance of payments. This suction of gold to the United States was augmented from time to time by the flight of foreign capital. The resulting acute shortage of gold reserves abroad, as well as rampant nationalism, brought about further exchange controls, quotas, and barter transactions which seriously handicapped world trade and adversely affected our exports of agricultural products. This is the situation which existed at the outbreak of the present war.

POSSIBILITIES OF INCREASING AGRICULTURAL EXPORTS

Generally speaking, there are two ways to increase our agricultural exports: (1) By increasing foreign purchasing power for our products, and (2) by making more effective use of existing foreign purchasing power. When the various proposals for expanding our agricultural exports are thus grouped, the very small number of alternative measures for increasing exports becomes apparent.

Increasing Foreign Purchasing Power

In the long run our exports can be paid for only by the importation of commodities, including gold, or by services rendered by foreign countries or by their nationals. In the years of comparative peace before 1914, imports and exports and the mutual rendering of services were so well balanced that occasional small gold shipments sufficed to settle differences in payments and to maintain the currencies of the leading commercial nations on a parity level. Under present conditions gold is no longer a fully effective international medium of exchange, and few countries are able to settle exchange balances in gold. The United States, however, has received large amounts of gold as payment for exports and as the medium for foreign investments in this country. As a result we have so much of the world's gold that it may lose much of its traditional value as a world monetary base, and the acceptance of still more gold in payment for exports may be inadequate compensation from a national standpoint.

The balance of payments of the United States in 1933, 1937, and 1939 in comparison with the average for the 5 years 1924–28 is shown in table 1. This is an account in summary form of transactions which involve receipts from or payments to residents of foreign countries. Payments are received from foreigners for our exports of commodities and gold, for interest on our foreign investments, for services rendered to foreigners, and in the form of capital transferred from foreign countries to the United States. These items are classified as credits in the balance of payments of this country. On the other hand, payments are made to foreigners for our imports of commodities and gold, for interest on the investments of foreigners in this country, for services rendered by foreigners, and in the form of capital transferred to foreign countries. These items are listed as debits in our balance of payments. For simplification, table 1 shows only the net credit or debit arising from interest payments, gold movements, and capital transfers. The fact that total credits and debits do not balance is due to errors and omissions in available statistics.

It will be noted that in the years 1924 to 1928 exports exceeded imports by an average of $652,000,000 annually, which was nearly balanced by the annual outflow of capital from the United States. In other words, we were financing our own exports with loans, most of which have never been repaid. By 1933 the outflow of capital had diminished nearly to one-half of the 1924–28 average and exports, which had fallen to about one-third of the 1924–28 average, had become smaller than imports. In recent years there has been a large flow of capital into the United States. With exports exceeding imports this capital has been transferred in the form of gold. Payments for services, tourist expenditures, and other invisible items were in 1933 less than one-half those of the predepression years. Although these invisible items had revived somewhat by 1937, they decreased in 1938 and 1939 and probably will be further reduced by the present European war. Commodity imports will also tend to decline, and commodity exports will be weighted on the side of munitions rather than on that of agricultural products. Unless they are financed by loans or by further gold imports the outlook for agricultural exports in wartime is not bright.

Table 1.—The balance of international payments of the United States, 1924–28, 1933, 1937, and 1939 [1]

[In millions of dollars]

Item	1924–28 average	1933	1937	1939 [2]
Credits (items for which payments are made to the United States):				
Exports of agricultural commodities	1,962	694	797	655
Exports of nonagricultural commodities [3]	3,148	1,066	2,561	2,537
Exports of gold (net)	38	83		
Interest received on foreign debts (net) [4]	682	409	298	295
Net inflow of capital			881	1,232
Total	5,830	2,252	4,537	4,719
Debits (items for which payments are made by the United States):				
Imports of commodities [5]	4,458	1,977	3,176	2,403
Imports of gold (net)			1,386	3,040
Miscellaneous invisible items (net) [6]	777	347	576	427
Net outflow of capital	603	336		
Total	5,828	2,660	5,138	5,870

[1] Compiled from reports of Bureau of Foreign and Domestic Commerce.
[2] Preliminary.
[3] Includes exports of silver which in 1939 amounted to $15,000,000.
[4] Includes principal payments on war debts.
[5] Includes imports of silver which in 1939 amounted to $85,000,000.
[6] Includes payments for freight and shipping, tourist expenditures, immigrant remittances, charitable and other contributions, government transactions (excluding war-debt receipts), and miscellaneous services and transactions.

The best long-view plan for increasing agricultural exports, looking to the restoration of peace, is the mutual lowering of trade barriers to permit a resumption of the normal trade relations which existed before 1914. This lowering of trade barriers has been accomplished to some extent through the reciprocal trade agreements, which have been appraised in the preceding article in this Yearbook.

Aside from an increase in imports of commodities, foreign purchasing power for American exports could be increased by a more extensive use of foreign services, such as shipping, insurance, and banking. Such an extension, however, is limited by our attempts to build up our own merchant marine and the fact that our insurance and banking facilities are equal to those which might be obtained in foreign countries. Any increased use of foreign shipping under the restrictions of the Neutrality Act will tend to create foreign purchasing power for American exports.

Foreign travel by American tourists is one of the most effective means of creating foreign purchasing power for American exports. Aside from merchandise purchased abroad by travelers, large sums are spent for transportation, hotel accommodations, amusements, fees, and taxes. Estimated aggregate payments by American tourists to foreigners reached a peak of $821,000,000 in 1929. After a very sharp decline during the depression, aggregate payments increased to $563,000,000 in 1937, a sum still far short of the 1929 figure. The war probably will reduce these expenditures (they amounted to only $485,000,000 in 1939) and thus weaken the effective demand for American agricultural products.

Loans abroad during the 1920's were a very important means of expanding our agricultural exports. The average net export of capital from 1924 through 1928 was approximately $600,000,000. In contrast, in recent years there has been a large net inflow of capital into the United States. The net inflow reached a total of $1,400,000,000 in the calendar year 1935, declined to $330,000,000 in 1938, and increased to $1,232,000,000 in 1939. Since the beginning of 1935 the total net inflow of capital has been about $5,000,000,000. This large net inflow was made possible principally by heavy imports of gold, which amounted to nearly $9,000,000,000 from 1935 to 1939, inclusive.

During the last 5 years United States investments in foreign countries have decreased $2,000,000,000. If we were again to become a net exporter of capital, our whole foreign-trade situation would become much healthier. Loans to South America appear to have the greatest possibilities at the present time, but if a duplication of the record of previous loans in that area is to be avoided, it will be necessary for the United States to accept imports in payment of interest and principal. Most loans in the past have not led to any permanent increase in foreign purchasing power for our exports, chiefly because we did not adopt those foreign-trade policies that a creditor nation must follow in order to maintain its exports.

In September 1939 the foreign investments in the United States consisted of $5,635,000,000 in the form of long-term investments (stocks, bonds, and branches and subsidiaries of foreign enterprises) and $3,195,000,000 in the form of short-term investments (bank balances and brokerage funds). This is a total of $8,830,000,000, which equals more than 2½ times our commodity exports in 1939. These investments constitute foreign purchasing power potentially available to pay for exports of American goods because they could be withdrawn in the form of commodity exports. The withdrawal of foreign investments might be brought about by improved investment opportunities in other countries or by legal restraints against foreign investments in this country. Obviously any increase in exports as a direct result of reduction in foreign investments would be only temporary, and since a large part of these investments are owned in countries that are at war military considerations will prevail in determining what commodities will be purchased.

The flow of gold into the United States in recent years probably is in great part a result of more fundamental conditions impeding world trade rather than a cause in itself of reduced trade in commodities. Nevertheless, it seems clear that a reversal of this flow would do much to improve world trade generally. One possible course of action which would help, though in a small way, to reverse the recent gold flow would be to use some of our gold stocks to purchase strategic war materials, such as tin and rubber, from foreign countries. This would be effective, of course, only if the exchange were made under arrangements that would prevent the quick return of the gold to this country. If governments lacking adequate gold for their banking and monetary systems should agree to use the gold for that purpose, the excuse for some forms of international trade barriers would be gradually eliminated. Any substantial outflow of gold, however, could come about only from an increase of commodity imports, from the withdrawal of foreign investments from this country, or from the investment of American capital in foreign countries.

Making Foreign Purchasing Power Go Further

In order to take full advantage of the foreign purchasing power that may be available for our agricultural products, it is essential that production for export take account of the needs and preferences of foreign markets and the situation in other exporting countries. This requires that we have the best possible information in regard to foreign developments, their significance, and their probable future trends. Since 1921 the work of the Department of Agriculture has included collecting and disseminating information relating to foreign markets for American agricultural products. Under the authority of legislation enacted in 1930 the work of the Department of Agriculture in the foreign field has been reorganized and expanded. The collection of current foreign crop and market information has been continued, but greater emphasis than in the past has been placed on securing and analyzing basic information bearing on the relation of foreign conditions to the welfare of American agriculture.

A number of countries, notably Denmark and New Zealand, have increased their volume of agricultural exports by very careful control of the quality of their merchandise and conformity to the tastes of the consumers in the importing countries. The work of the Department of Agriculture also includes efforts to secure acceptance of standard grades and to encourage cooperative marketing associations and individual farmers to improve the quality of their products.

If all the foreign purchasing power available for commodity purchases and investments in the United States were devoted to the purchase of agricultural commodities, we would have the largest agricultural export trade in the history of this country. But attempts to require that all foreign purchasing power be used for purchasing farm products undoubtedly would stop some of the flow of purchasing power to this country. Individuals investing money in American securities for safety are not interested in securing agricultural products for exportation. Moreover, at the present time many foreign powers have a distinct preference for war materials rather than agricultural commodities. Turning to this country, there would be obvious difficulties in resolving the conflicts of interests that would be involved in restricting the use of foreign purchasing power to payment for exports of particular commodities, such as agricultural products. Nevertheless, certain measures to this end are theoretically possible, and their nature and objectives should be understood.

Bilateral trade agreements represent one of the familiar devices used by foreign countries to exercise control over the use made of foreign exchange. Such agreements are discussed in considerable detail in the preceding article in this Yearbook.

A country with a highly centralized government may carry on an extensive foreign trade by means of barter agreements. Under such an arrangement a very positive control is exercised over the use made of foreign purchasing power. Through barter agreements it is also very easy to subsidize certain exports by offering a larger quantity of the exported product in exchange for a given quantity of the imported commodity than would be justified by current market-price relationships.

Although some opportunities undoubtedly exist for the governments of two countries to make mutually advantageous exchanges of commodities to be used for special governmental purposes or to be reserved for certain contingencies, the placing of the foreign trade of a country entirely on a barter basis is not likely to be the most advantageous course of action in the long run. Usually the compelling force leading to the adoption of barter is the need for certain imports rather than the desire to increase exports. Some countries may seem temporarily to gain from a barter system where the true costs are obscured by hidden subsidies or the over-all controls employed by a totalitarian form of government. On close examination barter transactions are usually found to involve an economic loss, that is, smaller real returns than could be obtained under normal marketing methods. This loss may in particular cases be justified by military considerations or as a preferred method of favoring certain commodities over others in export markets.

Since exports of commodities from the United States already exceed imports of commodities into the United States, the placing of all this trade on a barter basis would immediately call for either a decrease of exports or an increase of imports. Subsequently exports would increase only as imports were increased.

Assuming, however, that barter could be restricted to exchanges of selected commodities, a hypothetical example—the exchange of American cotton, let us say, for hides from country X—will demonstrate the economic loss that would occur. Such an exchange would result in an increased export of cotton to X only (1) if American consumption of X hides were increased, (2) if the price of American cotton to X were decreased, or (3) if the United States paid an increased price for X hides.

(1) Our consumption of X hides could be increased either by increasing our total consumption of hides or by substituting X hides for domestic or other foreign hides. An increase in the total consumption would require some reduction in the price, but if the price paid to X is to be decreased our cotton price would also need to be reduced to maintain the volume of cotton taken by X. That is, it would be necessary for the United States Government to finance a reduction either in the price of X hides or in the price of American cotton exported to X. Likewise, the substitution of X hides for other hides would require that the former be made cheaper or that other sources be shut off, which would pass the extra cost of the barter deal on to consumers in this country.

(2) It is obvious that to decrease the price at which cotton is offered to X would involve either a reduced return to American cotton growers or a financial loss assumed by the United States Government.

(3) The possibility of paying an increased price for hides imported from X is similarly unattractive. Unless our Government were to absorb this increase it would be necessary to pass it on to American consumers. This would require that the quantity of hides taken from other sources be decreased by more than the increased imports from X, because the higher price would cause the total consumption of hides to decrease. Insofar as the transaction with X required that imports of hides from other countries be decreased, it would serve to decrease

the purchasing power of these other countries for our exports and thus defeat the purpose for which barter frequently is urged, namely, to increase our exports.

Such a barter deal would increase our exports only at a cost to the United States Government, to American consumers of the commodity received, or to producers of one of the commodities exchanged through the barter. True, the cost may be justified under certain circumstances.

Barter deals made by private agencies without government aid or supervision are simply transactions in which an exporter is also an importer. It may be assumed that such an arrangement is to be adopted only if it gives the agency a competitive advantage. The adoption of barter arrangements under other conditions will require some control of foreign trade by a governmental agency. The degree of control exercised could vary from a requirement that foreign-trade transactions be approved by the agency to a government monopoly of all foreign trade. Once a country begins to substitute barter for normal foreign trade, it is almost certain to become necessary to use barter for all foreign trade and place complete control in the hands of the government.

Foreign purchasing power can be made to go further not only by restricting its use but also by cheapening United States products for export. An obvious method of accomplishing this purpose would be to devalue the currency. Usually, however, the effect of devaluation is temporary and is soon offset by devaluations of foreign currency and by higher domestic price levels for commodities having a large export demand.

The exports of a commodity could be stimulated by subsidizing an expansion of production of the commodity and thereby causing a fall in the price of the subsidized commodity in relation to prices of other commodities. Some forms of domestic farm-allotment proposals would achieve this result.

Another plan for expanding our export market for certain agricultural products would provide for the reduction of export prices below domestic prices. The reduction in export prices could be accomplished in several ways. Perhaps the best-known procedure is to offer a direct payment to the exporter. Exports will then increase and a smaller supply will be left for domestic consumption, the result being that the spread between domestic and export prices tends to become equal to the amount of the payment.

Another method of subsidizing exports would be to set up a national marketing organization to handle the total production of a commodity, charging domestic consumers a higher price than that prevailing in the world market. Producers could be paid on this two-price basis or on the basis of a single blended price which would enable the marketing organization to offset losses on exports with profits in the domestic market.

An alternative to the above proposal would be the so-called equalization-fee plan, whereby the commodity would be handled through the usual channels, over which a central organization would have supervisory powers. A tax or fee would be levied on the handling of the commodity, and the proceeds of this tax or fee would be paid as a bounty on exports.

One form of export subsidy that has been proposed is the granting of certificates on the exportation of the commodity to be subsidized. These certificates would have a stated value and could be used in payment of tariffs on articles imported. Proponents of this plan argue that it would also increase imports, thereby increasing the total volume of foreign purchasing power for the products of this country.

The use of export subsidies to increase the volume of exports raises several fundamental problems. One problem is that a payment on the exports of a commodity tends to bring about an increase in the domestic price of the commodity and thereby to stimulate production. Hence, to avoid the accumulation of unsalable surpluses, with their violent repercussions on producers, as well as to avoid constantly increasing costs to the Government, it is necessary that any export payment program be accompanied by adequate measures to control production. In the second place, it is necessary to recognize the fact that existing export outlets are definitely limited regardless of the price at which our products are offered for export. The adoption of export subsidies as a permanent program would tend to decrease the possibility of removing these limitations. A third problem is that the use of export payments to obtain more than our normal share of the world trade in, or to depress the world price of, a commodity would doubtless lead to offsetting measures by other countries.

Any internal arrangements in a country which have the effect of holding the price of any commodity above the competitive world level also tend to decrease exports of that commodity. Hence, the removal of any arrangement of this kind would help to increase exports. These price-supporting measures usually are adopted as a means of satisfying certain requirements with respect to the incomes of the producers of the commodity. Alternative methods are available for increasing producers' returns without having the effect of impairing export outlets. This could be accomplished by permitting the price of a commodity for export to follow competitive changes in world markets while maintaining the price, or cost, of the commodity for domestic consumption at a higher level. Proposals of this type include Government price fixing for domestic consumption, processing or excise taxes on a commodity for domestic consumption to finance payments to producers, and the use of marketing certificates to enable producers to obtain higher returns on the domestically consumed portion of their production.

In determining the relative merits of the alternative forms of this approach, there are considerations other than the direct effect of each upon exports of agricultural products. For example, price-fixing plans raise serious problems as to practicality of administration under our form of government and as to their capability of including adequate provision for controlling production. From the long-time standpoint, and looking toward the restoration of peace, the elimination of internal restrictions on the free play of world conditions on prices of products for export seems to be the most promising method of making available foreign purchasing power go further, just as the removal of barriers to world trade in general appears to be the most effective approach to the problem of increasing the amount of foreign purchasing power available for our exports.

The Industrial Market for Farm Products

by W. B. VAN ARSDEL [1]

ONE WAY to expand the farmer's market is to develop industrial uses for farm products. Since any such development must be based on research of the type conducted by modern industry, Congress recently authorized the establishment of four regional laboratories specifically devoted to research of this type. The object, says the author of this article, is to hold the market for farm products, and expand it if possible, "by aggressive use of the same resources of science and technology that in the past have been used almost exclusively by the farmers' competitors." But science is impersonal, and such an effort cannot depend on wishes and fantasies; it must include a hard-headed analysis of all the factors involved. Here is such an analysis of some of the major possibilities in the industrial field—rayon, casein and soybean protein, plastics, motor fuels, starches, and vegetable oils.

MORE and more the farmer sells his produce to a highly developed processing industry, which in turn sells some conversion product to

[1] W. B. Van Arsdel is Principal Chemical Engineer, Bureau of Agricultural Chemistry and Engineering.

consumers. In some cases the return to the farmer is only a small proportion of the final cost—for instance, a man's shirt contains only a few cents' worth of cotton. There is an evident trend toward extension of processing into new fields, as well as toward more elaborate transformation of farm products in the old industrial fields. The grinding of wheat, for example, which once was done for the individual family, has been gradually concentrated at large industrial flour mills. For a long time the housewife still made her own bread, but today many families buy bread not only baked but sliced and wrapped in a great industrial plant.

For many of his products, then, the farmer's market is already largely an industrial market. Improvements in technology in these processing industries may open up a whole new field of consumption by decreasing costs or improving quality. That is what has happened, for instance, in the processing of grapefruit for juice and in the packing of frozen fruits and vegetables.

The terms "industrial market" and "industrial uses," however, have come in recent years to have a narrower special meaning. Traditionally the farmer has produced the raw materials for food, clothing, and shelter. That is still his main business. But our highly complex civilization also provides a rapidly expanding market for other kinds of goods in bewildering variety, ranging from cosmetics to airplanes. Human wants for these things have no discernible limit. To what extent does the farmer supply the raw materials for the industries based on these new wants, and what are the possibilities of expanding his proportion of that market?

The full catalog of present industrial uses of products of the farm and the forest attains a really impressive size. Thus, from animal carcasses the processing industries produce leather, glue and gelatine, soap, greases, glycerin, and fertilizers, as well as the meat and cooking fat which are their primary products. The cereal grains furnish starch for sizing and finishing textiles and paper, dextrin adhesive, glucose used in the rayon and leather industries, and a whole series of industrial chemicals and solvents. About 40 percent of the cotton used in this country goes into industrial outlets—cordage, automobile tires, explosives, bags, paper, packing and stuffing, artificial leather, and the like. While more than 90 percent of our commercial soybean production goes into human food and animal feed, there has been a rapid growth in the use of soybean products for making adhesives, plastics, paint and varnish, and other industrial materials. Wood-conversion products find scores of uses—paper, turpentine and rosin, lacquers and protective coatings, plastic molded articles, rayon, and artificial leather, to name only a few.

Though there is a wide field for industrial use of farm products, the picture in closer detail is by no means all favorable. Some of these industrial markets, it is true, are expanding rapidly, but others are barely holding their own or are shrinking under the pressure of competition from other raw materials. For instance, such important industrial chemicals as acetone, acetic acid, and even alcohol are now being made cheaply from coal or petroleum. One of the most important fields of all, that of liquid fuels and lubricants, is almost wholly monopolized by petroleum products. Petroleum is an irreplaceable and dwindling resource, and eventually the cost of producing it will rise enough to destroy its competitive advantage; but if our annual crops can contribute to the supply of vital fuels should we wait until the scarcity of petroleum forces us to investigate this possibility?

It is worthy of note that the areas of intensified competition with farm products are, by and large, those in which intensive industrial research has been carried on. Certain private industries have poured millions of dollars into a persistent search for expanded markets. They have commanded every resource of science and engineering. Some of their achievements, if judged solely from the points of view of technology and corporate profit, have been brilliant. But a private industry cannot in the nature of things feel any concern if a new advance destroys a market for cotton or corn, for example. In fact, there has been a rather general preference for nonfarm products as raw materials wherever they could be used, mainly because of seasonal and regional variations in the quality and wide and rapid fluctuations in the prices of farm products

THE FARMER MUST ENLIST TECHNOLOGY ON HIS SIDE

The farmer cannot hope to defend his interests by striving to arrest this impersonal tide of technology. The people of this country, including the farmer himself, have come to prize impersonal material progress as a distinctively American contribution to life. Nor can the millions of farmers combine into a single giant corporation which can play the industrial game in its own behalf. There are, however, some other courses open to the farmer.

First, he may strive, as he has done with measurable success, to raise the quality and the uniformity of his raw materials and so to keep his grasp on existing markets. Single-variety cotton communities are doing that kind of thing. Soybean growers are handling their crop more and more as an industrial raw material, with industrial standards of quality. Advances like this are generally the outcome of patient and thoroughgoing research and careful extension work among the farmers.

A second line of attack is the stabilization of the supply of farm commodities, and incidentally the stabilization of prices, through cooperative, democratic control of farm programs by the farmers themselves. Price stability for raw materials, as has already been pointed out, is a most desirable factor in the eyes of any consuming industry.

But the third possibility—the one with which we are here chiefly concerned—is that the farmers may, after all, meet private industry on even terms through research conducted in their interest by Federal and State and in some cases private agencies; that they may succeed in evening the scales by throwing the resources of science and technology as strongly on their side of the balance as they have been on the side of nonfarm materials for the past generation or more.

What Research Has Already Done for Agriculture

This is not, of course, a new idea. The Department of Agriculture and State experiment stations have discovered and nursed into independent maturity a considerable number of new consuming outlets for farm products. For instance, the work of Department scientists provided the basis for far-reaching improvements in the sugar industry, for the production of high-grade American casein, and for the rejuvenation of the naval stores industry in the South. All this was accomplished in spite of the fact that until recent years the farmer has been pressed always for production and more production to feed and clothe the rapidly expanding population and that Federal and State research also have looked mainly in that direction.

A little more than 10 years ago research began to place emphasis on utilization as well as on the strictly agricultural aspects of farm production. In 1933 a Federal laboratory was established at Ames, Iowa, to investigate the industrial possibilities of such agricultural residues as straw, cornstalks, corncobs, and hulls. Several years later a laboratory was set up at Urbana, Ill., to widen the field of use for soybeans. This particular venture into farm-sponsored research of the industrial type illustrates very well the complex impact of technologic changes upon agricultural economy. Farmers of the Corn Belt had traditionally followed a corn-oats or corn-oats-clover cycle. The rapid disappearance of the horse from the American scene seriously restricted the market for oats. The possibilities of soybeans as a replacement crop were known to some feed manufacturers and to the Department and the midwestern experiment stations. A vigorous extension campaign and careful selection of suitable varieties resulted in an increase in production from 8 million bushels in 1928 to about 80 million bushels in 1939. The market absorbed this new crop readily, but its products go mainly into the food and feed markets, where they compete directly with cottonseed products. The only discernible remedy for this situation is to discover, through research, other destinations for the soybean crop than the nonexpansible human or animal stomach, and on this the Urbana laboratory is working.

The Four Laboratories—A Comprehensive Research Program

In 1938 Congress authorized the Department to extend this type of aid to agriculture upon a really comprehensive scale. A research laboratory was to be established in each of the four major farm areas, for the purpose of discovering and developing new uses and new and wider outlets for farm commodities—primarily for those of which there is a surplus (fig. 1). The scale of the enterprise was determined by Congress by its authorization of not to exceed 4 million dollars annually, to be divided equally between the four laboratories. Experience indicates that such an outlay on a research program will provide for a total professional personnel of about 800. By any criterion, the effort thus authorized by Congress compares favorably as to scale and resources with the research undertakings of the most important private industries. It is still comparatively small if measured against the total expenditure for private industrial research or that for Federal and State research into agricultural production problems.

The four laboratories envisioned by Congress are now being established in Peoria, Ill., New Orleans, La., and in the vicinities of Philadelphia, Pa., and San Francisco, Calif. (fig. 2). In cooperation with

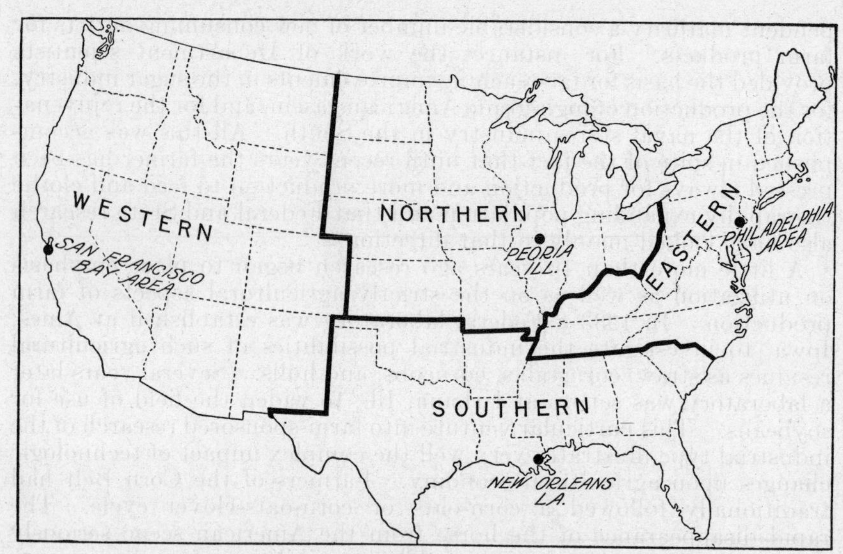

Figure 1.—Locations of the farm research laboratories and the regions they will serve.

State experiment stations, universities, private industries, and farm organizations of their regions, they start active investigation in the fall of 1940.

This whole undertaking must be regarded as a measure of self-defense taken by farmers in recognition of their increasing vulnerability if they fail to adapt their methods to a rapidly changing world. The market for farm products is to be held—and expanded wherever possible—by aggressive use of the same resources of science and technology that in the past have been used almost exclusively by the

Figure 2.—The laboratory at Peoria, Ill., is typical of the four regional research laboratories, which are being established by the Department of Agriculture to search for new markets and outlets for agricultural commodities.

farmers' competitors. That, at least, is the purpose. The desired result may not be attainable, but the game is not to be lost by default, at any rate. The history of scientific research leads to confidence that it need not be lost at all.

PRESENT AND POTENTIAL INDUSTRIAL MARKETS

A complete survey of the present and possible future industrial markets for farm products would be beyond the scope of this article. The most that can be done here is to analyze some of those markets in the broadest terms and indicate their present status and their potentialities in a qualitative way. In the following pages six classes of products will be discussed: (1) Rayon, (2) casein and soybean protein, (3) plastics, (4) motor fuels, (5) starches, and (6) vegetable oils.[2]

Rayon[3]

Rayon, a typical example of the new products introduced into modern life as a result of scientific research, illustrates the complex effects of technologic advances on agricultural markets. As a new textile fiber, with desirable properties of its own, it has largely created its own new demand; but with a world production of almost 2 billion pounds in 1938, it has also cut into established markets for cotton, wool, and silk. Rayon, however, is itself made from agricultural products—in this country, about 75 percent from wood pulp and about 25 percent from cotton linters (the relatively short fiber adhering to cottonseed after ginning and removed by a subsequent operation). To the extent that there has been direct replacement of cotton goods by rayon goods, wood-pulp producers have taken part of the market of cotton growers; but the new market created by the rayon industry has also increased the demand for one of the cotton growers' by-products, linters.

What are the present trends in the industry, and how are they likely to affect markets for agricultural products?

The total world production of rayon has increased steadily every year since 1915, and on a steeply rising curve since 1920. The yearly increase since then has averaged about 27 percent, so that production has doubled, on an average, about every 3 years. Until 1936 the United States was the leading producer. In that year Japan forged ahead, and in 1937 and 1938 Japan and Germany each produced more rayon than did the United States. In 1938 Japan and Germany together produced more than half of the world supply.

The amounts of rayon produced do not seem so huge if they are viewed in relation to the production of other textiles. The total consumption of textile fibers in the United States has averaged about 3.5 billion pounds a year. Of that total, about 80 percent has been

[2] These discussions are based on a survey (results unpublished) conducted in the summer of 1939 by an interbureau committee consisting of W. B. Van Arsdel, chairman, Bureau of Agricultural Chemistry and Engineering; R. J. Cheatham, Agricultural Marketing Service (now with the Bureau of Agricultural Chemistry and Engineering); E. O. Whittier, Bureau of Dairy Industry; H. S. Betts, Forest Service; and R. S. Kifer, B. R. Hurt, and F. L. Thomsen, Bureau of Agricultural Economics. Factual studies were supplied to the committee by K. S. Markley, G. H. Brother, P. B. Jacobs, and F. H. Thurber, all of the Bureau of Agricultural Chemistry and Engineering.

[3] For a detailed study of this subject, see: ROBINSON, CARL H., CHEATHAM, ROBERT J., LYNCH, D. F. J., and HOLMAN, H. P. REPORT ON DEVELOPMENT AND USE OF RAYON AND OTHER SYNTHETIC FIBERS. Bur. Chem. and Soils Spec. Rpt. MC-38, 50 pp., illus. 1938. [Mimeographed.]

cotton, about 9 percent has been wool, another 9 percent has been rayon, and about 2 percent has been silk. Nevertheless, the effect of rayon has not been negligible. The proportion of cotton in the total consumption has dropped from 86 percent to 80, while rayon has risen from less than 1 percent to 9. If the steep rate of increase in rayon production continues much longer, the seriousness of the situation will be aggravated.

The probability of such an occurrence cannot be estimated without taking a closer look at the rayon industry itself. In the first place, what is rayon?

Rayon is a man-made synthetic fiber. There are three main varieties, named after the chemical processes used to produce them, viscose, acetate, and cuprammonium. The starting point for all three is cellulose in some form—the same cellulose which is the characteristic substance of cotton itself and of the stems and woody parts of plants in general. The process consists essentially in dissolving cellulose in the proper chemical solution, forming continuous filaments or threads from the resulting sirup, and setting the filaments to a solid form again.

About 70 percent of United States rayon production is of the viscose type, about 25 percent is acetate, and less than 5 percent is cuprammonium. A considerable part of the recent increase in world rayon production has been in "staple fiber"—that is, rayon made in continuous filaments as usual, then cut into relatively short lengths and spun like cotton or wool, often in admixture with them. The significance of the proportions of the three types of rayon lies in the fact that the standard raw material for viscose rayon is wood pulp and for the other two varieties, cotton linters. The reasons for the ascendancy of wood pulp are its lower—and relatively stable—cost and the fact that unremitting research by producers has resulted in a product the quality of which is uniform, day after day and year after year. Manufacturers of acetate and cuprammonium rayon have long endeavored to adapt wood pulp to their processes in place of cotton linters because of these advantages, but certain unsolved technical difficulties still stand in the way.

The rapid growth in consumption of rayon is, of course, traceable to many factors, including style movements and intensive advertising; but not least among these factors are the strength, softness, and other desirable physical properties which have been developed through research and the marked drop in price. During the period from 1925 to 1937, when our rayon production was rising from 50 million pounds to 340 million, its price was falling from $2 a pound to about 60 cents; during the same period the price of a standard cotton yarn dropped only from about 70 cents a pound to about 45 cents, and the consumption of cotton in textiles remained almost unchanged.

Economists who have studied the situation believe that further expansion of rayon production and utilization will occur during the next few years but that the era of rapid growth is nearly over. A level of comparative price stability has been reached. Improvements in quality, particularly in the field of special finishes that enhance durability, are still being made, but in the broad market that demands above all else high durability and low price rayon cannot compete successfully with cotton. The possibilities of staple fiber, on the other hand, have not yet been fully explored. A large part of the recent expansion of rayon production in Germany, Japan, and Italy has been in this particular item, while in this country it is still of comparatively minor importance. Expansion of American staple-fiber consumption comparable to that which has occurred in the countries named would require a further substantial growth in viscose-rayon production. As already pointed out, the standard raw material for that process is wood pulp.

On the other side of the picture, acetate rayon more than tripled its share of the total rayon production in this country in the 9 years 1929–37, and acetate still looks to cotton linters for its raw material. It is believed that the proportion will continue to increase for some time. Although the price is slightly higher than that of viscose rayons, the spread has been decreasing, and the physical properties and durability of the product have given it a good competitive standing.

To sum up, rayon is a textile fiber with definite and distinct properties which for some uses give it advantages over cotton, silk, and wool and for others are definitely restrictive. It has expanded very rapidly into the fields for which it is best suited, but it is approaching industrial maturity. Production of certain types, paricularly of acetate rayon and staple fiber, is likely to continue to expand rapidly for some time to come. The bulk of the raw material will probably continue to be wood pulp. Cotton farmers have a divided interest in the future of the industry; further growth in rayon-textile consumption will affect the cotton-textile market adversely, but growth in the production of the acetate type of rayon will offer a wider outlet for cotton linters. Every major development in the product has been an outgrowth of persistent research, and its future course is likely to be determined by the same factor.

Casein and Soybean Protein

All living organisms, including the plants and animals classed as farm products, contain certain very complicated chemical compounds known as proteins. Lean meat, hair and skin, egg white, cheese, corn and wheat gluten, and cottonseed and soybean meal are typical examples of high-protein animal and plant products.

Some uses for proteins or for high-protein tissues, which we would now class as industrial uses, are actually prehistoric. The production of leather from hides and of glue from skin and bones are instances. In general, though, the proteins have been relatively neglected as industrial raw materials. To a considerable extent this may have been due to the excessive difficulty and complexity of chemical research in this field.

Casein, a purified curd produced from skim milk, has been used for a long time as a component of waterproof glue, cold-water paints, paper coatings, and molded articles, particularly buttons. Soybean meal, relatively a newcomer, is establishing itself in the production of adhesives, water-resistant coatings, sizes, and plastics. What is the status, and what are the foreseeable possibilities, of these two typical protein products?

About 20,000 to 30,000 tons of casein is produced annually in this

223761°—40——40

country, requiring as raw material well over a billion pounds of skim milk. Even that large quantity, however, is only about 1 percent of the total milk production. The largest single use of the casein is in paper coating, to produce the highly finished papers used, for instance, in some of the so-called "slick" magazines. There is no evidence of any large undeveloped field there. About 4,000 to 5,000 tons a year is used in the production of buttons, in competition with natural horn, bone, and the cheaper plastics. The growth in this use has been rapid, but the total conceivable consumption is still comparatively small—perhaps 10,000 tons. About 1,500 tons of casein is used to make cold-water paints. This usage is also growing steadily, in competition with both wallpaper and other types of paint, but no prediction of ultimate consumption can be hazarded.

Transparent casein wrappings were produced commercially for a short time several years ago. The company which holds the patents on the product has announced that it is about to manufacture this film in much improved form. It will, of course, enter the market in competition with the familiar transparent wrappings made from cellulose, and its industrial success will therefore depend upon whatever advantages it may have in cost or physical characteristics over the cellulose product, which is produced by the viscose process (see the section of this article on rayon) from wood pulp as a raw material.

Casein, like wood pulp and cotton linters, may come to serve as raw material for another synthetic textile fiber. The first fiber of this type was produced in Italy, as a result of research directed specifically toward the replacement of imported wool. Small but unknown quantities are being made also in Belgium, the Netherlands, and Germany. None is being produced in the United States, but much experimentation is going on, and it is reported that construction of a commercial plant has been started. The fiber produced so far is in no sense of the word fully a substitute for wool. It is a new type of textile fiber, with possibilities still unknown. The analogy with the early history of rayon is apparent, but how far the analogy will go, no one can say.

When soybeans are processed for the recovery of their oil, about 80 percent of their weight remains as a high-protein cake or meal. All but a small percentage of the million-ton production is now used for livestock feeding and for fertilizer. That small percentage—perhaps 50,000 tons—has, however, awakened great interest.

The largest single industrial use is for making a water-resistant adhesive for plywood. About 16,000 tons of meal a year is so used. Since plywood construction in the building industry is spreading, the possibility of substantial increase in soybean-meal consumption for that purpose is seen. The next largest use at present is for coating washable papers, especially wallpapers, and a similar outlet is being developed in the manufacture of cold-water paints. In all three of these uses there is some competition with casein, as might be expected, particularly because of the considerable advantage in price possessed by soybean meal.

A small quantity—about 5 or 6 tons a day—of purified protein is being produced from soybean meal. The major part of this goes to the paper industry, where it is being used as a component of special sizing agents. Other uses are being developed in the leather-finishing, adhesive, film, and plastic fields. Research on a soybean-protein fiber, analogous to the casein fiber mentioned above, is also being pushed.

Soybean meal, like casein, then, is an agricultural product which has a wide variety of interesting industrial uses, none of which has sufficient volume as yet to exert any marked effect on the total demand for the farm commodity itself. They are significant, though, as pointing the way toward expanded markets. It may be that the real development of protein uses will come only after the scientist has worked his way through the baffling inner complexity of such commodities as soybean meal and casein.

Plastics From Farm Products

The last two decades have witnessed a remarkable growth in the use of plastics in articles of everyday use. The term "plastics" covers an extraordinary range of materials, natural and synthetic, from the old familiar glaziers' putty, sealing wax, and celluloid, to the crystal-clear organic glasses now used in highway reflector buttons and the like. All have one property in common: Under some condition of heat, pressure, or softening with a liquid, they can be pressed or molded into a desired form, which they will then hold under the conditions of use. Their growing importance arises from the fact that once a suitable mold, or die, is constructed, thousands of molded pieces can be turned out rapidly and at low cost, and each of those pieces will be an accurate replica of the original design, exact to the finest detail. Molded plastics thus lend themselves to wide use in the mass-production industries. Up to the present time they have not been used to make very large articles, partly because of the high cost and relatively slow operation of large dies, and partly because of the high cost of materials. If a continuous process for forming strips, sheets, and other structural forms from a cheap plastic material could be developed, a wide new field of use in the construction industries would be opened up.

Agricultural products furnish several important raw materials to the plastics industry. Cellulose enters into many plastics, either as a fibrous reinforcement (cotton fabric, paper, or wood flour), or as a constituent of the plastic itself (such compounds as cellulose nitrate or acetate). Casein (from skim milk), furfural (from oat hulls), rosin, various conversion products of vegetable oils, and soybean meal are also used to a minor extent. Synthetic products made from nonagricultural raw materials like coal, petroleum, limestone, sulfur, and salt, which furnished the impetus to the industry through the development of such molding resins as Bakelite, continue to supply a large portion of the present demand for plastics.

An important general principle is involved here. The desired final products are invariably made up of complicated giant molecules, and so also are the main constituents of farm products—cellulose, starch, lignin, protein, resins, and so on. A relatively simple modification of such a substance as cellulose may give it desirable plastic properties; the chemist brings about such a modification when he makes celluloid out of cotton. But there is a draw-back. Complicated structures are not easily changed into other complicated structures of an entirely different type. It is as though we were to try to change a radio set into an adding machine by lopping off some corners, compressing some parts, and cutting up and drawing out some others; it would be considerably easier to start afresh with some plain, flat sheets of metal. Similarly, the chemist may find it easier to start with some very simple molecules—such things, for instance, as phenol, formaldehyde, urea, or vinyl chloride—and build up his complicated structure to please himself. Now these simple chemicals are exactly the ones that may be obtained cheaply from coal, petroleum, limestone, and other nonagricultural raw materials.

Does this seriously circumscribe the possible use of farm products in plastics? Not necessarily. To continue our metaphor one step further, it may be possible to develop a superior type of adding machine that is constructed along the general lines of a radio set; in that case, old radio sets might become the preferred raw material. In other words, there may well be thousands of possible molecular structures that would give us plastics superior to those we have today and at the same time could be made most cheaply from complex raw materials such as starch or protein. The question must be left in the hands of the research worker.

Motor Fuels[4]

Future motor-fuel requirements of the United States, as estimated by the American Petroleum Institute, are given in table 1.

Table 1.—Future motor-fuel requirements of the United States

Year	Total demand	Available from—		Estimated fuel consumption per automotive unit	Estimated total vehicles registered
		Benzol and natural gasoline	Crude petroleum		
	Barrels [1]	*Barrels*	*Barrels*	*Barrels*	*Number*
1940	563, 880, 000	45, 000, 000	518, 880, 000	17. 38	29, 200, 000
1950	636, 570, 000	47, 000, 000	589, 570, 000	16. 90	33, 900, 000
1960	657, 490, 000	48, 000, 000	609, 490, 000	15. 95	37, 100, 000

[1] 42 gallons each.

Automobile fuel in the United States is now practically limited to petroleum, but the rate at which resources are being used has caused concern for the future. Coal, shale oil, and natural gas are possible mineral sources of motor fuel, but like petroleum they are irreplaceable. Their time of exhaustion cannot be predicted, but a gradual advance in the price of fuel from such sources may be anticipated as the better and more available supplies are exhausted.

Under present rates of consumption, our present petroleum reserves, which the American Petroleum Institute estimates at 17 billion barrels, would approach exhaustion in perhaps 15 years; but this estimate cannot be taken literally, as the actual appearance of shortage would raise prices and react upon the consumption of both straight and blended fuel to an unpredictable degree. Furthermore, engines developed in the future may use some other form of fuel.

[4] For a comprehensive analysis of this subject see: JACOBS, P. B., and NEWTON, H. P. MOTOR FUELS FROM FARM PRODUCTS. U. S. Dept. Agr. Misc. Pub. 327, 129 pp., illus. 1938.

Something less than 10 percent of domestic gasoline consumption already comes from natural gas, which cannot be viewed as an important substitute as it is usually associated with petroleum in the earth. On the basis of chemical composition, oil recoverable from shale rock may be the most logical successor to petroleum. Shale deposits in the United States are exceedingly extensive, the American Petroleum Institute having estimated that 108 billion barrels of oil are potentially available from this source. However, the cost of extracting the oil is still several times greater than that of crude petroleum.

The use of coal to produce liquid fuels and lubricants by the process known as hydrogenation is receiving intensive study, particularly in Europe but also recently in the United States. However, it is difficult to visualize this process in the role of principal supplier of motor fuels, because the supply of soft coal of the better grades has already been depleted.

Synthetic chemical compounds obtained from waste refinery gas, coal gas, water gas, coke-oven gas, natural gas, and similar abundant sources of light hydrocarbons constitute suitable replacement motor fuels, and competition with future fuel materials produced from agricultural sources will most likely come from this rapidly expanding field. Most of these synthetic fuels introduce no new problems in engine performance or design.

Many foreign countries enforce by legislation the blending of alcohol from agricultural sources with gasoline, benzol, or similar substances for motor-fuel purposes. To some extent this has been an attempt to accomplish certain agricultural readjustments, but there are usually other contributory causes, such as a lack of adequate fuel resources and a desire for national self-sufficiency in raw materials.

Ethyl alcohol is the only fuel of agricultural origin yet to attain extensive use, but while no others are in plain sight, chemists believe that several other compounds which might be produced from starch, cellulose, or sugars deserve further study.

There has been much controversy as to the value of ethyl alcohol as a fuel for internal-combustion engines as compared with gasoline. After a comprehensive study of this complex problem, Jacobs and Newton [5] conclude that "blends of ethyl alcohol with gasoline function satisfactorily as fuels for present-type internal-combustion engines, especially with increased engine compression ratios and other favorable changes in design." They also point out, however, that uniformity of concentration and employment of alcohol blends are desirable and that all motor fuels should therefore be nationally standardized.

Such a national program would entail economic readjustments and present difficult legal and sociological problems. Use of a national alcohol blend containing alcohol produced from diversified crops as well as from crop wastes and surpluses would entail some method of equalizing the production costs incurred, which would vary both geographically and for the several materials.

Gasoline-alcohol blends containing from 5 to 10 percent of anhydrous alcohol probably represent the optimum mixtures obtainable on a national scale under present conditions. The use of such mixtures

---

[5] Reference cited in footnote 4.

would require roughly the annual production of 1 to 2 billion gallons of alcohol.

The production of alcohol from agricultural materials in quantities sufficient to have a significant bearing on petroleum conservation would necessitate a marked increase in crop production, as shown in table 2.

Table 2.—Acreages of principal farm crops required to produce a quantity of alcohol equivalent to 10 percent of the gasoline consumed in the United States in 1935, and actual acreages in that year

Raw material	Acreage required to produce alcohol equal to 10 percent of gasoline consumed in 1935	Acreage actually harvested in United States in 1935	Raw material	Acreage required to produce alcohol equal to 10 percent of gasoline consumed in 1935	Acreage actually harvested in United States in 1935
	1,000 acres	*1,000 acres*		*1,000 acres*	*1,000 acres*
Barley	40,000	12,371	Wheat	51,500	51,229
Corn	16,300	95,804	Jerusalem-artichokes	9,500	---
Grain sorghums	25,000	4,222	Potatoes	12,600	3,541
Rice, rough	18,500	817	Sweetpotatoes	11,000	969
Rye	47,500	4,141	Sugarbeets	6,000	809

Corn is the only crop now produced in excess of such requirements. The entire 1935 wheat crop does not quite equal the amount required to produce the necessary quantity of alcohol, while all other crops taken together total less than the required amount.

On the basis of estimated motor-fuel requirements in 1960, the use of a 10-percent alcohol mixture would require something like 25,000,000 additional acres in cereal-grain production, apart from any increase that might be required for food.

Wood, in the form of hydrolyzed wood waste or of waste liquor from the sulfite process of pulp making, offers a potential source of alcohol. Technical and economic difficulties have so far prevented commercial exploitation of either process in the United States.

Agricultural wastes, such as sugarcane bagasse, corncobs, cornstalks, cotton stalks, and cereal straws, offer another potential source of cellulosic material which might be converted to alcohol by a process similar to that used for wood waste. Besides the technical difficulties, which are still largely unsolved, the difficulty and expense of collecting large and assured supplies at central points would impose a serious initial handicap. The total amount of these materials available to industry appears to be about 135 million tons a year, from which a maximum of about 4 billion gallons of alcohol could be obtained.

At present the lowest-cost raw material for alcohol production in the United States is blackstrap molasses. However, costs of alcohol produced from molasses at 5 cents a gallon have been estimated as ranging from 15 to 30 cents a gallon of anhydrous alcohol in tank cars, as compared with about 4 cents a gallon for gasoline at the refineries. Furthermore, the supply of byproduct molasses is at present entirely insufficient to have any marked significance for an extensive motor-fuel program.

The cost of alcohol produced from the usual farm crops is substantially higher than that of alcohol produced from molasses. Direct competition of agricultural alcohol fuel blends with gasoline could be made effective at present price levels only through some form of supplementary financial support. But even though the raw material were furnished to the distillery free, conversion costs alone under the best present practices amount to at least twice the present base price of gasoline.

Present Outlook

In summary, it may be said that the enormous demand for fuels in our modern civilization is now being met by depletion of our abundant and cheaply developed resources of coal and petroleum. The American consumption of motor fuel alone amounts to over 500 million barrels a year. It is foreseen that as oil fields approach exhaustion costs will rise, and the way will be opened for the development of other fuels suitable for use in internal-combustion motors. Among these new fuels may be some prepared from agricultural raw materials. At the present time alcohol is the only such substitute fuel that has been extensively investigated. A blend of, say, 10 percent of alcohol with gasoline can be used in present engines, and it is now being used in some foreign countries. At present costs of production the use of such a blend is not economical in the United States. Its use on a national scale would call for the conversion of farm crops far beyond any probable surpluses, and might require the production of cereal grains on as much as 25 million acres of land now devoted to other purposes. Chemists foresee the possibility of developing other types of motor fuel from farm products and of hastening the day when annual crops will supply at least a part of the tremendous market for the concentrated fuels on which modern life depends.

Starches

Starch, the main energy-storing component of most food crops, has long served mankind also for a wide variety of nonfood uses. Its value for sizing textiles and papers and for making adhesives is traditional. In recent years its uses have been extended into diverse fields through the development of new physical and chemical methods of processing. While it has not yet shown the versatility of its near relative, cellulose, those most familiar with it believe that there are many unexplored possibilities of widening its use in the arts.

Starch is widely distributed in the vegetable kingdom. It is apparently used by plants generally as a means of storing the energy of sunlight against the time when a large expenditure of energy will be needed for germination or growth. Thus, the most important sources are tubers and the seeds of the cereal grains.

Pure starch may be separated with comparative ease from some of these tubers and seeds. In this country, corn is by far the most important source of pure starch, but potatoes, rice, sago, and cassava (the source of tapioca) are each the main raw materials in some parts of the world, and all of these varieties of starch, as well as some other types of domestic origin, such as sweetpotato starch, are used to some extent in the United States. Approximately 300 million pounds of tapioca and sago are imported into this country annually, as well as a large proportion of the potato starch used here.

Starches from any of these sources have certain fundamental similarities that make it possible to use any of them indiscriminately for some purposes. Thus, any starch may be converted quite readily into the simple sugar, dextrose, familiar as glucose sirup or corn sugar. Actually, however, the geographic location of the glucose industry and the economics of the situation have resulted in almost complete dependence upon corn as a raw material.

For many other uses the natural varieties of starch do show marked individuality, so that root starches, such as tapioca and sweetpotato, have a real advantage over others in the production of dextrin adhesives for postage stamps, and potato starch is in demand for the finishing of some fine cotton goods. To some extent, then, each starch enters a field in which its individual characteristics give it a quality advantage. The imported starches also have been favored by the low costs of production in tropical countries, but research work now under way and contemplated may make it possible to supply a larger proportion of our requirements by products made from domestic crops, both by reducing the cost of production and by improving the quality.

The most important domestic raw material for starch at present is corn. About 9 percent of the domestic crop of 2½ to 3 billion bushels is used for all "city" purposes, including the production of starch. The corn kernel contains about 60 percent of starch, so that the total corn crop alone produces the tremendous total of about 50 million tons of starch annually. Less than 1 percent of that total is now actually being recovered as cornstarch.

Some dry-milled corn flour is used in cold-water paints, wallpaper paste, foundry flours, fillers, and sizes. Cornstarch, however, and therefore its conversion products—dextrin, sirup, and sugar—are made by the wet-milling process. Corn oil, corn-oil meal, and gluten feeds are recovered as byproducts. The major uses of these corn products are in foods and feeds, but in addition they go into the laundry, into rayon, and into leather industries, and are used in sizing paper and textiles, in explosives, in adhesives, and in colors.

The total sales of corn products in 1937 were, in million pounds: Cornstarch, 731; corn sugar, 418; corn sirup, 1,035; dextrins, 83; corn oil, 133; corn-oil meal, 58; gluten meal and feed, 1,084.

Potatoes comprise the largest vegetable crop in the United States. During the 10-year period 1928–37, the average yearly commercial production was 372 million bushels.

Potato-starch production in this country, however, has been based not upon the primary crop, but upon the utilization of culls and off-grade potatoes in some of the large shipping centers. The industry has therefore been comparatively small, irregular in operation, and none too stable. Many of the starch plants are so small as to make operation expensive and the product very uneven in quality. This fact has been reflected in low prices for the domestic product and unprofitable operation for the plants. In 1937, an unusually large crop led to the diversion of some first- and second-grade potatoes to the production of starch, with the aid of benefit payments for such diversion.

Pure potato starch has a somewhat specialized market in the sizing of paper and textiles, and the economic recovery of a good grade of starch from culls and wastes may become possible on the basis of redesign of plants and further experimentation with processes. It appears unlikely that any large part of the main potato crop can be seriously considered as a source of commercial starch.

Next to potatoes, sweetpotatoes are the largest vegetable crop, averaging 70 million bushels during the 10-year period 1928–37.

The average yield during this period was 85 bushels an acre, but varieties grown primarily for starch have yielded as high as 400 bushels an acre, with 200 bushels representing a fair attainable average. At the latter figure, starch production would be about 2,500 pounds an acre, as compared with about 1,700 pounds from corn.

Experimental efforts in this country led in 1934 to the establishment of a small commercial sweetpotato-starch plant operated by a local cooperative in Mississippi, under technical supervision furnished by the Department of Agriculture. In 1938 the plant processed about 165,000 bushels of sweetpotatoes into about 1,600,000 pounds of starch, most of which was used in the textile industry. The plant is still in an experimental stage, with many technical problems to be overcome before maximum efficiency can be obtained.

The characteristics of sweetpotato starch indicate that its natural fields of use will be in sizing textiles, making high-grade dextrin for adhesives, and in various food products to which it imparts desirable qualities. It is not at present competitive with cornstarch for conversion into glucose sirup or sugar.

A gradual growth may be expected in the traditional uses of starch—for laundry work (fig. 3), for sizing paper and textiles, and for the preparation of dextrin adhesives—but such growth will not have any marked effect on the production of primary starch crops.

The conversion of cornstarch into glucose sirup is a long-established industry, but the further step of preparing pure crystalline dextrose, or corn sugar, from the sirup is a comparatively recent development that is still growing rapidly. Both the sirup and sugar find their major uses in the food and beverage industries, although large quantities are used in tanning, rayon spinning baths, tobacco products, and the pharmaceutical industry.

The fermentation industries are large users of starch, generally in the form of ground grain, and there has also been some industrial production of important chemicals such as acetone, butanol, acetic acid, lactic acid, citric acid, and gluconic acid. The first three of these, however, face difficult competition from the synthetic chemical industry, which uses nonagricultural raw materials. The chemical conversion of starch to various esters, ethers, and polymers is a comparatively new and undeveloped field. A small but growing quantity of such starch derivatives is already being used in protective coatings, adhesives and water-resistant binders, explosives, beverages, and plastics. A quantitative evaluation of this potential new outlet for starch is, of course, impossible now; too much depends on the outcome

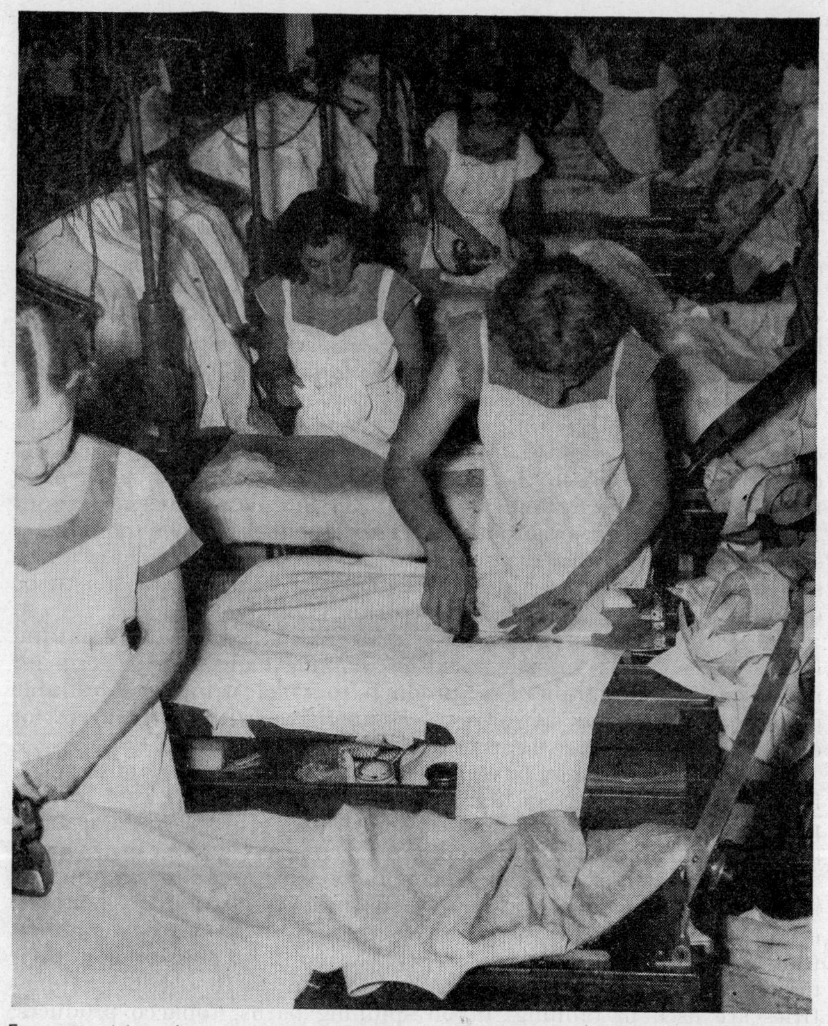

Figure 3.—Many large commercial laundries such as this one now use high-grade root starch made from sweetpotatoes.

of future research. But it might be remarked that some of the outstanding triumphs of chemical technology have occurred in the analogous field of cellulose derivatives—nitrocellulose lacquers and rayon, to mention only two.

Although tremendous supplies of starch are potentially available at prices that are low relative to those of other highly refined raw materials, and although the relatively undeveloped state of its chemical technology makes expansion in domestic use likely, it should be emphasized that an increase even of several hundred percent in the consumption of starch could occur without necessitating any substantial increase in the total acreage requirement. Thus, replacement of the entire quantity of imported starches by expansion of the domestic sweetpotato-starch industry would require a shift of only about 200,000 acres, or about 1 percent, of present cotton acreage in the Southeastern States to industrial sweetpotato production. However, increases of such a magnitude would have a decided effect on the cash income of considerable groups of farmers.

Vegetable Oils

Three great common constituents of farm crops—cellulose, protein, and starch—have been considered in relation to the industrial market. The fats and oils make up a fourth broad class of constituents of plants and animals. As with protein and starch, by far the most important use of fats and oils—led by butter and lard—is for food. Two other major uses, however, are very ancient; oils are essential in manufacturing paints and varnishes and in making soap.

The total annual consumption of fats and oils in the United States is somewhat more than 9 billion pounds, or over 70 pounds per capita. Almost a quarter of the total is represented by butter; about a sixth by lard. Cottonseed oil, tallow, coconut oil, linseed oil, soybean oil, palm oil, corn oil, fish oil, tung oil, peanut oil, whale oil, and perilla oil follow in the order named, and a score of minor fats and oils, both domestic and imported, make up the remainder. Among the oils in this list, all but cottonseed, soybean, corn, and peanut oils are either entirely or mostly imported.

A summary of the present distribution of the more important fats and oils according to their main uses is given in table 3, which lists factory consumption during the year 1938.

Table 3.—Factory consumption of primary vegetable and certain animal fats and oils, 1938[1]

Oil or fat	Total	Shortening	Oleomargarine	Other edible products	Soap	Paint and varnish	Linoleum and oilcloth	Printing inks	Miscellaneous products
	Million lbs.	*Million lbs.*	*Million lbs.*	*Million lbs.*	*Million lbs.*	*Million lbs.*	*Million lbs.*	*Million lbs.*	*Million lbs.*
Vegetable oils:									
Cottonseed	1,540	1,051	143	198	3				3
Peanut	62	52	4	2					
Coconut	555	26	90	61	343	1			4
Corn	73	1	1	57	3				3
Soybean	237	137	40	11	11	15	4		5
Linseed	298				1	217	55	17	8
Tung	87					78	4	2	3
Perilla	33					24	7	2	
Castor	28				2	5	1		20
Palm	253	115			92				20
Animal oils:									
Inedible tallow	764				702				61
Grease	183				96				85
Whale	71				66				4
Fish	153	17			80	16	14		26

[1] Adapted from U. S. Bureau of the Census, Animal and Vegetable Fats and Oils; Production, Consumption, Imports, Exports, and Stocks, Quarterly for Calendar Years 1934 to 1938, 29 pp. 1939.

The figures in table 3 show that the fats and oils may be grouped roughly into three classes: Cottonseed, peanut, and corn oils are used almost exclusively for edible products—shortening, oleomargarine, salad dressings, and the like; inedible tallow, coconut oil, grease, and whale oil go mostly into soaps; and linseed, tung, and perilla oils are used in the drying-oil industries—in paint and varnish, linoleum and oilcloth, and printing inks. The lines are not sharp. Coconut oil is used as an edible oil as well as in soaps. Palm oil is almost evenly divided between those two fields. Soybean oil finds substantial outlets in all three groups. In summary, about a third of our total consumption of fats and oils is in industrial—that is, nonfood—markets. About 18 percent is in soaps and other detergents, 7 percent in the drying-oil industry, and the remaining 8 percent in a great variety of miscellaneous uses.

These divisions are determined in the first place by inherent characteristics of the natural oils. Peanut oil does not make a high-grade soap and has none of the drying property necessary in a paint, but it is an excellent article of food. Tung oil is a valuable constituent of varnishes but is inedible. Miscellaneous products in table 3 include such other characteristic uses of certain oils as the medicinal use of castor oil.

But there is also a considerable degree of interchangeability between oils—a degree that is increasing year by year with advancing chemical knowledge and improving techniques. This has been particularly evident in the edible-oil industries. For instance, 15 or 20 years ago cottonseed oil was the standard source of oil for making oleomargarine; then coconut oil began to supplant it and by 1935 was supplying more than half of that market; and finally cottonseed oil began to take back the market, sharing it with the newcomer, soybean oil, while the consumption of coconut oil in oleomargarine dropped 100 million pounds in 2 years. Somewhat similar shifts are constantly occurring in the industrial markets for oils. Obviously, the more nearly interchangeable the various oils become, the more exclusively will their relative consumption be governed by price levels.

While the competitive replacement of one domestic commodity by another naturally pleases one group of producers, it may be a tragedy to another group. From the national standpoint such situations are certainly undesirable. The specific case of soybean oil has been referred to; to the extent that soybean oil enters the relatively fixed total market for food oils it must displace other oils there. It is true that the nonfood market—the industrial market—itself is not perfectly flexible, but at least that is where we must look for any substantial expansion of the total demand for oils. What are some of the main trends in the industrial market?

The traditional drying oil, linseed, still holds first place in consumption in this field, which includes the manufacture of paints, enamels, and varnishes, linoleum and oilcloth, printing inks, certain synthetic resins, oil lacquers, core oils, and putty and other caulking compounds. Since the World War, however, the proportion of the market supplied by linseed oil has fallen from 95 percent to only 60 or 65 percent. Linseed oil is still supreme among drying oils for the production of exterior house and maintenance paints, but other natural oils and synthetic products are being adapted to many of the uses formerly dominated by linseed oil.

The development of quick-drying nitrocellulose lacquers was the first important departure from traditional practices. Then the demand for faster-drying and more waterproof varnishes and enamels led to the increased use of tung oil instead of linseed oil for this purpose. The popular wrinkle finish on many types of metal goods also became possible with the introduction of tung oil. New air-drying or baked-enamel finishes were formulated, using synthetic resins and considerable quantities of soybean oil, along with linseed and other drying oils. In the linoleum and oilcloth industry linseed oil has apparently held its own, but the proportion of linseed to total drying oil used in printing inks has dropped from nearly 90 percent in 1931 to about 75 percent in 1938. Tung and perilla oils constituted the principal replacements.

With the discovery that castor oil could be chemically processed to yield a synthetic oil with properties intermediate between those of linseed and tung oils, a new competitor entered the drying-oil field. The fish oils have also become more important as a result of improved processing and chemical treatment. Even the petroleum industry has furnished a competitor to linseed oil, with a resin which has attained importance in foundry core making.

Linseed oil, then, has been gradually surrendering its pre-eminence in the drying-oil industry. At the same time the farm production of flax for oil has undergone heavy curtailment, so that in 1937 the United States imported four-fifths of its flaxseed, principally from the Argentine, the Union of Soviet Socialist Republics, and British India. Progressive increases in the tariff on flaxseed have apparently stimulated the development of cheaper oils and synthetic products rather than an increased production of domestic flaxseed.

The total consumption of drying oils is, of course, closely related to activity in the construction industries as well as, more generally, to total consumer income. This particular industrial market is therefore likely to continue to be characterized by intense internal competition between products and high variability between periods of depression and prosperity.

The soap and detergent industry is the largest present industrial user of fats and oils. As already shown, the animal fats and coconut oil are the most important fatty raw materials, although palm oil and palm-kernel oil also are used in substantial quantities. The tropical fats and oils have enjoyed the double advantage in this industry of low cost as compared with domestic oils, and superior quality for soap making, particularly for free-lathering and hard-water soaps. Minor quantities of linseed and soybean oils are used in special-purpose soaps. The soap industry also constitutes an important outlet for soap stock, a byproduct of the refining of crude vegetable oils.

The total usage of fats and oils in soap is, as might be expected, highly stable in good times and bad. The growth from year to year is slow. Within the field of suitable fats and oils competition is intense. The low price level of the main raw materials discourages serious attempts to develop new ones, but as an indication of possibilities, European countries such as Germany, which are chronically short of oils, have made substantial progress toward the development of soaps from the heavy and waxy fractions of petroleum. Improved methods of processing whale oil and fish oils have increased the importance of these low-cost oils to the American industry. Under present conditions there is little incentive to broaden the use of our principal domestic vegetable oils for soap making.

The other industrial consuming outlets for vegetable oils cover a wide range of products. The total volume of use for these purposes, while relatively minor, still amounts to several hundred million pounds. Some of the more important of these miscellaneous uses are for softening and lubricating fibers during textile operations (olive oil), in manufacturing tin plate (palm oil), in making fat liquors for leather manufacture, in cosmetics, in insecticides, in candles, in rubber compounding, in metal-cutting oils, as plasticizers and softeners for synthetic resins, and as lubricants, especially the modern extreme-pressure lubricants. Each of these fields is highly specialized, and there is no general pattern of prospective expansion. No one of them can be pointed out as an embryonic major use of the future. Intensive research is under way in several of these fields, however, under both governmental and private auspices.

Technological improvements, agricultural advances analogous to that in soybean production, and the discovery of entirely new fields of use will doubtless continue to characterize the vegetable-oil industry as they have in the last two decades. The natural conservatism of producers, the weight of investment in existing plant and equipment, the large amount of capital required to finance new processes, and the social impact of shifts in production, all act as deterrents to radical change in established systems of agriculture and processsing. Nevertheless, it is obvious that such changes must occur, else under our competitive economic system established products and markets will be gradually supplanted by newer, cheaper, and often better products from other sources.

Reducing the Costs of Food Distribution

by A. C. Hoffman and F. V. Waugh[1]

WHERE DOES most of the consumer's food dollar go—to the farmer or to the middleman? Is the spread between the farm price and the retail price justified or not? What part is played in this spread by wage rates, by profits, by efficiency or inefficiency in business methods, by consumer demands for services? What are the possibilities for reducing costs within the framework of the present marketing system? What about cooperative marketing, direct marketing, terminal wholesale facilities, new developments in retailing? Are there possibilities for reducing costs through a rather complete reorganization of the whole marketing system or large segments of it? Would such a method be consistent with our conception of free enterprise and competition? Here is a thoughtful and illuminating discussion of all of these questions.

THE MARKETING spread between farmer and consumer has always been a matter of keen public interest and not a little criticism.

[1] A. C. Hoffman is Agricultural Economist and F. V. Waugh is Chief Agricultural Economist, Division of Marketing and Transportation Research, Bureau of Agricultural Economics.

To many people it has seemed unreasonable that on an average the farmer receives only about 40 percent of the price paid for food products by the consumer. This situation has been variously ascribed to monopoly, to high wage rates, to inefficiency, to a wasteful increase in expenditures for competitive selling, as well as to numerous other factors. Ways and means of reducing marketing spreads have consequently taken many forms and have received the attention of governmental agencies for many years. But there is still a rather widespread misunderstanding of why marketing charges are as high as they are and what is necessary to effect significant reductions.

Let us see at the outset what the trend of food margins has been during the last 25 years. The Bureau of Agricultural Economics has compiled figures to show the retail cost to the consumer as compared with the farm value of 58 food products in the amounts purchased annually by a typical workingman's family (table 1). The difference between the two represents roughly the charges made for processing, transporting, and distributing this quantity of foods to the consumer. These data should not be taken as exact measures of marketing spreads but they are believed to be accurate enough to warrant several important conclusions.

Table 1.—Retail value, farm value, and margins of 58 food products, 1919–38

Period	Retail value	Farm value	Marketing spread	Farmer's share of consumer's dollar	Index of hourly wages (1926=100)
	Dollars	*Dollars*	*Dollars*	*Percent*	*Percent*
1913–17	285	157	128	55	48
1918–22	437	227	210	52	88
1923–27	400	187	213	47	98
1928–32	361	154	207	43	96
1933–37	317	130	187	41	90
1938	321	130	191	40	102

The first thing to be noted from table 1 is that marketing charges represent a large and increasing part of the price paid for food products by the consumer. During 1913–17 the average annual retail cost of 58 foods for a typical workingman's family was $285, of which the farmer received $157. As of 1938, the same bill of goods cost the purchaser $321, of which the farmer received $130. The spread between the farm and retail value of these goods thus increased from $128 to $191, while the farmer's share of the retail price decreased from 55 to 40 percent.

The first inclination is to say that here certainly is evidence that the marketing system is becoming increasingly monopolistic or increasingly inefficient or both. But let us look a little closer to see what comprises these marketing spreads, and why they behaved as they did.

FACTORS AFFECTING MARKETING SPREADS

Changes in food margins from year to year are to be explained by one or more of the following factors: (1) Changes in hourly wage rates and other cost factors; (2) changes in profits and rates of return to capital invested in marketing enterprises; (3) changes in the efficiency of the marketing system; and (4) changes in the amounts and kinds of marketing services rendered.

Wage Rates

Of these four factors, the first is by far the most important in explaining changes in marketing spreads during the last 25 years. The reason is simply that most of the charges for getting food products from the farm to the consumer are made up, either directly or indirectly, of wages. This being the case, one would expect to find a close relationship between changes in hourly wage rates and food margins. That such a relationship does indeed exist is obvious from table 1. Hourly wage rates have more than doubled during the last 25 years, which is the chief explanation of why food margins widened as they did.

This brings us to the first choice with which we are confronted in any effort to reduce marketing spreads significantly: Either (1) the amount of labor required to process and distribute food products must be decreased by means of increased efficiency, or (2) the wage rate per hour must be reduced.

It goes without saying that in general the objective of public policy ought to be to reduce marketing costs by the former method rather than by wage cutting. Any reduction in wage rates would of course affect the farmer in two ways. Insofar as it curtailed consumer purchasing power for food products, the farmer would be adversely affected. On the other hand, the farmer stands to gain directly from any measures that reduce marketing costs. From the farmers' standpoint, it is not easy to say which of these considerations is the more important. But from the public standpoint, which takes account of the interest of all groups, it is obvious that a reduction of marketing costs by means of wage cutting alone represents no net social gain, but merely a transferring of advantage between different economic groups.

Profits

A second component of the spread between farmer and consumer is the profits or earnings of capital invested in marketing enterprises. The notion is not infrequently held that exorbitant profits are largely responsible for the present width of this spread and that the solution is merely to force middlemen to disgorge their profits. Unfortunately the matter is not so simple as this.

The profits of some of the leading food corporations and the relation of these profits to total marketing spreads are shown in table 2. The ratio of earnings to capitalization—which gives a close approximation to the rate of return on invested capital for the companies involved—has varied from as high as 23.9 percent for the grocery chains in 1928 to as low as 0.4 percent for the large meat-packing concerns in 1932. At no time in the last 15 years have the meat packers netted more than 6 percent on their investment, which makes it difficult to establish a case against them on the grounds that their profits have been excessive. On the other hand, the corporate grocery chains at one time were among the most profitable enterprises to be found anywhere

223761°—40——41

in the country. They enjoyed these profits, however, not because they had a monopoly of retail food distribution, but mainly because their competitors were unable to match them in distributive efficiency. In this connection it is significant that chain-store profits have fallen steadily as competition between the chains themselves has increased and as the independents have been able to meet them on more equal terms through their own voluntary and cooperative associations.

Table 2.—Ratio of earnings to capitalization and profit margins of leading grocery chains, dairy companies, and meat packers, 1928, 1932, and 1936

Year	Ratio of earnings to capitalization [1]			Profit margins [2]		
	5 grocery chains	4 dairy companies	4 meat packers	5 grocery chains	4 dairy companies	4 meat packers
	Percent	*Percent*	*Percent*	*Percent*	*Percent*	*Percent*
1928	23.9	18.0	5.5	3.1	7.3	2.1
1932	14.7	7.1	.4	2.9	4.8	.2
1936	11.5	10.0	5.6	2.1	4.4	2.0

[1] Earnings represent the amount of money available for dividends on stocks, interest on bonded debt, and Federal income taxes. Capitalization represents the sum of the outstanding stocks, surplus reserves, and long-term debt.
[2] The profit margin is computed by dividing the earnings of a corporation by its dollar sales.

More significant for our present purpose than the ratio of earnings to invested capital is the profit margin. The profit margin is computed by dividing the earnings of a corporation by its dollar sales. It therefore shows how important these earnings are as a component of marketing spreads.

It is evident from the profit margins as shown in table 2 that earnings do not represent a very large part of the margin between farmer and consumer. Out of every dollar of sales made by the five leading food chains in 1936, only about 2 cents went to the capital invested in these enterprises. For the big dairy companies and meat packers, the corresponding figures are 4.4 cents and 2 cents, respectively.

Obviously the total marketing spread would not be greatly reduced even by the complete elimination of all earnings to capital invested in food enterprises. For most food products probably not over 5 percent of the retail selling price is represented by the combined earnings to capital at all stages in the marketing process. To suggest that we must look elsewhere than at profits is not to imply that any savings, however small, are unimportant; and certainly it is not meant to condone an exorbitant rate of profit derived from monopolistic or unfair trade practices. The point is that other factors such as wage rates, material costs, and the over-all efficiency of the marketing system are considerably more important than are profits in the determination of marketing spreads.

Marketing Efficiency and Increase in Marketing Services

The charge most commonly made against the marketing system is that it is inefficient and becoming more so. The increase in absolute marketing spreads, together with the fact that the farmer's share of the consumer's dollar has tended to decrease, is often cited as evidence of this. Taken by themselves, however, neither of these things gives any direct measure of efficiency as that term is properly used.

If the farmer were to process his own products, transport them to market, and sell them direct to the consumer, there would of course be no margin between him and the consumer and he would get 100 percent of the latter's dollar. Obviously this would not be an efficient way to market most farm products, and for some of them it would be patently impossible. The proportion of the consumer's dollar received by the farmer, then, is not a measure of efficiency but rather of the degree to which farmers concentrate on the business of production rather than on marketing. Some farm products—for example, eggs that are produced near the point of consumption—do not require expensive processing or transportation. The farmer selling such products will normally receive a much larger share of the consumer's dollar than one producing peas for canning, for instance, even though both products are marketed with equal efficiency.

It is generally agreed that consumers receive more in the way of marketing services today than they once did. Examples of this are better grading and standardization, more convenient packages, and added processing. It is impossible even to estimate how much has thus been added to marketing costs. But so long as these things add to consumer satisfaction, it is self-evident that any resulting increase in the spread between farmer and consumer does not mean that the marketing system has to that extent become less efficient.

From the social standpoint, efficiency ought to be measured in terms of the amount of labor and capital required for the performance of any given marketing operation. The amount of labor required should be clearly distinguished from the wage rate or the compensation paid to labor for its services. Thus the marketing spread might increase either because more labor and capital are used for a given operation or because labor and capital are better paid. The first would be evidence of growing inefficiency but not the second. As we have seen, the increase in marketing spreads during the last 25 years is to be explained largely by the increase in hourly wage rates. But it does not follow that the marketing system is less efficient in terms of the amount of productive resources used per unit of marketing services rendered.

As a matter of fact, there is some evidence to indicate that food distribution is becoming more, rather than less, efficient. One thing which points in this direction is that food margins have not increased in proportion to the increase in hourly wage rates despite the fact that consumers are receiving as much in the way of marketing service as they ever did.[2]

Still another thing should be kept in mind when considering marketing efficiency—the distinction between those marketing costs or expenditures made for the purpose of satisfying demand and those made for the purpose of influencing it in favor of a particular firm's product. Most costs incurred in connection with the physical han-

[2] Too much significance cannot be attached to the varying ratio between wage rates and food margins as a precise measure of efficiency, because the ratio of labor to capital may also have changed. There is no way of estimating the change in the ratio of labor to capital used in food distribution, but probably it has not been sufficient to invalidate the above conclusion.

dling of the commodity such as assembling, processing, transporting, and storing are of the former sort. So also are part of those for selling and transferring ownership of commodities at various stages in the marketing process. But it is also true that many—though not all—of the expenditures for salesmen's salaries, brokerage fees, and brand advertising are made for the purpose of influencing the buyer to patronize a particular firm or to use a particular brand or type of commodity. Insofar as expenditures of this kind contribute to the creation of new wants, larger total sales, and reduced production costs, they serve a socially necessary and useful purpose. But if the effect is merely to take business from one firm and give it to another, then clearly there is no net social gain but only a transfer of advantage between individual firms. We should, therefore, take care to distinguish between the over-all efficiency of the marketing system and that of individual firms, since the two are not necessarily synonymous.

REDUCING MARKETING COSTS WITHIN THE FRAMEWORK OF THE PRESENT SYSTEM

How much marketing costs can be reduced depends largely on how far we are willing to go in reorganizing the marketing system. Many gains have been and can be made within the framework of the present system. Improvements in the efficiency of individual firms, cooperative marketing, reorganization of terminal wholesale facilities, changes in types of retail stores—all of these offer possibilities for some reduction in marketing costs without any drastic reorganization of the present system of food distribution. But not infrequently the savings possible by these means are exaggerated in the public mind, with the result that there is disappointment when they do not come up to expectations.

Most of the efforts on the part of the farmers themselves to reduce marketing costs have been made by means of cooperative-marketing organizations. For the most part, these ventures have been confined to the processing and marketing operations at the producer end of the marketing system. Outstanding examples of the progress in cooperative marketing are of course the thousands of local cooperative creameries, grain elevators, cotton gins, livestock-shipping associations, fruit-packing plants, etc.

It goes without saying that the farmers' cooperative movement has led to great improvement in the local marketing sphere within which it has mainly operated. It has resulted in larger and more efficient local plant facilities, a better competitive situation, improved quality, and various other gains calculated to improve returns to member farmers. (See the article, Cooperative Marketing by Farmers, p. 684.) But it must also be said that the costs of these local marketing functions represent only a small part of the total marketing spread, so that the greatest possible gains to be made here do not bulk large in relation to the retail price of the commodities involved. The cost of making butter, for example, might be reduced as much as 1 or even 2 cents per pound within the creamery; and the local costs of handling a bushel of wheat by as much as several cents. But important as such savings are to the farmers who receive them, it is obvious that more than this is necessary if the total cost of marketing is to be greatly reduced.

Greater potential gains are to be made in the field of food processing and in the terminal and wholesale markets, but even here it is easy to overstate what might be done without a complete reorganization of the marketing system. The most significant development affecting the terminal marketing of most farm products is the tendency toward direct marketing—as, for example, the selling of livestock direct to meat packers or the sale of fruits and vegetables by growers to chain-store systems. In effect this has meant the elimination of one or more specialized intermediaries at some point in the marketing system.

Elimination of the broker or the commission man does not mean that marketing spreads are reduced by the amount of the fees or margins formerly taken by these agents. Direct marketing involves some compensating costs on its own account, and in some cases these may be almost as great as those costs which it displaces. Generally speaking, however, direct marketing does appear to have led to some economies, particularly by mass distributors who no longer have need for the services of specialized intermediaries between them and the producer.

Among the most inefficient and disorganized terminal wholesale facilities are those for fresh fruits and vegetables. In most of our large cities, these facilities are antiquated, ill-adapted to the handling of motortruck receipts, and altogether inadequate for the efficient wholesaling of perishable produce under modern conditions. As a result, waste and spoilage is higher than it should be, intracity cartage costs are excessive, and the margins taken by wholesalers and jobbers are somewhat wider than they might be if modern market facilities were provided. Studies made by the Bureau of Agricultural Economics indicate that savings approximating 2 or 3 percent of the retail price of perishables are possible within the terminal wholesale market.

Most important of all marketing functions from the standpoint of the costs involved is retailing. Because of its remoteness from the farmer, the retail function is sometimes overlooked when ways and means for reducing marketing costs are under consideration. In selling nearly all farm products, the retail margin is the largest single element in the marketing spread, and in many cases it is larger than all other marketing costs combined. The retail margin for fruits and vegetables, for example, commonly amounts to 30 to 35 percent of the retail price; for meat products, 25 to 30 percent; for bread, 20 percent. This does not mean that the retailer is less efficient in his operations than handlers at other stages in the marketing process or that his profits are necessarily exorbitant in relation to his labor and invested capital. But it does mean that here is one of the most likely points at which to effect significant savings in food distribution.

The outstanding development in food retailing has been the growth of the corporate grocery chains and, in recent years, of voluntary and cooperative chains of independent retailers. The changes brought about in food retailing as a result of this development are of two kinds: (1) Those resulting from the integration of the wholesaling function with that of retailing; and (2) changes in the operation of the retail grocery store itself.

Next to the function of retailing itself, some of the most costly links in the marketing system are those between the processor and the retailer. The key to many of the advantages possessed by chain systems lies in the fact that they have dropped some of these links by the integration of successive marketing functions within a single firm. Nearly all of the chains have set up their own wholesaling establishments to service their retail units, and the larger systems have gone actively into country assembling and processing of many food products. In consequence of this, their stocks move toward the consumer without the numerous and costly bargaining transactions and selling operations necessary to move goods in the regular channels.

Equally important are the changes which mass retailing has brought about within the retail store itself. The emphasis of chain stores as well as of many independents has been on rapid turn-over, larger volume per store, and the application of labor-saving methods—notably the self-service feature. The corporate chains took the initiative along these lines, but in recent years the voluntary and cooperative chains have not been far behind in the application of many of these cost-saving features.

How much mass retailing has contributed toward reduced marketing costs it is of course impossible to say. Data compiled by the Federal Trade Commission in connection with its chain-store inquiry indicated that, in the four cities studied, the chains were selling at prices approximately 7 percent below those of their independent competitors. Numerous studies made by other agencies confirm this general relationship between the prices of chains and those of independents, although there are of course many individual exceptions to these averages. It is probable that the reduction in food costs brought about as a result of mass retailing is even greater than these price differentials would indicate, since all retailers must follow the lead of their low-price competitors to some extent if they are to stay in business in competition with them.

Another important development in food distribution is the introduction of new low-cost methods of retailing, notably the supermarket. The essential features of the supermarket are tremendous store volume (often amounting to 10 or 20 times that of the average grocery store), low rent and store overhead, and a reduction in store labor by means of customer self-service. Within the short span of a few years, stores of this type have become an important factor in the grocery trade, particularly since the older grocery chains have begun converting their retail units into markets of this type.

Somewhat the same general idea is embodied in the milk depots recently set up in several large cities at which milk is sold at greatly reduced prices to those willing to forego the regular service of doorstep delivery for this product. All low-cost marketing developments of this kind are likely to have a special appeal for those whose income is limited or who prefer lower prices to extra marketing services, and they ought to be permitted to develop in accordance with the wishes of those who use them.

OVER-ALL REORGANIZATION OF THE MARKETING SYSTEM

Thus far we have discussed only those savings which can be made within the framework of the present marketing system. To a considerable extent, however, all of these leave untouched one of the main causes of high marketing costs—the duplication of processing, transportation, and marketing facilities arising out of competition itself. We have indeed made great progress in improving the efficiency and reducing the costs of individual firms; but this has not resulted in a proportionate improvement in what might be called the over-all efficiency of marketing because the nature of our marketing system is such that no limitation has been placed on the number of firms or the quantity of labor and capital used in food distribution.

It is not possible on the basis of present information even to approximate how much the needless duplication of marketing facilities at all stages of food distribution adds to marketing spreads. But it can be asserted positively that the number of retailing, wholesaling, processing, and assembling establishments has multiplied out of all proportion to what would be needed if food distribution were organized on what might be called a social-engineering basis.

The number of grocery stores, for example, has increased from about 160,000 in 1900 to 355,000 in 1935. Population per store has decreased in this same period from 486 to 358. Part of this increase in retail facilities is due to the fact that a larger proportion of the population now lives in cities and requires more in the way of retail facilities. But it also signifies a growing excess of retail facilities, the cost of which must be reflected either in wider marketing spreads than would otherwise be necessary or in a lowered rate of recompense to the labor and capital employed in retailing enterprises.

Nor is this situation confined to food retailing. To some extent at least it is to be found at every point in the marketing system. We do not need all our creameries and canneries and grain elevators to handle our present food supply. Studies have repeatedly shown that many of these plants are operating at far less than capacity and that substantial cost savings could be made if all of the supply were to move through the most efficient types of plants operating at full capacity. In general this would probably mean a substantial increase in the average size of plant and handling agencies, and it would certainly mean a reduction in numbers of handlers so as to bring the over-all capacity of the marketing system more in line with the facilities actually needed to process and distribute food products.

Generally speaking, proposals of this kind have not yet received much discussion so far as the food industries are concerned. During recent years, however, an increasing number of people are beginning to think of fluid-milk distribution in these terms. Careful students of the problem know that the costs of fluid-milk distribution are high mainly because of the duplication of pasteurizing facilities and the overlapping of milk routes and that these costs can be reduced significantly only by a fundamental reorganization of the fluid-milk marketing system. How much these costs can be reduced and whether or not the necessary measures are feasible, considering all the factors involved, is of course conjectural. A recent study of fluid-milk marketing in Milwaukee, Wis., indicates that savings of more than 2 cents per quart might be achieved through a unified, noncompetitive system of milk distribution. A gain even approximating this estimate would far exceed any saving likely to be obtained in any other way.

To achieve the maximum efficiency in food distribution by limiting the number and kind of marketing facilities to those actually needed to provide consumers with the goods and services they desire would obviously involve some fundamental changes in our present conception of free enterprise and competition. It would probably mean that some limits would have to be placed on the right of private enterprisers to erect plants and engage in marketing operations unless there was a real need for the added facilities. In some cases it might even mean the abandonment of competition as the regulator of economic forces and the substitution of public control somewhat along the lines of that now being exercised in those industries classified as public utilities. At the present time most of the food industries are too ramified and their economic units are too numerous and too separate to permit an easy transition to such a system. The thing to be emphasized, however, is that this is the general direction in which food distribution will probably have to go if the sole objective is to process and distribute food products at the least possible cost in terms of man-hours and capital equipment.

Assuming that it were possible to operate our marketing system with far less labor and capital than is now used, it will immediately be asked what is to be done with the additional productive resources thus made available for other means of employment. With many of our resources already idle, many will argue that no good purpose will be served by adding to present unemployment. If the alternative to employment, even though it be relatively unnecessary and unproductive, is no employment, then this argument indeed has considerable logic. There is, of course, nothing novel either in this contention or in the situation which has given rise to it. The same objection was raised at one time to the introduction of the power loom, the steam engine, and many of the other labor-saving instruments which are basic to our modern way of living.

The fundamental problem of how to give full and productive employment to all economic resources is beyond the scope of this article. It has generally been assumed that labor and capital displaced in one line of enterprise would ultimately find employment in another. Over the centuries this has in the main been true; but the lag has been so great and the adjustments so slow that the ultimate gains for mankind have been achieved only at the expense of great loss and suffering during the transition period.

PUBLIC POLICY TOWARD NEW MARKETING DEVELOPMENTS

One thing further might be said regarding the reduction of food costs. Nearly everyone pays lip service to the need for doing everything possible to reduce marketing spreads and lower the costs of food distribution. But not even governmental agencies themselves have always followed a consistent policy in this matter.

One of the economic premises on which the Federal Government was founded was that there should be free and unrestricted commerce between the States. In another article in this Yearbook (pp. 656–666) the way in which this premise has been violated by various State and local barriers to internal trade is described in some detail. It is self-evident that this tendency cannot but result in an uneconomic use of productive resources and that it must mean some addition to the Nation's food costs.

Another contradiction is sometimes to be found in governmental policy toward large-scale marketing organizations. It goes without saying that private monopoly in any of its forms is intolerable and must be abolished either by the restoration of competition or by public control of monopolized industries. Sometimes, however, governmental measures go beyond this and seek to help or preserve a particular type of marketing system on the grounds that this, rather than a possible reduction in marketing costs, is in the public interest. Examples of this are some of the State chain-store tax laws, trade-practice acts, and State and Federal legislation for resale price maintenance. It may be that, when all factors are considered, measures of this kind are in the public interest. But when their effect is to maintain food prices at levels higher than they would otherwise be, it should be frankly recognized that there may be an inconsistency between these measures and the goal of narrower marketing spreads.

Marketing-Agreement Programs as a Means of Agricultural Adjustment

by Budd A. Holt and Donald M. Rubel [1]

FOR A good many years certain groups of fruit growers and producers of other products have dealt with their marketing problems through cooperative action. Because of its practical value, this method has now become established on a much wider scale, with national sanctions, in the form of a program of marketing agreements covering fruits, vegetables, nuts, and milk. Essentially, this program gives farmers some of the advantages long enjoyed by industry. What is the background of the marketing-agreements program? How does it operate? What devices are used to get the desired results? What are the principal problems it faces? What are its possibilities and limitations? This article deals with these questions.

MARKETING-AGREEMENT programs combine voluntary and regulatory control of the marketing of agricultural commodities for the purpose of increasing returns to producers. They differ from other agricultural adjustment programs having the same objectives

[1] Budd A. Holt is Economic Adviser and Donald M. Rubel is Agricultural Economist, Surplus Marketing Administration.

in that they are not directly concerned with production; their purpose is to regulate the marketing of available supplies.

PROGRAMS ESTABLISHED FOR TWO GROUPS OF COMMODITIES

Authority to undertake marketing-agreement programs was given in the Agricultural Adjustment Act of 1933. They have been established for two general types of commodities—(1) milk and dairy products and (2) specialty crops, particularly tree fruits, tree nuts, and vegetables.

While the results that producers of these two main groups of commodities seek to obtain by regulation—principally increased income, greater price stability, and more equitable sharing of the market—are similar, the marketing problems in these two types of industries differ, owing largely to the inherently different characteristics of the commodities themselves. Fluid milk is a highly perishable commodity which must be delivered to the consumers at a relatively constant rate, and producers usually ship their fluid milk to one consuming market.

The producers of the specialty crops, on the other hand, are usually concentrated in areas favorable to the production of their commodities and ship their products to many scattered consuming markets.

A second main difference in the marketing of these two types of commodities is in the number of buyers of the product for distribution to consumers. Conditions surrounding the retail distribution of fluid milk favor the growth of large distributing organizations, and relatively few organizations buy and distribute the bulk of the fluid milk in most markets. In contrast, there are many local buyers of most specialty crops, and these commodities are shipped to widely distributed consuming markets in each of which many buyers are located. To offset the tendency for prices of fluid milk to be determined in a buyers' market, organizations of producers have been established for the principal purpose of bargaining with distributors. Bargaining between large buying and selling interests is not common in the fruit and vegetable field. Furthermore the several different market uses for milk—as fluid milk, cream, butter, etc.—have led to the development of pricing plans involving two or more prices for the producer's product depending on the use made of the milk. Such multiple pricing is seldom found in the producers' markets for fruits and vegetables.

The approach to the problem of improving the income of producers through regulation of marketing differs for the two general types of commodities with the differences in marketing problems and marketing institutions of these commodities. In the case of milk, regulations involve classification according to use and determination of prices for the various uses. The price of milk for fluid distribution is established at a higher level than prices for other uses, and the seasonal and operating surpluses which cannot be sold for fluid distribution are diverted to use for cream or manufactured products. On the other hand, regulations for specialty crops, such as tree fruits and nuts or vegetables, approach the problem of growers' prices indirectly from the supply side. That is, the quantity, quality, rate, and method of shipment from the producing areas to all markets are controlled, and prices received by producers are thereby indirectly affected.

In this article some of the basic problems involved in marketing-agreement programs for the tree-fruit, tree-nut, and vegetable industries will be discussed. The principal conclusions are applicable to all commodities for which marketing-agreement programs have been established.

MARKETING PROGRAMS IN SPECIALTY-CROP INDUSTRIES

The general problem of regulating marketings of various fruit, nut, and vegetable commodities should be viewed in the light of recent trends in these industries, most of which have undergone important changes since the early 1920's or are now in the process of undergoing such changes.

Production of fruits and nuts in the United States averaged more than 40 percent greater during the 3-year period ended in 1938–39 than during the period 1919–20 to 1923–24. At the same time many changes have occurred in the composition of our national fruit supplies. Average production of all citrus fruit, for example, increased 2½ times, while average production of apples declined 6 percent between the same periods. Along with the increase in production, new outlets have been developed. Production of canned fruits doubled between the above periods, while the United States pack of dried fruits increased one-third. A phenomenal increase has occurred in the production of fruit juices. Domestic production of tree nuts has increased substantially since the World War, while during recent years imports of like types of nuts from foreign countries have decreased, resulting in a partial replacement of foreign supplies by domestic production. The outlook is for a continued increase in production in most of the tree-fruit and tree-nut industries in the United States during the next few years.

The acreage and production of vegetables have also expanded greatly since the World War period. In 1919 the area planted to 21 crops for fresh market was about 500,000 acres; by 1926 a total of 1,000,000 acres was in these crops; and since 1936 the acreage has been maintained at about 1,750,000. Nearly twice as many pounds per person of fresh vegetables for market are availabe at the present time as were available 20 years ago.

The growth in these industries may be attributed in a large measure to the relatively high returns received during the post-war period. The expanding production has been accompanied by declining prices which in turn have brought about economies in production and marketing, together with new channels of utilization. Important shifts have also taken place in the regional distribution of supplies, and in a number of cases the pressure of increased supplies has resulted in some changes in the marketing institutions of the various commodities. In general, therefore, marketing-agreement programs for specialty crops have been established for growing industries which have been in a state of flux or in which continued growth is indicated.

Voluntary Programs Preceded Marketing Agreements

The downward trends in prices accompanying the increased supplies encouraged the development of marketing programs designed to resist further price reductions. It was a relatively common occurrence, particularly during seasons of above-average yields, for terminal-market prices for the less preferable grades and sizes of many fruits and vegetables to go below the cash costs of harvesting and marketing. Such situations often resulted from abnormal weather conditions which advanced or retarded the harvesting period in specialized production areas. At times producers, possibly encouraged by shipping agencies interested in receiving service charges, shipped extremely large volumes, with the result that markets were glutted and the prices received gave little or no return to the producers. Situations of this kind were particularly acute in those producing areas located at a great distance from terminal markets so that large marketing and transportation charges were involved.

For a number of years producers in some of these industries had been attempting to increase their returns by various means of controlling the supply. In some of the Pacific-coast fruit industries voluntary agreements prohibiting shipments of discounted grades and sizes of fruit had been established. In other industries, where cooperative organizations controlled large proportions of the total supplies, these organizations had established regulation of volumes of shipments.

The decrease in consumer purchasing power during the early 1930's, with its further depressing effect upon prices of agricultural commodities, resulted in extremely low prices to growers. In some industries, volumes of supplies remained unharvested owing to the low prices. These conditions led to particular emphasis on marketing programs, and producer groups that had attempted surplus controls within their organizations tried to obtain the cooperation of other organizations in carrying out industry-wide marketing programs. Some voluntary marketing programs were developed that involved the elimination of a portion of the available supplies, with the formation of surplus pools for diversion of supplies from the customary commercial channels or of reserve pools of supplies not to be sold in commercial channels except at satisfactory prices. These voluntary schemes had limited success, however, chiefly because the handlers and producers who were not cooperating in the programs could benefit at the expense of those who were cooperating. The expanded activities of those operating on the outside eventually caused a break-down of these industry programs, since their continued success depended upon complete cooperation.

Development of Marketing-Agreement Programs

The legislation providing for marketing-agreement programs grew out of an acute need on the part of agricultural producers for additional means of increasing their returns. At the start it was felt that marketing agreements constituted a possible alternative approach to the production-adjustment features for basic commodities in the Agricultural Adjustment Act, and their applicability to specialty-crop and fluid-milk markets was not generally recognized. The Secretary was authorized by the act to enter into marketing agreements with and to issue licenses to processors, associations of producers, and others engaged in the handling of any agricultural commodity in interstate or foreign commerce. Marketing agreements constituted voluntary contracts between the handlers of farm commodities and the Secretary of Agriculture and were authorized for the purpose of controlling interstate marketings as one means of increasing returns to producers. The authority to issue licenses, however, seems to have been aimed at the elimination of unfair trade practices or charges tending to prevent efficient practices in the marketing of agricultural commodities.

With the passage of the act, industries confronted with acute price situations and desiring assistance under this legislation developed marketing programs, which were submitted to the Secretary of Agriculture for consideration. One of the first problems in developing marketing-agreement programs was to bring into line the recalcitrant minorities that were unwilling to participate in marketing schemes proposed by the industries. To accomplish this, licenses were issued by the Secretary of Agriculture compelling all shippers to comply with the provisions of the marketing agreements. This early use of licenses as a complement to marketing agreements established the basis for a type of program that could not be rendered ineffective by a small minority within an industry.

Under the authority provided by the Agricultural Adjustment Act of 1933 the various agricultural industries proposed those types of control they believed would be most helpful in solving their marketing problems. Additional legislation, provided by the amendments to the Agricultural Adjustment Act in 1935 and by the Marketing Agreement Act of 1937, further clarified marketing-agreement programs and specifically stated the types of control that could be effected and the agricultural industries for which programs could be established. Provision was made for the issuance of orders to take the place of the licenses in the earlier marketing-agreement programs. Furthermore, producers were given a more definite place in the development and operation of marketing-agreement programs. It was provided that no order could go into effect without the approval of two-thirds of the growers by number or by volume of the commodity involved. In addition, authorization was given the Secretary of Agriculture for the selection of industry committees or agencies to assist in the administration of marketing agreements and orders.

Certain general features of the marketing-agreement programs and the legislation under which they are developed distinguish them from other agricultural programs and legislation. (1) These programs embrace both voluntary control, represented by marketing agreements, and regulatory control, enforced by orders. They are initiated within the production or marketing area by producer groups or others interested in improving marketing conditions. The regulatory aspect of the program is essential to its success, and the authority to proceed on a regulatory basis is necessary for the protection of producers' interests. (2) The programs are primarily applicable to localized production or marketing areas for individual commodities and are designed to meet the particular problems of such areas. The provisions of the legislation are, in general, sufficiently broad to permit the development of programs flexible enough to meet many of the peculiar marketing problems of various individual areas or commodities. (3) The legislation alone imposes no control over the marketing of any commodity; neither does it assure that such control will necessarily be established over any commodity. It is enabling legislation, under which programs may be undertaken with respect to specified commodities provided conditions within the area are such that a satisfactory and practical program can be developed within the authority and limitations of the act. (4) The programs are financed by the interested industry, and they provide for as great a degree of democratic control by the industry in their development and operation as is legally possible, with sufficient governmental supervision to protect the interests of individuals and the general public.

Procedure and Conditions of Operation

Marketing-agreement programs for specialty crops are established in a production area after a request for a program has been made by the industry concerned and a hearing has been held at which evidence is presented by industry groups on all circumstances relating to the proposed program. In general, the agreements and orders provide for an administrative agency and for the issuance of special regulations to govern the handling of the commodity. The administrative agency is dominated by the producer-members. It usually consists of a committee appointed from among nominees elected by growers and handlers to represent the respective group interests. In some instances there are two committees—one of growers, which is responsible for administrative action, and the other of handlers, which acts in an advisory capacity.

Recommendations for regulations to govern shipments are made by the administrative agency to the Secretary of Agriculture, who is responsible for putting any regulation under marketing-agreement programs into effect. The nature of the regulation varies with conditions both in the producing area and in the markets and is governed by limitations prescribed in the marketing agreement and order and by the Marketing Agreement Act.

The problems involved in regulation of shipments differ with each crop and with each season. One consideration is the length of time during which a commodity may be stored. This, of course, varies with the degree of perishability of the product. The length of the harvesting season likewise affects the nature of the regulation that may be issued. Many commodities must be harvested as soon as they are mature; others may be held for a time without damage—certain varieties of citrus fruits, for example, may be held on the tree for several months after maturity has been reached.

Also, the problem of regulating shipments varies with the nature of the marketing institutions in the various industries. In the Pacific-coast hop industry the product is processed and made ready for final sale by the growers, whereas in all other industries for which marketing agreements have been established some form of packaging or processing is performed by handlers. In the Pacific-coast walnut and the California-Arizona orange industries more than 85 percent of the total volume of shipments is made through cooperative marketing organizations, while in the California-Arizona cantaloup and the

Pacific-coast hop industries the volume handled by cooperative marketing organizations is relatively small.

A large number of the commodities marketed under marketing-agreement programs are of a perishable nature, and the time of marketing exerts a considerable influence upon returns received by growers. A difference of a week or two in the period of maturity of Colorado vegetables, for example, may result in a marked difference in the incomes to growers of these commodities, since shipments of competitive vegetables may or may not be heavy during that particular period. Furthermore, since there is no carry-over from year to year in the case of most perishable commodities, damage to crops from weather may result in extreme variations in marketing conditions. Since it is impossible to forecast accurately the marketing conditions that may prevail from time to time, marketing policies under these programs must be flexible enough to be modified readily as conditions change during the season.

TYPES OF REGULATION

Three main types of regulation—volume regulation, regulation of grade and size, and price-posting requirements—have been used in marketing-agreement programs for general crops, and each program contains provision for one or more of these methods of regulation.

(1) Volume regulation is designed to control the volume of shipments of a given commodity in specified channels during a given period of time. One form of volume regulation is the limiting of the total quantity shipped over the season. Where conditions of demand are such that the proportionate increase in price to growers resulting from the restriction is greater than the proportionate restriction in volume, returns to growers will be improved by such a limitation in shipments. A more complex form of volume regulation may be established where two or more market outlets for the commodity exist and where conditions of demand are such that the producers' returns may be improved by protecting prices in one outlet through the diversion of supplies to other outlets. This, in effect, is what is accomplished in milk-marketing programs through the classification of milk and the establishment of prices in the various channels of use. In the specialty-crop field, returns to walnut growers, for example, are improved by diverting supplies from the domestic unshelled market to the shelled and export markets.

Another form of volume control is regulation of the rate of flow to market. It has been found that total returns to growers from many semiperishable and perishable commodities can be raised by such regulation, which may or may not involve elimination of part of the available supplies. This form of regulation is usually designed to prevent the periodic gluts and scarcities of supplies in consuming markets that often occur when perishable commodities are concerned and the control of shipments is determined by the usual competition in the industry. Benefits to producers through this type of regulation come from more uniform prices throughout the shipping season and from the prevention of actual losses on shipments to glutted markets. Regulation of the rate of flow to market might also be designed to achieve different prices at different times in the marketing period if the demand conditions were known to be such that this form of control would improve returns to producers. Thus far, however, this form of volume control has not been undertaken in any marketing-agreement program.

(2) Regulations of grade and size relate to the prohibition of shipments of particular grades or sizes of the product during a given period of time. To the extent that these regulations increase or decrease the total volume of shipments during any given season or accelerate or retard the rate of shipments during given periods of the season, they tend to influence growers' prices and returns in the same manner as regulation of volume. Likewise, regulations of volumes of shipments tend to result in limitation of discounted grades and sizes, since usually the most preferred supplies are shipped when volumes are limited. Grade and size regulations, however, influence growers' returns through affecting the quality as well as the quantity of the product which may be shipped in the period during which the regulations are in effect. They have, in some cases, been established for the purpose of improving the quality of shipments early in the season by prohibiting shipments of immature fruit. (Shippers often ship immature fruit in order to take advantage of high prices existing during those weeks when the volume of shipments is small.) Grade and size regulations, furthermore, have been established for the purpose of preventing losses to growers for those discounted grades and sizes that would occasion a loss if they were shipped during the period of regulation.

(3) Price-posting provisions require that no shipper may quote or sell his commodity at prices other than those contained in his posted schedule. This is not designed to effect price fixing, since shippers may file new price schedules. They are not permitted to quote or sell the commodity at the new schedule of prices, however, until a designated period of time has elapsed. The primary purpose of price posting is to make available more reliable information concerning the prices prevailing in the market. At the same time this may prevent destructive price cutting.

As would be expected, regulations limiting the total volume shipped during the season have proved to be the most effective in improving prices and returns to growers. Regulations of this type were more widely used during the earlier years of marketing-agreement programs than they are at the present time. During the first 3 years (1933–34 to 1935–36), 11 marketing-agreement programs, on an average, were in operation each season. Of these programs, 3 limited total season shipments, 5 regulated the rate of flow of shipments, and 4 limited the grades or sizes of the commodities shipped. During the 3 crop years ended in 1938–39 an average of 9 programs operated annually. In this period, 7 of the programs limited the grades or sizes of the commodities shipped, 5 regulated the rate of flow of shipments, while 1 limited the total season shipments. In addition, 2 of the programs in 1935–36 and in 1938–39, and 1 program in each of the intervening years, contained price-posting provisions.

Performance under marketing-agreement programs has demonstrated that regulation of volumes or of grades and sizes of shipments of specialty crops provides an effective means of increasing growers'

223761°—40——42

returns. Experience has indicated, however, that only during short-time emergency situations are growers and handlers willing to undertake the adjustments in supplies that are necessary to have substantial effects upon prices to growers.

TYPES OF PROBLEMS RELATED TO REGULATION

The successful operation of marketing-agreement programs is, of course, contingent upon full compliance with the regulations established. Aside from the legal problems of enforcement, which required major consideration in the initial development of these programs, a number of broad general problems are involved in the establishment of regulation. (1) The existence of regulation connotes a change in marketing practices or methods on the part of a few or many individuals in the industries affected. These individuals are often reluctant to make the changes, and their resistance, in turn, necessitates activities to overcome it. (2) Regulation must be applied to a certain group of individuals. The programs are directly applicable to the handlers of the commodities, even though their objective is to benefit the producers. This approach is used not for the purpose of regulating handlers as such but because it is the most practical method of controlling market supplies. Handlers, however, operate in different ways, and the size of their individual operations varies greatly. For these reasons many of the problems encountered concern the relative effects of regulation on different handlers. (3) Regulations, if they are to be effective and enforceable, must be relatively simple and well defined. Simplicity and definiteness of regulations are difficult to attain in complex marketing situations. Furthermore, oversimplification may mean a less effective regulation. For example, if regulation of grades or sizes is undertaken, it can be well enforced only if shipments of all of certain grades or sizes are limited, even though from an economic standpoint the industry would benefit more if a portion of the prohibited grades and sizes could be shipped. Similarly, regulation of volume to interstate channels might be improved from an economic standpoint if shipments to various consuming areas could be regulated instead of only the total flow outside of the production area, which is the only way at present that effective control can be established.

A most important problem of regulation, which concerns both handlers and growers, is the question of equity. Control over the volume, rate, or composition of shipments necessitates the use of formulas or rules which, even though they are uniform for all individuals, are found to have different effects. Equitableness is largely a matter of judgment and must be considered in respect to the objectives of the program. In addition to the problems involved in the determination of standards of equity, the question may be raised whether all handlers or producers should be treated alike, for this may tend to enable the less efficient individuals to remain in the field while more efficient and aggressive individuals may be prevented from expanding.

The long-time economic problems of an industry must be recognized in the operation of marketing-agreement programs for that industry. This consideration is an extremely important one in connection with many specialty crops, particularly those the production of which is expanding rapidly. Expansion in a given industry may be due to the fact that funds invested in that industry return more than in alternate investments; to maintain prices at levels satisfactory to the industry might encourage additional plantings, thereby increasing the marketing difficulties of growers in the future. On the whole, however, the interests of growers as individuals in selling as much of their product as possible have sufficiently outweighed their desires for improvement in total returns to result in reasonable price levels for their commodities even when under regulation.

RESPONSIBILITIES AND ADJUSTMENTS OF PRODUCERS AND HANDLERS

The producer plays an important role in the operation of marketing-agreement programs, even though these programs apply to handlers and not to farmers in their capacity as producers. The responsibility for proposing marketing-agreement programs and also that of formulating the provisions of prospective programs rests largely with producers and their cooperative associations. The administrative agencies for the operation of marketing-agreement programs for specialty crops are made up largely of growers, and no program can be made effective until it has been approved by the majority of the producers in the industry.

Through these programs the Department of Agriculture has endeavored to indicate to growers the marketing responsibilities they must accept along with their responsibilities relating to production. Until very recently producers of certain agricultural commodities appeared to believe that their job was completed after their crops had been harvested and that the problem of marketing should be undertaken by a separate agency. Many marketing problems, however, particularly those which marketing-agreement programs are designed to solve, are too closely associated with agricultural production to justify the reliance of producers on outside agencies for solutions. The generalization may be made that a marketing agreement extends the principle of cooperative marketing to all growers and handlers of the commodity within the area embraced by the program. The program is established for the purpose of bringing about a change in either the volume or the composition of supplies shipped to commercial markets. This implies that growers and shippers must relinquish some of the rights which heretofore they had considered to be inalienable—those of the quantity and timing of the sales of their commodity—to an organization directing the marketing of the commodity for the welfare of growers as a whole. For marketing-agreement programs to operate successfully, it is essential that growers be thoroughly acquainted with the implications of regulation of shipments and thoroughly aware of the obligations they must assume and the rights they must relinquish in order to effectuate the purpose of the program.

Marketing-agreement programs necessitate adjustments on the part of handlers as well as of growers. For example, in the event a marketing-agreement program includes a regulation in which allotments to handlers are based on the volume of fruit controlled by each handler, independent handlers may find it necessary to contract, at the beginning of the season, for the volume that they intend to ship during the season. This involves a change in operation on the part of those independent handlers who, prior to the agreement program, operated on a hand-to-mouth basis, purchasing fruit concurrently with their shipments to commercial channels. Market regulations restricting shipments of certain grades and sizes would curtail operations of shippers whose activities had been confined largely to the shipping of the grades and sizes excluded by the regulations. The regulation of shipments may require fewer adjustments by handlers if their volumes are increased to a given size. Thus, shippers may find it desirable to merge their operations with those of other shippers to facilitate such adjustments. Adjustments on the part of handlers, however, are borne in a large measure by the growers whose produce they ship. In fact, handlers could not make these adjustments without the consent of their growers who, in turn, share the responsibility of administering the programs.

SHORT-TIME AND LONG-TIME OBJECTIVES OF REGULATION

The operations of marketing-agreement programs directly affect the interests of three main groups. The producer group is interested in the improvement of price levels within a short period, which means an increase in returns to the individual producer. Over a longer period, however, it is to the best interests of this group to maintain prices at as high a level as possible without encouraging an increase in supplies of the same commodity through additional plantings or increases in supplies of competitive commodities. Similarly, handlers are anxious to ship large volumes, since their profits are largely determined by the volume handled, although in the long run it is to their best interest to maintain volumes at levels consistent with reasonable returns to producers. The consumer group, on the other hand, is interested in immediate low prices, although in the longer period prices must be kept at a level that will insure continuation of the volume of supplies.

It is the function of the Department to bring about a reasonable adjustment between the interests of these three main groups in the administration of marketing-agreement programs. Generally speaking, the purpose of a program is to raise prices to growers, since the programs are established at the request of industries which hope thereby to improve a condition caused by low prices. The short-run objective of farmers, therefore, appears to be the first consideration in the establishment of marketing-agreement programs, and regulations are established generally for the purpose of increasing producer prices through some form of control on shipments to commercial channels.

The long-time objectives of the major group interests involved must be taken into consideration, however, in the administration of marketing-agreement programs that are to remain in effect year after year, since continued emphasis on the short-run objective of growers may not be consistent with their best interests in the long run. The obvious limitations to continued curtailment as a solution to marketing problems of growers have led to particular emphasis being placed upon the importance of expanding outlets, developing new uses for products, and marketing practices tending to enable the marketing of larger volumes. During the first years of marketing-agreement programs, when producer returns were extremely low owing to excessive supplies in relation to the low level of consumer purchasing power, many marketing-agreement programs were designed to improve growers' prices through rather substantial limitations on the volumes of shipments. During recent years, however, with consumer income at relatively higher levels, more emphasis has been placed upon marketing an increased volume of merchantable supplies in an orderly fashion. Moreover, as previously stated, producers are generally reluctant to restrict volumes of supplies much beyond those that would not return costs of harvesting and marketing. Since shipments of the crop of an individual producer exert no appreciable influence upon price, producers as a group continue to be highly individualistic. During recent years, however, there has been evidence of more interest on the part of producers in the long-time aspects of marketing programs.

With regulations that do not restrict the movement of merchantable supplies appreciably beyond the point of loss to the grower, marketing-agreement programs do not effect a much greater elimination of supplies from market than intelligent and informed growers and shippers would impose upon themselves in the absence of regulation. Regulation of this type is consistent also with the long-run interests of producer groups. When marketing conditions have not been of an emergency nature, more attention has been directed toward achieving stability of prices, adjusting the rate of flow of shipments, and educating producers and handlers concerning their mutual responsibilities in marketing.

Regulation of supplies to this extent under normal marketing conditions appears reasonable when recognition is given to the place of marketing agreements in the general field of marketing. The problems of marketing are by no means confined to securing adequate regulations of supplies and prices. There are many other problems the solution of which requires the mutual understanding and cooperation of producers and handlers. From the long-time viewpoint such problems as reducing marketing costs, improving marketing organizations and services, and eliminating unfair trade practices are more fundamental than the control of shipments and prices. Marketing-agreement programs that continue to operate year after year must be considered in relation to these problems.

Marketing agreements and orders have been upheld by the courts as constituting a legal means of regulating interstate commerce for the purpose of improving returns to producers. They present a unique means of providing laws and regulations for individual industries. What direction these programs may take in the future it is difficult to foresee. In addition to continuing their present objectives, the possibility is at least suggested that eventually they may be found applicable to many other marketing problems.

Thirty Million Customers for the Surplus

by MILO PERKINS [1]

AMONG methods for making use of surplus farm products, the food-stamp plan has aroused exceptionally widespread interest and received extraordinary public support—probably because, as this article describing the plan points out, it kills at least four birds with one stone. The author also deals briefly with the school lunch-program and the new cotton-stamp plan. All of them, he says, are modest experiments toward wiping out "the black plague of the twentieth century"—underconsumption—which must be conquered if democracy is to survive.

HITHERTO we have concentrated on methods of production until we know how to produce almost anything efficiently. We do not know how to distribute the things we produce. The black plague of the twentieth century is underconsumption. It must be wiped out if democracy is to survive. It can be wiped out if we will fight it as we would a foreign enemy. If we will redirect our genius as a people to solving the problems of efficient, businesslike distribution, we can

[1] Milo Perkins is Administrator, Surplus Marketing Administration.

utilize our total resources, reach full employment in a few years, and give initiative and free enterprise a chance such as they have never had before.

The food-stamp plan is a modest effort to attack the plague of underconsumption insofar as it affects certain agricultural products. Farmers suffer from surpluses of dairy products, poultry products, fruits, vegetables, meats. To call them surpluses is merely a polite way to avoid saying that there is a shocking amount of underconsumption of many of these products. Millions of low-income people would eat more of these surpluses if they had the chance.

The stamp plan is designed to give some of them that chance. It kills four birds with one stone. (1) The farmer sells the so-called surplus through (2) the grocer, who thereby increases his business, to (3) low-income families, whose health is bettered by eating these foods; and finally (4) the Nation gains all around through partially solving an acute economic problem and lifting the standards of health at the point where they are usually lowest.

Some simple but significant arithmetic is back of the stamp plan. The average income of two-thirds of our families is $69 a month. They need twice that much for a minimum standard of living, and their unsatisfied wants make a potential market beyond the rosiest dreams of our manufacturers and farmers—a market, incidentally, that we can develop if we have enough imagination and courage. The stamp plan reaches part of the lowest fringe of this vast group. In this lowest fringe there are 30,000,000 people whose income per family averages $9 a week. Over half of them have been getting some form of public assistance. Studies show that approximately 20,000,000 people spend an average of about $1 a week per person for food at retail prices—5 cents a meal. The stamp plan enables such a person to get food worth $1.50 for each $1 expenditure. On the average, then, these low-income families will be spending 7½ cents for each meal instead of 5 cents. All of the extra 50 percent increase in food purchasing power is concentrated among the 12 or 15 foods officially designated as farm surpluses. That these extras still make for very modest meals is shown by the fact that United States Army rations cost 15 cents per man per meal at wholesale, not retail, prices.

The stamp plan does not reach all of the 20,000,000 people who get public assistance—not yet, at any rate. By the end of 1940 it will be reaching only about one-fourth of them—5,000,000 people—in some 200 communities in the United States out of the thousand or more communities that have applied for it. The aim from the beginning has been to make haste slowly and have a solid foundation of experience back of every advance. Even with only 5,000,000 consumers sharing the benefits of the plan, however, experience so far indicates that it means a new market among low-income families for over 60,000,000 pounds of butter a year, over 60,000,000 dozens of eggs, probably more than 200,000,000 pounds of pork products, and over $40,000,000 worth of fruits, vegetables, and other surplus foods. If 20,000,000 people were eligible for this form of assistance, these figures might be multiplied.

Such an advance estimate must be regarded as a rough approximation—though it is based on analyses of actual results in various communities since the stamp plan was started in Rochester, N. Y., on May 16, 1939. The amounts represented are of course small compared with the increased market for farm products that would be opened by full industrial employment and better family incomes. When a man can go off relief and get a job at good wages, he spends about 12 cents a meal instead of the 7½ cents spent by those on relief, using the stamp plan. Whenever an unemployed man gets a job, therefore, every farmer ought to shout Hallelujah! That is the real answer to many of his surplus problems.

It should be noted that the stamp plan affects mostly products for which there is an elastic demand—dairy and poultry products, meats, as well as fruits and vegetables—those a family cuts down on, or does not buy at all, when income is drastically reduced. It would not, for example, materially increase the consumption of wheat because a family with very little to spend for food will use that little to buy bread first of all.

HOW THE STAMP PLAN WORKS

Now how does the stamp plan operate?

On a voluntary basis, a person getting public assistance may buy a minimum of $1 worth of orange-colored stamps for each member of his family. He gets the stamps from the local welfare agency, and they can be exchanged for any food at any grocery store.

Those buying orange stamps receive half again as many blue stamps free. The blue stamps also are good at any grocery store but only for foods found to be "in surplus" by the Secretary of Agriculture (chiefly dairy and poultry products, meats, fruits, and vegetables).

Grocers paste the stamps, each worth 25 cents, on cards and redeem them for cash through their banks, their wholesalers, or the Surplus Marketing Administration. The orange stamps cost the Government nothing because welfare clients buy them from their own resources. Free blue stamps are redeemed from funds authorized by Congress to be used to encourage domestic consumption of agricultural products. The grocer does the buying, through regular commercial trade channels; the consumer chooses what he wants instead of having to take what is handed him. There is no price fixing or price regulation. Banks perform a public service by handling the stamps without charge.

The stamp plan is not a substitute for local relief but a supplement to it. Local units of government must sign a contract that they will not reduce relief grants on account of the program. In other words, every effort is made to see that the blue stamps actually represent increased purchasing power. Otherwise they would not carry out the double purpose of the plan—to broaden the farmer's market and to better the diets of low-income consumers.

The full effect of the stamp plan upon farm income cannot be reached until there is practically a national coverage. Studies made by the Surplus Marketing Administration and the Bureau of Home Economics show that the plan brings about an extraordinarily high per capita consumption of the commodities classed as surplus.

One of the important phases of the stamp plan approach is that it provides a mechanism for increasing sales of surplus commodities among all consumers. Increases of 30 percent to over 300 percent have been found for individual commodities. The attention focused on the surplus foods by the stamp plan seems to stimulate the trade to put greater effort into selling these products to all customers. This is in line with the intent of the program—to utilize existing economic machinery more fully and effectively by giving everyone concerned a motive for moving the surpluses.

In the long run, the nutritional effects of the program should be fully as important as the economic effects. In announcing the plan to a gathering of grocers in March 1939, Secretary of Agriculture Wallace said:

> If this plan is fully successful, it means that the day is not far distant when all of the people of the United States will be adequately nourished. Our goal might well be to use surplus foods to end vitamin deficiency in the United States. * * * Shortage of vitamins is in my opinion responsible for more sickness and lack of abounding, joyous energy in the United States than the various kinds of preventable disease. * * * Gentlemen, it may well be that you are pioneers in one of the most significant public health movements of our time.

THE SCHOOL-LUNCH PROGRAM

Providing free, nourishing lunches for undernourished school children is another method used to get surplus farm products eaten by the people who need them most. There are 9,000,000 children in low-income areas who need this kind of assistance. During the peak last spring, 3,000,000 received the lunches in 35,000 schools in more than 2,000 counties. By the end of this year the number should reach 6,000,000. It costs the taxpayers $100 a year to educate a child in the public schools. It costs the Surplus Marketing Administration about $7 a year to furnish surplus foods for lunches to a child who ought to have them if he is to be physically fit for school work. Records show that children who received the lunches gained materially in weight, were absent from school less frequently, and had fewer illnesses than before the lunches started.

In the school-lunch program, the Surplus Marketing Administration provides the surplus foods and State agencies distribute them. Nonsurplus foods, which of course are necessary to round out the lunches, are provided from local funds. The Work Projects Administration and the National Youth Administration often furnish cooks and other help and build necessary equipment. The Bureau of Home Economics helps in preparing menus. Local organizations, such as the Parent-Teacher Associations, take full responsibility for running the program. Few programs are so completely cooperative or have such wholehearted support as this one.

THE COTTON-STAMP PLAN

The cotton-stamp plan attacks domestic underconsumption on another front. It approaches the problem from a wear-the-surplus, rather than an eat-the-surplus, viewpoint. In its essential details, however, the cotton-stamp plan follows the pattern established earlier under the food-stamp plan.

Particular significance is attached to the cotton-stamp plan at this time because the war in Europe has sharply reduced our export markets. Heretofore, cotton growers in the United States have shipped about half their marketable crop into foreign consumption—some 6 million bales out of a normal annual production of about 12 million. Domestic consumption has seldom risen above 7.5 million bales. It would seem obvious, therefore, that the most sensible way to compensate, in part at least, for reduced foreign outlets is to enlarge home markets. Such is the primary objective of the cotton-stamp plan.

As in the case of food, there is a tremendous untapped market right here in our own back yard for more cotton goods among low-income groups. Evidence of that fact is underscored by these figures. Families of four, with incomes of $500 a year or less, spend only $17 a year for cotton goods. On the other hand, families of four, making $5,000 a year or more, spend $111 a year for cotton goods. Unquestionably, there exists a potential market for greatly increased domestic consumption.

Started in Memphis, Tenn., on May 7, 1940, the cotton-stamp plan was extended to only a few other cities during the next several months. In order to keep down administrative costs, we have stipulated that the plan could be established only in those places already operating the food-stamp plan. We propose to move forward very gradually until more experience has been gained.

Like the food-stamp plan, the cotton-stamp plan enjoys the enthusiastic endorsement of retail business groups. Because it operates through normal trade channels, the plan depends largely for its success on the front line support of local drygoods merchants. Their cooperation during the first experimental months foreshadows a new era of business-government cooperation in the interest of the general welfare.

The plan works simply. The Government gives eligible needy families special cotton-order stamps which can be used at retail stores in exchange for new cotton goods made of cotton produced and manufactured in the United States. For every dollar's worth bought, a dollar's worth is given free. Purchases are made in an amount approximately equal to expenditures before the inauguration of the program. Thus the plan provides for doubling former consumption of cotton goods among eligible low-income families. The stamps are redeemed by retail merchants just like food stamps.

The need for this additional cotton purchasing power is pointed up sharply in the kinds of cotton articles that have been purchased by users of cotton stamps in cities already operating the plan. They bought sensible articles—sheets, pillowcases, dresses, work pants, work shirts, and piece goods. One of the outstanding successes of the food-stamp plan was the ability of the food trades to move more than a dollar's worth of surpluses for every Government dollar spent to redeem free food stamps. If dry-goods merchants can successfully push the sale of cotton goods to families who are not getting public assistance, then the cotton-stamp plan can become one of the major ways to expand domestic consumption.

One nationally significant aspect of the cotton-stamp plan remains to be discussed briefly here. Something like 15 cents of the consumer's dollar spent for cotton goods at retail under the cotton-stamp plan gets back to the cotton farmer directly. Most of the remaining 85 cents goes to employ labor directly and indirectly in our transportation systems, in our cotton mills, in our garment factories, and in our wholesale and retail stores throughout the country. That has always been inherent in the process of distributing cotton goods. This reemployment aspect of a cotton-stamp plan is one of its very great advantages, however, particularly since it is a rather ingenius way of letting industry itself hire the unemployed all along the line. The program benefits not only farmers, but labor, business, and low-income families as well. If ever the Nation decides to expand the cotton-stamp plan to cover the country, therefore, consideration should be given to charging part of its cost to the broader goal of reaching full employment.

Barriers to Internal Trade in Farm Products

by E. L. Burtis and F. V. Waugh [1]

THE ERECTION of trade barriers that shut off normal commerce is not confined to European countries. Within the United States there are many such barriers, built on a mistaken theory of shutting out the competition of other communities, other States, other products. Many and devious are the methods here described to accomplish this end—oppressive restrictions on motortrucks, misuse of milk-inspection procedures, excise taxes on margarine, taxes on "outside" alcoholic beverages, dubious or nonuniform commodity "standards," illegitimate quarantine regulations. To correct these stifling restrictions, these authors argue that "what is required is a widespread and keen appreciation of the advantages and the importance of keeping our great national market open to all American producers, and a greater sense of responsibility and accountability to the Nation at large on the part of those who see some immediate gain for themselves in fencing off a corner of the national market and keeping their fellow citizens out of it."

[1] E. L. Burtis is Assistant Agricultural Economist and F. V. Waugh is Chief Agricultural Economist, Division of Marketing and Transportation Research, Bureau of Agricultural Economics.

THE SMOOTH and efficient flow of products from the farm to consumers is constantly interrupted by the existence of a large number of laws, ordinances, regulations, and administrative decisions that set up unnecessary restrictions on interstate trade and sometimes even on intrastate trade. These restrictive measures, formerly almost unnoticed, began to multiply after 1929.

Administrative officials in the various States, through their national organizations, were among the first to recognize the seriousness of the development. As early as 1925, the United States Live Stock Sanitary Association, national organization of the State officials in charge of animal quarantine regulations, had set up a committee on unification of laws and regulations. At its annual meeting in 1937 the National Association of Marketing Officials devoted a full day to a consideration of internal trade barriers. In November 1938 the National Association of Secretaries, Commissioners, and Directors of Agriculture passed a resolution condemning attempts to discriminate against the products of other States. At a regional conference of the Council of State Governments, held the same month, internal trade barriers were the chief subject of discussion.

A few examples of trade barriers are described in this article. A recent report made by the Bureau of Agricultural Economics and sponsored by the National Association of Secretaries, Commissioners, and Directors of Agriculture [2] cites many examples. When the whole picture is drawn in, it becomes evident that a kind of unpremeditated, partial economic warfare exists among the States of the Union.

This is a development which the Federal Constitution was specifically designed to prevent. Article 1, section 8, gives to the National Congress the power "to regulate commerce * * * among the several States"; and article 1, section 10, provides that "no State shall, without the consent of Congress, lay any duties on exports or imports except what may be absolutely necessary for its inspection laws."

As the Supreme Court said in 1824, in the case of *Gibbons* v. *Ogden*: "If there was any one object riding over every other in the adoption of the Constitution, it was to keep commercial intercourse among the States free from all invidious and partial restraints." And, indeed, one of the main purposes in calling the Constitutional Convention had been to provide an opportunity to consider ways and means of haiting the commercial wars raging between some of the Colonies.

One of these wars had been between New York and neighboring States. New York had levied high harbor entrance fees on small ships from New Jersey and Connecticut with the purpose of discouraging New Jersey and Connecticut farmers from shipping their firewood, dairy products, and garden vegetables to New York City for sale and thereby taking money out of New York State. In retaliation, New Jersey had levied a real estate tax of $1,800 a year on a small plot of ground at Sandy Hook where New York had erected a lighthouse to aid shipping in New York Harbor. In Connecticut, the merchants of New London had pledged themselves to boycott all

[2] TAYLOR, GEORGE R., BURTIS, EDGAR L., and WAUGH, FREDERICK V. BARRIERS TO INTERNAL TRADE IN FARM PRODUCTS. U. S. Dept. Agr., Bur. Agr. Econ., Spec. Rpt., 104 pp., illus. 1939.

New York goods. By 1786 almost all of the States of the northern half of the Confederation had levied import duties on each other's products, duties so high as to be protective measures. In the same year the Massachusetts Legislature had passed an act totally prohibiting the importation of some 58 articles.

A contemporary leader speaking before the Massachusetts Legislature [3] to urge ratification of the Constitution described the existing situation as follows:

> As to commerce, it is well known that the different States now pursue different systems of duties with regard to each other. By this and for want of general laws of prohibition through the Union we have not secured even our own domestic traffic that passes from State to State.

The adoption of the Constitution by the Colonies did, in large measure, "secure domestic traffic." As the United States expanded in area and grew in population during the following decades, it became one of the largest and most populous free-trade areas in the world. When all parts of the country were bound together with a network of rails in the latter half of the nineteenth century, producers of many commodities and articles found that they could reach a large part of the population of the Nation at prices the people could afford to pay. This mass market has made possible the phenomenal development of mass production in industry, mass distribution in merchandising, and specialized areas of production in agriculture.

Without an enormous market, easily and freely accessible, the great intensely specialized citrus-growing areas of California, Florida, and Texas—to mention a single example—could not have developed, and consumers in northern cities would not enjoy such ample supplies of oranges and grapefruit at such low prices. Even potatoes, which are raised almost everywhere, are heavily concentrated in about a dozen areas, such as Aroostook County, Maine, Long Island, N. Y., and the Eastern Shore of Virginia. Without a wide national market the Corn Belt, the Wheat Belt, the Cotton Belt, and the great cattle ranges of the West would not have developed, although a readily available foreign market also contributed to their growth. It is apparent how closely both the prosperity of American agriculture and the well-being of our great city populations are bound up with the maintenance of the Nation-wide market that is made possible by free internal trade.

MOTIVES FOR RESTRICTIONS

Why, then, have restrictions on trade been imposed—restrictions so numerous and severe that they seriously threaten free trade within the United States?

An urge to protect local industries and local producers is always present. The ills at home are easily seen and keenly felt, while those farther away are harder to appreciate. It is a natural thing, therefore, to try to aid home industries even if the action taken is detrimental to others. When the depression set in, this perennial tendency was powerfully reinforced by the acute distress of many groups of agricultural producers. American agriculture had already felt the pinch of narrowing foreign markets, and when purchasing power

[3] Dawes, in the Independent Chronicle and Universal Advertiser, Boston, January 31, 1788.

slacked off so rapidly at home, farmers were under great impulsion to hold as much as possible of what was left of their markets and to protect themselves against encroachments by their competitors. Farmers appealed to their legislatures and to their State and local officials, and many protective laws and regulations resulted.

At about the same time, the motortruck and the merchant trucker became major factors in the transportation and marketing of farm products. They upset old patterns of marketing; and although often offering higher prices to some farmers than other agencies of transportation and marketing, they exposed other farmers to unwonted competition, perhaps bringing competing products into areas not so well or so cheaply served by rail. Merchant truckers, in particular, often "went around" established middlemen at both the country and the city ends of their hauls. This situation added to the incentive of some farmers and middlemen to protect themselves against competition.

It must be recognized, nevertheless, that the protectionist motive is not the only factor that has been responsible for the erection of trade barriers. Contributing factors have been the reluctance of States to forego sources of revenue and a simple lack of coordination among States in their efforts to regulate, resulting in nonuniformity of requirements from State to State.

In much of the legislation designed to protect in-State producers, the constitutional provision giving Congress the power to regulate interstate commerce has been circumvented by disguising restrictions upon interstate trade as revenue measures, measures for the protection of public health or safety, or measures for the prevention of the spread of plant and animal diseases. Also, in some fields Congress has not exercised its constitutional power to regulate interstate commerce. In the absence of regulation by Congress, the courts have ruled that the several States may (within limits) exercise control over interstate commerce.

DISADVANTAGES OF EXCLUSION COUNTERACT BENEFITS

Most trade barriers have been promoted by local groups of producers with the motive of keeping as much of the local markets as possible for themselves by preventing or hindering the sale of competing products produced in other States. This policy may, of course, raise prices at least temporarily in the local markets and give the local producer a kind of monopoly advantage. Nevertheless, agricultural producers are harmed in two ways by these market-exclusion practices. (1) Although they may be able to get some measure of protection on their local markets, they are harmed by similar measures in outside markets to which they might want to ship their surpluses. (2) The monopolistic advantages gained by market exclusion are likely to be short-lived.

When a local group of dairymen succeeds in establishing unnecessarily high and complex inspection requirements on milk, they not only shut out some of the supply which might compete with them, but they also raise their own costs of production. Moreover, by excluding outside milk and cream they add to the national surplus of cream and butter, which tends to demoralize the butter market.

Since the prices of dairy products all tend to be based on butter prices, this situation is not a healthy one for the dairy industry.

Let us take another example—that of a dairy State which imposes a prohibitive tax on margarine. This is intended, of course, to benefit the local dairymen. Yet it is a question whether Wisconsin dairymen have been benefited or hurt by the margarine tax of 15 cents a pound in that State. It is true that the tax has been almost completely effective in stopping the sale of margarine in the State of Wisconsin. This probably means that a little more butter is sold in that State; but the price of butter in Wisconsin, of course, is determined by what the national market will pay for it. Probably the margarine tax has had no significant effect on butter prices. Moreover, the tax in that State has led to a great deal of resentment in the South, and although there has not yet been any official boycott of Wisconsin products, it is quite apparent that the present situation does not help Wisconsin producers to find markets in the South. Many more examples could be given, but perhaps these are typical.

When exclusion of outside products leads to retaliation, the local producer is more likely to be harmed than helped. It is clear that in the long run agriculture would be better off with free and open markets throughout the country.

TYPES OF RESTRICTIONS

What are the restrictions and regulations that most seriously hamper trade in farm products? They are most numerous and most serious in the following fields: (1) Regulation of motortrucks and merchant truckers, (2) regulation of the marketing of dairy products, (3) margarine taxes and regulations, (4) taxation on and regulation of the sale of alcoholic beverages, (5) grading, labeling, and standardization measures, and (6) plant and animal quarantines.

Regulation of Motortrucks and Merchant Truckers

Some States, among them Massachusetts, New York, California, and Ohio, permit motortrucks owned by nonresidents to enter the State without payment of any fees so long as they do not engage in intrastate business within the State, this arrangement usually being contingent upon reciprocity of treatment. Such freedom of interstate movement, however, is not typical of the country as a whole. There are a few States that will not allow an out-of-State motortruck to come in even for a single or occasional trip without purchasing a State license tag or without paying a ton-mileage tax higher than that charged in-State trucks. Most States place similar but less extreme restrictions on out-of-State trucks. It is plain that requirements like these must necessarily discourage interstate movement by motortruck.

Another serious impediment to interstate movement of goods by truck is the great variation among the States in requirements as to the width, length, and weight of trucks and as to the safety appliances they must carry. Two examples might be cited. Kentucky and Tennessee allow a maximum gross weight of only 18,000 pounds, and Kentucky will not permit a motortruck to use the roads if it exceeds 30 feet in length. These limits prevent any but the lightest trucks from crossing two States which stretch from the Mississippi River to the crests of the Alleghenies, and hence constitute a serious barrier to transportation by trucks between States north of the Ohio River and States to the south. A South Carolina law that was enacted in 1933, but was never enforced and was repealed in 1938, would have limited the width of motortrucks to 90 inches, 6 inches less than the standard width, and their gross weight to 20,000 pounds. This law would have set up a very serious barrier to the movement of citrus and other produce north from Florida, and out of North Carolina southward. Together with the Tennessee and Kentucky laws, it would have stretched a barrier from the Mississippi River to the Atlantic Ocean interfering with north-south truck movement.

The merchant trucker—the trucker who buys goods in one locality, carries them to another, and there sells them—is especially likely to be affected by the requirement of having to purchase a license plate for his truck even for occasional visits to a State. In many States he is also required to take out a license to do business as a merchant trucker. The fee charged for such a license ranges from $10 annually in Iowa, for a light truck, to $100 annually in Montana and $300 annually in each county in Idaho and Washington in which the trucker wishes to do business.

High fees charged merchant truckers are not in themselves restrictive to interstate trade, except in cases where a trucker might wish to do business in two States having them. However, most legislation of this kind, by exempting from its scope farmers carrying produce grown on their own farms, has the effect of favoring producers close to a consuming market at the expense of those located farther away. This is true because only farmers close to the market, say within 20 or 30 miles, can economically haul their own produce to market. Those farther away must get someone to do the hauling and merchandising for them.

In passing, it may be noted that railroad freight rates have a profound effect on the movement of goods. Differences exist in the level and structure of rates in different parts of the country, and these differences have been the cause of many controversies. For example, the rates that apply in the southern territory (the Southern States lying east of the Mississippi River) are materially higher, generally speaking, than those in the eastern or "official" territory (the Northern States east of the Mississippi River). An intermediate level of rates has been established for shipments between the two regions. Therefore, it is typically more expensive to ship from one point to another in southern territory than to ship an equal distance from a point in eastern territory to one in southern territory, and more expensive to ship from a point in southern territory to a point in eastern territory than to ship the same distance between two points in eastern territory. Whether this or any other specific set-up of rates can properly be regarded as a trade barrier, unfairly hindering the movement of goods into or out of a particular area, is a question that can be answered only after general agreement has been reached as to what are correct economic principles in the setting of transportation rates. Any conceivable set of rates must necessarily be unfavorable in comparison with some other set of rates to some groups of producers.

223761°—40——43

A set of principles of rate making, generally agreed upon, is indispensable to the impartial appraisal of a rate situation.

Regulation of the Marketing of Dairy Products

The importance of a safe milk supply is well known and unquestioned. To insure that it will be safe most towns and cities, and in some cases the State authorities, inspect the farms where the milk is produced. The usual procedure is to permit only milk from farms that have been inspected and approved to enter the city or town or the State, as the case may be.

There can be no question of the necessity of making sure that milk is germ-free and healthful. But by refusing to inspect the farms of all producers who desire inspection, or by charging a high fee for such inspection, the authorities in charge of inspection can exclude healthful milk. For example, Haverhill, Mass., will not accept milk shipped in from a distance of more than 40 miles. Walpole, Mass., places the limit at 30 miles, and North Attleboro at 8. Similarly, New York City will not send inspectors west of Pennsylvania. While it probably would not be profitable to ship milk from Ohio to New York City, western cream is kept out of the New York City market by this action.

There is a real opportunity to remove the barriers to interstate trade in milk and cream and other dairy products by devising a system under which each State and each municipality will accept inspection by accredited inspectors located in other States.

Margarine Taxes

Prior to 1929 several unsuccessful attempts had been made by dairy States to discourage the consumption of margarine. In the years from 1885 to 1897, five States had enacted laws requiring margarine to be colored pink. These laws had become inoperative, however, when the United States Supreme Court declared the New Hampshire law void. In the 1920's three States had passed legislation prohibiting the sale of butter substitutes in which milk or cream had been combined with edible oils. (Some milk or cream is necessary if the substitute is to be palatable.) But these laws had been defeated by popular referendum in two of the States, and in the third the State supreme court had granted a permanent injunction against enforcement of the law.

Then in 1929, Utah placed an excise tax on margarine. In 1931 10 other States followed suit, and by 1939 half the States in the Union were taxing the sale of margarine. These taxes have been upheld by the Supreme Court of the United States as legitimate revenue measures. Three States now impose a tax of 15 cents a pound; 1, a tax of 12 cents; 17, a tax of 10 cents; and 3, a tax of 5 cents.

There are no statistics of the consumption of margarine by States, but a rough indication of the effect of the margarine taxes on consumption is given by a comparison of the figures on the number of retailers federally licensed to sell uncolored margarine in 1929 with the same figures for 1935. If the figures for the States taxing uncolored margarine are examined, it will be found that in those levying a tax of 5 cents a pound the number of retailers licensed to sell uncolored margarine dropped 52 percent between 1929 and 1935; in those with a tax of 10 cents a pound, 91 percent; and in those with a tax of 15 cents a pound, 99 percent. In comparison, there was a 10-percent increase in the States that have no excise taxes on uncolored margarine.

In the face of these figures, it is hard to doubt that the excise taxes on margarine effectively discourage consumption.

Probably no other measure that limits interstate trade has aroused so much resentment and active opposition as margarine taxes. Cottonseed oil is an important ingredient in the manufacture of margarine, and cottonseed is an important source of cash income to southern farmers. Cotton farmers regard margarine taxes as an attack on their legitimate markets. They have threatened to impose retaliatory taxes on Wisconsin dairy products and other Wisconsin products. For example, the last session of the Arkansas Legislature considered a bill that would have imposed a 25-percent sales tax on milk, cream, butter, and apples grown in Wisconsin and three other States that have margarine taxes.

Perhaps the worst danger in margarine taxes is the possibility that their example will spread to other commodities. Having granted protection against outside competition to one industry, a State may soon find itself under considerable pressure to grant similar favors to other industries. If excise taxes may be used against margarine, why not also against other commodities that compete with State industries?

Here, indeed, would be a revival of the interstate tariffs that the framers of the Constitution were so anxious to eliminate from our national life.

Regulation of the Sale of Alcoholic Beverages

Commerce between the States in alcoholic beverages is not subject to regulation by Congress. "Since the Twenty-First Amendment," said the Supreme Court in a decision handed down early in 1939, "the right of a State to prohibit or regulate the importation of intoxicating liquor is not limited by the commerce clause."

Many States have moved quickly to turn this exemption to the advantage of their own brewing and distilling industries. Some have imposed heavier license fees on wholesalers or retailers who sell alcoholic beverages produced outside the State than on those who sell only home liquors. Some have imposed special sales taxes or "inspection fees" on out-of-State liquor, in addition to those imposed on liquor produced in the home State.

Agriculture has been directly affected by efforts of several States, in their regulation or taxation of the sale of liquor, to give their own farmers an advantage over other farmers. For example, Arkansas, Georgia, Michigan, and New Mexico place a higher sales tax on out-of-State than on domestic wines. Maine taxes materials produced outside the State but used by State wineries. North Carolina limits the sale of wine to the native product. Iowa, Minnesota, and Wisconsin require beer to be made from 66⅔ percent or more of barley malt. Presumably the purpose is to discourage the use of substitutes for barley, particularly brewers' rice.

Grading, Labeling, and Standardization Measures

Nonuniformity of specifications and requirements forms perhaps the most serious hindrance to interstate trade, as far as State grading and labeling laws and State standards are concerned. Hardly less serious, however, is the deliberate choice of specifications and requirements designed to place out-of-State products at a disadvantage when sold in competition with home-State products.

Nonuniformity among the States in grades, standards, or labeling requirements does not hamper interstate trade as long as they are not made compulsory. But nonuniform compulsory State requirements obviously are a potential source of countless annoyances and hindrances.

For example, one Western State has promulgated compulsory grades for fruits and vegetables which are based on United States grades but differ in some particulars. This State refuses to accept certificates of inspection issued by the Federal-State inspection service and insists on making its own inspection of all fruits and vegetables coming into the State by truck, charging a fee for the inspection. Another Western State does the same thing, except that it does not charge an inspection fee. Many shipments of apples arriving from Washington by truck have had to be regraded and repacked at the California border because the Washington and California grades are not uniform.

A ludicrous but unhappy situation was created when Oregon made its berry-box standards compulsory for shipments out of the State, and California declared such boxes illegal within its borders.

Two examples will show how specifications or requirements may be chosen with an intent to place out-of-State produce at a disadvantage. Formerly some of the Southeastern States required eggs to be classified as "Cold Storage," "Shipped," or "Fresh." Cold storage eggs were those that had been in cold storage; shipped eggs, those that had not been in cold storage but had been shipped in from outside the State; and fresh eggs, those produced in the home State that had not been in cold storage and that were not "partially or wholly decomposed." Labeling so patently misleading could hardly fail to defeat its own purpose, but the purpose was plain: to prejudice consumers against out-of-State eggs.

In Rhode Island the specifications are so drawn that eggs produced in other States cannot qualify for the topmost grade. There are three grades of eggs in Rhode Island: "Rhode Island Specials," "Fresh eggs," and just eggs. Only eggs meeting the strictest quality tests can qualify as Rhode Island Specials. But this is not enough. They also must have been produced in Rhode Island. No out-of-State egg, no matter how fresh, can be a Rhode Island Special. It is true that the State regulations do not prohibit the sale of eggs graded in accordance with the Federal grades, under which eggs of the same quality as Rhode Island Specials but laid outside the State could be sold as U. S. Specials. But Federal egg grades are not in common use in Rhode Island. Rather, the State bureau of markets actively promotes the Rhode Island grading system.

Nonuniformity is an ill that can be solved by consultation and cooperation among the States. Failing this, Congress can exercise its power to regulate commerce between the States by providing for Federal grades to be used in interstate commerce in fruits and vegetables and other farm products not now covered by such legislation.

Plant and Animal Quarantines

Agricultural quarantines are indispensable to American agriculture. They have proved themselves again and again an effective means of preventing the spread of pests and diseases, and in many cases they have been a necessary part of successful efforts to completely eliminate pests and diseases from the United States.

Quarantines used for these purposes are legitimate and desirable, but there are a few quarantines that appear to be used for economic reasons—to protect in-State producers against competition—rather than to prevent the spread of a disease or pest.

Nonuniformity is another defect in some State quarantine regulations that tends to hamper interstate trade. Nonuniformity was perhaps to be expected when the States first undertook to protect themselves against threats of new pests and diseases. However, it is too serious a handicap to internal trade to be allowed to continue when uniform regulations can be just as effective, if not more so, in preventing the spread of pests and diseases.

A good beginning has already been made by the four Regional Plant Boards and the National Plant Board toward removing the defects present in some of the State quarantine regulations. These boards, consisting of State enforcement officials, meet periodically to review the regulations in force in the States represented. After a discussion of the factors involved, both from the point of view of the State imposing a regulation and from that of the other States affected, the boards often go on record as approving the regulation, recommending that it be rescinded, or recommending that it be amended in a certain way. The recommendations of the boards are nearly always followed, and as a result a great deal of progress has already been made toward achieving more uniformity among the State regulations and toward eliminating measures that are not well justified as means of controlling pests and diseases.

POSSIBILITIES FOR REMOVAL OF BARRIERS

How can the barriers to internal trade be removed? In the foregoing discussion a few suggestions have been made with respect to particular fields. In general, there seem to be three possible means: (1) Action by the courts, (2) action by the States, and (3) action by the Federal Government.

Not all of the legislation under which barriers to internal trade have been established has been reviewed by the courts. It may be expected that some of it will be found unconstitutional. But much restrictive legislation has already been reviewed by the Supreme Court, and some of it has been approved. Some of the margarine excise taxes have run the gauntlet of the courts, even taxes so high that they produce virtually no revenue. The Court has ruled that the States are not bound by the commerce clause in regulating and taxing alcoholic beverages. The Court is not always guided by the economic effects of a measure in deciding whether or not in law it is an interference with the powers of Congress to regulate commerce between the States.

In brief, it is too much to expect that the Constitution will work automatically—that as soon as an unwise law, detrimental to interstate commerce, is passed, the courts will declare it void. What is required is a widespread and keen appreciation of the advantages and the importance of keeping our great national market open to all American producers and a greater sense of responsibility and accountability to the Nation at large on the part of those who see some immediate gain for themselves in fencing off a corner of the national market and keeping their fellow citizens out of it. We can hardly hope to keep our Federal system intact unless the various producer interests in each State accept the responsibility that is theirs not to urge upon their legislatures laws that are injurious to the Nation as a whole or in contravention of the principles which have made it great, merely in order to snatch some quick and probably temporary advantage over competing producers in other States.

The chief responsibility for keeping internal trade in the United States free rests primarily, then, not on the courts but on the legislatures and administrative officials as representatives of the people.

There is room for considerable difference of opinion as to whether the Federal Government or the State governments should take the lead in getting rid of our present interstate trade barriers. But it would seem to be common sense that the problem is one needing cooperative action by both. There are some barriers, such as margarine taxes, that the States alone have the power to attack. Then there are some barriers that arise out of the difficulty that 48 different governments are bound to have in keeping together on a coordinated program. Problems of nonuniformity are of this nature, and it may be that some Federal legislation may be needed to assist in the solution of problems of this kind. Action by the Federal Government, however, should be taken as part of a general program in which the States are collaborating. Many problems of nonuniformity can be solved by closer consultation and collaboration among State enforcement officials. The example of the Regional and National Plant Boards, whose activities are described above, would seem to be an excellent one to copy in other fields.

Many organizations of State officials have concerned themselves with internal trade barriers and are anxious to help remove them. The National Association of Directors, Secretaries, and Commissioners of Agriculture, the National Association of Marketing Officials, and the Governors' Conference have all gone on record as being opposed to trade barriers. The Council of State Governments, which officially represents 44 States, is holding a series of important conferences to consider the problem. With such full support of the States and with whatever assistance the Federal Government can render, the attack on internal trade barriers may confidently be expected to succeed.

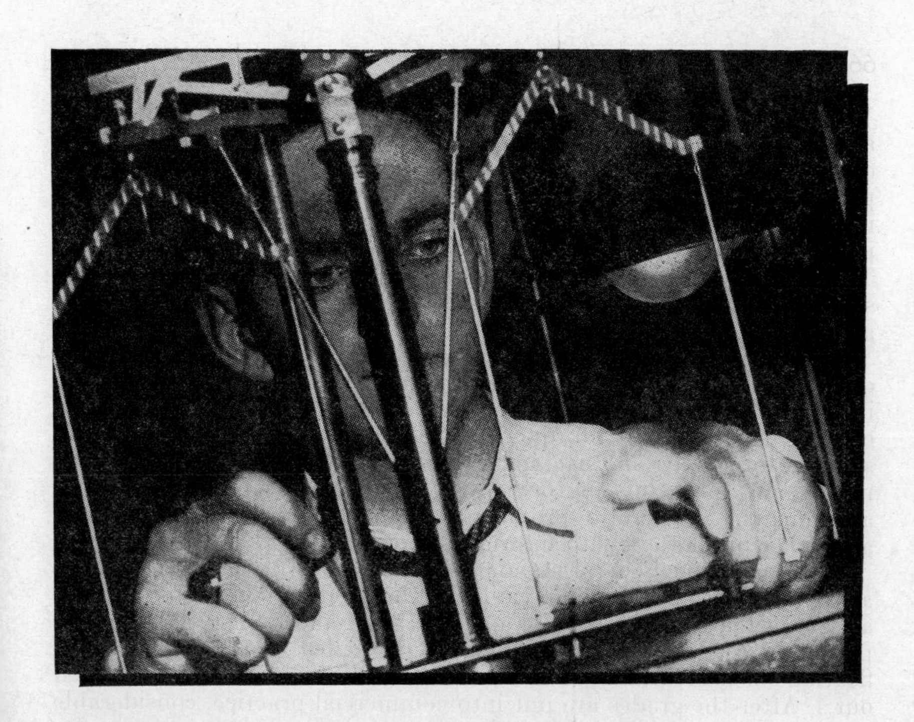

Standardization and Inspection of Farm Products

by C. W. KITCHEN [1]

STANDARDIZATION is essentially an aid to orderly marketing and efficient buying and selling. It reduces confusion, waste, and chicanery. Since the widest possible uniformity is the first objective in standardization work with farm products, the lead in this work is taken by the Federal Government. This article describes the whole process in a nutshell, discussing the historical background, the basic principles involved, the procedure followed with various products, the limitations and problems, and the need for continued research and education if the work is to have its full potential usefulness.

STANDARDIZATION and inspection of farm products trace from the desire and need of producers, dealers, and consumers for a uniform "yardstick" with which to measure important variations in quality. The producer is interested in getting the price to which the quality of his product and the condition of the market entitle him. The processor and distributor need a quality gage to facilitate buying and selling, particularly at long distances. The consumer wants assurance that he is obtaining a product of a quality in line with the price paid.

[1] C. W. Kitchen is Chief of the Agricultural Marketing Service.

These needs and wishes, translated into group and legislative action, have resulted in the development of United States standards of quality for nearly all of the important agricultural commodities produced in this country. For some commodities the standards are mandatory, that is, no other standards may be used lawfully if the product is sold by grade and shipped in interstate or foreign commerce. This is true for grain and for cotton. For other farm products the standards are permissive—in most instances these are used voluntarily as quality guides in buying and selling.

As a means of describing variations in quality and condition, the official standards, whether of the mandatory or permissive type, are important in the marketing process. They provide a basis for merchandising contracts, for quoting prices, for loans on products in storage, for sorting and packing by producers to meet market requirements, and for regulating or controlling shipments under marketing agreements. They also provide a means of furnishing consumers and other purchasers with information on quality.

In formulating Federal standards, the various factors that may in any way affect the economic value or relative desirability of a product are subjected to careful study and appraisal, and their gradations are placed in certain definite quality groups called grades. The specifications or descriptions of these separate grades are carefully worked out. After the grades are put into commercial practice, considerable time may elapse and numerous changes may be made before the grades are adopted as the official standards. The standardization program for a commodity remains flexible in the sense that the standards may be revised from time to time to meet significant long-time changes in the character of the product, in marketing practices, and in technological progress.

Establishing descriptive standards for products produced by nature is more complicated than establishing standards of weights and measures, inasmuch as the former involves many relatively intangible factors that are not easily determinable. But if such standards are to be practical, they must be reasonably specific and uniformly interpreted. Furthermore, unlike standards of weights and measures which are definite in their terms, descriptive standards require interpretation and the exercise of independent judgment. Consequently, any program of such standardization, to be effective in commercial practice, must be accompanied by competent and unbiased inspection.

With the marketing of farm products now largely on a national basis, local or State standards and local or exclusively State inspection agencies cannot provide the degree of uniformity needed for transactions in interstate and foreign commerce. Therefore, if uniform standards are to be established, they must be developed and maintained by a recognized agency in position to consider the problem from a national point of view. An agency of the Federal Government, operating in close cooperation with State agencies and other interested groups, can best perform these services.

ORIGIN OF STANDARDS

Standards for identifying and describing farm products according to quality are the result of a process of evolution. They have developed with the commercialization of American agriculture.

During the early days of American agriculture, when most farms were self-sufficient units and marketing was largely a local function, there was no great need for standards. But even then, when certain farm commodities moved in commercial channels, the buyer and producer used some form of standardization, as E. E. Edwards points out in an article elsewhere in this volume (p. 171).

This early period, however, was a time when farmers in this country produced mainly for home consumption. Their surpluses were bartered for articles needed or were sold to nearby merchants, and questions of quality and price were argued between them. As settlement increased in the great grain-producing areas of the Middle West and as vast quantities of grain began moving long distances to centers of consumption and to foreign ports, marketing problems arose that had not existed in the earlier days. These problems, common also to the marketing of other farm commodities, centered around the difficulty of buyer and seller, a thousand miles apart, in achieving a meeting of minds on questions of quality and price. Grain was bargained for by buyers far removed from the wheatfields, and because of wide differences in the quality of grain a common language for trading purposes became necessary.

Early Standards for Grain

In those early days, grain was sold by sample or by personal inspection. If it was not possible to submit samples or for the buyer to inspect the grain personally, the dealer made a statement or filled out a certificate as to the general quality or condition of the grain offered for sale. But as the volume of trading increased, this practice became too cumbersome and generally unsatisfactory.

To remedy this situation trade organizations, chambers of commerce, and boards of trade adopted systems of grading grain. They employed grain inspectors for grading carload lots upon arrival in the principal markets. Later grading and inspection were undertaken by several State governments.

But the grading rules under which inspectors worked in those early days differed in many important respects, depending upon the agency issuing them. Each market had its own grades and methods of interpreting grades. Sometimes the certificate of grade issued in one market was not recognized in another. Some standards, for example, required that No. 2 corn be dry, others reasonably dry; one would require not more than 16 percent of moisture, another perhaps not more than 15.5 percent; some one weight per bushel, some another. No. 3 oats were described under more than 30 different sets of specifications, and the test-weight requirements for this grade ranged from 22 to 29 pounds per bushel. A study of the phraseology of the grain trade in 1906 disclosed 338 names or grade titles: 133 for wheat, 63 for corn, 77 for oats, 53 for barley, 10 for rye, and 1 each for "no grade" and "no established grade."

The confusion of grades was only one element in the chaotic condition of the grain trade. Other abuses grew out of the situation. Growers were systematically defrauded by short weighing and undergrading. Shipments of good-quality wheat could easily be mixed with cheaper grain. When the grower sent his grain to market he had little idea what grade designation if any would be assigned to it. Likewise the buyer could not be sure what quality he would receive. Furthermore, many buyers had little or no confidence in the inspection certificates issued at some markets.

This loose and unregulated system of grading imposed many hazards on the various elements of the grain trade. Traders took wide margins of profit wherever possible in order to protect themselves against these hazards. Farmers naturally suffered, since these tolls cut down their returns.

The confusion arising from a lack of uniform standards was increased by the lack of uniformity in the application of such grades as were in use. The situation became well-nigh intolerable. As a result, producer groups, grain-dealer associations, and others began to consider ways and means for bringing about uniformity and confidence in grades and in inspection methods. To some extent these efforts were successful. It was found impossible, however, to maintain uniformity, for there was no accepted authority to enforce rules or to compel the use of the same standards in all markets.

Cotton Standards Old Yet New

Much the same situation existed at first in trading in cotton. True, standards were adopted early. The term "middling"—the basic grade for the modern system of standardization—was apparently in use in England at the turn of the nineteenth century. Such terms as "good," "fair," and "ordinary" were in general use in New Orleans by 1825, when Andrew Jackson and his Tennessee neighbors were shipping cotton down the Mississippi River.

The meaning of grade terms, however, caused much confusion, inasmuch as no specific standards were established. The result was an unintelligible set of price quotations and frequent and costly arbitrations. Efforts were made later to set up a unified system, and in 1874 most of the exchanges adopted the standard American classification. But this classification was discontinued after a few years, and the disorder in quality designation was as great as ever. During this period, however, and in the decade after 1900—a period of general disorder in cotton marketing—public sentiment was shaping itself for legislation, first for permissive and later for mandatory Federal standards for American cotton. The need for uniformity was expressed by producers and domestic spinners as well as by cotton merchants and exporters.

Federal Legislation Provided Uniform Standards

The situation in the grain and cotton markets paralleled that existing with respect to many other farm products. Conditions naturally varied with the peculiarities of the product, but in general lack of uniform and adequate standards resulted in the same sort of confusion in marketing fruits and vegetables, tobacco, livestock, and dairy and poultry products. The failure of attempts to correct the situation through a multiplicity of private, semiprivate, and State standards and the unnecessary expense and waste were important in crystallizing public opinion on the necessity for Federal standards.

In 1907 the need for Federal standards was recognized by Congress in appropriations of funds granted for the Department of Agriculture to study Federal standardization. The studies were rapidly initiated. Later, the demand for Federal standards was closely coupled with the operation of certain federally administered regulatory and service functions. And during the World War the demand for food conservation and the elimination of waste provided a substantial impetus to the movement. Gradually a degree of order emerged out of the chaos existent for so many years in the marketing of farm products.

The passage of the Cotton Futures Act in 1914 (reenacted in 1916), which requires the use of Federal standards in trading in cotton futures, definitely established the Department of Agriculture in standardization work. The Grain Standards Act of 1916, which followed, requires the use of Federal standards when grain is sold by grade in interstate commerce. The United States Warehouse Act, also passed in 1916, requires that Federal grades, if they exist, be shown on warehouse receipts except when storers of products request their omission.

The Food Products Act of 1917, a war-emergency measure for conserving food supplies, provided authority for the establishment of standards and for a permissive inspection service on fruits and vegetables as well as on other products. The Cotton Standards Act of 1923 provided for the compulsory use of the official cotton standards of the United States in all interstate and export transactions based on standard descriptions (fig. 1). In 1929 the Tobacco Stocks and Standards Act was passed, authorizing the Secretary of Agriculture to establish standards for the classification of tobacco

Figure 1.—Making up the United States official standards for cotton. The standards are used in all countries trading in American cotton.

for stocks reports. And the Tobacco Inspection Act of 1935 provided for mandatory and free inspection at designated auction markets.

These various statutes, together with the authority carried annually in the Agricultural Appropriation Act to formulate standards for farm products and to inspect and certify their quality and condition, provide the groundwork for the Department's standardization, grading, and inspection work as now conducted by the Agricultural Marketing Service. Under the authority contained in this legislation the Department has developed standards of quality for most of the important agricultural commodities and has established various types of inspection and supervision to insure their uniform application throughout the country.

STANDARDIZATION WORK OF THE DEPARTMENT

Establishing national standards, especially of the permissive type, and having them generally accepted in merchandising practice are problems that comprehend more than a determination of a logical and scientific scheme of classification. Neither the mandatory nor the permissive standards thus far developed by the United States Department of Agriculture,[2] nor the two combined, necessarily represent a complete program of quality standardization for all agricultural products. The mandatory standards are limited to those quality and condition factors that are readily determinable in commercial practice. In the permissive standards, it has been necessary to make rather broad classifications in many instances, to be refined as experience in actual use indicates a need and as rapidly as further refinements will be accepted for merchandising purposes.

The individual grades have been based on the results of Department research and after consultation with various groups in the industry concerned. The Agricultural Marketing Service ascertains facts concerning varied conditions and practices throughout the producing areas and in both domestic and foreign trade, and assists wherever possible in harmonizing divergent views of competing areas and interests.

Official grades promulgated or formally recommended by the Department have been subjected to extensive tests and study to determine their practicability under actual commercial conditions. When the demand for grades for immediate use has been such that this procedure could not be followed, the Department has, on occasion, issued in tentative form descriptions of grades which, although based on the best available information, had not been tried out in actual use.

Basic Principles Followed

The work in developing Federal standards has been based on certain

[2] A mandatory standard may be defined as an official standard the use of which is compulsory in the conditions specified by the law under which that standard is promulgated; for instance, the official grain standards of the United States for wheat are compulsory for such grain when shipped by grade in interstate commerce, according to the United States Grain Standards Act. A permissive standard may be defined as a standard which has been worked out and recommended officially for optional use. Permissive standards are used by the Department in such lines of work as inspection and market news. They are often adopted by States as mandatory under certain conditions. A tentative standard as here used may be defined as a standard that is offered by the Department for use under commercial conditions to test its practicability or as a basis for discussion. It is still subject to further study and investigation before being officially recommended. Such a tentative standard may later become either a permissive or a mandatory standard, according to circumstances.

broad principles that have come to be recognized as fundamental. One of these is that a standard must recognize significant gradations in quality of the entire supply of a commodity. Consequently, standards must be applicable to all segments of the supply in order to afford a basis for trading in all qualities of the product.

In general, grades are defined in such a way as to recognize commercial distinctions, so that the highest grade in a set of standards represents those quality characteristics and degrees of condition that are most wanted and that command the highest prices in the market. Lower grades include characteristics of quality that are usually found in inferior portions of the supply of a particular product. Merchandising preferences are usually based directly or indirectly on utility or on what is sometimes called intrinsic value or use value. The uses to which farm commodities may be put vary a great deal. They include food for human consumption, feed for livestock, and raw materials for manufacture. The wide variety of alternative uses for many of our farm commodities naturally presents an extremely complicated situation in the setting up of quality classifications based on utility values of the commodity.

A grade in a set of standards specifies, in most cases, the lower limits of quality permissible within the grade and may prescribe both upper and lower limits. The limits for a practical grade must be broad enough to avoid unnecessary technicalities and must conform to some extent to trade acceptance. As a result there may be some difference in merchandising value between products near the bottom of the grade and those that fully meet the average of the grade or reach its top limits. The extent to which a standard reflects the relative value of the product depends on the completeness with which it deals with the various factors influencing quality, on the range of quality permitted in any one grade, and on the merchandising practices followed.

There are, however, various interrelated supply-and-demand forces that affect not only the level of prices at which all grades of farm commodities may be sold, but also the prices received for any particular grade or quality classification. Consequently, premiums or discounts for certain classifications may be based as much or more on the prevailing opinion of the supply of those grades in relation to the demand for them as on the variation in quality between grades.

Inspection and Supervision

In evaluating a product for growers, processors, manufacturers, or consumers, standards must be uniform within reasonable limits throughout the country. Federal standards, being national in scope, cannot vary from region to region or from market to market. Neither can they be changed from season to season to conform to the quality of the crop produced during a particular season. The standards, therefore, cover the chief quality characteristics common to products grown in all major regions of the country. They may not always reflect special quality factors peculiar to products in limited areas, unless the differences in varieties, types, and strains of the product are so marked as to differentiate them as separate classes of the same product.

Standards of description, however, are uniform in reality only to the extent that they are interpreted accurately and applied consistently.

This necessitates that only competent inspectors be licensed to apply the standards and that these inspectors be centrally trained and supervised. For this reason, a carefully supervised system of inspection by persons particularly qualified for this work is maintained.

Best Test of Standards Is Their Use

The best test of the practicability of permissive standards is the use that is made of them. The Federal standards have not as yet completely established themselves in all branches of marketing farm products, but their use is rapidly being extended and increased. As the standardization program of the Department of Agriculture has been in progress for only about 25 years and as most of the standards are of a permissive character and their use is wholly voluntary, their widespread acceptance has been a real achievement.

Only a few years ago the use of the standards was limited almost entirely to facilitating the movement of commodities in wholesale channels of trade. Now the standards are being applied rather generally to the sale of small lots by farmers directly to consumers and to purchases in retail stores.

Though the inspection and grading of small lots is expensive and often does not justify the cost, farmers who sell in this manner usually are affected indirectly by the grading system. The price they receive depends partly on the quality of products produced in their community as shown by grading records. The Agricultural Marketing Service, therefore, is endeavoring to develop grading methods that are inexpensive and that can be applied to small lots. As a result, an increasing number of farmers now sell their products according to grade.

Retail and consumer organizations are showing a marked interest in standardized grades. In 1938 approximately 320 million pounds of butter was officially graded, more than 85 million pounds of which was sold in consumer packages each containing a certificate of quality showing the purchaser the score or grade of the butter and the date on which the grade was determined. Nearly 720 million pounds of meat (most of it fresh beef) was graded by the Department, and the carcasses were so stamped that retail cuts showed the grade designation for the information of consumers (fig. 2). At present, permissive grades especially adapted for retail or consumer use have also been developed for eggs (fig. 3), dressed turkeys (fig. 4), rice, dry beans, and the more important canned fruits and vegetables.

In addition to providing a common language for buyers and sellers of farm products, Federal standards have been useful in many of the marketing functions. Standard grades are, of course, the basis of Nation-wide market reporting. Without uniformly applied standards and an understanding of them, efficient market reporting and an intelligent interpretation of market reports would not be possible. The standards have been an important factor in the gradual elimination of a "flat price" inspection of quality from our marketing system; and, together with the market news work, the standards have been instrumental in equalizing prices by grades between markets. Marketing risks that formerly caused wide price spreads have, to a large extent, been reduced or eliminated. Other important results of the standardization program have been incentives to growers to increase

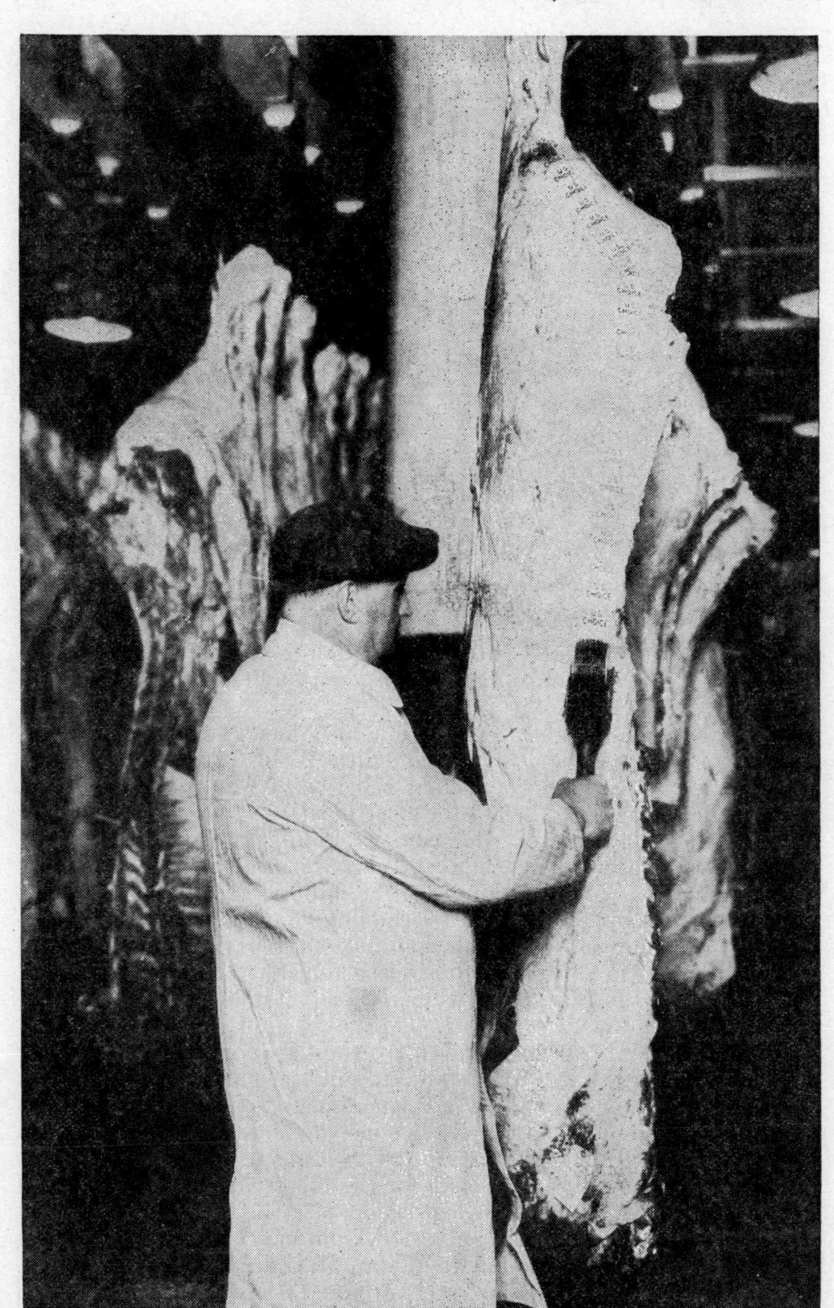

Figure 2.—The roller stamp repeats the grade name on the carcass in such a way that it appears on the principal retail cuts of meat.

Figure 3.—United States grades of eggs are carried through to the consumer by means of certificates of quality and seals.

their production of the varieties and qualities that best meet consumer requirements and to decrease production of varieties that have proved unremunerative.

Federal standards and certification also have greatly facilitated futures trading in agricultural commodities. In futures trading, the buyer cannot choose the particular seller with whom he will trade, so his protection lies in the accurate certification of the product under standards that adequately describe it. This protection is a safeguard to prices of futures in that it precludes refusals to accept delivery of a commodity on the ground that it fails to meet specifications, thereby withdrawing support from the buying side and creating pressure on the selling side. Legislation makes the use of Federal standards mandatory in futures trading in cotton, butter, grain, potatoes, and wool top, and in eggs when official standards for eggs are promulgated.

Federal and State agencies and institutions are constantly increasing the use of the United States standards in the purchase of supplies. Marketing-agreement and surplus-commodity-purchase programs have brought about a more extensive use of the standards for certain products. Proration of shipments, restrictions as to grade and size, and surplus-commodity purchases for the most part have been based on the standards. Canadian legislation of 1939 requires that most of the fruits and vegetables imported from the United States must meet the minimum requirements of specific United States standards.

To satisfy the increasing interest being shown in the Federal standards, education and demonstration programs are conducted in cooperation with State extension services, State departments of agriculture, and other State and private agencies. Each year thousands of persons attend the Federal-State tobacco-grading demonstra-

Figure 4.—The label on each turkey tells the consumer the grade.

tions, the grain-grading schools, the cotton-classing meetings, and the livestock-, meat-, turkey-, and other commodity-grading demonstrations.

LIMITATIONS AND PROBLEMS

It is recognized, of course, that Federal standards have their limitations. By reason of their very nature they cannot be expected to meet all the requirements of producers, distributors, and consumers.

Difficulty of Measuring Certain Factors

In some instances the standards have been criticized for being expressed in terms that are too general or purely descriptive. Here the lack of precise terminology or specification arises out of difficulties inherent either in the product itself or in the limitations of our present knowledge in measuring quality variations. There is at present no known method of "measuring" quantitatively many quality factors, and in these instances there is no alternative to descriptive terms based on observation and judgment. Fortunately, research is yielding more and more accurate measures of the factors of quality.

Size and weight are easily determined by simple measurement or by weighing, and they may therefore be clearly and definitely defined in grade terms. But shape, color, and flavor, which may be important factors in the grade of a product, cannot be precisely "measured" in commercial inspection practices. This is true in evaluating flavor in scoring butter and in judging whether a fruit or vegetable is "well-

223761°—40——44

formed," as required in determining certain fruit and vegetable standards. These defects in inspection technique lead to criticisms that the grades are too technical and that they cannot be interpreted uniformly.

Until more precise inspection methods can be found, it is necessary to rely in such instances on the personal skill of trained inspectors. Inspectors representing the Department must show conclusively that they are competent before they are permitted to make inspections and to issue grade certificates. Furthermore, their work is constantly supervised.

Many ingenious methods and devices have been developed, however, to reduce the element of error in human judgment. Photographs are used extensively to illustrate certain quality factors such as conformation in livestock, types of defects in fruits and vegetables, and color requirements for certain grades of eggs, meats, fruits, and vegetables. In the case of staple crops such as grains, beans, tobacco, cotton, wool, and hay, type samples illustrating grades and qualities are used to obtain greater uniformity in interpretation of standards and to acquaint growers, dealers, and others with the requirements of the various grades. Plaster models are used in illustrating minimum requirements of shape, color, and other grade factors for fruits and vegetables.

Figure 5.—Using a specially constructed precision instrument, a worker measures the color of cotton. Color measurement is an aid in the preparation of standards for farm products.

Mechanical and chemical tests are increasing in number and efficiency and promise to facilitate the measurement of various special and chemical quality factors. Mechanical devices include an electrical apparatus for quickly determining the moisture content of grains, and others show the color of honey, of hay, and of cotton (fig. 5). A candling apparatus aids in determining internal quality of eggs. Puncture testers show the maturity of raw and canned corn, and pressure testers are used to determine the maturity of apples, pears, and other fruits. Hydrometers, refractometers, and other laboratory equipment are used in grading certain processed products to determine density, percentages of sugar, the relationship of soluble solids to juice, and the cloudiness of liquor in canned foods. Other devices include machines to aid in determining dockage in grain and test weight per bushel. Experiments with artificial daylight show promise of reducing some of the uncertainty in classifying cotton to the extent that more uniform conditions of judging may affect results.

Attitude of Trades

A major obstacle to the general adoption of permissive standards has been the slowness of dealers and of the trades generally to accept Federal standards. In certain instances, in fact, general use of the standards has been actively opposed by trade groups.

A part of such opposition has been due to fear that the adoption of retail or consumer standards would permit the latter to supersede well-established and expensively advertised brand names, with a consequent loss in advertising value of those brands. To a minor extent this objection is being overcome by some processors who are linking their brand names with the appropriate Federal grade names.

Obviously, resistance to Federal standards could be expected from manufacturers and others who desire to market their products under brand names or other descriptions that do not convey specific information as to quality factors and provide wide latitude in adjusting output to seasonal conditions and variations in available supplies. This type of resistance to Federal standards is being overcome to some extent by consumer insistence on grade terms which are understandable and carry an assurance that the purchaser receives the quality for which he pays.

The degree of willingness shown by various industries and parts of industries to adopt the optional standards as a basis for trading varies considerably. The extent to which the standards are used, it is found, depends largely on the individual needs of the industry, on prevailing buying and selling practices within the industry, and in some instances on the demands of organized producer and consumer groups.

The increasing use of the motortruck for transporting products from farm to market has had the effect of bringing many buyers and sellers closer together and has caused many growers and shippers to believe that there is less need for standards for products so handled. A considerable portion of certain products that were formerly packed on the basis of Federal standards, loaded into freight cars, and sold on the same basis is now purchased for cash by truckers at the farm. In such cases personal inspection has taken the place of the standards as a basis for sales.

Some growers and shippers explain their failure to adopt the permissive Federal standards in their trading operations by stating that they cannot control the grade interpretations and fit such interpretations to changes in conditions. Obviously, such interpretation of grades would defeat the purposes of standardization.

There has been excellent cooperation on the part of the trades in the application of standards made mandatory under Federal legislation. General experience has shown that the mandatory standards permit trading safely on a small margin of profit and that as a result producers and consumers both have benefited.

Problems Associated with State Standardization

The lack of uniformity in standards and grades established and required by State legislation is an important problem. In some States legislation has been enacted requiring certain products to be graded according to official State grades. Some States have laws requiring that produce shipped into the State also must be graded in accordance with the State standard in order to protect home-grown products from competition. When State grade definitions differ in any way from those of other States, confusion arises.

All but two States, Iowa and New Mexico, have enacted one or more laws pertaining to the standardization of fruits and vegetables. A number of these laws, and the regulations under them, require that products be graded on the basis of United States standards and that containers be marked with the correct United States grade designation. But a still larger number of the laws and regulations conflict not only with the United States standards but also with grades that have been established across the line in adjoining States.

State laws regarding eggs furnish many examples of nonuniformity. Figures obtained early in 1939 showed that 10 States had statutory standards for egg sizes but no 2 States had exactly the same standards. Nine States still prescribed egg classifications not based on candling, which is the commonly accepted method of determining egg quality and the basis of the Federal grades.

Problems in Formulating Consumer Grades

A difficult problem is faced in developing a standardization program for some of the perishable commodities. A package of fruits or vegetables that would grade U. S. No. 1 in the morning might be out of grade within a very short time because of decay or some other kind of deterioration that developed after packing. It is the general, and no doubt the most economical, practice to grade and pack fresh fruits and vegetables at producing or shipping points, which often are long distances from consuming markets. Even under the best of handling, some deterioration occurs in transit. If practicable and acceptable consumer grades were formulated for highly perishable fruits and vegetables, regrading and repacking might have to be done in the wholesale markets or in the retail stores. Even then it might be difficult to keep certain commodities within grade.

From the standpoint of consumer or retail standards now in use the greatest need is for uniform and simplified grade names or designations that will readily give the consumer the desired information regarding quality. Grade names adopted as a result of long-established practices in industry may not convey to the consumer an understanding of the quality of the product. Alphabetical or numerical grade terms are most acceptable to consumers. This has been evidenced in the great interest shown by consumers in A, B, and C grades for canned fruits and vegetables. Consideration is being given to linking alphabetical or numerical terms with more of the present grade names in order to make them more understandable and acceptable.

An important step in the simplification of grade terms for the benefit of consumers was made in July 1939, when the official United States standards for grades of carcass beef were revised. Formerly beef standards were largely for use in wholesale trading, which required a higher degree of refinement than is needed for retail trading. Steer, heifer, and cow beef were graded on separate standards. The grade term "Good," for example, designated a different quality on each class of beef to which it was applied. Therefore, to purchase beef by grade intelligently, a consumer had to be informed not only as to the relative position of the grade name in the grade scale, but also as to the relative merits of steer, heifer, and cow beef. Since the revision, steer, heifer, and cow beef have been graded on a single standard, each on its merits as beef and without regard to class. Consideration is given only to the factors that make beef of value to the consumers. Under this new system, consumers need to familiarize themselves only with the few grades applied to carcass beef and with their relative position in the grade scale to be assured of obtaining the quality for which they pay.

FUTURE NEEDS IN STANDARDIZATION PROGRAMS

These problems point the way in which standardization efforts must be directed in the future. The Federal program for standardizing farm products is by no means complete. In many respects only a beginning has been made.

Farm products and the industries which handle them are in no sense static. Products and practices are undergoing constant change as progress is made. To be practicable, therefore, it is essential that standardization programs be kept sufficiently flexible to meet significant long-time changes.

Demands for modifications and refinements in existing standards and for the formulation of new standards come as changes and improvements occur in any phase of the production, marketing, or distribution processes. Growers lead in the demand for new and changed standards when new crops are introduced, when production of any agricultural commodity is extended to new areas, when the nature of a crop undergoes change as a result of weather, disease, or other factors, when improvements or changes are made in harvesting facilities or practices, and when new uses for farm products are discovered. To these changes, which also bring requests from the trade and processors, must be added changes that occur in transportation, in methods of packing and processing, and in further knowledge regarding intrinsic values of a product.

Improvements in transportation and refrigeration have greatly increased the movement of farm products from the points of production to all parts of the United States. And with these changes have come constant demands that more and better information be placed on the grade certificate which covers a particular lot of a product. It is realized that the terms used in the standards and on inspection certificates must be readily understood by the buyers throughout the entire country so that farm products will find a ready market wherever they can be utilized. For some products much remains to be done before all significant factors of quality can be adequately appraised and given their place in the grades.

The need for greater refinement in standards for the purpose of broadening the credit base of farm products stored in warehouses also increases the demands made on the Department for further standardization work.

Some of the most pressing demands now being received come from consumer groups who want retail grades formulated and stamped on products in such a way that consumers can easily determine the quality of the products they buy. A beginning has been made in the use of labels and certificates carrying the grade designation for the information of consumers (figs. 2, 3, and 4).

Need for Continued Research and for Education in the Use of Standards

It should be recognized always that the Federal standards, the inspection methods by which they are applied, and the certification as to grade are based on painstaking and comprehensive research. Continued research, which fully recognizes changes in production and uses, is essential in order to provide sound and practical bases for meeting the demands for standards that are made by the many interested parties.

Of equal importance, particularly to the producer, is the information obtained through research, which places the Department in a position to resist sectional or factional demands for standards, modifications, and tightening or widening of interpretations that would benefit only a few persons. Such information also shows whether the changes requested would be desirable only temporarily and whether, if adopted, they would seriously interfere with commerce in the commodity or with the purposes of standardization and grading.

Important as research is in the making of satisfactory decisions in answer to demands, it is even more important in developing information as a background for standards or for revisions that will serve a broad and useful purpose. It is impossible to formulate satisfactory standards for any commodity without careful study over a number of years of the production, handling, and uses of that commodity in all areas.

Particularly pressing is the need for research work directed along lines of developing mechanical devices for measuring factors of quality. The weak point in most of the present Federal standards is the reliance placed on observation and human judgment in the measurement of such quality factors as flavor and odor. A great deal has already been accomplished in this field. Many devices developed within the Department have simplified the inspection procedure and made exact interpretation possible. Though the difficulties yet to be overcome are numerous, the possibilities of more exact determination of various qualities are nearly unlimited.

The question of grades for consumer use is receiving increasing attention, but more research in this connection is needed. Individual consumers must think in terms of quality and buy on the basis of grade if we are to have the most sensitive adjustment of price to quality. More studies of consumer preferences are necessary, and more educational and demonstrational work as to the meaning of grades must be carried on among consumer and retail groups. As consumers register their preferences more accurately and effectively, they will indirectly be encouraging the development of grades they prefer and discouraging development of grades less suitable for their uses.

Obviously the use of Federal standards could be materially expanded if the various States had uniform laws recognizing and accepting Federal standards. This would greatly facilitate a Nation-wide program of education for the fullest use of standard grades. With many commodities, proper grades carried through to consumers would make possible more intelligent purchase by consumers in line with their pocketbooks. This in turn would reflect back to producers the type and kind of product that would bring them the largest returns. Cooperative efforts of State and Federal Governments would go a long way toward the realization of this objective.

Despite the lack of uniformity that still prevails and the fact that many individuals in certain industries have not yet adopted the official standards, it is encouraging that the use of Federal standards as a basis for buying and selling many products is increasing.

Cooperative Marketing by Farmers

by E. A. Stokdyk [1]

FARMERS' cooperative marketing associations have now gained a firm foothold in the United States and are showing a remarkably healthy growth. There are 8,300 of these associations today, with 2½ million farmer members, doing an annual business of over $2,000,000,000. Here is an account of this significant development. The author discusses the organization, nature, and functions of farmer cooperatives and devotes a good deal of attention to analyzing their legal status. He then summarizes the present position of the cooperatives handling each of seven major types of farm products—dairy products, poultry products, fruits and vegetables, grain, livestock, wool, and cotton. Even this, as he points out, does not tell the whole story, for there are now cooperatives in the United States handling many other farm products.

COOPERATIVE marketing of agricultural products is a well-established economic institution in the United States. In the 1937–38 marketing season approximately 2,500,000 farmers sold more than $2,000,000,000 worth of agricultural products through 8,300 cooperative marketing associations.

In every State of the Union, as well as the District of Columbia and Puerto Rico, cooperative-marketing associations are now in operation

[1] E. A. Stokdyk was formerly Deputy Governor of the Farm Credit Administration. The writer is indebted to F. M. Hyre, E. Marks, W. C. Welden, and J. G. Knapp of the Farm Credit Administration for generous assistance in the preparation of this article.

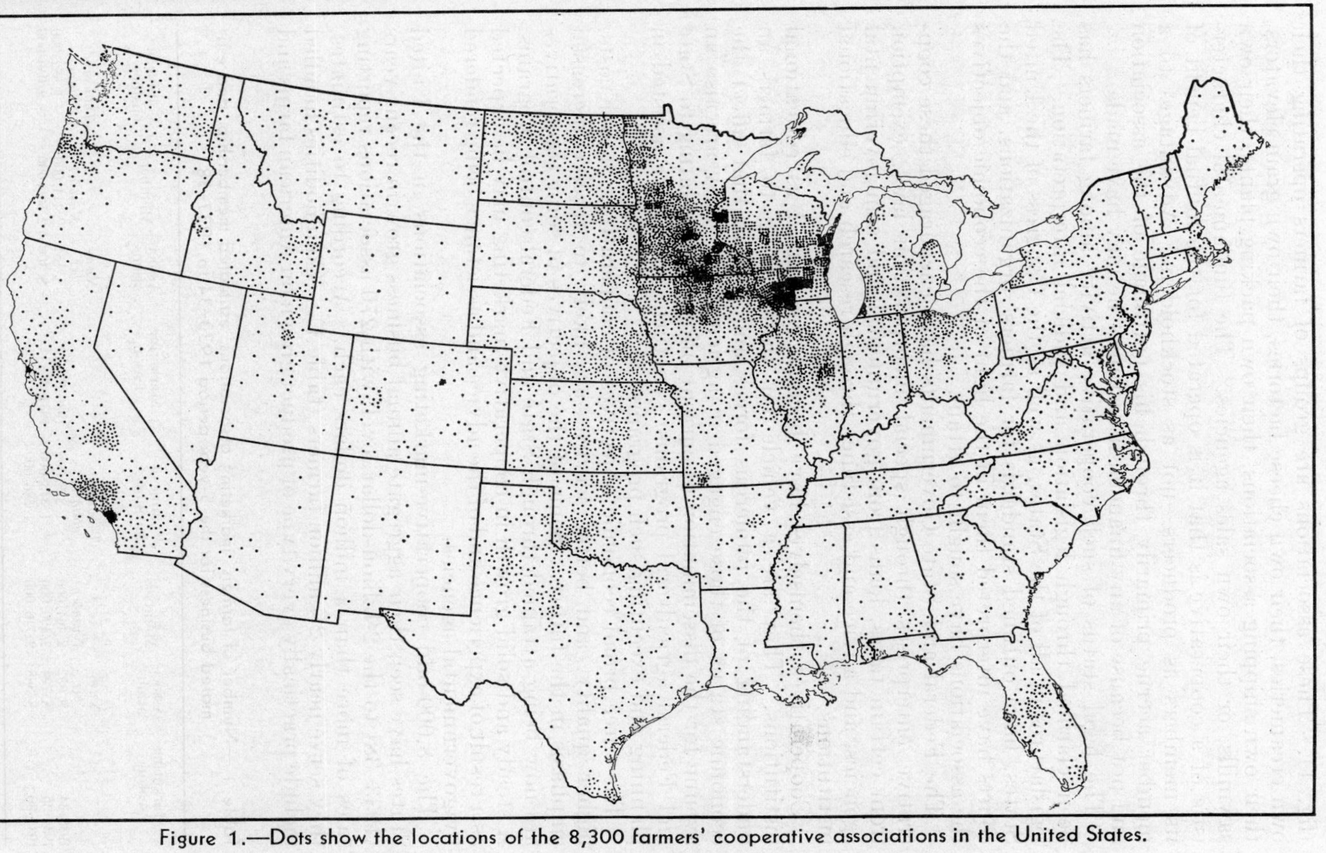

Figure 1.—Dots show the locations of the 8,300 farmers' cooperative associations in the United States.

(fig. 1). These associations are groups of farmers operating their own creameries, their own cheese factories, their own grain elevators, their own shipping associations, their own packing plants, their own sawmills, or their own sales agencies. The fundamental characteristic of a cooperative is that it is operated for the mutual benefit of its members as producers—not as stockholders. Advantages to a member accrue primarily through his patronage of the association and not because of any financial investment he may have made.

The legal status of such cooperative activity among farmers has been clarified through legislation and judicial interpretation. The legislatures in all of the States, as well as the Congress of the United States, have outlined standards for farmers' organizations, and the courts have interpreted them in the light of the economic objectives the associations have sought to attain.

The Federal and State Governments have encouraged these cooperative enterprises through special incorporation laws, exemption from certain taxes, loans from governmental and semigovernmental agencies, and advice and assistance through research and educational institutions.

Cooperatives themselves have become recognized as educational institutions. They are a vehicle for transmitting to farmers an understanding of the numerous forces and factors that affect the economic status of those engaged in agriculture. They are also an avenue for the dissemination of current information relating to State and Federal agricultural programs. In turn, they have assisted in planning and executing such programs.

The three broad economic objectives of cooperatives—lower costs, higher quality, and better service—are likely to receive increased emphasis in the future. Some of the objectives of some cooperatives are now being attained through State and Federal control programs. A steady and solid growth in cooperative marketing may be expected as a result of experience and of the advice and assistance being rendered by governmental agencies.

The 8,000-odd cooperative-marketing associations in the United States have seen their aggregate annual business grow in recent years (1933–38) to the 2-billion-dollar level, with 270 associations reporting sales of more than a million dollars each. According to estimates, they serve nearly 2½ million farmers (table 1). Commodities handled include practically every type of product grown on American farms and

Table 1.—Number of farmers' marketing associations, estimated membership, and estimated business for the 5-year period 1933–34 to 1937–38 [1]

Marketing season	Associations	Members	Volume of business [2]	Marketing season	Associations	Members	Volume of business [2]
	Number	*Number* [2]	*Thousand dollars*		*Number*	*Number* [2]	*Thousand dollars*
1933–34	9,052	2,464,000	1,213,000	1936–37	8,151	2,414,000	1,882,000
1934–35	8,794	2,490,000	1,343,000	1937–38	8,300	2,500,000	2,050,000
1935–36	8,388	2,710,000	1,586,000				

[1] Compiled from data assembled by the History and Statistics Section, Cooperative Research and Service Division, Farm Credit Administration.
[2] Estimated.

ranches: Livestock, grain, cotton, fruits, vegetables, dairy products, eggs and poultry, wool, tobacco, rice, sugar, and many other items of lesser importance.

BACKGROUND OF THE COOPERATIVE MOVEMENT

Cooperative marketing as it exists in the United States today does not represent a sudden or spectacular change in the method of handling farm products. For more than half a century our farmers have participated in cooperative enterprises. As early as the 1870's, and in isolated cases even before that, groups of farmers were convinced that they could obtain certain services cheaper or better by providing these services for themselves on a cooperative basis. From that time to the present, through periods of prosperity and periods of depression, this idea has grown. In thousands of rural communities throughout the United States cooperative enterprises have been undertaken, with varying degrees of success or failure, but each experience has added to the knowledge of the cooperative way of doing business.

Many of the earlier associations have disappeared; but a few of those now active date back to the early days of the Granger movement, and over 2,000 associations have been operating continuously for more than 25 years (table 2). These older associations are most numerous in Minnesota, Wisconsin, and Iowa. This group is composed chiefly, though by no means exclusively, of creameries and cheese factories. Many of the grain elevators now operating were formed between 1910 and 1920. Many livestock-shipping associations also were organized in that period, their organization reaching a peak about 1919.

Table 2.—Marketing associations classified according to age [1]

Age (years)	Associations	Ratio to total	Age (years)	Associations	Ratio to total
	Number	*Percent*		*Number*	*Percent*
Less than 6	1, 142	14	21 to 25	1, 275	16
6 to 10	1, 063	13	Over 25	2, 028	24
11 to 15	890	11			
16 to 20	1, 753	22	Total	8, 151	100

[1] Compiled from data assembled during the 1936 Nation-wide survey of farmers' cooperatives. For a complete tabulation of the statistical data assembled during this survey see Farm Credit Bul. 26.

ORGANIZATION OF COOPERATIVE ASSOCIATIONS

Cooperatives are often referred to as nonprofit organizations. This, of course, does not mean that a cooperative association does not have capital; nor does it mean that an organization of this type will never make a purchase-and-sale transaction at a profit. What it does mean is that the earnings of the association—or the savings, as they might better be called—are returned to the patrons of the organization as dividends, whether in cash or in capital equities. These dividends are called patronage dividends. Patrons may be members or nonmember users of the association's services.

Patronage dividends do not necessarily provide a good measure of the benefits derived from cooperative organizations; however, they do represent one of the tangible evidences of these benefits. A bargaining association may do much toward stabilizing a market and increasing the price paid to farmers. But this type of activity does not lend itself readily to accurate measurement. There is always the question of what the price would have been had the association not operated.

In 1936, the latest year for which complete information is available, patronage dividends returned by the marketing associations amounted to $17,342,750 (table 3). This figure, of course, does not represent the total savings effected by cooperatives during that year. Part of the earnings were retained to build up the farmers' investment in their associations. Furthermore, many cooperatives have a policy of rendering services as near cost as possible and do not attempt to build up any earnings or surplus for later distribution to their members.

Table 3.—Patronage dividends paid in 1936 by marketing associations of each commodity type [1]

Commodity type	Associations paying dividends	Patronage dividends paid	Commodity type	Associations paying dividends	Patronage dividends paid
	Number	*Dollars*		*Number*	*Dollars*
Fruits and vegetables	350	7,529,850	Livestock	227	583,950
Grain	1,121	3,035,200	Miscellaneous selling	89	224,900
Dairy	647	2,915,950	Wool	15	4,250
Poultry	43	2,044,900			
Cotton	147	1,003,750	Total	2,639	[2] 17,342,750

[1] Compiled from data assembled during the 1936 Nation-wide survey of farmers' cooperatives.
[2] In addition to the $17,342,750 returned by the marketing associations, $8,037,250 was returned by purchasing associations, making a grand total of $25,380,000.

If an association is to be truly cooperative, the control must be in the hands of its members. Equality among the members in the control of the affairs of the association is one of the oldest principles of cooperative endeavor. The association is managed by a board of directors selected from the ranks of the farmer-members. The one-man-one-vote rule is generally accepted, but it is not indispensable. Sometimes equality in voting among the members of a capital-stock association is furthered by limiting the number of shares a member may own. A few associations use patronage as a basis of voting rights (table 4).

Table 4.—Marketing associations classified according to basis of voting [1]

Basis of voting	Associations	Ratio to total	Basis of voting	Associations	Ratio to total
	Number	*Percent*		*Number*	*Percent*
One member, one vote	6,976	86	Other and unknown	55	1
Stock, or other forms of equity	1,003	12			
Patronage	117	1	Total	8,151	100

[1] Compiled from data assembled during the 1936 Nation-wide survey of farmers' cooperatives.

Eighty-six percent of all the farmers' cooperative-marketing associations operating in the United States use the one-member-one-vote principle, while in 12 percent of the associations voting privileges are based on the ownership of stock or other types of membership equity. This latter practice is most prevalent in Illinois and Missouri.

In 117 marketing associations, most of which are located on the Pacific coast, voting privileges are based either on patronage alone or on a combination of patronage and membership. Where a combination of patronage and membership is used, the usual procedure is to allow each member 1 vote plus additional votes based on his patronage of the cooperative.

COOPERATIVE MARKETING AS AN EDUCATIONAL FORCE

An examination of the history of American agriculture, especially during the past 25 years, will show that probably no influence has been so potent in the economic education of farmers as their own efforts in cooperative marketing. In many cases these efforts have been apparently unsuccessful, but the very attempt on the part of farmers to solve their problems together has taught them basic economic truths. For example, such experience has tended to teach farmers how the law of supply and demand actually works, how the export market affects the particular commodities in which they are interested, and the relation of a sound condition in industry to agricultural prosperity. Much of this knowledge has come incidentally through their struggles to develop a cooperative-marketing system for their products.

The process of education in cooperatives comes largely through the way in which they function as democratic organizations. Experience in the operation of these associations has shown that they cannot succeed without full membership understanding, and this requires that members be kept informed on the problems of their industry by their hired executives. As a result, these associations hold membership meetings, issue publications, conduct market tours and grading demonstrations, hold cooperative institutes, and in many other ways stimulate thinking.

The operation of cooperative-marketing associations teaches farmers that agriculture is primarily a form of business. Many of the associations have even gone so far as to directly encourage farmers to keep detailed records on their individual business operations. For example, the many poultry associations encourage their members to keep records on egg production, while the dairy cooperatives often encourage similar studies of milk production. The annual reports and statistical information developed and distributed by such associations are of great importance in teaching business principles to farmers.

Cooperative-marketing associations have also taught farmers that the problem of marketing is closely related to the problem of production, since the efficient marketing of any agricultural product depends upon the adjustment of supply to demand. These associations have been forced to study the market to determine the demand for particular products. They have found from experience that the demand for agricultural products can be increased by an improvement in production methods that results in products of higher quality. The significance of such a cooperative association as the California Fruit

Growers Exchange is, in effect, as great in the field of quality improvement of its products as in the actual process of selling.

In many cases farmers are not willing to undertake general reforms in agricultural practices without a definite economic incentive for such action. Cooperative-marketing associations have in many cases provided this incentive through the assurance of higher returns or patronage dividends as a result of following recommendations. The cooperatives' method of paying returns on the basis of quality has directly furthered quality improvement and also standardization of grades.

Thus cooperative effort on the part of farmers has had a direct effect in improving the quality of products placed on the consumer's table. For example, the large egg-marketing associations have taken the lead nationally in raising the quality of eggs, while cooperative creameries have raised the general quality of butter. The fluid-milk bargaining associations have likewise done much to raise the hygienic standards for fluid milk. Again, until the advent of cotton cooperatives, cotton was largely sold as just cotton. There was little encouragement to growers to produce cotton of any particular grade and staple length, although cotton was sold to cotton mills on a grade and staple-length basis. Cotton cooperatives have done much to change this situation through premiums and discounts based on the ultimate commercial value of the product. Although much remains to be done in this direction, it is true that, through the activities of these associations, cotton growers, both members and nonmembers, have become conscious of the importance of staple length. Likewise through efforts in cooperative marketing farmers have been made aware of the importance of the protein content of wheat.

Until farmers attempt to market their products in cooperation they have little knowledge or experience of market abuses which may greatly reduce the economic value of their products. When they undertake a marketing program of their own, these abuses quickly come to the surface, and through the mechanism of the cooperative marketing association become known to the members. Some of the valuable legislation designed to remove marketing abuses and certain Federal services established for the same purpose have come about through the insistence of cooperative groups that these abuses be abolished. Cooperative-marketing associations, for example, played an important part in bringing about the enactment of the Packers and Stockyards Act, in improving the Federal crop-reporting service, and in securing more adequate statistical information on agricultural products and marketing, as well as in the enactment of Commodities Exchange legislation.

Cooperatives also serve an important function in transmitting information on the many forces that affect the economic status of farmers. The State colleges of agriculture, the United States Department of Agriculture, and the Farm Credit Administration disseminate their findings through cooperatives as well as through other agricultural agencies.

Cooperatives have taken an active part in the formulation and execution of State and Federal surplus-control programs and marketing agreements. In fact some of the most successful of such programs owe a large part of their success to cooperative-marketing associations.

FUNCTIONS OF COOPERATIVES

The three broad economic objectives of lowering costs, improving quality, and rendering improved service are common to most cooperative associations. Some have more specific objectives, and a few have attempted to obtain what were considered reasonable prices by limiting the quantity of goods moving into the ordinary channels of trade. A general objective—that of increasing farmers' bargaining power—is either stated or implied in all cooperative structures.

The majority of cooperative associations handle products sold in competitive markets where prices are made through the bids and offers of numerous buyers and sellers. They deal in commodities produced in many areas under highly competitive conditions. As a consequence, they can exert little influence on wholesale prices. They do, however, have a marked influence on local prices by narrowing the margin between wholesale or terminal-market prices and local prices. The method employed is to operate efficient local units, whether creameries, elevators, packing houses, or livestock-shipping associations. At the same time, the cooperatives have aimed to furnish more and improved marketing services by facilitating the delivery and handling of members' products.

After a cooperative has become established and attains efficient operation, its existence forces competitors to narrow their margins and render better service. Then the objective of the association becomes one of maintaining a reasonable margin and satisfactory services. In many agricultural areas in the United States cooperatives handling staple products have accomplished about all that can be expected in the way of narrowing the spread between terminal and local prices, improving marketing services, and improving the quality of their products. In some areas, however, there is need for the establishment of cooperatives to set the competitive pace. In still other areas there is an opportunity for cooperatives to correct an unsatisfactory competitive condition caused by an excessive number of dealers, each operating with a small volume and high overhead costs. In a few areas there is a chance for producers to increase their returns by forming cooperatives to utilize improved techniques or equipment which proprietary dealers are slow to adopt because of present investments.

Cooperatives that handle specialty crops usually have one or more objectives not common to those that handle staples. These include (1) the expansion of markets through advertising, (2) the timing of sales to the periods of strong and slack demand, (3) the distribution of a given available supply among markets to put equal pressure on all markets, (4) the promotion of reasonable dealers' margins, and (5) the adoption of grades and packages to meet the demands of various income groups.

It is likely that these objectives will receive increased emphasis in the future because, with the advent of State and Federal programs some of the problems which cooperatives formerly undertook single-handed are now undertaken by the entire industry. This development has had a wholesome effect on cooperative activity, because it makes a distinction between marketing problems and the surplus problem. Some cooperatives have attempted to handle a surplus for an entire industry, but they have found that such activities placed undue burdens on their members, upon whom the entire cost of the removal of the surplus fell while nonmembers benefited equally. As a result, with few exceptions, cooperatives have abandoned surplus-control programs, and where such action is advisable they now insist that such programs be undertaken by the industry as a whole.

Some surplus-control programs have tended to weaken cooperative activity. On the other hand, control programs that are primarily volume-proration programs and leave the function of pricing to those who handle the products have stimulated associations that were efficient and weeded out the inefficient.

LEGAL STATUS OF COOPERATIVE MARKETING

During the early history of cooperative marketing in the United States cooperatives employed the corporate structure of private business. Some still do today. However, certain difficulties that arose in the maintenance of patron control of voting rights and in the conduct of business operations made it desirable for cooperatives to seek special incorporation acts which would permit restrictions on the transfer of shares and allow the distribution of earnings on a patronage basis.

Beginning in 1865, when the first cooperative statute, although not applicable to farmers, was enacted in Michigan, increasing legislative recognition has been accorded the special staus of cooperative associations. The early statutes retained the capital-stock concept that prevailed in the field of corporations organized for profit, and it was not until 1895, when the California nonstock law was adopted, that the organization of nonstock cooperative associations was authorized by statute.

Each of the 48 States now has statutes for the incorporation by farmers of cooperative-marketing associations. These statutes have been construed by the courts as desirable and essential for organizations of a nonprofit character dealing in agricultural products. Generally speaking, the courts have come to recognize that cooperative-marketing associations are formed and are intended to operate on somewhat different principles from general corporations and that the members have, aside from their monetary interest, a common interest in the objects for which the associations are formed.

The comparatively few cooperative rights conferred by the early statutes have been greatly expanded as a more widespread recognition has been obtained of the public need for and benefit from cooperative efforts, and as experience in cooperative activities has demonstrated the necessity of additional legal safeguards and new procedures for accomplishing the proper purposes of cooperative associations.

In a large and increasing number of cases, farmers' cooperatives have availed themselves of the privileges and safeguards afforded them by these laws. Of the 8,151 farmers' cooperative marketing associations operating in the United States in 1936, 74 percent were incorporated under cooperative laws, 14 percent were incorporated under general corporation laws, and 12 percent were unincorporated (table 5).

Table 5.—Marketing associations classified according to legal status [1]

Law under which incorporated	Associations	Ratio to total	Law under which incorporated	Associations	Ratio to total
	Number	*Percent*		*Number*	*Percent*
Cooperative stock	4,166	51	Not incorporated	966	12
Cooperative nonstock	1,904	23			
General corporation	1,115	14	Total	8,151	100

[1] Compiled from data assembled during the 1936 Nation-wide survey of farmers' cooperatives.

The cooperative character of an association does not depend upon whether it is incorporated under cooperative laws. Unincorporated associations or even associations incorporated under general corporation laws may be thoroughly cooperative if properly organized and operated. Fundamentally, the cooperative association must be operated for the benefit of its members as producers, not as stockholders.

The Capper-Volstead Act

The legal status of cooperative associations was by no means secure from the start, and much litigation and legislative effort was required before it was made so. Thus it was not made clear until 1922, with the enactment of the Capper-Volstead Act,[2] that a cooperative association was not, by reason of the manner in which it was organized and normally operated, a combination in restraint of trade in violation of the Federal antitrust statutes, even though no Federal court had so held. The Sherman Act did not exempt cooperative associations from its provisions, and although the Clayton Act[3] recognized in a sense the nature of cooperative associations as such, it applied only to nonstock associations and afforded no protection for certain established practices of cooperatives. One of the distinct contributions of the Capper-Volstead Act was the definition of a cooperative association which it contained. This definition has served generally as a standard for cooperative organizations and activities.

In the meantime, in some of the States, the courts had held that the contracts or bylaws of cooperative associations operated to unduly restrain trade,[4] or that the association was a combination in restraint of trade, and was unlawful under the State antitrust laws.[5] Subsequent legislation and court decisions have led to a reversal of the holdings in these earlier cases.[6]

As a result of court decisions and statutory provisions, it is believed at the present time that a cooperative association which is properly organized and functions in a normal manner is not acting in violation of the antitrust statutes. It should be borne in mind, however,

[2] 42 Stat. 388, 7 U. S. C. 291.
[3] 38 Stat. 730, 15 U. S. C. 12.
[4] *Reeves* v. *Decorah Farmer's Cooperative Society*, 160 Ia. 194, 140 N. W. 844; *Burns* v. *Wray Farmers' Grain Company*, 65 Colo. 425, 176 P. 487.
[5] *Ford* v. *Chicago Milk Shippers' Association*, 155 Ill. 166, 39 N. E. 651.
[6] *Clear Lake Co-Op. Livestock Shippers' Association* v. *Weir*, 200 Ia. 1293, 206 N. W. 297; *Rifle Potato Growers' Cooperative Association* v. *Smith*, 78 Colo. 171, 240 P. 937; *Milk Producers' Marketing Company* v. *Bell*, 235 App., 222.

that the antitrust statutes do apply to cooperative associations, and if they engage in prohibited practices, such as boycotting, or in other activites the effect of which is in fact unduly to restrain trade, they may be prosecuted or held liable in damages in the same manner as other business enterprises.[7]

Special Statutes

As previously indicated, it may be said that the special character and functions of cooperative associations have received rather full recognition by both Federal and State Governments. Thus, a cooperative association which meets the statutory requirements is exempted from the payment of income [8] and other Federal taxes and from the necessity of registering its securities with the Securities and Exchange Commission.[9]

A cooperative association is also entitled to receive advice and service from the Cooperative Research and Service Division of the Farm Credit Administration [10] and, upon meeting the statutory requirements, is entitled to borrow from the banks for cooperatives;[11] is entitled to representation on boards of trade under the Commodity Exchange Act; [12] and is also entitled to certain exemptions under the Motor Carrier Act.[13]

In addition, the special nature of cooperatives has received recognition in the Soil Conservation and Allotment Act as Amended,[14] the Robinson-Patman Act,[15] the Agricultural Marketing Agreements Act of 1937,[16] and other Federal statutes.

Cooperative associations, like other corporations, are the creatures of statutes, and at present the cooperative acts of the 48 States, generally speaking, give associations properly incorporated thereunder rather broad powers for organization and operation and a certain latitude in such matters as financing, membership control, marketing contracts, distribution of earnings, and the character of business which may be transacted. In many of the States, by statute, an association may recover liquidated damages for breach of its contracts [17] and injunctive relief against its members and against others for interfering with the performance of the marketing agreements of members.[18]

Further recognition of the special character of the cooperative associations is reflected in State statutes exempting such associations from various tax and licensing statutes.

Many of the State statutes have copied the Bingham Cooperative Marketing Act of Kentucky [19] and contain provisions either identical with or similar to provisions of the Kentucky act. Under these statutes there has developed and is developing a body of case law that is

---

[7] *United States* v. *Borden*, 308 U. S. 188, 60 S. Ct. 182, 84 L. E. 143; *State* v. *Standard Oil Company et al.*, 130 Tex. 313, 107 S. W. (2d), 550; *Hy-Grade Dairies* v. *Falls City Producers' Association*, 261 Ky. 25, 86 S. W. (2d), 1046.

[8] 52 Stat. 480, 26 U. S. C. 101, par. 12.

[9] 48 Stat. 74, 15 U. S. C. 77c.

[10] 44 Stat. 802, 7 U. S. C. 455.

[11] 48 Stat. 262, 264, 49 Stat. 317; 50 Stat. 717, 12 U. S. C. 1134c.

[12] 49 Stat. 1491, 7 U. S. C. 1.

[13] 49 Stat. 545, 49 U. S. C. 303 (b) (4b).

[14] 52 Stat. 31, 16 U. S. C. 590.

[15] 49 Stat. 1526, 15 U. S. C. 13.

[16] 50 Stat. 246, 7 U. S. C. 601.

[17] *Milk Producers' Association of San Diego County* v. *Webb*, 97 Cal. App. 650, 275 P., 1001.

[18] *Local Dairymen's Cooperative Association* v. *Potvin*, 54 R. I. 430, 173 A., 535.

[19] Acts of Kentucky, 1922, Ch. 1, Carroll's Ky. Statutes, Baldwin's 1936 Revision, S883f 1-41.

becoming rather well defined and establishes the rights and liabilities of cooperative associations under stated circumstances.

Since cooperative associations are usually incorporated, the general corporation statutes and court decisions on corporate procedure and practices are frequently applicable to situations in which the special character of a cooperative association is not directly in question, and many cases concerning cooperative associations treat such associations just like other corporations.

Although much remains to be accomplished in improving and perfecting the cooperative statutes, and particularly the corporate structures, forms, practices, and contracts of individual associations, it may be said that cooperative associations have established a definite legal status in both Federal and State law, and have won general recognition and understanding of their special character and functions.

THE PRINCIPAL TYPES OF FARMER COOPERATIVES IN THE UNITED STATES

Dairy Products

In volume of business and number of members, dairy cooperatives lead those of all other commodity groups. Scattered throughout 45 States are more than 2,400 dairy cooperative organizations selling milk, cream, butter, cheese, and other dairy products for almost three-quarters of a million farmers (fig. 2). Approximately 48 percent of all the fluid milk, 39 percent of all the butter, 25 percent of all the cheese, and lesser amounts of other dairy products pass through the hands of cooperative-marketing organizations at one stage or another

Figure 2.—Modern plant of one of the 2,400 dairy cooperative organizations.

as these products move from farmer to consumer. During the last 5-year period, the number of cooperative dairy marketing organizations increased from 2,286 to 2,421, and during this same time sales increased from $380,000,000 to $687,000,000 (table 6).

Table 6.—Number of dairy marketing associations, estimated membership, and estimated business for the 5-year period 1933–34 to 1937–38 [1]

Marketing season	Associations	Members	Volume of business [2]	Marketing season	Associations	Members	Volume of business [2]
	Number	*Number* [2]	*Thousand dollars*		*N mber*	*Number* [2]	*Thousand dollars*
1933–34	2, 286	757, 000	380, 000	1936–37	2, 338	656, 900	577, 100
1934–35	2, 300	750, 000	440, 000	1937–38	2, 421	700, 000	686, 000
1935–36	2, 270	720, 000	520, 000				

[1] Compiled from data assembled by the History and Statistics Section, Cooperative Research and Service Division, Farm Credit Administration.
[2] Estimated.

Oldest of the dairy associations are the cooperative cheese factories. Concentrated largely in Wisconsin and surrounding States, 543 producer-owned plants are making each year approximately 150,000,000 pounds, or about one-fourth of all the cheese made in this country. In 1936 the output of these 500-odd plants was valued at $24,133,000. Averaging about 30 members each and with annual sales that average less than $50,000 for each association, the cheese factories are the smallest of the dairy cooperatives.

More than 200,000 dairy farmers producing milk and cream for fluid use look to cooperative organizations to find a market for these products. About 140,000 of these dairy farmers are members of fluid-milk bargaining associations, of which there are more than 100 now in operation. The others are members of associations that go a step further than bargaining, actually taking title to the milk and processing part of the supply. In some cases the milk is pasteurized, bottled, and carried to the consumers' doorsteps by the cooperative, but usually the fluid milk is sold on a wholesale basis.

The conversion of milk or cream into butter is the primary work of approximately 1,400 cooperative creameries. Through these cooperatively operated plants, farmers are selling about 500,000,000 pounds of butterfat each year. Scattered across the country from Vermont to California, cooperative creameries now are operating in at least 28 States; but, as would be expected, they are most numerous in the heavy butter-producing region comprising the North Central States. Minnesota alone has 600 such creameries, Iowa has 260, and Wisconsin 220. In each of these three States more than half of the factory-made butter comes from cooperative plants.

Poultry Products

The principal business of 194 associations is marketing eggs and poultry for 106,000 farmers. During the 5 years ended in 1938, the number of poultry associations increased from 147 to 194 and the volume of business from $48,000,000 to $91,000,000 (table 7). In addition to these 194 egg and poultry associations, some 700 other cooperatives are handling poultry products as side-line enterprises.

Chief among these are a number of local cooperative creameries, most of them in the Middle Western States.

Table 7.—Number of egg and poultry associations, estimated membership, and estimated business for the 5-year period 1933–34 to 1937–38 [1]

Marketing season	Associ- ations	Members	Volume of business [2]	Marketing season	Associ- ations	Members	Volume of business [2]
	Number	*Number* [2]	*Thousand dollars*		*Number*	*Number* [2]	*Thousand dollars*
1933–34	147	73,000	48,000	1936–37	180	112,500	72,000
1934–35	164	85,000	53,000	1937–38	194	106,000	91,000
1935–36	154	93,000	69,000				

[1] Compiled from data assembled by the History and Statistics Section, Cooperative Research and Service Division, Farm Credit Administration.
[2] Estimated.

In California, Oregon, Washington, Utah, and Idaho, where intensive commercial poultry production has developed on a large scale, poultrymen now own and operate some of the world's largest egg, poultry, and turkey marketing associations. At least eight associations located in this area transact an annual volume of business in excess of $1,000,000 each. The business of some of these associations exceeds the $10,000,000 level when feed and other supplies handled are included. Many progressive practices have been instituted by this group of organizations; for example, box packing of turkeys on a Government-graded basis, oil treatment of shell eggs to improve their keeping quality, and the cleaning of eggs by the sandblast process.

In the Eastern States, where the producing areas lie within easy reach of large consuming centers, the auction method of selling eggs and poultry has become very popular. In this area, 26 egg and poultry auctions are now in operation. The first of these was organized in Flemington, N. J., in 1930. Since that time additional ones have been formed in Pennsylvania, New York, Connecticut, Massachusetts, Rhode Island, New Hampshire, Ohio, Indiana, and Maryland, as well as at four other points in New Jersey. Through these associations 13,068 poultrymen in 1937 sold 947,210 cases of eggs and 172,314 crates of poultry, the combined value of which was more than $10,000,000.

In the Middle Western States, the production of eggs and poultry is a side-line enterprise on most farms, and the marketing of these products is likewise a side line with many cooperatives in this area. In contrast with the specialized and commercial poultry farms of the far West, production is on a much smaller scale. A farm flock of not more than 100 hens is the general rule. These producers pay less attention to quality and grade and know less about the value of their eggs than the large-scale poultrymen. This situation is not particularly conducive to the development of poultry marketing organizations as such. It is here that most of the 700 or so cooperative associations that market poultry products as a side line to the handling of other commodities are located.

The greatest development of this type has occurred in Missouri. Here the eggs and poultry are assembled through local exchanges and then moved to concentration points, where the eggs are candled, graded, and packed, and much of the poultry is dressed before being moved to eastern markets in full carlots. In some other parts of the Middle West, especially in Minnesota, the local creamery provides a convenient place for assembling and handling eggs. The farmer can deliver his eggs and cream at the same time.

Fruits and Vegetables

In all of the important commercial growing areas, producers of fruits and vegetables have developed cooperative marketing organizations. More than 1,100 such associations are now operating in 45 States. During the 1937–38 marketing season these associations marketed approximately $300,000,000 worth of products for 164,000 members (table 8). The greatest development has occurred in production areas farthest from the large eastern markets. California, with 371 associations, through which 37,000 growers marketed $151,000,000 worth of products during the 1937–38 season, leads all other States. Florida, with 85 associations, is the second leading State and is followed by Oregon, Colorado, and Washington (table 9).

Table 8.—Number of fruit and vegetable marketing associations, estimated membership, and estimated business, 5-year period 1933–34 to 1937–38 [1]

Marketing season	Associations	Members	Volume of business [2]	Marketing season	Associations	Members	Volume of business [2]
	Number	*Number* [2]	*Thousand dollars*		*Number*	*Number* [2]	*Thousand dollars*
1933–34	1, 194	185, 000	182, 000	1936–37	1, 104	144, 700	282, 000
1934–35	1, 082	158, 000	200, 000	1937–38	1, 164	164, 000	300, 000
1935–36	1, 063	166, 000	212, 000				

[1] Compiled from data assembled by the History and Statistics Section, Cooperative Research and Service Division, Farm Credit Administration.
[2] Estimated.

Table 9.—Number of fruit and vegetable marketing associations, estimated membership, and estimated business for leading States, 1937–38 marketing season [1]

State	Associations	Membership	Volume of business [2]	State	Associations	Membership	Volume of business [2]
	Number	*Number* [2]	*Thousand dollars*		*Number*	*Number* [2]	*Thousand dollars*
California	371	37, 000	151, 000	Michigan	54	8, 500	9, 380
Florida	85	5, 400	21, 000	New York	39	5, 800	7, 000
Oregon	57	9, 800	19, 000	All others	458	76, 100	64, 120
Colorado	32	12, 400	15, 000				
Washington	68	9, 000	13, 500	Total	1, 164	164, 000	300, 000

[1] Compiled from data assembled by the History and Statistics Section, Cooperative Research and Service Division, Farm Credit Administration.
[2] Estimated.

Approximately 60 percent of all the citrus fruit produced in this country is marketed by cooperative organizations. In the California-Arizona area, the proportion marketed cooperatively reaches 85 to 90 percent. Cooperatives have done much to increase the consumption of citrus fruits—oranges, lemons, and to a lesser extent, grapefruit and tangerines—by judicious advertising and by placing on the market a well-graded product.

In the cranberry industry, also, cooperatives have been an important factor in expanding markets by carefully planned advertising and by wise handling of the crop. Fully 60 percent of the cranberry crop is placed on the market by cooperative organizations.

Possibly no other vegetable is handled more widely by cooperatives than are potatoes. More than 180 associations scattered over 33 States are now marketing this product. Not all of these are strictly potato associations, as many of them also handle fruits and vegetables of other types. Apples coming mainly from the Pacific Northwest, the Shenandoah Valley, and the commercial areas of Michigan and New York are handled by 78 associations. Strawberries from Louisiana, Missouri, Arkansas, Kentucky, the Eastern Shore of Virginia, and other commercial areas find their way to market through 125 cooperative associations.

Many other fruits and vegetables are handled in substantial volume by cooperative organizations. Some of the more important of these are included in the list below:

Product	*Net sales by cooperatives* [1]	*Product*	*Net sales by cooperatives* [1]
Citrus	$124, 748, 000	Pears	$3, 883, 000
Potatoes	21, 073, 000	Celery	3, 146, 000
Grapes [2]	17, 279, 000	Cherries	2, 627, 000
Apples	11, 740, 000	Tomatoes	1, 933, 000
Prunes	7, 640, 000	Apricots	1, 604, 000
Strawberries	7, 607, 000	Lettuce	1, 468, 000
Cranberries	6, 155, 000	Avocados	1, 363, 000
Peaches	4, 632, 000	Olives and olive oil	1, 249, 000
Lima beans	4, 092, 000	Asparagus	1, 242, 000
Peas	4, 063, 000	Beans, green	1, 240, 000

[1] Data from 1936 Nation-wide survey of farmers' cooperatives.
[2] Includes table grapes, raisins, grapejuice, and wine.

At least 16 other vegetables, 4 other kinds of fruit, and 2 other types of berries are now handled by cooperatives, but in volumes of less than $1,000,000 each.

Grain

Starting well back in the 1800's, the cooperative movement among grain growers had a rather firm foothold in this country before the turn of the century. However, the most active period, as measured by the number of new associations formed, did not occur until 15 to 20 years after 1900. Stimulated by an increasing acreage of wheat and corn during the World War period, cooperative elevators made their most rapid growth between 1915 and 1921. The peak in number of grain marketing associations was reached in the early 1920's, when about 4,000 such organizations were operating.

Since that time there has been some decline in the number of associations, but this has not necessarily been accompanied by a corresponding decline in volume of grain handled. As changing conditions have brought better means of transportation, a considerable number of weak local associations have been eliminated, the members and business gravitating to the larger and more efficient organizations.

Nearly all the local elevators handle coal, feed, salt, and other farm supplies. In some instances, particularly in northern Ohio and Indiana, the volume of supplies handled now exceeds the volume of grain marketed, and these associations are more logically classified as purchasing associations, although they still handle considerable quantities of grain for their member-patrons.

For the 1937–38 marketing season, 2,619 grain associations reported an aggregate business of $475,000,000 and a total membership of 360,000 (table 10).

Table 10.—Number of grain[1] associations, estimated membership, and estimated business for the 5-year period 1933–34 to 1937–38 [2]

Marketing season	Associations	Members	Volume of business [3]	Marketing season	Associations	Members	Volume of business [3]
	Number	*Number* [3]	*Thousand dollars*		*Number*	*Number* [3]	*Thousand dollars*
1933–34	3,178	[4] 600,000	285,000	1936–37	2,614	362,000	397,900
1934–35	3,125	[4] 580,000	315,000	1937–38	2,619	360,000	475,000
1935–36	3,010	[4] 610,000	360,000				

[1] Includes dry beans and rice.
[2] Compiled from data assembled by the History and Statistics Section, Cooperative Research and Service Division, Farm Credit Administration.
[3] Estimated.
[4] Includes an unknown number of patrons who were not members.

The typical local cooperative elevator has a membership of 100 to 200 persons, each of whom owns one or more shares of stock in the organization. Ordinarily dividends on capital are limited to 8 percent or less and voting to one vote per member, regardless of the number of shares owned. Grain is received from both members and nonmembers, and generally the prevailing price is paid at the time of delivery. Supplies likewise are sold at going prices. Any earnings or savings made by the associations are later distributed as patronage dividends on the basis of the volume of business transacted. Some associations distribute patronage dividends to all patrons, and others only to members.

Many of the local elevators hold membership in large regional sales agencies through which much of the grain is marketed.

Livestock

Meat animals are one of the most important commodities produced on American farms and ranches. Cooperative organizations are playing an important role in the marketing of these animals (fig. 3) Approximately 600,000 producers now hold membership in 900-odd associations engaged in shipping and marketing livestock. During the 1937–38 season the business transacted by these associations exceeded $300,000,000 (table 11).

Table 11.—Number of livestock associations, estimated membership, and estimated business for the 5-year period 1933–34 to 1937–38 [1]

Marketing season	Associations	Members	Volume of business [2]	Marketing season	Associations	Members	Volume of business [2]
	Number	*Number* [2]	*Thousand dollars*		*Number*	*Number* [2]	*Thousand dollars*
1933–34	1,371	410,000	162,000	1936–37	1,012	549,000	320,000
1934–35	1,197	410,000	175,000	1937–38	926	600,000	312,000
1935–36	1,040	600,000	250,000				

[1] Compiled from data assembled by the History and Statistics Section, Cooperative Research and Service Division, Farm Credit Administration.
[2] Estimated.

Figure 3.—"Market toppers" in a pen of the Central Cooperative Association, South St. Paul, Minn. Cooperative commission associations handle approximately one-fifth of all the livestock received in public stockyards.

Cooperative livestock-marketing associations may be divided roughly into two groups—those operating primarily at terminal markets and those operating primarily in the country. The first group is composed mainly of large terminal sales agencies handling livestock on a commission basis. The latter group is composed chiefly of local associations engaged primarily in assembling and shipping. A few of the local associations do their own selling, but a large majority of them consign the livestock to commission associations at the terminal market.

Dating back to 1883, the local livestock-shipping associations represent a much older movement than does the terminal agency. In many areas local shipping associations were well established when the present terminal agencies first made their appearance. The years 1917–23 proved to be the period of maximum growth in the local-shipping-association movement. At its peak more than 2,300 associations were shipping livestock cooperatively. One of the primary purposes was to assemble livestock in carlots and thus take advantage of carlot transportation.

With the coming of hard-surfaced roads, the movement of livestock by motortruck caused the local shipping associations to become less active and in many cases to cease operations altogether. During recent years direct buying on the part of packers has caused the number of active associations to decline still further. In 1938 approximately 850 were still in operation. Many of these had turned their attention to truck transportation. Some of them own their own trucks and do the hauling themselves. Others function more or less as "bargaining" agencies in arranging with private truckers to haul the livestock under terms and conditions favorable to the livestock producers.

Judging from the increase in the number of members served (table 11), the decline in number of local shipping associations has not seriously affected the terminal agencies. Many farmers who once shipped through the local associations now are sending their livestock by truck direct to the cooperative commission associations on the terminal market.

Cooperative terminal sales agencies are now operating on practically all of the larger livestock markets in this country as well as on some of the smaller ones. On many of these markets the largest single agency is a farmer-owned organization. Receiving each year from 10 to 15 million head of cattle, calves, hogs, and sheep, the cooperative commission associations handle approximately one-fifth of all livestock sold at public stockyards.

In 1917 the Farmers' Union of Nebraska established the Farmers' Union Livestock Commission on the Omaha market. This was the first of the present commission associations. From that time on, the movement expanded rather rapidly; in 1925, 28 cooperative commission associations were in operation. By May 1939, 43 associations with 12 branch agencies were operating on 42 markets and, in addition, 5 regional or State associations were operating at places other than terminal markets. In 1938 these 60 large-scale cooperative agencies handled 12,286,914 head of livestock (table 12).

Table 12.—Livestock handled by cooperative sales agencies, 5-year period 1934–38 [1]

Year	Agencies [2]	Livestock handled	Year	Agencies [2]	Livestock handled
	Number	*Head*		*Number*	*Head*
1934	51	13, 710, 949	1937	57	13, 052, 441
1935	55	11, 965, 517	1938	[3] 60	[3] 12, 286, 914
1936	55	13, 846, 348			

[1] Compiled by the Livestock Section, Cooperative Research and Service Division, Farm Credit Administration.
[2] As used here, an agency means a complete operating unit with its own manager, staff of salesmen, and accounting system. Some associations maintain agencies at more than one market.
[3] Preliminary.

The commission associations at the terminal markets receive the consigned livestock and take care of the yarding, feeding, watering, sorting, and selling. In addition to handling livestock for sale, they also purchase stockers and feeders for their member-patrons.

Wool

Approximately 50,000 ranchers and farmers scattered throughout the United States are marketing wool cooperatively. During the 1937–38 season this group of wool growers sold $11,300,000 worth of wool through 130 cooperative organizations (table 13). The greater part of the wool marketed cooperatively is handled by 25 or 30 large-scale centralized associations, which operate on a State-wide or regional basis. These cooperatives assemble, grade, warehouse, and sell the wool for their member-patrons. Much of the wool handled by this group of associations is marketed through the National Wool Marketing Corporation in Boston.

Table 13.—Number of wool and mohair associations, estimated membership, and estimated business for the 5-year period 1933–34 to 1937–38 [1]

Marketing season	Associations	Members	Volume of business [2]	Marketing season	Associations	Members	Volume of business [2]
	Number	*Number* [2]	*Thousand dollars*		*Number*	*Number* [2]	*Thousand dollars*
1933–34	120	63, 800	13, 700	1936–37	139	79, 200	11, 500
1934–35	119	71, 000	15, 700	1937–38	130	50, 000	11, 300
1935–36	114	51, 400	11, 000				

[1] Compiled from data assembled by the History and Statistics Section, Cooperative Research and Service Division, Farm Credit Administration.
[2] Estimated.

The remainder of the associations are mostly local wool pools. Generally, these organizations are small and often serve but a single county. In most cases they are informally organized and are frequently inactive except for a month or two after shearing time. The wool is assembled and offered for sale to the highest bidder, consigned to another cooperative or a private sales agency, or sold direct to mills.

Cotton

Cooperation among cotton farmers has developed along three distinct lines: (1) Cotton marketing associations, (2) cotton gins (fig. 4), and (3) cottonseed-oil mills.

Figure 4.—Cotton being delivered to a farmer-owned ginning plant. No other phase of cooperation is making greater gains in the South at present than the ginning movement. More than half the 500-odd cooperative gin associations now operating in this country are less than 5 years old.

Located at strategic points throughout the Cotton Belt are 15 large-scale centralized marketing associations, most of which are operating on a State-wide or regional basis. These associations report a total aggregate membership of 280,000 cotton farmers, and during the crop year of 1938–39 they handled 1,522,037 bales of cotton. Approximately half of this was Government-loan cotton. During the 5 years ended in 1939 the proportion of the total cotton crop handled by the marketing associations ranged from 12.2 percent to 17.5 percent (table 14). Only once during the last 15 years has the aggregate annual volume dropped below the 1,000,000-bale level. Three times during that period it has exceeded 2,000,000 bales.

Table 14.—Cotton handled by large-scale cooperative cotton-marketing associations, 6-year period 1933–34 to 1938–39 [1]

Marketing season	Associations	Cooperative deliveries			Total ginnings handled cooperatively [3]
		Bales for sale	Bales for Government loan [2]	Total bales handled	
	Number	*Number*	*Number*	*Number*	*Percent*
1933–34	15	1,104,975	651,111	1,756,086	13.9
1934–35	15	847,397	811,193	1,658,590	17.5
1935–36	15	1,456,238	59,365	1,515,603	14.5
1936–37	15	1,863,629		1,863,629	15.3
1937–38	15	1,541,355	691,091	2,232,446	12.2
1938–39	15	723,005	799,032	1,522,037	13.1

[1] Compiled from data assembled by the Cooperative Research and Service Division, Farm Credit Administration.
[2] This service consisted mainly of classing and filling out loan documents.
[3] Running bales as reported by the U. S. Bureau of the Census.

The cotton-gin movement has reached its greatest development in Texas and Oklahoma, where 20 to 25 percent of the crop is ginned through farmer-owned and farmer-operated plants. In these two States alone more than 400 cooperative gins have been organized within the last 20 years, fully half of them within the last 5-year period. At present there are more than 70 gin associations in Mississippi, nearly all of which are less than 5 years old.

The movement is gradually spreading to other cotton States, and at least a few such organizations are now to be found in New Mexico, Arizona, California, Louisiana, Alabama, and several other Southern States. In some regions where ginning charges were high, opportunities for savings have been great. Some of the earlier cooperative gins were able to pay for their plants out of savings within a relatively short period.

In addition to ginning seed cotton and supplying the bagging and ties necessary for wrapping the bales, the cooperative gin ordinarily markets the cottonseed for its members. In some instances these organizations also market a part of the cotton lint.

Ordinarily cottonseed is sold by the cooperative gins to private oil mills, but during recent years cotton growers in certain areas have undertaken to extend their cooperative activities into the crushing field. At the present time there are six cooperative oil mills in operation. The oldest of these is at Minter City, Miss. This association was organized in 1922 and has operated continuously since that date. Of the other five, two were organized in 1934, two in 1937, and one in 1939. During the 1937–38 season the five associations then operating crushed a total of 107,900 tons of seed at an estimated saving of more than $350,000 for the member-growers.

All told, 415 cotton associations were in operation during the 1937–38 marketing season (table 15). As indicated previously, 15 of these were large-scale selling agencies, 5 were oil mills, and the remainder were cooperative gins. During the year the aggregate sales of these 415 associations amounted to $110,000,000.

Table 15.—Number of cotton associations, estimated membership, and estimated business, 5-year period 1933–34 to 1937–38 [1]

Marketing season	Associ-ations	Members	Volume of business [2]	Marketing season	Associ-ations	Members	Volume of business [2]
	Number	*Number* [3]	*Thousand dollars*		*Number*	*Number* [3]	*Thousand dollars*
1933–34	250	200,000	100,000	1936–37	401	341,800	138,500
1934–35	305	255,000	100,000	1937–38	415	350,000	110,000
1935–36	311	300,000	110,000				

[1] Compiled from data assembled by the History and Statistics Section, Cooperative Research and Service Division, Farm Credit Administration.
[2] Includes some Government-loan cotton.
[3] Estimated.

Probably no other phase of cooperation in the South is making greater gains at the present time than is the gin movement. The number of "co-op" gins has increased since the close of the 1937–38 season, and well-informed persons have stated that the number now exceeds 500.

Other Products Handled Cooperatively

More than 15,000 farmers, located mainly in California, Oregon, Georgia, and Virginia, are marketing nuts cooperatively. During the 1937–38 season, 52 active nut associations reported an aggregate business of $15,800,000.

Eleven associations, having a combined membership of 70,000, are marketing tobacco. Marketing hay is the principal enterprise of 8 associations and a secondary enterprise of at least 40 others. There are 25 to 30 sugar-beet bargaining associations. In the Southern States 8 or 10 cooperatives are manufacturing cane sugar. And one or more associations are handling each of the following products: Maple sirup and maple sugar, honey, timber, nursery stock, pulpwood, tung oil, broomcorn, and fox fur.

The Growth of Farm-City Cooperative Associations

by SIDNEY N. GUBIN [1]

FARMERS' marketing cooperatives are described elsewhere in this Yearbook. They represent only a part of the cooperative movement in agriculture. On the other side of the picture there are the purchasing cooperatives, which have also had an impressive growth in recent years. There are four types of rural purchasing cooperatives: (1) Those including only farmers and handling only farm supplies, (2) those including only farmers but handling consumers' goods as well as farm supplies, (3) those including both farmers and city people and handling both consumers' goods and farm supplies, and (4) those including both farmers and city people and handling only consumers' goods. The first two types are by all odds the most numerous and influential. The last two types are relatively new and have developed in spite of the fact that some sincere elements in the rural cooperative movement do not approve of them. Although the author of this article is interested primarily in outlining this new development, he presents a striking picture of the growth of rural purchasing cooperatives as a whole.

THE PAST decade has witnessed the development of a new form of joint activity by farmers and city workers—the growth of local, regional, and national cooperative purchasing associations designed to serve consumers in cities as well as on farms. This is one of the

[1] Sidney N. Gubin is Associate Agricultural Economist, Consumers' Counsel Division, Agricultural Adjustment Administration.

major developments in the cooperative purchasing movement during the present century, although it has not attracted widespread notice because it has proceeded at a relatively slow rate, is still quite limited in its scope, and is as yet in its early stages. This development has widened the scope of operations, increased the variety of goods handled and produced by cooperative associations, and thereby transformed a number of purchasing cooperatives from associations serving farmers solely in their capacity as producers to organizations serving both the producer and the consumer needs of farmers and their families, and in a number of cases the consumer needs of city families as well. In other words, it has partly bridged the gap that existed for many years between two types of purchasing cooperatives.

Both farm and city people have used cooperative purchasing associations for some time as a means of reducing the costs of the goods and services they had to buy. But until about 10 years ago they were considered as two distinct and unrelated groups, and to a large extent are still considered so. This distinction was made despite the fact that both kinds of associations had the same primary object and adhered to the same basic methods—the Rochdale cooperative principles—in their operations.[2] The purchasing associations in which farmers were members were termed "cooperative purchasing associations" and were regarded generally as organizations established to furnish producers with supplies needed in farm operations as aids to more economical production. The purchasing associations to which city people belonged were considered in a class by themselves as "consumers' cooperative associations" established to supply food and other products for consumption in the home.

Differing philosophies, as well as legal restrictions,[3] were responsible for this distinction between classes of purchasing cooperatives. The earliest-formed farmers' purchasing cooperatives still operating were offshoots of cooperative marketing associations and for that reason limited their activities to the purchase of supplies needed in farm production. The view that they were producers' organizations created to assist the farmer only in his business of running a farm persisted even after purchasing cooperatives were formed independently of the marketing cooperatives. Although leaders of the weaker city cooperatives wanted to join with the strong farmers' cooperatives in a united movement, some farm leaders discouraged this

---

[2] The basic Rochdale principles are: (1) Democratic control through limiting each member to one vote regardless of the number of shares he owns, (2) distribution of annual savings to members in proportion to their patronage, (3) payment of a limited amount of interest on a member's share capital, (4) sales for cash only, and (5) sales at market prices.

[3] A number of different types of legal restrictions have encouraged this separation of purchasing cooperatives into classes. In some States a cooperative purchasing association can qualify under the special cooperative incorporation laws only if it limits its membership primarily to farmers.

The Agricultural Marketing Act of 1929, as amended by the Farm Credit Acts of 1933 and 1935, defines a purchasing cooperative as an association in which farmers act together in purchasing farm supplies and/or farm business services. Under this restriction the Farm Credit Administration can make loans only to cooperatives which (1) do business only in farm supplies or farm services (insurance, power, transportation, etc.), (2) limit their membership to farmers, and (3) do at least half their business with members. However, there are no restrictions to the services rendered to cooperatives by the Cooperative Research and Service Division of the Farm Credit Administration, because the Cooperative Marketing Act of 1926 under which the Division was established does not restrict its services.

The Internal Revenue Act of 1938 (section 101) exempts farmers' purchasing cooperatives from income and certain other Federal taxes. However, in order to qualify for exemption, a purchasing cooperative must, among other things, (1) be organized and operated on a cooperative basis for the purpose of distributing supplies to farmers, (2) not transact more than 15 percent of its total business with persons who are not producers or members, and (3) limit ownership of substantially all its voting stock to producers who patronize the association.

affiliation on the grounds that (1) each of the two groups of associations handled a distinct type of goods, and thus neither one would be benefited by joint action; (2) urban cooperative associations were consumers' organizations, whereas the farmers' cooperatives were producers' organizations; and (3) joint action was impossible because farmers' cooperatives were merely an improved method of distribution in the prevailing economic system, whereas one element in the consumers' cooperative movement believed in the ultimate establishment of a cooperative commonwealth. These leaders not only objected to affiliation in principle but also advised farmers' cooperatives on practical grounds to limit their activities to handling farm supplies, pointing out that farmers' associations that had taken on consumers' goods had frequently encountered financial difficulties. Even after a number of farmers' organizations began to handle groceries and other consumers' goods used by the farm family and thus were no longer producers' cooperatives exclusively, many farm leaders continued their opposition to affiliation with purchasing cooperatives formed by city people.

One of the major reasons for the partial break-down of these objections was the action taken by a small group of farm leaders to promote joint farm-city purchasing cooperatives on the ground that both farmers and city people were consumers and therefore had a common interest in reducing living costs by cooperative action. These leaders stressed the fact that the average farmer spends more each year for food, clothing, housefurnishings, and other goods used in the farm home than he spends for the feed, seed, fertilizer, and other supplies used in farm production. In 1935–36, when the Department of Agriculture made its last complete check on farmers' annual expenditures, nearly 60 percent of all the money spent by farmers was for commodities and services used by the farm family, and only 40 percent was expended in producing farm products. Store-purchased food and clothing comprised 25 percent of farmers' total expenditures. Farmers spent the most money for these two items, an amount that in each case was larger than that spent for feed, seed, and fertilizer combined. Six of the twelve largest items in the farmers' budget, as indicated in figure 1, were consumers' goods. The amount spent per farm for each of the items in the farm budget in 1935–36, as well as their relative importance, is given in table 1.

On the basis of such data, this group of farm leaders argued that farmers had placed too much emphasis on improving their well-being through cooperative activities aimed at reducing production costs and too little on cooperative activity aimed at lower living costs. As a remedy they urged the farmers' purchasing cooperatives (1) to handle goods used in the farm home as well as farm supplies, (2) to admit nonfarmers as members, and (3) to affiliate with city purchasing cooperatives in regional and national cooperative associations. Joint action with city consumers and with purchasing cooperatives formed by city people was deemed essential to the success of cooperative activity in the household-goods field, since urban people comprise about three-fourths of the population and the larger membership made possible by drawing from them would provide the broader base necessary for successful operation. Because farmers purchase food and other

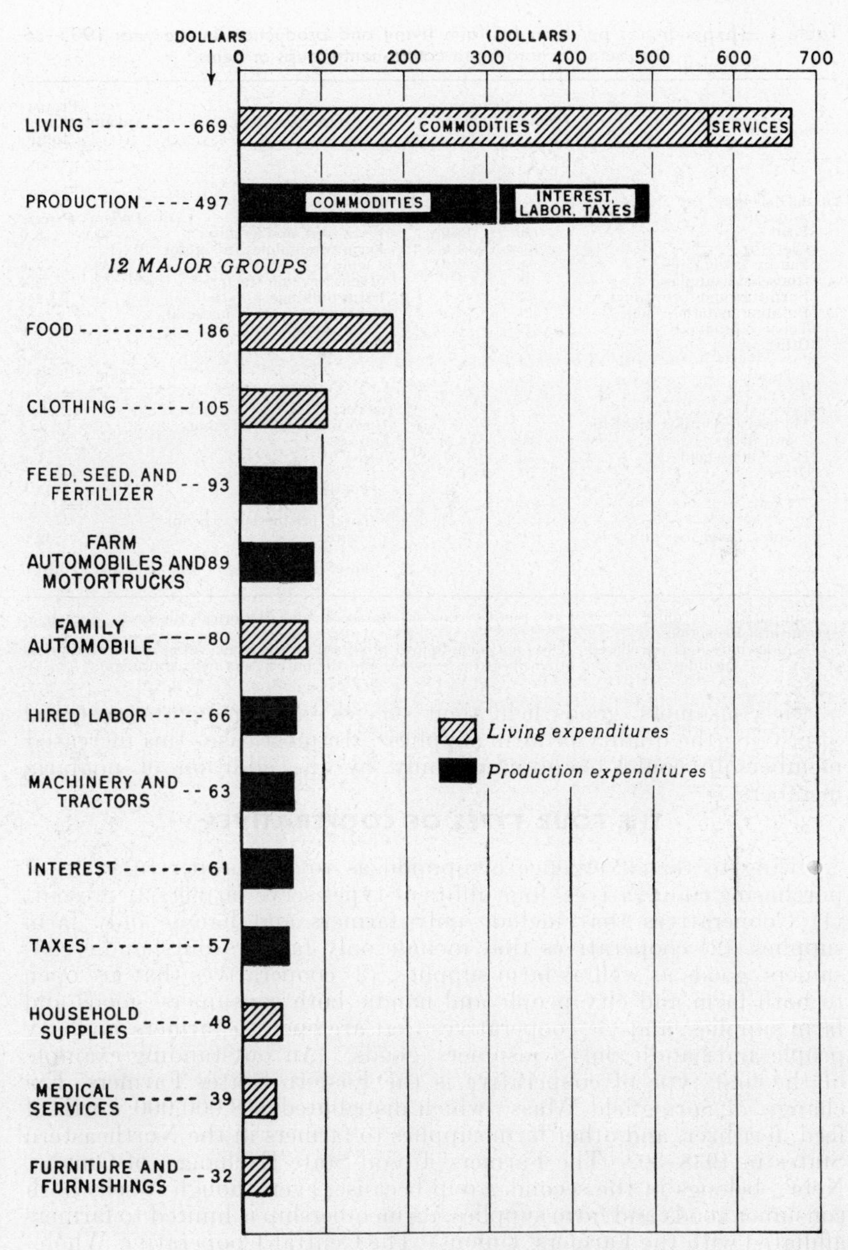

Figure 1.—Living and production expenditures of the average farm family, 1935–6.

consumers' goods in much smaller quantities and more frequently than they purchase farm supplies, local retail and regional wholesale associations had to have larger memberships to be able to duplicate

Table 1.—Expenditures per farm for farm living and production in the year 1935–36 distributed according to component groups or items [1]

Group or item	Amount	Proportion of total	Group or item	Amount	Proportion of total
Living expenses:			Production expenses:		
Commodities:	*Dollars*	*Percent*	Commodities:	*Dollars*	*Percent*
Food [2]	186	16.0	Feed, seed, and fertilizer	93	8.0
Clothing	105	9.0	Farm automobiles and motor-trucks [3]	89	7.6
Family automobile [3]	80	6.9	Machinery and tractors [3]	63	5.4
Household supplies	48	4.1	Farm buildings [3]	25	2.1
Furniture and furnishings	32	2.7	Containers, spray material, and twine	15	1.3
Building materials, house	21	1.8	Other	28	2.4
Tobacco products	15	1.3			
Other	82	7.0			
Total	569	48.8	Total	313	26.8
Services:			Services:		
Medical (excluding medicine and drugs)	39	3.3	Cash wages to hired labor	66	5.7
Hired household	10	.9	Interest	61	5.2
Other	51	4.4	Taxes	57	4.9
Total	100	8.6	Total	184	15.8
Total, living expenditures	669	57.4	Total, production expenditures	497	42.6
			Total expenditures	1,166	100.0

[1] Computed from data compiled by the Division of Statistical and Historical Research, Bureau of Agricultural Economics.
[2] Includes only food purchased. Does not include food produced on the farm, valued at market prices at $311. [3] Includes repairs and other operating expenses and the purchase of new equipment.

in the consumers' goods field their success in reducing the cost and improving the quality of farm supplies. In most cases this increased membershlp could be obtained only by the addition of nonfarm members.

THE FOUR TYPES OF COOPERATIVES

Owing to the divergence of opinion as to the proper function of purchasing cooperatives, four different types serve farmers at present: (1) Cooperatives that include only farmers and handle only farm supplies, (2) cooperatives that include only farmers but handle consumers' goods as well as farm supplies, (3) cooperatives that are open to both farm and city people and handle both consumers' goods and farm supplies, and (4) cooperatives that are open to farmers and city people and handle only consumers' goods. An outstanding example of the first type of cooperative is the Eastern States Farmers' Exchange, of Springfield, Mass., which distributed $18,000,000 worth of feed, fertilizer, and other farm supplies to farmers in the Northeastern States in 1938–39. The Farmers' Union State Exchange, of Omaha, Nebr., belongs in the second group because, even though it sells both consumer goods and farm supplies, its membership is limited to farmers affiliated with the Farmers' Union. The Central Cooperative Wholesale, of Superior, Wis., illustrates the third type of cooperative. The Farmers' Union Cooperative Hospital Association, of Elk City, Okla., the oldest cooperative medical association in the United States, is an example of the fourth type, since it provides medical care, hospital service, and limited dental service to both farm and city people in Oklahoma.

Although no adequate data are available to indicate the extent to which farmers have joined each of the four types of purchasing societies, there is considerable evidence of an unusually rapid growth in recent years in the number of associations in the third group—those that serve both farm and city people with farm supplies and consumers' goods. Cooperatives that are open exclusively to farmers and handle only farm supplies have always been the leading type of rural purchasing association. Many associations that originally were in this first group have shifted into the second group by adding consumers' goods. Unquestionably most of the farmers' purchasing associations now operating come under one or the other of these two classifications. But in recent years a limited number of cooperatives of the third type—those serving both farm and city people—have evolved from organizations originally catering to farmers alone. In order to visualize the relative importance of this third type of purchasing association to which farmers belong, as well as some of the reasons for its recent development, it is necessary to obtain a general picture of the entire cooperative purchasing movement among farmers in the United States.

EXTENT OF COOPERATIVE PURCHASING BY FARMERS

Cooperative purchasing by farmers has increased considerably during the present century. It is estimated that about one-sixth of all the farm supplies used by farmers are bought cooperatively. No estimate as to the proportion of goods other than farm supplies that farmers purchase through cooperatives is available, but it is believed that though the proportion is small, it is steadily increasing.

If their recent rate of growth continues, purchasing cooperatives to which farmers belong may attain a volume of business and a membership equal to that of the marketing cooperatives. In 1938 these purchasing cooperatives transacted 15 percent of all cooperative business done by farmers, as compared with only 2 percent in 1915, 23 years before; they enrolled 26 percent of all the members of cooperative farmers' societies, as compared with 9 percent in 1915; and they represented 24 percent of the number of cooperative associations to which farmers belong, as compared with 5 percent in the earlier year.

Nearly half of the purchasing cooperatives to which farmers belong have been formed within the last 10 years. Records of the Farm Credit Administration show that in 1913 there were only 111 cooperative purchasing associations with farmer membership. By 1929 there were 1,454 such associations, with a membership touching the half-million mark. By 1933 the number of associations had increased to 1,848, and the membership amounted to nearly 700,000. In the marketing year 1938–39 there were about 2,600 purchasing associations, with nearly 1,000,000 farmer-members. Thus in the last 10 years the number of associations has increased 80 percent, and membership has practically doubled. In the last 5 years the increase in the number of associations has amounted to 40 percent, and the gain in membership has been about one-third.

The volume of business transacted by these associations has increased at a much faster rate in recent years than either membership or number of associations, indicating that expansion in sales probably has resulted from the increased variety of goods and services furnished by purchasing cooperatives. In 1913 the total business of purchasing cooperatives to which farmers belonged amounted to only $6,000,000. By 1929 it had jumped to $190,000,000. The volume declined slowly to $152,000,000 in 1933 because of falling prices coupled with reduced farmers' incomes. But during the next 5 years the volume shot upward, in the 1938–39 marketing year reaching $340,000,000, more than double its 1933 total.

These data reflect only part of the growth of cooperative purchasing because they concern only those associations whose members are mainly farmers and whose principal function is the cooperative purchase of goods. In addition cooperative purchasing to the extent of about $100,000,000 annually is conducted as a side line by about half the farmers' cooperative marketing associations. Farmers also obtain an unknown amount of goods from purchasing associations located in cities in which they comprise a minority. An unreported volume of services from telephone, electrical, insurance, burial, and similar cooperatives [4] also contributes to the total value of the goods and services farmers obtain through purchasing cooperatives. If the cooperative purchasing business of marketing associations is added and the small cooperative marketing business done by purchasing associations is subtracted, total cooperative purchasing by farmers in the 1938–39 season amounted to somewhat in excess of $420,000,000. This compares with a total volume of approximately $215,000,000 in 1933–34.

The development of regional wholesale purchasing cooperatives patronized by farmers' associations has been an important factor behind this rapid expansion in business volume on the part of retail cooperatives. Wholesale associations, through their manufacturing operations, their large volume, and their purchase of goods on quality specifications have increased the benefits to farmers considerably over those that could be obtained solely through retail cooperatives. In the 1938–39 marketing season there were nearly 40 regional wholesale cooperative purchasing associations. These organizations transacted a business of about $200,000,000, or almost half the total volume of business of all cooperative purchasing associations patronized by farmers. The wholesale total duplicates part of the retail business included in the total cooperative purchasing volume of $420,000,000 in 1938–39. The extent of this duplication in 1938–39 is not known, but it may be close to $100,000,000 in view of a recent Farm Credit Administration study, which shows that the total purchasing volume for 1936 included a duplication of $98,000,000 in supplies sold by one purchasing association to another and consequently reported by both.

GOODS AND SERVICES OBTAINED BY FARMERS FROM PURCHASING COOPERATIVES

The marked expansion in the number, membership, and business of purchasing cooperatives to which farmers belong has been accom-

[4] In 1937, when the last check was made by the Farm Credit Administration, there were about 1,900 farmers' mutual fire insurance companies, 2,100 farmers' mutual telephone companies, and 600 electric power and light associations.

panied by an even more notable increase in the variety of goods and services that cooperatives provide for their patrons. The earliest purchasing cooperatives formed in the present century handled primarily the three important products used in farm production—feed, seed, and fertilizer—and dealt only with farmers. Today these three original products are still important in volume and comprise about half the annual business of these organizations. But in addition to these and a number of other farm supplies, about 50 percent of the purchasing associations sell a limited amount of consumers' goods to farmers and in some cases open their facilities to city people. Moreover, a number of these products are sold under the "Co-op" label that the city cooperator finds in his cooperative store.

Some idea of the extent to which purchasing cooperatives patronized by farmers have been transformed from associations handling farm supplies alone to associations handling both farm supplies and consumers' goods is indicated by two Nation-wide studies of the types of goods purchasing associations now handle. The first of these studies, made by the Bureau of Labor Statistics in 1936, covered only purchasing cooperatives with farmer members that handled some consumers' goods. The other study, made by the Farm Credit Administration in 1936, covered purchasing cooperatives in which farmers comprised the majority of members.

Nearly half—1,215—of the 2,500 retail purchasing cooperatives patronized by farmers in 1936 carried some consumer goods, according to the Bureau of Labor Statistics survey. Of this group of 1,215 cooperatives included in the Bureau's study, 73 handled no farm supplies but only consumer goods. The majority primarily distributed supplies used in farm production, but they handled also sizable proportions of goods used by the farm family. This sale of consumers' goods is in decided contrast with the situation in the early 1920's, when practically all the operating associations limited their business to farm supplies. The study showed that in 1936 there were 92 of these purchasing cooperatives that specialized in the sale of groceries, 114 whose major business was general merchandise, 52 that sold mainly fuel, and 498 that dealt primarily in petroleum products, which were used in farm tractors, automobiles, and trucks and in family automobiles. If petroleum products are regarded as farm supplies, then goods for the farm family constituted the major business of about 10 percent of all purchasing cooperatives patronized by farmers in 1936. However, if petroleum products are considered as consumers' goods, then the proportion of farmers' cooperatives whose major activity is the distribution of consumers' goods rises to 30 percent. Since not all petroleum products purchased by farmers are used exclusively for farm production or for the farm family,[5] the proportion of these associations whose major activity was handling consumers' goods for the farm family can only be stated as falling between 10 and 30 percent. The Bureau's study did not indicate the amount of consumers' goods handled by these associations.

A similar tendency toward the increased distribution of consumers' goods by farmers' cooperatives is indicated by a Farm Credit Admin-

[5] In response to an inquiry by the Bureau of Labor Statistics as to the proportion of total petroleum products which were used for "consumer" purposes, the estimates ran from 5 percent to 30 percent.

istration study in 1936, which showed that business in consumer merchandise represented between 3 percent and 36 percent of the total business of these associations. The exact proportion of consumers' goods handled by these associations again is not known because the coal and petroleum products they sold were used both by the farm family and for farm production purposes. But it is believed that the proportion falls in the lower part of this range owing to the widespread use of these two products in production. One part of this study covered the products handled by 2,000 of the 2,500 farm purchasing associations operating in 1936. It showed that 891, or 45 percent, of these 2,000 associations handled petroleum products. There were also 451 associations (23 percent) that sold groceries and flour, 319 (16 percent) that handled general merchandise for the farm family, 229 (12 percent) that distributed coal, and 42 (2 percent) that sold clothing. Another part of this same study covered the products that farmers purchased cooperatively through marketing associations in which purchasing was a side line as well as those obtained through purchasing associations. It showed that in 1936 there were 983 associations that handled over $8,000,000 in consumer merchandise. This report did not include as consumer merchandise any part of the $73,000,000 worth of petroleum products sold by 1,798 associations or the $19,000,000 worth of fuel (mostly coal) handled by 2,149 associations. Some of these products were used by farm or city families. Hence, in 1936 the amount of consumer merchandise handled by associations in which farmers were the principal members amounted to between $8,000,000 and $100,000,000, probably being closer to the lower than to the upper figure.

That many purchasing associations supplying farmers not only have expanded their activities but are considering still further expansion in the field of consumers' goods is indicated by testimony presented by the leaders of five midwestern purchasing associations before a Senate subcommittee on July 21, 1939. Representatives of the leading farmers' wholesale purchasing cooperatives in Indiana, Minnesota, Ohio, Pennsylvania, and Wisconsin told the committee that cooperative benefits to farmers could be increased considerably if cooperatives could freely expand their activities in the sale of goods for the farm family and could admit city people to their organizations without legal restrictions. The executive secretary of the Ohio cooperative wholesale pointed out that farmers were demanding that their cooperatives handle consumers' goods, such as food and clothing, in order to lower prices and to improve quality. The manager of the Wisconsin cooperative wholesale, which has a farmer membership of more than 80 percent, advised the committee that his cooperative was a community enterprise, providing everything that was needed on the farm and in the home. The manager of the Minnesota wholesale cooperative, which was the first farmers' association to handle petroleum products at wholesale, said that narrowing margins in gasoline had forced his cooperative to add other lines of merchandise such as groceries and tires, and that farmers are now demanding expansion into other lines. The manager of a large Indiana cooperative pointed out that his association, which had begun operations by handling feed, seed, fertilizer, and machinery, had finally acceded to members' requests and added coal, building materials, electrical equipment, and many other products. He stated that almost half of his association's business now was in products other than farm supplies and that 70 percent of the net savings of his association were obtained through the sale of these other articles.

The greater variety of goods distributed by three typical wholesale purchasing cooperatives patronized by farmers further illustrates the change in the activities of local retail cooperatives. The rural electrification program induced cooperative wholesale associations to add household electrical appliances. The addition of small stocks of groceries and household goods as side lines by local cooperative gasoline stations made it advisable for the wholesale organizations to handle these consumers' goods. The Grange Cooperative Wholesale at Seattle, Wash., which was organized in 1919, at present distributes groceries and meats, limited lines of clothing and shoes, fuel, household goods, petroleum products, automobile tires and accessories, students' supplies, machinery, and farm supplies. The Farmers' Union State Exchange at Omaha, Nebr., established in 1914, handles the same lines of goods with the exception of meats and farm machinery. The Central Cooperative Wholesale at Superior, Wis., which was established by farmers in 1918 and still has a membership over 80 percent of which is farmers, distributes groceries, clothing, bakery goods, petroleum products, automobile tires and accessories, and farm supplies.

THE DEVELOPMENT OF PURCHASING COOPERATIVES SERVING FARM AND CITY PEOPLE

This expansion in the number and volume of goods other than farm supplies handled by purchasing cooperatives formed by farmers has resulted in a rapid growth in the number of associations that jointly serve city people as well as farmers. If purchasing cooperatives formed by farmers had continued to confine their activities to farm supplies, joint cooperative activity by farmers and city people would scarcely have developed. But when these associations added gasoline, groceries, insurance, electrical appliances, and other consumers' goods to the list of products they distributed, many city people became anxious to join, and many urban retail purchasing associations wanted to affiliate with farmers' wholesale purchasing associations. A number of farmers' organizations in turn were willing to serve city workers and city cooperatives in order to increase the scale of their operations and their savings.

This joint activity is still conducted on a very limited scale, despite the fact that it has expanded at a rapid pace recently. However, no data are available which show its full extent. Half of the retail purchasing associations to which farmers belong handle consumers' goods, but the number of these cooperatives in which city people also are members is not known.

The ways in which farm and city consumers have organized in joint cooperative purchasing ventures have varied considerably in different areas. In the Western and Middle Western States, where purchasing associations to which farmers belong have been most active in expanding into the distribution of consumers' goods, there are numerous instances in which farmers and city workers are members of the same retail association. In the Northeastern States, where purchasing cooperatives still deal mainly in farm supplies, less joint action on a local scale has occurred. Farmers and city people appear at present to have combined mainly in regional and national cooperatives rather than in local retail associations. Thus a number of the purchasing associations to which farmers belong have joined with purchasing cooperatives located in cities to form (1) the only Nation-wide wholesale purchasing cooperative and (2) a national cooperative educational association.

In the automobile-supply field in particular a number of purchasing cooperatives formed by farmers have opened their membership to city dwellers. They did so because they found that nonfarmer business in gasoline, oil, and auto accessories was needed to increase their operations and enable them to compete more effectively with noncooperative dealers, who draw business from all consumers regardless of occupation. The position taken by a wholesale association in Minnesota, the first farmers' cooperative to enter the wholesale petroleum business, is indicative of the attitude of a number of wholesales serving farmers on the question of admitting city people. When this association was organized in 1927 the original members were practically all farmers, because farmers were the only consumers able to buy gasoline in large quantities from bulk tank stations. But the number of members who were not farmers gradually increased when local retail cooperatives established service stations in villages all over their territory to service members' cars. As a result the proportion of nonfarmer members in the wholesale now amounts to about 10 percent, and in some localities it has exceeded this figure. In at least one affiliate which was able to start in the cooperative oil business because of credit extended by the wholesale association practically none of the members are farmers. The recent action of the wholesale association in adding groceries to its commodity list and in assisting the formation of local retail cooperatives to handle groceries in its territory points to increased joint activity between farmers and city people in this association.

The phenomenal growth of the automobile-insurance business transacted by an Ohio purchasing cooperative is another outstanding example of joint cooperative activity by farm and city dwellers. This mutual insurance company was organized 13 years ago to serve farmers in Ohio. The association found, however, that it could not grow rapidly in competition with other insurance companies unless it served cities as well as farm areas. After it had adopted a policy that permitted city people to become members, there was an unprecedented increase in the number of policies written. By 1939 the society had extended its operations to 9 States and the District of Columbia and had over 250,000 policyholders. As a result of this rapid increase, in 1939 it was the fifth largest of the mutual casualty insurance companies that write automobile insurance, rated on the basis of the number of policies outstanding and premiums collected on automobile insurance.

Through the Cooperative League of the United States of America many farm purchasing associations have joined with urban purchasing cooperatives to develop a Nation-wide joint educational program for the cooperative purchasing movement. Not all purchasing cooperatives to which farmers belong are members of the league, and those that belong are affiliated mainly through their wholesale or regional organization. The league reported in 1939 that 14 regional farmers' associations, or about two-thirds of the large regional purchasing cooperatives, participated in its activities. These 14 large regional wholesale associations had a volume of business of $40,000,000, or about 20 percent of the total wholesale business transacted by farmers' purchasing cooperatives in 1938–39.

Farmers' associations did not join the league until some time after it was formed by city consumers. From 1916 until recent years, most affiliates of the league were associations composed of city consumers. But in 1939 the league had more retail and wholesale member associations from rural areas than from urban areas. Eight of the fifteen members of its board of directors were representatives of purchasing associations in which farmers were the principal members, and 14 of the 20 affiliated regional wholesale associations were farmers' associations. The addition of these farm associations has been one of the major factors behind the recent rapid growth of the league, which has raised the number of affiliated retail and wholesale associations to close to 2,000. It has given the cooperative purchasing movement for the first time a Nation-wide educational association that is representative of consumers in general. This additional support has enabled the league to carry out on a wider scale its dual function of (1) schooling members of affiliated associations in the principles of cooperation and (2) broadening the public's knowledge of the aims and operations of the cooperative movement.

Farmers have likewise joined with city people to form the only Nation-wide wholesale purchasing cooperative association, National Cooperatives, Inc. This federation was organized by farmers' purchasing associations, and urban cooperatives joined later. In 1933 only 7 regional farmers' associations were affiliated. By 1939 the number had increased to 14, and 5 additional associations were affiliated indirectly through 1 of the 14 cooperatives. This direct membership list includes 2 large cooperative wholesales (Eastern Cooperative Wholesale of New York and the Cooperative Wholesale, Inc., of Chicago) which handle only consumers' goods and serve city people almost exclusively. As a result of this growth, National Cooperatives acts as the purchasing agent for nearly 1,000,000 farm and city consumers in 26 States and an additional number in Canada. It has reported that nearly two-thirds of the large regional wholesale cooperative purchasing associations use its brokerage facilities.

Farmers' purchasing associations saw that there was an immediate need for a national wholesale cooperative soon after they entered the petroleum field. They formed National Cooperatives, Inc., to pool their petroleum orders and to act as their broker. At first this association limited its purchases to gasoline, grease, kerosene, and lubricating oil, but it gradually expanded its scope to include many additional items and thus was able to serve city people as well as farmers. By 1939 it had added automobile tires and accessories, radios, household electrical equipment, uniforms for employees of cooperative associations, binder twine, farm tillage machinery, and farm tractors. Today the national association purchases many of its goods on the basis of quality specifications and has them labeled with the "Co-op" brand. Each wholesale association receives its goods directly from the manufacturer, since National Cooperatives is a broker and not a distributor. Nevertheless any worker who buys a radio, tire, or other item bearing the "Co-op" label from his city cooperative is assured of getting the same quality the farmer receives when he buys a similarly labeled product through his purchasing association.

In addition to their joint action in the distribution of goods through retail and wholesale purchasing cooperatives, farm and city people have also acted jointly to produce some of the consumers' goods that their cooperatives distribute. These joint production ventures are much less numerous than the joint cooperative purchasing societies. Their number and output also are relatively small as compared with the number and output of plants that purchasing cooperatives have erected to produce their own farm supplies, such as feed and fertilizer.

Soon after farmers' purchasing cooperatives began to distribute consumers' goods they found it necessary to repeat in connection with these products the work they had done to improve the quality of the farm supplies they handled. In the case of farm supplies—such as feed and fertilizer—these associations saw that the best way they could give their members the kind of feed and fertilizer they ought to use, improve and standardize the quality of these items, and reduce prices by eliminating unnecessary manufacturing costs was to produce these farm supplies under their own label. In a few cases purchasing associations have found that similar action was desirable in consumers' goods and have started their own plants to produce such goods. In many more instances they have sought to purchase goods on the basis of specifications and have tried to distribute these goods under a "Co-op" label.

While most of the plants owned by purchasing cooperatives produce feed or fertilizer, there nevertheless has been a marked expansion recently in other fields. A number of regional associations, including the Indiana and Pennsylvania Farm Bureau Cooperative Associations, the Midland Cooperative Wholesale, and the Consumers' Cooperative Association of North Kansas City, Mo., now blend the lubricating oil used by their urban and rural members. The Missouri cooperative also produces its own grease and paint. The Central Cooperative Wholesale of Superior, Wis., owns its own bakery, a coffee-roasting plant, and two feed mills. In 1939 purchasing cooperatives, in addition to producing farm supplies, produced paint, bakery products, flour, and grease, blended lubricating oil, and roasted coffee. In 1940 they will begin to operate the first oil refinery owned by cooperatives in the United States. This will supply a large portion of the petroleum products distributed by cooperatives in the immediate vicinity of the plant and about one-fiftieth of the petroleum products distributed by all cooperatives. These cooperatives handle "Co-op"-branded groceries, tires, tubes, batteries, and household electrical appliances, many of which are purchased on the basis of their own specifications.

This joint activity of farm and city people developed during a period in which cooperative purchasing societies were expanding not only in size but also in the variety of goods handled. To some extent joint activity has been an important factor in this growth, but farmer members of purchasing cooperatives still outnumber urban members. Cooperative purchasing of farm supplies still is much more important than cooperative purchasing of consumers' goods. Though joint farm-city activity in cooperatives is still on a very limited scale, it is nevertheless significant because it has developed from the realization that farm and city people have similar problems and interests as consumers.

The Transportation Problem of Agriculture

by RALPH L. DEWEY and JAMES C. NELSON [1]

FARMERS have a long-standing interest in the efficiency of the transportation system and also in the cost of shipping farm products to market and supplies to the farm. In fact the early Granger movement was a form of farmer agitation that resulted in the first positive control over railroad rates in this country. Today farmers are again concerned over serious transportation problems. The plight of the railroads and the development of other forms of transport make the situation more complex than it used to be, but this is all the more reason to see fundamentals and opposing viewpoints clearly. Here is a forthright discussion with special emphasis on the interests of agriculture.

IN OUR modern agricultural structure, transportation bridges the gap between the producers of agricultural commodities and the markets in which these products are sold and also that between the producers and their sources of farm supplies. Transportation, whether provided by commercial agencies or by the farmer himself, is a vital necessity to the economic functioning of agriculture. The effective exchange of goods between groups and individuals depends

[1] Ralph L. Dewey is in charge of the section of Transportation in Relation to Agriculture, and James C. Nelson is Senior Transportation Economist, Division of Marketing and Transportation Research, Bureau of Agricultural Economics.

on locating production economically in relation to markets, and this in turn depends on a first-rate transportation system. Evidence that farmers have clearly recognized this fact is to be found in their historic role in the promotion of adequate transport facilities and the regulation of rates, discriminations, and services.

HOW FARMERS ARE AFFECTED BY TRANSPORTATION

Since transportation, whether of persons or goods, inevitably involves the expenditure of time and effort, farmers and consumers are interested not only in having available a transportation system of the necessary geographical extent but also in having it function so that the minimum amount of time and cost will be involved at various service levels. The functioning of the transport system affects farmers in a variety of ways. The focal points of concern to farmers as both producers and consumers are their ability to reach markets at which to sell and buy goods; the timing of shipments of farm products and purchases of farm supplies in accordance with their needs relative to market conditions; the preservation of the quality of commodities during shipment; and the rates, charges, and other direct and indirect costs of transportation.

The relative emphasis accorded to these various aspects of transportation in relation to farming operations and rural life varies with circumstances peculiar to particular periods in the development of agriculture, transportation, and industry. Of importance also are the period of time over which the effectiveness of the transport system is observed and measured, the distance from markets of particular farming and production areas, the nature of the product in relation to market needs, the phase of the business cycle, the existence of a war economy, and numerous other factors. Consequently, it is difficult to draw valid generalizations in brief compass regarding the shifts in emphasis on various aspects of the transportation system. The effort at one time is to promote the development of the physical facilities of transport; at other periods it may be to secure improved services from existing facilities by negotiation with the carriers or by regulation, to secure reductions in operating costs, to obtain rate adjustments by negotiation, or to promote additional transport services. The periods of special emphasis also overlap. The history of agricultural movements through which favorable transportation adjustments have been sought is voluminous as well as complex in its interrelations with other farm objectives.

GENERAL LINES OF EFFORT BY FARMERS TO IMPROVE THE TRANSPORTATION FACTOR

A brief review of the role of agriculture in promoting transportation development in the past, though incomplete, may serve a useful purpose as background for an analysis of present problems and a discussion of policy.

During the early history of this country, the development of agriculture in frontier areas was limited by the lack of adequate transportation facilities. Availability of transportation tended to determine the direction of settlement. As population increased along the eastern and southern coasts, the farmers settled on navigable streams which furnished a means of transporting their products to market. As the seaports grew in population and wealth, with an attendant increase in their requirements for food products, the fertility of the interior portions of the country proved attractive to many pioneers, who steadily pushed the agricultural frontier westward and established industrious rural communities hard upon the heels of the departing Indian and the American huntsman. However, the meagerness of transportation facilities and the difficulties, dangers, and excessive cost of marketing seriously hampered this movement and early directed public attention toward the urgent necessity of establishing better means of transportation and communication.

In successive overlapping phases, this public concern led in little more than a century to the promotion and development of the early trails and land routes across the Appalachian barrier, canals to supplement the natural water routes, toll roads, the early Government-aid roads, such as the Cumberland Road, trails across the West to the Pacific coast, railroads, pipe lines, modern motor highways, and finally airways. While it would be inaccurate to attribute the promotion of the present elaborate transportation network in the United States solely to the efforts of farmers to exploit the undeveloped lands of the West, it cannot be gainsaid that agriculture played an important role in the marvelous development in this field. Many other forces contributed, of course, such as concern over national unity and defense, the needs of industry, the availability of foreign capital, and the profitable adventure of the railroad barons in spanning the continent. The westward movement and all it implies in terms of location of specialized regions of agricultural production and farm population depended significantly upon the rapid development of rail transportation in the last half of the nineteenth century. Moreover, rural life and farming operations would be back in the horse-and-buggy days of isolation from neighbors and urban culture, restricted educational opportunities, self-sufficient farms, and inaccessible markets were it not for the modern highway and motor-vehicle facilities, in the promotion of which agriculture has been vitally interested in recent decades.

Farmers are today less concerned with promoting the development of additional transport facilities than they have been in times past. This is because the domestic system of transport has apparently reached a state of maturity, except perhaps in the fields of highway and air transport and in restricted areas where special agricultural or industrial development may yet take place. Many economists, transport experts, high public officials, and others frequently voice the opinion that the Nation is now oversupplied with transport facilities and services. Attention has tended to shift to the problem of improving service in terms of speed, preservation of the quality of perishable commodities en route, safety, and other factors. The question whether the total cost of operating our present transportation system, which amounts to $20,000,000,000 annually, could be reduced without sacrificing essential services through terminal unification, coordination of facilities and traffic, consolidation of the railways, regulation of all agencies, and other measures has come to the fore since 1920, especially during the depression of the past decade. Since farmers bear a large though undetermined share of the total expense for transport, they have a significant stake in these problems, including the question of determining proper highway tax and finance policies.

Agriculture has also played a decisive role in the development of governmental regulation of rates and services, particularly of the railroads. The objective of those who advocated effective regulation in the seventies and later was to secure reasonable rates and to eliminate uneconomic discriminations in rates. In view of the frequent price and other economic maladjustments which have studded our history and the indispensability of transport connections with markets, it is not surprising that in an effort to restore their economic health farmers have given unusual attention to railroad rates and charges on farm products and supplies. The Granger movement of the seventies, for example, developed in significant part as a protest against the exorbitant and highly discriminatory freight rates which were extremely burdensome at a time when agricultural prices and income were at low levels. The Granger agitation led to the first positive control over railroad rates in this country, beginning with State action in Illinois, Iowa, Wisconsin, and Minnesota, and spreading to the Federal Government in 1887 with the passage of the Act to Regulate Commerce. In part, too, this agitation by farm groups reflected disappointment in the lack of dividends on their railroad investments and protest against the tax load farmers had to bear to pay off the bonds voted to provide subsidies to encourage railroad development. An inevitable reaction occurred because of high expectations of the benefits to be received, high-handed railroad practices, and what were regarded as arbitrary rates and rate discriminations.

However, agriculture has not found in the mere establishment or even in the subsequent enlargement and improvement of the regulatory legislation granting control of rail rates and services to the Interstate Commerce Commission an effective answer to its complaint against extortionate or unduly discriminatory freight rates. The regulatory process requires the bringing of adequately prepared cases before the Commission and the courts, which is often an expensive undertaking and one for which agricultural interests are not always adequately financed and staffed. In many cases it has been necessary to rely upon representatives of middlemen dealing in farm products to present the farmer's case. The interests of the two groups have coincided frequently, but not always. Speaking of rate relationships between grain and flour and service practices such as transit for storage, milling, and processing purposes, Chairman Joseph B. Eastman of the Commission recently said in an address before the National Farm Institute: [2]

> It is quite possible that I have a slight obsession on this point, because my own views seem to run counter to the general trend. The dealers and the millers and the mixers all insist, and at great length, that the parity of rates between grain and flour and all the alleged free transit service are of great advantage to the farmer and give him, through the force of competitive bidding for his products, a better net price after deducting freight rates than he would otherwise receive. They appear before us, in fact, in the guise of guardians and protectors of the farmer. It may be so, but I have yet to be convinced. I suggest only that the farmers

[2] Eastman, Joseph B. Transportation charges and agriculture. Natl. Farm Inst. Proc. 3:82-87. 1939. See p. 86.

ought not to take too much for granted on this general subject, but give it some careful independent study on their own account.

This is not to say that farm problems and interests have always been inadequately presented to the Commission for consideration, but merely to emphasize that the problems of rate adjustment, in both the level and the structure of rates, are continuous and can never be finally solved in a dynamic economy subject to ceaselessly changing domestic and international economic and political conditions. Serious and unrelaxed attention must constantly be given this matter.

The timing of the Granger agitation and subsequent political action by farm groups in relation to rate regulation show that farmers tend to understand the significance of freight rates and charges, particularly during periods of agricultural depression, when prices for farm products and farm income and purchasing power seem out of line with previous standards. In the early 1920's economic difficulties due to post-war adustments in price, demand, and supply relationships in the agricultural regions of the West and South precipitated another political protest against the level and the structure of freight rates, which culminated in the passage by Congress of the Hoch-Smith resolution in 1925. By means of this legislation it was hoped to compel rate adjustments in order to relieve agricultural distress. Under the mandate of the resolution, the Interstate Commerce Commission instituted a widespread investigation of freight rates and accorded unusual attention to such agricultural products as grain and grain products, cotton, and livestock. The results achieved were disappointing to farmers, largely because of the interpretation placed upon the resolution by the United States Supreme Court in the Ann Arbor case in 1930.[3] The Court ruled that the resolution did not "purport to make unlawful any rate which under the existing law is a lawful rate, but on the contrary leaves the validity to be tested by that law." However, as Commissioner Porter has aptly observed, "The command to afford to agriculture the lowest possible lawful rates has not been in the slightest altered or annulled."[4] The Commission is still required within the flexible limits of its jurisdiction to prescribe the lowest lawful rates on the products of agriculture.

With the coming of the economic depression of the 1930's, agricultural dissatisfaction with the relatively high freight rates, particularly with the 15-percent increases sought by the railroads late in 1937, led to the passage of section 201 of the Agricultural Adjustment Act of 1938, which authorized the Secretary of Agriculture to present economic data relating to the agricultural situation to the Interstate Commerce Commission and make complaints against rates and charges on farm products. Shippers of farm products have made frequent use of this section, and the Department has been active in the many cases falling under the mandate of the legislation, including rates and charges on cotton, grain, fresh fruits and vegetables, and livestock.

CURRENT TRANSPORTATION PROBLEMS OF AGRICULTURE

Trends in the level of freight rates and freight-rate relationships have probably given farmers as a group more concern during the last

[3] *Ann Arbor R. R. Co.* v. *United States*, 281 U. S. 658 (1930).
[4] *Livestock-Western District Rates*, 176 I. C. C. 1, 161 (1931).

decade than any other aspect of transportation. This does not mean that agriculture has dropped its traditional interest in the availability of essential transport facilities, improvements in service, and general promotion and regulatory policies. In general, however, the problem of securing sufficient service to transport agricultural products to market and supplies to the farm has presented little difficulty during the last few years. The low levels of general production and consumption, especially in industry, the great growth of motor transport and highway facilities, and the improvements in service stemming from increased competition for traffic by transport agencies explain this situation. On the other hand, because of the severe depression in agriculture after the crash of 1929 and the incomplete recovery of farm income and prices since 1933, the ability of the farmers to pay for the excellent transportation services available has been sharply restricted. This has inevitably raised the question whether freight rates have been adjusted in line with changed economic conditions in agriculture.

A comparison of the trends of index numbers of farm prices and rail freight rates in the United States for wheat, cotton, beef cattle, sheep, and hogs for 1913–39 is shown in figures 1 and 2. A similar comparison for fresh fruits and vegetables is seen in figures 3, 4, and 5. Using pre-war figures as a base, farm prices for these significant commodities, with the exception of oranges in 1934, oranges and lemons in 1936 and 1937, and cotton in 1934, were lower than freight rates for every year after 1930.

The failure of rail rates to decline in proportion to market demand for farm products has contributed to the disproportionate decline in prices at the farm. The relative stability of rail rates during the recent periods of low farm prices and income has resulted in a rebirth of farm agitation for lower freight rates. In the early part of the depression following 1929, negotiations by shippers of farm

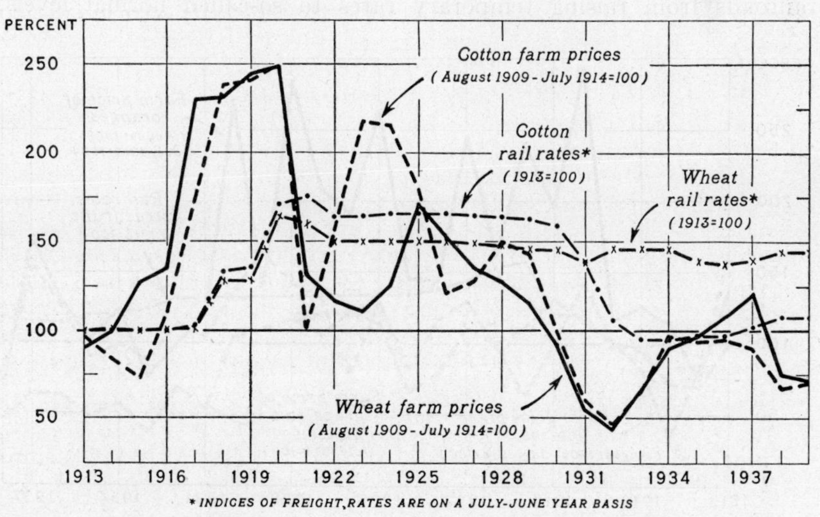

Figure 1.—Trends of farm prices and freight rates on wheat and cotton, 1913–39.

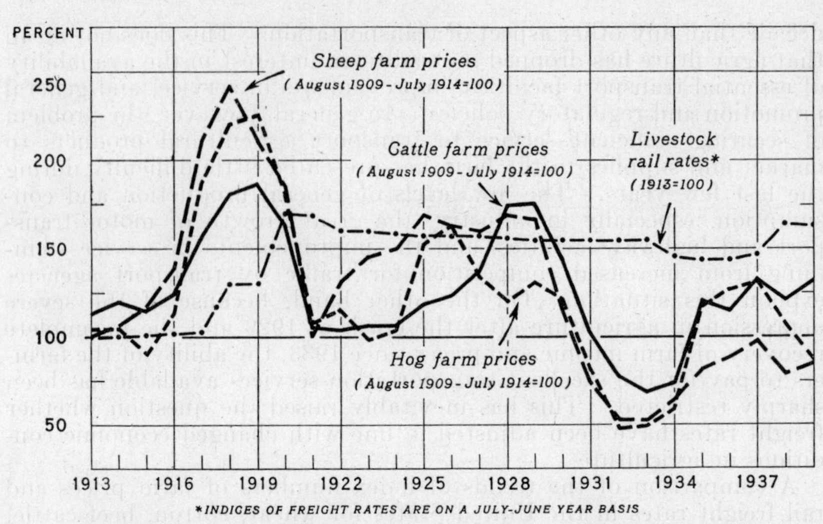

Figure 2.—Trends of farm prices and freight rates on livestock, 1913–39.

products with the railroads, during which the serious economic plight of specialized agricultural areas far from markets was presented, led to some voluntary but temporary reductions in freight rates—for example, on transcontinental shipments of certain fruits and vegetables. However, since voluntary reductions were regarded as insufficient, farmers and shippers of farm products have looked to the Interstate Commerce Commission to prescribe reductions in rail rates on farm commodities. They have been especially vigorous in protesting the frequent attempts of the railroads to raise rates in the last 5 years. Though these protests did not generally prevent the railroads from raising temporary rates to so-called normal levels,

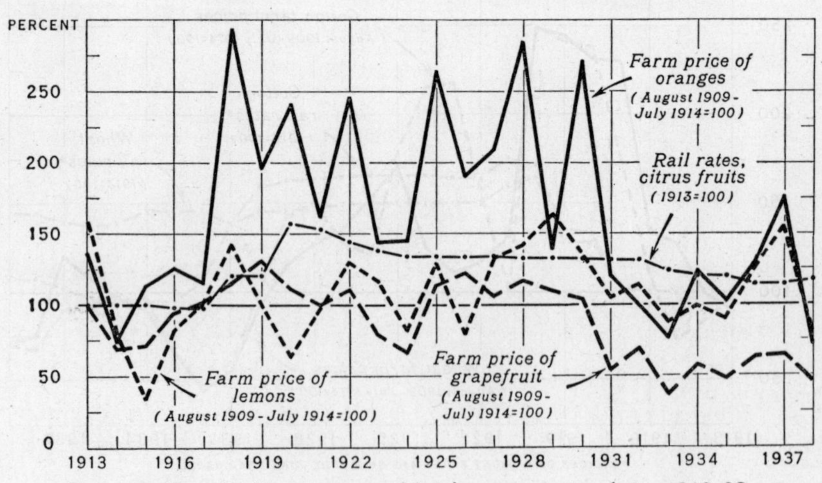

Figure 3.—Trends of farm prices and freight rates on citrus fruits, 1913–39.

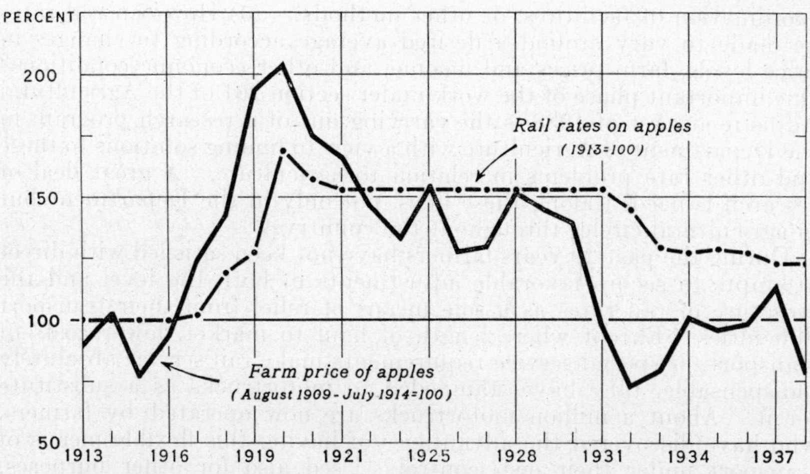

Figure 4.—Trends of farm prices and freight rates on apples, 1913–39.

they were effective in limiting the increases in the Fifteen Percent Case, 1937–38,[5] to 5 percent on farm products as compared with 10 percent on other commodities.

Some of the questions regarding railway freight rates to which farmers demand answers require much study and research as a basis for preparation for rate and other regulatory actions. Among these are: (1) Can a greater portion of the total average amount which the revenues of the railroads should be expected to cover be raised from other sources than the freight rates on agricultural traffic? (2) Can the average amount of revenue required by the railroads to cover necessary expenses be reduced by retrenchment in railway service,

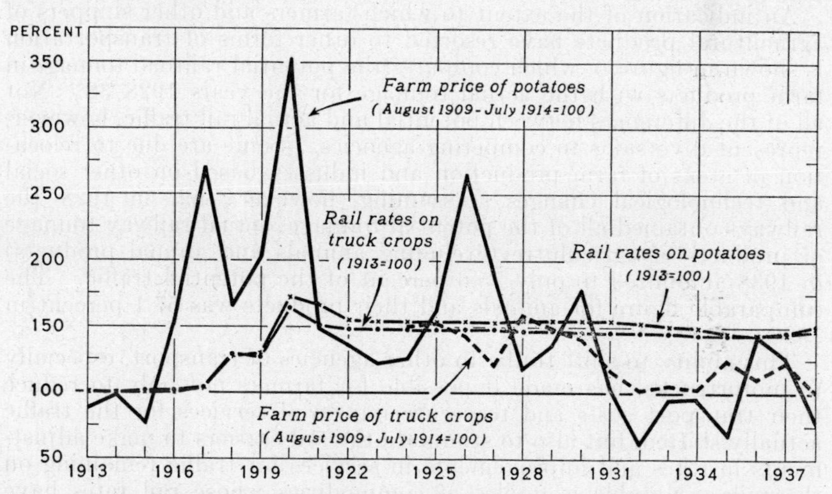

Figure 5.—Trends of farm prices and freight rates on potatoes and truck crops, 1913–39.

[5] Ex Parte No. 123, 226 I. C. C. 41 (1938).

coordination of facilitites, or other methods? (3) How can rail rates be made to vary around a desired average according to changes in price levels, farm prices and income, and other economic conditions? One important phase of the work under section 201 of the Agricultural Adjustment Act of 1938 is the carrying out of a research program in the Department of Agriculture with a view to finding solutions to these and other rate problems in relation to agriculture. A great deal of research is needed along these lines, not only in the Department but in agricultural circles throughout the country.

During the past 20 years farmers have not been satisfied with direct attempts to secure favorable adjustments in both the level and the structure of rail rates as a sole means of relief from their transport difficulties. Except where length of haul to market, lower costs of transport, or special service requirements make rail service absolutely indispensable, they have stampeded to motortrucks as a substitute for it. About a million motortrucks are now operated by farmers, who have discovered the advantages of having this flexible means of transport under their own control. Used also for other purposes, such as interfarm and intrafarm plant operations, family passenger service, hauling products to railroad sidings and to warehouses and elevators located on rail lines, and hauling supplies from trading centers, these farm motortrucks do substitute to a considerable but unknown extent for railroad and other common-carrier service. In addition, much agricultural traffic now moves to market by means of common and contract motor carriers, although it is impossible to estimate at this time the proportion of the total of such traffic. It is well known, however, that the railroads have lost to motortrucks significant portions of the traffic in fat livestock—especially hogs, cattle, and calves—as well as in cotton, most fruits and vegetables, milk, butter, poultry and eggs, baled hay and straw, sugar beets, and other farm products.

An indication of the extent to which farmers and other shippers of agricultural products have resorted to other forms of transportation is shown in figure 6, which compares the potential railroad tonnage in farm products with the actual tonnage for the years 1928–38. Not all of the differences between potential and actual rail traffic, however, represent diversions to competing agencies. Some are due to relocation of areas of farm production and industry based on other social and technological changes. Assuming, however, that in 1928 the railways obtained all of the potential tonnage, actual railway tonnage of products of agriculutre (excluding animals and animal products) in 1938 amounted to only 75.6 percent of the potential traffic. The comparable figure for animals and their products was 57.1 percent in 1938.

This ability to shift traffic to other agencies of transport, especially to motortrucks, has made it possible for farmers not only to reduce their transport costs and to secure improved services for the traffic actually shifted, but also to stimulate the rail carriers to make adjustments in rates and improvements in services for traffic remaining on the rails. Notable examples of commodities whose rail rates have voluntarily been cut in response to motortruck competition are cotton, citrus fruits (particularly from Florida to the Northeast), apples,

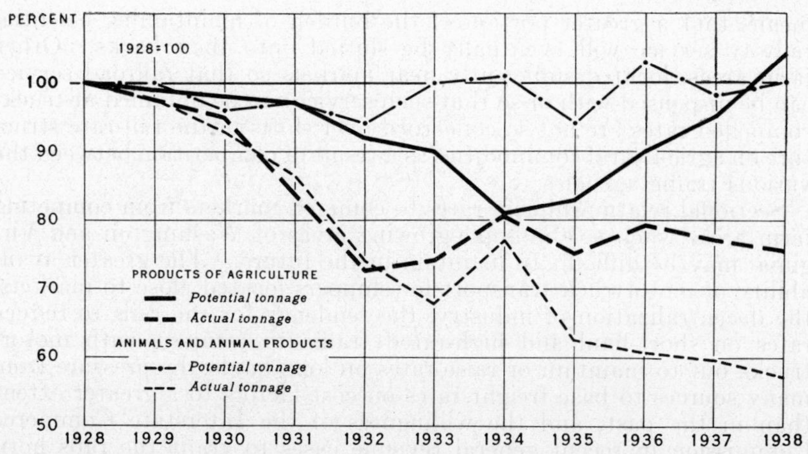

Figure 6.—Potential tons and railway tons by commodity groups, class 1 steam railways, 1928–38.

California raisins, dairy products from Wisconsin and Iowa, and hogs. Cotton is one of the best examples of the rate responses of the railroads to vigorous motortruck competition Railroads serving the Texas ports instituted reductions in 1928, but the first reductions in the South occurred mainly in August and September 1930. On the basis of 1913 figures as 100, the Bureau of Agricultural Economics index numbers for cotton rates dropped from 163 in 1929 to 159 in 1930, 139 in 1931, 106 in 1932, and 95 for 1933 and 1934. Subsequently the trend was reversed, the index reaching 108 in 1938 and 1939. As a result of the earlier slashes the railroads regained much of the diverted traffic, although recent rate increases may again cause significant losses.

On the other hand, lack of vigorous motortruck competition may be a significant factor in explaining the relative stability of rail rates on such commodities as stocker and feeder cattle and sheep, wheat and other grains, berries, peaches, cantaloups, cabbage, tomatoes, potatoes, and other fresh vegetables, and tobacco, all of which frequently move long distances. While motortruck competition may have been effective in reducing rates for these commodities on particular hauls, it is possible that the railroads and the Interstate Commerce Commission in maintaining these rates and even increasing some of them during the recent depression had in mind the fact that many of these products are more or less tied to the rails. This would be especially true of certain fruits and vegetables produced in specialized areas across the continent from markets, as well as of stocker and feeder livestock. The tendency of the rails to maintain or increase rates on farm and other commodities which must generally utilize this form of transportation, at least for significant proportions of the tonnage and on significant hauls, sharply raises a question in the minds of farmers as to the final implications of diversion of high-rated and short-haul traffic to the motortrucks. Southern, southwestern, and western farm groups are concerned with finding out whether it means that a greater portion of the burden of maintaining essential railway service will eventually be shifted onto their backs. Other farm areas, located sufficiently near markets so that railroad service can be dispensed with or so that such service can be obtained at truck-compelled rates are not so concerned over shifts in the rail-rate structure on agricultural commodities as a result of competition between the various traffic agencies.

Sectional relationships in rates to common markets from competing farm areas, such as the apple-growing areas of Washington and Virginia, may be difficult to maintain in the future. The greater availability of motortruck transport for shippers located close to markets, the decentralization of industry, the tendency for the rails to reduce rates on short-haul and high-rated traffic to compete with motortrucks but to maintain or raise rates on long hauls, the pressure from many sources to base freight rates on cost factors to a greater extent than in the past, and the willingness of the Interstate Commerce Commission in recent general revenue cases to grant the rails horizontal percentage rate increases are some of the factors that appear to be bringing about changes in the basic rate structure. The demand by industrial shippers, particularly in the South and Southwest, for rate equalization, distance considered, on shipments of industrial products to eastern, or "Official," territory may cause the rails to attempt to shift a greater part of the revenue burden to agriculture. These dynamic influences are likely to bring considerable changes in the shape of the railroad rate structure, with shifts in the relative burdens between various areas of production and various commodities. The impact of probable changes upon interregional competition is of especial concern to transcontinental shippers of farm products such as fresh fruits and vegetables and to other long-haul shippers in the South and West. Here is a problem to which serious and extended study should be given by affected agricultural groups and their representatives.

THE RELATION OF GENERAL TRANSPORT POLICY TO AGRICULTURE

In seeking solutions to current transportation difficulties of agriculture in the fields of rates and services, it is important to recognize that these problems of farmers are merely special cases of a more general problem or group of transportation issues facing the Nation. Very few transport facilities, whether railway, highway, waterway, or other types, were originally designed to, or indeed actually do, handle farm products and farm supplies exclusively. Throughout our history the agencies of transportation have been built to accommodate farm and industrial products and to serve rural and urban populations. Hence, the solution for many of the key problems of agricultural transportation is dependent to a considerable degree upon finding solutions applicable to the general public issues in this field. Moreover, the general transportation problem itself must be considered as a part of the great economic problem of our era, which is to restore and maintain the national economy under democratic controls so that it will function at the highest possible levels of production, consumption, and employment compatible with the wants of the people.

The dependence of profitable and serviceable railroads upon economic recovery in agriculture and industry is frequently overlooked in discussions and proposals with respect to freight rates. In seeking to solve their financial troubles since 1929, the railroads have made numerous and vigorous attempts to raise the general rate level and rates on particular commodities and hauls. They and other interested groups have sought the support of agriculture and the public generally on the recently expressed theory that "It is impossible to envisage a healthy American economy without healthy transportation, and it is difficult to envisage it without healthy railroads."[6] But farm groups and other representatives of the public which bear the burden of transport charges believe the reverse of this proposition lies nearer the truth—namely, that it is impossible to envisage healthy transportation or railroads without a healthy American economy. And being unwilling to succumb to the pressure for increased transport charges, these groups raise the vital question: What contribution can the railroads and other agencies of transport make to an active economy and a healthy agriculture, not by raising rates and restricting service, but by the adoption of more effective managerial and governmental policies?

To answer this significant question in economic policy, the nature of the difficulties experienced by transport agencies must be diagnosed. While present-day transport ills are multiple and some may appear to be unrelated to the others, fundamentally the United States transportation problem consists of making adjustments in our transportation system to dynamic economic influences. All agencies are subjected in greater or less degree to these forces. Most important on the demand side are the low levels of business activity in recent years and changing social habits and wants. Other influences of some significance center in technological developments such as the increasing decentralization of industry, improved quality of industrial products, substitution of electricity for coal, etc. The principal influences on the supply side are the rapid development of other means of carrying persons and goods, especially highway and air transport, and the overbuilt and obsolete condition of a considerable portion of rail plant. The impact of these influences has been mainly upon the railroads, whose financial plight has been of serious national concern throughout most of the last decade.

EXTENT AND CAUSES OF THE FINANCIAL DIFFICULTIES OF THE RAILWAYS

Since many of the most serious current transportation issues of public consequence have grown out of the changing role of the railroads in the transport system and attempts by the railroads and affected groups to safeguard their traditional economic position, a brief analysis of the sources of the financial difficulties of railroads will be profitable. It will lay the basis for a discussion of the probable cures and of a

[6] THIRD FORTUNE ROUND TABLE. TRANSPORTATION POLICY AND THE RAILROADS. Fortune 20 (2): 50–90. 1939. [Reprinted.]

desirable policy for bringing about a more efficient transportation structure for agriculture and industry alike.

The railroad financial problem can be set forth in a few words. About one-third of all railroad companies, operating more than 70,000 miles of line, are in equity receivership or trusteeship. Of the remainder, only a small fraction are paying dividends, and others have been saved from bankruptcy, for the time being at least, by Government loans. Considerable mileage has been abandoned during the depression years, and new construction has practically ceased. Purchases of materials, supplies, and equipment have been curtailed as compared with the sums spent during the 1920's. The volume of employment has declined drastically, and there are today less than 1,000,000 persons regularly employed by the railroads as compared with a peak of 2,000,000 in 1920. The class I roads had a deficit in net income in 1938 of $123,000,000 after deducting operating expenses, taxes, interest, and rent for leased road. Deficits were also incurred in 1932, 1933, and 1934. While net income was earned in 1935, 1936, and 1937, it was slight in 1935 and less than $100,000,000 in 1937.

The primary cause of the economic reverses sustained by the railroads has been the relatively low average volume of traffic and revenues during the past 8 or 9 years. Back of the decline in traffic and earnings have been two factors of outstanding importance: (1) The general industrial depression; and (2) the increasing competition of other forms of transportation, which has accentuated the reduction in rail traffic. There is little, of course, that the railroads can do directly about a general recession in economic activity which reduces the volume of their traffic. Indirectly, they can assist by adjusting their rates to take into account the lessened ability of shippers and passengers to pay. But lower rates alone will not restore general prosperity for the reason that many other elements of cost enter into the economic picture.

In 1926 the railroads hauled 75.4 percent of the ton-miles of inland freight in the United States. This proportion declined to 64.6 percent in 1937, most of the difference being taken by inland waterways, motor vehicles, and pipe lines. Rail passenger traffic declined in total volume and in relation to competing forms after 1923. In some respects the railroads are powerless to meet the increasing competition of these other agencies of transportation. Large sums of public money have been spent to promote the construction and operation of highways and waterways. Large sums have also been lavished by Government on the railways. Some of these expenditures have been wasted. The investments of private interests have also on occasion turned out badly. In any event the railways have lost ground in both passenger and freight traffic to their rising competitors. They have themselves in part to blame. Passenger rates for standard coach service were maintained at 3.6 cents per mile from 1920 until 1936, with some exceptions, although the volume of passenger traffic declined steadily from 1923 onward. The burden of freight rates was distributed among commodities and hauls in such a way as to invite the motortrucks to enter the field. This was done by the device of making rates comparatively high on valuable goods (in proportion to weight-space) and on short hauls. The trucks were able to offer particularly effective competition in these fields. As a result the railroads came more and more to depend upon their long-haul and low-value traffic. Unfortunately for them, the policy of keeping these rates low acted as a boomerang, first, because shippers resented efforts to maintain or raise these rates, and, second, because the lower truck rates on the short hauls were diverting markets from competing long-haul shippers. Moreover, where water competition for long-haul traffic existed, the railroads faced additional difficulties in their attempt to withstand the trend of events.

Other factors of some significance in the railroad picture were: (1) The substitution of natural gas, fuel oil, and hydroelectric power for coal; (2) the greater efficiency in the utilization of coal; (3) the curtailment of our foreign trade; and (4) the decentralization or relocation of industrial operations to shorten the hauls of raw materials and finished products.

In addition to these causes, several contributory factors should be mentioned. One is the shady record of past financial manipulation in the histories of many railroads. The New York, New Haven & Hartford, for example, was seriously weakened financially on the eve of the World War by an attempt on the part of a prominent banking group to monopolize New England railroad, electric railway, and steamship facilities. Also plaguing the railroads in their time of distress has been the great volume of indebtedness incurred over a period of several decades. The railroads have always been heavy borrowers, with the result that the return paid to investors has largely been in the form of interest on bonds rather than dividends on capital stock. Out of the total railway net capitalization of $18,000,000,000 in the hands of the public in 1938, the amount represented by funded debt was $11,000,000,000, or 61 percent. The same year interest on debt amounted to $488,000,000 and constituted by far the largest item among the fixed charges of the carriers. There is no legal obligation to pay dividends, but fixed interest is a contractual obligation, and default may lead to bankruptcy. When their earnings decline to low levels, the railways quickly get into financial trouble. Naturally, in an attempt to stay out of receivership, they cut their expenses drastically, particularly for personnel and for maintenance of way, structure, and equipment. While this expedient has thus far saved some carriers, it nevertheless serves chiefly to underline the need for revamping the capital structures of many railroads. Until the amount of interest is scaled down to a level which will permit the carriers to meet their obligations in periods of deep or prolonged depression, there can be no financial stability for railroads.

The ills of the railroads have also been accentuated by: (1) The failure of their managements to recognize at an early date the potency of the competition offered by moter carriers and water lines; (2) the wasteful and extravagant construction of railroads during the second half of the last century; (3) the construction of costly and largely unnecessary passenger and produce terminals in certain large cities for competitive reasons; and (4) the apparent inability of individual carriers to submerge their selfish interests and coordinate their lines and services for the purpose of rendering an improved service at lower cost. Moreover, the increase in railway employees' wages of approximately 8 percent in the autumn of 1937 at the moment when the unforeseen decline in economic activity precipitated a headlong fall in traffic and revenues added greatly to their difficulties.

If, therefore, the railroad situation is judged solely in terms of profit to security holders, there can be no doubt that there is a "railroad problem." But the ability of the carriers to operate is not determined principally by their net income under present conditions of mature development in this industry. As long as operating expenses and taxes can be met out of current revenues, shippers need not fear stoppage of service, although without Government assistance the quality of service will eventually be impaired if inadequate amounts are earned for depreciation and return on investment. At no time during this depression, even in the darkest days of 1932 and 1933, have the railroads as a whole been in danger of securing inadequate revenues to meet operating expenses and taxes. In 1932, for example, class I railroads earned, above operating expenses and taxes, about $450,000,000. The comparable figure for 1938 was $500,000,000.

It is not to be supposed that all transportation enterprises are in a state of physical and economic decadence. The past 10 or 15 years have witnessed a wonderful development technically in all forms of transportation both in quality and availability of service. The public has not suffered diminution but on the contrary has enjoyed expansion of facilities, especially in air and highway transport, throughout the depression. The financial records of numerous individual carriers of key importance disclose that they have made profits sufficient to expand their operations, improve their plant and equipment, and keep out of bankruptcy or trusteeship.

Agricultural Interest in the Railroad Problem

While farmers are concerned primarily with their own economic problems and their own struggle for profit and a living and, except for interest in the future of rail securities held, do not worry much about the trend in rail profits as such, they nevertheless should be—and many of them are—vitally interested in proposals and steps taken to solve the "railroad problem."

(1) For much agricultural traffic, especially that from the West and Southwest, rail service is indispensable. Accordingly farm leaders and organizations would be deeply concerned if rail operations became so unprofitable as to threaten necessary services. However, considering the failure of the railroads to take various means open to them to reduce operating expenses, such as terminal unification, farmers are not easily persuaded to support demands for increased rates, at least on farm products, the traffic in which is far more stable than is industrial traffic. Nor are they willing to assume that depression conditions and shifts of traffic from rails to other agencies are necessarily to be regarded as permanent. After all reasonable steps have been taken by management and Government to correct the uneconomic rail structure and inefficiencies in operation, farmers would be sympathetic to action to assist the roads if the only alternative was likely to be restriction or abandonment of essential services.

(2) As has already been said, the plight of many railroads exerts

pressure upon them to attempt to maintain or even raise long-haul rates in the face of economic conditions that frequently make falling rates desirable. When they are successful in such a policy, the result means higher transport costs on transcontinental and other long-haul traffic in farm products, where the transport factor is a significant part of the wholesale price at destination. Higher charges are not only hard to bear in themselves; they also seriously affect the competitive relationships of specialized farming areas far from market as compared with those nearer the points of consumption. Hence, it may be in the interest of these long-haul farm areas to have profitable railroads, to lessen the pressure of needed revenues on rates.

(3) Concern over the railroads' future has become so widespread, whether as a result of propaganda by minority groups or genuine public interest, that the Government has been considering proposals to change national transport policy and has to some extent been putting significant changes into effect. It should be understood that not all problems of national transport policy spring from financial difficulties of the railroads. It is probably true that the Nation developed its modern motor highways in the last three decades largely without serious consideration of the impact of this new means of improved transportation upon the railroads. A host of special but important problems have arisen in connection with this development. However, intelligent thinking and discussion have necessarily been devoted to proper relationships between the various agencies of transport and redefinition of promotion and regulatory policy in relation to the true transport needs of the Nation. Selfish interests in all quarters are active in forging policies for the future, which necessitates that the shippers and ultimate consumers be adequately represented in the ultimate decisions made. Farmers and farm organizations appreciate that policies adopted by Congress with respect to these problems may affect the efficiency of the transport system and its functioning for a long time to come. Consequently they demand a voice in policy formation in all its stages from the voter through the legislative process to administrative action and judicial review.

WHAT CHANGES SHOULD BE MADE IN NATIONAL TRANSPORT POLICY?

It is clear enough that the railroads as a principal means of transportation must be preserved. But this policy should not be applied in such a way as to place unwise curbs on the other agencies of transportation. The motortruck, bus, and airplane are here to stay, as well as the ship, and it would be contrary to the public interest to try to turn the hands of the clock back even a decade in transportation history. Government policies should not be deliberately shaped with a view to fostering any particular vested interest in transportation at the expense of economic competition.

We have seen that railroad earnings have been low for some years. There are two general lines along which an effort could be made to increase them. One is the use of methods to increase gross revenues. The other is by the hard road of reducing operating costs and other charges and expenses.

The proponents of the railroads naturally prefer the first method—that of increasing gross revenues. In order to achieve this result efforts are made from time to time to increase the rate level through horizontal percentage advances, such as the one proposed in the Fifteen Percent Case, 1937–38.[7] Endeavors are also frequently made to increase particular rates or schedules of rates. This is sometimes attempted by the direct process of filing tariffs raising the rates, as has been done lately on cotton,[8] livestock,[9] and fresh deciduous fruits and vegetables,[10] or by the indirect method of increasing the estimated weights on commodities, such as citrus fruits, shipped in boxes, crates, or packages.[11] Some of these efforts have succeeded, while others have not had the approval of the Interstate Commerce Commission.

But it is not always feasible to attempt to increase the rates, particularly when competitors are able and anxious to divert traffic by offering lower rates or improved service. Under these circumstances the carriers seek to curb the competitive power of the motortrucks, water lines, etc., by attempting to bring them under regulation. The two chief regulatory devices are minimum-rate control and restriction of entry into service by the use of certificates of public convenience and necessity and of permits. Much is said about unregulated competition being destructive. Stress is laid upon the argument that fair and equal regulation of all agencies of transportation is needed in order to preserve the inherent advantages of each. This is the spirit that permeated the discussions preceding the passage of the Motor Carrier Act of 1935 and that has governed the deliberations of Congress in connection with the omnibus transportation bills introduced in a recent session.[12] While there are important differences between the bills, all provide for the extension of the jurisdiction of the Interstate Commerce Commission to include domestic common and contract water carriers.

Such is the trend of thinking on the subject of regulation. It reflects a drastic departure from the public policy which prevailed in the main at least until 1920 for railroads and until more recently for motor and water carriers. The former basic purpose of regulation, as originally embodied in the Granger legislation of the seventies and in the Act to Regulate Commerce of 1887, was to protect the public against extortionate rates, unjust discriminations, and undue preferences. This policy of protecting the public against abuses was continued for many years without significant modification.

With respect to railroads the traditional policy was greatly changed by the passage of the Transportation Act of 1920 in which the public

[7] Ex Parte No. 123, 266 I. C. C. 41 (1938).

[8] Cotton shippers requested the Interstate Commerce Commission to suspend the proposed increases, but the request was not granted and the rates were allowed to become effective in the summer of 1938.

[9] *Livestock—Western District Rates*, Rate Structure Investigation, Part 9, No. 17000, decided May 14, 1940. (Mimeographed report.) The substantial increases in rates as proposed by the railroads were disallowed by the Commission.

[10] *Transcontinental Rates on Fresh Deciduous Fruits and Fresh Vegetables*, I. and S. No. 4501. These proposed rates were suspended in June 1938, and before hearings were held in September the carriers voluntarily canceled the schedules.

[11] *Estimated Weights on Citrus Fruits*, I. and S. No. 4511. A decision denying the rail proposals was issued February 13, 1940. (Mimeographed report.)

[12] S. 2009 (the Wheeler-Lea bill); H. R. 2531 (the Lea bill); and H. R. 4862 (the Committee of Six bill). The Senate and House passed S. 2009 in 1939 in substantially altered versions and then adjourned before reaching final agreement. The bills were sent to a conference committee which reported out a compromise on April 26, 1940. It was sent back to conference by the House on May 9. At this writing (September 4, 1940), a second conference committee bill has been reported out and passed by the House on August 12, but it is still pending in the Senate.

definitely undertook, for the first time, to assume considerable responsibility for the financial well-being of the carriers. This attitude explains the enactment of such measures as the rule of rate making (a fair return on a fair value), the recapture clause, permissive pooling, voluntary unification and consolidation, restriction on new construction of plant, control of new security issues, and regulation of minimum rates. An endeavor was made to restrict the competition of railroads with each other and with other types of carriers, notably water lines. As has been noted, similar policies were adopted with respect to motor-carrier competition in 1935 and are proposed for water carriers.

Is there proper justification for centralizing regulation of all forms of transportation for hire in the hands of one agency and for applying to their operations such restrictive devices as minimum-rate control and certificates and permits? Centralized administration of such regulation as is required to protect the public interest has much to commend it. However, proposals to extend to all agencies centralized control of minimum rates and of restriction of entry into service can be defended only if it can be demonstrated that the policies in question are necessary to prevent harm to the public growing out of destructive competition. Thus far, there has been no convincing evidence that shippers of farm products and consumers have benefited, or are likely to benefit, from these particular methods of regulating motor or water carriers.

It will be helpful to examine the premises underlying the arguments of the proponents of "unified" and "fair" regulation of all agencies of transportation. Unified regulation of rates and services is warranted only when the economic characteristics of the carriers are similar. As a matter of fact significant differences exist between rail, water, and motor carriers, even though all of them generally undertake to handle freight and passenger traffic.

Consider first railway economics. The railroads have large, costly plants, and a large proportion of their expenses does not vary with changes in the volume of traffic, except perhaps in the long run. Excessive rail capacity, while generally in evidence, has been especially marked for some years past, owing largely to depression conditions. Hence the railroads not only have an incentive to lower their competitive rates to out-of-pocket cost-plus levels if necessary, but because of their size and financial strength they have the ability to engage in vigorous destructive competition for considerable periods of time, if unrestrained by Government.

Moreover, unless regulated, the railroads can charge high rates on noncompetitive traffic for the purpose of making up revenue deficiencies on the competition-compelled traffic. If the power to destroy their motor and water competitors were not curbed, as it is by the long-and-short-haul clause and minimum-rate regulation, the railroads could eventually destroy or absorb their smaller rivals. This is what happened to most water carriers on the rivers, canals, and lakes prior to the World War. The history of railroad competition affords ample justification for strict control of their rate-cutting activities when designed to throttle legitimate competition.

It appears otherwise in respect to the water and truck industries. The rights-of-way upon which the water and truck lines operate are publicly owned, and the overhead costs incidental to their maintenance are therefore borne by Government rather than by the individual water and motor carriers. Moreover, the investment in motortrucks, and frequently in water equipment, is relatively small, and most of the costs of these carriers, especially of the motor carriers, vary directly with traffic. Taxes paid for the use of the highways are largely on a use basis. Depreciation of trucks is frequently computed on a mileage basis, and thus reflects changes in the volume of traffic. Variations in traffic can be handled by appropriate additions to or deductions from equipment, since each vehicle or small combination is a complete carrying unit. Rates for different carriers providing these services tend toward a common level, for the operations are essentially small scale and competitive in nature. Very little, if any, complaint has been registered against discriminations in truck or water rates. This is what might be expected because, in competitive industries, the opportunity to discriminate is curtailed by the shipper's ability to transfer his custom to another firm. Obviously there is much less opportunity for industries possessing these characteristics to engage in destructive competition than for the railroads.

This is not to imply that motor and water carriers should be free of Government regulation. Control of safety and the requirement of public responsibility are unquestionably justified. But serious doubt exists that identical regulation of all forms of transportation on the railroad model is required in the public interest. Failure to make proper economic distinctions between these industries only postpones socially desirable solutions of the transportation problem. It is frequently asserted that water and motor carriers are subsidized and that their competition with railroads is neither fair nor economic. The validity of this claim is difficult to assess because the railroads have been the recipients of free lands, labor service, cash grants, and other public assistance in the past. But if Government subsidies are distributed unwisely or unfairly, the sensible policy would seem to be to make changes in promotional policies and not to add uneconomic regulation to uneconomic transport subsidies.

The advocacy of thorough regulation of the minimum rates of motor and water carriers by a centralized agency appears to represent an attempt to use Government power to bring competing transportation agencies into a cartel and in this manner to share traffic and adjust rates in such a way as to earn a return upon all transportation capital of these agencies. An umbrella would thus be held over the inefficient plant, and the present high rate level would be protected from the impact of vigorous competition. Undoubtedly such a policy would also result in more rigid rates in times of depression, since the motor carrier and boat line could no longer play their role as an effective competitive force in bringing down rail rates on commodities susceptible to rail-or-truck and rail-or-water movement. Rather than requiring farmers and other shippers to pay rates based upon transportation costs of properties improvidently built, wastefully operated, or partially obsolete, it is suggested that the advisability of effecting a rationalization of the railroad plant to eliminate uneconomic transportation services be considered. Serious doubt exists whether all possibilities along these lines have been exhausted.

IN CONCLUSION

In recent years trends in the level and structure of freight rates have been of great concern to agriculture. Many efforts have been made to induce the railroads to reduce freight rates on agricultural products more or less in sympathy with the depressed farm prices and the low levels of farm income during recent years. Vigorous efforts have been exerted through the regulatory process to prevent the railroads from using the "greater revenues" approach—which generally means increased rates on farm products—to solve their admitted financial difficulties. Not all of these representations either to the railroads or to the Interstate Commerce Commission have been successful, but that they have been of real value is shown by the general rate increase on agricultural products granted by the Commission to the railroads effective March 28, 1938, of 5 percent, as compared with a 10-percent increase on industrial products.

Considering that many railroads are in a precarious financial condition, that the public is much concerned about their future, that the railroads are reluctant to experiment with general rate reductions, and that the Commission has consented to resort to rate increases in depression as a remedy for rail problems, the securing of lower rates and greater flexibility in rates is likely to be an uphill battle in the future, as it has been during the last decade. Therefore, farmers and other shippers should not overlook the economy and efficiency approach to the problem of securing lower transport charges.

Shippers and consumers should insist that the transportation system be as efficient and economical as possible. Waste and extravagance, whether in terms of excessive plant facilities with attendant overhead costs or of unnecessary operating expenses, should be eliminated. All efforts on the part of carriers to restrict service for the purpose of increasing profits—especially profits on obsolete or overbuilt facilities —should be resisted. The power of Government should not be employed to create a transportation cartel, permitting the railroads or other carriers to escape necessary and desirable adjustments in rates, service, capitalization, and fixed charges. In this dynamic age, failure to change means ultimate destruction.

Agricultural Credit

by E. C. JOHNSON [1]

IN 1900 it took $3,000 to start an average farm. In 1930 it took $8,000. These figures are merely one indication of the need for increased and better coordinated credit facilities for farmers in modern times. There are three types of financial aid to farmers—direct grants, with no expectation of repayment; loans by Government-subsidized agencies to farmers in a weak financial position; and loans on a regular business basis, with repayment at interest. This article deals with credit of the last type, which in turn may be long-term credit, intermediate credit, or short-term credit. In addition to the other facilities for credit to farmers in the United States, the article describes the present Farm Credit system with its main divisions—the Federal land banks and national farm-loan associations, the Federal Farm Mortgage Corporation, the production credit corporations and production credit associations, the Federal intermediate credit banks, and the banks for cooperatives. The article gives advice about where to get credit and how to use it wisely and discusses some of the

[1] E. C. Johnson is Chief, Economic and Credit Research Division, Farm Credit Administration.

basic considerations involved in a credit system adequate for current needs.

FINANCING agriculture in the United States involves extensive use of credit. Many farmers do not have sufficient capital of their own to acquire or operate a farm. They must therefore borrow money if they are to purchase or improve land for farming, and many farmers find it necessary to borrow to meet current expenses in producing crops and livestock. Some of the most important of the many problems facing farmers today grow out of the difficulty of obtaining adequate credit, of making proper use of it, and of meeting financial obligations as they fall due.

Credit is a means by which the borrower acquires immediate purchasing power in exchange for a promise to make certain payments in the future; in addition to the return of the sum advanced, these payments usually, though not necessarily, include interest for the use of the funds. In such a transaction a definite financial and legal obligation is undertaken, or, as it is commonly expressed, a debt is incurred.

The ability of farmers to obtain such advance purchasing power differs greatly. Some farmers, because of superior ability or because they already have substantial capital of their own, can obtain comparatively large sums by borrowing; other farmers experience difficulty in obtaining loans of even small amounts from regular credit channels. The ability of farmers to make use of credit likewise varies considerably. By intelligent use of credit some farmers can expand and improve their farm operations and increase their income. On the other hand, unwise and unproductive use of credit may load a farmer with heavy financial obligations which are likely eventually to lead to distress and perhaps to the loss of his farm and home. Too often more and easier credit has been advocated as a means of solving the problems of farmers. Additional credit may get farmers who are already heavily obligated even deeper into debt without solving the fundamental problem, which is to increase the income of farmers, improve their capacity to repay, and raise their standard of living.

THREE TYPES OF FINANCIAL HELP TO FARMERS

Present activities associated with the financing of farmers may be divided into three main classes. The first is aid to farmers by direct grants. In this class are grants to farmers who, because of misfortune and, in many cases, lack of ability in farming, have practically no resources of their own and therefore cannot be expected to repay regular loans. Assistance to this group can hardly be classed as credit since it is recognized that comparatively few advances will be repaid in full and that losses will be large. Perhaps all aid to this group should be in the nature of outright grants to avoid confusing relief payments with credit.

In the second class of financing are loans by agencies subsidized indefinitely by the Government in order that they may make loans to farmers who have ability but whose financial position is weak. Many farmers of such a group can make financial progress if intelligently directed; but lending to a group of even this character is likely

223761°—40——48

to mean losses for the lending institution, although under the supervision it can give, losses may be held to a minimum. Loans of this class, accompanied by definite plans for improved farming practices, will help many farmers to build up their resources to a point where regular credit agencies can take care of their needs. Part of the activities of the Farm Security Administration fall in this field.

The third class of financing includes loans made on what may be referred to as a business basis. In making such loans creditors seek assurance that the borrower will try to pay the loan when due and that his resources and earnings are such that it may reasonably be expected that the loan can be paid. Furthermore, credit on a business basis means that the borrower pays interest at a rate sufficient to cover costs and risks and to net the investor furnishing the funds the prevailing market rate of interest. The majority of the loans of commercial banks and life-insurance companies fall in this class. The permanent agencies of the Farm Credit Administration, except for certain emergency provisions, are directed by statute to follow loan policies in line with what is here called business credit. In application of these policies the interests and welfare of the farmer borrowers are given full consideration. It is expected that over a period of years the earnings on loans will cover losses, operating costs, and a fair return to investors purchasing the bonds of these institutions. The discussion which follows will deal largely with this third type of agricultural financing—credit to farmers on a constructive business basis.

TRENDS IN FARM INDEBTEDNESS

From early colonial days to the present the financing of agriculture has been a major economic problem. The pioneers who settled the country needed capital. Land was plentiful, labor was usually available, but capital for improvements and equipment was scarce. Even then farmers used credit to obtain capital, but the amount used was relatively small. With the shift in agriculture from self-sufficing farms having low cash incomes to commercialized and, in many cases, highly specialized farms with most of the income from the sale of farm products, credit became increasingly important as a means of providing the capital necessary for farming.

A major reason for the great increase in the use of credit by farmers is the much larger investment now called for in farm real estate and

Table 1.—Value of farm property in the United States, census years 1890 to 1930

Year	Total value			Value per farm		
	Land	Buildings	Machinery and equipment	Land	Buildings	Machinery and equipment
1890	$13, 279, 000, 000	(1)	$494, 000, 000	$2, 909	(1)	$108
1900	13, 058, 000, 000	$3, 557, 000, 000	750, 000, 000	2, 276	$620	131
1910	28, 476, 000, 000	6, 325, 000, 000	1, 265, 000, 000	4, 476	994	199
1920	54, 830, 000, 000	11, 486, 000, 000	3, 595, 000, 000	8, 503	1, 781	557
1930	34, 930, 000, 000	12, 950, 000, 000	3, 302, 000, 000	5, 554	2, 059	525

[1] Included in value of land.

equipment. This is illustrated by table 1, which gives the value of farm property in the United States by census years from 1890 to 1930.

Whereas in 1900 the average farming operation might have been undertaken with an investment of $3,000, in 1930 the amount of capital required for this purpose was about $8,000, and even this represents a substantial decline from the high point of a decade earlier.

Farm-mortgage indebtedness constitutes by far the largest share of total debts of farmers. Mortgage debts on fully owner-operated farms, according to the census, totaled approximately 1.7 billion dollars in 1910, increased to 4 billion dollars in 1920, to 4.3 billion in 1930, and then declined to 3.7 billion in 1935. The total farm-mortgage debt, according to recent estimates, reached a high point of 10.8 billion dollars in 1923, declined to 9.6 billion in 1930, to 7.8 billion in 1935, and to 7 billion dollars in 1939.

It is significant that the greatest increase in farm-mortgage indebtedness came during the period of rising farm income, 1910 to 1920. The rise in farm income resulted in a sharp increase in farm land values, particularly during 1917–20, when these values reached boom proportions in many regions. For the United States as a whole the index of farm real estate value per acre increased from 100 for the period 1912–14 to 170 in 1920. In some Midwestern and Southern States real estate values more than doubled during this period, and many farms were sold at what later proved to have been highly inflated values. Farmers who purchased real estate during the years of high prices, giving a mortgage for a large share of the purchase price, found themselves in financial difficulties when the decline in agricultural prices after 1920 greatly reduced their incomes. Periods of rising farm incomes are favorable for liquidation of debts, but unfortunately many farmers actually increased their indebtedness during these years.

Although a sharp drop in farm real estate values occurred after 1920, farm-mortgage debts continued to increase until 1923. Part of this increase included refunding of short-term, unsecured obligations into long-term mortgage loans and did not represent an additional increase in total debts among farmers. Farm income, although not so low as in more recent years, declined to a level materially below that of the war years, and foreclosures increased in many regions.

Since 1930 there has been a material reduction in farm indebtedness. Farm income fell to very low levels in 1930–34, and delinquency on loans was widespread; an increase in the number of foreclosures followed, and many farms passed into the hands of creditors. That the farm-mortgage debt declined sharply during these depression years was a result of this transfer of farms to creditors, who held them in most cases without encumbrance, and of the scaling-down of debts through refinancing. The further reduction in farm debt that has occurred since 1936 has been due to a larger extent to the amortization and repayment of loans from farm earnings or other income. The number of foreclosures has declined materially.

Debts represent a larger percentage of the value of real estate on mortgaged farms now than in former years. For the United States as a whole, mortgage debts on full owner-operated farms mortgaged in 1910 amounted to 27.3 percent of the value of land and buildings.

In 1920 this percentage was 29.1; in 1930, 39.6; and by 1935 it had increased to 50.2 percent.[2] The higher ratio of debt to value in 1935 as compared with that in 1930 was not due to an increase in debts—the average mortgage debt per farm in the United States actually declined from $3,521 in 1930 to $2,899 in 1935—but to the great decline in the value of farm real estate, which reduced the equity of farmers in their farms.

Changes in the average debt per mortgaged owner-operated farm by census years and regions are shown in table 2. From this table it is also apparent that, as might be expected, the average mortgage debt varies greatly between regions because of differences in size of farm, type of farming, and other factors.

Table 2.—Average debt per mortgaged farm [1] in stated years

Region	1910	1920	1930	1935	Region	1910	1920	1930	1935
New England	$1, 088	$1, 855	$2, 547	$2, 414	West South Central	$1, 255	$2, 316	$2, 663	$2, 286
Middle Atlantic	1, 508	2, 278	3, 009	2, 583	Mountain	2, 221	3, 824	3, 683	3, 094
South Atlantic	851	1, 870	1, 917	1, 617	Pacific	2, 405	4, 736	4, 979	3, 853
East North Central	1, 783	3, 362	3, 758	3, 098					
West North Central	2, 568	5, 398	5, 616	4, 602	United States	1, 715	3, 356	3, 521	2, 899
East South Central	701	1, 606	1, 448	1, 311					

[1] For fully owner-operated farms reporting mortgage debts.

It should not be assumed that most farms are mortgaged; on the contrary, a majority of farmers are free from mortgage debts. In 1935 according to the census only 39.6 percent of the fully owner-operated farms in the United States were mortgaged. This means that most farmers are at least not faced with loss of their farms from failure to meet mortgage obligations. But a comparatively large number of the others have debts large enough to constitute a heavy burden.

Prices of farm products began a sharp decline in 1930 and reached very low levels in 1932 and 1933. The serious effect of this decline on farm income is indicated by the fact that estimates of gross income from farm products in the United States amounted in 1929 to 11.9 billion dollars and in 1932 to only 5.3 billion dollars. Besides the disastrous decline in gross income the widening disparity between agricultural income and nonagricultural prices made it exceedingly difficult for farmers to pay current operating and living expenses, and many operated at heavy losses with insufficient income to pay taxes and debt charges. Credit from regular sources was not available to tide farmers over the period of emergency. A considerable number of the banks in the country closed their doors during the period 1928–33, and many rural communities were left without banking facilities. Where banks remained in operation they were forced to restrict their loans, and in many regions even farmers in good financial condition found it difficult to borrow for current operations.

[2] These ratios vary from region to region. In 1935 corresponding ratios were highest in the West North Central region, 58.6 percent, and lowest in the Pacific region, 39.8 percent.

CREATION AND ACTIVITIES OF FEDERAL CREDIT AGENCIES

One of the first attempts to relieve the serious agricultural credit situation was the establishment by the Reconstruction Finance Corporation of a regional agricultural credit corporation in each of the 12 Federal land bank districts. Authority for their establishment was granted under section 201 (e) of the Emergency Relief and Construction Act, approved July 21, 1932; control and supervision of these regional corporations was transferred to the Farm Credit Administration, created May 27, 1933, by Executive order. Proceeds of loans by the regional agricultural credit corporations were used for refinancing existing agricultural indebtedness as well as for financing current operations. From their organization in the fall of 1932 to December 31, 1938, these corporations made loans aggregating $325,684,348, exclusive of renewals. Repayment of these advances has been very satisfactory; by the latter date 96 percent of the total amount advanced had been repaid. The corporations were placed in liquidation May 1, 1934, and their liquidation is now nearing completion.

For some years Congress has provided funds annually for emergency crop and feed loans. Since 1933 these have been made through the Farm Credit Administration. These loans have been restricted to farmers who could not obtain credit from other sources. They reached a peak in 1933 when 633,586 loans were made, amounting to $57,375,940; since then the number has declined each year, many farmers having been able to place themselves in a position where they could obtain credit from regular sources or meet expenses by using their own capital.

The year 1933 was one of important developments in the farm-credit field. The Emergency Farm Mortgage Act of 1933, approved May 12, made funds available for emergency loans to farmers in addition to expanding the activities of the Federal land banks, which had been established as permanent credit institutions in 1917. The Farm Credit Administration, established May 27, 1933, brought all Federal agencies dealing with agricultural credit into one unit (fig. 1). The Farm Credit Act of 1933, approved June 16, provided for the establishment of production credit associations to make short-term and intermediate-term loans to farmers. These associations obtain funds for loans by discounting notes with the Federal intermediate credit banks established in 1923. The same act also provided for the establishment of 12 district banks and 1 central bank to extend credit to farmers' cooperative associations.

Under the Farm Credit Administration the country has been divided into 12 farm credit districts. In each district there is a Federal land bank, which makes long-term mortgage loans; a production credit corporation, which supervises the production credit associations making short-term loans; a Federal intermediate credit bank, which serves as a dependable source of funds for financing institutions making short- and intermediate-term loans; and a bank for cooperatives extending credit to farmers' cooperative associations. The Farm Credit Administration is headed by the Governor, in the Washington office, and each of the four separate fields of credit activity referred to is under the immediate supervision of a commissioner.

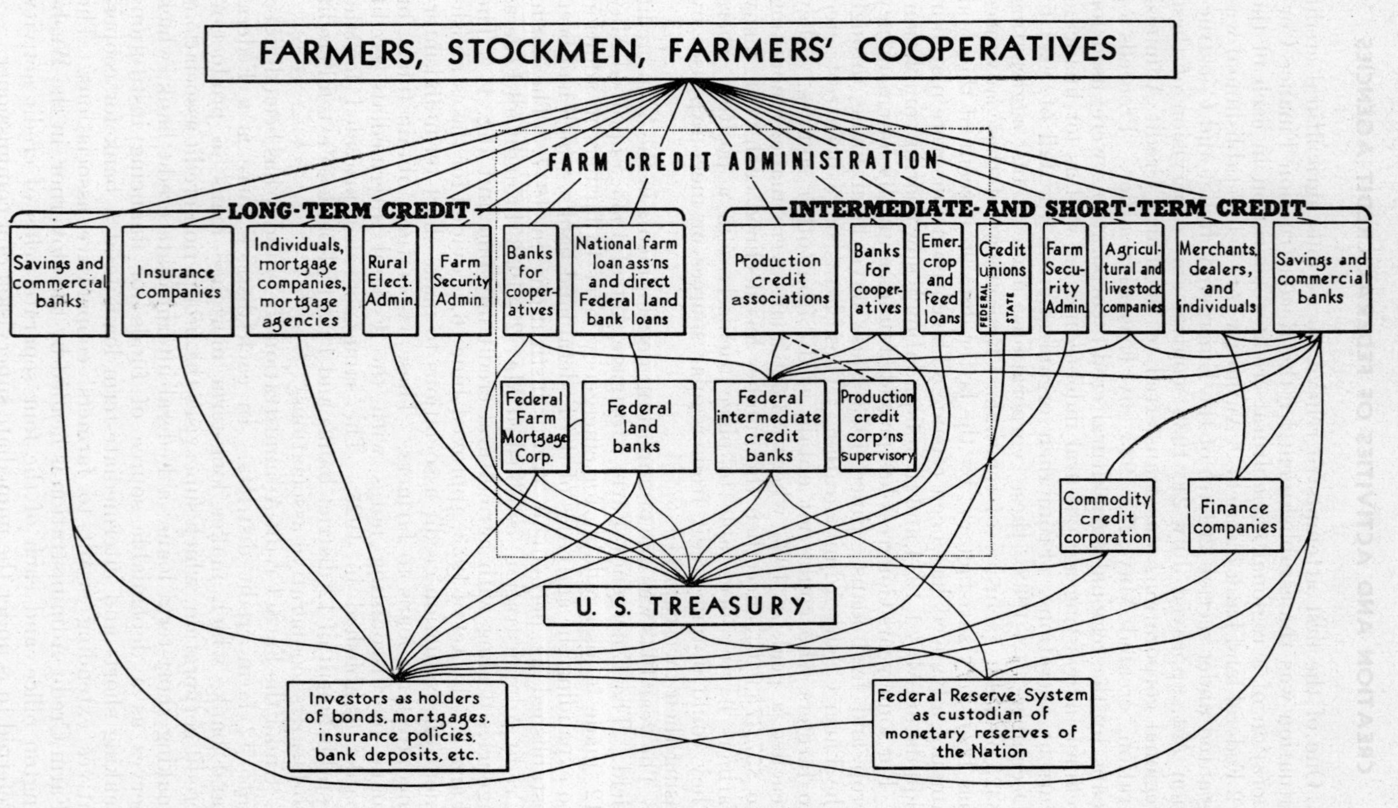

Figure 1.—The agricultural credit structure.

As a result of the 1933 legislation thousands of farmers refinanced their outstanding debts through the facilities of the Federal land banks and the Land Bank Commissioner. Land banks are restricted to first-mortgage loans not to exceed 50 percent of the appraised normal value of the land plus 20 percent of the value of insured improvements. However, the Land Bank Commissioner may lend up to 75 percent of the appraised normal value of the property, secured by either a first or a second mortgage. Many farmers wishing to refinance debts were enabled to do so by obtaining a first-mortgage loan from the Federal land bank and a second-mortgage Commissioner loan, provided the total of these loans did not exceed 75 percent of the normal appraised value. Some farmers were able to obtain a reduction in their debts from their creditors by making a cash settlement from funds obtained through their land bank or Commissioner loans. Almost without exception the refinancing was at a lower rate of interest, which further reduced the debt burden.

An extensive refinancing program was carried on during 1933, 1934, and 1935. During these 3 years the Federal land banks made 287,683 loans, amounting to $1,130,672,451, and the Land Bank Commissioner made 441,397 loans totaling $820,343,777.

By the end of 1933 it was apparent that the $200,000,000 fund originally provided for the Land Bank Commissioner loans would be insufficient to meet the demands for emergency loans. Congress accordingly created the Federal Farm Mortgage Corporation by the Federal Farm Mortgage Corporation Act, approved January 31, 1934. This Government corporation has an authorized capital of $200,-000,000 and obtains funds for loans by the sale of its bonds, which are guaranteed both as to principal and interest by the United States Government.

In addition to long-term mortgage loans, many farmers were aided in obtaining short-term loans to finance current operations. The latter are made by production credit associations, organized as farmers' cooperative credit associations (fig. 2).

Government emergency lending to farmers was carried on as one of the functions of the Resettlement Administration, established by Executive order on April 30, 1935. This lending was part of the activity to rehabilitate dispossessed and destitute farm families who had lost their capital during the depression. Individual loans were usually small, at the most a few hundred dollars, and the funds were used to buy livestock, equipment, and supplies and to rent land. The farm- and home-management plans worked out for each borrower, together with the capital advanced, enabled many distressed and low-income farmers to improve their standard of living and establish themselves on a more secure basis.

On September 1, 1937, by order of the Secretary of Agriculture, the Farm Security Administration replaced the Resettlement Administration, and this agency has continued to make rehabilitation loans. It also makes loans to farm tenants for the purchase of farms under the provisions of the Bankhead-Jones Farm Tenant Act, approved July 22, 1937. Limited funds have been available for loans to selected farm-tenant families for purchase of farms up to the full value of the farm on a 40-year repayment plan at 3-percent interest. Trained

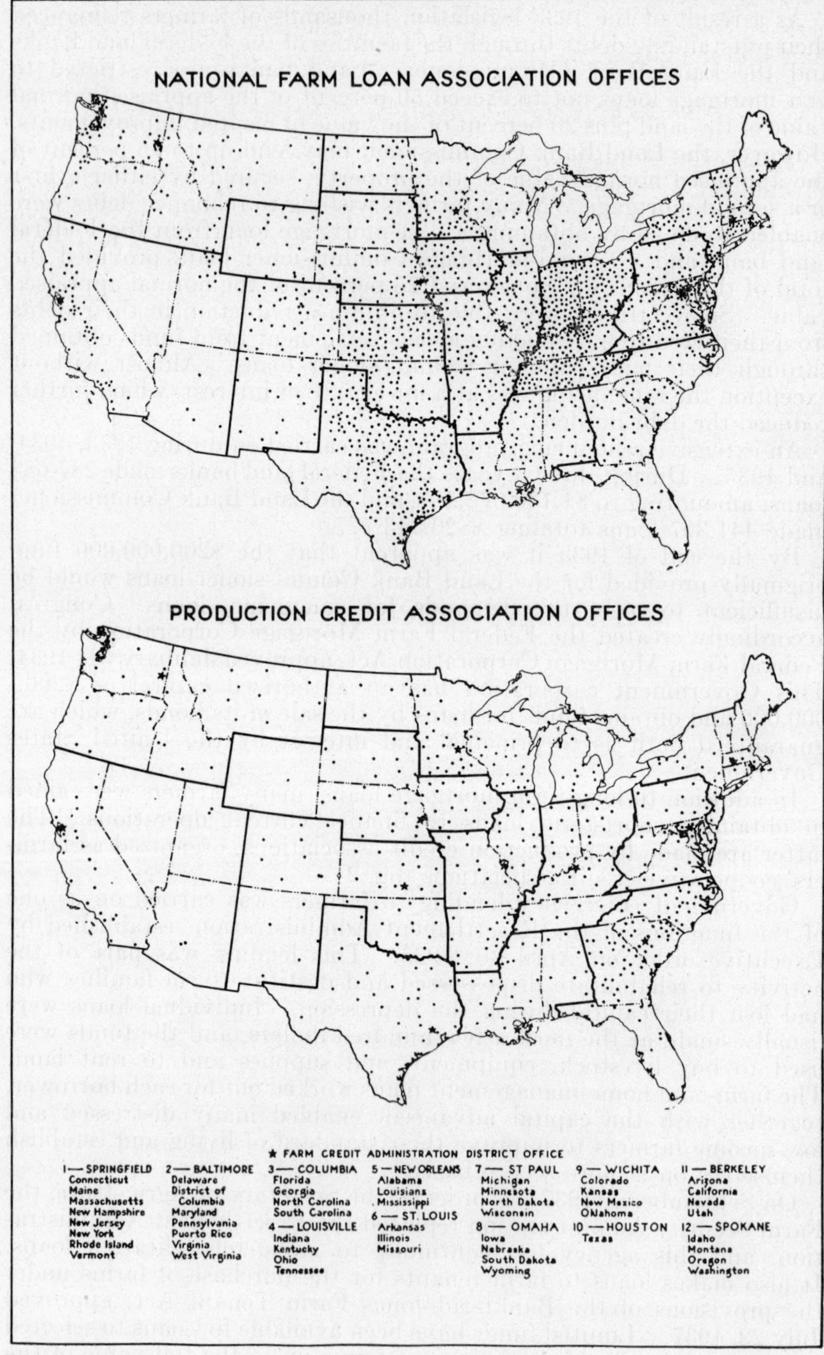

Figure 2.—Locations of national farm loan association and production credit association offices are indicated on the maps by dots. Stars represent district offices.

personnel assist the purchasers in developing sound plans for organizing and operating the farms.

IMPROVED FINANCIAL SITUATION OF FARMERS

Since 1934 the financial position of farmers generally, except in areas affected by drought, has improved. Refinancing in large volume reduced the debt charges for thousands of farmers, and higher prices during 1934–37 increased the income of farmers, enabling many to remove delinquencies on debt and tax obligations. The number of foreclosures in the United States per thousand farms mortgaged January 1, 1935, estimated at 27.8 in 1934, declined to 15.0 in 1939. Of the Federal land bank loans outstanding at the end of 1933, 48.8 percent were extended or in default, while at the end of 1939 only 20.5 percent were extended or in default. In 1934, the year of the greatest refinancing activity, the Federal land banks and the Land Bank Commissioner made approximately $1,300,000,000 worth of loans, but in 1939, the loans closed had declined to $78,998,000. Meanwhile other credit agencies have again become active in agricultural lending, indicating renewed confidence. For example, estimates of farm mortgages recorded by life-insurance companies increased from $46,000,000 in 1934 to $138,000,000 in 1939, and those recorded by commercial banks from $110,000,000 to $218,000,000 for the same years.

About three-fourths of the farmers having farm-mortgage debts have been able in recent years to meet their interest obligations and in many cases make payments on the principal of loans. It is difficult, however, to generalize on the credit situation of farmers. In many regions, such as the Great Plains, where there have been severe droughts for several years, delinquency on loans is great and farmers and creditors still face serious problems. In all regions individual farmers whose obligations are too heavy to carry may be unable in the long run to carry on farming activities because of their heavy debt load. More careful analysis by creditors of applications for loans to determine whether the funds desired can be used to advantage and can be repaid from farm earnings will do much toward developing a more stable agricultural situation.

PRINCIPAL SOURCES OF AGRICULTURAL CREDIT

Long-Term Loans

Because a large share of the capital of farmers is invested in land and buildings, a large share of the credit obtained is in the form of long-term mortgage loans. Approximately three-fourths of the agricultural debt falls in this class. When a farmer wishes to obtain a long-term mortgage loan, he may apply to one of a number of agencies—individual investors, commercial banks, insurance companies, or the Federal long-term loan institutions. Individuals provide probably one-fourth of the total amount of mortgage loans. The relative position of institutional lenders in the mortgage field shifted during the agricultural depression (table 3). Between 1929 and 1938 Federal land banks greatly increased the total of their loans to farmers, the Federal Farm Mortgage Corporation came into existence as an important source of credit, and the life-insurance companies and commercial banks declined in importance in the long-term credit field.

Table 3.—Lending-agency farm-mortgage loans outstanding on December 31, 1929, 1935, 1937, and 1938

[In thousands—i. e., 000 omitted]

Year	Estimated total farm-mortgage debt	Loans by Federal land banks	Loans by Federal Farm Mortgage Corporation [1]	Loans by life-insurance companies	Loans by commercial banks
1929	$9, 631, 000	$1, 185, 765		$2, 105, 477	[2] $945, 172
1935	7, 639, 000	2, 059, 845	$794, 121	1, 054, 770	487, 505
1937	7, 214, 000	2, 024, 473	811, 489	895, 470	501, 450
1938	7, 071, 000	1, 971, 630	751, 392	887, 336	519, 276

[1] Land Bank Commissioner loans.
[2] June 30, 1931.

The Federal land banks were established in 1917 as provided for in the Farm Loan Act of 1916. The country was divided into 12 districts (now referred to as farm credit districts), and a bank was organized in each district for the purpose of making long-term amortized loans secured by first mortgages on farms. Loans by the Federal land banks, as previously mentioned, may not exceed 50 percent of the appraised normal value of the land mortgaged plus 20 percent of the appraised value of the permanent insured improvements on the farm. Loans may be made for the purchase of land, equipment, fertilizer, and livestock; to provide buildings and other farm improvements; to provide funds for general agricultural uses; and to liquidate all debts incurred prior to January 1, 1937, and debts incurred for agricultural purposes without regard to time incurred. Funds for loans are obtained by the sale of land bank bonds to investors. The contract rate of interest charged by the land banks on loans made through national farm loan associations generally may not exceed by 1 percent the rate on the last issue of farm loan bonds. In 1940 the contract rate on loans was 4 percent, but under provisions of law the temporary rate paid is 3½ percent. Under existing legislation this temporary reduced rate will be in effect until July 1, 1942.

Federal land bank loans are usually made through national farm loan associations. When a farmer obtains a land bank loan he subscribes for stock in his association equal to 5 percent of the amount of the loan. The association then subscribes for an equal amount in stock of the land bank. Capital stock of the Federal land banks on December 31, 1939, totaled $236,475,965, of which $107,786,870 was held by national farm loan associations, $125,000,000 by the United States Government, and $3,689,095 by borrowers obtaining loans direct from the land banks.

The Federal Farm Mortgage Corporation provides funds for Land Bank Commissioner loans. In making and servicing these loans the Corporation utilizes the services of the national farm loan associations and the facilities of the Federal land banks, which act as its agents.

Funds for loans are obtained through the sale of bonds, which in the aggregate may not exceed $2,000,000,000. Land Bank Commissioner loans may be made for the same general purposes as Federal land bank loans but may be secured by either first or second mortgages on farm property, either real or personal. The maximum Commissioner loan to any one farmer is $7,500, and the loan may not exceed 75 percent of the "normal or prudent investment value of the property." Loans are made on a long-term amortization plan and bear interest at the rate of 5 percent, which by act of Congress was temporarily reduced to 4 percent for all interest payments falling due on or after July 22, 1937, and prior to July 1, 1940; the rate has been set at 3½ percent for the 2-year period ending June 30, 1942. Authority to make Commissioner loans expires June 1, 1942.

Life-insurance companies for well over half a century have been a major source of farm-mortgage credit. During the 1920's they were very active in farm-mortgage lending, and by 1928 the estimated volume of outstanding farm-mortgage loans by life-insurance companies reached $2,172,863,000. Foreclosures and refinancing during the depression had reduced this to $887,336,000 in January 1939; although the trend again turned upward in recent years. Most of their loans have been made in an area bounded on the east by the Appalachian Mountains and on the west by the one hundredth meridian, with about three-fourths of them in 12 Midwestern States. Their loans average larger than those of other agencies because a greater proportion are on the larger and higher-valued farms. The loans are generally made as straight loans with 5- or 10-year terms, although in recent years the practice of making longer-term, amortized loans has become more common. Interest rates of 4 to 4½ percent are common on new loans in the better agricultural areas.

Commercial banks in rural areas, both State and National, make farm-mortgage loans. Such loans have been of service to farmers, but as students of banking have often pointed out, since liabilities of commercial banks are largely payable on demand, their assets should be in sufficiently liquid form to permit payment on short notice. However, the farm-mortgage loan, although not so liquid as some other assets, if properly made may be a desirable type of loan for banks in rural areas, particularly banks that have a relatively large share of their deposits in the form of savings rather than demand deposits. Total farm-mortgage loans by commercial banks, estimated at $945,-172,000 on June 30, 1931, declined rapidly during the depression, increased slowly after 1937, and in January 1939 amounted to $519,276,000. Their loans are usually made for a term of 5 years or less, and interest rates vary greatly from region to region.

Short- and Intermediate-Term Loans

As in the case of long-term credit, a number of agencies are available to which a farmer may apply whenever a short-term loan, a seasonal loan, or perhaps a production loan extending over several seasons is desired. Commercial banks are a convenient source, and farmers with a proper credit rating can usually obtain reasonable terms. During the depression, however, banks were not always an available source, and this was one factor leading to the establishment of the cooperative production-credit system.

Approximately 500 production-credit associations in the United States provide short and intermediate credit to farmers who have the basis for credit. Unlike the commercial banks they do not have deposit liabilities and therefore need not curtail lending because of fear of withdrawal of funds by depositors. These associations have access to capital in the money markets of the country through the Federal intermediate credit banks, which discount the loans and obtain funds through the sale of debentures. A production-credit association may make loans for any agricultural purpose. Loans must have a satisfactory repayment plan and usually are secured by a chattel mortgage on livestock, equipment, or crops. They are drawn to mature when crops or livestock are marketed. The term usually does not exceed 1 year, but loans may be renewed for limited periods if the security and other credit circumstances are satisfactory. Associations charge a rate of interest which may not exceed by more than 3 percent the rate of discount of Federal intermediate credit banks. The latter rate at present is 1½ percent, and the rate charged farmers is 4½ percent. A borrower must hold class B (voting) stock in his association in an amount at fair book value not to exceed par, equal to $5 for every $100 borrowed. In 1939 production-credit associations made 234,266 loans, and advances on these loans, including renewals, totaled $320,961,046.

Merchants in many regions are a leading source of credit. No data are available as to the total amount of credit granted farmers annually by merchants, but the figure is undoubtedly large, as many farmers purchase supplies and equipment on credit. Since poorer credit risks are often accepted by merchants than by lending agencies, some farmers may find merchants their only source of credit. Studies have shown that merchant credit is more expensive than that from regular credit agencies. Goods purchased on credit usually cost the farmer more than if purchased for cash, and interest and other charges are high, particularly on installment contracts. It is expensive for merchants to extend credit, and this is reflected either in the sale price of goods or in credit charges. Many farmers who can borrow from regular credit sources find it advantageous to do so and to pay cash for goods purchased from merchants.

AGRICULTURAL CREDIT PROBLEMS

As the policies and practices followed in the past in extending credit to farmers are reviewed, it is obvious that too much attention has been paid to the value of the collateral securing a loan and insufficient attention given to analyzing the income of the farmer as an indication of his ability to repay the loan. This emphasis on collateral by both creditors and farmers has resulted in excessive lending during periods of rising prices for farm products and farm real estate and in difficulties for both farmers and creditors during periods of low prices when the debts become a heavy burden. Unless ability to repay is given careful consideration by the borrower and the creditor, both suffer. A loan based on sale value of collateral and in excess of the earning power necessary to carry the debt is likely to become delinquent during periods of low income, and the collection of it in such periods may mean foreclosure with loss to both borrower and lender. It becomes apparent, therefore, that it is in the interest of both borrowers and lenders to keep loans within the capacity of the farmer to repay out of earnings from the farm.

Proper appraisal is the key to successful long-term loans on farms. Too often in former years appraisals were based on current sale values of land and loans approved on the basis of a ratio of such values. This procedure led to excessive loans during years when land values were high, and in succeeding years, when values had declined, the farmer often found he had no equity, since the debt then exceeded current values of the real estate. Sound appraisals require not only a careful estimate of the value of the farm, but also an analysis of earning power to determine the size of loan that can be carried by the farmer over a period of years.

Studies of the experience of creditors in different areas indicate clearly the importance of determining carefully the economic productivity of land. The great range in economic productivity that exists between areas has not been properly reflected in land values. The result has been overvaluation of lands of low productivity and in some cases undervaluation of lands of high productivity, although with respect to the latter, appraisals have, as a rule, been more satisfactory. Not only creditors but farmers have tended to overvalue poor lands and to set prices out of line with productivity, with the result that many farmers on the poorer lands have failed.

The importance of credit and credit policies to conservation of soil resources should not be overlooked. The farmer who assumes a heavy debt obligates himself to make certain definite payments and must plan his farm operations to meet these. Faced with large interest payments that must be made if he is to continue to hold his farm, he may be forced to use his land for the production of crops that will give him the largest immediate cash return, even though this means depletion of the soil. Also, under the pressure of heavy debt payments he may be unable to repair and prevent rapid depreciation of farm buildings. On the other hand, with only a moderate indebtedness, the farmer should be able to maintain a cropping system that will give him the greatest net return over a period of years and will also conserve the productivity of his land. Creditors can aid in conservation of soil by holding loans to conservative figures in line with the farmers' ability to pay while maintaining a proper cropping system.

As another means of conserving soil resources, creditors might well give attention to including in mortgage contracts more specific provisions calling for practices that will prevent rapid depreciation of the farm. The usual wastage clause now used in mortgages merely provides that the borrower shall maintain the buildings in a good state of repair and use the land in a husbandmanlike manner. However, it is difficult to define "waste" under such general terms, and courts have been reluctant to enforce penalties for breach of mortgage contract other than failure to pay interest and principal when due. Therefore, it appears that creditors might find it advisable to draw up more specific terms relating to soil conservation in mortgage contracts. Such terms might call for a certain type of farming, for keeping a certain proportion of the farm or certain tracts in grass, and for other conservation practices and might stipulate that failure to meet these requirements would make the loan due and payable. Farmers interested in conserving their farms should raise no serious objections to such provisions if they conform to sound farming practices. This program would require that creditors check farms at intervals for the purpose of noting their condition, but farmers would be left free to carry on current operations without restriction so long as they conform to the general plan agreed upon.

Not only do excessive loans tend to result in depletion of the soil, but they also tend to increase the number of farms operated by tenants. When a farmer loses his farm through foreclosure it is usually transferred to the creditor, who often operates it for a period through a tenant. Unwise use of credit, in other words, may increase the percentage of farms operated by tenants. On the other hand, proper use of credit may provide funds that will enable tenants or others to purchase and operate their own farms.

While it is true that many tenants—and in this group are many successful farmers—do not care to assume the risks associated with ownership of a farm, preferring to remain tenants, it is probably fair to say that most tenant farmers wish to own a farm. Ownership of a farm gives a certain security and an opportunity for home and farm development that are difficult for a tenant to attain. Credit is helpful in the purchase of a farm, but loans must be held within the carrying capacity of the farm if the owner is to have security of ownership. To reduce the risk assumed in the purchase of a farm the farmer should have capital of his own that will enable him to establish a substantial equity and hold his debts to a minimum. The long-term amortization loan is well adapted to the needs of the farmer who is paying for a farm over a long period of years. It eliminates the hazards of the frequent and often expensive renewals of the shorter-term mortgage loans which were common in former years.

Experience indicates that if used intelligently credit may be very useful but that it has often been used in a manner that resulted in great difficulties for the farmer. Certain fundamental rules relating to the use of credit which farmers may well keep in mind are:

(1) Use credit only for productive purposes.

(2) Obtain credit from sources of lowest cost, all charges and service rendered by the creditor considered.

(3) Analyze the plans for paying the loan and develop a satisfactory program of repayment.

(4) Since income usually varies greatly from year to year, during favorable years pay debts and build up reserves to draw upon during years of low income.

(5) Maintain a high credit rating by making every effort to pay loans when due, or if necessary, by arranging in advance of maturity for renewal or extension of the obligation.

It may be well to emphasize again that while credit properly used may help farmers to increase their income and raise their standards of living, the fact must not be overlooked that more credit will not cure all the ills of agriculture. The greatest need is to assist the farmer in getting out of debt, not deeper into it.

Crop Insurance

by William H. Rowe and Leroy K. Smith[1]

INSURANCE has long been used by businessmen as a means of sharing certain business risks. Private companies have provided fire and hail insurance on farmers' crops. All-risk crop insurance is a new experiment to reduce the impact of a major crop loss on the individual farmer. So far it is being tried only with wheat. Here is a careful analysis of the theory back of this experiment; an account of how it works, including the results of the first year's operations; and a frank discussion of the problems involved. Finally the authors analyze the merits and disadvantages of some of the changes that have been proposed. If crop insurance is to be extended to commodities other than wheat, they conclude, the advance must depend upon careful studies of the new problems that will arise with each crop. Such studies are now being made in connection with cotton, corn, and citrus fruits.

INSURANCE is a device whereby the losses sustained by a few are shared by all in a group exposed to the same risk. Developed several centuries ago to lessen the hazards of marine shipping, today insurance is available in connection with most business risks.

In the agricultural field, insurance on their buildings and equipment against such risks as fire, windstorm, and hail is available to farmers from stock or mutual companies. Insurance on crops by such companies is available only against fire and hail, yet these are not the most important risks in producing a crop. Some companies have attempted to write "all-risk" insurance on crops, but the projects have not been successful. Such contracts were written against loss of income from the crop for any cause, and price declines were, on the whole,

[1] William H. Rowe is Senior Agricultural Economist, Division of Agricultural Finance, Bureau of Agricultural Economics, and Leroy K. Smith is Manager, Federal Crop Insurance Corporation.

more important causes of loss than crop failures. The insurance of price would be desirable if it were feasible, but prices are to a considerable extent determined by human actions and are not predictable. On the other hand, factors affecting production are largely physical and, in considerable measure, can be predicted.

All-risk crop insurance, covering only losses in production, has now been made available on wheat by the Federal Government. This will cushion the shock of partial or total crop losses and reduce for the wheat farmer the possibility of accumulated debts, a lowered standard of living, and impairment of morale.

Crop insurance on wheat is proving itself an aid not only in regions where failures are frequent but also in those where production is relatively certain and failures are not ordinarily contemplated nor provided for. By this method the burden of loss is spread over a large group of wheat farmers throughout the country. Each farmer, by payment of his premium, purchases security against crop failure. The total premiums collected constitute a reserve with which to pay the losses. Those who harvest a good crop thus share the loss of those not so fortunate.

From another point of view, a farmer who buys crop insurance each year distributes the burden of his losses over a period of years. By this device he can substitute for an unpredictable loss that occurs infrequently a definite annual cost item in the form of an insurance premium. By paying annual premiums into the insurance reserve he is really setting aside part of his production each year to take care of his losses in years when they occur.

Crop insurance for farmers is the counterpart of the unemployment insurance for industrial populations provided for in the Social Security Act. The industrial worker is dependent from week to week and month to month on the continuance of his employment. The farmer is dependent from season to season on the production of his crops. Both live in more or less constant uncertainty as to whether their source of income will fail. The Social Security Act provides for Federal assistance to States to operate unemployment insurance systems whereby the industrial worker is assured of a limited payment in the event that he loses his job. The Federal Crop Insurance Act provides for insurance for the wheat farmer against the loss of as much as three-fourths of his average crop.

In years of crop failure the farmer who does not have crop insurance or some other reserve to fall back on must resort, if he needs funds, to borrowing, or he may have to seek private or public relief. His chances of obtaining money in these ways are uncertain. Crop insurance introduces certainty in place of uncertainty. It is less expensive than borrowing, because it eliminates the payment of interest and other borrowing costs which are apt to be high at those times when the farmer is pressed for funds. It is undoubtedly less expensive to the Government than public relief, because the farmer contributes through payment of premiums to his own need for funds following crop failure. It is less embarrassing to farmers to provide in advance through insurance for their own needs in years of misfortune than to have to accept public relief. The Federal crop insurance program helps farmers to help themselves.

The function of crop insurance is to supplement rather than to supplant various other means of stabilizing income, such as diversifying the sources of income or protecting the crop from damage. The farmer's income usually can be stabilized somewhat by arranging his farming plans so that the income arises from various sources. He might plant several crops, some of which can be consumed on the farm, rather than a single crop which he must sell; or he might be able to keep livestock as another source of income. But carried beyond a certain stage, such practices are frequently more expensive than insurance. Farms are often best adapted to the production of a certain crop; a reduction in yield or net income must be accepted if other crops or livestock products are to be produced. At some point the loss through diversification will probably exceed the cost of insurance.

Similarly, there are many ways in which the crop can be protected from hazards, but protective measures, too, if carried beyond a certain point are often more expensive than insurance. For society as a whole, it may be cheaper to let the weather destroy crops under certain circumstances and in certain areas than for each producer to expend large amounts for equipment and labor to protect his crop. Especially is this true in the case of specific commodities of which the Nation, as a whole, produces a surplus that cannot be either consumed or exported.

Because many of the major problems of American agriculture during recent years have resulted from the existence of unmarketable surpluses due to the loss of foreign markets, the decline of domestic purchasing power, and other economic factors, public attention has been focused on the problem of agricultural surpluses. The American farmer might, indeed, be said to have a surplus psychology. Crop insurance, on the other hand, deals with the problem of deficits—individual deficits may exist even in years when there is a general surplus of production. It should not be forgotten that while public interest is focused on surpluses over the country as a whole, many farmers each year produce little or nothing. This is the problem that crop insurance is designed to solve.

The Federal crop insurance program is not a subsidy program. The premium rates are determined in such manner that, over a period of years, premiums collected will be sufficient to pay indemnities. The Federal Government takes care of the expense of administering the program as its contribution toward stabilizing agriculture. By and large, the program is designed to be supported by the farmers.

As a national program, crop insurance is designed to bring security to the individual farmer and, as a consequence, to bring more stability to agriculture as an industry. Financial security for the farmer will enable him in many cases to continue farming, when otherwise he would be compelled to find other means of livelihood because of failure to meet his debts or inability to live on his income in a year of crop failure. Thus it may eliminate a part of the shifting in the farm population and perhaps reduce some of the migratory movements that have been so pronounced following the drought years. It should tend to stabilize local business conditions in farm communities by providing purchasing power in years of crop failure; it should stabilize local financial institutions by enabling farmers to pay their debts with

223761°—40——49

greater regularity; and it should stabilize land and other property values by reducing foreclosures.

THE FEDERAL CROP INSURANCE PROGRAM

The Federal Crop Insurance Act, passed as title V of the Agricultural Adjustment Act of 1938, approved February 16, 1938, provided for crop insurance for wheat. Such insurance was made available for the first time on the crop seeded for harvest in 1939.

The Federal Crop Insurance Corporation, established by that act, is an agency of, and within, the United States Department of Agriculture and subject to the supervision of the Secretary of Agriculture. The board of directors of the Corporation consists of three persons employed in the Department of Agriculture who are appointed by the Secretary. The present directors are the Administrator of the Agricultural Adjustment Administration, the Chief of the Agricultural Marketing Service, and the officer in charge of Land-Policy Credit Coordination. The executive officer of the Corporation is the manager, who is appointed by the board of directors with the approval of the Secretary of Agriculture. The headquarters of the Corporation are at the Department of Agriculture in Washington, D. C.

Insurance operations are conducted from branch offices under the supervision and control of the Washington office. The branches are located at Kansas City, Mo., Minneapolis, Minn., Chicago, Ill., Spokane, Wash., and Washington, D. C.

The detailed field work of writing insurance, checking acreage, inspecting crops, and adjusting losses is administered by the same county committees who administer the agricultural conservation program. This work is done with the assistance of the community committees and is subject to the supervision and review of the State agricultural conservation committees. The crop insurance program is, in large measure, farmer-operated, the committeemen themselves being farmers who are elected to their positions by farmers.

Insurance Coverage

Insurance protection under the Federal crop insurance program is not against loss from specific hazards but against losses from all unavoidable production risks. The insured farmer is protected against loss in yields below 75 percent or 50 percent of his average yield, depending ordinarily on the plan chosen by the insured. If the yield of the insured crop is less than 75 percent or 50 percent of the average yield and such decrease in yield is due to unavoidable hazards, the insured is indemnified for the shortage. If the loss is due in part to the use of poor farming methods or to some other avoidable risk, the indemnity covers only that part of the loss which is due to unavoidable causes. The insurance takes effect upon the seeding of the crop and payment of the premium. It terminates upon the threshing of the wheat or on September 30, whichever occurs first.

Insurance In Kind

The Federal crop insurance program is based on the principle of insurance in kind; that is, the amount of the premium and the amount of the loss is determined in bushels of wheat. Payments of both premiums and indemnities may be made in warehouse receipts for wheat, but they are ordinarily made in the cash equivalent thereof. The price used in determining the cash equivalent is one that tends to reflect the local market price and is obtained by using central market prices with deductions for freight and handling charges.

As the obligations of the Federal Crop Insurance Corporation are in bushels of wheat rather than in dollars, it is necessary if losses from price fluctuations are to be avoided that the Corporation invest its cash premiums in wheat. Otherwise, if the price of wheat increased materially between the time when premiums were collected and the time losses were settled, the premiums might be inadequate to meet losses merely because of the increase in price. Thus it has been the policy to invest in wheat the premiums received in cash equivalent and to pay losses by selling the wheat and giving the farmer a check for the cash equivalent. This plan places the Corporation in essentially the same position as if it had accepted wheat for premiums and paid wheat for indemnities. The activities of the Corporation with regard to dealing in wheat are limited, however, because the Federal Crop Insurance Act stipulates that it can buy wheat only to the extent of the premiums collected and can sell wheat only to pay losses, prevent deterioration, or change the location of the wheat. In the latter two cases, the wheat sold must be promptly replaced by purchase of comparable stocks.

Since premium rates are based on average loss experience over a period of years, it is to be expected that in years of abundant crops the premiums collected will be more than enough to meet indemnities and that in years of widespread crop failures the premiums will be inadequate to meet indemnity payments. The reserve accumulated in years of good crops will act as a cushion to absorb the shock of fluctuations in losses from year to year, functioning as a kind of ever-normal granary. Its operations will be automatic. It should contribute to stabilizing the supply of wheat on the market, and insofar as it stabilizes supply it should have some tendency toward stabilizing prices.

An annual accounting by the Corporation in terms of profit and loss on insurance operations is not possible. An excess of premiums collected over indemnities paid in any year cannot be deemed a profit for the Corporation, and, conversely, an excess of indemnities paid over premiums collected in any one year is not considered a loss. Both of these conditions merely reflect the normal functioning of the insurance reserve.

The wheat farmer who is insured regularly each year may obtain a somewhat higher price for his wheat if his production fluctuates with the Nation-wide production of wheat. If he collects his indemnities for loss in years of widespread crop failures when the national production is small and the supply is short, the cash equivalent for his indemnity will ordinarily be on the basis of higher-priced wheat than the cash equivalent for the premiums which he paid. If his wheat crops do not vary consistently with the national production, or if factors other than supply become the major factors affecting the price of wheat, such an advantage would not be gained.

Individual Farm Ratings

One of the basic principles on which the crop insurance program has been built is that of individual farm rating—that is, each farm has its own coverage per acre based on its average yield and its own premium rate based on its risk. It is doubtful whether crop insurance would be feasible under a plan by which each farm would have the same insurance terms. If each farm were insured for an equal number of bushels of wheat per acre, the low-producing farms would be overinsured, and the high-producing farms would be underinsured. Low-yielding farms would tend to collect indemnities frequently, whereas the high-producing farms would seldom collect any indemnities. The owners and operators of high-producing farms would not take insurance, and the only farms in the program would be the overinsured low-producing farms. The ultimate goal of the individual-rating plan is that over a long period of years each farm shall carry its own losses. The individual-rating plan is deemed necessary to fit the insurance to the farm. Otherwise the high-yield, low-risk farm will be penalized for the low-yield, high-risk farm, and the industrious, capable farmer will be penalized for the less industrious and less able farmer.

The average yield is determined, if possible, from reliable and applicable data regarding yields for each year of a base period. Such averages are adjusted to a longer, more representative period. In the 1940 crop insurance program the base period was the 9 years 1930–38, and the data for this period were adjusted to the 13-year period 1926–38, except that in certain areas where the base period contained an exceptionally large number of drought years, the 20-year experience, 1919–38, was reflected in the adjustment factor. If historical yield data were not available or were unreliable or inapplicable for a few years of the base period, the yields for such years were appraised. If reliable and applicable annual-yield data were not available for two-thirds of the years of the base period, the average yield was appraised on the basis of a similar farm.

To determine the premium rate for a farm for which annual-yield data are available, the loss experience or loss history is determined by an analysis of the amount of indemnity that would have been required had the farm been insured in past years. This is illustrated in table 1. The average yield for the base period is determined and the amount of loss that would have been paid had the crop been insured for 75 percent (or 50 percent) of such yield is determined for each year. This gives an annual loss cost. The losses are then averaged for all years of the base period, which gives an average loss experience for the base period. This loss experience for the base period is adjusted to the longer period used in establishing yields. After such adjusted loss experience is determined for the farm, the premium rate is obtained by averaging this loss experience with the loss experience for the whole county, which has been determined by actuarial studies with the use of sample farms. For those farms for which annual-yield data are not available, the premium rate is appraised on the basis of a similar farm for which data are available. A minimum premium rate of 0.5 bushel for 75-percent insurance and 0.3 bushel for 50-percent insurance applies if the computed premium is less than such amounts.

Table 1.—Computation of insurance coverage and premium rate per acre for an individual farm for 75-percent insurance

Crop year	Yield per seeded acre	75 percent of average yield	Annual loss cost per acre
	Bushels	*Bushels*	*Bushels*
1930	14.5	9	0
1931	16.0	9	0
1932	8.2	9	.8
1933	14.0	9	0
1934	17.2	9	0
1935	2.5	9	6.5
1936	12.8	9	0
1937	15.9	9	0
1938	7.0	9	2.0
Total	108.1		9.3
Average for period (total divided by 9)	12.0		1.0
Adjustment	+.3		−.1
Adjusted average	12.3		.9
Adjusted average loss cost for county			1.3
Total			2.2
Premium per acre for farm (total divided by 2)			1.1
Insurance coverage (75 percent of adjusted average yield)	9.2		

In the 1940 crop insurance program yields and premium rates were determined for all wheat farms in the county in advance of the application-writing period. First, a group of representative key farms for which annual-yield data were available was selected. The yields and premium rates were computed for these farms. All other farms for which annual-yield data were available were treated in the same manner. For most of the farms, however, the yields and premium rates were appraised by comparing each such farm with a key farm for which average yield and premium rate had been computed (fig. 1). All yields and rates were set up on listing sheets. These listing sheets and supporting papers were submitted first to the State office of the Agricultural Adjustment Administration and then to the branch office of the Corporation for approval.

To provide a further control over the work done by county committees, the yields established for crop insurance purposes were required to average out to a check yield established for the county. Such check yields were based on 13-year (or 20-year) average county yields, as determined by the Division of Crop and Livestock Estimates of the Bureau of Agricultural Economics. If the average of the yields originally established for crop insurance did not meet the county check yield, they were required to be factored so that they would meet the county check yield. This placed an automatic control over the level of yields established. Similarly, a county figure was determined from actuarial studies to which the premium rates established should check, or, if they did not check, should be factored. This placed an automatic control over the level of the premium rates.

In certain counties where wheat is produced under different practices—such as summer fallow and continuous cropping or irrigation and dry land—separate yields and premium rates were established for each practice on the farm, so that if the farmer followed different

Figure 1.—Three members of the county committee appraise yields and premium rates for individual farms for which annual yield data were not available.

practices on the same farm he could have a separate yield and rate for the acreage under each practice.

Some indication of the yields and the cost of insurance in different

Table 2.—County check yields and check premium rates for selected counties for the 1940 wheat-crop program

County	County check yield per acre	County check premium rate per acre for insured percentage of—[1]		County	County check yield per acre	County check premium rate per acre for insured percentage of—[1]	
		75 percent	50 percent			75 percent	50 percent
	Bushels	*Bushels*	*Bushels*		*Bushels*	*Bushels*	*Bushels*
Pembina, N. Dak	12.2	1.0	0.4	Sedgwick, Kans	13.2	.9	.3
Stark, N. Dak	8.0	1.6	.9	Blaine, Okla	12.5	.7	.3
Walworth, S. Dak	7.6	1.8	1.0	Carson, Tex	10.6	1.9	1.0
Perkins, Nebr.:				Young, Tex	10.0	.9	.3
General	9.7	2.0	1.1	Judith Basin, Mont	10.7	2.0	1.1
Continuous cropping	9.2	1.9	1.0	Whitman, Wash	26.4	.6	.2
Summer fallow	15.6	3.0	1.7	Umatilla, Oreg	25.9	.7	.2
Dodge, Nebr	19.4	1.3	.6	Lafayette, Mo	15.8	.7	.3
Thomas, Kans.:				Morgan, Ill	18.8	.6	.2
General	7.2	1.9	1.1	Putnam, Ohio	19.4	1.6	.7
Continuous cropping	6.7	1.8	1.0	York, Pa	20.8	.5	.1
Summer fallow	10.7	2.7	1.5				

[1] Subject to minimum premium rates of 0.5 bushel per acre for 75-percent insurance and 0.3 bushel for 50-percent insurance.

parts of the county can be obtained from the county check yields and check premium rates. A few of these are given for scattered counties in table 2. These figures are county averages; within each county there will be a wide range of yields and premium rates.

How it Works for the Farmer

The farmer who wants insurance must make application for such insurance and pay the premium before seeding the crop, and in no case later than the final date established for his county for the acceptance of premiums (fig. 2). It is necessary that applications for

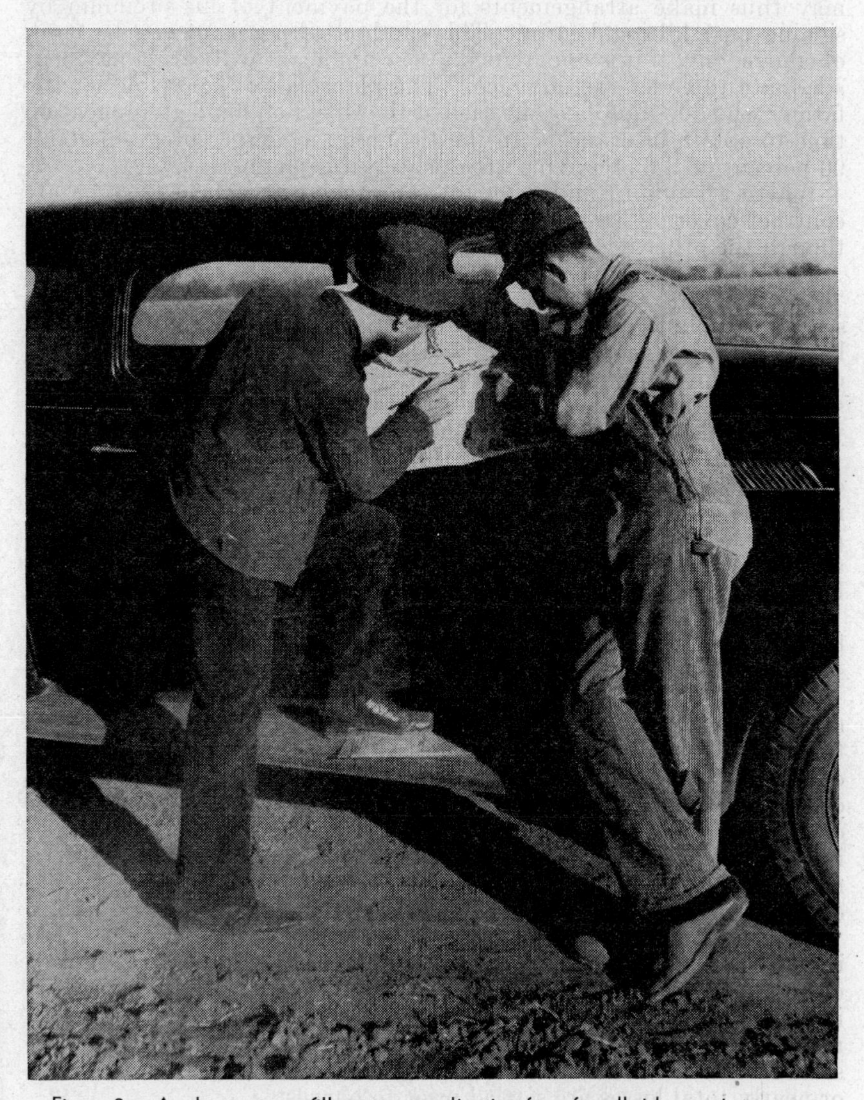

Figure 2.—A wheat grower fills out an application form for all-risk crop insurance.

insurance be made before the seeding of the crop, so that the possibilities of loss may not be known by either the insured or the insurer before the contract is made. If insurance could be obtained some time after the seeding of the crop, it would be possible for a farmer to insure a crop that had had a poor start. Such an adverse selection of risks would, in a few years, wreck the program.

A plan has been provided whereby the premium in the form of the cash equivalent may be paid by obtaining an advance from the Secretary of Agriculture out of payments to be earned under the agricultural conservation program. A farmer who applies for insurance may thus make arrangements for the payment of his premium by signing an additional form. This method of payment can be used, of course, only if it is apparent that the applicant will earn a payment adequate to cover the advance. The plan makes it possible for the farmer who does not have the cash or the wheat on hand at application time to obtain insurance. In the 1940 crop insurance program about 90 percent of the premiums were paid in this manner.

Where a landlord and a tenant are involved, each has a separate contract covering his interest in the crop, and either may insure even though the other does not.

The insurance covers all acreage of wheat on the farm except "succotash" (a mixture of wheat and other small grains) and self-seeded or volunteer wheat. A farmer may not insure only a part of his wheat acreage. Crop insurance does not appear to be feasible on a field-insurance basis because of the possibilities of an adverse selection of risks under such a plan and because all data acquired on yields are on the basis of the farm as a whole.

After the seeding of the crop, the insured notifies the Corporation of the exact acreage seeded. This figure must check with measurements for wheat acreage made under the agricultural conservation program. If the acreage seeded is greater than the wheat-acreage allotment for the farm, the wheat-acreage allotment is used as the basis for determining the total insured production and the premium.

The insured must notify the county committee if it appears before harvest that there will be a loss under the contract. Upon receipt of such notice, an inspection is made of the crop.

Claims for loss must be filed within 30 days after threshing, and always before October 15. Settlement of loss is made on the basis of the extent to which the production falls below the total insured production, with adjustment for any loss that may have occurred due to causes not insured against. In determining the amount of loss, the county committee and the adjuster working for the committee have information gained through inspections of the crop before harvest, measurements of wheat in bins or elsewhere on the farm, and evidence of production from threshers' reports, sales invoices, etc.

After the adjuster and the insured have agreed on the amount of loss in bushels, the papers are forwarded to the State office and the branch office for review and for payment of the indemnity. If the papers are in order and no question is raised as to the validity of the claim, payment is ordinarily made within 2 weeks. Although most losses are settled after harvest when actual production can be determined, total or nearly total losses are settled prior to harvest.

Results of First Year's Program

Nearly 166,000 policies were issued on the 1939 wheat crop, representing insurance on 7¼ million acres, on a part of which only the landlord's or only the tenant's interest in the wheat crop was insured. The total premiums collected in wheat, or its cash equivalent, were a little over 6¾ million bushels. Insurance was written in 1,289 counties of 31 States. Losses paid on the 1939 crop amounted to about 10,000,000 bushels.

PROBLEMS INVOLVED IN CROP INSURANCE

One of the most difficult problems involved is setting up the individual basis for crop insurance contracts. The reason for this is the lack of reliable and applicable wheat-yield records for the farms. Under previous agricultural programs, yield data for some individual farms were obtained. In some parts of the country these data were obtained for most of the farms; in others, for only a relatively small proportion of the farms. In some counties these data were proved figures; that is, the production had been substantiated by sales invoices, threshers' receipts, or some other evidence. But in most cases the acreage figures, until recent years, were estimates; consequently the yield figure contains a substantial element of estimation. At the present time, data are being acquired regarding yields of wheat for current years, on which it is hoped dependable records can be built up for yields on most of the farms.

Avoiding Adverse Selection of Risks

A problem encountered by all insurance organizations is that of avoiding adverse selection of risks. One of the principal ways used to avoid this in the crop insurance program is to require that all applications for insurance be made and all premiums paid before the wheat is seeded. To a considerable extent, this practice makes it possible to avoid insuring only those farms on which the prospects of the wheat crop are poor.

Other problems also must be met in selecting risks to be insured. With an annual contract and yields based on the average productivity of the farm, the farmer might take insurance only in those years when he planted his crop on that part of his farm least suited to the production of wheat. Or, he might base his decision whether or not to take insurance on the effect of the preceding crop on the possibilities of the wheat crop. One way to avoid some of these difficulties would be to have a contract extending over a period of perhaps 4 or 5 years.

It will always be difficult to avoid adverse selection of insurance risks, but it is expected that, as new experience is gained, fewer loopholes will be left for those who would take unfair advantage of the program.

Desire for Temporary Advantage

Some farmers attempt to obtain as much advantage as possible for themselves, and sometimes persons who are administering the program in counties or communities try to gain as much advantage as possible for their people. They may attempt to establish unduly high yields and low premium rates or to make liberal loss adjustments. A temporary advantage gained in these ways will ultimately work as a disadvantage, for if losses exceed premiums, the cost of insurance will soon be increased, and the yield bases will be decreased. Those who are most interested in crop insurance as a permanent program do not seek such temporary advantages.

Adjusting Losses

The problem of adjusting losses appears to be less difficult than was originally contemplated. This is undoubtedly because the work is done by local people. Ordinarily insurance companies do not ask their local representatives who write insurance also to adjust losses. But since the county committees are responsible for the success or failure of the program in their counties and are familiar with all the factors involved, it was decided that they should adjust the losses.

The experience with settlement of losses under the 1939 program indicates that the county committees can adjust or supervise the adjustment of losses in a satisfactory manner. This is a major item indicating the feasibility of crop insurance.

Reducing Costs of Operations

One of the main problems facing the crop-insurance program is that of reducing the unit costs of operation—that is, the cost per contract. One way to accomplish this is to get larger participation. In the 1940 program more than twice as many contracts were issued as in the 1939 program, which tended to reduce considerably the cost per contract. Furthermore, procedure has been simplified in many ways that will reduce the actual cost of operation.

A very important factor is the high cost per policy in minor wheat-producing areas. One way to solve this difficulty would be to confine the program only to the major wheat areas. Since the program is national in scope, however, it should be available to all wheat farmers. Furthermore, if crop insurance is successful for wheat, it may, in the future, be extended by Congress to include other crops. In that event, experience in the minor wheat-producing areas will be extremely valuable in applying the program to other crops.

The cost per acre is also excessive for farms with small wheat acreage. When the program was inaugurated consideration was given to limiting insurance to those farms on which a substantial acreage of wheat was planted. It was felt, however, that it would be unjust to refuse crop insurance to small farmers, and consequently no minimum limit was placed on the acreage that might be insured.

SUGGESTED CHANGES IN THE PROGRAM

A number of proposals have been made for changes in the crop insurance program. Each has some merits and some disadvantages. A few of the principal ones are outlined here.

Long-Term Contracts

Although the present insurance program is on an annual-contract basis, much consideration has been given to the possibilities of a long-term contract, perhaps for as long as 5 years. This was, in fact, the original plan, but the act limits the operations for the first 3 years to annual contracts. A long-term contract, if enforceable, would rule out the "in and outers"— persons taking insurance in years when the prospects for a crop are poor and not taking insurance in years when the prospects are good. This would be a desirable feature. Furthermore, since the premium rates are based upon experience over a period of years, it is probable that the insured, over the period of the contract, would be more likely to pay in as premiums practically as much as he collected in indemnities.

On the other hand, many difficulties are involved in the use of a long-term contract. Within a period of 5 years a large proportion of the farms would no longer be owned by the same persons who signed the original contracts, and there would be a great many more changes in tenants. Furthermore, there is no practical way of enforcing contracts for a large group of farmers except by requiring a down payment on the premium. It would be virtually impossible to collect advance payment on the premium for such a period of years. Despite the difficulties, the advantages of the long-term contract are such that serious consideration should be given to the plan.

Variable Annual Premiums

Consideration has been given at various times to the possibility of requiring larger premiums in years following good crops and smaller premiums in years following poor crops, rather than charging the same annual premium each year. One of the first plans considered was to charge a premium only if the yield exceeded the average, making the premiums in such years large enough so that it would not be necessary to charge premiums in years when the crop was below the average. Such a plan would make it easier for the farmer to pay his insurance premiums because he would be required to pay only following years when he had some surplus production. But, in view of the fact that price declines might make the income from large crops smaller than the income from short crops, such a plan might work better if premiums were collected only in those years when the income from the crop was above the average. Other plans might be devised that would provide for some premium being paid every year, the amount varying with the size of the preceding crop.

There would be many difficulties in the application of a plan providing for payments in varying amounts. In the first place, it would probably be necessary under such a plan to use a long-term contract so that over a long period the farmer would have to pay as much premium as would have been required on an annual-payment basis. As pointed out previously, many difficulties are encountered in the long-term contract for insurance. Thus, while in theory the plan appears to have merits and would undoubtedly emphasize the ever-normal granary aspects of the crop insurance program, there are practical difficulties which at the present time do not seem to be surmountable.

An attempt has been made to modify the annual-payment plan so that some of the benefits of a variable-payment plan could be obtained. Provision was made that the farmer could pay his premium for 1 year in advance, so that if he had a good crop he could of his own volition pay 2 years' premiums. Relatively little use, however, has been made of this provision.

Deferred Payment of Premiums

The question of whether or not insurance should be written on the basis of credit was given careful consideration before the present plan of requiring all premiums to be paid in advance was adopted. Undoubtedly many more farmers would take insurance if it were possible to obtain the insurance at the time of seeding and pay for it out of the insured crop. The principal difficulty with such a plan would be the problem of collecting the premiums after the crop was harvested. There would undoubtedly be some accounts that would be uncollectible. Where an indemnity was paid, the premium could be deducted from the indemnity, but where no indemnity was due it might be difficult to collect.

In view of the fact that the Corporation is primarily in the insurance business, it was deemed unwise that it should also extend credit. Approximately the same results are obtained, however, under the plan whereby an applicant for insurance may receive an advance out of his agricultural-conservation payments with which to pay his premium. Under this plan the amount of the premium is collected from the farmer by deducting such amount from the payment due him, so that the problem of collection of debts is eliminated. This plan appears, therefore, to be more workable than that of issuing insurance with the premium to be collected after the crop is harvested.

Insurance Based on Soil-Moisture Conditions

Another proposal that has been suggested is that, in areas commonly subject to drought, insurance be written on the basis of the amount of soil moisture at the time of seeding the wheat crop. In other words, if the soil-moisture conditions were good, insurance might be written for yields higher than the average of all years and at a premium rate lower than the average based upon the experience of all years. Conversely, in those years when soil-moisture conditions were bad the insurance, if written at all, would be written on the basis of yields lower than the average and premium rates higher than the average.

This proposal is based on experience of individual farmers and experiments by agronomists, which show that to a certain extent yields can be predicted by the amount of soil moisture at the time of seeding the crop. Such a plan might be feasible, but it would require that special soil-moisture tests be made on each farm before writing insurance. From the viewpoint of the insurer, this arrangement might be more desirable in some ways, because it would fit the insurance coverage and the premium rate to the actual condition of the insured crop. But from the viewpoint of the insured, it would not meet his needs in periods of widespread drought. The insurance program is offered so that farmers will have an income in years when they cannot, through conditions over which they have no control, produce a crop. Under such a plan the farmer would be insured for a substantial amount in years when his prospects of a crop were good and would receive little or no insurance protection in years when prospects were poor. In such years he would have no crop and no income from insurance. It was to provide an income to farmers in years of poor crops that crop insurance was initiated. Such a plan, therefore, would fail to accomplish one of the principal objectives of the program.

The Upper 75-Percent Plan

A plan commonly known as the "upper 75-percent plan" has been proposed, and legislation has been introduced in the Congress to provide for insurance on such a basis. The essence of this plan is to insure the upper 75 percent of the average yield, rather than the lower 75 percent as is now done. Under the proposed plan a farmer would receive indemnity for loss whenever his yield fell below the average yield, but in no case would he receive an indemnity in excess of 75 percent of his average yield. Thus, if a farmer has an average yield of 12 bushels per acre, he would, under the present plan, not receive any indemnity until his yield fell below 9 bushels. Under the proposed plan he would receive indemnity whenever his yield fell below 12 bushels, but he would never receive an indemnity in excess of 9 bushels an acre.

The reasons advanced in favor of this plan are that the farmer has a loss whenever he has a yield lower than the average and needs indemnification for his loss. This is particularly true in the Great Plains region where the average yield represents an average of successful crops and of failures, and the average yield itself is not considered a very successful crop. It is believed that the limitation of the amount of indemnity under the upper 75-percent plan to three-fourths of the average yield would not work undue hardship on those who have a complete crop failure because the farmer in such instance would not have to harvest the crop and his actual financial loss would not be the value of the full average yield. This plan would probably simplify the administration of the program in the cases of complete crop failures, because ordinarily it would not be necessary when adjusting losses to appraise the yield of the wheat left standing in the field, for such wheat would, in most cases, fall within the uninsured lower one-fourth of the average yield. It would be necessary only for the adjuster to determine that the yield of wheat left standing did not exceed one-fourth of the average yield. For instance, in the illustration given above it would be necessary for the adjuster to determine only that the yield of wheat unharvested was less than 3 bushels. It is believed by many that the additional premium necessary would be gladly paid by farmers in order to secure the additional coverage. This is probably the case, for throughout the whole program it has been obvious that farmers are more concerned over the amount of coverage per acre than they are over the premium rate per acre.

The main objection to this plan appears to be that insurance protection up to the average yield might result in overinsurance, with an increase in the so-called moral hazard. It is a sound principle of insurance that property should not be overinsured because under such circumstances the insured could benefit more by obtaining an indemnity for loss than by proper care of his property.

The adaptability of this plan may differ between areas. In some areas the average yield represents the typical yield, or the yield the farmer expects to get when the crop is planted. In other areas the average yield may represent a yield somewhere between a crop failure, on the one hand, and a successful crop on the other. In such areas the crop is planted in the hope of making a successful crop rather than an average crop, and insurance up to the average might not constitute overinsurance. In other words, in these areas it may not be necessary that the farmer carry the first 25 percent of the loss below the average yield because such average yield is, itself, 25 percent or more below the yield hoped for when the crop is planted. Therefore such a plan might be considered sound insurance practice in some areas of the country but not in others.

INSURANCE FOR CROPS OTHER THAN WHEAT

The Federal Crop Insurance Act not only provides for an insurance program for wheat, but also for research looking forward to the possibilities of insurance of other crops. Presumably if wheat crop insurance proves successful, the Congress may from time to time add other crops to the program. Research work is now in progress in the Bureau of Agricultural Economics on cotton, corn, and citrus fruits, and it is anticipated that the work may be extended to other crops.

The research work on cotton is further advanced than that on other crops. In fact an actuarial basis for cotton crop insurance has already been established, and a plan for such insurance has been developed.

The plan proposed for cotton is similar, in most respects, to that now used for wheat. It provides in addition, however, a feature for insuring against the loss of cottonseed as well as against the loss of lint cotton. This would be accomplished by increasing both premiums and indemnities by a percentage which reflects the average relationship over a period of years between the income from cottonseed and the income from lint cotton.

The application of crop insurance to cotton would involve some new problems. Cotton is a cultivated crop, whereas wheat is not. Cotton crops require insect control and in some areas are dependent in large measure on the fertilizer used. Furthermore, in insuring cotton it will be necessary to provide some arrangement whereby sharecroppers' interests in the crop can be insured. This will probably require some sort of master policy for the farm, with separate parts for each cropper.

In the application of crop insurance to corn, also, special consideration will have to be given to the fact that it is a cultivated crop. Furthermore, much of the corn that is grown is used for silage or is fed to livestock without being measured, and consequently accurate figures on production will be difficult to obtain. This has already presented a problem in the determination of an actuarial basis for insuring corn and would also be a difficult operating problem in any program.

The application of crop insurance to fruits presents further new problems. Control of insects and disease, variations in production with the age of trees, extreme variations in risks due to topography and location of the orchard, all present problems different from those encountered in the insurance of wheat. Furthermore, the present plan of reserves in kind used for wheat, which is contemplated for cotton and corn also, would not be applicable to fruit, a highly perishable commodity. It appears, therefore, that if crop insurance is to be extended to other commodities, the advance into new fields will be conditional upon careful studies of the new problems that will arise with each crop.

Rural Taxation

by ERIC ENGLUND [1]

SEVENTY percent of the taxes paid by farmers, the author of this article points out, are in the form of taxes on property; and the tax on farm real estate makes up 85 percent of the total property tax. If tax reform is needed by farmers, then, the real estate tax is the place for it. Since farmers pay the real estate tax solely to meet State and local expenses for such things as schools and roads any changes in the system would be a matter for State action; though the Federal Government is involved when State taxes other than the property levy compete with Federal taxes and when Federal subventions are urged to relieve the pressure on the States. This thoughtful article on a complex subject has no easy reforms to offer. It discusses trends in taxation, shows the use made of taxes, points out both faults and advantages of the property tax, and finally discusses the question of public revenues and expenditures in the large framework of the rural-urban balance.

FARMERS like others are interested in taxation chiefly because of the probable effect of taxes and public expenditures on their income, the value of their property, their community life, and the economic and social prospects for themselves and their children. Abstract questions of fairness in the distribution of the costs and benefits of governmental services and improvements are usually of less immediate interest except as the practical effects are felt in the daily affairs of the people.

Some indication of the bearing of these questions on the welfare of farmers may be found in considering the more significant facts and

[1] Eric Englund is Assistant Chief, Bureau of Agricultural Economics.

trends in rural taxation in recent decades. The causes of increased tax levies, the chief characteristics of the tax system of which these levies are parts, and their economic effects and possible relation to public policy in agriculture are also briefly discussed in this article.

RISING EXPENDITURES AND TAX LEVIES

Total expenditures of Federal, State, and local Governments have increased rapidly in recent times, especially in the past 25 years. This increase has not been confined to rural communities, to particular States, or even to the United States; it has been a world-wide experience, fully recognized everywhere. If measured in dollars, this increase in expenditures—and therefore in taxes—is due to higher prices of goods and services bought with the taxpayer's money and to expansions in public improvements and services and governmental subsidies.

The question whether these extensions of the role of government are desirable is beyond the scope of this article and outside the definitive judgment of any individual. It belongs rather in the fields of social philosophy and political science, which study the scope and function of government and that fusion of opinion, judgment, prejudice, and conflict of interests from which public policy emerges in a democratic society.

Of immediate interest and bearing directly on the present subject, however, is the trend of farm taxes in recent decades, especially since the beginning of the war of 1914–18. The past 25 years has seen not only a very rapid increase in public expenditures and tax levies but also sharp variations in farm income and property values and rural-urban economic relationships. Against these changes and as a part of them the major trends in farm taxes will be considered, largely in terms of national averages, though regional and even local differentiation would be apropos and significant in a more extended treatment of the subject.

Farm real estate taxes per acre in the United States throughout the

Table 1.—Taxes on farm real estate, farm prices and income, and wholesale prices of all commodities, specified years, 1890–1939

Year	Total taxes on farm real estate	Index of tax per acre (1909–13=100)	Tax per $100 of full value of real estate	Prices received by farmers (1909–14=100)	Gross cash farm income [1]	Wholesale price of all commodities (1910–14=100)
	Million dollars		*Dollars*		*Million dollars*	
1890	82	63	(2)	(2)	(2)	82
1900	107	62	(2)	(2)	(2)	82
1910	166	91	0.47	102	5,785	103
1915	243	128	.57	98	6,391	102
1920	483	244	.79	211	12,553	225
1925	517	270	1.07	156	10,927	151
1930	566	277	1.30	126	8,883	126
1935	394	180	1.14	108	6,969	117
1938	407	186	1.16	95	7,599	115
1939	(2)	(2)	(2)	93	7,711	113

[1] Exclusive of Government payments. These were $573,000,000 in 1935, $482,000,000 in 1938, and $675,000,000 in 1939.

[2] Data not available.

decade 1890–1900 remained practically constant at about 60 percent of the 1909–13 level (table 1). Meanwhile the acreage of land in farms increased materially, with an approximately corresponding advance in total farm real estate taxes from $82,000,000 in 1890 to about $107,000,000 in 1900. Then began a rise which by 1913 carried the average tax per acre to 117 percent of the 1909–13 average and the total real estate tax to $218,000,000. This advance, caused in part by a rising price level, was the beginning of a sharply accelerated rate of advance in farm property taxes up to 1921, followed by nearly another decade of less rapid increase. These advances were a part of increased taxes levied on property in general, both rural and urban, associated with advancing prices and public expenditures.[2]

FARM TAXES AND PRICE TRENDS

In earlier decades expenditures and taxes advanced while prices declined, as shown by property-tax movements and price trends from the Civil War to the low point of the price decline that ended in 1896. Prices fell from the Civil War peak in 1864, which was 98 percent above the 1910–14 level, to 32 percent below that level in 1896. Meanwhile all property-tax levies per capita in the United States, both rural and urban, increased gradually, from about 42 percent of the 1912 level in 1870 to 54 percent of that level in 1890 and 66 percent in 1902. The year 1896 marked the end of a declining price trend lasting more than three decades and the beginning of 25 years of advancing prices. Meanwhile total farm real estate taxes also advanced, as shown by data for the country as a whole after 1890 and for a few areas in the preceding decade.

The general urge toward increased expenditures and rising property-tax levies in the thirty-odd years after the Civil War was more than strong enough to offset the counteracting influence of falling prices. But it should be noted that taxes in general, including the property tax, were very low from 1865 to the close of the century as compared with recent levels. This is a major consideration in the reasons for the upward trend of property taxes for some time prior to 1896 despite declining prices.

The much higher level of taxes in more recent years, both on a per capita basis and in relation to income and property values, makes it inevitable that taxes should be somewhat more responsive to changes in the general price level and that farm property taxes should vary more closely with the rise and fall in farm prices and income. It does not necessarily follow, however, that year-to-year expenditures in general will fluctuate closely with prices and income, because of certain relatively new elements in social and economic policy affecting public finance. Chief among these elements are the large expenditures to relieve distress and to stimulate employment in time of economic depression.

That farm taxes have responded sharply to the trend of prices and income in agriculture in the past decade needs only a passing mention here, because the statistical facts are generally known. In 1929, the

[2] For a more extended discussion of trends in property taxes in the United States and local rates in Great Britain since 1860 in their relation to price levels, see Literature Cited, p. 788, (*6*). Italic numbers in parentheses refer to this list.

223761°—40——50

peak year of these taxes, property levies per acre of land in farms averaged in the United States 181 percent above the 1909–13 level. By 1934, however, they had fallen to 78 percent above the pre-war level, advancing to 86 percent above in 1938 (table 1).

NATURE OF THE PROPERTY TAX

The property tax has long accounted for the major share of State and local revenues. Lately, however, this share has diminished somewhat, as shown in table 2, by reason of increased State revenues from other sources—chiefly the gasoline tax, motor-vehicle registration, the income tax, and sales taxes. Local government, particularly in rural areas, still depends to an overwhelming extent on property taxes, these taxes yielding 92 percent of all local tax revenues in the United States in 1938. It is of interest, therefore, to consider the relative importance of this tax among the direct taxes paid by farmers and to examine its characteristic feature as the major element in the present system of rural taxation.

Table 2.—Total direct taxes affecting farmers in the United States and the percentage of the total represented by each type of tax, specified years, 1927–34 [1]

Year	Total	Real estate	Personal property	Gasoline and automobile licenses	Other
	Million dollars	*Percent*	*Percent*	*Percent*	*Percent*
1927	787	69. 2	12. 2	14. 7	3. 9
1930	850	66. 6	11. 8	18. 8	2. 8
1932	699	64. 3	11. 4	21. 7	2. 6
1934	608	60. 2	10. 7	26. 2	2. 9

[1] From A Graphic Summary of Farm Taxation, by Donald Jackson (*8*).

In broad outline the existing tax system in rural communities is essentially the same as that applied to other properties and communities. The system, wherever applied, may be divided into two great classes of taxes—direct and indirect. Of the direct taxes paid by farmers, the general property tax constituted in 1934, the last year for which specific data are available, about 70 percent. Of this property tax, about 15 percent was paid on personal property—livestock, implements, crops on hand, household goods, etc.—and 85 percent on real estate. It is evident, therefore, that any substantial alteration or improvement in taxation as it affects the farmer must necessarily revolve largely around this tax.

The general property tax is levied under State law, the Federal Government levying no taxes on property as such. Therefore possible improvements in the property tax itself or in its administration is a State matter. But it should be noted that some of the improvements needed in the position of the property tax in the prevailing tax structure as a whole in large part depend upon the relation of Federal taxes to those of the States. In this sense there is an important and practical relation between the Federal tax structure and the general property tax in the revenue system of the several States.

The property tax seems to have been based upon the implied assumption that ability to pay is proportional to the taxpayer's possession of property, as measured by the valuation of the property for taxation. That this assumption is no longer valid, whatever may have been its merits in earlier times, will be brought out later.

The tax rate in each taxing jurisdiction is ordinarily determined by dividing the sum of money required as revenue under the property levy by the total valuation of the property within the jurisdiction. This makes it apparent that equality of valuation as among different properties of taxpayers is essential to an equitable application of the theory that property represents ability to pay. Even though a tax may be levied upon property as such, irrespective of domicile or status of the owner, this does not obviate the fact that the tax is collected from the owner and is based upon the implied assumption that his ability to bear it is measurable by the value of his property.

INEQUALITIES OF PROPERTY VALUATION

Valuation is usually based upon the "true value" of the property, or some specified fraction thereof, assuming a willing seller and willing buyer. It is apparent, therefore, that fairness in the distribution of the property tax, even within the implied theory of ability to pay as represented by ownership, depends upon the extent to which the tax assessor is able to determine the true value of one man's property as compared with that of another. In practice one of the worst faults of the general property tax appears in the failure to assess property uniformly in relation to its value. Many studies in the Department, in various State experiment stations, and elsewhere have shown very wide differences in the valuation of properties for tax purposes.[3]

Extensive inequalities appear not only among individual properties but also among classes of property and among taxing jurisdictions. One of the most commonly occurring inequalities appears between large and small properties. Larger properties generally are assessed at a lower percentage of their true value than are small properties, and land of low value per acre is very often assessed at a higher ratio to full value than is land of high value per acre (*1*, *9*).

Inequality of assessment results in discrimination among taxpayers, because the tax is levied at a uniform rate on assessed valuation within the taxing jurisdiction. The owner of a small property assessed at a higher ratio to full value than the large property bears a burden proportionately higher than intended by the strict application of the principle upon which the property tax rests. Land of low value per acre, probably reflecting its inferior quality, bears a burden disproportionately heavy as compared with the better and more valuable land. This inequality, it may be noted, is significant from the standpoint of its effect on land use and on tax delinquency, of which more will be said later.

When the property of one county is assessed at a higher ratio to full value than the properties of other counties, that county bears a disproportionately heavy part of the State property tax, which is

[3] See Assessment and Equalization of Farm and City Real Estate in Kansas (*3*) and other studies in this field in Oregon, Delaware, Minnesota, and elsewhere, several of which are summarized in Taxation of Farm Property, by Whitney Coombs (*2*).

applied at a uniform rate throughout the State. From this has grown, in a number of instances, a noticeable competition among counties and other local jurisdictions to report for the county a low valuation in order to escape a part of the State levy. This tendency, however, may become less important with the increased use of other taxes for State purposes and consequent reduction or elimination of the State levy on property.

Although real effort has been made through State boards of equalization to promote greater uniformity of assessment among local jurisdictions and individual properties, the problem of assessment and equalization is far from solved, and glaring inequalities remain. These are probably more serious now in their practical consequences than they were many years ago, because higher tax rates accentuate inequalities of valuation. Overassessment of low-value land, for example, was less likely to cause serious tax delinquency in earlier years of relatively low tax rates. The much higher tax rates in recent years, coupled with overassessment of such land, undoubtedly have contributed much to tax delinquency, especially in areas that include large amounts of low-value land.

On strictly logical grounds it appears that, within a given taxing jurisdiction, tax delinquency would not be more likely on low-value land than on land of higher value if both were assessed uniformly in relation to their real value. In this it is assumed that the tax rate itself is not higher in areas of the low-value land. If the land really has a market value, some buyer will come forward with an offer for it. The offer may be to purchase preceding delinquency, or it may be in the form of purchase of the tax lien established by delinquency.

As a practical matter, however, a given piece of land may appear to be of so little value to its owner that he may not find it to his advantage to pay the tax, however low, and to meet such other responsibilities as may be associated with ownership. Yet the land may have at least a trace of value which would become more concrete through transfer to other hands.

The effort to apply the general property tax equally on all property long ago created certain practical problems which have compelled significant changes in the property-tax laws and their administration in an increasing number of States. When the property-tax rate was low the pressure on the taxpayer and the inducement to escape the tax were, of course, less than under the much higher rates of recent years. The increase in the effort to escape the tax legally and even to evade it illegally, resulting from the higher rates, has been of real significance to farmers and other real estate owners. It has caused the "general" property tax to become little more than a tax on real estate.

Other forms of wealth have in large measure found their way out from under the general property levy. Intangibles usually have either escaped altogether or been subjected to much lower rates in order to lessen the inducement to escape. As a practical matter, since such property is difficult to assess except with the owner's cooperation, the reduced rates have yielded at least as much revenue and sometimes a good deal more. The lower rate was not infrequently a concession to the owner in exchange for his less unwilling cooperation with the taxing authority. Strong compulsory methods of reaching intangibles either have been found inexpedient or have been avoided altogether.

Property Levy Concentrated in Real Estate

It has been less necessary to make similar concessions of expediency to the farmer and other real estate owners. Their property is in the open for all to see. The same is largely true of the farmer's personal property—livestock, equipment, crops. Consequently the real estate and the farmer's personal property so closely and visibly associated with it have remained in the "general" property-tax base. With rising expenditures, therefore, and with characteristic public reluctance to turn to other sources of revenue, the property-tax rate advanced sharply in the years of rapidly advancing State and local expenditures.

Along with widening escape of intangibles, another inadequacy of the general property tax appeared and became increasingly evident with economic changes that produced large numbers of citizens whose income and taxpaying ability were not represented by ownership of property. Whatever may have been their uncertain contribution to the cost of government in the form of taxes levied on others and in some part shifted to them, they were not called upon to pay taxes directly and systematically until other taxes—income taxes, excises, etc.—were devised to broaden the tax base. This base had rapidly become too narrow, especially from the standpoint of the good old principles of fiscal adequacy and taxation according to ability to pay.

Fiscal Adequacy of Property Tax

Among the advantages of the general property tax, that of fiscal adequacy is of particular interest. While revenue requirements were well within the practical capacity of the property-tax base, it was readily possible to meet these requirements of a given taxing jurisdiction by the simple expedient of varying the tax rate. By dividing a figure representing the revenue sought by another figure representing the valuation of taxable property in the jurisdiction, a tax rate could be established that would yield the necessary revenue, assuming that taxpayers generally met their obligations. In this way it was quite possible to secure the necessary elasticity of revenue when expenditures of government were low and revenue requirements correspondingly moderate.

With increased cost of government, however, a new problem arose. With growing demand upon State and local government for more and better schools, larger property-tax expenditure for roads and numerous other improvements and services that go with a higher standard of community living, the pressure for revenue gradually approached the practical limit of taxable capacity of property in many States and communities. This was particularly true during the early years of the depression, beginning in 1930. Income from property and the income of citizens from all sources declined sharply. Expenditures by State and local government did not fall in proportion; on the contrary, demands for increases appeared for relief and other outlays necessitated by the depression. The result was a sharp rise in tax delinquency, indicating that for the time at least the property tax had lost its elasticity—that is, its ability to yield the required revenue. In some areas it appeared to have passed the point of diminishing revenue returns.

This situation showed itself not only in increased tax delinquency but also in tax transfer of property, which is the culmination of delinquency. The estimated number of farms changing ownership by reason of tax delinquency increased from 4.7 per 1,000 of all farms in the year ended March 15, 1929, to 15.3 in 1933. With the subsequent improvement in farm prices and income, the number declined to 3.4 in the year ended March 1939.

It is hardly possible to determine the ultimate limits of the revenue-producing power of any particular tax. Yet it appears that this limit under the property tax was reached and even exceeded in the depression years in some parts of the country, especially in large areas of agricultural land.

The practical limitations of the property tax as a means of raising additional revenue have caused State governments generally to turn to other sources. They have done this also out of considerations of fairness in the distribution of the cost of government and in recognition of possible economic consequences of still higher property taxes. Chief among the other sources are gasoline taxes and motor-registration fees, income taxes, and sales taxes. These represent a growing share of the farmer's direct taxes. The amount of the sales taxes paid by farmers in the period covered by table 2 (p. 774) is not known. A tentative estimate suggests that the amount in 1935 may have been in excess of $25,000,000, but this figure does not include any allowance for such effect as sales taxes may have had on prices received by farmers.

It will be noted that the "other" taxes in table 2, which represent income taxes, poll taxes, etc., constitute a very small part of the total, while automobile and gasoline levies are a large and rapidly growing part. This is indicative not only of the part represented by the automobile in the yearly balance sheet but also of the importance of the motor vehicle and gasoline as sources of revenue for highway purposes. Some of these tax funds are diverted to general purposes, but by far the greater share (86 percent in 1937) goes for roads and streets. This has had the effect of providing better roads in rural areas, for the benefit of urban as well as rural people, without placing the increased load on farm property, the farmers, however, bearing a substantial part as users of motor vehicles.

Rigidity of the Farm Property Tax

The elasticity of the property tax from the standpoint of revenue requirements is in fact inelasticity to the taxpayer. The tax varies very much less than does his income. This is especially true of the farmer, whose income is closely associated with his taxable property. Hence the property tax is high in relation to his income in years of low returns, as contrasted, for example, with the income tax, the amount of which varies automatically with the income of the taxpayer.

The inelasticity of the farm property tax is shown in table 3. The tax was 4.7 percent of the gross cash income in 1925 and 9.8 percent, or more than double the proportion in 1932. The total real estate tax had actually declined about 11 percent, but income had fallen 58 percent.

An even more striking illustration of the inelasticity of the real estate tax from the farmer's standpoint is found in its relation to the cash income which the farmer has left for family living and taxes after deducting the other estimated costs of producing that income. This relation, also shown in table 3, changed from 5.7 percent in 1925 to 14.1 percent in 1932.

Table 3.—Relation of farm real estate taxes to cash farm income in the United States, specified years, 1910–39

Year	Gross cash farm income	Income available for family living and taxes	Farm real estate taxes	Ratio of tax to gross cash income	Ratio of tax to income for living and taxes
	Million dollars	*Million dollars*	*Million dollars*	*Percent*	*Percent*
1910	5, 785	5, 267	166	2. 9	3. 2
1915	6, 391	5, 621	243	3. 8	4. 3
1920	12, 553	9, 679	483	3. 8	5. 0
1925	10, 927	9, 067	517	4. 7	5. 7
1930	8, 883	6, 724	566	6. 4	8. 4
1932	4, 682	3, 261	460	9. 8	14. 1
1934	[1] 6, 720	5, 349	384	5. 7	7. 2
1936	[1] 8, 499	6, 974	397	4. 7	5. 7
1938	[1] 8, 081	6, 401	407	5. 0	6. 4
1939	[1] 8, 581	(2)	(2)		

[1] Cash income for 1934, 1936, 1938, and 1939 includes Government payments.
[2] Data not yet available.

Notwithstanding its disadvantages, the general property tax will continue to be the major source of local revenue and furnish a substantial part of the State revenue as well. This is in spite of the transformation of this tax into little more than a real estate levy under pressure of rising revenue requirements and its failure to reach taxpaying ability not represented by property. But if every tax were judged by its faults alone none would be acceptable.

INDIRECT TAXES

Each tax must be judged in its place and in relation to other taxes in a revenue system. This is especially true at the high level of revenue requirements now reached. In any tax, and in all taxes constituting a system, it is necessary to recognize certain basic principles, including fiscal adequacy, reasonableness, convenience of the taxpayer, ability to pay, and economic effects. Yet in the face of pressing demand for revenue, the taxing authority sometimes must recognize the principle of fiscal expediency. On this principle rest some of the indirect taxes which are becoming increasingly important in a growing number of States despite the fact that little can be said in their favor except that they yield substantial revenues to hard-pressed governments.

An indirect tax is ordinarily shifted wholly or in part by those on whom it is levied and borne by others either as higher prices paid for goods and services bought or as lower prices received for goods and services sold. It is finally paid, usually as part of price, by those who in the game of shifting taxes are the last in line, and so are unable to pass it on to others.

Indirect taxes are of many kinds, but for the present purpose they may be classified in two general groups. In one group fall taxes that are levied with the intent or expectation that they will be shifted to others, at least in large part, by those from whom they are collected. This group includes the general sales tax and various special taxes such as those on tobacco and admission to theaters and other amusements. The other group includes taxes that enter into price transactions but are not levied with the intent or understanding on the part of the taxing authority that they will be borne by persons or concerns other than those from whom they are collected. This kind of indirect tax can be illustrated by that part of the tax on houses and other improvements which under certain circumstances may be shifted to others and by a tax on transports and utilities which may be taken into account in fixing rates charged to the public.

The amount of indirect taxes paid by farmers or by any other group is unknown. Yet it is possible, on the basis of the known characteristics of particular taxes and their economic relation to the farmer, to formulate reasonable judgment as to whether more taxes are shifted to farmers as a group than are shifted by them to others. An effort to trace the shifting of taxes would involve essentially very complex questions of price analysis. It is far less a matter of conscious effort of individuals to escape the tax by shifting it to others than of the impersonal economic influence of a tax on prices of goods and services. The economic principles involved underlie the whole field of value and price.[4]

SALES TAXES

In recent years an increasing number of States have levied sales taxes upon various kinds of transactions. Twenty-five States have general sales taxes, which in 1939 yielded a revenue of $442,300,000. All State sales taxes, both general and selective, exclusive of the gasoline tax, yielded $685,100,000.[5] Many of the recent sales taxes were adopted to raise revenue for public relief and were assumed for the most part to be temporary measures. It is possible, however, that these general sales taxes will remain for a long time as part of the tax structure of a considerable number of States. They might even expand in scope if there should be strong demand for still further increase in revenue.

Unless a sales tax is a so-called luxury tax, restricted to articles of wide use but not of first importance, the chief objection to it is its regressiveness; that is, it falls most heavily upon persons of small income in the sense that it takes a larger share of their income than of the income of wealthier taxpayers. Such a tax violates the generally accepted principle that taxes should be levied in accordance with ability to pay.

This characteristic of the sales tax has many implications from the standpoint of its effect on such matters as volume of consumption and

[4] For a comprehensive treatise on these principles as they relate to taxation both in their historical development and practical application, see The Shifting and Incidence of Taxation, by Edwin R. A. Seligman (*10*).

[5] BUREAU OF THE CENSUS. STATE TAX COLLECTIONS, FISCAL YEAR 1938-39. Revised report, February 24, 1940. [Mimeographed.] See p. 5.

standard of living of low-income groups, but these implications are in large part outside the subject of rural taxation as such. It is pertinent, however, to note that the sales taxes, whether levied to afford tax relief for general property or to raise revenue which it would be difficult to get by increasing the property tax, fall upon farmers as upon other consumers to the extent that they buy the commodities subject to the tax.

Sales Taxes and the Property Levy

A general sales tax levied to relieve taxable property is not likely to afford tax relief to a very large part of the rural people. In the first place 38 percent of the total value of all farm real estate in the United States is in farms operated by tenants. The landowner may or may not be a farm resident or even live within the State where his property is situated and where the sales tax is levied. If he lives within the State, as a buyer of the goods subject to the sales tax he pays a part of the tax. If he lives elsewhere, he does not pay it. In any event, if the revenue from the sales tax is used to reduce the real estate tax or to maintain it at a level lower than it would be without the sales tax, the tenant and his family bear the tax and the landowner gets the relief. The difference may not be equalized soon, if ever, through adjustments in the rental contract.

This does not mean that the landlord necessarily gets an unfair advantage at the expense of the tenant, although that may sometimes be the case. Attention is called to sales taxes for property-tax relief to illustrate that an extensive shift of revenue collection from the property tax to the sales tax may possibly create new inequalities hardly less serious than those which exist within the property-tax structure itself.

It is possible also that a sales tax designed to relieve real estate may save the owner-occupant of a large property more in real estate taxes than he pays through the sales tax. To the extent that his expenditures for the taxable commodities bear a lower ratio to the assessed value of his property than those of the small landowner to his assessment, the large owner would receive more relief in proportion. Be this as it may, the regressiveness of the general sales tax itself, together with the tendency of the real estate tax to fall more heavily on small properties, makes it most unlikely that the sales tax can properly be regarded as a suitable means of correcting economic inequalities in the rural tax structure.

If the revenue from the general sales taxes in a State with a large urban population were applied to the cost of government in rural areas, the relief there would be substantial. This, however, is not the usual application of the tax. Even if it were so applied, the fact remains that the tax would still fall most heavily on the poor and also would have the usual characteristics of vexation and disturbance to business, especially when levied at retail.

On grounds of fiscal expediency, however, much may be said for the general sales tax. It is capable of yielding large revenues, and when it is paid as a hidden part of price and in small amounts as purchases are made the buyer is hardly conscious of it.

Shifting the Sales Tax Through Price

A tax levied on the sale of food and other farm products may be shifted in part to the producer by depressing the price he gets below what it would be without the tax. The amount of tax shifted would depend not only on the tax rate itself but also on the forces of supply and demand affecting each commodity taxed.

A sales tax may be characterized as a wedge driven into the price structure between the producer and the consumer. The result may be one or all of three things:

(1) The price to the consumer may rise, reducing consumption and damming up the supply with the producer. This is more likely with some commodtities than with others.

(2) If consumer resistance to higher price is strong, the price to the producer will go down and remain down unless the lower price causes a reduction in supply, which ordinarily is slow in coming and is less likely with farm products than with others.

(3) If the tax is not readily shifted to the consumer or to the producer or to both, it must come out of the middleman's margin.

Any one, or two, or all three of these price-and-margin adjustments may take place in varying proportions, depending on the supply and demand influences characteristic of each taxable commodity. This serves to illustrate the complexity of the question, Who bears the sales tax?

Numerous other indirect taxes are borne by farmers, including tobacco taxes and other levies of special types. Moreover, when he buys an imported commodity subject to tariff, the farmer contributes toward the revenues of the Federal Government. Added to these are the taxes levied on transport, which to the extent that they enter into the rate structure affect the price received by producers distant from the market. All in all, it appears probable that the various indirect taxes have contributed toward a widening in the price margin between producer and consumer. Although not measurable in dollars and cents, this has added to the disparity between prices paid and prices received by farmers, on the basis of 1910–14 prices.

The Farmer's Disadvantage in Shifting Taxes

Only a general qualitative answer is possible to the question as to the American farmer's net position in the shifting of taxes. His property tax, as noted earlier, amounts to about 70 percent of his total direct taxes. It is generally recognized that his property tax cannot be shifted either to the consumer or to the middleman but must be borne by the farmer and landowner because it does not cause reduction in supply and increase in price of farm products.

The gasoline and motor-vehicle taxes, amounting to more than a fourth of his total taxes, are borne by the farmer because there appears to be no reason to suppose that they either increase the price of what he has to sell or reduce the price of his purchases. His "other" taxes—poll taxes, income taxes, etc.—account for less than 3 percent of the total, and they, too, cannot be assumed to affect prices in his favor.

It is clear, therefore, that by and large the taxes collected from the farmer are borne by him, not shifted to others. On the other hand, many of the sales taxes, some of the property levies, including some that are levied on transports and utilities and taken into account in rate making, and others that tend to affect price are borne in part by farmers. All in all, the farmer's total taxes, both direct and indirect, are no doubt substantially larger than the direct taxes alone as shown in table 2 (p. 774).

ECONOMIC AND SOCIAL CONSEQUENCES OF TAXATION

Aside from questions of fiscal adequacy and fair treatment of taxpayers, taxes are capable of producing important economic and social consequences. On this subject perhaps even more than in other fields of taxation there is a distinct dearth of specific information. But conjecture and generalization may be helpful in suggesting major problems in the field of rural taxation as related to the economic effects of present taxes, especially the property tax.

The Property Tax in Relation to Land Use

The present property tax is often said to hinder conservation and proper land use. A land use and conservation program may be assumed to have two general objectives: (1) To put land into uses that will promote the well-being of the rural population consistently with the general public interest; and (2) to conserve the soil and other land resources, thus safeguarding the national interest and the well-being of future generations.

It is essential to a sound policy of land use and conservation, including adjustments in taxation in furtherance of such a policy, that land should be classified according to the uses to which it is best suited. Taxation in relation to the desirable utilization is then essentially a problem of devising and securing the adoption of the kinds and amounts of taxes and the improvements in their administration that would remove such hindrances as present taxes and tax administration may impose on wise utilization. In a number of States this might require significant changes in the property tax itself and in the tax system as a whole. Change in the property tax would most likely reduce property taxes on land that should be put to uses other than farming—forestry, recreation, or wildlife—at least in the years immediately ahead. Accompanying changes in the tax system would in all probability include new means of raising revenue to make up for reduction in the property levy (*5*).

The extent to which present tax levies stand in the way of desirable land use is as yet a moot question. There appears to be a tendency, especially on the part of some landowners, to overstress the point that taxes are the major deterrent to proper land use. For example, taxes were for many years called the major obstacle to private forest development and conservation. In order to get to the bottom of this matter Congress instituted and financed a comprehensive study of forest taxation, which was conducted by the United States Forest Service and published in 1935 (*7*). One of the conclusions of this study was that other deterrents to private forest development were on the whole more important than the inhibitions imposed by the property tax.

It has also been advanced that certain adjustments, or rather reductions, in tax levies on agricultural land would distinctly promote soil improvement and conservation. The land most in need of special conservation work probably is of less than average value and below the minimum quality for farming. The average tax per acre of all land in farms in the United States in 1938 was 39 cents, varying by States from $2.45 in New Jersey to 5 cents in New Mexico. The tax per acre of land near or below the margin of agricultural use in any State would ordinarily be lower than the average on all land, despite the general tendency to overassess low-value land.

Even if the tax on land requiring special conservation work were reduced by half, or even if it were eliminated altogether where certain recommended conservation practices were required, it is unlikely that this tax concession would induce the owner to do much toward land conservation that he could not afford to do without the concession. To illustrate, if a tax of 30 cents per acre were reduced to 15 cents, conditioned upon certain annual conservation practices, this tax reduction alone would not be a strong inducement. If the tax reduction were permanent and capitalized at 4 percent it would indicate that the farmer could be induced to spend $3.75 per acre for some permanent improvement for conservation.

Moreover, land-tax reduction on a large scale in the interest of conservation or for any other purpose would create a revenue problem for the community. It would be necessary to meet the reduction in revenue by other local taxes or by State taxes and subventions. These taxes probably would draw, at least in part, upon the income of the landowner.

All this is to the point that while tax adjustments have a distinct place in a comprehensive program of conservation and improved land use, they could easily be overemphasized as means of promoting these ends. At this stage much too little is definitely known of their place in such a program and how their influence could be utilized most effectively.

The Property Tax and Farm Ownership—Homestead Exemptions [6]

Another economic and social effect of the property tax is said to be its hindrance to farm and home ownership, especially on the part of small owners. The fact that small properties are often overassessed in comparison with larger properties points in this direction. A good deal has been done in recent years toward removing this supposed impediment to the ownership of small farms and homes and to turn the property tax into a positive inducement through homestead tax exemptions.

Thirteen States have joined this growing movement to grant tax preference to "homesteads," both rural and urban. The preferential treatment ranges from favorable rate differentials to outright exemptions from all levies. The preference is usually effective for only that part of an owner-occupied property which falls within specified limits of maximum value or area. In general the effect of homestead tax preference will reflect (1) the definition of an eligible homestead; (2)

[6] The section on homestead exemptions is based in large part on material furnished by Gerhard J. Isaac, Bureau of Agricultural Economics.

the proportions of various classes of property in the taxing jurisdiction; and (3) the means adopted to offset the revenue loss.

In defining an eligible homestead, it is usual to distinguish between urban and rural properties. An urban homestead is roughly restricted to a house used principally as a private residence and the lot on which it stands. A rural homestead, on the other hand, includes not only the farm residence but also the land and buildings making up the principal production facilities of the farm. This is of particular significance if the maximum eligible acreage is large enough to give complete exemption to most farms. If, however, a low maximum value limitation exists, it may be possible in some localities for a greater proportion of properties to get complete exemption in cities and towns than in farming areas.

For example, in Oklahoma, the value limitation is $1,000 and the area limitations are 1 acre for urban properties and 160 acres for rural properties. Under these restrictions it was found that more of the county taxes fell on rural property after exemption than before. That is, under the limitations mentioned there was a greater decrease in the taxable valuation of urban than of rural property. The decrease in rural valuations was least in those counties where many of the farm homesteads include extensive areas of grazing land in excess of the 160 acres granted exemption. In the same counties it is quite likely that a large part of the urban (small-town) homesteads have little assessed value in excess of the $1,000 exemption.

Even where homestead exemption reduces the farmer's real estate tax, the net effect on the farmer's tax contributions as a whole will depend on the nature of the fiscal adjustments adopted to meet the loss in revenue due to increased tax exemptions. It is quite conceivable that in some cases the substitute taxes which a given individual might be called on to pay would equal or exceed his tax reduction through homestead exemption. In other words, the mere fact of homestead exemption does not alone guarantee to the owner a lower total tax contribution.

Experience under homestead exemption has not yet been sufficient to show the extent to which these exemptions will serve the purpose of stimulating independent owner occupancy of small farms and homes. Moreover, adequate determination has not been made of the extent to which these exemptions really modify the distribution of the cost of government among individual taxpayers or between the lower income groups and the rest of the community.

Real Estate Taxes and Land Values

The effect on land values also must be considered among the economic effects of the farm real estate tax. A possible effect of the tax on land values may be indicated by converting the increase in taxes per acre since 1913 into land values at a given rate—5 percent, for example. Thus in 1920, at the peak of land values, the average value per acre would have been higher by $3.40 if the tax in that year had been the same as in 1913. As the average value in 1920 was $69.38, it might have been $72.78 but for the tax increase of 17 cents per acre. In other words, if there had been no increase in taxes from 1913 to 1933—from the pre-war base year, through the peak year of 1920, and to the low point of the depression—the trend of land values as compared with the actual trend might have been as shown in table 4.

Table 4.—Actual trend of land values as compared with possible trend if taxes had remained stationary, 1914–39

Year	Actual trend of land values[1]	Trend if taxes had remained at 1913 level	Year	Actual trend of land values[1]	Trend if taxes had remained at 1913 level
	Percent	*Percent*		*Percent*	*Percent*
1914	100.0	100.0	1927	115.3	130.0
1915	99.2	99.2	1928	113.6	128.7
1916	105.0	105.9	1929	113.0	128.6
1917	112.2	114.0	1930	111.5	127.1
1918	122.2	125.4	1931	101.1	116.3
1919	132.2	136.4	1932	84.4	97.3
1920	159.5	167.3	1933	68.7	78.4
1921	149.0	161.4	1934	70.1	77.0
1922	131.7	145.5	1935	71.6	77.6
1923	129.1	142.9	1936	74.6	80.6
1924	124.7	139.0	1937	77.2	83.7
1925	123.0	137.3	1938	77.9	84.8
1926	120.4	135.1	1939	77.1	84.0

[1] Since the land values are reported as of March 1 of a given year, they are here related to the taxes levied in the preceding year, which are the current levies at the time value is reported.

Figures based on unpublished computations by Janet L. Weston, formerly Assistant Agricultural Economist, Bureau of Agricultural Economics.

The maximum absolute influence on land values that could be attributed to the tax increase obviously appears in the years 1928 and 1929, when the tax per acre was at its highest, and the maximum relative influence in 1932, the year of highest ratio of taxes to land values. On this basis it appears that if taxes per acre had remained the same as in 1913 the index of land values per acre would have been 15.6 points higher in 1929 and 12.9 points higher in 1932. In percentage of difference and in average values per acre, this means that land values would have been higher in 1929 by 13.8 percent, or about $6.80 per acre, and in 1932 by 15.2 percent, or $5.60 per acre, if the tax had remained as in 1913. By the same computation it appears that land values in 1939 would have been 9 percent, or about $3, higher per acre.

The possible effect of taxes on the general rise and fall of land values in the past 25 years may also be of interest in this connection. As shown in table 4, land values by 1920 had advanced 59.5 percent above the 1914 level and could have made an additional advance of less than 8 points if taxes had not increased. By 1932, values had fallen from 59.5 percent above to 15.6 percent below those of 1914, a drop of 75.1 points. If taxes had remained at the pre-war level through these years, this wide range could have been narrowed by only about 5 points, and in 1939 land values would have been 16 percent below the pre-war level instead of 22.9 percent below. Obviously other factors have been of far greater influence than taxes in shaping the general trend of average land values in the United States over the past 2½ decades.

The above computations are more abstract than realistic. They merely help to particularize the obvious fact that the rise and fall of land values in the past 30 years have been influenced to some extent by tax levies. Moreover, it would hardly be realistic to suppose that the increase in local expenditures made possible by the higher tax had no relation to land values.

This recalls a remark by a Kansas farmer in a discussion following a speech by the writer some 15 years ago. In reference to the depressing influence of taxes on land values, he said,

> I know of some land out our way that wouldn't be worth anything if it were not for taxes. We wouldn't have schools, roads, and other things that make it worth while to live there. And land isn't worth much where nobody wants to live.

In that State about one-half the rise in farm real estate taxes was due to increased expenditures for schools and about one-fourth to increased expenditures for roads (*4, pp. 55–62*); and these proportions are probably not far from typical of the country as a whole.

TAXES AND THE RURAL-URBAN ECONOMIC BALANCE

It would be possible to go into many ramifications bearing on the question of whether rural property and rural people should be required to bear as large a share of the cost of schools and roads as they bore during the period of rapid advance in farm taxes. The decline of about 35 percent in taxes on farm real estate from 1930 to 1934 did not come without real sacrifices to rural institutions. In many places schools were closed, school terms were shortened, and other curtailments were made that weakened the educational opportunity of children and of youth held back in the country for lack of employment opportunities in the cities.

If rural taxation were viewed only in the light of fiscal balance sheets it would be possible to show that large subventions from revenues collected largely outside of rural communities go a long way toward counterbalancing direct rural taxes. As already noted, however, while the amount of taxes levied on others and shifted to and borne by agriculture is probably large, it is indeterminable.

If, however, rural taxation is viewed as a part of the larger field of public finance and as a part of the still larger field of urban-rural economic balance, it would soon appear that the economic contributions of rural people and resources to the national economy as a whole may outweigh by far the subventions which appear in the fiscal balance sheet.

The evolution of public policy in recent decades, especially in the 1930's, shows an unmistakable trend toward the view that public finance should play a larger part than in earlier periods in the relationships among economic interests and groups. The tariff, for example, has been considered always as having a large fiscal function, only occasionally as a program chiefly for revenue, and most of the time as a regulator of trade for the real or supposed benefit of one or another economic interest or group.

Income taxes and taxes on inheritance and related transfers of wealth are primarily revenue producers. Yet they find strong popular sanction, especially in their more sharply progressive features, because of the influence they exert on the distribution of wealth and income.

Processing taxes to finance agricultural programs were levied by Congress in response to the substantial national conviction that the price mechanism had failed to do justice to agriculture, that it is a proper function of Government to rectify that failure, and that the powers to tax and to spend public revenues are properly used in exercising that function.

Relief, welfare, and social security (including net additions to social security reserves) by Federal, State, and local Governments in 1938 amounted to more than 4 billion dollars, or 22.5 percent of the total disbursements of the three jurisdictions.

In addition, Government enters more and more into such wide and varied fields as education, research, conservation, public health, road and other construction, and numerous other activities that touch the daily life of the people as a whole.

In support of these activities, funds raised by this or that tax or under one or another jurisdiction are in large part intermingled in a flow of public services and improvements. These have become so definitely a part of the standard of living of the people that the methods and sources of revenue for their support are in large part indistinguishable.

Balance sheets and budget tables are necessary for reasons of law, accountancy, and administration, but they cannot show the economic effects of tax levels or expenditures, and they tell comparatively little as to the fairness of the distribution of the cost and benefit of these activities among groups and individuals.

From the standpoint of fairness to taxpayers, it is necessary to consider each tax, whether rural or other, in its relation to a revenue system in which fiscal and administrative requirements of each jurisdiction are considered in relation to all jurisdictions. It is an old idea, but important enough to justify repetition, that improvements in rural taxation must be considered in relation to and as a part of the fiscal system as a whole.

For this reason it is of special significance to rural taxpayers as well as to others that much attention is being given by Congress, the Treasury, the Council of State Governments, the National Tax Association, and other organizations to the better coordination of State and Federal taxes. This is essential in order to give room, in a logical and administratively feasible system, for those changes in the property tax itself which would mend some of its outstanding faults and yet retain it as the principal part of the tax structure in rural areas.

LITERATURE CITED

(1) Blakey, Roy G., and others.
1932. TAXATION IN MINNESOTA. Minn. Univ. Studies Econ. and Business 4, 627 pp.

(2) Coombs, Whitney.
1930 TAXATION OF FARM PROPERTY. U. S. Dept. Agr. Tech. Bul. 172, 75 pp., illus.

(3) Englund, Eric.
1924. ASSESSMENT AND EQUALIZATION OF FARM AND CITY REAL ESTATE IN KANSAS. Kans. Agr. Expt. Sta. Bul. 232, 70 pp., illus.

(4) ———
1925. THE TREND OF REAL ESTATE TAXATION IN KANSAS FROM 1910 TO 1923. Kans. Agr. Expt. Sta. Bul. 235, 97 pp., illus.

(5) ———
1931. CHANGES IN TAXATION REQUISITE FOR A SOUND PROGRAM OF LAND UTILIZATION. Natl. Conf. Land Util. Proc. 1931: 132–145, illus.

(6) ENGLUND, ERIC.
1932. ADJUSTMENTS NECESSARY IN TAXATION IN VIEW OF THE POSSIBILITY OF A LOWER GENERAL PRICE LEVEL. Jour. Farm Econ. 14: 94–105, illus.

(7) HALL, R. CLIFFORD.
1935. THE FOREST-TAX PROBLEM AND ITS SOLUTION SUMMARIZED. U. S. Dept. Agr. Cir. 358, 18 pp.

(8) JACKSON, DONALD.
1937. A GRAPHIC SUMMARY OF FARM TAXATION. U. S. Dept. Agr. Misc. Pub. 262, 17 pp., illus.

(9) JENKINS, WARDER B.
1933. TAXES ON FARM PROPERTY IN THE UNITED STATES. U. S. Census 1930, 120 pp., illus.

(10) SELIGMAN, EDWIN R. A.
1927. THE SHIFTING AND INCIDENCE OF TAXATION. Ed. 5, rev., 431 pp., illus. New York.

223761°—40——51

Rural Electrification

by Robert T. Beall[1]

THE MOST advanced country in the world in the use of modern methods in industry and agriculture, the United States has lagged astonishingly in making electricity available to farm communities. In 1935 about 10 percent of our farm families were receiving central-station electrical service as compared with almost 95 percent in France, 90 percent in Japan, 85 percent in Denmark, 100 percent in Holland. Since 1935 vigorous action has stepped up the number in this country to 25 percent. Here is the interesting story of the developments that have resulted in a more rapid advance in rural electrification than this country has ever seen. The author also tells how farmers can get electric service, and he lists over 200 uses of electricity on the farm and discusses the comparative costs of operating various kinds of electrical equipment.

PRIOR to 1935 an extremely small percentage of farms in the United States were receiving central-station electrical service. Industries and residents in urban areas, having recognized the value of reliable, low-cost power, had almost universally adopted electricity. Farmers, however, had not enjoyed electric power to any great extent—largely because it had not been made available on terms they could afford.

Of the more than 6.3 million farms in the country in January 1925, only 204,780, or 3.2 percent, were receiving central-station electrical service. During the succeeding 6 years the percentage increased slowly, reaching 10.2 in January 1931. From 1931 to January 1935 the increase was negligible, the percentage on the latter date being 10.9, or a gain of about 0.7 percent in 4 years. In terms of number of farms receiving central-station service during the 10-year period 1925–34 the record is but slightly more impressive; the number

[1] Robert T. Beall is Economist, Rural Electrification Administration.

increased from 204,780 in January 1925 to 649,919 in 1931, and to 743,954 in January 1935.

In contrast to the 10.9 percent of the farms in the United States receiving central-station service in 1935, other countries had achieved much more rapid progress in making electricity available to agriculture. For instance, in Ontario in 1935 about 20 percent of the farms were electrified, in New Zealand over 60 percent, in Japan and Germany about 90 percent each, in France between 90 and 95 percent, in Sweden about 65 percent, in Norway over 55 percent, in Denmark over 85 percent, and in the Netherlands practically 100 percent. Though conditions differ among these foreign countries in such factors as density of population, type of farming, per capita income, and form of government, it is significant that they have developed ways and means to make electricity available to such a large percentage of their farms. In most of these other countries, rural electrification has been characterized by wide availability, a high percentage of public or cooperative ownership, and long-term programs under government sponsorship. It is unlikely that rural electrification would be so extensive in these countries except under such auspices.

THE LAG IN RURAL ELECTRIFICATION IN THE UNITED STATES

In view of the growing but relatively ineffective demand of American farmers for electricity on their farms during the decade prior to 1935 and the contrasting substantial progress in rural electrification achieved by many foreign countries during the same period, it is important to note briefly the reasons why relatively few farms in the United States were being served with central-station power. After a careful study of the rural electrification problem, the Mississippi Valley Committee reported, in October 1934, that—

> several reasons might be advanced to explain why only 10 percent of the Nation's farms purchase electricity. These are the lack of interest by operating companies in rural electrification, high cost of line construction because of the unnecessarily expensive type of line used, onerous restrictions covering rural line extensions, and high rates.[2]

Inasmuch as the private utility companies own and control wel over 90 percent of the electric-power industry in the United States, the extension of lines into rural areas prior to 1935 depended primarily on the willingness of these companies to serve farmers. However, it was the assumption generally of the great majority of these companies that the average farmer was unable to use sufficient quantities of electric power to justify the costs of rendering service; that electricity could be brought to only a few farms except when lines had to be built for some other purpose; and that justifiable extensions were dependent on factors other than the use of electric power in household and ordinary farm activities.

Of particular importance in creating the apathetic attitude of the private industry toward rural electrification was the fact that the companies did not want to invest large blocks of capital in thinly

[2] United States Federal Emergency Administration of Public Works, Mississippi Valley Committee. report of the mississippi valley committee . . . 234 pp., illus. Washington, D. C. 1934. See p. 51.

populated rural territory when they were experiencing a satisfying increase in business from the more profitable and easily accessible markets in urban areas of denser population. This attitude was in accord with the dominant policies of conserving invested capital and selecting markets that promise the greatest profit. Rural areas did not offer the conservative investment opportunities of urban communities where the uses for electricity were rapidly expanding—particularly for street lighting, commercial and industrial power, household appliances, and more recently display advertising—and it was normal from a strictly business point of view for private industry to select for development these more conservative yet more profitable opportunities for investment. From a business point of view the companies did not need the rural market.

The most important barriers restricting rural electrification prior to 1935—and these reflected generally the attitude of private industry—were the conditions and rates imposed on farmers if service were made available to them. Frequently the farmers had to pay for the distribution line, give the company title to the property, and then guarantee high minimum charges over a long period of years. Charges for rural service, often based on the costly urban type of construction and usually on high, nonpromotional rate schedules, made electrification prohibitive to all but a favorably situated class of farm people. The industry generally felt no responsibility to find out whether construction in rural areas might not be simpler and less expensive than that in urban centers and therefore require less capital investment per farm. It made little effort to work out promotional rate schedules that would enable and encourage farmers to employ electric power in their activities.

As already indicated, rural electrification prior to 1935 was on the whole restricted to a selected class of farm residents. Generally these farmers were located along the main highways extending out from urban centers, where density of population was relatively high, or in sections of the country where the nature of farm activities made large power loads immediately available. In the irrigated sections of the West, as in California, rural electrification was extensive because the pumping of water for irrigation required large amounts of power; in areas of specialized farm activities, such as dairying and poultry farming, farms required relatively large blocks of power and offered readily available and profitable loads to the utility industry. In most rural areas devoted to general farming, however, line extensions were usually short, frequently not more than a mile or two each, and usually to only a few customers in the more prosperous and densely settled communities. In very few localities were any attempts made to develop entire areas, including sections of thin as well as of dense population, in order that electric power might be available to substantially all the farms in an area. Rather, electrification was conducted on a highly selective, an almost individual-farm basis, a condition which meant that each farm or small group of farms was evaluated on its potential profitability as an isolated unit. The effect of this type of line-extension policy was not only to restrict in a large degree the number of farms served but also to make construction costs unduly high because of piecemeal additions.

RURAL ELECTRIFICATION AND RURAL PROGRESS

That only 1 farm in 10 in the United States was receiving central-station service in 1935 did not mean that farmers generally did not want or could not use electric service. On the contrary, extension of electricity to rural areas on conditions that promote its maximum use in farm operations stands out as a vital need for the all-round improvement of rural life. Not only does the wide use of electricity hold much promise in raising the standard of living of individual farmers and their families, but also it offers real opportunities to make a substantial contribution to community welfare and national well-being through its applications in promoting a more permanent and stable agriculture.

Electric power is a factor common to many parts of the broad program to restore farm life to its proper plane in the national economy, and it reinforces many of the activities being carried on to achieve that objective. The electrified farm, for instance, generally attracts and holds better tenants, and it may prove to be a constructive force in promoting an increase in owner-operated farms as well as better landlord-tenant relationships. Increased income and improved living standards resulting from the use of electricity on the farm may exert a favorable influence on the problems arising from the migration of rural youth to urban centers and the distribution of population. Many of the productive applications of electricity on the farm will reinforce and make more effective the programs of soil conservation and farm rehabilitation by facilitating wider diversification of crops and adjustment of farm operations to proper land use. In a very real sense the electrification of rural areas is of national concern, not only because of its contributions to the comforts and income of the individual farm family but also because of its influence on the welfare of agriculture generally.

Recognizing the need for rural electrification, farmers, farm organizations, and public-spirited leaders have for many years exerted much effort to make electric service widely available in rural areas. They have approached the problem from many angles, realizing that the inadequacy of this service to farmers is one of the distinguishing features of the gap between rural and urban living standards. Notwithstanding the slow progress of rural electrification before 1935, the desire of farmers for electricity increased rapidly. Every time a farmer visited a market center he observed the uses and convenience of electric power; educational and promotional literature confirmed these impressions.

In addition to the growing demand of farmers for electric service, a small but energetic group of public-spirited citizens has for many years been advocating widespread rural electrification. These citizens, among the earliest of whom were Senator George W. Norris and Gifford Pinchot, and somewhat later Franklin D. Roosevelt and Morris L. Cooke, may at the beginning have conceived of electric power on the farm as a desirable thing, but as their thinking expanded they recognized it as a necessity in modern life and a matter of national concern.

The October 1934 report of the Mississippi Valley Committee, of which Morris L. Cooke was chairman, after a careful review of the causes of the lag in rural electrification in the United States, emphasized the opportunities for extending electric power to farmers but added:

> Unless the Federal Government assumes an active leadership, assisted in particular instances by State and local agencies, only a negligible part of this task can be accomplished within any reasonable time.[3]

A similar point of view was expressed in the report of the National Resources Board of December 1934.[4]

These documents focused attention on the fact that something concrete should be done to bring electricity to the farmer. At the rate of progress of rural electrification during the decade 1924–33 it would take about 50 years to make electric service available to 50 percent of the farms in the United States.

PROGRESS IN RURAL ELECTRIFICATION

In his message to the Congress in January 1935, the President recommended the adoption of legislation which would reduce the rolls of the unemployed and cited the program of the National Resources Board as a guide for useful public expenditures. In the Emergency Relief Appropriation Act of 1935, Congress expressly included rural electrification as one of the classes of projects for which the appropriation was made available. Under this act, the President, by Executive Order No. 7037, on May 11, 1935, established the Rural Electrification Administration as an emergency agency "to initiate, formulate, administer, and supervise a program of approved projects with respect to the generation, transmission, and distribution of electric energy in rural areas." Relief funds were made available to be loaned to private companies, power districts, municipalities, and cooperatives. A year later Congress passed the Rural Electrification Act of 1936, which transformed the Rural Electrification Administration from an emergency to a more permanent agency of the Federal Government, established a 10-year program of rural electrification, and authorized for this purpose loans eventually totaling $410,000,000. Of this total, the Administration was authorized to borrow $50,000,000 from the Reconstruction Finance Corporation for loans during the fiscal year 1937, and $40,000,000 was authorized for each of the succeeding 9 years, the appropriation for each of these years being subject to a specific act of the Congress. In 1938 Congress authorized the Reconstruction Finance Corporation to lend $100,000,000 to the Rural Electrification Administration for the purpose of making rural-electrification loans, this amount being in addition to the regular loan appropriation of $40,000,000 for the year beginning July 1, 1938. In June 1940 Congress authorized the Reconstruction Finance Corporation to lend $100,000,000 to the Administration for similar loans during the year beginning July 1, 1940. The Administration was placed under the general direction and supervision of the Secretary of Agriculture on July 1, 1939.

---

[3] See reference cited in footnote 2, p. 791.

[4] [UNITED STATES] NATIONAL RESOURCES BOARD. A REPORT ON NATIONAL PLANNING AND PUBLIC WORKS IN RELATION TO NATURAL RESOURCES AND INCLUDING LAND USE AND WATER RESOURCES WITH FINDINGS AND RECOMMENDATIONS. 455 pp., illus. 1934. See p. 353.

Briefly, the Rural Electrification Act of 1936 provides that loans, which shall be self-liquidating within a period not to exceed 25 years, may be made to persons, corporations, States, Territories, municipalities, people's utility districts, and cooperative, nonprofit, or limited-dividend associations organized under the laws of any State or Territory of the United States, for the purpose of financing the construction and operation of generating plants, transmission lines, and distribution lines for the furnishing of electric energy to persons in rural areas who are not receiving central-station service. These loans are made on terms and conditions determined by the Rural Electrification Administrator and may be made payable in whole or in part out of income. The act also provides that loans may be made for wiring premises and the acquisition and installation of electrical and plumbing appliances and equipment. Such loans may be made to borrowers of funds loaned for line construction or to businesses supplying and installing wiring, appliances, or equipment. All loans bear interest, the rate for any year being the average rate of interest paid by the Federal Government on its obligations not maturing for 10 or more years and issued in the preceding year. The act specifies that no loan shall be made unless the Administrator finds and certifies that in his judgment the security therefor is reasonably adequate and that the loan will be repaid within the time agreed. In accordance with the terms of the act, the interest rate on Rural Electrification Administration loans made in each fiscal year has been as follows: 2.77 percent in 1937, 2.88 in 1938, 2.73 in 1939, and 2.69 in 1940.

Because it was created as an agency not only to extend rural electrification but also to stimulate business and relieve unemployment, the Administration had to make an initial assumption as to how it would function. The Rural Electrification Administration was established as a purely lending agency; it could not itself construct, own, or operate electric-distribution systems. As a lending agency having as one of its objectives to lend rapidly in order to put funds into circulation promptly, it was assumed that under the reasonable conditions established and low interest rates offered the private utility companies would constitute the principal borrowers of the funds inasmuch as they were going concerns, had generating plants, experience, and facilities for prompt action, and had signified their intentions to promote actively the development of rural areas. These conditions, including area coverage, economical construction, and simplified and lower rate schedules, were designed to remove or modify the barriers that had impeded progress in rural electrification before 1935. But of the $268,037,293 allotted by the Administration up to December 31, 1939, less than 2 percent has been borrowed by private companies for rural extensions.

Within a year after the Administration was established a new type of borrower came into being—the nonprofit local distributing organization, or cooperative; and soon these new associations of farmers became the principal borrowers of Government funds for the construction and operation of rural electric-distribution systems. This development began at a slow pace at first but accelerated as more farm communities discovered how they could organize to get electricity by forming cooperative, nonprofit enterprises under their State laws to borrow funds from the Administration. The Rural Electrification Act in fact provides that in making loans preference should be given to these associations as well as to States, Territories, municipalities, and people's utility districts. Of the total amount lent by December 31, 1939, over 92 percent had been borrowed by cooperative associations and about 6 percent by public power districts and other public bodies.

The Work of the Rural Electrification Administration

From the beginning the Rural Electrification Administration recognized that if the objectives of the rural-electrification program were to be achieved, a new approach would have to be made on many fronts in order to remove or modify substantially the barriers that had impeded progress in the past. This meant that comprehensive area coverage was needed, cost of line construction would have to be reduced, and more favorable rates and rate schedules must be made possible. Achievement of these objectives, it was recognized, would enable farmers to obtain maximum benefit from the full use of electric power in their activities. These objectives and the emergence of cooperative associations, a type of organization relatively new to the electric-utility industry in the United States, as the principal borrowers have involved pioneering work of many types.

One of the basic principles the Administration has encouraged its borrowers to follow is that of comprehensive area coverage. This simply means trying to reach all farms in an entire area by designing compact systems which do not leave gaps of unserved sectors within the area or some farms stranded on the fringes. The practice generally followed prior to 1935, of building only to those farms promising relatively large loads and ignoring all other potential consumers, often referred to as "skimming the cream," deprives the large number of remaining farms of the probability of ever receiving electric service, because lines can be extended to them in the future only at exorbitant cost. On the other hand, comprehensive area coverage as practiced by Rural Electrification Administration borrowers assures availability of service to most of the farms within a compact area, because mass-production methods of line construction can be utilized and the resulting lower costs averaged over both large and small consumers. The application of the principle of area coverage has eliminated one of the greatest barriers to widespread farm electrification.

By placing line construction on a mass-production basis and simplifying and standardizing designs and materials, the Administration engineers have been able to achieve substantial reductions in the costs of rural lines, the effect of which has been to broaden the area of economical widespread rural electrification. Every reduction in the cost of line construction is reflected in farmers' electric bills, from which must come the funds for amortization of the Government loans; lower line costs mean an increase in the number of farmers who can be supplied with electric power on a self-liquidating basis.

Before the establishment of the Rural Electrification Administration the reported cost of rural lines, depending on consumer density and on terrain, ranged from $1,500 to $1,800 a mile. The average total cost of R.E.A.-financed lines is now less than $800 a mile.

The average estimated construction cost of these lines has been declining each year, from $904 in 1936 to $858 in 1937, $768 in 1938, and $583 in 1939. These economies have not been achieved by inferior design and construction; R.E.A. standards of line design are now followed generally throughout the country by private companies as well as by borrowers of Government funds.

A substantial part of these reductions has been achieved by designing rural lines to fit the particular requirements of farm service. With few exceptions, rural-line construction in the past had followed the urban practice of heavy construction. The Administration recognized that urban-type lines were not required in farm areas; that light, simple line construction would be more economical and would

Figure 1.—Simple, long-span construction of single-phase distribution lines means lower costs and makes electricity available to more farms.

serve the needs of the farmer (fig. 1). This necessitated the application of new techniques to rural construction. Some of these had been known previously and had been used here and there by certain private companies; but because of the general lack of interest and particularly the absence of rural extension programs, they had not received any wide acceptance. A simple design for rural lines suitable for rural conditions was found in the now common vertical construction with the elimination of the cross arm. Another important technique in rural-line design that has resulted in substantial reduction in line costs has been the increased length of the span between poles with a consequent reduction in the number of poles per mile. In contrast to usual spans of 200 to 225 feet in 1935, the average span of R.E.A.-financed lines is now 400 to 425 feet.

While the new type of line-design standards for rural service is the best-known contribution of the R.E A. to more economical rural electrification, there are several other technical advances which should be mentioned.

In cooperation with manufacturers a cyclometer-type meter has been developed which permits easy, direct reading and reporting by the farmer. Reading the common clock-type meter requires a skilled reader and costs about 15 cents a month. With the new type of meter read by the farmer this cost is reduced to 3 cents a month.

The latest important development has been a new low-cost, small-capacity electric service—consisting of a small transformer, a new device for lightning protection, a new type of circuit breaker, and an underground cable—which will enable farmers with very limited incomes to have electric lights and small appliances for a minimum of about $1 a month instead of the average monthly minimum bill for regular service of $2.50 in the South and $3.50 to $4 in the North. Even at the substantially and progressively lowered costs achieved since the Government program started, many low-income farms have been unable to afford electric service. This new, small-capacity service will enable the small tenant farmer or sharecropper, for example, to have electric lights and radio, and possibly a limited number of other small appliances at very low cost.

Engineering advances relating primarily to technical construction and the operation of rural lines include a new meter for testing the efficiency of circuit grounding; a slide rule for computation of proper guy and anchor sizes; and another slide rule for accurate determination of proper equipment to regulate voltage.

The effect of these and other engineering advances in design and technique of rural-line construction has been not only to lower substantially the cost of rural lines, which in turn means lower rates for electric power, but also to make possible the extension of electric service to many farm areas where it had heretofore been considered uneconomical on the basis of urban standards of construction.

The Rural Electric Cooperative Associations

As has already been indicated, the principal type of borrower of R.E.A. funds is the cooperative, nonprofit association of rural residents organized for the specific purpose of constructing and operating a rural electric system. Although this type of organization for the distribution of electric power in rural areas has been widely used in certain foreign countries, notably Denmark, Sweden, and Finland, it was almost unknown in the United States until the establishment of the Government's rural-electrification program. In 1934 there were 34 such associations in existence in the United States. One of these had been organized in 1914, and the majority of them had been in operation 10 years or more. Most of these pioneer associations have been handicapped by unplanned and inadequately financed lines and lack of expert counsel, but it is significant that they have been in operation for many years.

The development of a cooperative association for the purpose of borrowing funds from the R.E.A. is a local matter and reflects the desires of the residents of a rural community for electric service. Usually a small group of farmers begins a cooperative by writing the Administration that they wish electric service in their community. Farmers usually find the county agent and local planning committees to be of great assistance to them in getting their organizations started, by calling mass meetings, sending out notifications, and acting as advisers. The Administration does not make loans to individual farmers because the cost of rendering electric service on an individual basis would be exorbitant; economical and efficient service must be obtained through collective action. It recommends that the cooperative association consist of farmers in a compact rural area with at least 100 miles of line and approximately 300 members, or a density of about 3 to the mile. After the residents of an area signify their desire for electric service, the Administration recommends procedures and helps them in many ways to perfect their community association in order that they may apply for a Government loan to finance the construction of their lines. The preliminary steps to the formation of a cooperative are usually taken at a community meeting called by the county agent or other farm leaders in the community. After selection of the tentative area where it is expected the lines will be built, the group selects the persons, usually not less than nine, to become the incorporators of the proposed cooperative. The cooperatives are incorporated under laws of the respective States, this being handled by local attorneys selected by the sponsors.

After the incorporation of the cooperative, the next step of the local group is to make a membership survey, obtain easements, collect membership fees, and prepare a map for the proposed lines, all of which is preliminary to and necessary for submission of a suitable loan application to the Rural Electrification Administration. In order that this work may be done properly, the Administration informs local people of the best procedures to follow. The cooperatives are democratic community organizations; every consumer receiving service from them is a member and pays a membership fee, which is usually $5. Each member is entitled to receive all the benefits provided by the cooperative and to have a vote in its management.

When a loan application is received, the Administration examines it for economic and engineering feasibility. The loans generally cover the total cost of constructing the electric-distribution lines, which constitute the entire security for the loan, so that members of the cooperatives are not personally liable for repayment. The rate schedule established by the cooperative makes provision for an income that will permit payment of principal and interest on the Government loan as well as costs of wholesale power and operating expenses.

A loan for the construction of a generating plant is not made unless it is found to be absolutely essential to the successful operation of a borrower's distribution system. Existing generating sources are used wherever practicable. In some cases, however, a loan has been made for a generating plant because of the absence of a satisfactory power source or because the borrower could not afford to purchase power at the wholesale rate demanded by an existing plant (fig. 2). A total of $6,529,000 had been allotted by December 31, 1939, for the construction of generating plants in 20 States.

In the organization, construction, and operation of their rural distribution systems, cooperatives may receive considerable guidance from the Administration. These expert and technical advisory services are to help cooperatives to become economical and efficient business enterprises capable of managing their systems successfully. R.E.A. experts aid borrowers in obtaining a satisfactory source of power and reasonable wholesale rates, essentials to successful operation of their systems. R.E.A. engineers counsel borrowers' engineers in the design and plan of the lines, review and approve

Figure 2.—Such a generating plant as this may be built by a cooperative with money borrowed from the Rural Electrification Administration when electric power from existing sources is not available or cannot be obtained under satisfactory conditions.

construction contracts, and assist in the supervision of line construction.

After construction is completed and the lines are energized, borrowers receive expert advice from the Administration in connection with the development of good management practices and the promotion of use of electricity on the farm. These activities are of an advisory nature and do not involve participation in the actual operation of the electric systems. The Administration also has trained specialists who work with borrowers in demonstrating the many uses of electricity on the farm and arranging exhibits of electrical equipment. Most of these load-building activities are conducted in cooperation with specialists from the extension divisions of State universities, county agents, and other representatives of the Department of Agriculture. Group plans for obtaining low-cost installations of plumbing and wiring have been developed in order to make these conveniences available to as many farms as possible. In all of these and other activities the primary objective has been to make electricity available to farmers at lowest costs and to safeguard the security of the Government loans.

In addition to loans for distribution lines and generating plants, the Administration makes loans for the acquisition and installation of wiring and plumbing. These loans are not made directly to individual farmers but to the cooperative or other group of borrowers, which in turn makes loans to individuals for these purposes. Wiring and plumbing loans bear interest and are made on a 5-year basis. By December 31, 1939, the R.E.A. had made wiring and plumbing loans totaling $5,001,862. Borrowers may also take advantage of the facilities of the Electric Home and Farm Authority, an agency of the Federal Government which lends funds for the purchase of all types of electrical equipment.

Accomplishments and Problems

Farm electrification in the United States has received a new stimulus from the Government's program of financing and aiding farmers to obtain electric power. Since the establishment of the program in 1935 the electrification of rural areas has gone forward at a faster pace than ever before. In the 4½ years since the Rural Electrification Administration was established, the number of farms receiving electric service has more than doubled; it is estimated that in December 1939 about 1,700,000 farms, or 25 percent of all farms, were receiving electric service. Table 1 shows the number and percentage of farms receiving central-station service for each year from 1925 to 1939, inclusive. This substantial increase in the number of electrified farms reflects the activities both of private utility companies that have been stimulated by the Rural Electrification Administration and of borrowers of its funds. Lines under construction at the end of 1939 by R.E.A. borrowers alone will make power available to almost 300,000 additional farms within the next year.

By December 31, 1939, the Administration had made allotments of loan funds totaling $268,037,293 to 690 borrowers for the construction of about 250,000 miles of rural power lines and other power facilities. When completed, these lines will make central-station service available to almost 850,000 farms, rural churches, schools, and business enter-

Table 1.—Progress of rural electrification in the United States, 1924–39

Year ended Jan. 1—	Electrified farms	Proportion of all farms electrified	Year ended Jan. 1—	Electrified farms	Proportion of all farms electrified	Year ended Jan. 1—	Electrified farms	Proportion of all farms electrified
	Number	*Percent*		*Number*	*Percent*		*Number*	*Percent*
1925	204, 780	3. 2	1931	649, 919	10. 2	1937	1, 042, 924	15. 4
1926	246, 150	3. 9	1932	698, 786	10. 7	1938	1, 241, 505	18. 2
1927	309, 125	4. 9	1933	709, 449	10. 5	1939	1, 410, 000	20. 6
1928	393, 221	6. 2	1934	713, 558	10. 5	1940	1, 700, 000	25. 0
1929	506, 242	8. 0	1935	743, 954	10. 9			
1930	576, 168	9. 2	1936	788, 795	11. 6			

Source: Number of electrified farms: 1925–30, Statistical Bulletin No. 2, April 1935, Edison Electric Institute; 1931–38, Electrical World, January 1938; 1939–40, R.E.A. estimates.

prises. It is reported that on December 31, 1939, there were about 435,000 consumers receiving service from Government-financed lines.

The distribution of R.E.A. allotments, number of borrowers, and percentage of total farms electrified, by States, are shown in table 2. In connection with the allotments among the States it should be pointed out that the Rural Electrification Act provides that 50 percent of the annual funds available for loans shall be allotted in the several States in the proportion which the number of their farms not then receiving central-station service bears to the total number of farms

Table 2.—Rural Electrification Administration allotments, number of borrowers, and percentage of all farms electrified, by States [1]

State	Allotments	Borrowers	Proportion of farms electrified, June 30, 1939	State	Allotments	Borrowers	Proportion of farms electrified, June 30, 1939
	Dollars	*Number*	*Percent*		*Dollars*	*Number*	*Percent*
Alabama	5, 466, 550	15	10	Nevada	227, 000	1	35
Arizona	703, 000	3	46	New Hampshire	392, 000	1	52
Arkansas	5, 608, 500	14	3	New Jersey	420, 300	2	78
California	1, 748, 500	4	75	New Mexico	710, 000	3	7
Colorado	3, 402, 500	11	17	New York	1, 375, 000	1	45
Connecticut			45	North Carolina	6, 219, 350	22	19
Delaware	878, 000	1	31	North Dakota	1, 988, 972	7	2
Florida	1, 763, 000	8	10	Ohio	14, 344, 025	26	42
Georgia	13, 864, 615	36	14	Oklahoma	6, 529, 000	18	5
Idaho	2, 545, 750	7	54	Oregon	1, 002, 500	6	50
Illinois	14, 952, 130	27	26	Pennsylvania	7, 222, 200	13	52
Indiana	17, 120, 195	43	37	Rhode Island			84
Iowa	17, 800, 628	50	23	South Carolina	4, 073, 328	12	14
Kansas	5, 761, 151	20	11	South Dakota	1, 738, 500	5	4
Kentucky	8, 658, 720	24	8	Tennessee	8, 695, 058	17	10
Louisiana	3, 064, 600	12	7	Texas	20, 306, 685	59	9
Maine	223, 000	2	44	Utah	579, 000	3	54
Maryland	748, 000	2	33	Vermont	280, 500	2	34
Massachusetts			48	Virginia	6, 356, 800	15	21
Michigan	11, 252, 500	14	62	Washington	3, 644, 200	13	57
Minnesota	18, 127, 236	39	17	West Virginia	582, 000	2	15
Mississippi	7, 911, 200	23	4	Wisconsin	13, 398, 800	28	36
Missouri	11, 568, 700	30	8	Wyoming	1, 719, 800	10	14
Montana	2, 393, 100	11	15				
Nebraska	10, 670, 700	28	13	United States	268, 037, 293	690	22

[1] Data on allotments and number of borrowers as of Dec. 31, 1939.

of the United States not then receiving such service; the remaining 50 percent shall be allotted at the discretion of the Administrator, provided that not more than 10 percent of the remainder of the annual sum may be allotted in any one State or in all of the Territories.

The program, in addition to providing funds for financing rural electrification, has exerted considerable influence on private companies by stimulating a renewed interest on their part in extending lines into rural areas. By designing lines particularly for rural areas, the Administration has demonstrated that construction and operating costs can be reduced substantially below previous levels and that adequate electric service can be rendered over wide areas at rates and under conditions more in accord with the purchasing power of farm consumers.

The general adoption of R.E.A. standards of line design by private companies has contributed to the extension of their lines into areas formerly considered to be uneconomical. In many areas, however, the proposed development of cooperatives has provided the major stimulus to the accelerated rural activities of the private companies.[6] Many private companies have modified their terms and have offered lower and promotional rate schedules. Many have eliminated or substantially modified their requirements of contributions by farmers to cost of line construction and are building lines without requiring immediate investment by the farmers. In some places the principle of area coverage has been accepted by progressive companies, but selective building, or cream skimming, practices are still common.

As a result of the Federal rural-electrification program and the increased rural activities of private companies, public interest in rural electrification has increased and many farmers have become acquainted with the uses and desirability of electric power on the farm. Manufacturers of electrical appliances and equipment have come to recognize the importance of electrified farms as an outlet for their products and are actively engaged in developing this market. Through periodicals, demonstrations, and exhibits and through the activities of the Extension Service, farm organizations, State colleges, and other public agencies, farmers are being informed of the applications of electric power to farm-household and farm-production activities.

Notwithstanding the current progress being made in extending electric service to rural areas, the major problem of rural electrification remains primarily one of wider availability, making electrification available to as many farms as possible on conditions and terms that will encourage its maximum use in agricultural activities. The magnitude of this task is apparent when it is realized that about 3 out of 4 farms in the United States are still without electric service. In

---

[6] In its report of October 3, 1936, the Wisconsin Rural Electrification Coordination stated that "startled out of a long sleep by farmers' R. E. A. cooperative activity, private electric companies in the State jumped to their feet with sudden, new plans to extend rural lines to farmers whose requests had gone begging some twenty years." (Wisconsin Rural Electrification Coordination, The First Year of R. E. A. Program in Wisconsin, October 3, 1936, p. 3.) The Kansas State Corporation Commission reported that "in addition to their electric supply lines constructed, the activity of the cooperatives has served to intensify the effort on the part of the private power companies to develop the territory immediately adjacent to urban and rural territories now served by the companies." (Kansas State Corporation Commission, Fourteenth Biennial Report, July 1, 1936, to June 30, 1938, pp. 17–18.) The Public Service Commission of Kentucky reported that "faced with competition, many private utility companies, formerly reluctant to run rural line extensions in any but the most profitable areas, have reduced minimum monthly bills, and waived former contribution requirements to encourage new rural business." (Kentucky Public Service Commission Report, 1936 and 1937, pp. 27–28.)

many States, as shown in table 2, less than 10 percent of the farms are receiving central-station service. The extension of electric service to the large number of unserved farms will require the coordinated efforts of the farmers, their organizations, the suppliers of electric power, and the research, planning, educational, and administrative agencies of every level of Government in developing and perfecting programs for its achievement.

RURAL USES OF ELECTRICITY

Electric power on the farm is beneficial—in fact, is feasible economically—to the extent only that it is used profitably and effectively in household and productive activities. In itself electricity is only a "tool" to be used. Urban industry has found it to be the most flexible and versatile of all sources of power; agriculture may find it of equal or greater importance in the performance of farm activities. Already there are over 200 separate uses for electric power on the farm, and the list continues to grow. While many of these uses relate primarily to household activities, a substantial number of them are directly concerned with labor-saving, cost-reducing, and income-producing equipment for farm operations. Since the farm provides both a home and a livelihood, many uses of electricity in the household have a direct influence on productivity by relieving the farmer and

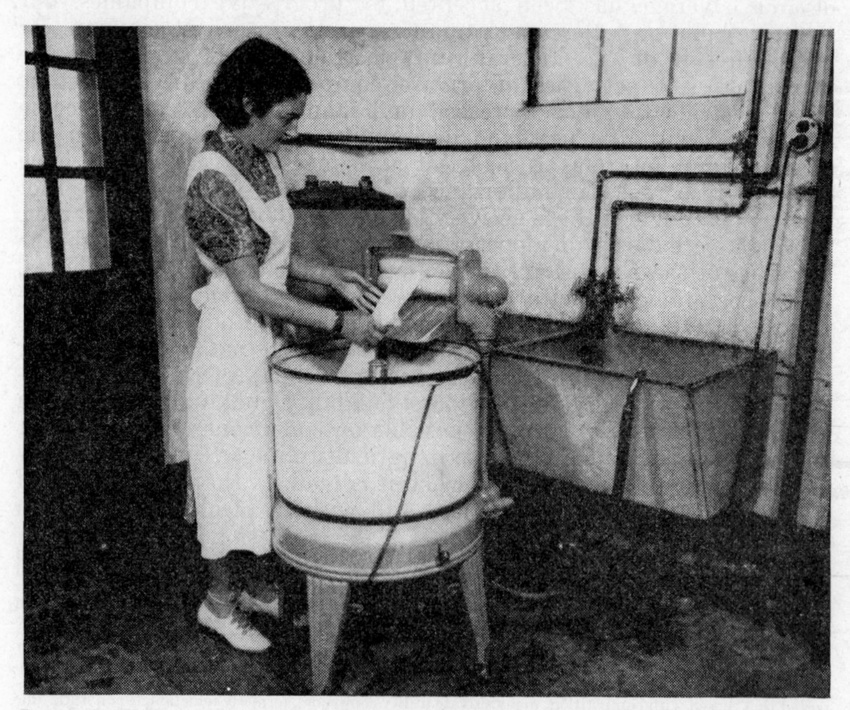

Figure 3.—Electricity lessens the drudgery of washday and performs many other chores in the farm household.

his family of much time-consuming drudgery and by adding to their comforts. The use of electric power in rural areas may be divided into three broad classes: (1) Household operations (fig. 3), (2) farm operations, and (3) rural community services.

Electricity in the Farm Home

The initial desire of farm people, particularly farm women, for electric service often arises from its use for electric lights and for performing common household tasks and chores. Electric service in the farm home means a better standard of living, greater freedom from drudgery, improved health, and greater contentment for the entire farm family. While electric lights are universally used on electrified farms, many other appliances are widely used because of their contribution to better living. It is a natural tendency for consumers of electricity to acquire first the more common and better-known electrical appliances and gradually to add to others as knowledge and information about them is acquired and as circumstances permit. An appliance survey conducted by the R.E.A. during the summer of 1939 among more than 72,000 consumers on the lines of 121 of its borrowers indicates the popularity of the more common household appliances among farmers who have been receiving electricity for a short time—an average of slightly over 10 months. The results of this survey are shown in the following tabulation:

Appliance	*Percentage of farms reporting use*	*Appliance*	*Percentage of farms reporting use*
Iron	84. 1	Hot plate	19. 1
Radio	82. 6	Electric water pump	18. 4
Washing machine	58. 7	Coffee maker	6. 3
Refrigerator	32. 2	Range	3. 1
Toaster	30. 8	Roaster	1. 6
Vacuum cleaner	21. 3		

In addition to the appliances listed above it is of interest to note that 9 percent of these consumers reported bathtubs or showers, 6.3 percent both septic tanks and water closets, and 1.2 percent electric water heaters. The percentages shown are significant not only because they indicate the popularity of various household appliances among farmers who have had electricity available for a short period but also because of the high saturation obtained in this relatively short period.

Many household appliances consume very little electric power, and their costs of operation are surprisingly low, especially when consideration is given to the amount of time saved and drudgery eliminated through their use. As the result of tests made by various State colleges, utility companies, and manufacturers, it is conservatively estimated that the average family of four or five persons uses the average amount of electricity shown to operate the following household appliances:

Kilowatt-hours of electricity used per month

Appliance:		Appliance—Continued.	
Clock	2	Curling iron	½
Coffee percolator	5	House heating (oil burner)	25

Kilowatt-hours of electricity used per month—Continued

Appliance—Continued.		Appliance—Continued.	
Household motor	1	Toaster	3
Iron (hand)	5	Vacuum cleaner	2
Ironing machine	10	Waffle iron	2
Lighting	20	Washing machine	3
Radio	8	Water heater	240
Range	140	Water pump (shallow well)	8
Dishwasher	2½	Water pump (deep well)	10
Fan (household)	2		*Kilowatts per hour of use*
Fan (kitchen)	8		
Refrigerator	45	Heater (glowing or radiant)	1
Sewing machine	½	Heating pad	½

By multiplying these consumption figures by the rate for electric energy, approximate costs of operation for each appliance may be obtained. At 4 cents per kilowatt-hour (1,000 watts for 1 hour), for instance, it would cost 8 cents a month to operate an electric clock, 32 cents a month for the radio, 12 cents for the toaster, and 30 to 40 cents for the water pump. In making such computations, it is important to remember that the more power used, the lower the rate.

Electricity in Farm Operations

Though the uses of electricity for productive farm operations are less well known than are home uses, electric power offers substantial opportunities to farmers for more effective and profitable performance of many of their farm operations.

Many farmers have discovered new sources of income because of the availability of electric power; others have found that they can reduce their operating costs below those of methods previously used; still others have been able to save time which they have used to profitable advantage in other activities. It has been stated that there is not a stationary operation on the farm today, indoors or out, in the doing of which electricity cannot be used. On the other hand, electric power has not been applied in the United States, except largely on an experimental basis, to mobile farm operations such as plowing and hauling. It is of interest to note that some electrical plowing is being done in certain European countries.

The survey of electrical equipment mentioned previously indicates the most popular items of farm electrical equipment purchased by farmers who have been receiving electric service for an average period of about 10 months. A list of these items of equipment, with the percentage of their use by the reporting farmers, is as follows:,

Equipment	*Percentage of farms reporting use*	*Equipment*	*Percentage of farms reporting use*
Motor, up to 1 horsepower	18. 0	Milk cooler (fig. 4)	0. 7
Cream separator	14. 0	Poultry water warmer	. 5
Poultry-house lighting	10. 0	Feed grinder	. 5
Milking machine	3. 8	Dairy water heater	. 3
Brooder	3. 2	Hotbed heating	. 1
Electric fence	2. 7	Stock-tank heater	. 1
Motor, 1 horsepower and over	2. 3		

Not every farm has need for all of these pieces of equipment; one farm may need a brooder, another a cream separator. Many farmers

Figure 4.—The electric milk cooler eliminates losses from spoiled or rejected milk and increases profits by making possible milk of high quality.

have developed plans for gradually electrifying their operations as conditions warrant.

Many of the most effective and profitable applications of electricity to farm operations require very small amounts of electric power per unit of productive activity. A list of some of these operations with the average unit power requirements of each is given in the following tabulation:

Appliance	*Kilowatt-hours*
Apple-butter stirrer	¼ per gallon.
Apple-cider mill	¾ per 100 gallons.
Barn ventilator (during season)	50 per month.
Bone and shell grinder	2 per ton.
Bottle washer	½ per 1,000 bottles.
Brooder	½ per chick raised.
Bull exerciser	¼ per hour of use.
Churn	1½ per 100 pounds of butter.
Clipper (for horse or cow)	¼ per hour of use.
Concrete mixer	½ per cubic yard of concrete.
Corn husker-shredder	30 per 100 bushels of corn husked.
Corn sheller	¼ per 100 pounds of shelled corn.
Cream separator	¼ per cow per month.
Dairy refrigerator (during season)	30 per 10 gallons of milk daily per month.

Appliance	*Kilowatt-hours*
Dairy water heater	7 per cow per month.
Fence	4 per month.
Fly screen (during season)	5 per month.
Grain elevator	4 per 1,000 bushels.
Grain grinder	1 per 100 pounds.
Grain, seed cleaner and grader	1 per 100 pounds.
Green-feed cutter and root shredder	2 per ton.
Hay baler	2½ per ton.
Hay drier	40 per ton of dry hay.
Hay hoist	½ per ton.
Hotbed	1 per square yard per day.
Incubator	¼ per chick hatched.
Irrigation (surface)	3 to raise an acre-foot of water 1 foot.
Milking machine (portable)	1½ per cow per month.
Milking machine (pipe line)	3 per cow per month.
Oat sprouter	75 per 1,000 chickens per month.
Paint sprayer	½ per 250 square feet.
Poultry-house lighting (during season)	5 per 100 birds per month.
Poultry water heater	1 per day.
Sheep shearer	2 to shear 100 sheep.
Silage cutter	1 per ton.
Straw cutter	2 per ton.
Threshing machine	½ per 100 pounds of grain.
Tool grinder	¼ per hour of use.
Ultraviolet lights for poultry	10 per 100 hens per month.
Utility motor (small ¼ horsepower)	½ per hour of use.
Utility motor (3 and 5 horsepower)	1 per horsepower per hour of use.
Water pump for all farm uses	25 per month.
Wood saw	2 per cord of wood.

The figures presented make possible an approximation of the cost of electric power for these operations. In estimating the cost of performing various farm operations by assuming a rate per kilowatt-hour, it should be borne in mind that promotional rate schedules provide for lower rates and therefore lower costs as consumption of power increases.

Electricity in Rural Community, Institutions

In addition to serving the individual farms of a community, rural electric service is making a real contribution to community activities and undertakings in a great variety of appliances. Community institutions such as churches, schoolhouses, community centers, and lodge halls are found to be of greater service and benefit to farm people when electricity is made available. Entertainment, movies, and educational meetings can be held at night under attractive conditions. Lights, ventilation, and controlled heat enable rural schools to equal urban schools to the benefit of farm children. Rural community enterprises such as stores, garages, and gas stations have many uses for electricity that enable them to render better service to their farm customers. All of these and many other uses of electricity contribute to a better rural community life, a higher standard of living for rural people, and generally more unified and stable agricultural communities.

The availability of electric power throughout rural areas is making possible a desirable combination of agriculture and industry. Already there are definite signs of a beginning of decentralization of certain types of industry from the large industrial centers where their requirements for power have forced them to locate. The increasing acceptance of cooperative enterprises in rural areas may well provide the foundation for small industries to utilize the products of the farm for processing into commodities, which in turn will find their market in the local community as well as in the cities. Some of these processing enterprises offer possibilities for whole or part-time employment of those who work and live on the farms in the community. For instance, a woodworking plant operated by electric power may be established to utilize the products of the farm woodlands. Other possibilities include the processing of dairy, fruit, and vegetable products and electrically operated cotton gins, grain elevators, and mills. In many sections of the country cooperative refrigerators and cold-storage plants are rendering a desirable farm service for promoting health, increasing income, and fostering improved farming practices. For these and other types of community enterprises rural electric service offers a flexible source of heat, light, and power.

New Conditions Demand New Opportunities

by Raymond C. Smith [1]

THREE great question marks stand out in American agriculture today: (1) How can we manage our soil resources wisely? (2) How can commercial farmers get a better and more secure livelihood? (3) How can the disadvantaged group in agriculture find a useful and self-respecting place in our economy? This article outlines the scope of the third question. The attention paid to this group in present-day agricultural thinking is no more sentimental or accidental than the attention paid to cancer in modern medicine. There are many parallels between cancer, with its growth of hungry, functionless cells, and this nameless disease which is characterized by the growth of enormous groups of human beings who have little or no apparent function in our society. By now, the disadvantaged group in agriculture includes between one-third and one-half of all the farm people in the country. Every country boy and girl who comes of age with no job and no prospects adds to the group. What can be done to stop this growth and to heal the damage?

FOR MANY decades during the period of the development of American agriculture the possibility was not considered that fixed

[1] Raymond C. Smith is Chief Program Analyst, Bureau of Agricultural Economics.

classes might develop within the farm population. Plenty of free or cheap land was available, and it was possible for almost anyone dissatisfied with his lot, either in the country or in the city, to begin farming with almost a certainty that if he applied himself he could become an actual landowner within a reasonable time. For a long time this movement up the "agricultural ladder" (fig. 1) was our assuranec against the development of agricultural classes in this country. Just how is this ladder performing now that the physical frontier is gone and the country is showing signs of maturity? Is our democracy functioning in such a way as to furnish opportunities for all able-bodied citizens to make a livelihood, either on the farm or in the city, and to enjoy the much-heralded "American standard of living"?

All students of the farm problem know that opportunities for young people to become farm laborers, for laborers to become tenants, and for tenants to become owners are greatly limited today as compared with a generation or two ago. Man-labor requirements on farms have been constantly decreasing owing to mechanization and other developments of scientific agriculture. This decreasing requirement for man-power on the farms of the Nation has been accompanied, particularly during recent years, by a marked increase in the farm population of productive age. Careful estimates made by the Bureau of Agricultural Economics of the United States Department of Agriculture indicate that the farm population on January 1, 1939, totaled 32,059,000 persons. This figure practically reached the all-time-high record of 32,076,960 on January 1, 1910.

While farm population has been increasing and man-labor requirements on farms have been decreasing, unemployment in urban industry has limited the opportunities for surplus farm population to make a living by migrating to the city. This combination of circumstances, together with continued relatively high birth rates in rural areas, is creating an increasing population pressure upon the land, especially in poor soil areas. The increase in population pressure is accompanied by lower living standards among some segments of the farm population. The depression and recent droughts have been contributing factors, but it is necessary to look for more deep-seated causes than drought or depression to account for an insecurity so acute at the onset of these disasters that approximately one-fourth of the farm families of the Nation were unable to withstand their effects without applying for public assistance.

Danger signals have appeared along the way. For a long time there has been evidence of land misuse which if continued was bound to get farmers into serious difficulty. Wind and water erosion and such farming practices as overcropping, the one-crop system, failure to use cover crops, overgrazing, and plowing up grasslands that never should have been broken have taken a heavy toll from the soil and have handicapped cumulatively each succeeding generation of farmers. This misuse of the land has made for poverty in segments of the farm population, and the poverty in turn has made for more land misuse, since people who are hungry today are not likely to be conservation-minded or interested in saving for tomorrow.

Large increases in farm mortgage indebtedness and violently fluctuating land values have accompanied traffic in land as a commodity

Figure 1.—The agricultural ladder.

and the increasing commercialization of farming on a large part of the better land in the Nation. Farm mortgage indebtedness increased from 3½ billion dollars in 1910 to 9½ billion in 1928 and then, owing principally to foreclosures, declined to about 7¼ billion by 1937. Interest payments on farm mortgages increased from 200 million dollars in 1910 to 400 million in 1937. Values of all farm property increased 90 percent from 1910 to 1920, but by 1933 had declined to a point below the 1910 level. Cash requirements for principal and interest payments on mortgages and for tax payments have tended to be more rigid than has gross farm income, and this in turn has tended toward insecurity for farm owners and caused periods of widespread bankruptcy and loss of farms. It has become increasingly difficult for tenants to become owners, and for one heir at the death of a farm owner to buy out the other heirs and become the full owner of a farm.

Much rural wealth has migrated to cities through ownership of equities in farms by people in cities and interest payments to such holders. With only 9 percent of the Nation's income, farmers subsidize urban education because they rear and educate 31 percent of the Nation's children, many of whom later migrate to cities; and this too has been equivalent to migration of wealth from the farm to the city. The failure of rural industries that furnished opportunities for part-time employment to farm people in many areas has also been a handicap.

Farm tenancy increased from 25 percent in 1880 to 42 percent in 1935 for the Nation as a whole, while in some States as many as 70 percent of the farms were operated by tenants in 1935. If this increase in tenancy, representing loss of ownership by those who operate the land, is placed alongside the increase in mortgage indebtedness, we find that the equity in the total farm land of the Nation held by those who cultivate the land declined from 62 percent in 1880 to 39 percent in 1935.

The agricultural ladder is still working, however, even though much more imperfectly than in the past. Some laborers are becoming tenants, and some tenants are becoming owners; but as they progress up the ladder they are meeting owners in larger numbers coming down the ladder to become tenants, tenants coming down to take the place of laborers, and many laborers as well as some tenants and owners moving into towns and villages, where limited opportunities for private employment are forcing many of them onto public works programs or direct relief rolls. Not all of these surplus farm people move to towns and cities. Some who have been "tractored off" or "blown out," or who have been forced off their farms for other reasons, have heeded at too belated a date Horace Greeley's advice to go west, only to meet disappointment when they found themselves a part of the army of migratory laborers on the Pacific coast.

AGRICULTURAL CLASSES

As farmers cease to move up the agricultural ladder or move up more slowly, we have the beginning of permanent stratification of our farm population. In some sections, particularly in the Southern States, this began a long time ago. In other sections it is only now becoming noticeable. To prevent the formation of rigid permanent classes, such as a permanent farm-laborer class and a permanent tenant class alongside a permanent landowning class is a challenge to agricultural leadership today.

There are many ways in which farmers might be classified. On the basis of tenure, the classes could be those of landlords, owner-operators, tenants, sharecroppers, and laborers. These groups can be broken down into almost innumerable subgroups.

There are resident landlords and nonresident landlords, corporation landlords and individual landlords, landlords owning, say, more than 100 farms and those owning fewer than this number, landlords who take a genuine interest in their farms and the welfare of their tenants and those who do not take such an interest, landlords who understand farming and those who know little about it, landlords who have a long-time interest in their farms and in conservation of the soil and those with a temporary interest and the hope for a quick turn-over of the farm at the maximum profit.

There are owner-operators who own all the land they cultivate and those who rent land in addition to that owned, owner-operators engaged in commercial farming and those engaged in noncommercial or subsistence farming, owner-operators on large farms who employ farm labor and those on family-size farms who do most of the work themselves.

Among tenants there are those who operate large farms and those who operate small farms, tenants who rent for cash and those who rent for a share of the crops or of the crops and livestock, tenants with oral leases and those with written leases, tenants with leases for 1 year only and those with leases for more than 1 year, tenants who move frequently and those who are relatively stable in location, tenants interested in the conservation of the land they cultivate and those with no such interest.

There are sharecroppers who are allowed to raise gardens and produce milk, meat, and eggs for home consumption and those who do not have such privileges, sharecroppers who live in decent houses and those who do not, sharecroppers who move frequently and those who move less often.

As for farm laborers there are those with full-time employment in agriculture and those employed part time in agricultural work and part time in work off the farm, migratory laborers and those who are relatively stable in location, farm laborers who work by the day and those who work by the month or year, farm laborers who live on the farms where they are employed and those who live in nearby towns.

During the last few years several of the above groups could have been subdivided further between those who were self-dependent and those who have had to rely partly upon some form of public assistance in order to live.

The census of the unemployed[2] taken in 1937 shows 879,321 registrants in the United States who reported farm residence and classified themselves as totally unemployed. In addition 295,002 farm residents

[2] U. S. National Unemployment Census. census of partial employment, unemployment, and occupations. preliminary report on total and partial unemployment. summary by states, counties, and cities as of nov. 16–20, 1937. v. Washington, D. C. 1938.

reported that they had emergency employment, and 627,053 more that they were only partially employed. Of the total registrants in the United States who reported themselves as totally unemployed, 617,949 gave their occupations as either farm operators (owners and tenants) or farm laborers. Among the registrants who reported themselves as having only emergency employment, 225,672 classified themselves as

Figure 2.—*A*, With the help of modern equipment, 50 percent of American farmers produce 90 percent of the commercial farm products, while, *B*, the other 50 percent of farmers, with outdated methods and often on poor land, produce only 10 percent.

farm operators or farm laborers. Among the registrants who reported themselves as being only partially employed, 531,339 classified themselves as farm operators or farm laborers. According to these data more than 1⅓ million persons who considered themselves farmers, that is, owners, tenants, or laborers, were totally unemployed, only partially employed, or had only emergency employment in 1937.

The fact that only about 50 percent of the farmers of the Nation are producing nearly 90 percent of the farm products marketed, leaving only 10 or 11 percent of the total market for the other half of the farm families (fig. 2, *A* and *B*), indicates another basis for classifying the farm population. These two groups are often distinguished as commercial farmers and noncommercial or subsistence farmers. In the past the problems of the commercial farmers have received relatively more attention than have those of the subsistence farmers.

The 1930 census classified farmers according to gross farm incomes, as indicated in table 1. According to the census in 1929, the year before the depression began to affect farmers' incomes, approximately one-half of all farmers in the country had gross yearly farm incomes of less than $1,000, while more than one-fourth had gross farm incomes below $600. In addition these farmers had the questionable privilege of living in houses most of which would be classed as substandard and received some income from work done off the farm, although not more than 10 percent worked as much as 150 days off the farm. It has been estimated by Taeuber[3] that the average gross farm income received by the group of farmers whose incomes were below $1,000 in 1929 amounted to $615, of which approximately $200 represented products consumed at home, leaving $415 as average gross cash income. Taeuber also estimated that the average gross farm income received by the group whose gross farm incomes were below $600 amounted to $375 and that approximately $180 of this represented products consumed at home. This would leave $195 as average gross cash income. Farm operating expenses for such items as rent or mortgage principal payments, interest, taxes, purchase of feed and fertilizer, and replacement of machinery and work stock, had to be met first out of these amounts of gross cash income. The remainder, if there was any, was available for the purchase of food, clothing, household furnishings, medical care and hospitalization, education of the children, radios—in fact, to

Table 1.—Gross farm income (value of products sold, traded, or used by operator's family) reported by farm families in the United States in 1929, by income groups [1]

Gross farm income (dollars)	Farm families		Gross farm income (dollars)	Farm families	
	Number [2]	*Percent* [2]		*Number* [2]	*Percent* [2]
Less than:			Less than:		
250	397,517	6.6	4,000	5,474,430	91.2
400	915,549	15.2	6,000	5,765,542	96.1
600	1,681,667	27.9	10,000	5,913,295	98.5
1,000	2,927,351	48.6	20,000	5,974,905	99.6
1,500	3,865,261	64.4		5,999,882	100.0
2,500	4,846,424	81.1			

[1] U. S. Census, 1930.
[2] Cumulative.

[3] Unpublished data, Division of Farm Population and Rural Life, Bureau of Agricultural Economics.

support an "American standard of living" and to provide security for the future. In addition to farm operators, there were about 2¾ million farm laborers in 1929 a large portion of whom were in the very low income groups.

Thus it appears that there is a class that can be termed a poverty class in American agriculture. To prevent this group from becoming a permanent poverty class is another challenge to leadership today.

Regardless of the basis used for classifying our farm population, the conclusion seems inescapable that we do have disadvantaged classes in American agriculture. Standards of living among these people are so low that to be realistic we must say that disadvantaged farm families are living under slum conditions.

> The sore spots in rural life, as elsewhere, appear when the total economic machinery is subjected to heavy strain. Periods of depression bring into highlight conditions which, unobserved, have been in existence for a long time and they reveal the operation of disadvantaging factors that have been consistently tending to reduce the standards of living of thousands of farm families to marginal and submarginal levels. It is probably shocking to those not well acquainted with these disadvantaged areas in rural America and especially to those who have been accustomed to thinking of rural life in idyllic terms, to realize that there are rural slums as well as urban slums. But if slum conditions mean poor housing, lack of household facilities and sanitation, ill health, insufficient income to buy even the physical necessities of life, and few or no opportunities to participate in the consumption of cultural goods and services, then rural slums are a reality in many sections; and in these rural slums, persons and families are denied some things which even great masses of people who live in city slums take for granted.[4]

While low living standards tend to be concentrated in certain problem areas such as the Appalachian-Ozark area, the Lake States cut-over area, the short-grass spring-wheat area, the short-grass winter-wheat area, the eastern Cotton Belt, and the western Cotton Belt, as described by Beck and Forster,[5] they are found to a certain extent in every State in the Union. Included among the disadvantaged classes are some owner-operators as well as many tenants and the greater portion of the sharecroppers and farm laborers. Many farm owners are living on poor and badly eroded land, often with an inadequate acreage for making a living. Many tenants are insecure in their tenure and are forced to move frequently. This handicaps the tenant in getting ahead, interrupts the schooling of his children, and prevents the family from becoming a real part of the community in which it lives. Large numbers of sharecroppers have poor diets, owing in part to the fact that many of them are not permitted to produce vegetables, milk, eggs, and meat for home use. Poor diets combined with inadequate housing and unsanitary surroundings make for ill health. Many farm laborers are unable to obtain sufficient employment during the year to enable them to be self-dependent. Particularly handicapped are migratory laborers, many of whom, with their families, are constantly on the move seeking employment opportunities. The schooling of their children is neglected, and the conditions under which they are forced to live, often with no housing whatever, are deplorable.

[4] Taylor, Carl C., Wheeler, Helen W., and Kirkpatrick, E. L. DISADVANTAGED CLASSES IN AMERICAN AGRICULTURE. U. S. Farm Security Admin. Soc. Res. Rpt. 8, 124 pp. 1938. [Processed.]

[5] Beck, P. G., and Forster, M. C. SIX RURAL PROBLEM AREAS; RELIEF, RESOURCES, REHABILITATION, ANALYSIS OF HUMAN AND MATERIAL RESOURCES IN 6 RURAL AREAS WITH HIGH RELIEF RATES. [U. S.] Fed. Emergency Relief Admin. Research Monog. 1, 167 pp., illus. 1936.

RURAL POVERTY SHOULD BE ATTACKED

Is there a real need for giving increased consideration to the means of improving the standard of living of the disadvantaged classes in the rural United States? If we follow the policy of applying grease to the wheel that squeaks the loudest we may not attempt much in the way of improving living standards for these people, because they are not organized or very articulate. No doubt most people would be interested from a humanitarian standpoint in giving disadvantaged farm people greater opportunities. But from the standpoint of enlightened self-interest alone, the more privileged people in the Nation must be concerned about the welfare of the disadvantaged groups in rural areas. If we can find some way to increase the purchasing power of low-income farm people and also of low-income urban workers, we can greatly expand our domestic market. It has been pointed out [6] that even a moderate increase in nutrition and clothing standards for the low-income people would contribute to a considerable increase in production and prosperity in the Nation as a whole.

Another good reason for improving living standards among disadvantaged classes in the farm population is that these people are furnishing more than a proportionate share of children to the Nation. Birth rates are relatively high among disadvantaged farm people, and their children, with no opportunities in the areas where they are reared, move to the cities and to other parts of the country as soon as they are grown. Again from the standpoint of enlightened self-interest, as well as from the humanitarian standpoint, it seems essential that these children should not be allowed to grow up with unhealthy bodies and with an inadequate education.

In these days when democracy is on test everywhere we should be particularly interested in the welfare of disadvantaged farm families. If the entire farm population can have a reasonable standard of living and an adequate rural life it can serve as a reservoir of stability for the Nation and a stronghold in preserving democracy in our country. Farm people make up the backbone of the Nation in many ways, and it will be advantageous at all times for the Nation's backbone to be strong. Poverty is unnecessary in a land as rich in natural resources as ours. A vigorous search for means of eliminating it is one of the major tasks before us.

ACTION NEEDED FOR IMPROVEMENT OF LIVING STANDARDS AND SECURITY OF DISADVANTAGED FARM PEOPLE

There is no simple solution of the problem of rural poverty. Many different kinds of action are needed in the field of rural welfare. We are living in a complex society in which problems are very much interrelated. Hence, improvements for disadvantaged rural classes cannot be planned except in relation to the welfare of the more privileged farm families and also in relation to national life as a whole. The elimination of rural poverty should be of very definite benefit to all of

---

[6] EZEKIEL, MORDECAI. $2,500 A YEAR. FROM SCARCITY TO ABUNDANCE. 328 pp., illus. New York. 1936.

society. Some measures designed to benefit other groups in our society may benefit indirectly the disadvantaged classes in agriculture. Any efforts to stabilize the farming industry, to reduce violent fluctuation in land values and in the prices of farm commodities, to hinder widespread speculation in land, and to promote conservation of the soil should be of help to low-income farmers as well as to their more prosperous neighbors.

Expansion in industrial production and employment would also be of great advantage to all farmers. Such expansion would create greater opportunities for a part of the surplus farm population to make a living in the city, and the migration of large numbers of farm people to the city would increase the opportunities for those remaining in the country. More complete employment in the cities would also benefit agriculture by increasing the purchasing power of the buyers of farm products and would create a better domestic market for the products of agriculture. An expansion of the surplus-commodity stamp plan, which has been so successful not only in improving the lot of low-income urban families but also in creating a larger market for farm products, should be helpful. Mordecai Ezekiel has pointed out [7] that a great opportunity lies before the Nation if it is possible to bring about the continuous industrial expansion that he believes is practicable. The interdependence of farm and city cannot be overlooked. Those interested in improving the welfare of low-income farm families and of farmers as a whole, therefore, should be interested in any measures designed to bring about improvements in industrial production and employment. At the same time we should not sit by idly and assume that some day great improvement in the urban situation will automatically solve the problems of agriculture. Many things can be done to improve the welfare of low-income farmers now.

Action on the Farm Tenancy Problem

The great increase in the number of farms operated by tenants and the increasing difficulties that tenants face in becoming farm owners have centered a great deal of attention upon the problem of tenancy. Encouraging the ownership of land by those who farm it has been considered a worth-while national goal by many people. The Bankhead-Jones farm-tenancy bill was in part an outgrowth of this sentiment. Historically, ownership of a farm has given a considerable amount of security to farm operators, much more than has been enjoyed by tenants or laborers. Recently, however, ownership in itself has not been as good an assurance of security as it was in the past. It becomes necessary, therefore, to think not only of farm ownership but also of particular types of ownership in the attempt to assist low-income farm families to attain a reasonable degree of security.

It has been assumed in the past that only a type of ownership in which the farm owner had a substantial equity in his property was desirable. Obviously, the greater the equity a farmer has in his farm the more security he would have. But the limited income of farm tenants during recent years has made it exceedingly difficult for them

---

[7] EZEKIEL, MORDECAI. JOBS FOR ALL THROUGH INDUSTRIAL EXPANSION. 299 pp., illus. New York and London. 1939.

to save sufficient funds while tenants to be able to make substantial down payments on farms of their own. Some means of acquiring farms and at the same time of having security other than starting ownership with substantial equities seemed to be required if many tenants were to have the opportunity to become farm owners.

The tenant-purchase loans authorized by the Bankhead-Jones Act and now being made by the Secretary of Agriculture through the Farm Security Administration give tenants without large savings the opportunity to become farm owners and at the same time, if they avail themselves of the privilege of following the variable annual-payment plan, to have a considerable degree of security in the ownership of their farms. This plan is discussed in more detail in an article in this Yearbook by Paul V. Maris, page 887.

The Farm Security Administration is assisted in the work of making tenant-purchase loans by committees of farmers in each county where the loans are made. It also gives some farm- and home-management guidance to the borrowers. This is the third year in which such loans have been made. From the success that the effort has met so far, it appears that a considerable expansion of this activity would be justified and that such an expansion would be a desirable approach on the part of society as a whole to creating greater opportunities for farm tenants to become owners. While a reasonable amount of farm tenancy is no doubt desirable, the prospect of further increases, particularly in States where more than 42 percent (the national average) of farms are already operated by tenants, is viewed with considerable alarm by a great many people. Expansion of the tenant-purchase program would be one method of stemming the tide of increasing tenancy. In time it might be effective in reversing the trend and reducing the amount of tenancy, particularly in the States where tenancy is unusually high.

It also appears that many owner-operators of farms mortgaged to other credit agencies might be enabled to raise their level of living and have greater security for the future if farm-credit agencies generally explored the possibilities of adopting a variable annual-payment plan.

Many farm tenants, particularly those related to landlords, already have considerable security of tenure, and some may be better situated as tenants than they would be as owners. However, the tenure of many other tenants is very insecure. They are forced to move frequently, with the accompanying disadvantages of moving expense, of starting over on a new farm to which their livestock and machinery may not be well adapted, of interrupting the schooling of their children, and of lack of opportunity to become established as a part of a rural community. As has often been pointed out, such tenants are not likely to be deeply concerned over misuse of the land, since were they to conserve the soil it would be for someone else's benefit. During the fiscal year 1938 the Farm Security Administration assisted 98,000 tenants in changing from an oral to a written lease.[8] Included among these tenants were 65,000 who obtained leases containing automatic renewal clauses. More attention to equitable leasing

[8] [UNITED STATES] FARM SECURITY ADMINISTRATION. REPORT OF THE ADMINISTRATOR. . . . 22 pp. 1938.

arrangements between landlords and tenants, landlord and tenant education along the lines of desirable forms of tenure, and encouragement of longer and more secure tenure would be helpful. Development of methods through which tenants might be compensated for the unexhausted value of improvements also should be helpful, not only in improving living standards but in contributing to soil conservation.

Rural Rehabilitation

One of the most direct methods of helping low-income farm families to improve living standards and attain a greater degree of security has been rehabilitation. The rural rehabilitation program administered by the Farm Security Administration has been of service to more than a million farm families during the last 4 years. While grants of direct relief and emergency loans have been made to thousands of needy families by this agency, the main part of the program has been concerned with assisting what are called "standard cases." County rehabilitation supervisors, some trained in farm management and some with home-management training, with the help of county committees, assist applicants for "standard loans" in analyzing their needs and in working out a program for their rehabilitation. The families, with the assistance of the supervisors, prepare farm and home plans for the year's operations. These plans provide for careful budgeting of expenditures and estimating probable income. A standard loan is made to finance necessary purchases of livestock, machinery, seed, fertilizer, household equipment, and other items needed to assure the soundness of the plan and the following of good farm- and home-management practices. These loans, which average about $350, usually are repayable within a period of 5 years. As described in the article Overcrowded Farms in this Yearbook (p. 870), credit of this type is one of several devices used in the rehabilitation process.

According to W. W. Alexander, who until recently was Administrator of the Farm Security Administration—

> The annual net cost of the rehabilitation loan program—including all losses and expenses of administration—amounts to less than $75 for each family aided. This is without doubt the lowest cost to the taxpayer of any kind of help for needy families. Moreover, rehabilitation differs fundamentally from all other types of aid, because its whole purpose is to help needy families escape the relief rolls and become self-supporting. It has proved eminently successful in achieving this goal. Although the normal period of rehabilitation is 5 years, and the program has been in operation for only 4, more than 87,000 families [the number has increased since this statement was made] already have paid off their loans in full and "graduated" into a self-supporting status. The remaining families have made surprising gains in their net worth, standards of living, and capacity for self-support.

The rehabilitation program is an effective instrument in improving the welfare of low-income farm families and has made a great deal of progress in starting such families once more on the way to self-dependency and higher living standards. Many thousands of low-income farm families have not been served, however, because sufficient funds were not available. Expansion of this program so that it could be of assistance to other needy families appears to be highly desirable. Since farm- and home-management guidance is such an essential part of the rehabilitation process, further strengthening of this aspect of the program should be especially helpful to low-income families.

223761°—40——53

Purchase of submarginal land by the Government and assistance to the families living on it in finding new locations have been a worthwhile form of aid to a few thousand farm families. Some of these families were assisted by rehabilitation supervisors in renting farms in new locations and received standard rehabilitation loans and farm- and home-management guidance in making a new start. Others were settled on resettlement projects administered by the Farm Security Administration, where they either rented farms or purchased them under a plan providing for payments over a 40-year period. On these projects, families from submarginal farms were included along with a number of rehabilitation-client families and farm-laborer families who had not had an opportunity to rise above the farm-laborer class.

The development of resettlement projects involved the purchase of good land, which was usually subdivided into family-size farms, and the repair of existing buildings and construction of new buildings suitable to the units. As a rule the good land purchased was in large farms and was developed in such a way as to provide opportunities for a considerably larger number of families to make a living on it than had been living there before. In a few cases the land, instead of being subdivided into family-size farms, was developed into large cooperative farms. These large farms were leased or sold to cooperatives formed by low-income families, in accordance with existing State cooperative laws. In these cases the cooperative associations rather than the individual farmers operate the farms. The members of the cooperative divide the profits from the farm operations, usually in accordance with the number of hours of work contributed by each member.

As has been pointed out above, one of the serious problems with which the Nation is confronted is the seemingly great pressure of population on the land. Since most of the resettlement projects, both those with individual farming units and those with cooperative farming units, have enabled a larger number of families to make a living on the land than were being supported by the same land before its purchase for the projects, these projects have great significance. They have developed a pattern that could be followed more generally if the Nation should decide to make a serious effort to relieve this pressure of population on the land and to provide opportunities for a larger number of needy farm families to make a better living. Even though urban industry should be able to absorb a considerable amount of surplus farm population—an eventuality that does not appear to be likely in the immediate future—there would be a place for a great deal of activity of this kind. Though up to now the resettlement projects have been considered more or less experimental, the experience gained and the results achieved thus far indicate that they now could be spread safely on a much broader basis.

In some sections of the country stranded rural industrial workers—for instance, coal miners and timber workers—have been trying to wrest a living from worn-out or unsuitable soil since their former sources of income disappeared. Many farmers, too, have become practically stranded in areas of eroded and worn-out soil. The development of rural industries should be helpful in many such areas in furnishing part-time employment to stranded families. In some timbered areas, particularly in the South, it would appear desirable to explore fully the possibilities of assisting low-income families in making a living in the forests through a sustained-yield program. (See The Place of Forests in the Farm Economy, p. 533 of this Yearbook.) The Government might well consider supplementing private initiative by making cooperative loans to groups of such families for the establishment of sawmills or pulp mills, or both. An expansion of the subsistence-homesteads idea, which has worked out so well for urban factory workers in some areas, might also be desirable in those situations where work in the forest or mill could be combined with tilling a sufficient amount of land for raising a substantial part of the family food supply.

The problems of thousands of subsistence, or noncommercial, farm families are not likely to be solved through methods designed to improve the welfare of the commercial farmers. The development of new types of farming and of new farm- and home-management techniques particularly applicable to their problems may be necessary. Entirley new patterns of living may have to be developed in order to assure many subsistence farmers an opportunity to be self-supporting.

It also appears that a rural public-works program is needed to supplement the income of the thousands of low-income farmers who either have access to no land at all or are unable to get enough good land to make all of their living from farming. Because of the crying need for conservation of the soil over widespread areas, a rural public-works program designed to provide part-time employment to low-income farmers in saving and improving soil and forest resources would appear to be especially desirable. Such a program would contribute not only to the conservation of the soil and to the public benefits usually derived from soil conservation but also to the immediate needs of the farmers who would be given employment. This would be a method of combining conservation of human resources with conservation of natural resources in a very practical way.

Agricultural labor has received much attention as a cost factor in production, but there seems to have been a lag in considering the problems of laborers as human beings. As pointed out above, many tenants and even some farm owners have dropped back to become laborers, and laborers have had increased difficulties in taking the next step up the agricultural ladder. The use of mechanized equipment has made for combination of farms into larger units and has increased the number of laborers in proportion to the number of tenants and owners in highly mechanized areas. In some sections mechanization has reached the point where unemployment among the farm-laborer class has become pronounced. Migration of such laborers seeking work opportunities has created a migratory-labor class in some areas. Examples may be found in parts of Texas and to a considerable extent on the Pacific coast. Agricultural laborers have been denied the benefits of most of the legislation designed to help industrial laborers. This subject is discussed more fully in Farm Labor in an Era of Change, page 907.

Efforts to improve the situation are needed in two directions: (1) To provide greater opportunities for farm laborers to become tenants and later farm owners, thus preventing the development of a permanent and static farm-laborer class, and (2) to improve the welfare of farm laborers while they are laborers. Any measures for the benefit of laborers should apply to sharecroppers in the South, since they too are essentially laborers. The labor-camp program of the Farm Security Administration has been of help to migratory laborers, at least to the extent of giving them a chance to live decently while moving about from place to place. The few permanent homes that this agency has provided in connection with the labor camps, along with mobile camp facilities, probably have been of much greater benefit. Efforts to assist migratory laborers to settle down, or at least to have a permanent home to which they can return between migrations, should be an effective means of improving their welfare. Under such conditions, the children could have much better schooling opportunities, and if a small amount of land were provided in connection with the permanent home, the standard of living could be raised through the production of food for home use. A well-coordinated information service conducted by employment-service offices and accurately reflecting employment opportunities should also be helpful.

Housing, Educational, and Health Needs

One of the real needs in rural areas, particularly for laborers and sharecroppers, and to quite an extent for tenants as well, is the construction of well-built low-cost houses. Hundreds of thousands of low-income farm families are literally living under slum conditions. This is not only socially undesirable but is a very real menace to health. A large-scale program of rural housing would be desirable not only from the standpoint of improving housing itself but also from that of providing employment opportunities in the construction program.

Action is needed in the fields of education and health for the benefit of disadvantaged farm families. The children of farm families in many sections, particularly in the South, have very limited schooling opportunities.

> The South must educate one-third of the Nation's children with one-sixth of the Nation's school revenues. According to the most conservative estimates, the per capita ability of the richest State in the country to support education is six times as great as that of the poorest State. . . . All Southern States fall below the national average in tax resources per child, although they devote a larger share of their tax income to schools. . . . There were actually 1,500 school centers in Mississippi without school buildings, requiring children to attend school in lodge halls, abandoned tenant houses, country churches, and, in some instances, even in cotton pens.[9]

There is also a place for the development of more adult-education facilities among disadvantaged farm families. The Farm Security Administration has made a contribution in this field with its farm- and home-management guidance. The National Youth Administration has done likewise in providing educational opportunities for rural youth. There appears, however, to be a need for much more activity along the line of increasing educational opportunity for adults and youth as well as for the younger children of low-income farm families.

Health problems, including sanitation, adequate medical and dental care, and hospitalization, are in need of a great deal more attention

---

[9] [UNITED STATES] NATIONAL EMERGENCY COUNCIL. REPORT ON ECONOMIC CONDITIONS OF THE SOUTH. 64 pp. Washington, D. C. 1938.

in many rural areas. The approach made jointly by county and State medical associations, together with the Farm Security Administration, in providing adequate medical care for low-income families on a county basis, has already accomplished a great deal in approximately 500 counties. More than 100,000 low-income farm families are receiving medical care under this plan. There is need for much more activity of this kind and for other efforts in improving sanitation, dental care, and hospitalization. If adequate health and educational facilities are to be provided for these families, national as well as local resources probably must form the base for them.

Adjustment to Technological Change

There appears to be a great need for action in assisting farm families to make adjustments to technological changes on farms. In the commercial farming sections, where mechanization has assumed considerable proportions, family-size farms more and more are being combined into larger units. Farm-management specialists on occasion quote figures to show that such changes in size of farm make for greater efficiency in agricultural production. When these figures are analyzed, however, they often show that the greater efficiency attained is measured in terms of labor income to the farm operator—the entrepreneur—without regard to the effect on the farm laborers and the families crowded off the land to make possible the use of mechanized equipment. A broader base than the income of the entrepreneur should be used in measuring efficiency in farming. The income of farm laborers should be considered, as should the incomes of any displaced farmers, many of whom under present conditions probably have had to go on relief. In the long run, the welfare of all farm families as well as efficiency in production will have to be considered in attempting to measure efficiency in agriculture.

If we had no concern whatever for the welfare of farm people we might be able to consider efficiency in agriculture simply in terms of production of food and fiber for the Nation and in terms of income or standard of living for only a part of the families in agriculture. However, if we are interested in the welfare of all the families that have had and would like to continue to have the opportunity to make a living on the land, we cannot accept this type of efficiency with complacency. This does not mean that we should attempt to stop technological change in agriculture, nor that we should fail to encourage a portion of the farm population to seek opportunities in the city when they are available. It does, however, show the need for assisting displaced farmers in making adjustments to technological change and the need to influence the rate of introduction of technological change in such a way as to prevent its impact from causing serious losses in human values.

In the long run the widespread combination of farms into larger and larger units would no doubt make for a static, stratified farm population with a permanent laborer class in agriculture. If the farm land of the Nation were all to be owned by a relatively small land-owning class there would be an opportunity for comparatively few farm laborers to become landowners There are those who argue that this would be desirable, as under such a system we could get the maximum advantage from modern technologies, have the most capable people managing the land and directing the less capable (who would be laborers), and have the maximum efficiency in agricultural production.

It would seem, however, that there is a point beyond which the trend toward larger farms is undesirable. Safeguards to protect the security of families on family-size farms who desire to continue to operate such farms are essential. Farms should of course be large enough to be sound economic units—and at present some families are handicapped by units that are too small; but when the population pressure upon the land is considered, it seems that farms should also be small enough to be sound social units. Many very large farms appear upon the market every year, offered for sale either by owners or by the estates of deceased owners. Without in any way disturbing the owners of large farms who desire to keep them, it should be possible to develop procedures whereby some of the larger farms annually put up for sale could be made available to farmers displaced by technological change. By subdividing into family-size farms the larger farms capable of being developed in such a way that the same land could support more families than before, the maximum number of displaced farmers who want to make a living on small family-size farms could be given an opportunity to do so.

THE PROBLEM TO BE SOLVED

Obviously no one type of action will solve the problems of agriculture in a complex society and in a period of rapid change. Since adjustments to changing conditions are usually more difficult when changes come about abruptly it is not surprising that we have had serious social maladjustments. The problem seems to be to determine what kind of agriculture and rural life we want, and then to set ourselves to the task of bringing it about. Further research studies and much educational work still need to be done, but there are some present lines of action that can be strengthened and some new ones that can be attempted.

An attempt has been made here to point out a few possibilities for action to improve the welfare of farm people. There is a real need for combining appropriate approaches and methods of action to the end that rural poverty may be eliminated and all farm people enjoy a decent American standard of living with a reasonable degree of security for the future. Any approach to improving the welfare of farm people also must take into consideration the welfare of the total population of the Nation. The real problem that lies before us is to see to it that by means of the democratic process every able-bodied citizen, whether he lives in the city or in the country, has an opportunity to earn a good living today, and, through the conservation of both our human and our natural resources, will have an opportunity to live better tomorrow.

The Rural People

by O. E. BAKER and CONRAD TAEUBER [1]

BY ARRANGING heaps of cold figures in intelligible order, the population expert is able to see what is actually happening to millions of human beings. Thus, dealing with population figures, the authors of this article show the gradual break-down of cultural differences between rural and urban, and native and foreign, groups in this country; the building up of sharper cleavages based on income; the implications of the declining birth rate and the increase in the relative number of older people. They trace the course of migrations to and from farms and discuss the significance of these shifts in population. They show that there are millions of young people backed up on the poorer farms because there are no opportunities for them elsewhere. Finally, the authors emphasize three needs that they believe emerge outstandingly from the situation disclosed by their figures.

WHEN the Constitution of the United States was adopted, some 150 years ago, probably 8 or more out of every 10 of the people were living on farms. More than three-fourths of the gainful workers secured their livelihood through work on farms. During the 70 years between that time and the War between the States, the population of the country doubled every quarter century. But the number of people living in cities increased much more rapidly than did the number living on farms, with the result that in 1860 less than 6 out of every 10 persons gainfully employed were engaged in agriculture. The rapid growth of cities continued, and by the turn of the century this

[1] O. E. Baker is Senior Agricultural Economist and Conrad Taeuber is Agricultural Economist, Division of Farm Population and Rural Welfare, Bureau of Agricultural Economics.

ratio had declined to less than 4 out of 10. Though the farm population was growing less rapidly than the urban population, the number of persons living on farms continued to increase until about 1915. After that it actually decreased, despite the fact that the total population of the country continued to grow. The 1920 census revealed for the first time that a majority of the Nation's people were living in urban centers, and the 1930 census indicated that 56 percent of the total population lived in these cities and towns of 2,500 people or more. The other 44 percent was divided between rural farm and rural nonfarm residents, 25 and 19 percent, respectively.

During the 1930's the farm population was increasing about as rapidly as the total population, and the percentage of the total living on farms probably is still 25 percent. Whether this means that the trend toward urbanization has been stopped or only temporarily interrupted is difficult to say. However, the shift from a nation in which more than three-fourths of the population lived on farms to one in which only one-fourth live on farms is of profound significance. Along with it has developed a growing urban influence, which has extended far beyond the limits of cities. In 1930 approximately one-half of the Nation's population lived within 50 miles of a city of 100,000 or more people.

At the same time, differences between rural and urban people are diminishing, as the schools, the automobile, the radio, city newspapers, magazines, mail-order catalogs, and moving pictures spread urban styles, attitudes, and ideals, as well as urban mechanisms, among the rural people. There is a marked trend toward uniformity within the rural population, as well as between the rural and the urban groups.

THE TREND TOWARD CULTURAL UNIFORMITY

The dominant people in the United States are of northern-European stocks. But in certain portions of the Nation other peoples constitute an important segment of the population. Of the nearly 54,000,000 people classified as rural in the 1930 census, about 12 percent were Negro. In the Cotton Belt about 33 percent of the rural population and 37 percent of the farm population were Negro (fig. 1). In rural Mississippi and on the farms of South Carolina the Negro population exceeded the white population. In Arizona the Mexican and Indian farm population was almost equal to that of all other races combined, and in New Mexico this segment constituted a very large proportion of the population. These peoples have a cultural heritage differing from that of the peoples of northern-European origin.

But the Negroes have been leaving the farms in large numbers. The decline in Negro farm population in the Nation was from 5,100,000 in 1920 to 4,680,000 in 1930, nearly twice as rapid a rate of decrease as that in the total farm population. In the Southern States, where practically all Negro farm population is located, the decrease was from 4,621,000 in 1930 to 4,506,000 in 1935—a decline of 115,000 in the 5 years despite a large natural increase (excess of births over deaths). During the same 5 years the white farm population of the Southern States increased 721,000. Negro tenants (including croppers) de-

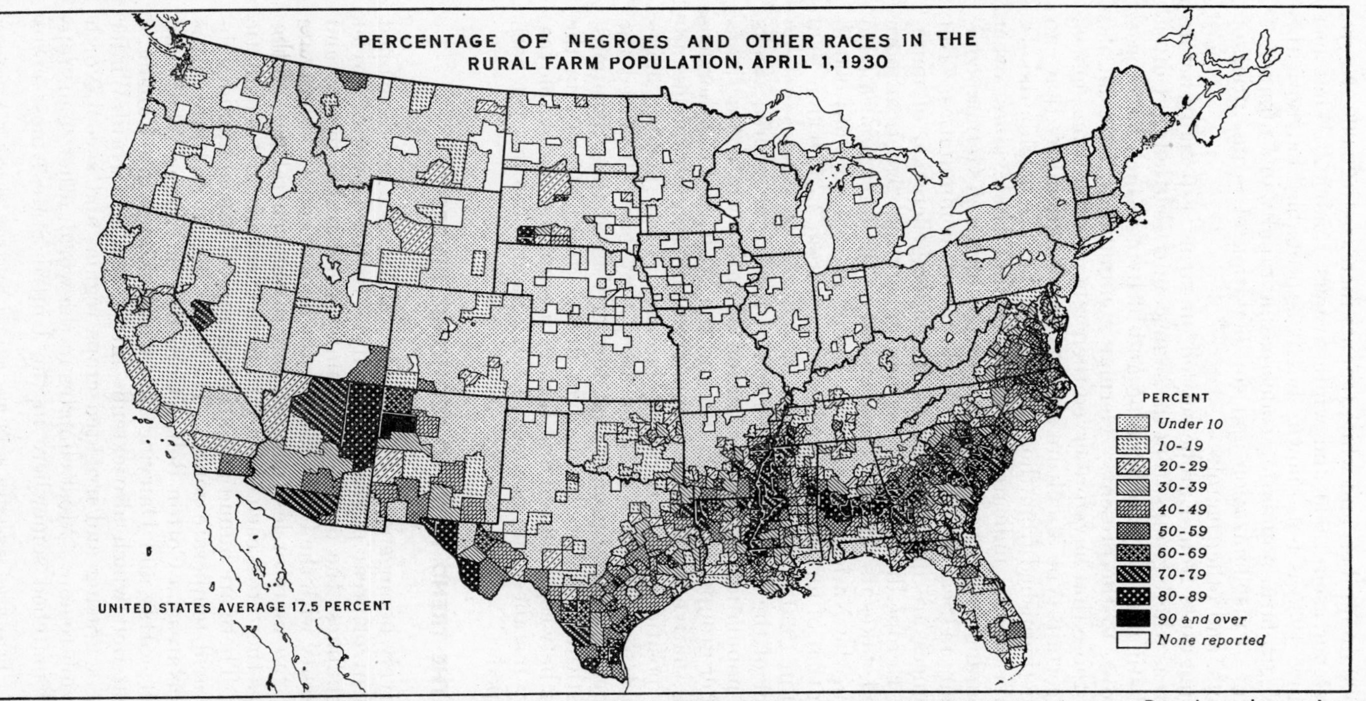

Figure 1.—In most of the United States the so-called white races constitute 90 percent or more of the farm population. But along the southern border, all the way from eastern Virginia to California and extending northward on the Coastal Plain to Cairo, Ill., is a belt in which nonwhite races constitute in most counties one-third or more—in some counties over two-thirds—of the farm population. In general, this belt of "colored" people is also a region of poverty, of tenants or wage hands, of highly commercial agriculture, except in parts of Arizona and New Mexico, and of retarded educational progress for most of the people. The other races include Mexican, Indian, Chinese, Japanese, Filipino, Hindu, Korean, Hawaiian, Malay, Siamese, and Samoan.

creased 70,000 in number, and white tenants increased 120,000; Negro farm owners increased 4,000 and white owners 155,000. What has happened since 1935 is not known, but it is probable that both the white and Negro farm population is decreasing rapidly in a number of States, owing to mechanization and consolidation of farms, prices of farm products, and other factors.

Many immigrants from Europe settled on farms, especially before 1890. In areas where groups from the same country settled they often developed distinctive ways of farming and of living which have been preserved down to the present. German communities, for example, particularly those that have preserved their religious traditions, generally have a certain type of culture and system of agriculture that can be readily distinguished from those of Irish or Yankee neighborhoods. Studies in Wisconsin [2] indicate, for example, that land values, other factors remaining equal, were 10 to 20 percent higher in German communities than in Scandinavian or Anglo-Saxon communities. But these differences are disappearing as the older generation of immigrants from Europe dies out and the new generation, American born and educated, takes its place. The decrease in the foreign-born farm population in the Nation was from 1,433,000 in 1920 to 1,084,000 in 1930, and in that of foreign or mixed parentage from 3,733,000 in 1920 to 3,305,000 in 1930.

One aspect of the declining proportion of foreign or colored stocks in the farm population is the substitution of native white Americans for these other groups. In the South and the West, and in other sections as well, native white farm people are competing for the less advantageous positions—as migratory laborers, farm hands, sharecroppers, and tenants—and in some cases they have displaced the other national and racial groups that formerly filled those positions. Such a substitution naturally involves drastic readjustments in the relationships between landlord and tenant or employer and employee, and in many instances the new set of relationships has not yet been fully developed.

THE TREND TOWARD ECONOMIC DIVERSITY

The relatively homogeneous culture of rural America has developed on a continent of great physical diversity. In the Union of Soviet Socialist Republics, the only other country comparable in size and natural diversity with the United States, the lines of equal temperature and rainfall run more or less parallel, but in the central part of the United States they cross each other, forming a checkerboard of climatic conditions. There are humid and arid subtropical zones; humid, subhumid, and arid temperate zones. There are humid and arid citrus areas and rice areas, a Cotton Belt, a Corn Belt, a Winter Wheat and Tobacco Belt, a Hay and Dairying Belt which extends into Canada, a Spring Wheat Belt which also extends into Canada, a Hard Winter Wheat Belt, a grazing and irrigated crops region, and a cool North Pacific dairying region. Most climates in the world, other than tropical, can be matched somewhere in the United States; most crops

[2] Taylor, C. V. Unpublished manuscript in Division of Land Economics, Bureau of Agricultural Economics.

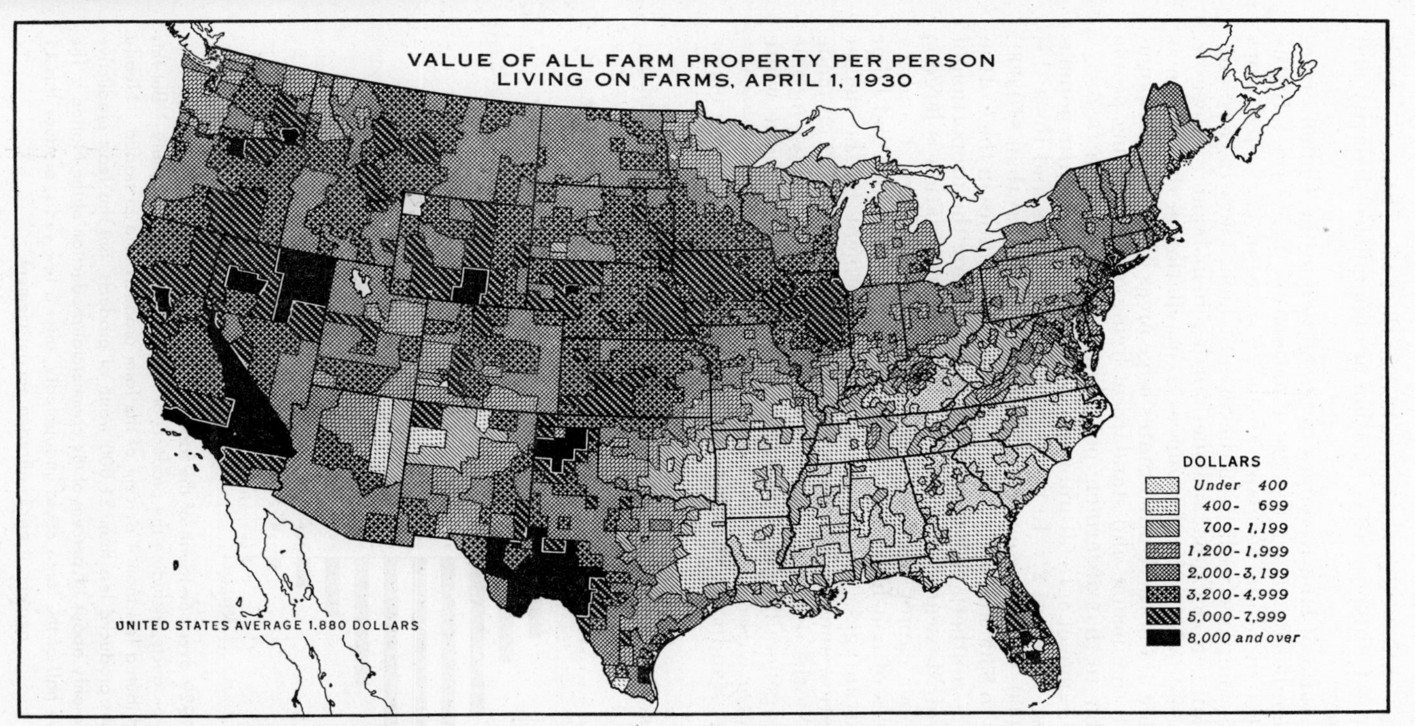

Figure 2.—The value of farm property per person living on farms is partly correlated geographically with the percentage of the farm population that is Negro, Indian, or Mexican (see fig. 1); partly with poor soils or hilly surface, as in the southern Appalachian and Ozark Mountains; partly with density of farm population and small amount of power available per farm worker; and with several less important factors. From southern Virginia and Kentucky to central Oklahoma and Texas, thence southward to the Gulf Coast and southern Florida—a region that contains one-third of the Nation's farm population—the value of farm property per person living on farms averaged in most counties less than $700 in 1930, and in some counties was as low as $300. Moreover, in most of this region the rural birth rate is high and the farm population is increasing rapidly. This region of relative poverty is destined to provide on increasing proportion of the Nation's citizens of the future.

grown in the world are grown somewhere in the United States. Agriculturally, the United States is a nation of unparalleled diversity and self-sufficiency.

The high ratio of land resources to population in the United States is also unparalleled among the great nations of the world. In the United States there are normally about 2½ acres of harvested crops per capita as compared with 1½ in the Soviet Union, 1 acre in Germany, about one-half acre in China, and one-fourth acre in Japan. However, despite the high ratio of land resources to population in the Nation as a whole, there are in the United States large areas of dense rural population where the income and standard of living of the farming people is comparable to that of farming people in these other countries.

The wide range of agricultural wealth per capita of the farm population is shown in figure 2. In many counties of Illinois and Iowa this value is $6,000; in a few counties in California it is more than $10,000; but it drops to $300 and even less in a number of counties in the Cotton Belt and the southern Appalachian region. Where the proportion of Negroes or of Mexicans or Indians in the farm population is largest, the wealth per capita tends to be least. (Compare figs. 1 and 2.) These peoples of non-European stocks are, in general, poor and labor under disadvantages. In the South the adjustment to the denser farm population and less productive soils has, apparently, been made principally by the tenant classes, both white and Negro, whose income per capita is generally only one-fourth to one-half that of the white owner-operator class.

From the standpoint of agricultural wealth there are two major

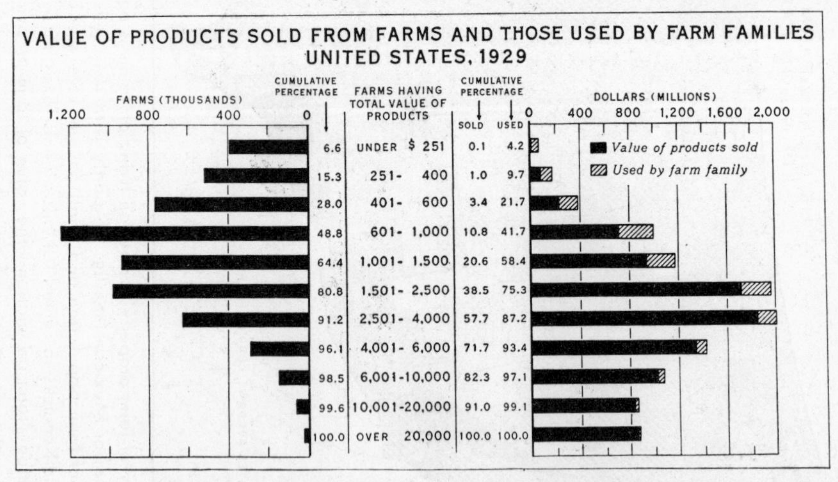

Figure 3.—In 1929 over one-fourth of the farms in the United States produced less than $600 worth of products, including the products of the farm used by the family. But this one-fourth contributed less than 4 percent of the farm products sold or traded. Nearly half of the farms produced less than $1,000 worth of products, but this least productive half contributed only about 11 percent of the commercial production of the Nation. The more productive half of the farms could undoubtedly, after a few years, produce this 11 percent, if prices afforded encouragement.

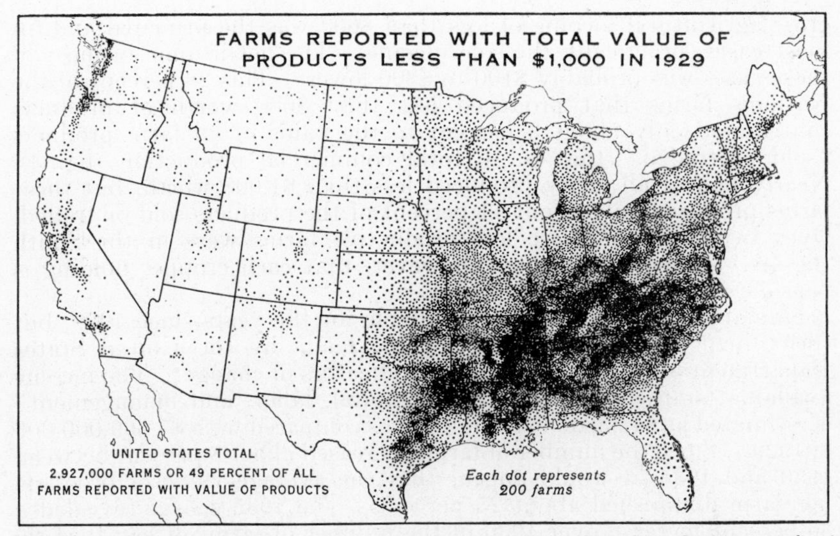

Figure 4.—Over two-thirds of all the farms that produced less than $1,000 worth of products in 1929 were located in the South. Two-thirds of all farms in the South produced less than $1,000 worth of products. It is probable that the peasants of northern Europe produce more than $1,000 worth of products on an average; and it is certain that the standard of living among the farmers of northern Europe is higher than among most farmers in our South. Nearly two-thirds of the net migration from farms during the decade 1920–29 was from the 16 Southern States.

divisions in the United States—the North and West, and the South. However, in the South there are areas of fairly well-to-do farmers in Florida and the Gulf coast of Louisiana and Texas; while in the North, the rural poverty in the upper Great Lakes region approaches that in the South. Value of farm property per capita, in both North and South, tends to run high in counties adjacent to large cities, partly because of residential value, partly because of opportunities for farmers to sell many products at almost retail prices. But rich oils are no t always associated with large per capita farm wealth. In Missouri, for example, the rich Mississippi Valley alluvial lands of Pemiscot and Dunklin Counties, famous for high yields of cotton, have no greater farm wealth per capita than the poorest counties in the Ozarks. On the other hand, the fertile Yazoo Delta counties of Mississippi have much higher per capita farm-property values than most other counties in that State. But this wealth does not belong to the Negro tenants and croppers.

In 1929, a good year for farmers, nearly 400,000 farms in the Nation produced less than $250 worth of products, including the milk, eggs, vegetables, and other products of the farm used by the family, and over 500,000 farms produced between $250 and $400 worth of products. Over 760,000 farms produced $400 to $600 worth of products. In all, 1,682,000 farms, or 28 percent of the 6,000,000 reporting value of products, produced less than $600 worth. Part-time farms numbered less than 340,000. For about 1,000,000 farm families the gross agricultural income of less than $600 was the principal and, in most cases, practically the sole income. The net income in most of those cases was probably $100 to $300 lower. This 28 percent of the Nation's farms that produced less than $600 worth of products contributed only about 3 percent to the value of all farm products "sold or traded," that is, to total commercial production (fig. 3). Nearly half of all farms produced less than $1,000 worth, but these farms produced only about 11 percent of the products sold or traded. Over two-thirds of these less productive farms were in the South (fig. 4). It should be noted, however, that each cropper holding is considered a farm by the census.

Similar census data are not available for the years since 1929, but the annual estimates of farm income made by the United States Department of Agriculture provide indicators of change. The income available for the farm "operator's capital, labor, and management" is estimated at $4,538,000,000 in 1935 as compared with $5,669,000,000 in 1929. Since the number of farms increased about 8 percent between 1930 and 1935, it would appear that the average value of products per farm diminished about 25 percent. The 1935 census revealed a 36-percent increase over 1930 in the number of farms of less than 20 acres; no change in farms of 20 to 50 acres; and 4- or 5-percent increase in farms of over 50 acres, except that farms of over 1,000 acres increased 10 percent in number. These changes clearly suggest an increasing number of little farms, measured by acreage and value of products, and also an increasing number of very large farms.

THE DECLINING NUMBER OF BIRTHS

These trends toward cultural and racial homogeneity on the one hand and toward economic diversity on the other have important effects on the rate of growth of the population. The decline in birth rates, which has been observed in this country as well as in most European countries, has been most pronounced in the cities and has spread more slowly to the country. The factors underlying it have been more effective in the native white population than among the people of other origins, including immigrants from Europe. But economic diversity opposes a barrier to the rapid spread of the decline in the birth rate. In rural as in urban areas, families tend to be smaller as incomes are larger and vice versa, but there are notable exceptions. In areas where commercial agriculture is less prevalent the older rural attitudes toward large families have been more nearly maintained. In the richer farming areas and where commercial agriculture is predominant, farm families are smaller, as in cities.

In the United States the birth rate has been declining for more than a century; but this declining birth rate was more than counterbalanced until 1921 by the increasing number of women of child-bearing age who were themselves born when the birth rate was higher and, for many years, by immigration from abroad. Since 1921 the trend in the total number of births, as well as in the birth rate, has been generally downward (fig. 5). In 1921 nearly 3,000,000 children were born and in 1924 about 2,900,000; but in recent years only 2,200,000 to 2,400,000 have been born annually.

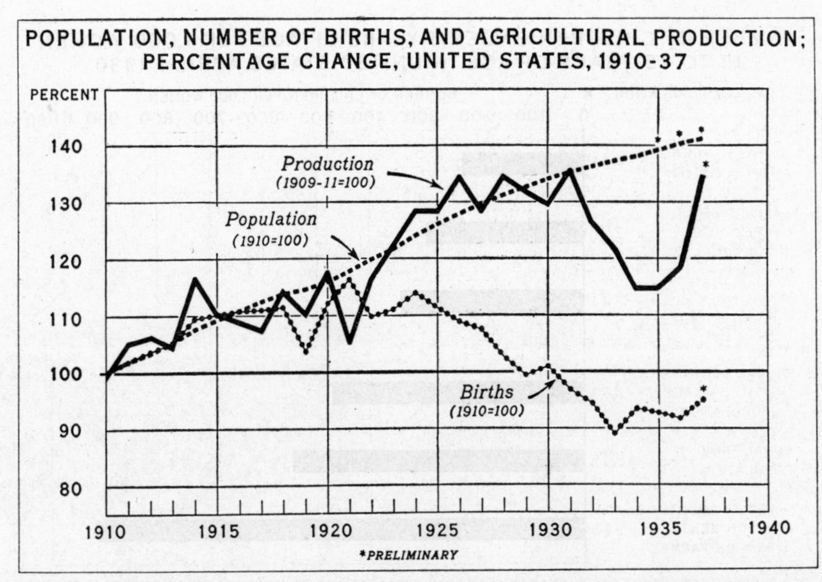

Figure 5.—The increase of population was remarkably steady until recently, only the influenza epidemic of 1918, which affected both births and deaths, causing a waver in the line. But since 1930 the decline in births and the restrictions on immigration have caused a slowing down in the increase of population. Agricultural production, on the other hand, has fluctuated notably. From 1931 to 1935 the trend was downward, largely because of extraordinary drought, the agricultural adjustment program, and soil erosion. But far more significant than the recent decline in agricultural production has been the 20-percent decline in births since 1924.

In the long run, this number of births is not sufficient to maintain the Nation's present population. At the present time the people of the United States are probably short of permanently replacing their own numbers by about 5 percent. For the time being, however, the population will continue to increase until the growing number of old people increases the number of deaths. The population is now increasing about 800,000 a year, as compared with 1,600,000, on an average, during 1920–30; but this increase will tend to become less and less until deaths balance births, probably 10 to 20 years hence. The population of the Nation will then remain almost stationary for about a decade, and after that decline slowly, unless births or immigration increase notably, which appears unlikely.

The decline in the birth rate was for many decades more rapid in the urban than in the rural population, and, as a consequence, in 1930 the reproduction rate in the cities of over 100,000 population was only about half that of the farm population (fig. 6). In the large cities the number of births lacked fully 20 percent of being sufficient to maintain a permanently stationary population without accessions from outside, while in the farm population there was a surplus of more than 50 percent. The deficit in the large cities is now probably 25 to 30 percent.

In the farm population the reproduction rate was highest in the

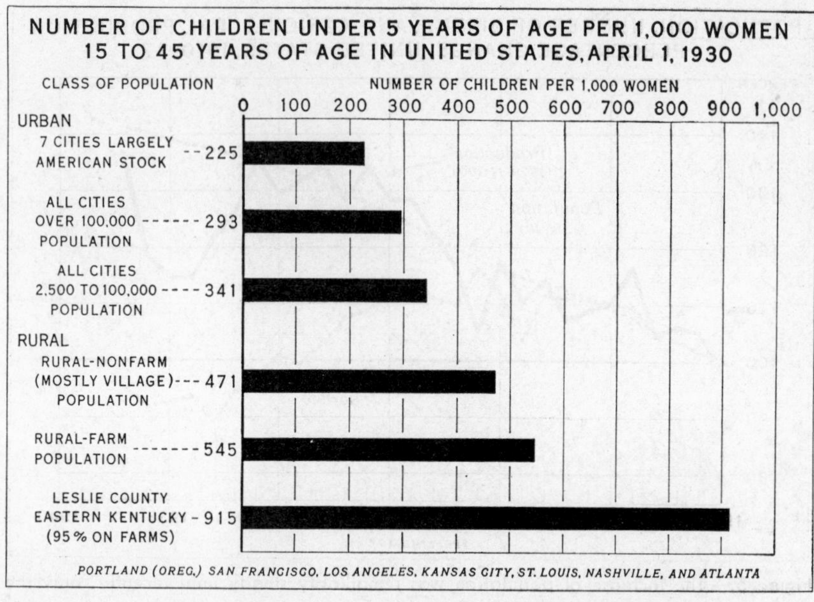

Figure 6.—About 370 children under 5 years of age per 1,000 women of 15 to 45 years (child-bearing age) are required to maintain a stationary population, with the 1930 expectation of life, in the United States, of 61 years. In 1930 the seven cities largely of American stock represented in the top bar of the graph lacked, therefore, about 38 percent of having enough children to maintain their population permanently without accessions from outside, and all cities of over 100,000 population had a deficit of over 20 percent. The smaller cities had a deficit of about 6 percent. On the other hand, the rural nonfarm (mostly villages and suburban) population had a surplus of 30 percent, and the farm population a surplus of 50 percent. In 1930 urban deficit and rural surplus nearly balanced. Now there is a national deficit of about 5 percent.

southern Appalachian Mountains, in portions of the Cotton Belt, in the Southwest, and in Utah—in brief, in areas that have been more or less isolated by physical barriers or traditions from the influences of modern urban civilization (fig. 7). The South, with only one-fourth of the Nation's population, has now about half of the natural increase (excess of births over deaths). The South is dominantly rural, and practically all of this excess is in the rural areas. An increasing proportion of the future citizens of the Nation will be the descendants of the people of the southern Appalachians, the tenants and croppers of the Cotton Belt, the hill folk along the Ohio River and its tributaries, the German-Russians of the Great Plains, and the Mormons of Utah and Idaho, for among these groups reproduction rates are comparatively high. By contrast, the reproduction rate among the professional and business classes of the large cities probably now does not exceed 60 percent. Among the skilled-labor group the rate may be as high as 80 percent. As these families die out, their places will be taken, in large part, by youth from the rural areas. The implications of this prospect for educational policy are profound.

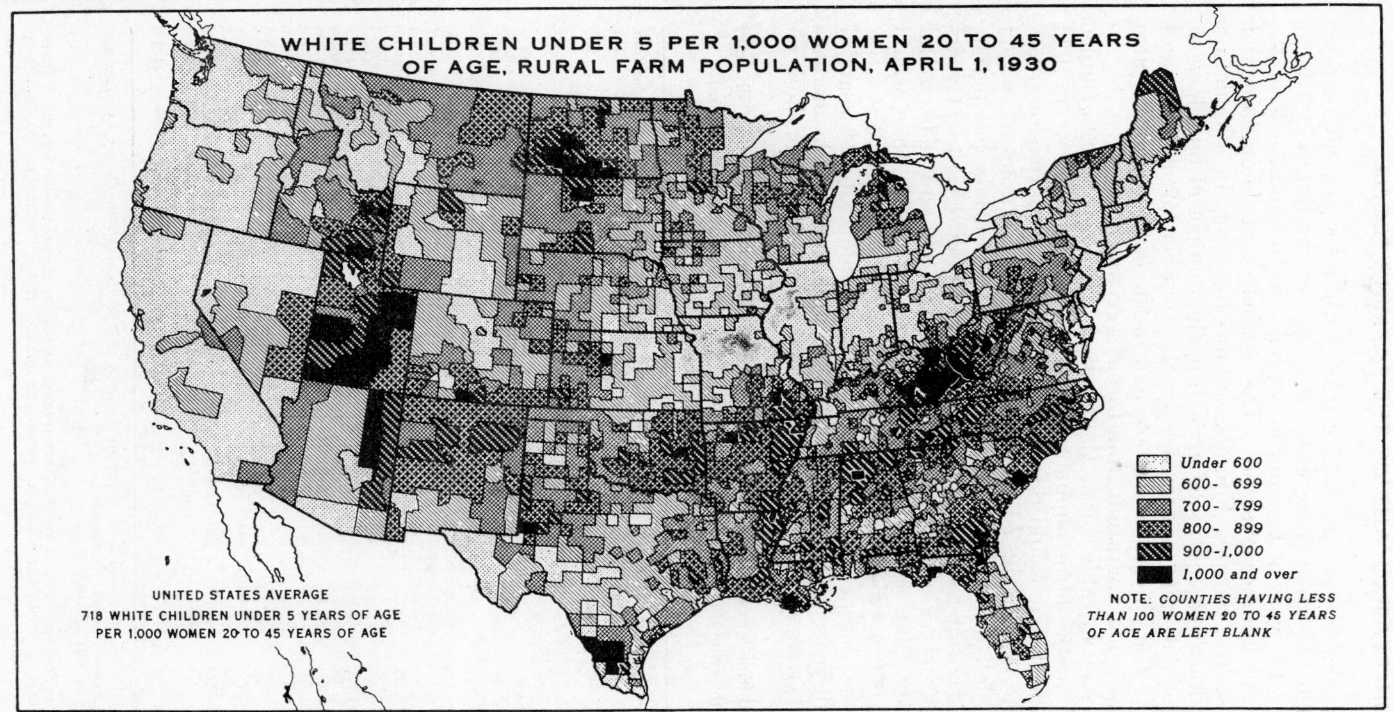

Figure 7.—The ratio of children under 5 years of age to women of child-bearing age (assumed in this case to be 20 to 45 years) is a better measure of the fertility of a population than the average size of the family or the crude birth rate (births per 1,000 population). About 440 children under 5 years of age per 1,000 white women 20 to 45 are now necessary to hold the population permanently stationary. In the Northeast and the Corn Belt the surplus of children in the farm population above this number was 20 to 50 percent in 1930, and in some suburban counties of the Pacific Coast States a deficit has developed. By contrast, the surplus exceeded 100 percent in many counties of the southern Appalachian and Ozark areas and in a number of counties elsewhere.

INCREASING AGE OF THE FARMING PEOPLE

Important changes are also taking place within the farm population. Between 1920 and 1930 there was a decrease in the number of farm people under 40 years of age and an increase in the number over 40, notably in the number over 65. The estimates of Thompson and Whelpton, of the Scripps Foundation for Research in Population Problems,[3] indicate a continued growth in the number of middle-aged and older persons and a decrease in the number of children and adolescents in the Nation as a whole and in the farm population also if the predepression migration from farms is resumed.

It will be seen in table 1 that the number of young children (under 5 years old) in the farm population decreased greatly between 1920 and 1930, but that it would remain fairly stationary until after 1950, under the assumption, based on present conditions, of a net migration from farms half as large as during the decade of urban prosperity, 1920–30. According to table 1, the number of children 5 to 14 years of age, which decreased about 565,000 between 1920 and 1930, would decrease more than 1,000,000 between 1930 and 1940, then would increase 300,000 between 1940 and 1950.

On the other hand, the number of young people 15 to 24 years of age, which increased slightly between 1920 and 1930, would increase a little more than 1,000,000 between 1930 and 1940, then show an

Table 1.—Rural-farm population of the United States by 5-year age groups, 1920 and 1930, with estimates for 1940, 1950, and 1960, by numbers and percent of 1930 population

Age group (years)	1920 [1]		1930 [1]		Estimates [2] assuming one-half the net migration from farms of 1920–30					
					1940		1950		1960	
	Number [3]	Percent, 1930	Number [3]	Percent, 1930	Number [3]	Percent, 1930	Number [3]	Percent, 1930	Number [3]	Percent, 1930
Under 5	4,143	119.2	3,476	100.0	3,451	99.3	3,505	100.8	3,252	93.6
5–9	4,113	108.7	3,783	100.0	3,112	82.3	3,422	90.5	3,255	86.0
10–14	3,979	106.3	3,744	100.0	3,248	86.8	3,245	86.7	3,346	89.4
15–19	3,267	95.5	3,422	100.0	3,589	104.9	2,953	86.3	3,304	96.6
20–24	2,487	102.2	2,434	100.0	3,346	137.5	2,916	119.8	3,017	124.0
25–29	2,131	117.2	1,819	100.0	2,889	158.8	3,122	171.6	2,646	145.5
30–34	1,882	112.6	1,671	100.0	2,031	121.5	2,965	177.4	2,654	158.8
35–39	1,906	106.6	1,788	100.0	1,600	89.5	2,659	148.7	2,939	164.4
40–44	1,601	97.4	1,644	100.0	1,534	93.3	1,902	115.7	2,835	172.4
45–49	1,538	98.5	1,561	100.0	1,634	104.7	1,476	94.6	2,520	161.4
50–54	1,266	90.6	1,398	100.0	1,479	105.8	1,393	99.6	1,760	125.9
55–59	975	87.8	1,110	100.0	1,351	121.7	1,434	129.2	1,314	118.4
60–64	845	95.2	888	100.0	1,128	127.0	1,219	137.3	1,170	131.8
65–69	599	92.4	648	100.0	838	129.3	1,041	160.6	1,126	173.8
70–74	386	84.3	458	100.0	586	127.9	762	166.4	842	183.8
75–79	228	88.0	259	100.0	342	132.0	458	176.8	587	226.6
80 and over	172	91.5	188	100.0	261	138.8	352	187.2	479	254.8
Total	31,518	104.1	30,291	100.0	32,419	107.0	34,824	115.0	37,046	122.3

[1] Census figures, allowing 4 percent for underenumeration by the census of children under 5 years of age.
[2] For source of estimates see text footnote 3.
[3] In thousands—i. e., 000 omitted.

[3] THOMPSON, WARREN, and WHELPTON, P. K. ESTIMATES OF FUTURE POPULATION BY STATES: A SERIES OF TABLES PREPARED . . . FOR THE NATIONAL RESOURCES BOARD. 1934. Washington, D. C. [Photolithographed.]

almost equal decrease between 1940 and 1950. The younger middle-aged groups, 25 to 39 years old, inclusive, which decreased 641,000 between 1920 and 1930, would increase 1,242,000 between 1930 and 1940 and over 2,200,000 between 1940 and 1950. The farm population 40 to 64 years of age, which increased nearly 400,000 between 1920 and 1930, would increase over 500,000 between 1930 and 1940, and 300,000 between 1940 and 1950. Finally, persons over 65 in the farm population, whose numbers increased more than 160,000, or 10 percent, between 1920 and 1930, would increase about 500,000, or 30 percent, between 1930 and 1940, and nearly 600,000, or nearly 30 percent again, between 1940 and 1950. The farm population as a whole would be more than 2,000,000 larger in 1940 than in 1930, increase 2,400,000 between 1940 and 1950, and 2,200,000 between 1950 and 1960, if migration remained only half as great as it was between 1920 and 1930.

POTENTIAL INCREASE IN NUMBER OF FARMS

In 1930 farm operators included about 14 percent of the farm population 20 to 24 years of age, rising to 40 percent in the 35- to 39-year age group and to over 50 percent in the age groups from 50 to 70 years, then falling to only 30 percent for ages 75 and over. If these (and intermediate) percentages are applied to the farm population estimates by 5-year age groups for 1940 and 1950 it appears that the number of farms would need to increase nearly 1,000,000, or 16 percent, from 1930 to 1940, and by 1,170,000, or 16.6 percent from 1940 to 1950, unless there is a much heavier annual migration from farms than took place during the period 1930–38.

During the decade 1920–29 about 410,000 farm boys reached maturity each year, but apparently nearly two-fifths of them (about 154,000) left the farms during that decade (and perhaps a third as many more left during 1930–39). During 1920–29 about 106,000 farm operators died each year, thus probably providing almost as many farm vacancies. The decrease in number of farms, as reported by the census, averaged 16,000 a year. Assuming that there were 90,000 farms for 256,000 maturing farmers, there remain about 166,000 farm males who must have become farm laborers each year unless they took over farms vacated by farmers who retired or resorted to other occupations. If we dare assume that all farmers 55 years of age and over who left the farms (excluding those who died) retired, this figure can be reduced to 150,000 as a rough estimate of the young men in the farm population who became farm laborers, either as hired hands or unpaid family laborers, or who took over farms vacated by farmers who entered another occupation or retired before 55 years of age.

Between 1930 and 1935 it appears that about 384,000 farm boys reached maturity each year, on an average. The yearly average increase in number of farms during this period was about 100,000. But the average annual increase in number of farmers who had not been living on farms in 1930 was about 90,000. The increase in number of farms was, therefore, probably only a little larger than that in number of farm operators included in the back-to-the-land movement. About 112,000 farmers died each year, on an average. There remain approximately 263,000 male youth a year who, apparently, left the farms, became farm laborers, or took the places of farmers who retired or resorted to other occupations during the 5-year period. Apparently 75,000 or 80,000 of these left the farms yearly.

THE RURAL-YOUTH SURPLUS[4]

Thus at the beginning of the depression and since, farm youth have been maturing at a rate fully twice that required to maintain at a stationary figure the number of farm operators. Increases in the number of farms have occurred since 1930 in spite of the fact that increasing productivity in agriculture has made it possible to produce the Nation's supply of food and fiber with only a part of the current farm population. Impending technological changes in agriculture may decrease further the need for farm labor, making a still larger number of farm workers available for urban employment if opportunities arise. Regardless of future developments, there is today a large group of persons living on farms who have little chance of employment either in commercial agriculture or in cities. Some of them may be absorbed in new rural industries or permanent public services at their present locations; the others will attempt to improve their condition by moving to other locations.

It is estimated that during the 20 years ending in 1955 the total population of working age (18–65) in the Nation will increase by approximately 14,500,000 persons. If there were to be no migration during this period 3,000,000 of these would be in cities, 4,000,000 in rural nonfarm areas, and nearly 7,500,000 or fully half of the total, on farms.[5] Prospective needs for agricultural production could be filled without drawing upon any of the 7,500,000, who, in that sense, would all be available for migration to towns and cities.

By 1929 the less productive half of all farms was producing only 15 percent of the value of all agricultural products. The same group contributed only 11 percent of the value of marketed crops—less than the value of agricultural exports. It seems entirely possible that the more productive half of our farms could, with proper management, have produced all of the agricultural products consumed by the Nation. Estimates in this field are extremely hazardous, but it seems likely that had there been sufficient demand, the Nation's farms could have given up at least 4,000,000 more persons—10,000,000 instead of 6,000,000—between 1920 and 1930 without endangering the volume of agricultural production if the additional migrants had left the least productive farms.

Here, then, was and is a population reservoir which might be tapped if superior opportunities were offered at locations other than those where these people now are and if such migration seemed to accord with the long-time national welfare. From this source alone cities might continue to grow for some time to come, if they were able to offer sufficient inducements. Apparently the large-scale rural-urban migrations of the 1920's could have been continued with beneficial eco-

[4] The manuscript of this article from this point to the end was critically read by Edgar M. Hoover, Jr., Department of Economics, University of Michigan, and Harry C. Woodworth, Department of Economics, University of New Hampshire, both of whom made helpful suggestions.

[5] T. J. WOOFTER, Jr. THE FUTURE WORKING POPULATION. Rural Sociol. 4: [275]–282. 1939.

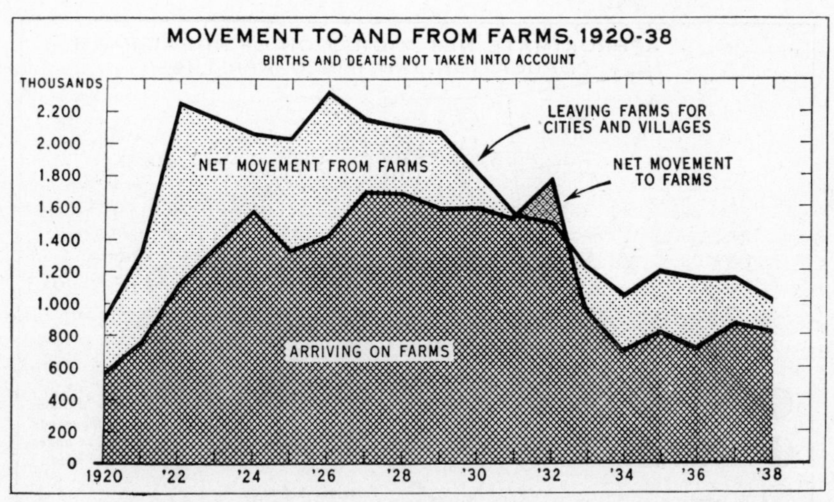

Figure 8.—From 1922 to 1929, inclusive, migration from the farms to the cities exceeded 2,000,000 each year—probably a larger movement than ever before in the Nation's history. Those were prosperous years in the cities and rather hard times for agriculture. But during those years many people also returned to farms. The net migration from the farms during these 8 years averaged about 700,000 annually. As the depression developed and jobs became scarce, the movement from farms dropped notably, while that to farms remained almost stationary through 1932. In that year it exceeded the movement from farms, but after that fell to one-half. During 1934–38 the net migration from farms averaged 351,000 a year.

nomic effects after 1930 had it not been for the characteristic instability of American industry and commerce and the present ineffectiveness of demands for the products required for customary standards of living or for those ordinarily regarded as adequate.

MIGRATION FROM FARMS, 1920–30

During the 1920's some 19,000,000 persons moved to towns and cities, while 13,000,000 moved from towns and cities to farms, with the result that farms lost more than 6,000,000 persons, net (fig. 8). Nearly 2 out of every 5 of the farm young people who reached their twentieth birthday during the decade had moved to cities by 1930.

The migrants were from all sections of the country (fig. 9). Except for parts of New England, the Great Plains, and the Pacific Coast States, hardly a rural area failed to give up more migrants than it received. Three-fifths of the net number of rural migrants came from the Southern States, Texas, Georgia, South Carolina, and Kentucky contributing the most. In general between 1920 and 1930 the rate of rural migration from the better land areas was almost as great as that from the poorer land areas. The migration to cities amounted to 20 percent or more of the rural population present at the beginning of the period in parts of the Cotton Belt and throughout much of the southern Appalachian and Ozark Mountain areas, in the cut-over

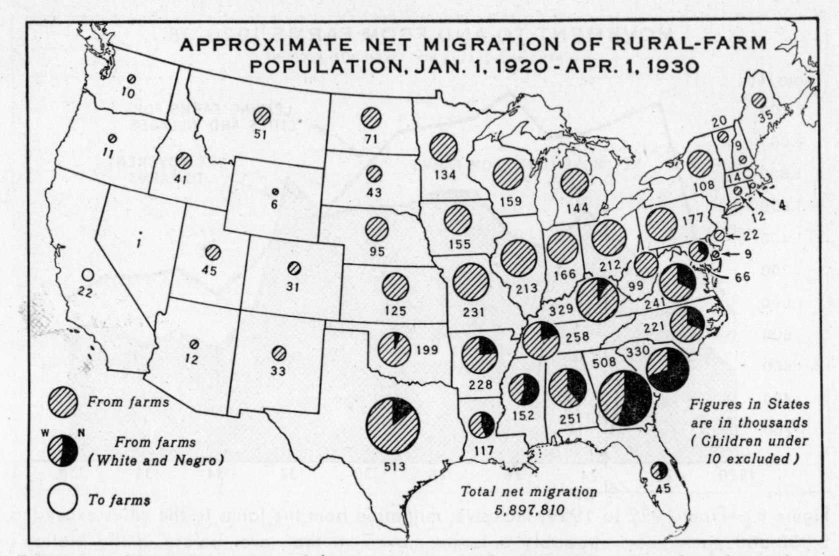

Figure 9.—About 60 percent of the net migration of 6,000,000 persons from farms during 1920–29 was from the South. Most of these migrants were young people. The birth rate is high among southern rural people, and economic opportunity is less than in the North. If it costs $2,000 to rear and educate a child to the age of 15 on farms in the South, these 3,800,000 migrants from southern farms represent a contribution of $7,500-000,000 made during the decade by the farm population of the South to other parts of the Nation, mostly to the cities.

sections of the Lake States, in Utah, and in scattered counties throughout the country (fig. 10).

Migrants from farms to cities generally went from areas of lesser to areas of greater economic opportunity. The manufacturing centers offered numerous opportunities. One hundred and sixty-seven counties in which manufacturing is predominant received almost three-fourths of the total. Three large cities—New York, Chicago, and Detroit—and their immediately surrounding territories accounted for one-fourth. The metropolitan area of Los Angeles alone received one-sixth—more than 1,000,000 migrants from other parts of the country.

MIGRATION DURING THE DEPRESSION

The period just considered, 1920–30, was characterized largely by farm depression and urban prosperity. But late in the 1920's migration to cities slowed down, and after 1929 further sharp reductions occurred in this movement. Since 1930 the attractiveness of cities for rural migrants has been sharply curtailed. Present indications are that during the current decade the net migration from farms to towns and cities will be under 2,500,000, or less than half as great as during the 1920's. Not only has migration to many cities been sharply curtailed, but some cities experienced a net out-migration after 1930. Special censuses taken in 1934 and 1935 showed decreases in the population of some of our largest cities, including Chicago and Detroit, which had previously been among the leaders in attracting migsants. With large numbers of urban workers unemployed, cities in general have not proved very favorable to the absorption of rural migrants.

The result is that since 1930 many potential migrants have remained in rural areas, where they know conditions and where their skills can be at least partly utilized. This tendency to remain on farms has been especially marked in the areas where opportunities in commercial agriculture are most limited, areas that before 1930 were generally sending migrants to cities. The failure to migrate out of rural problem areas in predepression volume has been a major factor in the increase in farm population in these areas during recent years. Migration from farms was greatest in those areas where commercial agriculture is most developed, and these same areas received very little of the back-to-the-land movement. The areas where commercial agriculture is less developed, as well as the areas where agricultural incomes are very low not only received migrants from cities but also retained a larger proportion of their own natural increase. In the Appalachian Mountains, the Lake States cut-over sections, New England, and some other areas, there was a net movement to farms.

Thus the increase in farm population was greatest in the noncommercial farming areas where soils generally are poorer and least in the commercial farming areas where soils generally are best. Areas

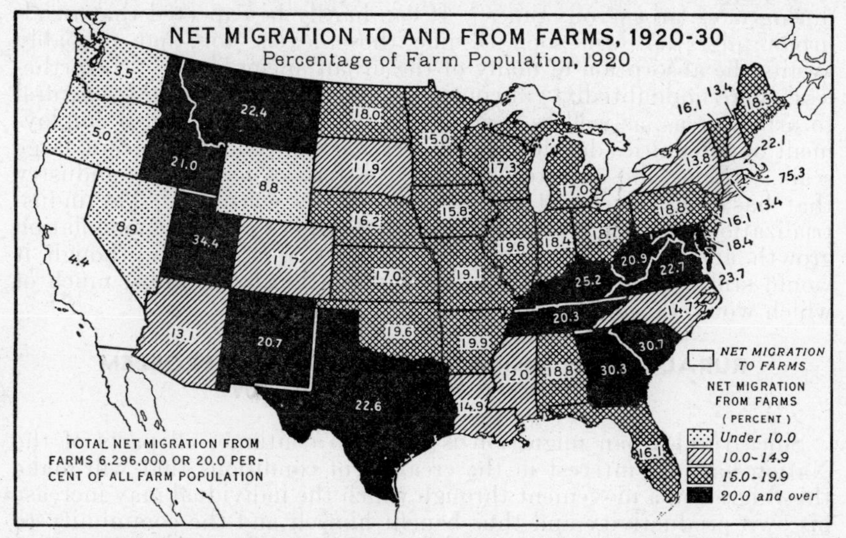

Figure 10.—Relative to the farm population in 1920, migration from farms exceeded 20 percent in eight Southern States, New Mexico, Utah, Idaho, and Montana. In these States the birth rate is high and the soils are poor to fair, or mostly arid. In the North the range in ratio was from 12 percent in South Dakota to nearly 20 percent in Missouri and Illinois, except that in Massachusetts and Rhode Island there was a net migration to farms. In California also there was a net migration to farms, and in Oregon and Washington the movement from farms was small.

where noncommercial farming is predominant appear to be more elastic for population growth—more able to absorb additional persons without disrupting their economic organization. Where standards of income and consumption are already low, the addition of a considerable number of persons or families may not have as serious effects as in areas where standards are high. Moreover, a man with little capital can normally produce more with his labor from a large area of cheap land than from a small area of good land. For example, it is better for a man with $1,000 to invest in land to buy 50 acres of land that will produce 20 bushels of corn per acre than 10 acres of land that will produce 50 bushels of corn per acre. It may be that rural problem areas thus serve as zones of absorption during depressions—a necessary function in our present economic order. However, if the necessity for such absorption of population continues over a long period of years, many persons who found temporary refuge in these areas may become stranded there. There is evidence that this has happened.

The present situation thus includes, on the one hand, a slowing down of the rate of growth of the population of cities, with a diminished demand for migrants from farms; and, on the other hand, an accelerated growth of the population on farms, although there is no immediate prospect that commercial agricultural production would require any increase in the number of available workers. Some migration from rural to urban areas continues to take place, but the volume of the movement is considerably below that which occurred during more prosperous times. It can hardly be expected that rural-urban migration will soon resume those levels, for that probably awaits the absorption of many of the urban unemployed. Nevertheless, there undoubtedly will continue to be some migration from rural to urban areas, as well as from urban to rural areas, and if employment opportunities develop, this migration will probably be on a large scale. It may be objected that the pattern of location of industry that has been developed will not necessarily continue. The industrialization of the South, for example, where rates of population growth are rapid, may decrease interregional migration, though it would still require a large volume of migration from farms, much of which would be across State lines.

RURAL-URBAN MIGRATION A NATIONAL PROBLEM NEEDING A NATIONAL POLICY

Since rural-urban migration is likely to continue, all parts of the Nation have an interest in the creation of conditions that will make this migration a movement through which the individual may increase his own productivity and thus benefit himself and the community to which he goes. At the same time, his going should not be a detriment to the community he leaves. With the present concentration of industry and distribution of population growth, these problems transcend State and regional lines and call for national planning. As an example, both Detroit, Mich., and Atlanta, Ga., are interested in the standards of health, housing, education, and community activities being maintained in rural Alabama, for both cities received, and may again receive, many migrants from that State. Conversely, isolated rural communities in Alabama are interested in developments in Detroit and Atlanta which mean employment opportunities or their absence. Such mutual interrelationships indicate that programs to deal with these movements must be on a national scale.

The persistence of a large volume of unemployment is a major factor in the development of rural-urban migration. The effects of a solution of this problem upon trends in migration would be far reaching. But along with efforts to solve the problem, it is important that attention be directed toward action specifically related to rural-urban migration. Three such lines of action are recommended for consideration: (1) Raising the level of living in areas from which migrants will be recruited; (2) raising educational levels in rural areas; and (3) developing an effective policy for the guidance of migration.

(1) Raising the level of living in areas from which migrants will be recruited is a matter of primary interest both to these areas and to those where the migrants will ultimately go. The influx to any city of a large group of persons with standards of living widely different from those of the city creates problems similar to those created in the past by the arrival of large numbers of foreign immigrants. Reports from some cities have already indicated that the migrants from poorer agricultural areas have filled the low positions previously held by foreign immigrants and have created similar serious problems of assimilation. In many cases the previous training, standards of living, and health of rural migrants have given them only a poor preparation for the life of the cities to which they have gone.

Raising the level of living in these areas cannot be done, except in small part, through an expansion in commercial agricultural production. It must come, if at all, through a more efficient utilization of available resources for the benefit of the residents there. This would require a new emphasis on a subsistence program of production for home consumption on the largest possible scale consistent with conservation of the land resources. This implies an extensive educational program in techniques, supplemented by loans; community facilities for curing, canning, and storing of farm products for home use; cooperative provisions for improvement of livestock, soils, drainage, and other physical facilities; a more thorough canvass of the possibilities of stimulating rural industries, including home industries; and the development of an extended program of public works and public services in rural areas to supplement farming activities there.

The development of such a program would improve morale and health among the people of the areas involved and would tend to develop an intelligent approach to local problems of utilization of available resources. It would further serve to bring about in problem areas the development of wants in relation to the ability to meet those wants. In part it would mean the restoration of some of the techniques and skills that were available to the older generations, but it is essentially not a return to the past so much as the development of a system to meet present needs. It would mean the possibility of maintaining a large part of the present population growth in rural areas at levels higher than those now prevailing, and it would also mean a greater ease of assimilation in cities should migration to cities occur.

(2) Increasing educational opportunities constitute a closely related line of activity. Educational facilities and adjustments in rural areas are a national concern, since many of the children now being reared in rural areas will ultimately live elsewhere. In 1930 over 4,000,000 of the 30,000,000 persons who had been born in the South were no longer living there; many of them had gone to northern cities. These States in 1930 had one-third of all children in the Nation then 5 to 14 years old, the group which has been passing through the elementary grades since 1930. That educational levels in the rural parts of these States, as well as in many other rural areas, are considerably below the average for the Nation, despite more than average effort to raise funds, has long been well known.

The shortage of educational opportunity, which is most marked in those areas where rates of population growth are highest, means a failure to equip the prospective migrants with the knowledge and skills needed for most effective adjustment in either city or country. Poverty fosters lack of educational opportunity, incentives are destroyed, and further poverty results. Lacking adequate training, these migrants press in upon the unskilled labor market, with the result that not only are they at a disadvantage so far as types of employment and rates of income are concerned, but in many cities they are forced to live under slum conditions. The development of adequate educational opportunities, realistically adapted to the situation in these rural areas, would serve not only to equip prospective migrants to take a better place in the new environment, but also to equip the nonmigrants for a better life in their own communities.

(3) More effective guidance of migrants to areas of greater opportunity is needed to eliminate much of the social cost of the present system or lack of system. Few areas offer so little opportunity that people will not move to them, and in all parts of the country there is a constant movement of people to areas from which many others are moving away at the same time. Migration is nearly always in response to a believed or observed differential in opportunities—opportunities for economic activities, health, education, recreation, new experience, or any other human want. The individual's decision to move or not to move is based on such information as is available, but rarely does the prospective migrant have the opportunity of assuring himself that this information is representative, reliable, or adequate. Tips, hunches, rumors, and indefinite promises are often the bases upon which migration is started, and when they prove incorrect there may be a return migration or a further movement to another place concerning which the information is no more definite.

The energy put forth by thousands of workers in securing jobs—as in traveling hundreds of miles for jobs that could not possibly last more than 3 months—might be used more effectively if there were means of providing more adequate information and guidance to prospective migrants. The development of an adequate system of disseminating necessary information about employment opportunities among potential migrants would eliminate many of the difficulties now encountered by individuals who go to areas where opportunities are much more limited than they appear to be or where they have entirely ceased to exist.

Not only is it desirable that migrants be assisted in going to locations that offer maximum opportunities, but in some areas it will become necessary to stimulate out-migration and to assist present settlers in finding adequate new locations. Resettlement, land use planning, rural zoning, and land-purchase programs are steps in the indicated direction, but these and related efforts have not always been effectively coordinated. In some areas public efforts have retarded migration, though a considered public policy might have called for partial or complete evacuation. But in other areas public efforts have stimulated migrations without adequate safeguards to assure beneficial results to the migrants. In some quarters it is advocated that a large part of the rural problems could be solved by moving the population involved to cities. So long as urban employment opportunities are lacking, this will remain wishful thinking. Where migration from rural areas appears in the public interest it may be encouraged in a variety of ways, of which subsidy is only one. Ordinarily, however, migration from rural to urban or to other rural areas is not to be positively encouraged unless there is ample justification for the expectation of beneficial results.

Areas that may ultimately become the recipients of rural-urban migrants have a vital interest not only in the education and training of potential migrants, but also in taking steps that will enable the migrants to make their fullest contribution at a minimum social cost.

Patterns of Living of Farm Families

by DAY MONROE [1]

DURING the past 40 years, the author points out, consumption patterns of farm families have changed more than those of urban families. "Whether these changes have increased the well-being of the rural population is a matter on which there is no general agreement because of differences in men's viewpoints and philosophies." Whatever the viewpoint, presenting these patterns in outline "provides a basis for a better understanding of certain human problems connected with agriculture." Here, then, are the most recent figures on what farm families at three income levels—moderate, relatively high, and low—are able to command in the way of food, housing, household conveniences, transportation and communication facilities, clothing, personal and medical care, recreation, and education.

PATTERNS of living of the Nation's families have changed markedly since the turn of the century. Technology has brought new goods and services to the market and thus enlarged the list of human wants. Standards of what constitutes an adequate living have changed too as science has increased our understanding of human needs. Consump-

[1] Day Monroe is Principal Home Economist, in charge of the Family Economics Division, Bureau of Home Economics.

tion patterns of farm families have changed more than those of urban families, lessening the differences that existed between the two groups 40 years ago. Whether these changes have increased the well-being of the rural population is a matter on which there is no general agreement because of differences in men's viewpoints and philosophies. But without passing judgment on the merits of the changes, the consumption patterns of farm families can be presented in broad outline, their divergencies from and similarities to urban patterns can be sketched, and the proportion of families at different levels of living can be estimated. This provides a basis for a better understanding of certain human problems connected with agriculture.

Income is a major determinant of a family's level of living. It is true that families with the same income may differ greatly in their ways of using funds. Some may spend all or more than they make for family maintenance; others may save appreciable amounts, limiting their expenditures for living. The large family will fare less well than the small with the same total budget. Ability to use income effectively is another factor. Despite these differences, however, consumption patterns of families in the same income group tend to be more similar than patterns of families with widely different incomes. Distribution of families by income—the proportion at the lower, middle, and upper parts of the income scale—therefore approximates their distribution by levels of living.

About one-fourth of the Nation's farm families during the period 1935–36 were in the nonrelief group with net incomes of less than $500, or had received direct relief (table 1). Slightly fewer than one-fourth had incomes of $1,500 or more. The remainder, a little more than one-half, were in the nonrelief group with incomes ranging from $500 to $1,500 (*9*).[2]

Table 1.—Percentage distribution of farm families by relief status and income level, 1935–36 [1]

Relief status and income level (dollars)	Percentage of farm families	Relief status and income level (dollars)	Percentage of farm families
	Percent		*Percent*
All families	100.0	Nonrelief families—Continued.	
		1,750–2,000	4.4
Relief families	8.9	2,000–2,250	2.8
Nonrelief families	91.1	2,250–2,500	2.2
		2,500–3,000	2.6
Under 250	3.4	3,000–3,500	1.5
250–500	12.7	3,500–4,000	.9
500–750	16.4	4,000–4,500	.5
750–1,000	15.2	4,500–5,000	.2
1,000–1,250	11.7	5,000–7,500	.6
1,250–1,500	8.9	7,500–10,000	.4
1,500–1,750	6.4	10,000 or over	.3

[1] From Consumer Incomes in the United States (*9*).

Income distributions differed markedly from one region to another; for example, the proportion of nonrelief farm families with incomes under $500 was about four times as great in the Southeast as in New England. Regional differences in patterns of living, therefore, are

[2] Italic numbers in parentheses refer to Literature Cited, p. 868.

associated with income distribution as well as with differences in customs, climate, and other environmental factors.

Receipts from the farm enterprise—not cash alone, but also the nonmoney income from occupancy of the farm dwelling, home-produced food, fuel, ice, and other products—provide the major part of the farm family's income. Earnings from other sources and returns from investments may be a helpful supplement, but such nonfarm receipts constitute less than one-fourth of the total net income of operators' families the country over (*2*). The level of living possible for the majority, therefore, depends in large measure on their income from farming.

FARM FAMILIES WITH MODERATE INCOMES

A picture of the manner in which American farm families live may well begin with the consumption patterns of an intermediate income group, which present neither the best situations nor the worst. Families with net incomes in the range $1,000 to $1,250 have been chosen for this purpose, a group with incomes a little above the median[3] for all the Nation's nonrelief farm-operator families. The median for 1935–36 has been estimated at $965 (*9*).

The income of this intermediate group was about 55 percent cash and 45 percent in kind; of the total net family income averaging $1,127, $634 was in money and $493 in the form of housing, food, fuel, ice, and other products furnished the household by the farm. With so large a share of its total income in a nonmoney form, the farm family has less cash to spend for the many offerings of our modern markets than has the city family at a comparable income level. The advantage, however, is not entirely on the side of the urban group. These nonmoney receipts help the farm family to protect its customary level of living against severe reductions in a depression period when money income and buying power are drastically cut. The city family, which purchases practically all its living, has no such safeguard against reduced money income except perhaps occupancy of an owned home.

The group of farm families at this intermediate income level just about achieved a balance between the value of their living and their total net income. Two-thirds of the families ended the year with a surplus or just balanced outgo with income, while one-third were "in the red." But the deficits of the smaller number exceeded the savings of the larger, making the balance for all families negative—an average net deficit of $10 for the year (fig. 1). The savings of a family include both decreases in liabilities and increases in assets. Payments on mortgages or other debts contracted before the current year represent an increase in net worth, as do increases in herds and other livestock, purchases of farming equipment not for replacement which adds to stocks on hand, and investments in securities.

Farm families show a greater tendency to save than urban families at a comparable income level. For example, Chicago families in the income range $1,000 to $1,250 had a net deficit of $63 in 1935–36, an amount appreciably greater than that of this farm group; a smaller proportion of the Chicago families—57 percent—broke even or had

[3] Half the families had incomes below the median, and half above.

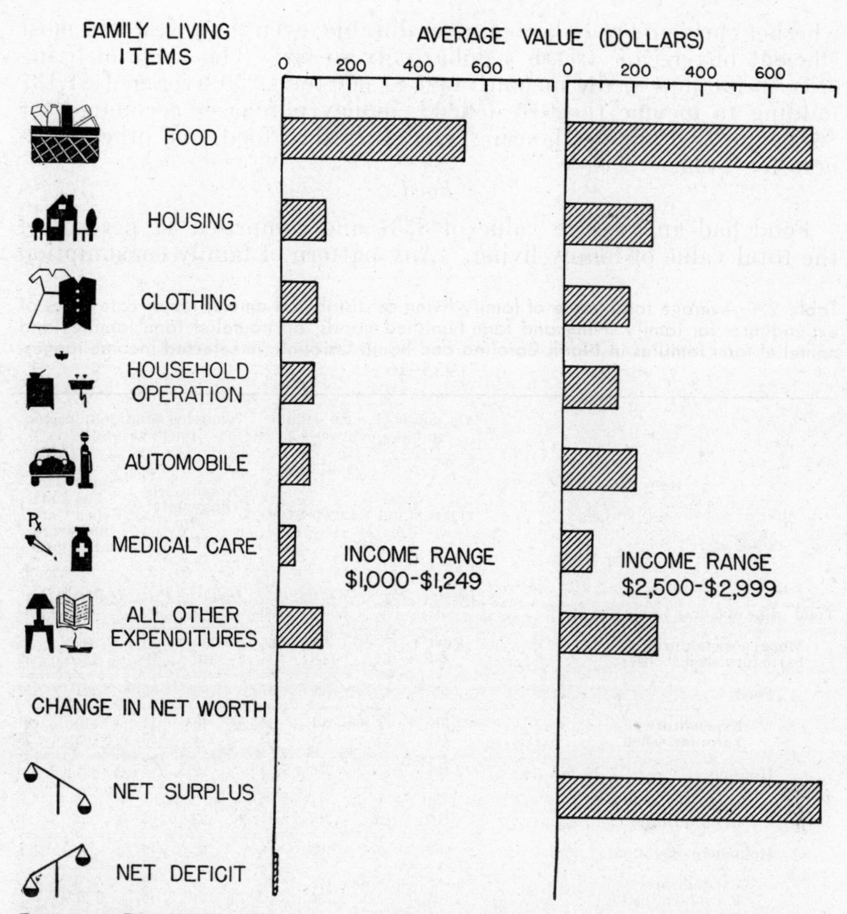

Figure 1.—Distribution of income among major categories of family living and change in net worth, all nonrelief farm families in selected income ranges, 1935–36.

a net surplus (*1*). City families may have less incentive to save; relatively few are building up a business of their own. In contrast, all families of farm operators are entrepreneurs; the farm enterprise is a family undertaking, the concern of all members old enough to work. Opportunities for participation in the business and interest in its success may explain why farm folk seem to place less emphasis than city folk upon competitive consumption, or spending to "keep up with the Joneses."

What the Income Provides

The money value of family living—expenditures plus value of farm-furnished housing, food, and other goods—and the pattern of distribution of the total among the various budget items (such as food and clothing) tell much as to the kind of living that farm families achieve. For example, the amount spent for clothing indicates something about a person's wardrobe even though it does not tell whether garments were becoming or durable; even the wisest and most efficient buyer can stretch a dollar only so far. The value of living of farm families in the income range $1,000 to $1,250 averaged $1,137 (adding to income the $10 deficit); money purchases accounted for $644, and the value of housing, farm-furnished food, and other products for $493.[4]

Food

Food had an average value of $537 and comprised 47 percent of the total value of family living. Any pattern of family consumption

Table 2.—Average total value of family living as distributed among major categories of expenditures for family living and farm-furnished goods, all nonrelief farm families and nonrelief farm families in North Carolina and South Carolina, in selected income ranges, 1935–36

Item	All nonrelief farm families in income range—[1]				Nonrelief families in income range $250–$499 [2]			
	$1,000–$1,249		$2,500–$2,999		North Carolina white farm operators		North Carolina and South Carolina Negro sharecroppers	
	Dollars	*Pct.*	*Dollars*	*Pct.*	*Dollars*	*Pct.*	*Dollars*	*Pct.*
Total value of family living [3]	1,137	100	1,939	100	440	100	388	100
Money expenditures	644	57	1,271	66	130	30	235	61
Farm-furnished goods	493	43	668	34	310	70	153	39
Food	537	47	729	37	293	66	221	57
Expenditures	194	17	291	15	49	11	119	31
Farm-furnished	343	30	438	22	244	55	102	26
Housing	128	11	256	13	22	5	24	6
Expenditures	13	1	41	2	([4])	([4])	0	0
Farm-furnished	115	10	215	11	22	5	24	6
Household operation	97	9	163	8	52	12	36	9
Expenditures	62	6	128	6	8	2	9	2
Farm-furnished [5]	35	3	35	2	44	10	27	7
Clothing expenditures	104	9	191	10	31	7	41	11
Automobile expenditures	88	8	217	11	5	1	16	4
Operation	40	4	126	6	3	1	5	1
Purchase	48	4	91	5	2	([4])	11	3
Medical care expenditures	50	4	90	5	12	3	15	4
Recreation expenditures	21	2	51	3	1	([4])	4	1
Formal education, reading expenditures.	18	2	42	2	3	1	3	1
Personal care expenditures	17	1	30	2	3	1	4	1
Expenditures for gifts, welfare, and selected taxes.[6]	24	2	58	3	5	1	5	1
Other expenditures [7]	53	5	112	6	13	3	19	5

[1] Estimates for all nonrelief farm families in the United States made by the National Resources Planning Board on the basis of data largely from the Farm Consumer Purchases Study conducted by the Bureau of Home Economics in 66 farm counties in 21 States.

[2] Preliminary data from samples taken as part of the Consumer Purchases Study, Bureau of Home Economics.

[3] Total expenditures for family living plus the money value of products furnished by the farm for family use.

[4] 0.50 or less. [6] Includes only income and poll taxes. [5] Fuel, ice, and other nonfood products.

[7] Includes expenditures for tobacco, transportation other than by automobile, household furnishings and equipment, and miscellaneous items of family expenditures such as funeral charges and legal fees.

[4] [U. S.] National Resources Planning Board. FAMILY EXPENDITURES IN THE UNITED STATES. 1940. (Unpublished manuscript.)

that shows so large a proportion of the total allocated to food will show restricted expenditures for reading, recreation, formal education, church and charities, and other budget items not closely related to physical needs. Although these farm families produced almost two-thirds of their food supply (average value $343), expenditures for what they bought amounted to an average of $194 (table 2). Even with a well-planned program of food production and preservation for household use, the farm family is far from self-sufficing; it depends upon the food industries for many products.

Good or fair diets [5] were probably obtained by about two-thirds of the families in this income group. Of the families whose diets were rated as poor, many had meals too low in money value to meet nutritional standards, no matter how wise their food choices. Others had meals whose money value was sufficient to provide an adequate diet, but because their choices of the foods they bought and produced were ill-advised, their diets were inadequate with respect to one or more nutrients.

Housing

Housing may be appraised in terms of space, of sanitary facilities, including running water and sewage disposal, and of other facilities that promote comfort, such as electric lights and central heating. For use in surveying large groups of families, the standard of one room per person has been generally accepted as a rough measure of the adequacy of space for wholesome living. It is recognized, however, that family composition (sex and age of members), size of rooms, ventilation, and other factors must be considered in determining whether a given dwelling unit provides the space needed.

Size of farm dwellings differs considerably from one part of the country to another, according to a survey made in 1934 (*6*). In New England, houses of families of all income levels combined had an average size of 8.9 rooms; those in the East and West North Central regions, 6.9 and 6 rooms respectively; those on the Pacific coast and in the south Atlantic region, 5.4 and 5.2 rooms; and those in the Mountain region and in the East and West South Central regions, 4.5, 4.4, and 4.2 rooms. Because of these regional differences, no estimate of the number of rooms per dwelling for families in the income range $1,000 to $1,250 has been made for the country as a whole.

Houses of families in this intermediate income range tend to meet the standard of one room per person. The average number of rooms was the same as or greater than the average number of persons per household in all regions except the Southeast. There, houses tended to be smaller and households tended to be larger than in other regions; as a consequence, there was less than one room per person, on an average, among the families of Negro operators and of white and Negro sharecroppers. In contrast, there were more than two rooms per person, on an average, in Vermont (*3*).

Averages do not tell the whole story, however. In every region some families lived in crowded houses. The proportion of families

---

[5] Diets may be classified as good if, according to their nutritive content, they meet standards insuring a liberal margin of safety in all essential nutrients. Fair diets meet minimum standards, and poor diets are in need of improvement in at least one nutrient. For a further discussion, see Present-Day Diets in the United States (*4*).

223761°—40——55

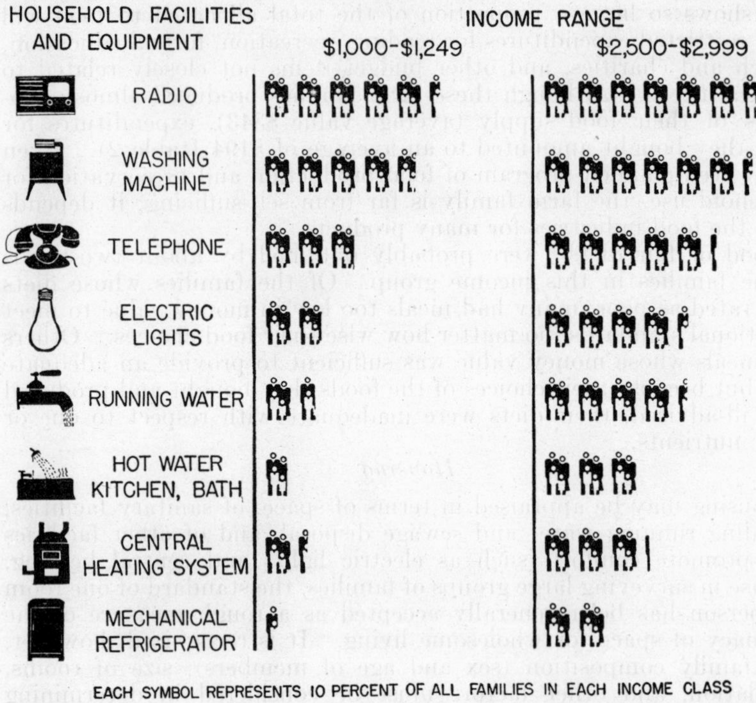

HOUSEHOLD FACILITIES AND EQUIPMENT | INCOME RANGE $1,000-$1,249 | $2,500-$2,999

RADIO

WASHING MACHINE

TELEPHONE

ELECTRIC LIGHTS

RUNNING WATER

HOT WATER KITCHEN, BATH

CENTRAL HEATING SYSTEM

MECHANICAL REFRIGERATOR

EACH SYMBOL REPRESENTS 10 PERCENT OF ALL FAMILIES IN EACH INCOME CLASS

Figure 2.—Percentage of families having specified household facilities and equipment in living quarters, all nonrelief farm families in selected income ranges, 1935–36.

at this intermediate income level living in dwellings that did not provide one room per person ranged from less than 5 percent in Vermont, Washington, and Oregon to about 60 percent of the group of Negro sharecroppers in the Southeast. For the country as a whole it was about one-sixth.

With respect to sanitary facilities—running water and sewage disposal—and facilities for lighting and heating, dwellings of many of the farm families at this income level still belong to the horse-and-buggy age. Only 16 percent had any running water; an even smaller proportion, 8 percent, had both hot and cold running water in kitchen and bath when surveyed in 1935–36 (fig. 2). Only 10 percent had an indoor toilet of any sort, flush or chemical (table 3). Although such facilities are less usual in urban communities than is sometimes supposed, about nine-tenths of the small-city families with comparable incomes have running water and indoor toilets, and about three-fifths have both hot and cold running water piped to both kitchen and bathroom.

The relation between family health and lack of modern sanitary facilities in dwellings is less certain in rural than in urban areas. A farm family can be served by a properly protected well and a sanitary outside toilet, whereas arrangements of this sort in a crowded metropolis would be a serious health hazard. However, there can be no

Table 3.—Percentage of families having specified facilities in family dwelling, owning specified equipment, and having expenditures for specified items, among all nonrelief farm families and nonrelief farm families in North Carolina and South Carolina, in selected income ranges, 1935–36

Item	All nonrelief farm families in income range—[1]		Nonrelief families in income range $250–$499 [2]	
	$1,000–$1,249	$2,500–$2,999	North Carolina white farm operators	North Carolina and South Carolina Negro sharecroppers
Families having—	*Percent*	*Percent*	*Percent*	*Percent*
Less than 1 room per person	18	9	23	57
Running water	16	43	6	0
Hot and cold water in kitchen and bath	8	30	1	0
No toilet	1	0	6	16
Indoor toilet	10	33	1	0
Central heating system	13	31	0	0
Electric lights	19	44	0	0
Telephone	29	52	0	0
Automobile	[3] 71	[3] 80	6	21
Radio	54	81	5	1
Refrigerator, any	39	70	0	6
Refrigerator, mechanical	4	20	0	0
Washing machine	47	64	0	0
Sewing machine	86	90	56	40
Home-canned food	95	96	100	77
Families having expenditures for—				
Newspapers	85	96	30	14
Magazines	58	82	8	11
Motion-picture admissions	51	75	6	15
Laundry sent out	8	16	3	
	Number	*Number*	*Number*	*Number* 1
Average visits to doctors	5.09	6.00	0.41	2.00

[1] All figures except those on automobile ownership are estimates made by the Bureau of Home Economics on the basis of the Consumer Purchases Study in 66 farm counties in 21 States.
[2] Preliminary data from samples taken as part of the Consumer Purchases Study, Bureau of Home Economics.
[3] Preliminary estimates by the National Resources Planning Board on basis of data largely from the Farm Consumer Purchases Study conducted by the Bureau of Home Economics.

doubt that lack of modernization of this kind means discomfort and a considerable expenditure of strength and time.

Undoubtedly farm families want comfortable homes; but a much greater money outlay is required to provide hot and cold running water and an indoor flush toilet for a farmhouse than for a house in a city where a water supply and sewage system are provided. Almost half—44 percent—of the farm families at this intermediate income level lived on rented farms. The landlord offering a farm for rent feels little pressure to modernize the house, since facilities for farming usually are a more important consideration in rental rates than are housing facilities. The city landlord, in contrast, must provide certain facilities to meet local sanitary regulations; competition forces him to provide others, since urban tenants choose their dwellings on the basis of livability rather than of business opportunities.

Electric lights, standard equipment of the so-called modern urban home, are lacking in the majority of farm dwellings. Approximately one-fifth of the farm families in the income range $1,000 to $1,250 had electric lights in 1935–36. Undoubtedly this proportion will be considerably larger by the end of 1940. The Rural Electrification Administration has greatly stimulated extension of electric service in many areas; but the most optimistic estimates place the percentage of all farms that will be served by electric power lines by January 1941 at less than 30.

Stoves heat most farm dwellings; only one in every eight families of this intermediate-income group had a central heating system. Some of the farmhouses are well heated by stoves and well lighted by kerosene lamps; but the expenditure of human effort necessary to achieve comfort is far greater than in cities where central heat is prevalent and more than 95 percent of the families have electricity. Then, too, despite the effort spent, many farm homes doubtless are inadequately heated in winter; many have but one comfortable, well-lighted room. For the small family this is not a serious limitation of space, but for the large family with members of different ages it may restrict opportunities for entertaining friends, for study and reading, for other relaxation, and for privacy.

Household Operation

Money outlays for operating the house—for heat, light, refrigeration, household help, and such incidental supplies as those for cleaning and laundry work—averaged $62 for farm families in the income range $1,000 to $1,250. This sum is considerably below that reported by small-city families with comparable incomes. Farm families curtailed their expenditures for heat by the use of farm-furnished wood and other fuels, and besides, their houses probably were less well heated than those of urban groups. Their lower expenditures for refrigeration reflect the fact that a relatively smaller number have equipment for this purpose. Approximately 40 of every 100 farm families had refrigerators; fewer than 5 had mechanical refrigerators. Some had springhouses or specially built coolers; but carrying food back and forth to the springhouse usually means more work for the homemaker than using a conveniently located refrigerator.

Farm families spend little for having washing done away from home by a commercial laundry or a laundress; average outlays of this income group for laundry were $1.70 for the year. Only 8 percent ever sent laundry out, and evidently many of these families seldom used such services, for their expenditures averaged less than 50 cents a week. In many instances, almost as much time would be spent in taking clothes and household linens to the laundry as would be required for doing the work at home.

Washing machines help materially in reducing the work of household laundry, but only about one-half of the farm families at this intermediate income level had such labor-saving devices. The proportion differed greatly from one region to another, however. Approximately four-fifths of the families in the north central sections had washers, and two-thirds had motor-driven machines. In contrast, only 2 percent or fewer of the families of white operators at this income level in four farming sections of the Southeast had washing machines of any sort—a reflection of the availability of domestic help in this region.[6]

In addition to laundry work, farm families perform many other

[6] MONROE, DAY, and KYRK, HAZEL. FAMILY EXPENDITURES FOR HOUSING AND HOUSEHOLD OPERATION. U. S. Bureau of Home Economics. (Unpublished manuscript.)

household tasks that city families are more likely to turn over to commercial agencies. More than four-fifths of the farm families in this intermediate-income group had sewing machines, as compared with fewer than three-fourths of the small-city families with comparable incomes. This would seem to indicate more home sewing, mending, and making of clothes and furnishings by farm homemakers.

More than nine-tenths of the farm families did home canning, putting up an average of 200 quarts of food. Family members also were responsible for care of gardens and poultry, for milking, and for other tasks involved in producing their farm-furnished food. With these many household production activities, it would seem that modern houses with facilities and labor-saving equipment that lighten the work of homemaking are more needed by farm than by urban families; yet the latter more often have them.

This picture of the operation of farm households raises the question of what is a good balance between use of money and use of other resources such as time and energy—a question also faced by the farm operator. Initial costs of modernizing houses and buying new equipment are considerable. In addition, electric lights, a mechanical refrigerator, and an oil-burning furnace would materially increase expenditures for household operation if farm-furnished fuel and ice had been used previously. Farm families with limited money incomes must make many decisions one way or the other. For some, the use of money to buy leisure—as by purchasing labor-saving equipment—does not provide as great satisfaction as its use for books, a radio, more gasoline for the family car, or other means of broadening horizons; but for others—those with unusually heavy burdens of work or unusual need for husbanding strength—purchases that save energy may be all-important.

Transportation and Communication Facilities

Improvements in transportation and communication are gifts of technology that have had far-reaching effects on patterns of farm-family living. Hard-surfaced roads, the automobile, the rural bus line, rural mail service bringing daily papers, the radio, and the telephone all serve to increase social contacts of farm families and bring them in close touch with neighborhood and world events.

The automobile seems to be one of the products of technological advance most appreciated in rural areas; approximately 70 percent of the farm families in the income range $1,000 to $1,250 were car owners as compared with 30 percent of the Chicago families with comparable incomes. This larger proportion of car owners among the farm families may reflect their greater use of cars for business. But there is the possibility, too, that the automobile ranks higher in the scale of wants of farm people. Certainly the farm family is far more dependent upon its automobile for social contacts and opportunities for commercial recreation than is the metropolitan family, since distances are greater and often there is no bus or trolley service available. In addition, the city family frequently does not have a place to keep a car.

Willingness to buy a used automobile may have enabled many of these intermediate-income farm families to become car owners; in 1935–36 three used cars were bought to each new one by the families included in the Consumer Purchases Study. These farm families expected their automobiles to give several years of service; of the cars owned in 1935–36 that had been new when purchased, more than half had been bought in 1929 or earlier and thus had been used 6 years or longer.

Radios were less prevalent than automobiles, being owned by only about half the farm families at this intermediate income level in 1935–36. The proportion of radio owners in small cities was considerably higher, approximately 90 percent—a difference probably associated with the greater availability of electricity. Radio ownership has increased the country over in the past 5 years, but farm families still lag behind those in cities in this respect, according to trade reports.

Fewer than one-third—29 percent—of the farm families in this income group had telephones. Subscriptions to newspapers were reported by 85 percent; to magazines, by 58 percent. Daily newspapers were taken by relatively more families than were weeklies, except in the Plains and Mountain regions, where distances from the cities are great and news in the daily papers is old by the time it reaches many farms.

Clothing

Dress, fashion trends, and grooming undoubtedly are of more interest to farm families than they were at the turn of the century. Increased social contacts made possible by better transportation facilities, consolidated schools, daily papers, and moving pictures have made rural people more style conscious. Range of choice of clothing has expanded, too; families drive to larger trading centers to shop. Stores carry more varied stocks of ready-made garments than when more home sewing was done. Notwithstanding this urbanization of standards of dress and increased availability of style goods, farm families restrict money outlays for their wardrobes more than do city families.

Clothing expenditures of farm families in the income range $1,000 to $1,250 averaged $104 for all members—husbands, wives, and children—for the year (table 2). This amount seems small in view of the standards of personal appearance general among farm families of the middle income group. That so much is achieved with so little is the result in part of careful planning of purchases. In addition, farm homemakers and their daughters economize by making some garments and by mending, remodeling, and otherwise extending the life of their families' wardrobes.

The kind of wardrobe provided by such limited expenditures is indicated by average prices paid for garments and the average period of wear before replacement. A wife whose expenditures were similar to the average would pay about $16 for her winter coat and wear it for 5 years. A rayon or silk dress costing about $4.50 would be bought every other year; a cotton street dress costing about $1.35, each year. Two pairs of shoes a year would be purchased at a price of about $3 a pair. Many farm homemakers seem to have disregarded style trends in headgear; the average number of hats bought was 1.2 a year, which indicates that few purchased both a spring and a winter model.

A husband whose clothing expenditures resembled the average for the group would spend about the same amount as his wife, but he would apportion the amount differently among the several groups of clothing items. He would buy four shirts a year, for which he would pay about 85 cents apiece. A wool suit bought for about $19 would last approximately 4 years; a $3 mackinaw or heavy wool jacket, 3 years. About $14 would be paid for a winter overcoat, and it would be worn many years. (Only 1 husband in 14 bought an overcoat.) A pair of work shoes usually would not last quite a year, and its purchase price would be about $2.80. The total outlay for underwear, nightwear, and hose would be approximately $4 during the year.

Personal and Medical Care

Personal care—including cosmetics, toilet articles, services of beauty and barber shops—has a more important place in the family budget than it did a generation ago. Farm families undoubtedly have increased their expenditures for such items; yet this intermediate group spent an average of only $17 during the year—less than small-city families with comparable incomes. Fewer than half, 43 percent, of the wives had expenditures for personal services such as haircuts, permanent waves, or shampoos.

The expenditures of families for medical care at this intermediate income level averaged about $50—approximately half the estimated cost of adequate care provided on a group basis (*8*). Family expenditures do not tell the whole story of outlays for medical care, since Government, philanthropic agencies, and industry also spend for this purpose and many families unable to pay are given free services by physicians. It is probable, however, that farm groups benefit less than urban groups from such provisions because of greater difficulty in reaching health centers and clinics.

Lack of income is not the only reason for inadequate medical care for farm families; medical facilities and personnel also may be lacking. Many rural counties have no hospitals; many others have hospitals too small to meet the needs of their population. In many there are too few doctors and nurses, and public-health programs are below national standards. Distances may make it impossible for farm families to obtain medical aid in emergencies and often cause physicians to charge higher prices for visits than current charges in cities.

Recreation and Education

Recreation, formal education, reading, furnishings and equipment, travel and transportation other than by the family automobile, gifts to persons outside the family, community welfare, and income and personal taxes accounted for money outlays that averaged about $100 for the farm families at this income level.

Recreation may be bought by payments for admissions to motion pictures and other entertainments and by such purchases as radios, toys, and equipment for hunting, fishing, and other sports. These intermediate-income farm families spent $21 for recreation during the year. Chicago families at the same income level spent the same average amount for recreation, but the patterns of the two groups differed; motion pictures took more than half the outlay of the metropolitan families and only about one-third that of the families on farms. For the latter, attendance at the movies or a concert usually means a trip to town—an expenditure in addition to the price of admission. Whether one group fared better or worse than the other is open to question, since their ways of recreation are so different. Farm families follow patterns that call for active participation. They have picnics; they hunt, fish, play games, and in general are less often merely spectators than are families in cities.

Family expenditures averaging $18 for formal education and reading are only slender evidence of what families receive along this line. Costs of public schools are borne by the State, and textbooks usually are furnished free. However, educational opportunities provided by the schools are far from equal throughout the country; farm children fare less well than those in cities. Rural schools spent an average of $67 per child attending in 1935–36; city schools, $108 (*5*). The lower expenditures probably mean shorter school terms and less well trained teachers for children on farms.

Education goes on in the home as well as at school, and the farm home may offer better opportunities than the urban home for the child's development. The farm boy or girl can learn by doing, by participating in work that leads directly toward better family living and thus gives a sense of accomplishment. Not all farm parents utilize these possibilities to the full, but more widespread adult education will increase their appreciation of the opportunities that farm life offers.

Farmers and farm homemakers who look at learning as an on-going process and who seek help in meeting their day-to-day problems have opportunities not generally available to city folk. Various agencies of the United States Department of Agriculture, of State colleges of agriculture, and of home economics (such as the field staffs of the Extension Service and the Farm Security Administration) provide an educational program designed to promote sound agricultural practices, rich family living, and a broad understanding of the current economic situation.

Opportunities for reading good books are fewer in rural than in urban communities. With expenditures for reading matter—newspapers, magazines, and books other than school texts—averaging less than $10 a year for these intermediate-income farm families, few books were bought. Libraries are not to be depended upon to provide the books that cannot be purchased, as in cities. It is estimated that about 39,500,000 persons live in rural areas served only by school libraries (*5*). These and the public libraries in small towns have limited stocks of books, many of them sadly out of date in scientific information.

THE MORE WELL-TO-DO FARM FAMILIES

An income of $2,500 to $3,000 makes possible a comfortable living even for a large farm family, barring unusual situations such as serious illness or heavy debts to be paid. Families at this level, therefore, have been chosen for depicting the consumption patterns of farm groups in comfortable circumstances. Some farm families achieve still higher incomes, but the proportion is small—less than 5 percent in 1935–36.

Total net incomes (money and nonmoney) of these more well-to-do families were more than double those of the intermediate group just described. Average net money income was more than three times as great, while nonmoney income—that from farm-furnished housing, food, fuel, and other products used by the household—was only about one-third higher. The upper-income families thus had a larger proportion of their net income in cash than did the intermediate group, as is shown in table 4.

Table 4.—Average income, change in net worth, and value of family living, for all nonrelief farm families in selected income ranges,[1] 1935–36.

Item	Families in income range—		Item	Families in income range—	
	$2,500–$2,999	$1,000–$1,249		$2,500–$2,999	$1,000–$1,249
	Dollars	*Dollars*		*Dollars*	*Dollars*
Money income	2,028	634	Change in net worth	777	−10
Nonmoney income from farm-furnished products	688	493	Total value of family living[2]	1,939	1,137
			Money expenditures	1,251	644
Total net income	2,716	1,127			

[1] Estimates for all nonrelief farm families in the United States made by the National Resources Planning Board on the basis of data largely from the Farm Consumer Purchases Study conducted by the Bureau of Home Economics in 66 farm counties in 21 States.

[2] Total expenditures for family living (including gifts, welfare, and selected taxes) plus the money value of products furnished by the farm for family use.

Families with net incomes of $2,500 to $3,000 saved an average of $777, 29 percent of their receipts—a marked contrast to those at the intermediate level, who just about broke even. The relatively large savings of these families are characteristic of the general pattern of use of income by the more well-to-do farm groups the country over. An average increase in net worth of more than $600 for the year was reported by white operators at this income level in each of 11 farming sections. As was true of the intermediate group, these farm families tended to save more than urban families with comparable incomes. For example, Chicago families with incomes in this upper range had an average net surplus of $185 (*1*), only about one-fourth that of farm families. Twenty-two percent of the families in Chicago as compared with 7 percent of those on farms reported a deficit.

Perhaps some farm families save too much; future security should not be bought at too great a sacrifice of current living. No one can lay down rules as to how much should be spent and how much saved from a given income; each family must decide this question for itself. But there can be no doubt that the feeling of independence and the other satisfactions that come from ownership of land and of herds, of modern equipment and other working capital have a high place in the scale of values of most farm families. To them, these are goals to be achieved even at the cost of giving up some of the comforts and pleasures enjoyed by urban groups.

The value of living of these upper-income families averaged $1,939, or about $800 more than that of the intermediate-income group. Thus value of living accounted for a little more than half and savings, or increase in net worth, for a little less than half the difference in average income of the two groups, approximately $1,600.

The money value of the food consumed by these farm families indicates that practically all could have had diets rated good according to nutritional standards had they planned their purchases and their production programs wisely. That some families had diets inadequate in one or more respects was because of their failure to make the most of their resources. Education in nutrition and in household management might have enabled them to raise their dietary standard.

Houses of the more well-to-do families tended to be larger than those of the intermediate-income group; but although some probably had more rooms than were needed, about one-tenth did not provide one room per person. The houses of the former group were better equipped, also; yet many lacked the facilities that the majority of urban families consider essential for comfort. Fewer than half—43 percent—of the farm families with incomes of $2,500 to $3,000 had running water; 29 percent did not even have a hand pump inside the house but carried water from outdoors. Only 30 percent had both hot and cold running water in the kitchen and bathroom. One-third had indoor toilets; fewer than one-third (31 percent), central heat.

More than three-fourths—77 percent—of these families owned their farms. Failure to modernize their homes, therefore, must be attributed to the large money outlays involved rather than to a landlord's reluctance to improve rented property. That tenure is a factor in modernization, however, is shown by a special study of families of farm operators in Pennsylvania and Ohio. At this income level ($2,500 to $3,000), owners fared appreciably better than renters with respect to the relatively costly improvements; running hot and cold water in both kitchen and bath was reported by 45 percent of the owners and 33 percent of the tenants; flush toilets by 41 and 23 percent, respectively; central furnaces by 47 and 27 percent. The proportion of families having electric lights was practically the same for the two groups, 69 percent of the owners as compared with 73 percent of the renters.[7]

Families in this upper-income group had more opportunities than their lower-income neighbors for making social contacts and keeping in touch with local and world events. More than nine-tenths—96 percent—subscribed to daily papers, and more than four-fifths subscribed to magazines and had radios. About half had telephones; three-fourths went to the movies, but attendance was not frequent since total expenditures for recreation for all family members (4.8 persons per family) averaged only $51 for the year and included all paid admissions, toys, games, sports equipment, and the like.

Automobiles were owned by relatively more of these families than of those with smaller incomes. They traveled more, too; their mileage was at least one-third greater than that of families with incomes of $1,000 to $1,250 in each farm section. With less need for strict economy, more of the former families bought new than used cars, the ratio between the two types of purchases being about 2 to 1.

With increased opportunities for social contacts, husbands and wives in these more well-to-do families spent more for clothes than did those in the intermediate income group, but their average outlays were less than $75 apiece. More than half—57 percent—of the wives spent

[7] See the reference in footnote 6, p. 856.

money for haircuts, shampoos, waves, and other services at beauty shops, as compared with 43 percent of the wives in the intermediate income group.

Probably the wives in the upper-income families had more leisure, but their records of household production indicate that time did not hang heavily on their hands. Those who canned food (96 percent of the group) put up an average of 262 quarts each. Only 16 percent sent laundry out, but many must have used such services rarely since their average expenditures were less than $20 during the year—under 40 cents a week. A comparatively large number of these women had facilities and equipment for lessening housework such as kitchen sinks, running water, washing machines, and electric lights. Nevertheless the burden of household production they carried must have been heavy.

LOW-INCOME FARM FAMILIES

Some families of farm operators in all commercial agricultural areas are in the low-income classes. Within this group, however, individual families may differ greatly with respect to their plane of living. Some are accustomed to better incomes, having had only temporary reverses. Their resources, built up in more prosperous times, enable them to secure credit and thus maintain their expenditures for living at a level materially higher than current income would permit. Others, whose incomes have been low over a long period and whose resources are meager, must fit their consumption patterns to their net receipts in cash and in kind. In addition to these families of operators in commercial crop areas there are many families with low incomes and low levels of living in the sharecropper group in the Southeast, in the group of agricultural laborers the country over, and among the operators concentrated in sections where land is poor, where most of the farms are of the self-sufficing type, and where receipts from sales of farm products are low year after year.

Only families having both a low value of living and a low income are discussed here. Those able to spend appreciably more than they made are excluded since they do not belong in a picture designed to show how the less fortunate farm families live. No attempt has been made to combine data for all low-income farm families in the country; instead, two tenure groups, operators and sharecroppers, in two different sections are described. Families receiving relief are excluded since receipts in kind from welfare agencies may cause consumption patterns to differ considerably from those of self-supporting groups.

Whether a low-income farm family maintains itself above or below the poverty line depends in part on its size. Obviously, a large family will be less able than a small one to stretch a limited income so that the needs of all members are adequately met. To divide a group of families having a low value of living into those above and those below a health-and-decency level would call for a detailed appraisal of each case—a task impossible in a large-scale survey. But the over-all picture of a low-income group, without a rigid classification as to degree of adequacy of living, indicates the kind of deprivation that such families face and the problems to be solved if they are to be helped toward more wholesome living.

The lower-income families of farm operators in Jackson and Macon Counties, N. C., in the Appalachian Mountains, provide a picture of the general pattern of consumption of a group whose incomes are largely in farm products rather than cash. The average value of living of those in the income class $250 to $500 was $440; of this, $310 was farm-furnished housing, food, and other products and $130 purchased goods and services (table 2).

Food took two-thirds of the net income, in cash and in kind, used for living. The average value of the year's total food supply was $293, of which home-produced products represented $244 and cash purchases $49. More than one-third of the money expenditures of these families went for food that they could not or did not produce.

Although these families sacrificed other needs and wants in order to provide food, the value of their meals per food-expenditure (money value) unit[8] indicates that probably at least a third had diets that would be classed as poor—that is, failing to provide average requirements for all important nutrients—and another third, diets that would be classed as only fair. The food of these latter families would provide some but not much margin for safety over average minimum requirements. While the proportion of these farm families having good diets is low, it is higher than that of urban families at similar economic levels. The home-produced food of the farm group included many of the protective foods, which are relatively expensive to purchase.

The dwellings of many of these low-income families failed to meet the housing standards accepted for cities. There was overcrowding; approximately one-fourth of the families had less than one room per person. More then one-third of the houses had only two or three rooms. Apparently the provision of adequate housing for low-income families is a rural as well as an urban problem.

Sanitary facilities were not a part of the equipment of the houses of this low-income farm group. Only one family in the whole group had an indoor toilet; 6 percent had no toilet whatever. Almost all of the families carried water from some outside source; only 6 percent had running water (table 3). Whether the outdoor water supply and the toilet were so located that there was no health hazard was not determined in this survey, but it is likely that adequate care was not exercised in all instances.

About nine-tenths of the houses were heated by fireplaces. The mean temperature in this section commonly falls below 50° F. for 3 winter months and at times may be as low as 6°. Whether houses heated by fireplaces were comfortable in such weather is uncertain; perhaps some of the smaller ones were, and some of the larger were not. All of the houses were lighted by kerosene lamps; none had electric lights.

Money expenditures for household operation averaged only $8 a year for this low-income group; the farm-furnished fuel was valued at $44, bringing the total value of this budget item to $52. None of the families had refrigerators; hence they spent nothing for ice.

With an average of only $81 to spend for all items of family living except food ($130 minus $49; see above), yearly expenditures were

[8] The relative value of food for different individuals based on the value of food for the moderately active adult.

divided as follows: Clothing, $31; medical care, $12; household operation, $8; travel and transportation (including the expenditures for automobiles owned by four families), tobacco, reading, formal education, recreation, gifts to persons outside the family, church contributions, and all other expenditures, $30 (table 2).

Poverty of contacts with world events was marked. Only 30 percent of these families subscribed to newspapers; 8 percent, to magazines. All were without telephones, and only 5 percent had radios. Eight percent paid admissions to moving picture shows or local sports events such as ball games; they could not attend commercial amusements very often and keep their total outlay for recreation at an average of $1 a family a year.

To dress the entire family on $31 meant limitation of wardrobes to sheer necessities. Husbands' clothing expenditures for the year averaged $11, almost one-third of which, $3.60, went for shoes and about $4 for shirts, overalls, trousers, and suits, leaving only $3.40 for hats, coats and sweaters, underwear, ties, belts, and other articles. Wives spent an average of $9.21 a year, more than one-third of which went for shoes; hats took only 59 cents.

Medical care must have been grossly inadequate for almost all families. An average of $12 means much lower outlays by some of the group. The number of visits to physicians averaged 0.41, or less than one for every two families in this low-income group. Routine dental care must have been almost unknown; average expenditures for such services were 68 cents per family. A little more than one-fourth of the total expenditure for medical care, an average of $3.48, went for medicines; self-medication must have been common.

A group of Negro sharecroppers at the same income level ($250 to $500) in the eastern part of North Carolina and in South Carolina received an average of $153 of their income in kind, less than half the average of $310 received by the low-income white operators just described. The money income of the former group was appreciably greater, an average of $230 as compared with $88 (table 5).

The consumption patterns of the two groups reflect these differences in ratio of money to nonmoney income. Family size helps

Table 5.—Average income, change in net worth, and value of family living, nonrelief farm families in North Carolina and South Carolina in the $250–$499 income range, 1935–36 [1]

Item	North Carolina white farm operators	North Carolina and South Carolina Negro sharecroppers	Item	North Carolina white farm operators	North Carolina and South Carolina Negro sharecroppers
	Dollars	*Dollars*		*Dollars*	*Dollars*
Money income	88	230	Change in net worth (net deficit)	—42	—5
Nonmoney income from farm-furnished products	310	153	Total value of family living [2]	440	388
Total net income	398	383	Money expenditures	130	235

[1] Preliminary data from samples taken as part of the Consumer Purchases Study, Bureau of Home Economics.

[2] Total expenditures for family living (including gifts, welfare, and selected taxes) plus the money value of products furnished by the farm for family use.

account for some differences in expenditures. The Negro sharecropper families were larger, averaging 4.18 persons as compared with 3.41 in the low-income operators' families.

The food of the low-income Negro sharecropper families had an average money value of $221, $72 below that of the families of the operators who raised so large a proportion of their supplies. Since the Negro families were larger, too, the average value per meal per food-expenditure (money value) unit was 5.2 cents for the group, as compared with 7.9 cents for the operators' families. A larger proportion of the Negro families, therefore, had diets that failed to meet accepted standards of nutritive adequacy; probably more than four-fifths had diets deficient in one or more respects.

That the degree of adequacy of diets achieved by low-income families depends in large part upon their programs of food production for household use is evidenced by this comparison. The Negro families had less than half as much farm-furnished food as the white operators; even though they purchased more food, they did not spend enough to provide meals as good, nutritionally, as those of the white families. Man's food wants are strong, but not strong enough to lead him to buy adequate food when his money is too limited to supply his many other needs. Tenure status may be partially responsible for the smaller amounts of food produced by the sharecropper families; they may have been less free to make decisions as to use of land than the families of the low-income operators. In addition, the sharecroppers were in a better farming section, where there was doubtless greater emphasis on use of land for cash crops.

The houses of these Negro sharecroppers tended to be less adequate than those of the white operators. They were smaller, with an average of 3.5 rooms per dwelling as compared with 4.1; 57 percent did not meet the standard of a room a person. The large families, those of five or more persons, suffered especially from overcrowding; 92 percent had fewer rooms than family members, and 13 percent reported two or more persons per room. Whether yards provided living space for these families and thus lessened the ill effects of overcrowding in their houses is not known. But examples of overcrowding of land are not limited to cities; crops may be planted to the door of the tenant's little house, leaving him no space for outdoor living or for a garden.

One out of six of the sharecroppers' houses lacked even an outdoor toilet. None had indoor toilets, running water, or electric lights. Fireplaces heated 86 percent of the houses—about the same proportion as for the operators.

Wretched as is the lot of these low-income farm groups—sharecroppers and operators on poor land—migrant agricultural workers fare even worse. These uprooted families, estimated to number from 200,000 to 350,000, lack the security that comes with arrangements for a year's use of land and a dwelling, inadequate though the shelter and the income from the land may be. They cannot produce any of their food supply. They have no land for gardens unless they are among the fortunate few living in one of the permanent camps established by the Government; they have no livestock or poultry. Their children attend school intermittently, if at all. Their earnings are irregular and usually far too low for their needs. Their levels of living are below those of the city's poor (7).

THE SITUATION AS A WHOLE

Patterns of farm family living have common characteristics the country over. City ways are reflected in these patterns more than they were three decades ago, before automobiles, radios, and other improvements in transportation and communication were so widely used. But though the consumption habits of rural families are becoming increasingly like those of urban families, certain dissimilarities persist and probably will exist for years to come, since the agricultural and industrial economies differ so fundamentally.

Desire for financial security is characteristic of all population groups—urban as well as rural. Farm families seek such security through ownership of land and through acquiring herds, equipment, and other working capital. Building up the farm business, either by decreasing debts or increasing assets, competes with family living for use of income and with recreation for use of time. The increases in net worth of farm families tend to be greater than those of city families at comparable income levels, perhaps because the farm business is a family undertaking, enlisting the efforts and interest of all members.

A considerable degree of self-sufficiency is another characteristic of the patterns of living of farm families; they still perform many of the tasks that urban groups have turned over to workers outside the home. Food and fuel are produced. Laundry work and canning and preserving of foods are more usual undertakings of farm than of urban households. With this greater dependence upon their own labor and other resources comes a lesser dependence upon money income and thus greater security against a major economic depression than is found among city groups.

Many elements in farm living reflect this tendency to carry on production for household use. Diets, while not universally good even for the more well-to-do, tend to be better than those of families in cities at comparable income levels. Most farm families can produce protective foods, so important for good nutrition, at less cost than they can be purchased in urban markets. Insofar as health is served by good nutrition, farm families thus have an advantage. But from the standpoint of medical care their position is far less favorable because of lack of hospitals and inadequate numbers of doctors and nurses in many rural areas.

Houses of farm families are more likely to provide adequate space than are those of families in cities, especially those in metropolitan areas. But the farm group has fewer of the comforts provided by modern facilities. A surprisingly large proportion of farm homes lack electric lights, hot and cold running water, an indoor toilet, and central heat.

With an appreciable share of its net income in kind, the farm family has less money to spend than the family in the city. In stretching funds, personal appearance is sacrificed to other needs and wants. Dress tends to be simpler and services of barber and beauty shops fewer than is the case with city groups.

The automobile holds a more important place in the standard of living of the farm than of the large-city family. Good roads, better mail service bringing daily papers and magazines, the radio, and the extension of motion picture theaters to small towns all lessen the isolation once considered a necessary part of farm living. Yet many families still lack these advantages.

Schools for formal education of farm children tend to lag behind those provided for children in cities; library facilities are far more limited, too. But adults in farm families have better opportunities for continuing their education than do those in cities, and children have more chances to learn through doing.

Many of the advantages of the farm over the urban family are not shown by statistics. Farm life offers more opportunities for strengthening family ties through sharing responsibilities. The farm business is a common undertaking; family members work together in making a living instead of depending upon one earner, as the majority of city families do. They have opportunities to produce goods for themselves and to have a degree of independence from the ups and downs of money income not possible for families employed in industry. They thus have greater security than do members of the city family in the insecure world of today.

These pictures of farm and urban living are in the main those of the middle- and upper-income groups. The ways of living of low-income families, whether in cities or on farms, resemble in general outline those of the middle group insofar as resources permit, since patterns of consumption of any group tend to follow those of families one step above in the income scale. But lack of adequate income is reflected in lack of the goods and services needed for wholesome living. On farms there are families that are inadequately fed, clothed, and housed and cannot obtain needed medical care, just as there are in cities. Which fares better and which worse, it is difficult to say.

It is the purpose of this article to give facts regarding rural living conditions rather than to suggest remedies. The latter are dealt with in many other articles in this volume. In general it may be said that the purpose underlying most of the agricultural programs in recent times is to enable farm families to work effectively toward wiping out rural poverty and achieving for all the Nation's agricultural population a level of living that measures up to our American standards.

LITERATURE CITED

(1) Kaplan, A. D. H., Williams, Faith, and Hartsough, Mildred.
1939. FAMILY INCOME AND EXPENDITURES IN CHICAGO, 1935–36. U. S. Bur. Labor Statis., Bul. 642, v. 2, 256 pp., illus.

(2) Martin, D., Monroe, Day, Brady, D., and Phelps, E.
1940. FAMILY INCOME AND EXPENDITURES, MIDDLE ATLANTIC, NORTH CENTRAL, AND NEW ENGLAND REGIONS, PART I, FAMILY INCOME, FARM SERIES. U. S. Dept. Agr. Misc. Pub. 383 (in press).

(3) Kyrk, Hazel; Monroe, Day; Pennell, Maryland Y.; and Dyer, Edith M.
1940. FAMILY HOUSING AND FACILITIES. U. S. Dept. Agr. Misc. Pub. 399, 229 pp., illus.

(4) Stiebeling, Hazel K., and Coons, Callie Mae.
1939. PRESENT-DAY DIETS IN THE UNITED STATES. U. S. Dept. Agr. Yearbook 1939: 296–320, illus.

(5) [UNITED STATES] ADVISORY COMMITTEE ON EDUCATION.
1938. REPORT OF THE ADVISORY COMMITTEE ON EDUCATION . . . 75th Cong., 3d sess., H. Doc. 529, 148 pp.

(6) [UNITED STATES] BUREAU OF HOME ECONOMICS.
1939. THE FARM HOUSING SURVEY . . . U. S. Dept. Agr. Misc. Pub. 323. illus.

(7) [UNITED STATES] FARM SECURITY ADMINISTRATION.
1939. REPORT OF THE ADMINISTRATOR . . . 1938–39.

(8) [UNITED STATES] INTERDEPARTMENTAL COMMITTEE TO COORDINATE HEALTH AND WELFARE ACTIVITIES.
1938. PROCEEDINGS OF THE NATIONAL HEALTH CONFERENCE, JULY 18, 19, 20, 1938 . . . 163 pp. Washington, D. C.

(9) [UNITED STATES] NATIONAL RESOURCES COMMITTEE.
1938. CONSUMER INCOMES IN THE UNITED STATES: THEIR DISTRIBUTION IN 1935–36. 104 pp., illus. Washington, D. C.

223761°—40——56

Overcrowded Farms

by W. W. ALEXANDER [1]

"**CONSERVATIVE** estimates show that, all told, 3,000,000 farm families are existing today on abnormally low incomes and at unwholesomely low standards of living," says the author of this article. "Many of these families who are so often marked down as misfits are just as able and anxious to earn their own way as any other group in this country. Given a chance—given the tools and the guidance they need—these people can become self-respecting citizens again. There is nothing fundamentally wrong with them. The problem is to devise a system that will enable them to become assets instead of liabilities." Here is the plain tale of efforts to make these people assets to the United States. The head of the Farm Security Administration tells how a family in dire need can secure not only a loan but personal advice and assistance until they can again get a toehold on self-respect and independence. Those helped so far have paid out remarkably well. But the need continues to outstrip the efforts to meet it, and the author frankly sets down what he regards as the shortcomings of the present program. The article ends with a brief account of the historical evolution of the rural relief program now in effect.

IN THE old days most people felt no rural relief was needed. Farmers were supposed to be self-sufficient. A farm was considered a place

[1] W. W. Alexander was formerly Administrator, Farm Security Administration.

to go when all other means of support failed. "You can always make a living on the farm," was the saying. The fallacy of this idea, however, began to appear after the World War.

When the rest of the Nation first felt the depression in 1929 the rural areas had been struggling through hard times for several years. One of the first effects on the farmers had been to send them to the cities in increasingly large numbers. Literally millions of rural workers went to the cities in the 1920's. Some of them were soon to suffer from this ambitious move, for when the depression did reach the cities this group again was the first to feel its force. They had been the last to be hired, and they were the first to be fired. Remembering the distress they had felt on the farms, however, they stayed in the cities as long as they possibly could.

The fact that many of these rural people were still in the cities when the first accounting of the relief needs was made in 1933 gave an inaccurate perspective to the picture. That many unemployed farm workers lived on their meager savings or were supported by their families also served to make the need for rural relief seem less than it really was. As time went by, however, these people exhausted their resources and went on relief. As a result the rural relief rolls continued to mount for almost 2 years after the first Federal emergency relief was granted in May 1933.

In January 1935 the rural relief rolls reached a peak. Estimates indicate that at this time 2,500,000 rural families were receiving some form of relief. In the following spring there was a steady decline until the ravages of the 1936 drought again caused rural distress to mount in the Plains States sufficiently to offset the declines elsewhere. Again in the later months of 1937, the interruption in the upswing of industry, low prices for farm commodities, normal seasonal unemployment, and localized drought piled up rural distress in some sections. This trend continued through 1938, and it was not until 1939 that there was again a slackening in the rural relief load.

This recent decrease, however, like some of the past fluctuations, is not an entirely accurate index of the need. A large part of this cut was forced by a decrease in the funds available for aid from the Work Projects Administration [2] and was made without full reckoning of the existing distress. Jobs were not available for all those who were dropped from the Work Projects Administration rolls.

On July 1, 1939, it was estimated that about 1,000,000 rural families were obtaining public assistance through W. P. A. and the Farm Security Administration, excluding the direct relief grants of various Federal, State, and local agencies.

Large as this number is, it does not give a full idea of all those needing help. Conservative estimates show that, all told, 3,000,000 farm families are existing today on abnormally low incomes and at unwholesomely low standards of living.

Many of these families, who so often have been marked down as misfits, are just as able and anxious to earn their own way as any other group in this country. Given a chance—given the tools, the guidance, and the sympathy they need—these people can become self-respecting citizens again. There is nothing fundamentally wrong

[2] Formerly the Works Progress Administration.

with them. The problem is to devise a system that will enable them to become assets instead of liabilities.

HOW RURAL FAMILIES ARE HELPED BY THE F. S. A.

Several agencies have worked to relieve rural distress, among them the Farm Security Administration. The F. S. A. rehabilitation-loan program, which at the present time is one of the strongest arms of the Government in the so-called rural relief field, is not actually relief, any more than are loans to home builders, banks, or railroads. The loan program does, however, deal almost entirely with families who are near the border line, who without its help would have to depend on grants of one kind or another for their existence. Its field is limited to the needy. In terms of dollars and of numbers of people directly affected it is far larger than any existing grant program.

Briefly, the loan program works in this manner:

In the spring a farmer who needs fertilizer, seed, a plow or other equipment to carry on his work and who is not able to obtain the money to purchase these necessities from any other source calls at a county office of the Farm Security Administration and asks for help. If the farmer owns or can rent enough land to support his family and repay the loan under normal conditions, the county supervisor sits down with him and draws up a plan for working the farm under which it can be done. Included in the plan are provisions for raising the family's food supply and feed for its livestock, and for the development of two or more cash-crop enterprises. The plan also contains all the soil conservation measures necessary for rebuilding or retaining the fertility of the soil.

While the supervisor is helping the farmer plan his work, a home economist gives the farmer's wife similar help. A household budget is drawn up and a year-round balanced diet planned for the whole family. Emphasis is placed on the canning of the surplus garden products and the working out of time-saving and money-saving measures in the everyday household job of feeding, clothing, and sheltering the family.

The completed farm and home plan clearly indicates what equipment is needed to carry on the work. These items may range from a mule, a milk cow, and 100 baby chickens to a pressure cooker and 6 dozen glass jars. Whatever they are, if the estimated income of the family appears large enough to pay for them, the money for their purchase is loaned to the farmer. These loans carry a 5-percent interest rate and are made out usually for a term of 5 years.

After the loan is made and the year's work started on the farm, the supervisor and the home economist continue to work with the family. They help with the farm problems that arise—such difficulties as fighting tobacco blight and doctoring sick chickens—and they bring the latest information on the work of the State experiment stations to the families.

Throughout the year the rehabilitation clients are encouraged to keep record books of all expenses and income, putting down each week the money they spend and earn. In the fall, when the crops are harvested, they find themselves, under normal conditions, with enough food to last through the winter and a considerable gain in farming

Figure 1.—In the fall they find themselves with enough food to last through the winter.

equipment and experience (fig. 1). When the next spring rolls around the same sort of planning is repeated. After several years of continual progress, during which the farmer gains experience and pays off his loan, the family often is able to finance itself and proceed on its own. By May 1, 1940, nearly 115,000 of these families had reached this stage of development and graduated from the program with their loans fully repaid (fig. 2).

A typical story of the rehabilitation of a one-time relief family into an independent, self-supporting family unit can be told by Lee Barnes, of Jackson County, Okla.

Back in 1936, Barnes, who supports a wife and two children, had

Figure 2.—Through farm and home planning with adequate guidance families become independent and self-supporting.

very little to farm with, and what he had was threatened with foreclosure. He applied to the county rehabilitation supervisor for help.

Together, Barnes and the supervisor worked out a farm plan that called for him to raise all his livestock feed, most of his family's food, and several cash crops. Mrs. Barnes worked out a home-management plan with the help of the F. S. A. home-management supervisor.

One of Barnes' troubles had been one-crop cotton farming. The F. S. A. loan enabled him to diversify by developing a milk herd for supplemental income. Now he milks five cows, which provide a weekly cream check averaging between $3.50 and $4. This takes care of the few groceries he has to buy. He raises his own livestock feed and most of the family's food.

From a 1½-acre garden Mrs. Barnes keeps the family supplied with vegetables and fruit throughout the year. One year she canned 600 quarts, enough to carry her through the next year when grasshoppers got their garden.

By last year, Barnes was well enough fixed so that he said he would not sell out for $1,000. He was looking forward to 1940, when he hoped to be able to pay off his final installment on the loan and be debt-free.

The basic feature of the rehabilitation program today is the guidance the family receives. Although the extent of this guidance has increased markedly since earlier days, it is still far short of what it should be, owing to the large number of families each supervisor is expected to look out for.

County supervisors now have an average of nearly 150 families each. For proper supervision, the number of families should not exceed 75.

The grant program plays a smaller part than it once did. Drought years developed the heaviest demand for grants, and with the slackening of need in this direction fewer grants have been given. Many are still being made, however, in the areas of greatest need, and in emer-

Figure 3.—Participation in cooperatives helps to remedy one of the basic troubles that plague low-income families.

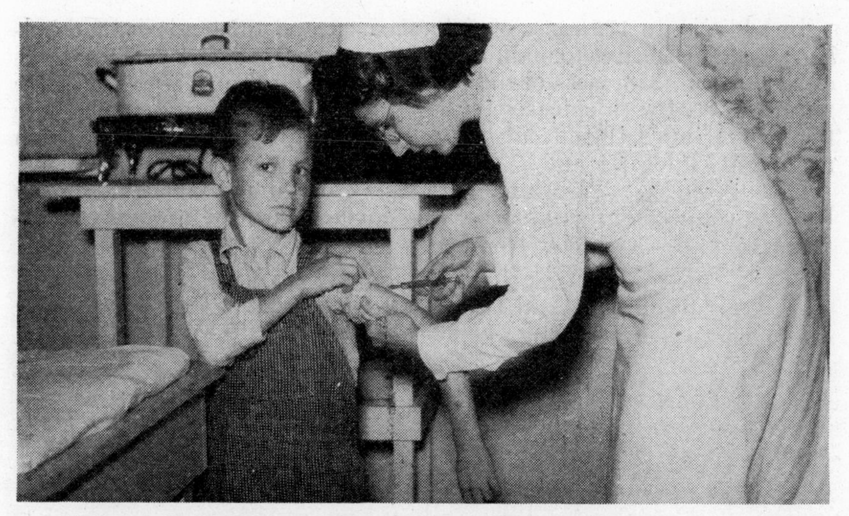

Figure 4.—By the beginning of 1940, 30 States had inaugurated cooperative medical programs

gency cases they are still used to supply food, clothing, or medical care to rehabilitation families.

Several other activities supplement the rehabilitation work. One of these, debt adjustment, was started as early as 1933. The other two—programs of medical care and participation in cooperatives—are of more recent development. In these auxiliary programs the Farm Security Administration attempts to remedy some of the basic troubles that plague low-income farm families (fig. 3).

If the farm family's debts are a hang-over from other days and are too big to be repaid, the F. S. A. helps to get them reduced to a size where they can be handled. If the family is unable to obtain adequate medical care, the Administration aids in the formation of a county health association through which the family can obtain the services of a physician at a price it can afford to pay. Also when the families need breeding stock, expensive machinery, or other equipment that they cannot afford individually, the Administration assists them to cooperate with neighbors in the joint purchase and use of such facilities.

The fastest growing of these auxiliary programs is the one providing for medical care. By January 1940, 67,542 families—357,973 persons—were covered by medical plans worked out by the Administration in cooperation with local physicians in 30 States (fig. 4).

The Administration has proceeded on the theory that, aside from humanitarian motives, it is good business for a lending and rehabilitation agency to do what it can to improve the health of its borrowers. Accumulated evidence shows that in a large percentage of failures poor health is one of the primary causes.

A health survey among 100 farm families in a Southeastern State last year disclosed the widespread need for medical aid for low-income rural families. The survey, conducted by the Administration and the local medical school, showed more than 1,300 health handicaps among the 575 people in these families.

In addition to 175 cases of rickets, suspected tuberculosis, and pellagra—afflictions due to malnutrition—the survey disclosed many cases of hookworm, 288 cases of diseased tonsils, 360 people with defective teeth, and 124 with defective eyesight. The 109 women among these families included 79 suffering from torn internal organs resulting from neglect at childbirth and 21 with suspected cancer.

Usually the F. S. A. health program is worked out on a county-wide basis in cooperation with the county medical society. Member fam-

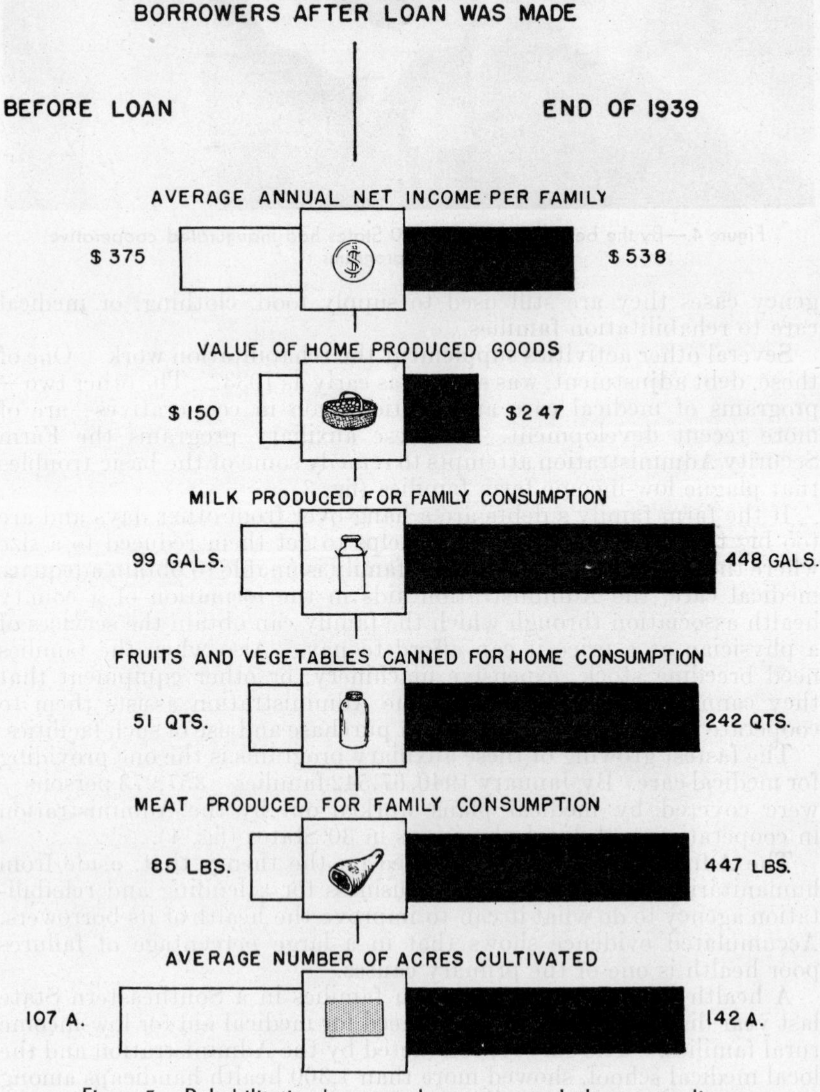

Figure 5.—Rehabilitation borrowers have progressed along many lines.

ilies form associations into which they pay in advance from $15 to $30 a year. This money is pooled and used to pay physicians on a pro rata basis. In most parts of the country both physicians and patients like the plan.

That the rehabilitation program has been a success so far is shown in a survey of progress made by borrowers taken at the end of the 1939 crop year. This report showed that 360,000 families had increased their aggregate net worth—over and above all debts—$82,954,656 since obtaining loans. This was an average increase of 26 percent. At the same time the average net income increased 43 percent.

Figures from the Nation-wide survey further showed that the borrowers had increased their production of food for home consumption from a total value of $54,160,657 before coming on the program to $89,038,910 in 1939. The average rehabilitation family in 1939 canned 242 quarts of fruits and vegetables, produced and used 448 gallons of milk (fig. 5), and produced 20 tons of forage for livestock feed.

Striking advances in tenure conditions also have been brought about among the rehabilitation borrowers. The survey showed that 206,384 tenants who formerly had only verbal agreements with their landlords were operating under written leases at the end of 1939. In addition, 67,458 borrowers had advanced from the status of sharecropper to that of tenant.

Nothing will do more to improve conditions among the Nation's distressed tenants or will contribute more to conservation of our soil than an improved system of tenure.

The Farm Security Administration has made rehabilitation loans totaling more than $370,000,000 since 1935. Although these loans are usually made for a period of 5 years, and much of the money is not yet due, these farmers who could not get adequate credit from any other source already have repaid more than $130,000,000 into the United States Treasury. Ultimately it is expected that at least 80 percent of these loans will be collected. In addition, grants have been made to nearly 550,000 farm families to prevent suffering in areas visited by drought, flood, or some other catastrophe.

Supplementing the rehabilitation-loan program and offering another step upward toward security for thousands of farmers is the program of loans to tenants for the purchase of farms, which the Administration administers under the Bankhead-Jones Act. This program is discussed in detail in the article Farm Tenancy, beginning on page 887 of this Yearbook.

More than 6,000 tenants, including many who were once on relief or on the rehabilitation-loan program, are now buying their own farms with money loaned by the Government and repayable over a 40-year period at reasonable interest rates.

This is the most direct attack on the growing tenancy problem, which has contributed to the other ills of agriculture. Tenants helped to ownership in this way are given the same guidance in modern farming methods that the rehabilitation borrowers receive. Ownership gives them an incentive for building up, rather than wasting, the soil.

OTHER AGENCIES ENGAGED IN RURAL RELIEF

Working today in the rural-relief field, in addition to the Farm Security Administration, are the Work Projects Administration, with its work program, and the Social Security Board and State and local agencies, with direct relief. Both of these programs serve a definite need. The first is designed to take care of the rural population capable of working and not eligible for F. S. A. aid, and the second is to provide for those needy persons who cannot work.

Since its inauguration in 1935, the Work Projects Administration has performed a herculean labor. For instance, a survey of its work program from the fall of 1935 to October 1937 showed that in rural areas, using rural labor, it had built or improved over 180,000 miles of roads. These roads vary in type as widely as the countrysides through which they run, but they have the common objective of linking farms, mines, resorts, and other sparsely settled or remote areas with important highways, with rail or water shipping points, and with schools, post offices, and marketing centers. In addition this survey showed that the W. P. A., using mainly rural labor, had built more than 19,000 new bridges, laid 200,000 new culverts, reconditioned 42,000 culverts, dug, cleaned out, or deepened 250,000,000 feet of drainage ditches, landscaped 14,700 miles of roadside, and extended or improved 24,000 miles of roadbed shoulders.

The conservation of soil, water, forests, fish, game, and other natural resources also has been the objective of many W. P. A. operations. For instance, 4,200 miles of stream beds and river banks have been improved, 17,000 check dams, diversion dams, and other small dams have been built, and 1,225 miles of firebreaks and 2,125 miles of fire and forest trails have been constructed.

The list of W. P. A. accomplishments is in fact almost endless and runs on into the fields of education, health, and many similar activities. The program has provided employment for as many as 550,000 rural workers at one time.

A great many rural families are also being aided by the direct-relief programs, which passed into the hands of the State and local agencies with the end of the Federal Emergency Relief Administration in the winter of 1935–36.

INADEQUACY OF THE EXISTING PROGRAMS

All of these efforts are helping to meet the widespread distress. But altogether they are falling far short of the need. The direct-relief programs are failing to care adequately for the unemployable, and the Farm Security Administration and the Work Projects Administration are falling down on the task of helping those who are able to work.

The resources of the local agencies providing direct relief have been inadequate to cover the field. Despite the fact that since February 1936 the Social Security Board has been helping immensely with the care of the aged and the handicapped, reports are constantly coming in that show a still large uncared-for need.

For instance in October 1938, 13 predominantly rural States were making relief grants that averaged less than $10 a month per family.

In some States funds were so limited that large numbers of those in distress were granted no relief except surplus commodities. Even as late as December 1939 cities were announcing their inability to provide the needed direct relief. In the light of this, the fact that cities have in general always been ahead of the rural areas in the provision of direct relief paints no bright picture for those in need on the farms. Similar inadequacy is evident in the relief available for those able to work.

The field workers of the Farm Security Administration report that they personally know of nearly 509,000 families who would be eligible for the Administration's aid if funds and personnel were available to do the job. Worse still, since the winter of 1938–39 the Work Projects Administration has removed more than 200,000 rural families from its rolls mainly because it lacked funds to carry them.

As good an indication as any of the failure of the Federal program and all the programs in general to provide for the existing need are the letters that pour daily into the Washington office of the Farm Security Administration. This mail brings a steady stream of requests for help, which for the most part are from families the Administration is unable to aid.

A typical letter was from a man who was born and raised on a farm, went to New York, got a job, lost it, and went on relief. Relief had been taken away from him, and he wanted to get back on the farm. The Administration, however, has more than it can do to help those who are already on farms and does not want to encourage folks to go into farming, knowing the thousands that are in line ahead of them and the slim chances that farming, in general, offers. Another man, in a typical letter, said that he and his family had been grubbing a small living out of a 3-acre patch of land and obtaining the rest of their income from the Work Projects Administration. They had recently been dropped from the W. P. A. rolls. Could the Farm Security Administration help them, he asked. Unfortunately the Administration could not.

SOME ESSENTIALS OF A BROADER PROGRAM

Little long-range planning has been done to date. Relief programs, with the possible exception of the F. S. A. loan program, have been planned on a year-to-year basis. This is possibly only an exception, because, although F. S. A. makes loans for periods of several years, it has never known from one year to the next what money or authority it would have. There is, however, a growing consciousness of the need for a definite program. What can that program be? To form one, a dozen and one factors must be considered. A few of the most important will high light the background against which such a plan will have to be laid.

Mechanization, for one thing, is going to be an increasing factor in the rural-relief picture. Already, with the aid of machinery and modern production methods, less than half of the Nation's farmers supply 90 percent of the demands of the farm market. There were 1,527,989 tractors on American farms in April 1938, more than a third of which had been purchased since 1935. More tractors were sold in 1937 alone than were in use on all American farms in 1929.

As a result, many thousands of tenants and sharecroppers have been pushed off the land and forced down to the status of day laborers, with little chance for more than a few months' work a year. On a typical Delta plantation, for example, the introduction of tractors and four-row cultivators reduces the necessary number of tenant families from 40 to 24. Other technological improvements, together with mechanization, have greatly decreased the demand for farm labor. Today it is possible for this country to meet the normal peacetime requirements for farm production, both domestic and foreign, with 1,600,000 fewer workers than in 1929.

In the face of this declining demand for farm labor, the farm population is still growing faster than any other group. The annual increase in the working farm population is now about 445,000 persons. In the past, most of these people would have sought work in the cities or opened up new lands on the frontier. Today the majority of them must join the army of migratory farm laborers, already swollen far beyond normal needs by the families forced off the land by drought and mechanization, or get onto the relief rolls.

Already the condition of migratory farm workers has become one of the most desperate in the field of rural relief. Hundreds of thousands of these families are following the crops in search of seasonal work, with no homes but roadside camps.

With incomes ranging usually from $250 to $400 a year, they live in almost unbelievable poverty, without sanitary facilities or any of the decencies of life. A small fraction of these families are now finding temporary shelter in camps established by the Farm Security Administration in the areas of greatest need. But even for this small number, these camps provide no permanent solution.

Many of these migratory families once operated farms and would still be farming except for conditions beyond their own control. They need good land, but there is none available for them except at prices far beyond their reach.

How much can industry help in providing for the surplus farm population? In the past the factories in the cities provided the answer. They no longer are able to do so. In 1937, and again recently, industrial production reached the level of 1929; yet there were millions unemployed.

True, industry can expand and should expand beyond the 1929 mark. Even then, however, it is doubtful whether it can take up the slack in the urban-labor field, let alone do anything for the countryman.

What is the solution? No one thing, of course. Probably a combination of a great many things. Ultimately, many of those people now seeking a living from farming must find some other occupation. But agriculture can be made to provide a better living for thousands of them who are now failing.

One way to do this is through an expansion of the kind of thing being done in the rehabilitation program. The Farm Security Administration is reaching little more than half of the families who are eligible for its loans. Many of them still unreached can be made self-supporting with guidance and credit.

Many more can be made self-supporting through intensive guidance and credit, supplemented by cash grants for capital equipment. The field covered by the rehabilitation program can be vastly expanded by frank recognition that grants can be used not only for urgent and immediate needs such as food and clothing, but also for the capital equipment necessary to make a farmer self-supporting.

Cooperative farming may be another answer. Some of the experiments now being carried on by the Farm Security Administration indicate that groups of low-income, marginal farmers can make a better living in competition with the modern industrial farms through farming in groups, cooperatively. This requires less land for a given number of families and less overhead for the modern machinery which the small farmer, as well as the big farmer, needs to do his work economically.

But the supply of good farm land is limited. Even with more emphasis on subsistence farming, not all rural families can make a decent living in agriculture. What is there for them?

They can be used ultimately, if we plan wisely, to provide the many things that our rural sections need today—better homes, better roads, additional schools, more doctors and nurses, reforestation, and many other forms of conservation.

The sanitation and health facilities of the rural areas offer an endless possibility for improvement. Such projects as drainage of swamps and lowlands that are breeding grounds for mosquitoes and installation of sanitary water supplies and sewage-disposal plants are examples.

It has been estimated that the Nation could give employment for an indefinite period to 3 million men in the national forests, saving and restoring one of our most valuable resources. Then the field of rural recreation has been almost ignored in our planning. In a hundred other fields there is ample need for the manpower that is now wasting on the farms. Many of these activities are by nature adapted to the purpose. They could be expanded or checked, depending on the volume of surplus labor.

These changes must come. A long-range program must be worked out to provide a sound economy for as many families as possible on the farms and new fields of activity for those no longer needed on the soil. The only alternative is a system of outright grants for subsistence on a far broader scale than anything we have witnessed to date.

BACKGROUND OF THE PRESENT RURAL RELIEF PROGRAM

It is worth while to take a brief backward glance to see the rural-relief picture in its proper perspective and trace the experience that led to the development of the present programs.

The country has always had the thin shadow of a rural-relief program. County poorhouses have existed for years in many rural areas, and nearly every winter some of the most destitute farm families have been "on the town." In a few instances, moreover, relief agencies, developed in the cities by local governmental or private agencies, have extended their aid to nearby farm areas. These instances of rural relief in the past, however, were few and far between. In no sense did they constitute a real program.

During the last half of the nineteenth century the homestead laws provided a backhanded but more or less direct form of relief. The Homestead Act passed in 1862 permitted the head of a family to obtain 160 acres of land practically free of cost by taking up residence on it for 5 years. Under this simple and liberal land policy, the public domain of the United States, which totaled some 1,400,000,000 acres of land, was settled in a remarkably short time. In this way, thousands of farmers who found themselves hard pressed in the East, moved west, took up new land, and got a fresh start. Long before 1935, however, when the homestead policy was ended, nearly all of the arable land of the country had been taken up. Indirect relief of this type was no longer possible.

After the World War, as homesteading came to an end, many of the forces that had speeded the country's growth began to weaken. The farmer, already in trouble, was almost submerged by the depression in 1929. For the farmer, as for the rest of the Nation, there were many adjustments to make. Flaws in the agricultural system that had escaped notice in the past then came to the front in rapid and often startling succession.

The bad side of our farm-tenancy structure appeared so quickly that it almost blacked out whatever good features the system possessed. All at once we became aware that one-third of our farm-tenant population moved every year and that our tenant farmers constituted 40 percent of our farm operators and were increasing at the rate of 40,000 a year.

The heavy farm debt, the dangers of one-crop farming, and the vast amount of eroded, wasted soil became apparent. Suddenly we realized that a million of our rural families were living in homes that were not fit for human beings, that 70 percent of our farmhouses lacked a kitchen sink with a drain, that only 1 in 10 had an indoor toilet. We discovered that one-third of the rural population of the average State did not have full-time health facilities, that hookworm, pellagra, and malaria contributed to what was called laziness in many parts of the rural South.

And we found out why these conditions had developed. We found that the farm population was trying to rear and educate nearly one-third of the Nation's children on a little more than one-tenth of the national income. We saw that in the so-called prosperous year of 1929 the value of the products from one-fourth of our farms, including the home-grown food that was placed on the table, averaged less than $600 per farm. We realized that tractors and trucks were taking the place of thousands of our farm workers.

Here suddenly was all of the ugly side of the picture. Here was an emergency which local government was unable to handle. The Federal Government had to step in—not only to provide the emergency help needed on all sides to prevent actual starvation but to eliminate some of the economic mistakes which showed up as our machinery came to a stop.

The first real rural-relief program got under way with the establishment of the Federal Emergency Relief Administration in May 1933. It was a program of cash grants to the States for direct or work relief under Federal supervision.

As soon as the Administration began to function, it found mass rural distress on a far wider scale than had ever been seen. It took different forms in different parts of the country. In the Plains, drought-stricken farmers were losing their crops and livestock; in the South, laborers and tenants were destitute because of the disorganization of the cotton economy; in the cut-over regions, New England, and the Appalachians, farmers who had been partly dependent on nonfarm wages had lost this supplementary employment. All over the country farmers who, through natural disaster or personal misfortune, were unable to keep up financially or to obtain credit from the existing agencies began to besiege relief offices.

From this situation there emerged the conviction that rural need was urgent and general and that the remedies required were of a different nature from those in urban areas. All during the early life of the Federal relief agency, therefore, experiments were made in adapting relief techniques to rural need.

A rural-rehabilitation program was tried on an experimental basis in several Southern States in 1933, but it was not until April 1934 that it took definite form. At that time a special division called the Rural Rehabilitation Division of the F. E. R. A. was established. The purpose of the Division was stated in very broad terms. Its goal was "to assist destitute farm families and other families residing in rural areas to become self-supporting and independent of emergency relief aid."

The program that was drawn up recognized a wide variety of the problems that such a goal presented. It did this of necessity. A glance at the situation showed clearly that no simple solution existed. If the purpose was to make farm families self-supporting, nothing as simple as a grant program would do the trick. Many farmers lacked good land, others needed tools and equipment, others needed education in new ways of farming, and those who used to work in lumber mills, mines, and quarries needed a whole new way of life.

Tentatively the program of the Rural Rehabilitation Division suggested the following: For those living on fertile land, it proposed to provide such resources as seed, livestock, equipment, buildings, building repairs, and more land if needed; to arrange debt adjustments if necessary; and to give training and advice in home economics and farm management. Displaced farmers would be relocated on the land. Farmers living on poor land would be located on better land purchased under a land program in which the Agricultural Adjustment Administration shared. Rural-relief families living in towns having less than 5,000 inhabitants would be provided with subsistence gardens. Selected families would be transferred from the towns to subsistence farms. Families stranded by the decline of local industries would be encouraged to develop subsistence gardens and community farmsteads.

This was a far-sighted rural-rehabilitation program. As it turned out, however, very little of the relocating of farmers or the rebuilding or reestablishing of stranded communities was carried on. In all only 29 communities were started, and on more than half of them development had proceeded no farther than the purchase of the land when their control passed out of the Relief Administration's hands.

Most of the work that was carried on was of the "rehabilitation in place" type, where aid was given to a farmer who was still located on the land but lacked the means for carrying on his farm work.

Though the general objectives of this program were determined by the Relief Administration, the details were worked out under State control. The State emergency relief administrations organized their own rural-rehabilitation divisions to outline local policies and conduct the work. Later most States organized rural rehabilitation corporations, which acted as legal and financial agents of the rehabilitation divisions.

Most of the Relief Administration grants to the States for rehabilitation went to the States in the southeastern part of the country. There were several reasons for this, the majority of which could be traced to the flaws in the sharecropping system.

Throughout the country the aid given to rehabilitation clients varied from area to area according to the type of farming. In the cotton areas, either mules or oxen and fertilizer were usually advanced to the families. In Tennessee some livestock were usually added to these items, and in a Wisconsin county the record shows that horses, pigs, cows, and chickens were supplied.

In only a few cases were the families advanced money with which to buy livestock and farm equipment, and in those cases they were required to make an accounting of their expenditures. Usually the rehabilitation agency assisted the farmer in selecting the required goods and made payment for him in the name of the rehabilitation corporation. When durable goods and livestock were bought in this way and sold to the client under a conditional-sales contract, the corporation retained the title.

The terms for repayment of these rehabilitation loans varied from State to State and even from county to county. Usually the cost of capital goods was to be repaid over a fairly long period, while advances for subsistence were to be repaid within a year. Crop mortgages and notes were given as security. Interest on these advances were fixed with regard to local rates; in some States no interest was charged until the notes reached maturity; in others the loans were free of interest for 1 year. In order to make repayment easier, some localities accepted payment in marketable produce. In a number of instances, especially in regions where there were no money crops because of the drought, the farmers were given work on Federal projects to aid them in making their repayments.

After continuing for a little more than a year, in June 1935 the rehabilitation program of the Federal Emergency Relief Administration was taken over by the newly formed Resettlement Administration, which at first planned to retain the established State administrative set-up. A ruling by the Comptroller General of the United States made this impossible, however, and starting in the summer of 1935, the administration of the program rapidly became centralized in 12 regional offices.

The policies of the Resettlement Administration were more sharply defined than those of its predecessor. The rehabilitation-loan program was changed. The F. E. R. A. had made rehabilitation loans to all farmers in need. The difference between those who received loans, those who received loans and grants, and the group that received only grants was often small indeed.

The Resettlement Administration began to sharpen these lines of distinction. This did not mean that only a few families were eligible for help. But the Resettlement Administration started stressing the difference between what it called a standard loan and an emergency loan. The standard loans—usually of about $300 or $400—were based on a farm- and home-management plan that the farm family drew up with the aid of the Administration's field staff. These plans incorporated a number of efficient farming methods. By following them the family could raise most of its own food, feed for its livestock, and two or more cash crops for market. In time it could become self-supporting. An important part was played in the development of these plans by the field workers of the Resettlement Administration—trained farm-management specialists and home economists. They brought to the farm family knowledge of the new farming and home-making practices that the State agricultural colleges and extension services were developing. The direction and guidance that these field workers gave was the keynote of the Resettlement Administration program. For various reasons—lack of trained personnel, lack of time, and lack of money—this supervision, though a part of the program, had not been extensively practiced by the Federal Emergency Relief Administration.

A sound farm- and home-management plan, however, could not be developed unless the farmer had enough good land and some experience in the newer ways of farming. Hundreds of farmers, it was found, lacked even these bare essentials. They had so little in the way either of experience or of fertile land that it was impossible to work out a plan that would give them enough to eat, clothe and house them, and permit them to pay back the loan. So to this group the Resettlement Administration made emergency loans. These loans were in general smaller in amount than the standard loans. They were made with the expectation that the family would slowly progress to the point where they would be eligible for a standard loan. All possible help was to be given to carry them in this direction.

The grant program was used to augment the emergency loans. Families like those in the hardest-hit drought areas, who had no chance whatever of repaying a loan, also continued to receive outright grants. Thus, the Resettlement Administration was covering the ground that the Federal Emergency Relief Administration had taken in, though in a different way.

During the winter of 1935–36, the rural-rehabilitation program expanded as a considerable shift took place in the whole field of rural relief because of the birth of the Works Progress Administration.

In July 1935, the F. E. R. A. started to pass out of the picture, and the W. P. A. took its place. The program of this new organization operated on an entirely different basis. The F. E. R. A. had made grants to families based on the amount of money they needed to keep alive. Often these grants supplemented the wages from private industry that were too small to give the family adequate support. The W. P. A. paid wages instead, and hired only the totally unemployed. Furthermore, while the F. E. R. A. had often made grants

223761°—40——57

to those who were unable to work, the W. P. A. made no grants. The Federal Government, so far as the W. P. A. was concerned, was out of the direct-relief field. Direct relief, of the type that the F. E. R. A. had been giving, was turned over to State and local agencies.

The shift from Federal work and direct relief to Federal jobs and local relief began slowly during the summer and fall and was finally accomplished in November and December of 1935. At that tmie farmers in need of aid who were not employed on the W. P. A. project or cared for by Resettlement Administration grants and loans became the responsibility of State and local relief agencies. This administrative division of the relief task has continued in general from that time until today.

Farm Tenancy

by Paul V. Maris [1]

THERE was an ideal in the United States that men should own their own homesteads and operate their own farms. What has happened to this ideal? Gradually it has come about that 42 percent of the farm families do not own their farms; they are tenants. Every year 40,000 more farm families are added to the tenant group. Here is a thoughtful survey of the whole tenancy situation—the economic status of tenants; the factors that have steadily driven more and more families away from ownership and created maladjustments between the people and the land; the new and proposed legislation designed to bring about a better adjustment, and the laws that have been passed in other countries for the same purpose; the lines of action that will tend to increase farm ownership; and finally, the proposals that have been made to correct the evils of tenancy—for tenancy in itself may be good or bad, depending entirely on the conditions under which tenants lease and operate their farms.

THROUGHOUT all the years of its history this country has adhered steadfastly to the ideal of owner-operated farms. When early colo-

[1] Paul V. Maris is Director, Tenant Purchase Division, Farm Security Administration.

nists who had received large grants of land in North America from the King of England attempted to exact rents from pioneer settlers they met with resistance because those settlers had come to America in quest of freedom and the right to have and to hold the land which they tilled. When the new national Government, after the close of the Revolutionary War, sought to recoup its finances by the sale of its vast public domain, it found that revenues from those sources were of secondary importance to the settlement and development of the country. So in order to facilitate and encourage farm ownership the Government, up to the year 1891, sold good land for 50 cents, $1, and $1.25 an acre. In 1841 the Preemption Act of Congress recognized the vested interests of squatters who had established farms and homes on the public domain and proclaimed their rights of possession. Still later (1862) the Homestead Act enabled persons desiring to acquire land for the purpose of farming it to do so without purchase.

Nor have we departed in recent years from this traditional ideal of private property in land, even though, in the words of President Roosevelt, "The rapid increase of tenant farmers during the past half century is significant evidence that we have fallen far short of achieving the traditional American ideal of owner-operated farms." This statement was made on November 16, 1936, to a committee which was asked to report "on a long-term program of action to alleviate the shortcomings of our farm tenancy system." [2]

The issues involved in the question of farm tenancy have deep social, political, and economic significance. The spirit of democracy cannot flourish where ignorance, poverty, insecurity, ill health, and despair are the lot of vast numbers of our rural people. National strength and solidarity spring from an independent, contented, home-loving rural citizenry. The national welfare is best served when this citizenry possesses capacity to buy the products of labor and industry as well as to produce the Nation's supply of food and fibers; when there is incentive for good practices of husbandry, for improving the land, and for developing homes; when there is an interest in good roads, good schools, and good churches; when there are facilities for conserving health; when there are recreational and cultural opportunities. These represent the constants in our national policy with respect to the land and to the people on the land. It has been and is our purpose to safeguard them in an ever-changing and evolving civilization.

CURRENT STATUS OF FARM TENANCY IN THE UNITED STATES

Against this background of national objectives and ideals, let us take stock of the situation in the United States as it exists at present.

Of the 6,812,350 farm families in the United States in 1935, 2,865,155, or 42 percent, were farm tenants. In 1880, 25 percent of the farms were tenant-operated. Between 1930 and 1935, the percentage of tenants did not increase, but the actual number of tenants did. The President's Committee on Farm Tenancy [2] reported in 1937 that "For the past 10 years, the number of new tenants every year has

[2] [UNITED STATES] SPECIAL COMMITTEE ON FARM TENANCY. FARM TENANCY, REPORT OF THE PRESIDENT'S COMMITTEE. Prepared under the auspices of the National Resources Committee. 108 pp., illus. Washington, D. C. 1937.

been about 40,000." The same report indicates that the actual equity of owners in their farms is decreasing.

Some tenants operate large farms, own ample equipment, obtain substantial incomes as farm incomes go, and are in general well to do. Many farmers of this type are tenants by choice, preferring to invest their capital in livestock and equipment rather than in land. They are thus able to operate on a larger scale than they otherwise could. These well-to-do tenants are found mostly on good land in the better farming sections of the country. Also included among the tenant class are some half million whose landlords are relatives and who may some day inherit part or all of the farms they occupy. Their outlook is often hopeful.

Contrasted with this group of tenants by choice is a larger and, from the standpoint of our democracy, a more significant group of tenants by necessity, who have low incomes and low standards of living. Many of them occupy poor land. However, some of the best agricultural lands are occupied by some of the most impoverished tenants. In a social research report of the United States Department of Agriculture, Disadvantaged Classes in American Agriculture,[4] the authors report:

> There were, in the United States in 1929, approximately 1,700,000 farms which yielded gross farm income of less than $600, based on value of products sold, traded, or used; a few more than 900,000 farms that yielded less than $400 income; and almost 400,000 farms that yielded less than $250. On these farms yielding less than $600 income, approximately 7,700,000 men, women, and children lived, whose lives were disadvantaged because of the lack of purchasing power.

All of these low-income farms are not tenant-operated. Some of them are operated by debt-burdened owners struggling against heavy odds of small uneconomic units, poor land, and inadequate capital and equipment.

In 1936 the Farm Security Administration made a study of the economic status of several hundred rehabilitation clients in selected type-of-farming areas in different States. The following facts were ascertained concerning 287 cotton tenant farmers in the hill section of Arkansas: Their total cash income from all sources averaged $134.71 per year. The average value of their household goods was $27.86. The average value of all their worldly goods was $305.61, against which there were debt obligations of $220.17, leaving an average net worth of $85.44.

The circumstances of 489 cotton tenant farmers in the Piedmont section of Alabama and 384 cotton tenant farmers in the Delta section in Mississippi, although slightly better, were not essentially different. Three hundred and seven tenants in the flue-cured tobacco section of North Carolina and 596 tenants in the Corn Belt sections of Illinois and Nebraska had total average incomes ranging from $425 to $499 and average net worths ranging from $438 to $594.

The reader would do well to contemplate these data. The tenants in the cotton areas of Arkansas, Alabama, and Mississippi included in the above study were among the estimated 400,000 in the United States whose income falls below the $250 yearly total. They had aver-

---

[4] Taylor, Carl C., Wheeler, Helen W., and Kirkpatrick, E. L. DISADVANTAGED CLASSES IN AMERICAN AGRICULTURE. U. S. Farm Security Admin. Soc. Res. Rpt. 8, 124 pp. 1938. [Processed.]

Figure 1.—His mules are the principal asset of most of the tenant farmers in the cotton areas of Arkansas, Alabama, and Mississippi.

age-sized families of about five members. In general they were old residents who had farmed on various farms in their respective counties for years. They had had time to climb the agricultural ladder, but they were not climbing. Their acres in crops ran 23 in Alabama, 23 in Arkansas, 20 in Mississippi. The mule was the principal asset (fig. 1). Homes and wardrobes were bare, diets meager, malnourishment and disease prevalent. It is these conditions that gave rise to the statement contained in the report of the President's Committee on Farm Tenancy[5] that "Approximately one farm family out of four occupies a position in the Nation's social and economic structure that is precarious and should not be tolerated."

Rupert B. Vance, of the social research staff of the University of North Carolina, says: [6]

> Unless one has actually observed the way tenants live, the meaning of such low incomes is hard to visualize. Tenant housing is the poorest in the nation, often consisting of two or three-room unpainted shacks with but one thickness of boards. Their customary clothing of patched overalls or faded gingham dresses show that tenants, black and white, get very little of the finished products of the cotton they grow. Their basic diet—fatback, cornbread, molasses, and sweet potatoes—has been well publicized by the researches of the United States Public Health Service in a study of the basic causes of pellagra.

Included among the 2,865,155 tenants are 716,000 sharecroppers,

[5] See reference cited in footnote 2, p. 888.

[6] COUNTRY LIFE CONFERENCE. DISADVANTAGED PEOPLE IN RURAL LIFE. Country Life Conf. Lexington, Ky., Proc. 21, 176 pp. Chicago. 1938. See p. 115.

who in general own no livestock or equipment and exchange their labor for a share of the crop. As farm machinery comes in, the tendency is to shift sharecroppers to the day-laborer status. In either category their position is at the bottom, considered from a standard-of-living or income viewpoint.

The regions of greatest density of tenancy, where the largest number of counties are found in which more than half the land is farmed by tenants, are in the southern cotton-growing areas and in the heart of the Corn Belt. The Appalachian and Ozark highlands, the Cotton Belt, the Lake States cut-over area, and northern New Mexico and Arizona are the areas characterized by the lower income groups of tenants.

FACTORS AFFECTING THE GROWTH AND CONTINUANCE OF TENANCY

Land Speculation

Speculation in farm land by persons seeking to profit from rising prices has contributed much to the growth of farm tenancy in the United States. When prices of land advance under the stimulus of speculative values to levels that are not justified by income-producing capacity, operators of such land who are dependent for their livelihood upon what it will produce are trending in the direction of bankruptcy. Many have arrived at that destination, especially during the depression years following the boom in farm prices. If overvalued farms are free of debt their operators may carry on by foregoing returns on their land investment and utilizing all their income for living and operating expenses. This, however, is not the prevailing situation. The farm-mortgage debt of this country was estimated at $7,071,-000,000 on January 1, 1939. It was $10,751,000,000 in 1923. Much of the decrease between these two dates was due to foreclosure proceedings and debt write-off. These mortgage debts represent generally inescapable obligations that must be met from farm earnings. Injudicious credit financing, coupled with overvaluation of land, has played havoc with farm ownership.

In the history of the country to date speculator interests have in general prevailed over operator interests. Land as a rule has been priced at more than it was worth on an earning-power basis, and as a result the lot of the tiller of the soil has been made continuously harder.

The jump in a half century from a free homestead to a farm salable at $250 an acre suggests a speculator's paradise. Now that the country has come of age the trend may be toward values based more definitely on earning capacity, but the ups and downs of business will doubtless provide continued opportunities for speculation in land. Unless controls are instituted, land speculation will in all probability continue to breed farm tenancy.

The Plantation Pattern

The pattern of farm economy in the Southern States that had its origin in slavery days also has contributed to farm tenancy in the United States. After the slaves were freed the only practical course open to plantation owners was to operate their holdings as nearly as possible as they had been doing, and the only practical course open to those who had previously worked on the plantation was to continue to do so. Hence the sharecropper system of tenancy came into existence. Plantations are still operated by sharecroppers and farm tenants. The transition from this pattern of tenure to an owner-operated, family-size-unit pattern is difficult of achievement. It can be accomplished best when entire plantations are subdivided into family-size units. This necessitates a special type of arrangement and financing. It is worthy of note, however, that there are certain elements of strength in the plantation system which it may be desirable to retain, either through the device of a high type of tenancy such as that described later or through a system of cooperative ownership and operation.

Mechanization

The transition from manpower and horse power to machine power, which has been gaining headway on the farms of this country for a generation, has likewise had its repercussions on the tenure situation. Mechanization fits in with large-scale operations. It involves larger outlays of capital. It makes farm ownership more difficult for the farmer of limited means. It crowds tenants and sharecroppers off plantations. In some instances it creates a demand for seasonal workers, who, in order to prolong their employment, move from community to community and from State to State. Thus we have developed a migrant class of land workers whose relation to the land and to society is anomalous and whose existence is precarious.

Credit

Satisfactory credit is the handmaiden of farm ownership. It is assumed that approximately 20 years constitutes a farm generation. Thus each year something like one-fifth of our 6,812,350 farm families are entering the farming ranks as inheritors or renters or purchasers of farms. They are the recruits filling the gaps created by the retiring generation of farmers. It was many years before a credit system was developed that met the requirements of this situation. An unscrupulous creditor, a farm mortgage falling due in the full amount on a given date, a widow who could not meet the payment, and a kind benefactor who saved the day have formed the basis for many a thrilling story in fiction that too often has had its counterpart in fact, though usually lacking the kind benefactor.

In passing the Federal Farm Loan Act (approved July 17, 1916), Congress set up a system of credit under which farm-mortgage debts may be retired by annual payments spread over many years, but until installments are permitted to fluctuate with income the credit need will not be fully met.

Prices, Taxes, and Other Factors

The continued drift toward tenancy has been augmented by the unfavorable price ratio between what the farmer sells and what he buys, which has prevailed in post-war years and at other times throughout history. The heavy share of the mounting tax load borne by real property has been another contributing factor.

High distribution and selling costs likewise have made it more difficult for owners of farms to retain their equities. In general all conditions that have affected agriculture adversely have had a bearing upon farm tenancy. Conversely, the many constructive measures for alleviating farm distress inaugurated in recent years have had a salutary effect.

Good Lands Largely Occupied

The remedy for declining ownership and mounting tenancy cannot be found to any measurable extent in the development of new farm land. While irrigation of arid land, drainage of swampland, and clearing of timbered or stump land may add to the sum total of tillable acres in the United States, the opportunities in this direction are relatively limited. Practically all of the good farm land is now in use, and much of it is occupied by more people than it can maintain in a manner compatible with American living standards.

ADJUSTING THE POPULATION TO THE LAND

Quite as difficult as the problem of providing security of tenure on the land is that of adjusting the population to the land. From the standpoint of logical sequence adjustment should command first consideration. The situation in this respect is now bad. If present economic and biological tendencies persist unrestrained, it promises to remain so for years to come, and this at the expense of national welfare. Let us consider some of the facts upon which these generalizations are based.

The land resources of the New England States are limited. Part-time farming has gained a foothold there. As industrial employment has declined, many part-time farmers have been deprived of their weekly pay checks in mills and factories. An extra burden has been forced upon the land. Relief rolls and Work Projects Administration rolls bear testimony to the fact that the land could not take up all the slack. Relatively the saturation point has been reached. But still many of the urban unemployed have contrived to establish themselves on little pieces of land in the country and have then sought expert advice on how to wrest a living from their meager holdings. Often the problem is beyond the ken of the expert. The pressure on the land is more than it can bear, even when subjected to intensive scientific cultural practices.

In the Southern States, Farm Security officials have asked State advisory committees, "How about the one-mule farm? Is it a satisfactory economic unit for a farm family?" The answer has been "No." There are instances in which "20 acres and a mule" are supporting families in reasonable respectability, but generally speaking there are not enough wealth-producing potentialities in that set-up to permit its acceptance as a standard at which to aim. Since the one-mule farm is prevalent in the South, a readjustment of population to the land is called for there before a foundation for security on family-size farms can be laid.

In the northern and southern Great Plains, where drought and duststorms have precipitated a gigantic battle between men and the forces of nature, the universal verdict appears to be that nature will be served and that a system of farming must be evolved that will utilize and conserve the resources that are there. More vegetative cover, less cultivation of the soil, larger dependence upon livestock and less upon crops are the remedial measures, and to apply them the farm units must be larger. It follows that as they become larger they must become fewer. Many families have already migrated from the area, but the adjustment of the population to the land along the one hundredth meridian is far from accomplished. Still more displacement may be anticipated.

The Dust Bowl refugees, emigrants from the drought-stricken areas of the northern Great Plains, and the displaced tenants and sharecroppers from mechanized plantations of the South have moved westward to the Pacific coast. The Pacific Coast States have been unable to absorb them as home-owning farmers or permanent tenants. The 1,200,000 acres to be reclaimed under the Grand Coulee project may accommodate as many as 30,000 families, but it is estimated that some 300,000 unsettled migratory farm families are in the area. All contemplated reclamation projects combined will not supply them with farms. They present an acute problem of adjustment of population to the land.

The Lake States likewise have an adjustment problem. Many units there are said to be too small for economic operation.

This brief review by major geographical regions of the United States merely serves to bring distinctive regional problems into focus. It is true that in all these regions some communities are supporting an optimum number of farm people on an acceptable level of well-being. Some sections are characterized by a high state of well-being among farm people. Usually these are good land areas where units are relatively large, investments are relatively high, and operating equipment is adequate.

Then there are the population-pressure areas where resources are meager, where poverty is chronic, and where no adequate remedy seems possible short of readjusting the population to the land.

The problem in general assumes still greater complexity when considered in relation to population increase. Reproduction of the race is proceeding at a more rapid rate in rural farm areas than in rural nonfarm areas or in urban areas (see The Rural People, p. 827). Without migration the population in the lowest-income farm counties of the country will double in 30 years. It goes without saying that the increase cannot be absorbed on the farms. Prospects for employment in the cities are not encouraging. The gains in industrial employment in recent years have just about been offset by like gains in the number of employable persons seeking jobs. The number of unemployed has therefore remained at a fairly constant level. It is estimated that 1,000,000 young people remained on the farm during the depression years who would normally have gone to the cities. It is further estimated that as a result of gains in efficiency through mechanization and scientific methods 1,600,000 fewer workers on farms could supply our present domestic and foreign needs for farm products.

These facts collectively constitute the evidence that our present serious maladjustment of population to the land promises to continue for years to come if present economic and biological trends are not altered.

Whether we as a people are prepared to come to grips with the issues involved and take whatever steps may be necessary to attain and preserve a distribution of people on the land that will provide the maximum number with economic units and with reasonable guaranties of security in their tenure remains to be seen. The governments of many nations have faced the problem and dealt with it in one way or another. Fortunately we have the record of their experiences for our guidance. Likewise we are accumulating some experience of our own under legislation enacted in recent years.

MEASURES FOR SECURING A BETTER ADJUSTMENT OF THE POPULATION TO THE LAND

Existing Legislation

(1) Homestead tax-exemption laws have been passed in recent years in Alabama, Arkansas, Florida, Georgia, Iowa, Louisiana, Minnesota, Mississippi, Oklahoma, South Dakota, Texas, Vermont, and Wyoming. These laws usually set up a stated acreage, not to exceed 40 acres in Iowa and Mississippi, 200 in Texas, and 160 in most of the other States, upon which there is at least State tax exemption up to a certain valuation. Wyoming exempts on the stated acreage up to a valuation of $500, whereas Florida, South Dakota, and Vermont exempt up to a $5,000 valuation. The amounts in other States fall between these two extremes. Alabama, Georgia, and Louisiana exempt up to $2,000; Oklahoma, Arkansas, and Mississippi to $1,000. In Alabama, Arkansas, Iowa, Mississippi, Oklahoma, Texas, and Wyoming the *assessed* value of the property is the basis of valuation for exemption; in Florida, Georgia, Louisiana, Minnesota, and South Dakota the "value" of the property is the basis; while the Vermont statute provides that the exemption shall be in accordance with the *appraised* value. Only State taxes are exempted in Alabama, Arkansas, Minnesota, Mississippi, South Dakota, and Texas; Georgia exempts State, county, and school taxes; Louisiana, State, parish, and special; whereas Oklahoma exempts all ad valorem taxes; Wyoming, all general taxes; and Florida, all taxes. The extent of exemption is variable in Iowa. (In Vermont the exemption is for new homes and is limited to 5 years. The exemption provision must be adopted locally by vote to be effective.) Usually the exemptions do not cover special assessments, such as those for irrigation and drainage-district improvements. These homestead exemption acts are a distinct protection to owners of family-size farms. They might appropriately be extended to other States and be drafted with a more definite view to safeguarding a suitable economic unit for a farm family.

(2) In 1939 the legislature of North Dakota passed an act providing that if the defaulting of any mortgage payment on farms results from crop failure or other disaster the mortgagor may petition the court for a continuation of proceedings. If the default occurred prior to March 1 the continuance will be granted until March 1 of the following year—if after March 1, until the second succeeding March 1.

(3) Title I of the Bankhead-Jones Farm Tenant Act, approved July 22, 1937, authorizes loans for the purchase of farms upon which competent, industrious families can make a livelihood. This gives legal recognition to the family-size-farm concept. Some farms are being purchased that have heretofore been family-size units operated by tenants. Hereafter they will be owner-operated. In other instances large units are being subdivided into family-size units. It cannot be claimed, however, that the operation of this law within its present scope is an adequate approach to the large and complex problem of adjusting the population to the land. It will be helpful in setting a pattern of family-size farms and providing valuable information with respect to their operation.

(4) The Taylor Grazing Act, which regulates grazing rights and usage on the public domain, is a distinct move in the direction of better adjustment of users to the land, but it touches primarily the great open spaces and not the areas of dense farm population.

(5) Thirty-six States now have laws authorizing the creation of soil conservation districts, which are clothed with certain authority in the matter of adjusting land use. The legislation is not designed or intended as a frontal attack upon the problem of adjusting the population to the land, but the local directors of such districts will, in the discharge of their duties, in all probability encounter problems of adjustment and propose courses of action. Such a result may be a minor and beneficial byproduct of this legislation.

(6) In connection with its rehabilitation program the Farm Security Administration is making some loans in the northern and southern Great Plains areas called unit-reorganization loans. These are loans to finance operating as a single farm what has heretofore been operated as two or three or even several farms. Setting up family-size units that will be successful in the area is the aim. It is a direct move toward correcting maladjustment of population to the land.

The above list of existing laws is not presented with the idea that singly or collectively they will have any material effect on the total problem under consideration. They were not drawn up essentially for that purpose.

Proposed Legislation

More specific and pertinent are the following recommendations quoted in full from the 1938 report of the Iowa Farm Tenancy Committee:[7]

Differential Taxation of Farms

It is recommended that a special committee be appointed to make a thorough study for the purpose of discovering the most equitable and effective way to discourage the concentration of large land holdings by means of differential taxation, such as a moderate surtax levied on land holdings exceeding a liberal amount of acreage, or, preferably, assessed valuation.

It is believed that if associated with ample credit facilities and other positive measures of encouraging farm home ownership, the gradual but steady pressure of differential taxation might exert an influence in favor of family-size farms by owners.

Tax on Capital Gains From Sales of Land

It is recommended that a provision be inserted into the State Income Tax Law

[7] Iowa State Planning Board, Farm Tenancy Committee. Report and Recommendations . . . 63 pp. Des Moines. 1938.

imposing a specific tax on capital gains from the sale of farm lands. Due allowance should be made for improvements or other enhancement of value brought about by the owner. Provisions should be made that losses sustained from the sale of farm land during the same year may be deducted from gains before the tax is levied.

Bills dealing with land use and land tenure have been introduced in a number of State legislatures in recent years. This reflects a growing public interest in the subject, but very little significant legislation has actually been enacted.

Legislation in Other Countries

The fundamental problems of land tenure now confronting this country have manifested themselves in many countries of the world and have given rise to significant legislation under which significant developments have occurred. When poverty, insecurity, and instability have become so prevalent and widespread among tillers of the soil as to constitute a grave national problem, remedial measures have usually been instituted by the governments concerned. In accomplishing land-tenure reform two general courses have been pursued: (1) Converting tenants into owners and (2) improving the status of tenants without converting them into owners. Legislation in other countries reveals the fact that the size or adequacy of farm units has been a problem there as well as here.

The land laws of England and Scotland have dealt primarily with establishing and safeguarding the mutual rights of tenants and landlords. The final result is a system of law, custom, and tradition under which tenants enjoy advantages and satisfactions usually achieved elsewhere only through ownership. However, England has also enacted legislation to facilitate ownership of small holdings.[8] Seventeen million pounds ($83,000,000) was appropriated for this purpose following the World War. Some of the conditions which the purchasers of holdings are required to meet are of special significance:

The holdings must not be divided, sold, assigned, let or sub-let. The holder or his family must cultivate it. No house may be erected without the consent of the council; there must be only one house to a holding; and dwellings must meet conditions imposed by the council in regard to healthfulness and freedom from overcrowding.[8]

Ireland and Denmark provide outstanding examples of the benefits of land-tenure reform wisely conceived and executed. In each of these countries the condition of farm tenants and farm laborers was very wretched before reforms were instituted, and in each country the transition from tenancy to ownership has been characterized by marked social, economic, and political progress.

A similar generalization can be made with respect to the Scandinavian countries, and France divided her landed estates and vested her peasants with ownership in 1789.

The most sweeping measure taken by any country in modern times to gain control of the distribution of its agricultural lands has been the complete socialization of land by the Union of Soviet Socialist Republics. Such a measure permits whatever adjustment of people to the land the Government may desire. Speculation in land is totally eliminated. Right to use the land may be made as permanent and

[8] See reference cited in footnote 2, p. 888.

secure as desired, and adequate safeguards may be established against abuse of the land. However, the people of this country are not likely to resort to so drastic a measure. Our pattern of individual ownership is too deeply rooted. There are fears that evils of public administration would enter in that would make the cure worse than the disease.

In 1917 the Mexican Government inaugurated a program consisting of—

> (1) Governmental regulation of private property rights in land; (2) promotion of land ownership by villages analogous to the tribal ownership existing before the Spanish conquest; and (3) creation of family-size farms for individual owners.[9]

Holdings desired for this purpose are "expropriated" by administrative action, and the owner is compensated on the basis of assessed value plus 10 percent.

In 1933 the German Government set up "inherited freeholds," consisting of family-size units of farm land which are passed in their entirety from one generation to the "next in line" in the succeeding generation. These freeholds are safeguarded by restrictive legislation precluding their sale or subdivision. They cannot be mortgaged An owner of an inherited freehold cannot own another farm. He must maintain his freehold in good repair, conserve the soil, and follow good farming practices. The effectiveness of this Freehold Act in safeguarding the owner-operated family-size farm in the German national economy should be carefully observed.

LINES OF ACTION THAT WILL TEND TO INCREASE FARM OWNERSHIP

Title I of the Bankhead-Jones Farm Tenant Act was listed among measures for securing a better adjustment of population to the land. It is primarily a measure for increasing ownership of family-size farms. Its purposes are carried out by direct loans to "farm tenants, farm laborers, sharecroppers, and other individuals who obtain, or who recently obtained, the major portion of their income from farming operations." Administratively, "other individuals" is being so interpreted as to avoid aid or stimulus to a back-to-the-farm movement. Actual farm families or recently displaced farm families are the beneficiaries.

> In making available the benefits of this title, the Secretary [of Agriculture] shall give preference to persons who are married, or who have dependent families, or, wherever practicable, to persons who are able to make an initial down payment, or who are owners of livestock and farm implements necessary successfully to carry on farming operations. No person shall be eligible who is not a citizen of the United States.

Loans are available "in such amount as may be necessary to enable the borrower to acquire the farm and for necessary repairs and improvements thereon." The period of the loan is 40 years. The interest rate is 3 percent. Annual repayments are amortized, and they may be large in good years and small in bad years, so long as they average out in such a way as to liquidate the loan in 40 years.

Each loan is secured by a first mortgage or deed of trust. Each borrower is required to maintain his property in good repair, keep it

[9] See reference cited in footnote 2, p. 888.

insured, and practice good husbandry. He agrees in his loan application to keep such records and accounts of his income and expenses as may be required. County committees consisting of three farmers pass upon the eligibility of applicants and upon the suitability and value of the farms which they desire to purchase.

Two years of experience have now been gained under the operations of this act. In 1937 Congress appropriated $10,000,000 for such loans, and 1,887 loans were made. In 1938 $25,000,000 was appropriated, and 4,340 loans were made. The appropriation for the current year is $40,000,000. This is $10,000,000 less than the law authorizes to be appropriated.

A total of 146,000 applications was received in 1938 and 1939 from persons desiring loans. This was an average of 34 applicants per loan. County committees report that many applicants, rejected because the loan fund was exhausted, were well qualified to receive loans. No great difficulty was experienced in purchasing family-size farms at prices believed by county committees and Farm Security Administration officials to be in line with their earning capacity. The limited check on borrowers' willingness and ability to repay their loans afforded by the first year's collection experience was favorable. No serious administrative difficulties have been encountered in carrying out the law.

Having inaugurated a program that gives promise of attaining the ends sought, the question is how far should it be carried and at what rate should it be expanded.

The President's Committee on Farm Tenancy recommended that the program be started in a small way and that "as the wisdom of the new policy is demonstrated, the program can be greatly expanded."[10] That Congress acted in conformance with this recommendation has been very advantageous from an administrative standpoint. But now the foundations are laid. It is appropriate to consider ultimate objectives. Since 1870, tenancy in Ireland has been reduced from 97 percent to 3 percent. Denmark has made a similar record in changing from large estates to small family-size farms. Should the United States, following the example of these countries, aim at the virtual elimination of tenancy in the next 40 or 50 years?

It appears that a wiser course would be to proceed along two lines of endeavor, one leading toward a better balance between owner-operated farms and tenant-operated farms and the other leading toward an improvement in the status of tenancy itself. The possibilities of improving the status of tenancy will be discussed separately. If landlords and tenants can be induced by enlightened self-interest or required by law to abandon certain vicious leasing customs and if security of tenure and incentive for protecting and improving leased property by tenants is provided, then tenancy can advantageously retain its place as a rung in the American agricultural ladder.

Young couples and others entering upon farming careers may benefit by spending a few probationary years as tenants while they gain experience and accumulate capital, livestock, and equipment. Some may prefer to concentrate their investment in operating goods rather than land and remain permanently in the tenant class. But tenancy

---

[10] See reference cited in footnote 2, p. 888.

should be a stepping stone from which the competent and enterprising may rise—not a destiny of degradation from which there is no escape.

Granting such improvement in the status of tenancy, it appears that we would have a very wholesome situation if something like 20 percent rather than 42 percent of our farmers were tenants—in other words, if we had about 1,000,000 or 1,500,000 tenants in the United States, instead of 2,865,155. Some $7,000,000,000 would be required to accomplish this reduction as against $14,000,000,000 to convert all tenants to owners. If this were spread over 25 years, which is a short time in the history of a nation, it would necessitate about 52,000 loans a year. This is not an impossible number from an administrative standpoint if worked up to gradually.

It is not assumed that such an expansion can take place under the Bankhead-Jones Farm Tenant Act as it is now written without encountering difficulties. Only about 10 loans have been made on an average in each of the 732 counties receiving Bankhead-Jones funds during the first 2 years. It has been possible to expand to new counties each year and to keep down the number of loans in any particular county. In several Southern States with large numbers of tenant farmers all agricultural counties are now designated to receive loans, and the number of loans per county will begin to mount progressively. What will be the effect on the price of land? Can family-size farms be bought continuously at prices in line with their earning capacity? There is grave doubt whether a Government-financed land-buying program can go on at an accelerated rate for several years without unduly stimulating land prices. The speculative impulse is deeply ingrained in human nature. There is no assurance that boom prices will not be grasped with open arms at every opportunity, whatever the cause of the boom and notwithstanding the disastrous consequences sure to follow.

The President's Committee on Farm Tenancy foresaw this situation and recommended the purchase of land by the Government and its subsequent resale to eligible applicants. It was thought that speculation could in some measure be forestalled in this manner and also that by retaining title for an extended period the Government could prevent borrowers from selling their farms for the sake of quick and easy profits. There was, however, opposition to the "Government's going into the land business." The process of Government purchase and sale of land is cumbersome and slow.

Nor can the Government itself escape the obstacle of price inflation unless it is clothed with authority to compel sales at appraised prices. This authority has been exercised by the Governments of the following 25 nations in achieving their purpose of dividing large land holdings into family-size units: Australia, Austria, Belgium, Bolivia, Brazil, Bulgaria, Chile, Czechoslovakia, Denmark, England, Germany, Greece, Hungary, Ireland, Mexico, the Netherlands, Norway, Paraguay, Poland, Rumania, Scotland, Union of Soviet Socialist Republics, Uruguay, Wales, and Yugoslavia. There is, therefore, ample precedent for exercising the right of eminent domain in the process of land subdivision. It remains to be seen whether a program for the development of family-size farm units can proceed to any great lengths in this country without legislation authorizing condemnation proceedings.

Should such legislation be found essential and desirable it should make provision for compensating owners on the basis of earning capacity.

A point advanced by advocates of Government purchase and resale of land, as contrasted with lending money to enable borrowers to purchase farms directly from private owners, is that under such an arrangement applicants can be granted probationary leases or conditional sales contracts, which can be exchanged for deeds after a suitable time when the prospects make good.

No system of selecting applicants that is infallible can be devised. Notwithstanding painstaking efforts on the part of county committees to choose wisely, nearly 0.5 percent of the borrowers approved for Bankhead-Jones farm-tenant loans during the first 2 years asked to be released from their obligations. This suggests the advantages to both buyer and seller of a probationary period during which uncertainties and doubts as to future plans and intentions can be reduced to a minimum.

The variable-payment provision of the Bankhead-Jones Farm Tenant Act, the effect of which is to permit borrowers to pay off their loans as they are able, is a great boon to the farm purchaser. It relieves him of anxiety with respect to foreclosure when seasons are unfavorable and fixed installments cannot be met. The creditor is protected by the administrative provision that abuse of the variable-payment privelege will result in its withdrawal. If this plan operates successfully it should be incorporated generally in land-purchasing financing.

More emphasis on earning capacity of farms in determining the price to be paid and less on their resale or security value should further facilitate ownership.

LINES OF ACTION THAT WILL TEND TO CORRECT EVILS RESULTING FROM CURRENT FORMS OF TENANCY

Improvement in the status of tenancy itself offers the most direct and immediate remedy for many of the current evils of the American land-tenure system. Attitudes, customs, and traditions are the principal obstacles involved in traveling this route to betterment, while law, economics, and credit must play a large role in the division of land holdings, transfer of titles, and subsequent safeguarding of farm ownership. Merely by common consent and the widespread adoption of tried and proved practices of land leasing, insecurity and instability can be substantially reduced and tenants be provided with incentive for improving their homes, the land they till, and their communities. Through guaranties of security and reasonable assurance of an opportunity to enjoy the fruits of productive effort, an environment may be created in which hope, courage, and enterprise may thrive (fig. 2, *A* and *B*).

Who profits by a situation in which a landlord will not repair a leaky roof because it leaks upon his tenant, and the tenant will not repair it because he expects to move to another farm before another season? To what end will such a policy lead in the long run? To what end has it already led in the poorer tenant and sharecropper sections of this country?

223761°—40——58

Figure 2.—*A*, This kind of tenant home represents insecurity and instability. *B*, An environment can be provided in which hope, courage, and enterprise may thrive.

Other countries have proved that tenancy and security are not incompatible. Charles L. Stewart, of the University of Illinois, in the October 1939 issue of Rural America,[11] describes his visit to the home of Vittorio Gelli located on an Italian farm which the present Signor Gelli and his ancestors have leased from Prince Borghese and his ancestors continuously for 932 years. The dwelling house was built in the year 902. As Dr. Stewart describes it, it is still habitable. Its durability cannot be questioned. Dr. Stewart reports further that in April 1938 announcements were made in Rome of the recognition of 81 families:

Two families had a tenure of over 800 years; three families over 700; one over 600; two over 500; fifteen over 400; thirteen over 300; seventeen over 200; and twenty-six for more than a century.

England affords an outstanding example of how stability, security, and well-being can be achieved through wisely conceived and well-administered tenure laws and leasing practices. English tenants are deeply rooted in the land they occupy. The results of generations of effort to solve perplexing land problems bear testimony to the fact that effort to improve the status of tenants has been worth while.

Since nearly half our farm land is farmed by tenants, since we have not yet stemmed the tide toward tenancy, and since increases in ownership under any program likely to be pursued will come about slowly, it follows that we should lose no time and spare no effort in moving at once on the broader front of improving the tenure system and landlord-tenant relations.

Two great obstacles confront us. (1) Customs and practices related to leasing are so deeply intrenched in the habits of the people as virtually to defy change or modification; and (2) legally responsible, property-owning landlords are reluctant to enter into contractual relations with tenants without property, against whom judgments are assumed to be worthless. Mutuality is the essence of all contracts, and it is difficult to attain in landlord-tenant lease agreements before resources of the tenants have been built up. Surrendering to these obstacles, however, clearly means the perpetuation of a vicious downward cycle which imposes heavy penalties on the landlords, the tenants, and the general public.

That these obstacles can be overcome in part is indicated by the fact that when the persons concerned face the facts together and explore remedies they find common ground upon which they can stand. Conferences on this subject have been held recently in many States. Farm Security Administration officials, State planning boards, farm-organization leaders, land-grant college representatives, the farm press, landlords, tenants, sharecroppers, and others have participated. The problem has been analyzed. Important agreements have been reached. In Iowa, 664 farmers, including 203 owner-operators, 366 tenants, 83 landlords, and 12 unclassified, responding to an exhaustive questionnaire on tenancy, were in hopeful accord both as to the flaws in their leasing system and the remedies that should be applied. Many present evils of tenancy cannot survive the critical analysis of

[11] STEWART, CHARLES L. MILLENNIUM AT MONTALE. ONE FAMILY FARMS LAND FOR TWENTY-SIX GENERATIONS. Rural Amer. 17 (7): 3-6. 1939.

the open forum. Action may be expected to follow if education is expanded.

Long-Term Written Leases

The remedy for insecurity and frequent moves is the written long-term or automatically renewable lease. Many tenants now operate under nothing more than a vague verbal understanding. The F. S. A. with its thousands of rehabilitation clients, mostly tenants, is doing much to introduce the written lease. It discovered that its borrowers were handicapped by insecurity of occupancy; satisfactory farm and home management planning is impossible when occupancy of a farm is limited to a year. Accordingly, after an exhaustive study of the terms and conditions of oral and written leases in various parts of the country, a standard flexible lease form was drafted. It is being widely adopted. Landlords and tenants alike are recognizing its advantages. It seeks to do justice to both.

Preferably a written lease should cover a period of at least 5 years. As experience is gained the mutual advantages of such long terms will be recognized by both landlords and tenants. Skepticism may, however, render such agreements impossible where there is the greatest need for written leases. Where shorter terms may be necessary for this or other reasons, written annual leases, providing for automatic renewal or continuation in the absence of a written notice of termination filed by either party prior to a stated date, provides an increased degree of security over no lease at all. This type may be necessary in the beginning.

Compensation for Unexhausted Improvements

To provide incentive for improving land, buildings, fences, and property in general, the lease agreement should include provision for compensating the tenant for improvements that are unexhausted when he leaves the farm. Conversely, the agreement should assess penalties against the tenant for damage to property due to his carelessness or negligence. Properly financed and assisted, tenants will ultimately build up equities against which penalties may be assessed.

Compensation for Disturbance

Compensation for disturbance when either party to a lease agreement breaks it on short notice without justification is another desirable feature of good leasing practice. A landlord is deemed to be justified in terminating a lease, and therefore not liable for compensation payments to his tenant, when he is bankrupt and compelled by eminent-domain proceedings to sell his farm, when he desires to operate the farm personally, or when the tenant has failed to pay the rent or does not follow good practices of husbandry. Annual leases that are automatically continued in the absence of written notice to the contrary and that contain compensation for disturbance provisions often continue in effect for years and are recognized as having some advantages over long-term leases with definite termination dates.

Provision for Arbitration

Lease provisions such as those described above tend to give rise to problems requiring adjustment between landlords and tenants.

Figure 3.—*A*, Nearly a half million farm families with incomes of less than $250 a year live in bleak homes. *B*, By appropriate steps, such houses as this can be built to strengthen the foundations of our democracy.

Hence provisions for arbitrating differences should be established in lease agreements, or in the lease laws of the State.

THE SITUATION CALLS FOR ACTION

The foregoing pages present an interpretation of our national objectives with respect to the land and the farmers who occupy it; point out how far we have fallen short of attaining these objectives; appraise the influences in a changing world that are operating to perpetuate maladjustment, reduce farm ownership, and increase farm tenancy; review remedial actions already taken, and suggest further desirable lines of action. The problem is admittedly complex and difficult to present clearly and precisely. It is, however, very real and very deeply rooted. It may be viewed at first hand by any one who flies by airplane above our eroded farm lands, travels by train across our great commonwealths, motors over country roads in any of hundreds of rural counties, or enters the bleak homes of some of the nearly half million farm families whose total cash incomes fall below $250 a year (fig. 3, *A*). The situation calls for action. Without undue delay, appropriate steps should be taken to bring about a better distribution of people on the land, to strengthen the ties that bind farm families to their farm homes, to increase farmers' purchasing power, and by all these and other means to safeguard and stengthen the foundations of our democracy (fig. 3, *B*).

Farm Labor in an Era of Change

by William T. Ham [1]

IT USED TO BE that the farm laborer could expect to rent a little farm, save up his money, and eventually have a place of his own. It used to be that the "hired hand" was almost part of the farm owner's family, eating his meals with them, entering into their plans. Today there is a growing army of farm laborers drifting over the country, not rooted to the soil, homeless, unemployed a large part of the time, able to provide only the most miserable living conditions for their children, and hopeless of ever doing any better. Is this a situation the United States can tolerate? Shall we shut our eyes to it and let it drift to some dangerous crisis? Or can we, by frankly recognizing new conditions and attacking them intelligently, do something to give these Americans a toehold in the changed world of today and a stake in the well-being of their country? These are the questions considered in this article.

LIKE ALL other rural groups, the farm laborers have been much affected, for the most part adversely, by the agricultural changes of recent years. However, being widely scattered and having no organization to speak for them, they have received little attention. The problems of farm operators and tenants have been discussed in detail and programs worked out to bring about improvement, but it has apparently been assumed that the difficulties of the hired laborers would disappear as the position of farm operators was bettered. Until recently it has been taken for granted that the man who remained a farm laborer lacked the initiative or capacity to rise to something

[1] William T. Ham is Principal Agricultural Economist, Division of Farm Population and Rural Welfare, Bureau of Agricultural Economics.

better and that the real labor problem was simply that of finding a sufficient number of competent hands to do the work of the farm.

THE PLIGHT OF FARM LABOR

Too Many Farm Laborers

Today, however, the farm laborer's problem is forcing itself to the front in other terms. In the first place—despite the complaints of farmers as to the scarcity of seasonal help—there is a superabundance of labor power on American farms. Much of this is among the members of the farm family, who in many cases have productive farm work only during a few months of the year. If these individuals were in the city and worked as intermittently at factory jobs, we should call them partially employed and not wonder at their resulting low standard of living. On the farms, however, the existence of unused labor power is commonly accepted as part of the order of nature. This was not so in earlier days.

The presence of these unemployed or partially employed members of the rural community who must be supported out of available resources although they lack opportunity to make a full contribution to the farm enterprise, is one explanation of the depressed standards of farm living in many areas. On the one hand, a high farm birth rate has been maintained. On the other, opportunities for farm-born persons have decreased. In agriculture this has been due to the disappearance of free land, the deterioration of much land already in use, the dislocation of farm markets, domestic and foreign, and the consequent necessity for crop adjustments. To some extent, also, it has been due to overemphasis upon cash income and cash crops and to neglect of diversification, with ill effects upon noncash elements in farm-family living and upon the opportunities for farm labor, whether in

Figure 1.—A diversified farm such as this requires the type of labor represented by the hired man.

Figure 2.—The hired man lives in the community and is often almost like one of the farmer's family.

the family or hired, to contribute to these elements (figs. 1 and 2). In industry the loss of normal outlets for rural people has been due to failure of production to expand into new fields and the development of labor-saving methods in fields already open.

From 1930 to 1932 there was an unusual movement of persons from the cities to the farms. Subsequently this movement was greatly reduced, but even so, the annual net migration from farms from 1930 through 1934 averaged only 120,000 as compared with an annual average of 600,000 during the decade 1921–30 (*4*).[2] Thus there was a damming up of the rural population. Moreover, a large proportion of those held on the farms were young persons whose presence tended to increase the competition for jobs and to depress farm wages. In addition, the increased use of farm machinery in some areas, together with the crop-reduction programs, has tended to reduce the number of tenants and croppers and to increase the number of wage hands. The protracted drought, too, drove thousands into the labor market.

Hired Labor for Life

One result of this damming-up of farm labor, both in the operator's family group and in the ranks of the workers available for hire, is that the farm laborer has less chance for advancement than used to be the case. (See New Conditions Demand New Opportunities, p. 810.) Before the depression it was the common view that the farm laborer was merely a person on the way to becoming a tenant or one temporarily engaged in agricultural employment before passing on to work in industry. In 1929 an authority asserted (*2*) that it is doubtful whether, in this country, farm wages ever have been high enough to warrant any man's deliberately adopting farm labor as a life occupation—that, as a matter of fact, wages have been only part of the

[2] Italic numbers in parentheses refer to Literature Cited, p. 921.

Figure 3.—Farms in the specialty-crop areas require a different type of labor from that on diversified farms.

remuneration, the rest consisting of training in the procedure of running a farm. In recent years, however, with farm tenants experiencing such difficulties in maintaining their status, it is obvious that the laborer's prospects have been poor. Hired farm work has become a permanent, rather than a transitional, occupation for an increasing number of farm people. Among them are fewer, proportionately, of the less competent, the tramps, hoboes, and drifters who figured so largely in early accounts of farm labor—and more, in proportion, of those who may be regarded as normal farm people, denied the opportunity for self-betterment which earlier they would have had, and which, if times improve, they may have again.

Associated with this relatively new permanency of status is the development in many areas of relationships and conditions which, in the past, have been associated with industrial rather than farm labor. In a recent volume of the Congressional Record is a passage describing the relationship of the farm hand to his employer (*6*):

> The habits and customs of agriculture of necessity have been different than those of industry. The farmers and workers are thrown in close daily contact with one another. They, in many cases, eat at a common table. Their children attend the same school. Their families bow together in religious worship. They discuss together the common problems of our economic and political life. The farmer, his family, and the laborers' [sic] work together as one unit. In the times of stress, in the handling of livestock or perishable agricultural commodities, of impending epidemics, and at many other times the farmer and laborer must stand shoulder to shoulder against the common enemy. This develops a unity of interest which is not found in industry. This unity is more effective to remove labor disturbances than any law can be.

Now while this state of affairs may once have been common, it cannot be asserted that today such community of interest prevails. Of course, in discussing farm labor problems, a distinction should be made between the regular farm hands, hired for all or most of the year, and the seasonal laborers, especially those in the highly specialized fruit- and vegetable-producing areas. On April 1, 1930, there were 2,732,972 persons whose usual occupation was working on farms for wages. In the agricultural census of 1935, of the 967,594 farms that reported hired help, 722,645 had only 1 employee, 137,670 had 2, while only 11,410 reported 10 or more wage hands. It is clear, therefore, that the more or less regular farm hands are widely scattered. They are characteristic of the regions given over to production of corn and livestock, wheat and the small grains, of the dairying districts and the western range. There is little reference to them in the writings on farm labor. For the hired man, undoubtedly, rural life has rewards aside from cash income received. Nevertheless, his position is not what it used to be. During recent years, wage rates have not kept up with the rise in farm income. Relations with the farm family are seldom as intimate as formerly. Mechanization has eliminated certain types of work and considerably changed the rest. Moreover the farm hand is frequently the principal sufferer from the failure to make the most of those rural resources which, if not at present productive of cash income, could contribute to better housing and other necessities.

With the seasonal laborers, particularly those in the specialty-crop areas, the situation is still more difficult because of the irregular and limited periods of employment and the lack of permanent or resident status in the community (figs. 3 and 4). At the height of the season there are well over 1 million persons employed on farms hiring 3 or more, and nearly half a million on farms hiring 10 or more workers.

In some areas there has been a considerable development of large-scale farms, of which a census investigation listed 7,875 in 1929 (*3*). This is only about 0.1 percent of all farms and represents less than 5 percent of American agriculture. However, this 0.1 percent paid 11 percent of the farm wage bill; on these farms the average wage bill

Figure 4.—In specialty farming, labor is irregular and not resident in the community.

Figure 5.—On large-scale farms the conditions of employment are more like those in a factory.

was $13,385, as compared with $135 for the 6 million other farms. Of these large-scale enterprises, more than 40 percent were fruit, truck, and specialty-crop farms, about 25 percent were stock ranches, and 10 percent were dairy farms. Of the total number, 2,892 were in California, and 731 were in Texas, as compared with 65 in Iowa and 21 in Minnesota. Of the large-scale enterprises in truck crops, California had 59.7 percent; of large-scale fruit farms, 60.1 percent; of large-scale cotton enterprises, 30 percent; of large-scale dairies, 40.5 percent; and of large-scale poultry farms, 52.9 percent. In this State in 1930 agricultural wage earners made up 56.4 percent of the total gainfully employed agricultural population 10 years of age and over, as compared with 26 percent for the United States. These figures indicate a development in agricultural organization quite different from that of the family-size farm.

On these large-scale farms the conditions of employment are more like those in a factory than like those on the traditional American farm (fig. 5). Hence the tendency on the part of labor sympathizers to refer to "factory farming." Aside from the number of workers employed, the work is of a highly routine character, being carried on by gangs under the direction of foremen or field bosses. The hiring of workers, their supervision, the payment of wages, and even housing and provisioning are often turned over to a labor contractor or to a representative of the packing or canning company or the cooperative marketing agency. Wage rates are very uncertain and may be cut without notice. Anything more unlike the variety and personal responsibility of the work of the hired man can scarcely be imagined.

The Forgotten Man

However, it is not only the increasing importance of seasonal labor or the change in the status of the regular farm hand that is complicating the agricultural labor problem. There is also the intrusion into agricultural circles of standards derived from industrial labor. Since 1933, despite vast unemployment, the laborers in industry have made gains. In 1935, after a period of experiment with the now famous section 7a of the National Industrial Recovery Act of 1933, the Wagner Labor Relations Act was passed. This act reasserted the principle of collective bargaining in industry, assured to labor the right to be represented by agents of its own choosing, and forbade employers to interfere with the freedom to organize. In 1935 came the Social Security Act, which outlined a far-reaching scheme of unemployment insurance and assistance for the aged, the blind, and other groups. In 1938 the Fair Labor Standards Act became operative, establishing a minimum for wages and a maximum for hours. The result of these legislative enactments has been to give impetus to the organization of industrial laborers and to create a new atmosphere in employment relations. Many powerful employers who in the past refused to countenance labor organizations have now accepted collective bargaining and appear to be satisfied that it offers a means of orderly procedure in their necessary dealings with their employees.

During all this period of debate and development the agricultural laborer has remained in the background. The legislation designed for the benefit of agriculture recognized expressly only sharecroppers and the workers in the sugar fields. From the benefits of the National Labor Relations Act, the Social Security Act, the Fair Labor Standards Act, the farm worker was definitely excluded. Accordingly, in 1939, unprotected in his right to bargain collectively, with no floor for his wages or ceiling for his hours, and denied the benefits of unemployment insurance and old-age assistance, the farm hand is worse off, by comparison with the industrial workers, than he was in 1933. Consciousness of this situation has undoubetdly done much in recent years to complicate already unsatisfactory employment relations on the farm.

With the specific conditions of which farm laborers complain—low incomes, low wage rates, irregular employment, unsatisfactory conditions of work, bad housing and living conditions, denial of civil liberties, and unsatisfactory status in the community—it is impossible to deal properly here. As regards income, it is obvious that if in 1929 1,700,000 farms on which lived probably 7,700,000 persons yielded gross farm incomes of less than $600 a year,[3] the income prospects of farm laborers during the troubled years since that date cannot have been favorable. In 1929 farmers paid about 1,284 million dollars in cash wages, board, and lodging. By 1933 this farm labor bill had dropped to 517 million. Total farm income had also dropped from about 12 billion dollars in 1929 to 5¼ billion in 1932, but by 1937 again amounted to about 10 billion (*5, 1938 report, pp. 91–92*). In that year total payments to labor, however, were still below 800 million dollars.[4] In all probability the full-time earnings of agricultural workers, including perquisites, average under $400 a year for the country as a whole.

[3] TAYLOR, CARL C., WHEELER, HELEN W., and KIRKPATRICK, E. L. DISADVANTAGED CLASSES IN AMERICAN AGRICULTURE. U. S. Farm Security Admin. Soc. Res. Rpt. 8, 124 pp. 1938. [Processed.]

[4] UNITED STATES DEPARTMENT OF AGRICULTURE. INCOME PARITY FOR AGRICULTURE PART II, EXPENSES OF AGRICULTURAL PRODUCTION. SECTION 1, THE COST OF HIRED FARM LABOR, 1909 38. PRELIMINARY. 45 pp., illus. 1939. [Processed.]

Data available since 1910 show that farm wage rates have maintained a fairly consistent relationship to farm income, gross and net, and also to prices received by farmers for their products. However, since 1933, when farm incomes turned upward after the catastrophic fall in 1932, farm wage rates, which had not fallen as far, failed to recover at as rapid a rate and have remained somewhat lower than the earlier relationship between wage rates and farm incomes would lead one to expect. Doubtless the inability of laborers to shift to industry is a factor. On July 1, 1939, the average rate of pay per month without board was $36.26, as compared with $37.28 the year before. Per day, without board, the rate for 1939 was $1.59; for 1938, $1.63.[5] In some areas—for example, on the Pacific coast—rates are considerably higher, but employment is highly seasonal and requires constant movement and expense in search of jobs.

According to the census of 1930 the wage worker has, on an average, 150 days of farm employment per year. To this instability of employment the trend toward larger farms in some areas and the gradually increasing mechanization of agricultural operations are contributing by reducing the need for regular hands. Where such equipment as the corn picker and the combine harvester is in use the seasonal-labor requirements are reduced also.

At this point, however, it should be noted that in agriculture, as in industry, the advent of the machine is not an unmixed evil. As a matter of fact, as a means of increasing income per worker, it is desirable that more, rather than fewer, machines should be introduced. Hand labor is inefficient as compared with human effort applied through machines; therefore, it is poorly paid. The presence of a plentiful supply of cheap labor in the Corn and Cotton Belts is thus an obstacle to that mechanization by which the incomes of those who are retained in agriculture would be raised. What to do with those who are not retained is another question.

As a consequence of the low incomes of farm laborers, their standards of living are incredibly low, their housing is inadequate, their means of preserving health are meager, and their community relationships are reduced almost to the vanishing point. In these respects the regular laborers and the sharecroppers are not much worse off than a large proportion of the farm operators, tenants, and owners.[6] But the seasonal laborers, who make up probably one-half of the 2 to 3 million hired workers in the country, are undoubtedly at the bottom of the heap—especially the quarter of a million or more who are migratory. Concerning the difficulties of the beet workers in the Lake, Mountain, and Pacific Coast States, the field hands of the great California valleys, the vegetable workers of New Jersey, the citrus workers of California and Florida, and the cotton, fruit, and truck-crop workers of Texas there has grown up an extensive literature of complaint.

During recent years there has been a sharp increase in the number of labor disputes in agriculture, particularly in the specialized crop areas. In 1927 there were 2 strikes, involving 322 agricultural

[5] United States Department of Agriculture, Agricultural Marketing Service. farm wage rate index down 3 points from year ago. 18 pp., illus. July 14, 1939. [Mimeographed.]

[6] See page 9 of reference cited in footnote 3.

workers; in 1928, 4, involving 410 workers. In 1933, however, the number of strikes rose to 47, with 58,701 workers participating. Since that time through 1938, there have been 159 strikes of agricultural workers reported, of which 24 involved 1,000 or more workers each. Although 24 States were affected, 80 of the strikes since 1933 have occurred in California. Many of these disputes have been characterized by extreme bitterness on both sides; they offer eloquent testimony to the urgent character of the agricultural labor problem in the special-crop areas.

LINES OF ACTION

The first line of attack upon the farm laborers' problems is part of the general offensive against low farm incomes and bad living conditions. As stated in the Report of the Secretary of Agriculture for 1937 (*5*)—

> Progress toward economic security and improved living standards among farm laborers depends in large measure, like the prosperity of agriculture in general, on the extent to which the country advances toward a fairer distribution of the national income as between agriculture and urban industry.

The farmer's ability to hire on terms satisfactory to laborers is limited by his ability to pay. Unless the conditions of agricultural prosperity can be restored, measures directed toward improving the lot of any particular group—owners, tenants, croppers. or laborers—will avail only to a limited extent.

Closely connected with this broad frontal attack upon the general problems of agriculture is another line of action which is equally basic, directed toward making labor power on farms a scarcer and therefore more effectively utilized and more highly valued article. Unless agricultural income—both cash and noncash—can be increased beyond all expectations, it is necessary, along with what can be done in that direction, to reduce the number of those among whom income is shared. To do this involves success in the efforts directed toward the increase of employment in factory, mill, and mine. As long as there are millions of unemployed in the urban areas, as long as farm youth lack the opportunity to take up industrial occupations but remain, perforce, on the farms, so long will it be difficult to improve materially the position of the farm laborers.

To say this, however, is not to advocate large-scale removal of rural population to the cities or to belittle the possibility of the further development of farm and other rural resources in such a way as to utilize existing rural labor more fully. What is needed is a resumption of the hitherto normal movement of a certain proportion of farm youth in response to opportunity in industry. There are those who would keep all farm people on the farms, who regard the hope of self-betterment in nonfarm occupations as illusory. They believe that agriculture and its allied rural industries can be so transformed as to afford a satisfactory living to all who are farm-born. Others believe that industry can be decentralized and brought to the rural centers to be combined with farming in a fruitful way of life. Such hopes should be cherished and every effort bent to secure their realization. But we are bound to recognize that if, from 1920 to 1930, two-fifths of all farm boys between 20 and 30 years old migrated to the cities, the cessation of this movement and the damming up on the farms from 1930 to 1935 of 2 million extra workers greatly complicated the farm problem (*2*). Fuller employment in industry would not only increase the demand for farm products and expand farm employment; it would also offer renewed opportunity to such farm people as prefer to seek jobs in the cities.

Better Labor Distribution

Emphasis upon such considerations, which apply both to the farmer and to the man he hires, should not blind us to the importance of certain special circumstances which affect the workers. Chief among these is the system of labor distribution, which is at present, as it long has been, nothing short of chaotic. In the special-crop areas, particularly, growers evidently assume that the seasonal workers needed at peak periods must and will be available without any responsibility on their part as to whether there is work enough to go round or what happens to the laborers after the need for them on the farms is ended. Indiscriminate advertising for labor often leads to oversupply, with low wage rates, low earnings, widespread distress, and hastily contrived methods of partial relief as the result.

If it is necessary for agriculture in these areas to be subsidized by the community, through provision of livelihood for the unemployed, the fact should be recognized by farmers as well as by the State and something better than the present haphazard methods of assistance worked out. But before taking this path it is desirable that every effort be made, locally and nationally, to adjust the supply of labor efficiently to the demand for it, through the development of an effective farm-placement and information service. Already notable steps in this direction have been taken in some States—for example, in Texas. But the progress is uneven. What is needed—since labor migrations are interstate in character— is more cooperation between Federal and State agencies, education of the growers to the advantages of effective placement, and regulation of frequently irresponsible private employment concerns. Such measures will not increase the volume of employment—indeed they will leave some laborers with less work than at present; but they will reduce the heavy cost of fruitless travel and lessen the distress which accompanies gluts in the labor market. Heavy movements of farm laborers from one area to another can be controlled, and means can be provided for assisting potential migrants to remain at home.

More Regular Employment

Closely connected with these measures looking toward the more effective placement of farm laborers is the modification of crop organization and farm practices so as to promote continuity of employment and increase annual earnings. In some areas there appears to be a possibility of the introduction of crop sequences that will reduce the need for seasonal labor. There are also certain types of processing which are now performed off the farm but which could well be combined with farm operations to increase the volume of available employment. In some areas there has been unjustified and uneconomic resort to the use of labor-saving machinery.

Precisely what adjustments of this sort can be made is not yet clear. It is frequently argued that the inevitable effect would be to increase the costs of production of the farmer and thus the prices of the commodities he produces, with consequent lessening of consumer demand and reduction of the amount of employment for farm labor. Indeed, it is asserted that the whole trend of development on the farms is in the opposite direction, that is, toward greater specialization in production and the use of equipment, which, although increasing the need for hired labor for short periods, lessens the dependence upon regular labor. This argument may be a sound one, especially for the individual farmer and in the short run. However, for the community there are additional costs involving serious social wastage. It may be best for society to assume these costs directly, leaving the farmer free to use labor as he sees fit; on the other hand, it may be preferable to induce the farmer to take a longer view. In any case it cannot be denied that it is desirable that farm operators who employ considerable seasonal labor should be encouraged to consider their responsibilities to the public in connection with the social problems arising from their present employment policies.

As a contribution, if a minor one, to the solution of these seasonal labor difficulties the provision of permanent and mobile camp facilities deserves to be encouraged. Of themselves these can contribute little to the permanent rehabilitation of the seasonal workers; they do, however, greatly improve the health aspects of seasonal farm employment. At present the Farm Security Administration has 25 permanent and 6 movable camps either in operation or in course of being established, in 7 States. More than half of them are in California. About 35,000 families use these camps in the course of a year. Such aid would be desirable for 10 times as many.

Widespread in rural areas is the need for the extension of the services of the public health authorities and for the establishing of rural medical centers. The experience of the Farm Security Administration in working out its system of cooperative medical care for low-income farm people has shown that it is possible to secure the active cooperation of State and local medical societies in providing more adequate health protection at lower cost. Through more than 100 medical-service plans, organized on a county or district basis, a number of experiments in types of organization and methods of approach are being worked out that should furnish a pattern for this type of service in the future, applicable to farm laborers' as well as farm operators' families.

More nearly adequate funds for housing and camp inspection in rural areas are in most States a real need. Coupled with this is the desirability of further effort directed toward low-cost housing construction such as will make it possible for families working on farms, permanently or temporarily, to escape what have been accurately described as rural slums. There should also be further experimentation with methods of providing home and garden quarters for agricultural workers and education in more efficient buying and consumption.

223761°—40——59

Equality Under Law

At the present time, as has already been noted, the agricultural laborers are almost entirely outside the system of protective labor legislation which has been established since 1933. The tendency of legislatures, both national and State, to exclude farm laborers is due (1) to a belief that the actuarial and administrative difficulties would give rise to administrative costs so high as to be prohibitive; (2) to a fear that the small farmer would be placed at a disadvantage; (3) to a tradition that the farm hand does not require protection; (4) to a fear that inclusion of farm laborers would mean defeat of any labor legislation proposed; and (5) to lack of any well-organized labor support.

The argument most frequently advanced by farm interests against extending protection to agricultural laborers, and to those in processing plants as well, is the largely fallacious one that such action would necessarily decrease the returns to farmers. As a matter of fact, it is becoming obvious to all disinterested persons that we cannot go on indefinitely denying to workers on farms and in allied occupations the benefits of legislation designed to improve the lot of labor generally. To do so is to create a class of pariahs, of really forgotten men, and to contribute to a definite inferiority of status which, in time, as industrial and agricultural conditions improve, the farmer himself will have cause to regret. Such action, moreover, is a type of negative class legislation which is repugnant to the spirit of American institutions.

Agricultural workers, like domestic and casual workers, were excluded from the social security legislation of August 1935 primarily because of the administrative difficulties anticipated on account of the high proportion of employers to employees, the payment of wages partly in kind, and the wide dispersion of the workers and their employers.

In its report to the President of December 30, 1938, the Social Security Board recommended the extension of old-age insurance—now estimated to include at any one time only 50 percent of the Nation's gainfully occupied population—to agricultural workers employed in large-scale farming operations; it suggested continuance of the exclusion of workers employed by small farmers to do the ordinary work of the farm. This recommendation was based on the grounds (1) that it is sound social policy to extend old-age insurance to as many of the Nation's workers as possible; (2) that, while the complete inclusion of agricultural employees leads to administrative difficulties, the inclusion of workers on large-scale farms would reduce rather than increase the administrative difficulties that now exist; and (3) that the financial soundness of the system is endangered by present arrangements, under which considerable numbers of farm workers come in by the "back door," so to speak, through acquiring rights to minimum benefits by working, from time to time, off the farm, in covered employments. It appears that at present it is almost impossible to delimit the field of agricultural labor with anything like the certainty required for administration. Particularly in enterprises concerned with processing and marketing as well as with agricultural production, the employer is plagued with perplexities involved in the keeping of necessary records of covered and excluded employees.

With respect to unemployment insurance, it was the view of the Board that, although in some foreign countries the systems have been extended to cover agricultural employees, in this country the agricultural wage-earning group is so much less clearly defined that extension of unemployment insurance to all agricultural employees at the present time is inadvisable. However, as in the case of old-age insurance, the Board recommended that the exception should apply only to the services of a farm hand employed by a small farmer to do the ordinary work connected with his farm. In addressing the Congress on the subject of social security on January 16, 1939, the President expressed his belief that under both the Federal old-age insurance system and the Federal-State unemployment compensation system "equity and sound social policy require that the benefits be extended to all of our people as rapidly as administrative experience and public understanding permit."

Inclusion of farm workers under the wages and hours regulations of the Fair Labor Standards Act should be governed by the facts as to employment status. Where workers are employed on the farm in considerable numbers, the individual workman is at the same disadvantage in dealing with his employer as the worker in industry and is entitled to the same protection. It is assumed, of course, that due consideration must be given to the peculiarities of agricultural production, especially as regards hours of employment. On those farms that have a man or two, regularly or at certain seasons, no questions as to wages or conditions of employment are likely to arise that cannot be settled equitably by the persons concerned. Similar considerations apply to the related question of including farm workers under the National Labor Relations Act, which was enacted by Congress for the purpose of protecting workers in their exercise of the right of collective bargaining. Farm workers, like all others in the United States, undoubtedly have that right and should be denied no guaranty that is extended by law to workers generally.

As regards farm wages, one may risk a reference to some foreign experience.

It is noteworthy that in each of the three countries—Great Britain, New Zealand, and Australia—where national minimum-wage legislation has long obtained, inclusion of agricultural workers has closely followed enactment of minimum-wage laws covering industrial workers. In England and Wales, despite a difficult beginning, an intervening depression, and an impoverished condition of agriculture, the legislation has been kept continuously in operation for 15 years and in 1937 was extended to Scotland. Its continuance appears to have been due to a belief in an interaction between agricultural and industrial wages of such character that if agricultural wage rates are not coordinated with those in industry the best elements of the agricultural labor supply are lost to the farmer. This relationship may be more marked in Great Britain, with its proportionally greater farm employment, than in the United States, but considerations of this kind are undoubtedly of some weight in explaining what is sometimes referred to as the "inland march" of the unions on the Pacific coast. Here, as in the southern textile areas, it is contended that the low standards of rural workers exert a depressing influence upon industrial wage rates, and thus justify a concerted effort to improve the conditions of rural employment.

Need for State Action

In the United States, of course, the situation, as compared with that in Great Britain, is complicated by the size of the country and the Federal character of our governmental arrangements. Hence the importance of State action in all matters that affect agricultural labor.

At present, under State laws relating to workmen's compensation, unemployment insurance, the hours of work of women and their wages, the employment of children, wage collection, and the like, agricultural workers are quite generally excepted; and, where they are included, enforcement leaves much to be desired. How this situation is to be remedied—whether by Federal assistance, pressure of organized labor, or the process of education—remains to be determined.

In all of the agricultural States the employment service should be expanded and improved and more effective methods of cooperation with the Federal service devised. In those areas where seasonal laborers are a necessity, public welfare imposes the duty of seeing to it that the workers have decent camping or housing facilities, public or private, and that proper standards of sanitation are maintained. The social importance of more adequate provision of educational opportunities for the children of agricultural workers need not be emphasized. The increase of labor organization and agricultural strikes in recent years suggests the desirability of working out methods of wage determination by joint conference of employers and employees, and also methods of stabilizing wage rates so as to prevent those violent fluctuations associated with ill-regulated movements of labor which so seriously reduce the earnings of seasonal workers. It is also desirable that facilities for mediation and conciliation in farm-labor disputes should be worked out. In certain counties of California an auspicious beginning in this direction has been made, and there has been considerable discussion of the possibility of a State board of conciliation for agriculture. When strikes of agricultural workers do occur, it is essential, as was noted by the President's Committee on Farm Tenancy, "that the civil liberties of the workers, and the right of peaceful assembly and of organization, be preserved" (7).

The possibilities of improvement of the status of farm labor through independent action on the part of organized producers and laborers remain to be explored. In some areas there is evidence that associations of producers are beginning to concern themselves with other aspects of the labor problem than that merely of providing an adequate supply of cheap labor. It is important that such associations should assume more responsibility for the social effects of the methods of labor utilization and management. Otherwise agriculture and its allied industries can hardly escape, not merely the inefficiency and loss involved in interruptions of orderly production, but also the growth of militant organizations of labor and the necessity for intervention on the part of government.

LITERATURE CITED

(1) Black, John D.
1929. agricultural reform in the united states. 511 pp., illus. New York.

(2) Ezekiel, Mordecai.
1939. jobs for all through industrial expansion. 299 pp., illus. New York and London.

(3) Jennings, R. D.
1933. large-scale farming in the united states, 1929. In Fifteenth Census of the United States: 1930. Census of Agriculture. 106 pp., illus. Washington, D. C. [Separately paged.]

(4) Lively, C. E., and Taeuber, Conrad.
1939. rural migration in the united states. U. S. Works Prog. Admin., Div. Res., Res. Monog. 19, 192 pp., illus. Washington, D. C.

(5) United States Department of Agriculture.
1937–38. annual reports of the secretary of agriculture, 1937 and 1938.

(6) United States Senate.
1939. national labor relations act—agricultural labor. Cong. Rec. 84 (37): 2565–2568.

(7) [United States] Special Committee on Farm Tenancy.
1937. farm tenancy, report of the president's committee. Prepared under the auspices of the National Resources Committee. 108 pp., illus. Washington, D. C.

Beyond Economics

by M. L. Wilson [1]

AN ECONOMIST by training, the author of this article is a rural philosopher by nature. He holds that economics, and in fact most social sciences, attempt the impossible when they try to fit human affairs into neat little cubbyholes and make rigid rules according to which human beings ought to behave. Not reason but custom is the force men obey, he says, and the problem of adjusting agriculture to the modern world is basically psychological and cultural rather than physical and technological. But to admit these things is not to be unscientific; in fact, the more scientific a man is, the more clearly he will see that our economic problems are really moral problems. On a foundation of these ideas the author builds a philosophy of agricultural reform. He deals especially with new possibilities for a better life for those whom we have been unable to fit into our economic system.

THE COMPLEXITY OF THE AGRICULTURAL PROBLEM

WHOEVER has studied the social and economic aspects of agriculture as they are presented in detail in the articles that make up this book

[1] M. L. Wilson is Director of Extension Work. The author wishes to acknowledge a debt of thanks to Paul H. Johnstone, of the Bureau of Agricultural Economics, for his generous assistance in the preparation of this article.

must be convinced that there is a problem of adjustment in agricultural and rural life that is not simple and cannot be solved by simple means. Even the major questions are numerous.

There is first of all the question of which we are most keenly aware—that of producing an adequate income for agriculture. This has received much attention, and a great deal has been done about it in the last decade. But although the grievousness of the condition of economic disparity has been alleviated, it is by no means cured. It remains a problem which will require for some time to come the best efforts of all those who seek justice for American farm people.

There is the problem of tenure. The long-time trends in tenure relationships do not fit into the pattern of what most of us believe is to be desired. The proportion of tenants in the agricultural population has continued to increase for a long time; and those farmers who are called owners have in general found their burden of mortgage debt mounting heavily, large numbers of them finding their hold upon the land ever more precarious. If the tenure trends that have now been operating for so long continue, there will soon be few small owners left—our land will be farmed by tenants and day laborers working on vast estates. Even if one assumes, as few people do, that the road toward greater technological efficiency must be based on huge units and high capital outlay, there are not many today who can ignore the tremendous social costs of such changes. And even if one assumes that tenancy is not in itself a bad thing, the particular forms and conditions of tenancy as they actually prevail in many places allow no security to the tenant and make no provision for proper care of the land. We tried liberalizing credit because that seemed the best way to halt the trend away from ownership, but the trend has continued. Undoubtedly liberal credit must be a key factor in efforts to assure greater security and continuity of ownership, but experience has taught us that credit alone cannot solve the problem.

Then there is a problem of population adjustment in agriculture. More people are now engaged in agriculture than can attain a good standard of living by ordinary commercial farming under prevailing economic conditions and institutions. This is the result partly of technological progress, partly of declining foreign markets, partly of urban industry's failure to maintain full production and employment opportunities. There are undoubtedly many other causes. The effect has been to burden agriculture as a whole with the support of a population out of proportion to agriculture's share in the national income. This disproportionate burden, moreover, has not been equally divided within agriculture; certain areas, certain classes of farmers, certain types of production have suffered far more than others. There can be no hope of immediate relief of the conditions that have produced a surplus rural population. But it is possible for agriculture to adjust itself in such a fashion as to support better and more equitably than at present all those who must make their living by the plow.

Closely related to overpopulation, tenure evils, and inadequate income for agriculture as a whole is the problem of the very low standards of living of a substantial portion of American rural people. Theirs is a poverty that so far at least has not been appreciably relieved by the momentary prosperity that has sometimes favored other farmers and farm groups. They live sometimes in houses that many prosperous farmers would not want as chicken coops. They frequently lack facilities for education and sanitation and medical care. Many of them lack the dietary elements required for good health. The kind of poverty in which they live has in many cases robbed them of the vitality, the incentive, and the means to improve their condition unless they get at least some small measure of outside aid. Yet it is people in such circumstances who produce a substantial part of some of our major crops and who likewise supply a disproportionately large share of our younger population because of their unusually high birth rate.

There is also a problem of land adjustment—of reforming our use of the soil so that future generations may live well upon it. This frequently means new methods of tillage. It sometimes means shifting agricultural production from one area to another or from one kind of production to another that is better from the point of view of total social efficiency.

There is the problem of adjusting production not only for the sake of soil conservation and of reducing surpluses but also for the purpose of supplying in a better way the diverse needs of our whole population. For instance, it seems apparent on the basis of our national dietary needs that we should produce relatively more dairy products, fruits, leafy vegetables, and other health-building foods, and relatively less of certain grains and fibers of which we have a superabundance.

In some parts of the country there is a crucial problem of taxation. This is especially acute in regions that were settled with booming optimism in expectancy of agricultural income which for one reason or another never materialized. Bonded indebtedness was assumed and tax-consuming institutions were established that have continued as an unbearable burden upon the agriculture of communities that were once so hopeful.

These brief notations are intended to suggest the complexity of the total agricultural problem which all of us who have rural welfare at heart must face. For however much we may wish that the problem were a simple one and even though many sincere and devoted friends of agriculture seem to believe it is simple, a careful exploration of the facts discloses an infinite complexity of causes and interrelationships. The problems of tenure, for instance, are closely interwoven with those of farm income, population, land use, increasing capital costs, the disappearance of a frontier of free land, and the rise of a metropolitan and industrial economy. They cannot be separated wholly from the influence of urban ways and thoughts and social standards extending into the countryside nor from the intangible but crucial change in attitudes that has accompanied the coming of the modern world. And all the problems of agriculture are affected, sometimes partially, sometimes crucially, by the conditions that prevail in industry.

Rural standards of living depend primarily upon income; yet in many places increased income by itself can never solve standard-of-living problems. Unless one is a thoroughgoing economic determinist, he must realize that such important matters as sanitation, education, medical care, and the birth rate are not determined exclusively by economics. Customary practices and traditional beliefs are vitally important determinants. The standard-of-living problems we have to deal with must be recognized as the product of the whole culture of a people and related to all of the prevailing customs, institutions, attitudes, and moral ideas. They add up to far more than straight economics. There can be no effective and lasting improvement of living standards in places where poverty is associated with disease, ignorance, and illiteracy or where there is an overcrowding of people upon slender or wasted natural resources, unless these conditions are altered first. Some of the poorer farm people have no fair chance to improve their lot because bad health and poor food have cut their vitality below the point where it is possible for them to lift themselves without outside help. In some places there are too many farmers for all of them to make a decent living by following prevailing agricultural practices, even if prices rose as high as there is any reason to hope they ever will. Absorption of a large portion of the population into industry seems the only hope of improvement in these cases—a faint hope in view of long-continued industrial unemployment—unless a new pattern of agriculture is adopted that can supply a higher standard of living without increasing cash costs. Much good would result from an extension of subsistence practices, with broad diversification and less dependence upon a single cash crop of which there is already a surplus and which consequently brings a low price. The adoption of such a program, embodying as it would farm practices so different that in many cases an almost totally different pattern of life would be involved, could not be accomplished quickly or by simple means but would entail, sometimes at least, much education and a change in the life philosophy of those who practiced it.

Because of this complexity of our farm problems there cannot possibly be a quick and easy panacea. Neither suddenness nor simplicity can characterize an agricultural program that would be really effective and lasting because the problem is not simple and its roots lie so deep in the past that they are embedded in many of our institutions and attitudes. There must be a long-time program of agricultural reform, but the reform must be slow and gradual, not for reasons of policy but because the very nature of the problem requires it.

SOME ESSENTIALS OF AGRICULTURAL REFORM

Reform in agriculture must grow from the ground up and be built upon the solid rock of democratic opinion. It must answer the desires of farm people, and they must determine its form. Its character must be shaped out of the native social soil of this country; and agricultural leadership can do no better than to provide devices whereby the rank and file may set their local problems into a national perspective, help to articulate the opinions that are formed on this basis, and finally assist in turning ideas into action.

Nothing is more important to the success of such a democratic program than that it be conducted upon a level of high tolerance. There must be on all sides a disposition to credit the other fellow with intelligence and sincere intentions. To do so is not only to recognize the fundamental decency of men, but also to avoid the bitterness that prevents both understanding and real accomplishment. The occasional reformer who seems more moved by hatred of those he deems oppressors than by love of the oppressed seldom aids the cause he enlists in.

THE CULTURAL APPROACH TO AGRICULTURAL PROBLEMS

The point of view best adapted to avoid oversimplification on the one hand and harsh intolerance on the other, and calculated to guide us toward the most practical methods of reform, is the cultural approach. The cultural approach is based upon a keen appreciation of the interrelatedness of all social phenomena. Both laymen and social scientists generally recognize that the facts of our daily lives cannot be clearly divided up and put in separate pigeonholes, as the artificial divisions of the social sciences suggest. Economists, political scientists, historians, psychologists, geographers, sociologists, and theologians all recognize that the crucial facts in the life of any individual or in any social situation cannot be correctly thought of as exclusively political, exclusively religious, exclusively economic, or exclusively anything else. They all merge into one another; and a single fact viewed from one angle may seem wholly economic, while from another, equally legitimate point of view it appears wholly psychological. Actually, of course, facts in themselves are not economic, political, or psychological.

The interrelationship of the whole range of social facts is at least vaguely perceived by everyone who gives serious thought to the subject. And it has been admitted by the social scientists of every specialized field. The point, however, is that while ordinarily this interrelationship is dimly recognized and grudgingly admitted, the cultural concept accepts the implications fully, gives them primary emphasis, and even makes them the foundation of its method.

One of the most important implications is that established attitudes and patterns of thought have as much to do with the total culture as more tangible, physical phenomena. Habits of thinking, special skills, social ideals, and customary judgments of value and of right and wrong develop and cluster around the material facts men live with. These all-important intangibles serve to make material traits function. Without them, the material traits would not exist. Things have effective being for men in society only to the extent that they integrate these things into their lives by the process of thought. This thought is partly skill or knowledge, partly explanation.

Man has an innate necessity for explaining to himself the reasons for the institutions and things he lives with. Whether or not he can explain them correctly, he must make the effort. If he does not have the necessary facts, he explains them by myths. Such myths are not to be disdained; they have a very necessary and important social function. Men are also inclined to think in absolute rather than in relative terms. In substance, therefore, we generalize from particular cases, and thus derive moral and social convictions which we consider absolute but which are based upon the temporary conditions of our own peculiar experience and social inheritance. This circumstantial origin of ideas that we are inclined to regard as universal and absolute is a very crucial matter in times of social change. Because of it, our traditional institutions, habits, and customs are associated with the abstract moral qualities and virtues that we most revere. And the changes in ways of doing things and in customs of living that inevitably come when our technological and physical environment is changed appear to be more than mere innovations; they seem an attack upon the very virtues with which the institutions they displace were associated.

The cultural approach sees a maladjustment, such as that of agriculture today, fundamentally as an unbalance between the world of things and the world of thought. Our customary institutions and ways of doing things, born in and adapted to a different set of physical conditions, are no longer wholly adequate and suitable to our needs. We are in the midst of a period in which these institutions and ways of doing things are changing relatively fast. Actually we submit to these institutional changes very slowly, generally only when we absolutely have to.

Why, it may be asked, do we change our customs so slowly if the need is really so pressing? Some people would answer this by saying that reform and change are prevented by the opposition of interests vested in obsolescent institutions or privileges. There is some truth in this, but the explanation seems to create personal devils—"the interests"—that seldom exist in large enough numbers to do all we attribute to them; nor does it explain the reluctance of the masses to change in matters in which, from the point of view of detached rationality, change would seem wholly to their advantage. The simplest explanation seems to be that we are creatures of custom rather than of reason. Not only are generalized ideas of right and wrong associated with customs and institutions, but in many cases they were actually developed as a moral justification of institutions that already existed. For this reason, many necessary innovations that amount essentially to a social accommodation to new factors introduced into the environment cannot avoid giving moral offense, for they seem to be an attack upon things that experience has taught were right and morally good.

Seen in this light, the problem of agricultural adjustment to the modern world appears to be basically psychological and cultural. We have the means already at hand for the desired technical and physical manipulation of the material elements in our altered environment. We have, that is, both machines and skills. We also have statistical inventories of physical resources and production techniques which enable us to calculate our capacity to produce goods to satisfy physical needs. On the basis of this knowledge of material things, it would therefore seem possible to direct our own destinies sufficiently well to avoid the kind of irrational maladjustments in the supply and distribution of goods to which actually we are grievously subject. But psychological and cultural obstacles so far have intervened to prevent a rational and feasible social control of these physical matters. This is so much the case that it is safe to say that the real genius of any feasible reform effort will reside not in its technical competence in any material concern but rather in its psychological and cultural insight. There are tens of thousands of men who can easily provide a blueprint of Utopia that is developed solely on the physical facts of our existing technology and natural resources. But because the crux of the problem is moral and psychological rather than physical and technological and because such blueprints are not based primarily upon psychic considerations, they are no more practical in specific application than so many phantasies.

We only admit the truth when we recognize that our economic problems are moral problems. The greatest difficulty in the traditional and accepted application of the social sciences to major social problems has arisen from the fact that they have tried to deal largely or exclusively with the material phases of social problems as opposed to the psychological and cultural phases. Among some social sciences and scientists there has been a distinct tendency to assume a rationality in man and a separateness in social phenomena that do not exist in fact. The social sciences and their applications have moreover tried to avoid dealing with moral and spiritual phases of social problems. This has seemed reasonable because of the recognized disposition of moral and spiritual things to be beyond the scope of recognized forms of scientific rationality. Yet the inner relationship both in cause and effect of these spiritual and moral factors with the kind of material things that science frankly deals with makes it impossible to ignore them. They have a mixed relationship with material facts that includes both cause and effect. They must be considered a part of the total picture from which there is no real escape. To ignore them is to be blind to the most important of social determinants. To take them for granted as absolutes that are unrelated to the transient conditions of the social and physical environment of man is to deny the most convincing evidence that has been presented upon the subject. To make a mere guess at them that is partly intuitive and largely unconscious—which is by far the most common practice—is to neglect the advantage of the systematic observations and theories of those who study such matters scientifically.

Analysis of attitudes toward important social issues generally discloses that a crucial determining factor underlying these judgments is very generally a moral consideration even when it is overlaid with a presumably rational explanation. Anyone who talks with farmers, businessmen, statisticians, wage workers, housewives, economists, scientists—in fact, people of any sort—about crucial issues and problems in agriculture, will find, if he analyses their opinions on the basis of the surest knowledge that psychology can supply, that the basis of judgment lies in moral ideas and attitudes not regularly considered by most social scientists. Very frequently the moral basis of the social opinion is unconscious. Sometimes it is candidly conscious. In point of method, the more conscious and candid the consideration of moral judgments is, the nearer is the approach to a scientific attitude toward that phase of social problems that is most commonly ignored. For it may be said fairly and without malice that in framing an opinion upon an issue that involves moral values—and very few social issues do not involve moral values—learning and logic and intellectual brilliance frequently serve principally to give an impressive and apparently rational argument in favor of opinions that really are formed for entirely different reasons.

The cultural approach recognizes the presence, influence, and importance of these moral considerations. It is, in fact, inclined frequently to concentrate upon them as the recognized crux of a social situation. In connection with contemporary agricultural problems, this would mean that psychological possibilities would form the starting point of all consideration of reform efforts. The psychological determinants within the total cultural situation would be considered as the first facts of the situation, and other matters would have to be bent to fit them rather than attempting to lay the major emphasis on bending psychological facts into conformity with physical factors.

Our thinking in matters that concern economic reform will be clearer and more useful if we learn to distinguish institutions from the human needs they exist to serve. Freedom and security may be accepted, for instance, as enduring human needs. But the particular institutions whereby they were attained in an age of free land may very well not continue to be effective in an age when there is no free land. And to confuse those older institutions with the freedom and security they once served is a dangerous kind of mistake.

The cultural point of view would indicate that educational processes and procedures must be a basic part of any serious reform effort. But since the cultural point of view regards conventional forms of education primarily as an institution for passing on to the younger generation the customs, techniques, and attitudes sanctioned by tradition and by established institutions, the specific content and procedures of education become very important in a period of cultural change. Good educational procedure adapted to present needs would not consist in experts telling farmers what the truth is, for experts frequently need educating just as much as do farmers. Education appropriate to contemporary needs would consist rather in an effort to stimulate the critical senses, to develop broader points of view, and to develop creative imagination by applying a scientific skepticism to those ideas we have that do not conform to the contemporary world of fact.

Both scientific analysis and popular demands indicate that continuing agricultural adjustment requires new kinds of action. New kinds of action programs are in fact already established and functioning in a way that suggests they will continue indefinitely. And in all probability many other new forms of action will evolve in the future. Since it is ordinarily impossible to do one thing and think another without developing serious conflicts, the matter of our attitudes and thinking becomes highly important. There should, therefore, be an expanding effort to increase both the amount and the intensity of thought and discussion concerning agricultural problems. And this thought and discussion should be popular and widespread because of the democratic ideal that is the first assumption of all our ideals of agricultural progress. There should be no restraint upon the philosophic implications of such thought and discussion. There should be no fear of pushing ideas beyond the frontier of what is known and factually proved into the region of philosophic ideals and moral preferences. It is obvious enough that no direct or scientific applications can come out of such exploration of ideals and opinions of ultimate goals in agricultural life. But philosophic probing, if it is sincere and deep enough, can realine our total thinking in such a way as to alter the nature of our attack upon those problems, for which immediate, calculable, and practical programs are possible.

TWO OPPOSITE DIRECTIONS OF AGRICULTURAL REFORM

There are in one sense two polar extremes of thought in respect to the direction agricultural development should follow in the future. The first extreme school of thought would follow the line set by sheer technological and production efficiency. Whether they are laissez faire theorists or socialistic theorists, the exponents of this point of view advocate agricultural development along lines for which technological efficiency is almost the sole criterion. If costs could be lowered by production units of 1,000 or 10,000 or even 100,000 acres, they feel that such units should be an important part of ultimate aims.

On the other hand, the exponents of the opposing school of thought seem to resent most of the mechanization and centralization of the modern world. This group is much impressed by the additional distribution costs that come with specialization and concentration of production. Whether it is for this economic reason, which contains a degree of truth, or whether it is because of a dislike for the more glaring aspects of modernity, those of this opinion advocate a return to the subsistence practices that were common before the industrial revolution destroyed the earlier individual self-sufficiency.

The members of the first group look upon the recommendations of the second group as an expression of defeatism and as inspired basically by an emotional reaction coming out of a maladjustment with the modern world. The second group is inclined to look upon the opinions of the first group as being headlong and lacking in a perception of the social and psychological maladjustments into which modernity in its industrializing and centralizing tendency may lead us. The difficulty in accepting either line of thought is the way it wholly excludes the other. Both lines of thought conform better to the rigidities of logic than to the variety of fact. Highly systematized social philosophies generally fail because they have a kind of geometrically perfect logic that assumes order and rationality within the social universe that seems to have no real existence outside the minds of those who create such systems.

If those things that deal with the psychic and more ultimate values of life are properly called philosophical, then there must be a greater disposition toward philosophy, for we need to strip ourselves of the preconceived notions and systematic ideas that so frequently prevent us from seeing things in the light in which they really exist. We see them too much according to the description that is handed down to us by tradition. This is an age in which we need to reexamine facts because a previous viewpoint entirely appropriate to an earlier environment is no longer wholly applicable. We must have philosophical consideration, but philosophical consideration does not mean making highly involved and rigidly logical systems. On the contrary, it should consist of a determined effort to test our dogmas in the light of the facts that are around us today. And if our dogmas do not conform to the facts, we should look for ideas that do.

The cultural approach follows no extremes of simple doctrine. Rather, it inclines to a program of many specific reforms varied in detail according to the peculiar needs of individual cases. It looks upon adjustment and reform of a social kind as an accommodation or a compromise between material facts and psychological factors. The cultural approach realizes the necessity for integration and harmony among the varied functions and phases of living, but this does not necessitate a systematic uniformity through all society.

It must be freely admitted that specialization, centralization, and interdependency seem to be the irresistible trend within industry. This trend does not seem by any means to be entirely spent. We must assume therefore that the industrial circumstances of modern society will continue indefinitely to necessitate a large degree of commercial agricultural production to supply raw materials for industry and to feed the industrial and metropolitan population. Since we are not headed for a return to handicrafts in industry, we must keep a large commercial agricultural plant that includes a great deal of specialized production for the urban market. But this does not mean that all agriculture can or should be established on an industrial basis. It is perfectly possible to have a specialized, highly interdependent, and even collectivized organization of industry and have beside it an agriculture that is in a large measure organized on a pattern of small individual units. Perfect conformity in ideas and organization does not need to extend from the factory into the field.

In agriculture, modern technology does not involve advantages to large units either universally or to the same degree as in industry. Specialized, large-scale agricultural production has sometimes appeared to be efficient when it really was not. It has sometimes created this appearance of efficiency by the device of shifting production costs to other agencies and institutions. It has utilized farm labor for short periods of the year at relatively low wages by shifting the living costs of that labor to relief or to charity during the seasons when it was not wanted. It has on occasion reduced the production costs of some individuals by dispossessing others and by increasing the proportion of individuals within the submerged social strata who live on the precarious border line of economic slavery and deprivation.

Much agriculture that is thoroughly commercial and highly specialized has been prodigal with the soil. Single cropping of various kinds has mined the soils and prepared them for rapid erosion. Concentration of production within specialized areas has increased the threat of diseases and insects and necessitated expensive operations for their control. It has run up the fertilizer bill and, by piling on transportation and handling charges, has increased those costs of distribution which have worried so many when they consider the difference between the price paid to the farmer and the price paid by the ultimate consumer.

Thus, while we may admit that commercial and specialized production is necessary and that on the whole it has provided great benefits, we must appreciate that its costs have not always been fully counted and that in many cases the social costs exceed the gain. We should not, therefore, make an all-embracing doctrine of it, but rather be prepared to let individual circumstances determine the nature of policies to be applied in specific cases.

A LIVE-AT-HOME PROGRAM OF REFORM

In many areas of our country more people are trying to make a living from the land than can possibly attain what has come to be recognized as a desired standard of living unless some of the prevailing customs and institutions of agriculture are altered. There is, according to all customary economic analyses, a surplus rural population. According to every economic theory that has any prestige to back it, the surplus of population that is in excess of the number required to produce most efficiently the goods that agriculture ordinarily supplies should be diverted into other occupations. This is a point upon which classical economists and Marxists are in perfect agreement.

But it is in fact the very condition of underemployment in industry that is partly or largely the cause of overpopulation in rural areas. The customary outlet for the excess rural population has been very much restricted. Industry has for a long time been unable to provide employment even for those who are dependent wholly upon it and not at all upon agriculture. To add to this number of unemployed all those from agriculture who are surplus by present commercial standards would be to aggravate an industrial unemployment situation that is already in many respects almost intolerable. Industry cannot be expected voluntarily to provide employment opportunities in the near future sufficient to take care of the surplus rural population. To force industry to take this surplus into decent and permanent employment would involve coercive measures that few if any people are prepared to accept. Regardless therefore of what pure theory might consider to be the most perfect solution of the problem, agriculture itself must provide a livelihood for a larger number of people than sheer production efficiency requires. In view of the fact that we have a national agricultural plant geared to produce more than the market will profitably pay for and since even with the best control measures we are still precariously near overproduction for the market, the only practical and expedient measure in many cases by which rural living standards can be raised is through the increase of subsistence practices.

Some people seem to imagine that an increase of self-sufficiency is a return to the Middle Ages. Perhaps that is because they have complete faith in the universal application of the theory of comparative advantage. Perhaps they like the quality of bigness and the outward appearance of rationalized system that characterize many aspects of modern economic organization. Or perhaps they do not know all the facts about twentieth-century methods of subsistence. Perhaps they are inclined to think of modern agriculture exclusively in terms of the most prosperous big farmers and to forget that a great deal of the specialized commercial production where self-sufficiency is lowest is pursued by means of relatively primitive technology under conditions of great poverty. Commercialization of agriculture, specialization in agriculture, and lack of self-sufficiency do not correlate very well with high living standards. Some of the very lowest rural living standards occur in areas of the most highly commercialized and specialized production. This is true in many of the cotton and tobacco regions of the South and in the truck and fruit areas of the South and of the Pacific coast. When we think of farm people we have to give a place to small farmers and tenants, sharecroppers, hired hands, and migratory workers along with big operators and proprietors.

For vast numbers of farm people that no other practical plan takes into consideration, small proprietorship with self-sufficient practices could produce a much higher standard of living than is now their lot. A change to self-sufficient agriculture would in these cases constitute material progress rather than retrogression. There is nothing medieval or retrogressive about a family supplying its own food from its own acres by means of progeny-tested hens, blooded sires, hybrid corn, pressure cookers, glass jars, electric refrigeration, and quick freezing. Yet it is precisely by such applications of modern technology that subsistence practices can be most effective. There are hundreds of thousands of farm families who produce practically nothing but a single crop of which there is such a market surplus that the price is too low to provide them with cash to buy the things they need. Yet they remain dependent upon the precarious and insufficient cash income from their one market crop to supply many things they could produce themselves with little or no out-of-pocket costs. Diversity of production to include a supply of their own consuming needs would in the first place reduce the need for cash outlay and in the second place tend to decrease the surplus which stands in the way of a good price for the crops that are sold.

A cash income for subsistence groups would continue to be necessary—a cash income sometimes greater than is now received. This would undoubtedly require a greater total cash income for agriculture as a whole than it now receives. But there is no cheaper way of taking good care of our disadvantaged rural people than by lowering the cash cost of a decent and secure living. To the degree that an increased cash income cannot be realized for agriculture by increased urban consumption of farm products, we should resort to a frank and open subsidy for as long a period as economic inequality exists. For the alternative to subsidy is peonage and the development of a proletarian group on a scale that is dangerously incompatible with the ideals of opportunity and democracy upon which our most cherished national institutions are based.

Self-sufficient farming, however, cannot be instantaneously embarked upon by those who have never practiced it. Self-sufficient farming practices are in the first place impossible in tens of thousands of cases unless tenure arrangements as they now stand are considerably changed. Many sharecroppers could not employ self-sufficient practices even if they would. Many who have the economic opportunity to do so cannot because they simply do not know how. In any case a change of farming practices from one or two cash crops to a rounded, live-at-home economy involves vastly more than the mere physical change of planting six crops instead of one or two and tending a score of animals instead of a lone mule. It means new foods to get used to. It means new kinds of concerns, new kinds of practices, and new kinds of knowledge. It means new kinds of pleasures and satis-

223761°—40——60

factions to supplant older ones, and new ideas about life's basic values. And it means almost certainly that there must be a great extension of cooperative activity. For in this modern world of technology, the humble little man can retain his independence generally only through devices of cooperative effort and action that will reduce his disadvantage in competing with vast organizations.

Raising the rural standard of living through increased subsistence practices or by any other means is bound to include educational procedures as a first essential to success. It is also bound in many cases to be a matter of very delicate social engineering. Some reform efforts in the past have come dangerously near to imposing standards that were neither desired nor needed by those whose condition was to be "improved." This has perhaps not been the case in sufficient degree to be a cause for much concern; but nevertheless it is well to remember that what individuals on one cultural level consider essential in a living standard may not seem either necessary or desirable to individuals within another culture or upon a different cultural level. The best and soundest way to introduce a desired practice or material benefit is to work somewhat by indirection—to encourage slowly the desire for a thing while developing at the same time the means of attaining it.

THE BASIC CRITERIA OF PROGRAMS OF REFORM

For the determination of reform programs and policies in agriculture, particularly those that apply to the less privileged groups, there is need for a more scientifically reliable understanding of the basic nature and needs of men. The physical sciences are already able to give us in reliable detail some of the physical requirements of health and well-being. There are certain needs—for food, housing, clothing, sanitation, and medical facilities—that have their basis in man as a biological being. These needs with only a little more clarification and specification than has already been attempted should be established as primary minimums of an agricultural program. There should be no hesitation or delay in adopting measures to remedy deficiencies on this score. In making programs to this end, the best rule would seem to be to devise different measures for specific purposes according to the nature of the circumstances. Proposals or programs that are practical for an immediate situation should of course not conflict with other special programs or with general programs and ideas that we can be sure are practicable and soundly based on fact. But we must for some time avoid generalized programs and ideals and give our attention rather to what is immediately factual and specific, with complete respect for the psychological conditions that are certain to be involved. Above all we must avoid the frequent mistake of deserting a practical and specific program because it seems to contradict a mere theory of how the economic system ought to work if only men and facts were different from what they really are. For we must know that fact precedes theory, and that much of our social theory amounts merely to a combined justification and explanation of the way something was once supposed to work.

Besides the physical requirements of men, certain psychic needs must be considered. In a sense they are more important than the material needs, for they are the ends that material things serve. They cannot in many cases be separated, because they are interdependent. A standard of living, for instance, is unintelligible unless it is set in a psychological and cultural context. Beyond the mere satisfaction of our most elementary biological needs, our wants are determined by the culture in which we live. We want and believe we need electric lights today in the same way that our grandfathers wanted kerosene lamps. Many of the things that are essential to our happiness are essential in no absolute sense but only in relation to the cultural background in which we live. The psychic needs of man may be, in a sense, universal; yet they differ in form and context in different cultures and at different times. Some of these psychic needs seem to be for security, for self-respect and prestige, for intimate experience, and for a relationship with the unknown.

Concerning the need for security, man needs not only to be fed well today but to feel some assurance that he will have food tomorrow also. He cannot enjoy the things he has today if he feels insecure or threatened in their possession. The need for self-respect and prestige means essentially that men desire to think well of themselves. The value standards upon which men may think well of themselves generally derive from their particular culture. A going culture should be expected to provide wide opportunity for the attainment of those things which its value system establishes as necessary to self-respect and happiness. The need for satisfactory intimate experience includes the need for warm fellowship and unquestioning loyalty and in our culture generally finds its most complete expression in relationships within the family. The relationship with the unknown is ordinarily provided for by the institutions of religion.

These psychic needs of man must for the present remain vague because we know relatively little about them. They deserve study and thought and, when they are better understood, must be included within our social goals; for we already know that the denial of these needs leads to maladjustment within individuals and dislocation within society. Because all of these psychic qualities are inextricably related to the material features of life wherever it is lived, we must be ready at all times to recognize not only their presence but also their primary importance, even though we cannot appraise them fully.

The cultural concept inevitably considers reform according to evolutionary principles. Because of the human basis of social institutions in personal habits and attitudes that ordinarily the individual clings to throughout his life, regardless of changes about him, profound social change is a matter of generations rather than of years. The cultural point of view conceives it highly unlikely that any great change in social institutions, however desirable, could be effected with rapidity.

If the evolutionary principle of social change and reform is to prevail peaceably during such a period of accelerated cultural change as the present one, there must be a rather widespread disposition among those of all views to credit their opponents with sincerity and honest motives, and there must be distrust of extreme views and violent language. For in a period such as this, two dangerous conditions almost inevitably develop: one is a confusion of ideas due to the dislocation of old institutions, and the other is a widespread feeling of insecurity that is both economic and psychological in character.

Although absolute certainty could be the only basis of intolerance in a purely logical sense, it actually works out that intolerance generally develops out of a sense of insecurity, which is at least akin to uncertainty. For it is insecurity and confusion that drive men into frantic loyalty to extreme ideas and into desperate and harsh oppression of those who disagree with them. Thus it is the very insecurity and uncertainties of this age that produce the harshest forms of bigotry and dogmatism and intolerance of action. This is the greatest danger, both in agriculture and throughout our national life, that confronts the hope for social progress with a minimum of grief. It is a threat to our spiritual and moral freedom. Tolerance of religious beliefs and practices that we do not ourselves subscribe to must go hand in hand with tolerance of political, social, and economic opinions that we do not agree with. For such tolerance provides a guaranty of a form of human liberty that is basic and a part of the most lasting and timeless of human needs. And above all, tolerance of minority groups and opinions leaves the door open for the development of the new dispositions and arrangements that will be necessary as long as society is dynamic and not static.

The preventive of the danger of intolerance seems to lie, first, in the continuation and practical elaboration of measures to increase the economic security of the vast number of people who are most in need of it, and, second, in the encouragement of a widespread and popular disposition on both an emotional and an intellectual plane to realize that social and economic truths are not absolutes to which mortals have ready access, but rather are valuable but shifting points of view which have immediate practicality.

A PRACTICAL AND PECULIARLY AMERICAN BASIS FOR A REFORM PHILOSOPHY

It is perhaps the greatest tragedy in American history that there has not been in this country a fully developed and distinctly indigenous philosophy of social reform that is applicable to the industrial situation that dominates so much of our modern social problems. The result of this lack has been that an unduly large share of socially minded Americans have attached themselves to creeds and doctrines that may suit the situation elsewhere but are rigid and unrealistic here.

Yet all the while there were in the United States the materials for just the kind of social philosophy that has been most needed. Those materials are to be found in the philosophy of pragmatism, in the economic thought of the so-called "institutionalists," and in the concept of culture. The philosophical pragmatism of William James, George Herbert Mead, and John Dewey considers rationality as an instrument for the prediction and control of experienced facts rather than as a device for grasping realities hidden from the ordinary methods of science, as was typically assumed by the older philosophers. Institutionalist economics, inspired by pragmatism, developed out of the perception that many observed economic facts did not jibe with accepted economic theory. As a consequence, among institutionalists emphasis came to be placed upon the observation and description of economic institutions as they actually exist rather than upon the elaboration or application of theories and principles conceived in the abstract. The concept of culture, which has already been described, though not so peculiarly American as either pragmatism or institutionalist economics, has so far been more widely explored and developed by American social scientists than by any others.

The essence of all of these philosophical concepts is an underlying sense of the relativity of things, a belief that the most ambitious hope that men can hold for their power of understanding is that it serve them well in the particular age and circumstance in which they live. We live upon this earth but once, and at best we see but one small segment of it during a very brief existence. And what we see, we see through limited senses, clouded by the mists of the particular ideas of the culture in which we live. Under such circumstances, wisdom would seem to reside in an effort to work with the materials at hand, trying to fit them together as best we may according to the needs of the moment and the powers we actually possess. In such an effort, man-made doctrines of immutable truth are likely to confuse our thinking more than they clarify it. The greatest intellectual task we have may well be that of stripping our minds of those misconceptions that prevent us from seeing things in the way that in our present circumstances would be most useful to us.

Out of the materials of such relativistic thinking should evolve a social philosophy that is peculiarly American in origin and character. It would not be a rigid creed in any sense, unless it were in a refusal to be a creed. It would be a philosophy that left no place for personal devils or for class or racial devils. It would be democratic, not for reasons of ideological loyalty but rather as a matter of practical effectiveness. It would be pluralistic in rejecting cure-alls and relativistic in rejecting pretensions to absolute or static perfection. It would recognize the interdependence of social phenomena all the way from the monthly creamery check and the Monday-morning washing to the highest aesthetic or philosophic or spiritual concern. It would perceive the impossibility of sharp separation of ends and means because it would see that means tend in the long run to become ends. And it would appreciate that the material things so generally the symbols of desires really exist only for the satisfaction of psychological or spiritual needs. Such a program of agricultural adjustment and reform should be able to avoid the equal evils of rashness on the one hand and dangerous delay on the other.

PART 4

Farm Organizations

Trends in National Farm Organizations

by DeWitt C. Wing [1]

CORRESPONDING to the great labor unions and certain associations of businessmen and industrialists, there are three outstanding national organizations of farmers in the United States—the Grange, the Farmers' Union, and the Farm Bureau Federation. The attitudes, policies, and legislative proposals of these organizations are vital to an understanding of American agriculture, even when they are most critical of this or that element in current programs. Here is a reporter's account of their backgrounds and their viewpoints on national problems, taken almost entirely from their own documents and from interviews with their representatives.

THE PURPOSE of this article is to sketch the origin and development of the National Grange, the National Farmers' Educational and Cooperative Union of America (usually called the Farmers' Union), and the American Farm Bureau Federation and, in the light of their more recent major activities and objectives, to indicate the direction in which nationally organized farmers appear to be moving. Interviews with executives of these organizations in the fall of 1939, along with an examination of their public reports and programs, supplied most of the material on which the article is based. Wherever possible direct quotation will be used so that the viewpoints of the organiza-

[1] DeWitt C. Wing is Senior Information Specialist, Office of Information.

tions or their representatives may be presented in their own words. The age of the organization will determine its place in the discussion.

Some consideration should be given at the outset to the evolution and philosophy of organization and its implications in the United States, where national farm organizations emphasize and continually test the idea of economic equality among industry, labor, and agriculture in a changing world. "Economic equality" is the phrase which the leadership of organized agriculture often uses synonymously with "the general welfare."

An organization may be defined as a group of people who have combined for the purpose of pursuing activities directed to common ends. Agricultural leaders are agreed that organization is a necessary mechanism for obtaining legislation in the interest of farmers and the general welfare. Organization by American business and labor and recurring depressions created the climate and seedbed for continued and increased organization by American farmers.

To business, labor, and farm leaders the advantages of combination have become increasingly evident. The important decisions upon which action is taken are more and more those of bodies of men rather than of single individuals. Farm leadership is concerned with balancing concentrations of power. National farm organizations are striving to develop such vigilant, protective, and continuing efficiency in their sphere of influence as is ascribed to the modern impersonal corporation.

In their origin and development all organized associations of farmers imply that the welfare of the individual member is best served through cooperation with his fellows. Organized farmers and many others subscribe to this thesis, but a common difficulty, usually mentioned by farm organization officials in reviewing their work, is that of maintaining and increasing membership.

A study recently made by Cornell University of 3,000 farmers in a typical rural neighborhood in New York State showed that 20 percent belonged to no organization and 30 percent to only one. It was disclosed by the study in this State that "the organization-minded farmer is usually past 30 years of age, and an owner rather than renter," and that "he has better education and a fairly large farm, with a higher assessment value" (*2*).[2]

> Nearly 60 million people are living in rural America. The National Grange * * * has a dues-paying membership of 800,000. The American Farm Bureau Federation * * * has a membership of 400,000. The C. I. O. has a membership of around 4,000,000, and the American Federation of Labor, excluding the United Textile Workers of America and the International Union of United Automobile Workers, which have just recently received their charters, has a total membership of 3,800,000. Thus organized labor boasts a membership of nearly 8 million as against agriculture's 1¼ million. [To this figure should be added the Farmers' Union membership of 100,000 farm families.] Farm organizations cannot be built up from the top down; growth must start from the bottom (*9*).

Owners as well as renters of family-size farms, small farms, and large farms are represented in the membership of the three national farm organizations. Some of their officials, however, point out that western and southwestern ranchmen who raise beef cattle, sheep, horses, and mohair goats, and farmers and ranchmen who produce

---

[2] Italic numbers in parentheses refer to Literature Cited, p. 978.

purebred livestock make up a very small percentage of the total membership of the three organizations. It is further pointed out that commercial producers of milk, wool, poultry, eggs, chicks, potatoes, fruits, vegetables, nuts, and special crops are most often allied with other organizations, chiefly cooperative marketing associations.[3]

So far as the total farm population of the United States is concerned, agriculture is far less than 50 percent nationally organized. "More than 90 percent of agriculture is still conducted by family size units" (*23*). Regional and local interests with which farm people are daily concerned tend to minimize in their minds the services offered to them by farm organizations which take a national view and seek to express it in terms of a national policy and program for agriculture. National issues do not possess much significance and vitality until they are defined and understood locally. Nevertheless, substantial membership gains have been made by the national farm organizations in recent years. Such gains are interpreted by most leaders as indicating that the conviction is spreading among farmers that since agriculture is a national problem it must be dealt with nationally as an industry. As Earl C. Smith, vice president of the American Farm Bureau Federation and president of the Illinois Agricultural Association put it:

> A great evolution has taken place in the life and work of farm people. Organization is the word that best indicates the evolution that has occurred. Everybody recognizes that business and labor made great strides in organizing their respective groups in advance of farmers. Such action forced farmers to organize in order to keep pace with the march of progress.

As a matter of established policy, the national farm organizations have long been helpful in many ways to the agricultural colleges, the experiment stations, and the Extension Service, which are associated with the United States Department of Agriculture in cooperative services to agriculture. In dramatizing the economic difficulties of agriculture and seeking legislation to assist farmers in dealing with them, these organizations have enlisted the sympathetic interest of many first-rate minds in business, labor, and professional circles. Education and cooperation are repeatedly stressed as major purposes of the farm organizations, which are fostering the application of science and technology to the farming business.

The early history of agricultural organizations in the United States has been sketched briefly elsewhere in this volume (American Agriculture—The First 300 Years, p. 171; Old Ideals vs. New Ideas in Farm Life, p. 111). The writer would like to point out here that as early as 1822 Nicholas Biddle was asking at a meeting of the Philadelphia Society for Promoting Agriculture, "Why is it that Pennsylvania farmers have never yet found leisure to associate for the advancement of their own best interest?" (*16*).

---

[3] Ranchmen and beef cattle producers are mostly members of the American National Live Stock Association, of the United States Live Stock Association, of regional groups such as the Texas and Southwestern Cattle Raisers' Association, Inc., and the Southwestern Sheep and Goat Raisers' Association, or of State associations in the western range country. All of these associations seek to influence State and Federal legislation in the particular interest of their members. A cooperative organization that serves a large and growing group of beef, pork, sheep, and wool producers is the National Live Stock Marketing Association.

Producers of purebred (pedigreed) beef and dairy cattle, hogs, sheep, goats, and horses are members of the various national pedigree registry associations. Horse, jack, jennet, and mule breeders support an over-all organization—the Horse and Mule Association of America—that deals with national, State, and municipal legislation as well as with special problems affecting the horse and mule industry. (Horses in the United States numbered 21,400,000 in 1915; by 1939 the total had dropped approximately 50 percent.)

Figure 1.—William Saunders, one of the founders and first master of the National Grange.

In 1853 talks at farmers' meetings began to center on a now familiar theme. In that year a speaker at a session of the New Hampshire Board of Agriculture said: "The only reason why American farmers are without power is that they have never learned to act in concert." Five years later a convention of middle-western farmers at Centralia, Ill., passed resolutions condemning railroads, middlemen, and speculators, and declared that farmers should have a voice in fixing prices.

After the Civil War, American farmers began to experience their first serious, widespread economic trouble. Instinctively feeling their way toward association with fellow farmers in a common distress, they were eager to join together. Farm organizations of the time were local, social, and educational in character, concerned chiefly with improving and exhibiting farm crops and livestock and increasing production. Distressed farmers whose farms were their only sources of income were not attracted to these organizations.

In Texas the Farmers' Alliance started a movement which spread over the whole Middle West (*20*). By 1890 this organization had a membership of two million. By this time farm organizations had become well aware of agriculture's economic interests.

Charles S. Walker, professor of economics at the Massachusetts Agricultural College, in a paper read at a meeting of the American Economic Association, August 24, 1892, said (*19*):

The farmer's industry has increased the supply of agricultural products beyond the demand, with the consequent fall of price. Here is revealed the efficient cause of his pecuniary condition. The trouble, however, is not that the supply is too great, but that the demand is too little. The other producers have not kept up with the tiller of the soil. * * * The farmers' movement is the awakening of these sturdy citizens from engrossment in manual labor to a sense of their duty, first to themselves and then to society. The movement may be slow, it may do much apparent damage, but it is irresistible, and though it may change the looks of things, in the end its results will prove beneficial.

THE NATIONAL GRANGE

Main Currents of National Grange History

Six of the seven men who founded the Grange on December 4, 1867, were employees of the United States Government; three were identified with the Department of Agriculture (figs. 1 and 2). One of this trio, Oliver Hudson Kelley, suggested the idea of "a secret farmers' organization," and from its founding to the present time the Grange has retained its "secret work and ritual service." The order had "a slow, feeble growth at the beginning * * * before arriving at the period of assured success in January 1873, when permanent organization of the National Grange was effected at Georgetown, D. C." [4]

"The Grange Creed," contained in the organization's declaration of purposes, reads (*11, p. 72*):

We desire a proper equality, equity and fairness; protection for the weak, restraint upon the strong; in short, justly distributed burdens, and justly distributed power. These are American ideas, the very essence of American independence, and to advocate the contrary is unworthy of the sons and daughters of an American republic.

Figure 2.—The birthplace of the National Grange. The Grange was organized December 4, 1867, in the office of William Saunders in this building of the Department of Agriculture, Washington, D. C.

[4] Quotations on Grange history in this section, unless ascribed to other sources, are from Atkeson's Semi-Centennial History of the Patrons of Husbandry (*11*). The official title of the Grange is The National Grange Order of the Patrons of Husbandry.

In 1875 the Grange had 850,000 members, but by 1889 the number had dropped to 106,782. During the 1869–72 period of the Grange's development (*11, p. 36*)—

It was evident that the western granges were finding the educational and social program, as given by the founders, rather tame. With the western farmer, they said, it was not so much a matter of raising crops as it was to market them. Why, they asked, should they study books on scientific agriculture * * * when corn was practically worthless in Indiana and Iowa because of middlemen's profits and exorbitant prices of transportation?

Oliver Hudson Kelley, one of the founders of the Grange, in a letter to William Saunders, a cofounder, wrote:

The idea of discussions upon how to raise crops is stale. They all want some plan of work to oppose the *infernal monopolies*. This seems to be uppermost in the mind of every member I have conversed with.

Kentucky in 1876 had 1,100 Grange chapters, yet the year before, in spite of a largely "agrarian" legislature, the only legislation the outmaneuvered farmers could get through was a reduction in interest rates from 10 to 8 percent (*12*).

At the time of the twenty-fourth annual session of the National Grange, held at Atlanta, Ga., November 12–19, 1890, J. J. Woodman, of Michigan, a past master, remarked (*11, p. 158*): "Other farmers' organizations have sprung up all over the country, and in some of the States [are] sapping the very life blood of the Order."

At the nineteenth session of the National Grange, held at Boston, Mass., November 11–20, 1885, Master Woodman said (*11, pp. 128–129*):

* * * our organization was founded upon the necessities of agriculture, and the principles which underlie it, if carried out, comprehend all that is required to place our interests and our class on a plane of prosperity approximating to that enjoyed by other great interests. * * *

In 1873, when farmers were moving in the work of organization, and the Order had obtained a foothold in nearly every State, the agitation of the question of correcting by legislation the abuses which railroad corporations were practicing in freight charges, began. Farmers of the great Northwest had voted taxes upon themselves, subscribed to stock, and mortgaged their farms to build the roads, in the vain hope that they would realize not only interest and dividends upon stock subscribed, but better prices for their farm products. But in all this they were doomed to disappointment. The money was used, stock absorbed, and farms were sold under the mortgages, and a system of spoliation in freight charges established by the companies which would have disgraced the feudal ages; and the managers of the corporations were raised, as if by magic, from gentlemen in comfortable circumstances to millionaires. No wonder farmers organized to resist these encroachments upon their rights. No wonder that, for once at least, they tore themselves from party ties, held conventions and nominated and elected men pledged to represent their interests. And it was not strange that legislative bodies thus elected should pass laws for correcting, as far as possible, these abuses. * * * Laws thus enacted were resisted by the companies, under the plea that they were operating under general laws and special charters, and were therefore above and beyond legislative control. There was scarcely a statesman or lawyer in all the land that did not coincide in this theory. * * * The parties to the suit were, practically, the farmers of the country, in their newly organized capacity, versus the great railroad corporations. * * * Horace Greeley was the first man of national reputation who espoused the farmers' cause. * * *

At the twenty-ninth annual session of the organization at Worcester, Mass., November 13–21, 1895, Master J. H. Brigham, responding to a request, spoke on "The Secretary of Agriculture: What He Should Be and What He Should Not Be" (*11, pp. 184–186*), giving an interesting sidelight on the agricultural thinking of that day:

* * * He should be a practical agriculturist, one whose associations and sympathies are with the real farmers of the country. * * * He should be ready at all times to aid every movement or enterprise calculated to help farmers. He should maintain harmonious relations, and meet with every national organization of farmers which is honestly striving by proper means to lighten the burdens and increase the social, intellectual and financial advantages of the grand army engaged in tilling the soil. * * *

He should search the world over for markets, and for information that will be of material advantage to the farmers; he should promptly advise them of every fraud or deception which is being practiced upon them in any section of the country. He should strive in every way to make the department useful to the farmers * * *.

If he should have had the advantages of a broad and liberal education, it would greatly increase his power for good, and in many ways aid him in his work.

* * * He should not be a man selected solely for political services rendered his party. He should not be a man who would not feel a sense of great responsibility as the representative of the most important of all industries. * * * He should not be a man who would discourage efforts to form organizations among farmers * * * that will enable them to profit by and enjoy a social culture and a mental training absolutely necessary to their proper development as good citizens * * * able to protect themselves and families from the abuse of power, made possible and probable by the unification and combination of all the great industries of our country. * * *

He, most emphatically, should not be a man who would remain silent or acquiesce in any proposed legislation that would be unjust to agriculture. * * * nor a man who will hesitate to demand rights, privileges and advantages for farmers equal to those enjoyed by other classes. * * *

The thirtieth session of the National Grange, 1896, found farmers somewhat more hopeful than for several years past (*11, p. 196*):

The Grange was essentially cooperative in all its work and methods, but for a number of years its efforts at cooperation were mainly along social, educational and legislative lines. The disastrous panic of 1893, which nearly crushed the life out of agriculture as well as other industries, and which had been dragging its blighting length along for four years, compelled the Grange and the farmers to renew their efforts at cooperative buying and selling, but these efforts were mainly limited to what was known as the "contract system."

An idea ascribed to David Lubin, founder of the International Institute of Agriculture at Rome, Italy, was presented in a resolution, endorsed by the California State Grange, to the National Grange meeting at Springfield, Ill., November 14–22, 1894. It read (*11, pp. 180–181*):

Resolved, That just so long as the protective tariff system is in operation for the protection of American industries, we demand an equal measure of protection for agricultural staples.

Resolved, That this be done by government bounties on agricultural exports from the United States to foreign seaports.

Resolved, That we pledge our most earnest efforts and support to have this proposition become a law of our country.

Grange leaders studied the "Lubin Proposition," and a committee of the order in 1895 resolved that "we urge upon Congress an early and thorough investigation of the subject, and that the legislative committee be directed to present the same to Congress."

At the 1896 session of the National Grange the Lubin Proposition came up again, and was finally disposed of in a resolution declaring that (*11, p. 193*) "this National Grange does not, and never has, indorsed what is known as the Lubin Proposition, to pay an export bounty on agricultural products." Twenty-five years later, however, Grange leadership was still interested in a farm program embodying the export-bounty device.

At the session of the National Grange at Washington, D. C., November 11, 1896, George B. Horton, master of the Michigan State Grange, in the course of a committee report, said (*11, p. 195*):

Trusts, combines and corporate greed are aggressive and persistent. Frequently accomplishing good in the successful execution of great enterprises, which are past the power of individuals to perform, more commonly their operations are a menace to the rights of the people. Those refined sensibilities of the individual man which lead him to regard his neighbor's landmark are absorbed and lost in the combine and trust, and the spirit of conquest, regardless of the rights of others, takes its place.

How can we rest in quiet composure with the handwriting on the wall, which reads to us: Your children and your children's children will gradually settle to lower positions in the social spheres of life, because of rights and privileges gone, and the history of other worlds will have repeated itself here, unless you are vigilant and watchful now?

James Wilson, of Iowa, Secretary of Agriculture for 16 years beginning in March 1897, "ran up from Washington to meet his fellow Grangers," and to make a speech at the thirty-first annual session of the order held at Harrisburg, Pa., November 10–18, 1897. "The National Grange," he said (*11, p. 200*), "represents the farming classes of our people, the half of the nation, the conservative half, the quiet, thinking half, the people who act as referees when there is commotion and settle things rightly."

Considerably more than half of the Grange's present members live in New England, New York, Pennsylvania, New Jersey, and Ohio. New England, with 150,000 members, is often referred to as "the Gibraltar of the Order." "During the past 12 months every New England State has made a membership gain," according to the National Grange Clip Sheet issued January 1940. Women, as well as boys and girls 14 years old or over, make up approximately 40 percent of the Grange's membership. Fred Brenckman, representative of the Grange at Washington, says, "The Order is a family institution before it becomes anything else."

Men and women are on a basis of equality in the organization. Early in the administration of Oliver Wilson, of Illinois, as master of the National Grange, the order indorsed "equal suffrage by amendment of the Federal constitution." Few women, however, have been given high offices in the organization. Mrs. Sarah Gates Baird, of Minnesota, was the first woman to hold the office of master of a State Grange. Mrs. Beulah Haase is now master in Montana, the latest State to organize a State Grange.

National Grange Master Interviewed

Louis J. Taber, of Ohio, thirteenth master of the National Grange, has held that office since 1922. He had served 17 years when he was reelected in 1939. Master Taber describes the organization and objectives of the Grange as follows:

Farming makes a man thoughtful and practical, and, most important of all, he early learns to plan for the future. I well remember, as a fatherless boy down on the farm, a family conference held early one spring. It ended in determination, and the venture to which it led was fairly successful. Farmers must plan their work, their crops, and what they intend to do. This is one of the reasons why the American farmer is the greatest producer per man of any tiller of the soil. This habit of the farmer in planning his work months in advance is followed in the Grange. For more than 70 years our Order has met in mid-November, to outline organization, legislative, fraternal, and business programs for the year ahead. Then officers are elected and committees appointed to try to translate this work into a reality. Every year our organization has some main objectives along with a complete, well-balanced program.

This year our program of almost 40 resolutions revolved around a central three-point theme: Keep America out of war; lift farm incomes; and make the processes of democracy function more efficiently. How may we expect to bring this about?

In the first place, we believe that public opinion is the court of last resort in America. We have 8,000 local Granges, 800,000 dues-paying members, and probably an additional million members who have at some time been active in the Grange field. Farm boys and girls marry, or go to town. They may become bankers, lawyers, or businessmen. They belong to city churches and clubs, but they never forget the obligation and training before the altar of the Grange. Of our 8,000 local Granges, almost 4,000 own their own halls. These are in reality community centers, each with dining room, lodge room, and frequently a juvenile room. Here the Grange meets and the community gathers to talk over farm problems and governmental affairs. Here public opinion is created. Here also start letters, telegrams, and resolutions to Congressmen, Senators, Governors, Cabinet members, and the President himself.

Our second objective—lifting farm income—is the real heart of the program. We just must bring another billion dollars to agriculture this year. Here is where the full legislative program of 20 or 30 different steps comes into full play. We want the American market to the limit of our capacity to supply it. Then we want to develop new markets, and here are great possibilities, not for overnight miracles, but for a long-time, slow march to improve farm conditions. Research is essential to farm progress.

Then we must have our share of the foreign markets. This is a big world; at the same time, with modern speed, it is a very small one. Agriculture must know what is going on and be prepared to meet changing conditions both at home and abroad. This requires cooperation with the national Department of Agriculture, the State college, and the Extension Service, with important research activities coming into the picture.

Here looms another force that is having a slow but definite and powerful influence on agriculture. This is cooperative marketing and cooperative buying. Farmers who help build a strong livestock marketing agency, for example, are better feeders and more careful in management than those who follow haphazard methods. Some of our wool, dairy, and fruit marketing agencies have been a factor in lifting farm income by millions. Standardization, advertising, grading, and quality all count. Here is another place where the Grange is different: We do not want Uncle Sam to do this work for us and tell us just how things should be handled. We want to do things for ourselves, keeping ownership, management, and control right where they belong—in the farm homes of the land.

The Grange realizes that we will not keep up farm income and get this extra billion dollars without doing many other things. Into this picture come conservation and a soil-betterment program as a prominent part of the agriculture of tomorrow. Temporarily we must rely on appropriations from Congress, but it is the Grange goal to give the farmer a price and a share of the Nation's income that will let him run his own business through teamwork, cooperation with his fellows, his Government, and those in other callings.

The Grange challenges business, labor, and Government to cooperate with agriculture to end unemployment, and to bring about permanent recovery. We believe that organization, cooperation, education, and research are effective keys to bring this about.

Now when it comes to the other one of our three major objectives—that of being good citizens and making our American methods work—this again comes back to the Grange, its order of business, its parliamentary procedure, and its program of work. We train people to take a greater interest in school district, town, township, county, State, and national affairs. The Grange is never partisan, but is always interested in public affairs. In all the 70 years of the Grange we have never nominated a candidate for office, and never endorsed one. We never

223761°—40——61

allow an individual to use Grange letterheads in asking for votes for himself or for a political party. On the other hand, we encourage every Grange member to get busy in seeing that the best men are nominated and elected. We believe the office should seek the man, and not the man the office.

The most important phase of Grange work is the opportunity that it gives to young men and women to find their places in the world and to do useful things. We have many men in State legislatures, in Congress, and in other fields of endeavor who received their first training as lecturers and officers in subordinate Granges. President Roosevelt is our most distinguished member, and he has recently been awarded his 25-year pin for a quarter century of continuous membership. But the most important Grange members are the boys and girls who are coming into the Grange by the thousand. They will be the Order of tomorrow. They will make the Grange function when we are gone. Grange women and farm boys and girls have an equal voice and vote with the largest landowner of the community.[5]

Probably the most interesting feature of the Grange is that it does Nation-wide work in a far-flung activity on the smallest dues of any comparable organization in the world. In most subordinate Granges the dues are 10 cents a month. The National Grange program functions on 1 cent per month per member. Many times this has seemed to be a weakness, as we do not have the amount of money we need. On the other hand, it is a source of strength because the first lesson that people must learn is that "it takes more than money to pay my dues: I must give some time and effort to my Grange." It is this sense of responsibility that has kept our Order alive.

The Grange has seen more than 50 farm organizations—State and national—rise and fall. It has gone through four great major depressions, and periods of boom and collapse, drought and bumper crops, and still moves forward because the soul of the Grange is its ritualistic side, and its emphasis is on moral and spiritual ideals. So it is possible for an organization with an annual income of only $100,000 to maintain membership from Alaska to the Gulf, from the Atlantic to the Pacific, and to have more than $25,000,000 in local Grange halls, and to be preparing for its Diamond Jubilee Anniversary in 1941 with the enthusiasm of youth.

National Legislative Program of the Grange

For 1940 the National Grange's legislative program was announced at its annual convention held at Peoria, Ill., November 15–23, 1939. A summary follows:

Farm Policies

In the development of a sound farm policy, we must keep in mind the fundamental American principles of self-help, equality of opportunity, and independence of thought and action. Agriculture asks for fair treatment rather than special privilege. It seeks economic justice rather than subsidy. We favor adherence to the following principles:

Give agriculture its fair share of the national income, in order that it may be raised to a position of equality with other groups.

Give the American farmer the American market to the limit of his ability to supply it.[6]

---

[5] In 1939 Mr. Taber made the following statement in a published article (*18*): "While the problems of agriculture are acute, the most outstanding question after all can be summed up in one word, markets. * * * Markets divide themselves in three great heads, namely, the home market, new markets, and foreign markets. * * * We must open up new markets for the abundance from the farm. * * * Farmers must learn to cash in on the scenery, beauty, health, and recreation of the farms and homes of our land."

[6] In an article in the April 1940 number of the Agricultural Situation (*21*), which is issued monthly by the Bureau of Agricultural Economics, F. L. Thomsen, of the Division of Statistics and Historical Research, says: " 'The American market for the American farmer' is a popular slogan which may be variously interpreted. To some, it implies that there is something undesirable about the export market, or that producers of commodities entering international trade are less fortunate than those producing only for domestic markets. Exported or imported products, it is believed, necessarily must sell for less because they come into competition with the output of producers in other countries with lower standards of living and generally lower costs of production. But the mere fact that a product is sold only in the domestic market, and does not come into competition with exports from competing nations, does not assure satisfactory prices or incomes to farmers. For example, if we compare recent prices of nine leading agricultural commodities which are consumed almost entirely in the domestic markets—and which receive little or no competition from

Speed national recovery by removing unnecessary restrictions from business, increasing employment in private industry and reducing the relief burden, recognizing that the benefits that will accrue will be shared by agriculture and the Nation as a whole.

Maintain the family-size farm as the standard of American agriculture and discourage large-scale or corporation farming, thus upholding America's greatest bulwark of democracy.

Continue the soil conservation program, but never as a means of crop control or a requisite for benefit payments; continue support for the present forestry and wildlife program.

Place the farm program on a voluntary basis, administered in accordance with democratic principles, with compensatory payments continued until farm prices reach parity; all benefits to be paid within the year earned, and not contingent upon compliance in future years.

Create a nonpartisan board, responsible to Congress and representing both producing and consuming interests, with power to regulate imports. Terminate all reciprocal trade agreements now in force that are injurious to agriculture.

Encourage sound cooperative marketing of agricultural commodities.

Remove discriminatory and punitive taxation on all legitimate forms of distribution. Remove unnecessary trade barriers between States.

Encourage research to find new crops and new uses for farm products.

Promote a more satisfactory rural life through development of educational facilities, good roads, and rural electrification.

Encourage cooperation, good will, and understanding between agriculture, labor, and industry to promote the common welfare.

The American market.—Since many artificialities and restrictions have been imposed upon our system of free enterprise during recent years which operate to increase our cost of production and of doing business, and since it is useless to attempt to maintain these artificial standards while permitting unrestricted competitive imports from countries where, because of substandard labor conditions, costs of production are lower than in the United States, it is manifest that proper steps must be taken to protect American interests. Under prevailing conditions, we favor the levying of excise taxes on all imports on the dutiable list when the landed cost of such goods falls below the American wholesale selling price; provided, however, that this rule should only apply to imports of commodities that are commercially available within the United States.

Reciprocal trade agreements.—The reciprocal-trade-agreements program has caused serious damage to American agriculture. It has depressed farm prices by encouraging imports of competitive products from countries where substandard labor conditions prevail. It is wrong in principle and violates the Constitution.

Farm credits.—We advocate the restoration of the independent status of the Farm Credit Administration and favor the creation of a bipartisan board, with staggered terms, to administer its affairs. Our farm-loan system was established as a cooperative enterprise, and farmers have invested huge sums of their own money in it. Continuity of policy and sound management are necessary if funds are to be available at reasonable rates of interest. These ends cannot be attained if the system becomes the prey of political manipulation and is subjected to the uncertainties of frequent changes. We consider it sound policy that low interest rates should be continued until normal farm income is restored. We likewise favor the extension of the Frazier-Lemke Farm Mortgage Moratorium Act under present economic conditions.

New uses for farm products.—The Grange commends Congress for the establishment of the four regional research laboratories, and we trust that these laboratories, as well as those that are privately owned, will put forth their best efforts to find industrial uses for farm products. The Grange favors specific appropriations to State experiment stations to develop new crops that can be profitably grown by farmers.

---

foreign supplies—with prices of nine leading commodities which enter into international trade, we find that both groups average close to 80 percent of parity.*** 'The American market for the American farmer' is a catch-phrase which has been used for many years by many different interests—for causes both good and bad—but it needs to be examined carefully by farmers before it is accepted as a guide to specific action designed to benefit agriculture. In some cases the application of this general 'principle' can be made to yield desirable results for both individual groups of farmers and agriculture as a whole; in others, only harm would result."

Forestry and conservation.—We recommend the adoption of a comprehensive Federal program relating to forestry and conservation and embracing: Encouragement and assistance to private owners in the extension of farm forestry and in the adoption of practices for sustained timber production; more adequate protection from fire to both public and private forest and range lands; greater emphasis on the control of insect pests and diseases and the prevention of floods and erosion; and provision for public acquisition of forests and other lands not suitable to private ownership, with adequate reimbursement to counties in lieu of taxes during a readjustment of the tax program. The Forest Service should remain in the Department of Agriculture and the administration of the Taylor Grazing Act should be transferred to that Department.

Railroads.—We favor continued private ownership and operation of the railroads. Under existing conditions, we believe that it would be good policy to liberalize railroad regulation so far as it can be safely done without jeopardizing the public interest. We believe this would be a more enlightened approach to the solution of our transportation problems than to impose unnecessary regulation on other forms of transportation in order to equalize conditions for the benefit of the rail carriers. We are opposed to the repeal of the long-and-short-haul clause of the Transportation Act.

Motor transportation.—We approve of the appropriations made by the Federal Government for highway construction and advocate the use of a large proportion of such funds for the improvement of farm-to-market and post roads. The interest and safety of the public require enforcement of proper restrictions regarding the size, weight, and speed of all motor vehicles moving over the public highways. Such regulations should be uniform among the several States, and there should be reciprocity between States based upon such uniformity. Every special tax collected for highway improvement should be conserved for that purpose alone. No diversion of such funds should be allowed. No taxation or regulation of motor vehicles should be permitted which has for its purpose any increase in cost or restriction of use in order to equalize competition between motor transportation and other forms of transportation. We oppose the establishment of ports of entry and State-line barriers. We likewise oppose Federal regulation of private motortrucks, including farm trucks.

Inland waterways.—Since the Federal Government, over a period of many years, has expended large sums of money for the development and improvement of our inland waterways, we are opposed to the adoption of any policy which would destroy the value of this wise investment. Our water-borne commerce should not be hindered or restricted by unnecessary regulation and interference on the part of the Government, since no question of monopoly is involved. We favor the early completion of the St. Lawrence Seaway project. We are opposed to any pork-barrel schemes for the improvement of streams that were never intended to be navigable.

Rural electrification.—We heartily approve the efforts of the Government to promote the cause of rural electrification through the agency of the Rural Electrification Administration, and we favor proper appropriations to further this work. In the making of loans, the present policy of giving preference to public power districts and nonprofit cooperative associations should be continued.

Taxation.—Excessive taxation is in large measure responsible for many of our national ills, including unemployment. It should be clearly recognized that spending borrowed money means the same thing as deferred taxation. The Federal budget should be balanced at the earliest practicable date. We oppose a general sales tax, because it is a tax upon the necessities of the people, and ignores the principle of ability to pay. We favor an amendment to the Constitution forbidding the issuance of tax-exempt securites. We are opposed to the levying of processing taxes of the type already declared unconstitutional. Heavy taxes now levied by the Federal Government constitute a growing threat to the sovereignty of the States, drying up the sources of revenue upon which they must depend to finance their activities.

Agricultural education.—We approve of proper appropriations for the land-grant colleges and for the support of extension work in agriculture and in home economics, together with adequate funds for the State experiment stations. We likewise approve of the expanded program for vocational education and for 4–H club work. Extension workers should be paid entirely from public funds, leaving them free to serve the people without favoritism or discrimination. Under no circumstances should any farm organization be allowed to graft itself upon the Extension Service or to dominate it to serve its own ends.

Reclamation.—We protest against bringing any more land under cultivation by irrigation and reclamation at Government expense, so long as the surplus problem presents one of the chief difficulties with which agriculture is confronted.

Truth-in-fabrics.—The fact that during the past 6 years 600,000,000 pounds of reclaimed wool or shoddy has been sold to American consumers as an undisclosed substitute for virgin wool makes it imperative that proper labeling legislation should be enacted by Congress without further delay.

Farm tenancy.—The Grange favors continued efforts for the further development of a sound program for the relief of farm tenancy. In attacking this problem, proper emphasis should be placed upon the correction of conditions which annually cause many thousands of home owners to slip into the tenant class.

Industrial mobilization plan.—Since it is a matter affecting the entire population, we advocate that full publicity be given to the industrial mobilization plan, which is to be made effective in the event of war. This plan should be in accord with the principles of our democracy, and agriculture should be given proper representation on all boards and commissions dealing with the farming industry.

Labor and industry.—It has been fully demonstrated that there is urgent need for revamping and amending Federal leiglsation with reference to the relationship between agriculture, labor, and industry. The Wage-Hour Act should be clarified and agriculture given the exemptions to which it is clearly entitled. The National Labor Relations Act should be made a two-way instead of a one-way act, as it now is, while the Labor Relations Board should be reconstituted so as to give proper representation to labor, industry, and the general public. While recognizing and endorsing the inherent right of labor to strike, we believe that labor unions and their members should be held responsible for unlawful and unwarranted acts occurring in this connection.

Imitation dairy products.—It is of vital interest to the dairy industry as well as the consuming public that all legislation for the control and regulation of manufacturers of and dealers in imitation dairy products should remain in full force and effect. We approve of the action of Congress in placing an excise tax on certain imported oils used in this country in the making of butter substitutes and for many industrial purposes. We advocate the extension of this tax to all imported oils that come into competition with the products of the American farm.

Imported starches.—Since nearly half a billion pounds of Asiatic starches, produced by coolie labor, entered this country duty-free during a single recent year, we favor adequate excise taxes on such products, which compete with domestically produced starch made from corn, potatoes, and rice.

Predatory animals.—We favor legislation providing for joint appropriations by the Federal Government, together with the States and counties, for the eradication of predatory animals in sections where such animals are a serious menace to agriculture. We also advocate more vigorous measures for the control and eradication of insect pests.

Stolen livestock.—The Grange favors renewed efforts to secure the early enactment of legislation making it a Federal offense to transport stolen livestock in interstate commerce.

Argentine Sanitary Pact.—Since American agriculture in the past has suffered heavy losses from the foot-and-mouth disease, brought in from other countries, we are opposed to the ratification of the so-called Argentine Sanitary Pact.

Sugar allotments.—With the United States proper producing less than 30 percent of the sugar consumed domestically, we favor larger and more equitable allotments to American growers.

Crop insurance.—We favor the continuance of the Crop Insurance Act, together with its extension to other crops besides wheat so far as conditions warrant. The granting of this insurance should not be contingent upon compliance with Government control programs.

General Policies

Control of monopoly.—It is manifest that the blessings of political liberty cannot be fully enjoyed under a system which permits monopolistic practices to rob the people of the fruits of their toil. We, therefore, favor more adequate enforcement of the antitrust law.

Socialized medicine.—While approving group health insurance on the voluntary basis, we are opposed to what is commonly known as State medicine.

Packers and Stockyards Act.—We advocate the amendment of the Packers and Stockyards Act to provide for more effective regulation by the Department of Agriculture of the marketing of livestock. Direct buying by the packers, merely to evade the law and depress prices, should not be tolerated. Buyers or factors at public stockyards should be licensed for the protection of the producer.

Motion pictures.—The Grange advocates the enactment of legislation prohibiting block booking and blind selling of motion pictures.

Lotteries and gambling.—We ask for the strict enforcement of the law against lotteries, whether foreign or domestic, and oppose gambling in all its forms.

Registration of aliens.—Since there are several million aliens in the United States who have manifested no intention of becoming naturalized, with many burdening the relief rolls and engaging in subversive activities, the Grange advocates legislation calling for the registration of all immigrants, with payment of a proper fee. Those who refuse to become naturalized within a reasonable length of time, together with those who have entered the country illegally, should be deported.

Un-American activities.—We favor continuance of the congressional committee investigating un-American activities, with an adequate appropriation for its use.

Trading in futures.—The Grange is opposed to gambling in the necessities of life and advocates the vigorous enforcement of the Commodities Exchange Act, together with any amendments that may be needed to make it effective.

Centralization of government.—The Grange reaffirms its stand against overcentralization of government, which violates the wholesome American principle of home rule in local affairs. We are opposed to all legislation, rules, or regulations that would abridge the rights of the States to control their own affairs within proper limits, or that would impair the legitimate rights of the people in matters relating to local self-government.

Temperance.—We recommend that Granges throughout the land join with other organizations in a campaign of education calling attention to the evils of strong drink and emphasizing the truth that decency and sobriety are virtues that bring their own reward.

Keeping out of war.—We approve of proper appropriations for national defense, and favor adherence to a sound neutrality policy that will save America from becoming entangled in foreign wars of greed, hatred, and aggression. We must take the profits out of war. Upon us rests the responsibility of protecting and preserving our free institutions of government and of doing all in our power to restore the blessings of peace to a war-torn world.

THE FARMERS' UNION

Origin and Membership

The National Farmers' Union had its beginnings in 1902 among low-income farmers in Texas. Representing 100,000 farm families in 40 States, it is organized in 21 States and has locals but is not organized in 12 more. Approximately 300,000 farmers are members of the organization's cooperative associations. The whole family become members of the Farmers' Union when the head of the family joins and pays his dues. Country school teachers, ministers, and a few editors desirous of working for the organization are eligible to membership. A strong junior program has been developed. Junior leaders are in training in 16 States, where their education includes leadership, cooperation, and economics. Juniors are 16 to 21 years of age, junior reserves are 12 to 16, and the maximum age of juveniles is 12. Special work is done by each group.

Plans for increasing the efficiency of the National Farmers' Union were formulated at a meeting of its officials December 16, 1939. Action was taken to departmentalize the organization's work. Each department is to have a head and well-defined responsibilities.

C. McCarthy, manager of the Nebraska Farmers' Union Exchange at Omaha, will have charge of the department of cooperation. The goal in this department will be to develop unity, standardization, and cooperation among and between the many Farmers' Union cooperative business enterprises. The importance of this department and the goal sought cannot be overemphasized. Long ago we should have been about the work of bringing our many cooperative enterprises, comprising insurance, farm supplies, livestock, butter, poultry, grain, and cotton marketing, into cooperation with each other. The National President will have the job of supervising and coordinating the work of the departments. He will also have general charge of the national paper. A staff of writers is being recruited from the editors of our other Farmers' Union papers who will contribute articles on subjects on which they are, so to speak, specialists (*8*).

In an article on the growth of the Farmers' Union grain terminal for the spring wheat area (*10*), John Andrews said, in part:

Thousands of grain producers all over the Northwest * * * for more than 40 years have endured * * * a system of marketing which, in effect, barred them from their own markets, and * * * made them pay tribute * * *. [Now, however], farmers * * * own the Farmers' Union Grain Terminal Association, direct its policies, and employ executives skilled in management and experts in the handling of their grain. * * * Following the withdrawal of the Farmers' National Grain Corporation from active service in the grain market on May 31, 1938, the Farmers' Union Grain Terminal Association opened for business on June 1, 1938 [fig. 3]. In the time that has elapsed since then, the Farmers' Union Grain Terminal Association has handled—either by marketing or storing—40,000,000 bushels of grain.

Figure 3.—The Farmers' Union Central Exchange at South St. Paul, Minn., handles grain and livestock for members and patrons and operates at Sioux Falls, Minn., a processing plant that compounds lubricating oil for the Farmers' Union Brokerage Co.

At the close of business of its first year, it showed earnings of $160,000, of which $15,000 was put in reserve. At the close of business on October 31, 1939, it had surplus and earnings of $260,000, in addition to the $15,000 reserve. It has paid all expenses and salaries, and these have grown with the increasing volume of business, with the addition of experts in the various grains, and, in the last few months, when much of the grain went on a loan-storage basis. * * *

When the Farmers' Union Grain Terminal Association began business, it secured a loan of $300,000 from the Farm Credit Administration. In less than 15 months this loan, with interest, had been paid off. That is one measure of the farmer-owned terminal. Another is the increase of local cooperative elevators throughout the Northwest—principally in North Dakota, Montana, South Dakota, and Minnesota. Within the year, 83 new cooperative elevators have become affiliates and members of the Farmers' Union Grain Terminal Association, bringing the total of such elevator members to 220. More than 250 local elevators market their grain through the Farmers' Union Grain Terminal Association, and this number is constantly increasing.

Interview With Farmers' Union President

John Vesecky, president of the Farmers' Union, made the following statement when interviewed early in 1940:

Cooperatives in England were organized with special reference to consumers. Exchange of production between all classes is a basic objective. Consumers want to buy as cheaply as they can. The Farmers' Alliance and the Grange started from the consumer angle. The Farmers' Union is trying to organize farmers into their own group, to educate them in economics, production, and cooperation, and to develop cooperatives, beginning with local cooperatives and going on, through processing and handling, all the way to consumers. Handling one-third of the farm business would be enough to do the job, according to the example set by Sweden. Our joint committee with labor unions is developing consumer cooperatives in cities.

Legislation is still needed for temporary relief. We are pushing legislation to help farmers who have been dispossessed to get a new start, as through the Farm Security Administration. Much more money is needed for this purpose. Help cannot be given to more than one-fifth of those who need it. Must farmers go broke before they can be helped?

We are for refinancing and composing farm debts that are larger than farmers can reasonably be expected to pay. Such debts should be adjusted to amounts that farmers can pay. Leaving them to try to pay out at the present level would force farmers to let their properties deteriorate until finally, when foreclosed, they would bring perhaps one-half of the amounts of the mortgages.

Price and income alone will not solve the farm problem. Our agriculture was at one time carried on by proud and contented homestead owners. Agriculture is now carried on by a few homestead owners free of debt on their land, a very large number of farmers whose land is mortgaged up to and beyond its price value, and by a very much larger group of farm tenants. * * * Our farmers have lost ownership of the soil. Our organization insists that restoration to ownership of the land by those who use it is a prerequisite to any permanent solution of the farm problem.

We remind our farmers of the vast need for them to take an active part in some organized movement for the betterment and stability of agriculture. If you are paying no dues in any farm organization, then we urge you to help support your trade or vocation by joining one of the three major farm organizations.

We are trying to increase the income of farmers by building cooperatives. We are trying to obtain legislation to secure to farmers prices equal to parity or cost of production, whichever is higher, with a view to getting for farmers parity income compared with that of other groups. There are differences between handling commodities in a surplus country and a deficit country.

As an organization, the Farmers' Union is insisting that some form of tax, earmarked for agriculture, similar to the gasoline tax which is earmarked for road construction, be enacted by Congress. Such an assured income for parity benefit or bonus payments to farmers is absolutely necessary to make the farm program workable. * * * Sentiment is decisive in the Farmers' Union against any fixing of prices for farm products. It is unsound to fix prices of goods and services by any method or agency.

We are training members for cooperation in dairy, cotton, and fruit production. We need mills and processing plants and bakeries, and as an outlet for these we need cooperative stores. We have many creameries in Nebraska. Most cooperatives make good butter. We have oil stations, compounding plants, and many wholesale supply outlets, and a few cooperative grocery warehouses and grocery wholesale houses. A cooperative at Arthurdale, W. Va., manufactures agricultural implements. The Grange started implement manufacturing long ago but failed. The Farmers' Union needs a full line of agricultural implements and machinery.

Our main objective is to safeguard family farm homes. All farm legislation must be built around the central idea of enabling farmers, whether tenants or owners, to become home owners. Our home-owning group is too small.

An outstanding purpose of the Farmers' Union is to extend and develop cooperatives among farmers. Its State divisions report progress in operating various cooperatives which they have sponsored. Local units, large wholesales, numerous marketing agencies, processing plants, insurance programs (including fire, life, and hospitalization insurance) and other cooperative services are affiliated with the organization.

According to the Farmers' Union, "democracy is built only by the masses of people; it exists only when the masses have economic democracy as well as political democracy." Cooperatives are essentially the means of achieving democracy in the economic field. Unless our cooperatives are built stronger, and thus the economic power of the masses is increased, neither economic nor political democracy will be continued for long.

In 10 years the Farmers' Union Central Exchange of St. Paul has built up a business, through affiliated local cooperatives, amounting to almost $5,000,000 a year. The Farmers' Union Grain Terminal Association of St. Paul has come to be, in a little more than a year, the largest grain-marketing cooperative in the world. In North Dakota, South Dakota, Montana, Wisconsin, Nebraska, Oklahoma, and other Middle Western States, Farmers' Union members are doing many millions of dollars' worth of business annually with themselves. Cooperatives sponsored by the Farmers' Union are progressing in the deep South, where sharecroppers are finding that these agencies offer new hope.

On the basis of 25 years of successful experience with crop insurance, the Colorado Farmers' Union is developing a broad program of life, health, accident, and property insurance coverage for farm families. Cooperating in this program are Farmers' Unions in Texas, Montana, and North Dakota. Some other States have requested the opportunity of participating. Credit unions of peoples' cooperative banks are being developed in most Farmers' Union States.

In the report of work done by Farmers' Union cooperatives the conclusion is emphasized that, without the educational work done by the parent organization, these accomplishments would not have been possible. We are finding many well-trained young people coming into our cooperatives with social vision, deep convictions, and a thoroughgoing understanding of what makes a cooperative successful.

Educational work done by the Farmers' Union has as its base an internationally known Junior Department, under the leadership of Gladys Talbott Edwards of North Dakota. A panel discussion conducted by Farmers' Union young people at their 1939 convention in Omaha was on "Forces Threatening Democracy." Junior work in 16 States is active under junior leaders.

The Farmers' Union is built to serve and aid farm owners and tenant farmers whose incomes fall in the lower and middle brackets. One of our first considerations in 1940 should be the building up of our membership. Our tentative goal in another year is 150,000 understanding, loyal members.

Farmers' Union Legislative Recommendations

In 1939 at its annual convention held at Omaha, Nebr., the Farmers' Union put on record its views on present and proposed legislation in substance as follows:

The Union believes that failure to pay various forms of poll taxes and property taxes should not be used as a basis for disfranchising any citizen; that the Wagner health bill should be amended so as to assist in constructing and operating cooperative hospitals; that the Federal Farm Mortgage Act should be extended; that agriculture, by amendment, should be included in section 77B of the National Bankruptcy Act; that county committees under the Agricultural Adjustment Act of 1938 should be given broader powers to allot acres to producers in the counties; and that the Farmers' Union should recommit itself to the principle that the cost of production or parity, whichever is greater, be paid for farm products domestically consumed.

The convention was in favor of legislation to protect the public against wool substitutes and legislation that will develop and disseminate to farmers information on marketing and purchasing farm products. It recommended that "State Farmers' Unions sponsor and actively support legislation in their respective States providing for homestead exemption and a graduated land tax."

A peace resolution was adopted. Two resolutions "deplored the tactics" used by the committee to investigate un-American activities, and "the color of publicity given the committee by the national press," and asked that "every action possible be taken fully to protect the civil liberties and civil rights of all American citizens."

The Farmers' Union is advocating a legislative program which includes a debt-adjustment plan; a dairy bill; a cotton certificate plan; a wheat income certificate plan, and a similar one for flax, rye, barley, rice, and other farm commodities. Pending the enactment of its proposed legislation, the organization requests that loans made by the Commodity Credit Corporation be at 75 percent of parity, which is permitted under the present law.

"Although recognizing that the Federal agricultural programs * * * have many weaknesses, and that legislation has not as yet provided farmers with either cost of production or parity price, * * * we believe it would be a serious set-back to American agriculture to lose any of the good points of existing Federal programs. * * * We must keep the present legislation and seek changes and corrective amendments."

Policies and Proposals

Historic principles reaffirmed.—The organization reaffirms the historic and basic principles of the Farmers' Union to attain equity and justice through maintaining a democratic political system, and building a cooperative income system, as the practical expression of the Christian ideal of brotherhood which alone can bring lasting peace and security; to cooperate with organized groups who genuinely seek to provide economic security, preserve democratic processes, provide distribution of abundance for all the people, and maintain our civil liberties. A system of cooperative business, owned by producers and consumers, is the only means by which the potential abundance of this Nation may be made available to all its people, and by which true democracy may be maintained and safeguarded. We urge that our membership continue actively to encourage and promote the development of cooperative business institutions.

To assure democracy.—In an admittedly legislated economy, to assure democracy, agriculture must be assured of a parity position with the other important and essential groups. * * * Legislation must first provide for a revaluation of the farm plant now under mortgage, so that debt and service charges may be related to the potential production of the plant, and also provide conservation of the plant and family. Production insurance and income assurance against drought, insect pests, speculative price changes and other causes beyond control by farm operators must be provided as a matter of national policy. We must soon be done with Federal programs which rest upon perennial political caprice and contribute to the continuing increase in the Federal deficit.

Four proposals.—The Union proposes (1) that payments to cooperators in the soil conservation program be made on the basis of needed soil conservation and be separated from commodity income programs; (2) that the Farm Credit Administration program be expanded to meet the needs of farmers with particular reference to farm tenancy, debt adjustment, land utilization, mortgage refinancing, rehabilitation and emergency relief; (3) that the Farm Credit Administration be transferred to the Department of Agriculture, which has demonstrated through its administration of the Farm Security Administration its capacity and intentions to deal sympathetically and intelligently with problems besetting farm people who, because of drought, insect pests, low prices and other causes, have been reduced to abject poverty; (4) that cooperatives, wherever available and serviceable, be used, giving assurance that the Government will stay out of the field of agricultural distribution.

In all Federal laws dealing with warehousing and distributing agricultural commodities, the Congress has provided directive language to use producers' cooperative associations when practicable. In too many instances Federal agencies have evaded the intent of Congress that producers' cooperative associations, when available, should be used. Large supplies of cotton, corn, and wheat are being accumulated by the Commodity Credit Corporation through loans to cooperators on a basis of a loan unit price above the current market price. It is making use of the facilities and services of producers' cooperative associations, yet gradually building the Government into the field of commercial distribution, to the detriment of all who have invested in the facilities and services of agricultural distribution. It would be a fatal policy in the long-time interest of producers for the Farmers' Union to continue to support appropriations for any Federal agencies which either fail to use existing facilities and services, or would eventually force, by competition, existing cooperative marketing associations to liquidate their enterprises.

Food-stamp plan, electricity, and insurance.—The organization proposes that the Federal Surplus Commodities Corporation be continued; that the food-stamp plan as a means of distribution be expanded; that the usefulness of the Rural Electrification Administration be expanded and accelerated; that the crop-insurance act be revised to insure the top 75 percent of the loss, provided that, in determining the loss, quality as well as quantity be considered; and provided, further, that indemnities paid be eligible to commodity loans, and that the crop-insurance program be extended to other basic commodities at the earliest possible date.

Opposition was expressed to "the assignment of any payment under the farm programs except for the purpose of paying crop-insurance premiums for which Congress has already made legislative provision."

Protection for the family-size farm.—A historic and abiding contention of the Farmers' Union is that "the protection of the family-size farm should be a constant and primary policy and aim in the formulation, amendment, and administration of all farm legislation."

The organization's leadership expressed the view that the "administrative personnel of Federal farm programs should be farmers democratically elected, so far as is legally possible; and all other administrative personnel should be persons who understand, participate in and are in sympathy with farm organizations and the cooperative movement."

Development of cooperatives.—"Adequate and effective legislation" was favored by the convention "to make possible the rapid development of cooperatives, and protect cooperatives in their infancy from large, established enterprises." Protection was asked for the domestic market for American agriculture. The organization seeks a permanent adjustment of interest rates on the indebtedness of agriculture to Federal agencies to those rates enjoyed by private industry. It is for the levying of all taxes on the basis of ability to pay, continued ability to pay being based on net income. It is opposed to the sales tax "because it exacts revenue from those least able to pay." It asks for "refinancing farmers' indebtedness at low interest and on the amortized payment plan," funds to be "provided by Government issue of currency." The organization repeated its demand "for the restoration to Congress of the power to coin and regulate the value of money."

Other Farmer's Union attitudes.—In addition to the foregoing proposals for incorporation or continuation in its 1940 program, the organization seeks to "abolish the practices under which tax-exempt Government bonds are issued"; favors conservation of all natural resources; opposes "regulation of truck and water transportation rates that tend to increase transportation costs"; opposes repeal of the Interstate Commerce Act "commonly known as the long and short haul clause"; and reaffirms "our * * * continued desire to cooperate with our brethren in the mills, mines, and factories." [7]

War and peace.—Farmers' Union officials hold that "war is a natural attribute of an economic system based on the profit motive. Seeds of hatred, intolerance,

[7] A Nation-wide, farm-to-farm poll of the opinion of 6 million farmers on the question, "Are you in favor of labor unions?" was conducted in 1938 and 1939 by Successful Farming, Des Moines, Iowa. In its November 1939 issue this magazine summarized the answers, which showed that in the fall of 1939 "67 percent of Midwest farmers favor labor unions, compared with 73 percent in the rest of the country," and that "farm approval of labor unions is consistently increasing."

and international conflict take root and flourish in a world where economic rivalry creates the tragic contrast of growing poverty for the masses and overwhelming abundance for a few. The brotherhood of men cannot be achieved in an environment distinguished by economic contrasts. * * * A secure and lasting peace can be achieved only through the establishment of an economic system based upon the principles of cooperation which offer a practical pattern for the creation of a warless world."

THE AMERICAN FARM BUREAU FEDERATION

Founding of the Federation [8]

The World War found farmers weak in effective national organization. After the war it became apparent that fundamental economic changes were in the making. The United States had changed from a debtor to a creditor nation. New land had been brought into cultivation all over the world. Soldiers in Europe laid down their guns and took up the plow. Power machinery was threatening to change agriculture as radically as the self-binder had changed it more than half a century earlier. The era of western frontiers had ended. Wartime expansion and wartime debts brought new and pressing problems to agriculture. As one writer put it a decade or so later in 1931 (*15*):

> The Department of Commerce declares that he [the farmer] gets the lowest income of all. In recent years it has usually been a deficit. In spite of this, farm taxes increased to 258 percent of the pre-war level in 1927, while the net composite farm price of 30 major products was but one-third above pre-war levels. Whereas the farmer gets little higher prices than before the war, his taxes have increased 2½ times, machinery costs him twice as much, building materials are two-thirds as much again, and wages he pays are also two-thirds higher than pre-war levels.

A few months of hectic post-war prosperity obscured these problems, but by 1920, when the Federal Reserve Board deliberately set about to answer the high-cost-of-living complaints in the cities by deflating agriculture, it was apparent to farmers that their wartime boom was gone. There was relatively little left of the aggressive, fighting farm organizations of the preceding century.

Just before the World War the idea of county agents, or "agricultural experts," had taken root. Originally financed by commercial companies and organizations for the purpose of increasing farm production and so creating a better farm market for city goods, the idea was later taken over by the United States Department of Agriculture and developed into the present system of agricultural extension, financed jointly by State and Federal funds.

To back up the work of county agents, a few county Farm Bureaus had been formed, composed chiefly of farmers who were interested in improving their farm practices and who welcomed the help of a scientifically trained man located in their county. Before the end of the World War, a few States had federated their county Farm Bureaus into State organizations. Even then the central idea was wholly educational; the purpose was to help farmers solve their individual problems of production on their own farms. But the new movement

[8] Except as indicated otherwise in the text, this account of the founding of the American Farm Bureau Federation and its work up to 1932 is an abridgment of The Good Old Days (*14*), by Clifford V. Gregory, for 25 years editor of the Prairie Farmer.

had vitality. Its personnel was mainly farmers who were aggressively trying to improve their lot by becoming better producers.

When war-inflated prosperity began to fizzle out in 1920, these same farmers were the first to see that a much broader program was necessary for agriculture if it were to save itself. It was only natural that these leaders should see in the embryo Farm Bureau organization an instrument that could be fitted to a new need.

Representatives of the 12 State Farm Bureaus of Delaware, Illinois, Iowa, Massachusetts, Michigan, Missouri, New Hampshire, New York, Ohio, Pennsylvania, Vermont, and West Virginia met at Ithaca, N. Y., in the spring of 1919 and appointed a committee to make plans for a national organization. Tentative organization was completed at a meeting at Chicago in November of that year. On this occasion Henry C. Wallace, then editor of Wallaces' Farmer, said:

> If the purpose of this organization is to carry on the sort of work which Farm Bureaus have been doing heretofore—which is for the purpose of education for the purpose of stimulating production * * * then the Farm Bureau organization * * * will serve no great useful purpose; in fact, it will do harm. But if this is anything at all it is a business organization to secure economic justice for farmers.

After ratification of the plan by the State Federations, the American Farm Bureau Federation was formally organized at Chicago, March 1, 1920, and permanent offices were set up.

The Farmer, St. Paul, Minn., in its issue of February 4, 1922, published an account of the National Agricultural Conference, called to order by Secretary of Agriculture Henry C. Wallace in Washington, D. C., January 23, 1922. President Harding thus addressed the delegates, to whom he had issued invitations to be present:

> Even in our times and under the most enlightened establishments, the soil has continued to enjoy less liberal institutions for its encouragement and promotion than most other forms of industry. * * * A score or more of manufacturers consolidate their interests under a corporate organization, and attain a great increase of their power in the markets, whether they are buying or selling. The farmer, from the very mode of his life, has been stopped from these effective combinations; therefore, because he buys and sells as an individual, it is his fate to buy in the dearest and sell in the cheapest market.

Editor Dan A. Wallace, of the Farmer, was present at the conference. He wrote that—

> a turning point in the history of American agriculture was reached in Washington last week as a result of the first national agricultural conference ever called by a President of the United States. * * * Of the 336 delegates at the conference, 202 were actual farmers. Twenty farm organizations were represented by delegates. The woman's part in farm life was represented by 15 women delegates. Sixty delegates represented agricultural colleges, State departments of agriculture, and marketing agencies, and the farm press. Sixty-two delegates came from business institutions allied with agriculture.

A. Sykes, an Iowa farmer, president of the Corn Belt Meat Producers' Association, spoke of "the pitiable plight of thousands of hard-working tenants who had made their first payments on homes of their own," and went on to say that—

> even middle-aged and old farmers who had accumulated a competence before the war broke out, have watched their assets melt away like ice on a summer day. Why is it, they ask, that they now have to pay 400 bushels of corn for a wagon which they used to buy for 150 bushels? Why must they pay 350 bushels

of corn for a gang plow which formerly cost 125 bushels, or 150 bushels for a suit of clothes that formerly cost 50 bushels, or 33 bushels for shoes that formerly cost 9 bushels? Farmers in the Corn Belt want to know why ham is sold at retail throughout the country at about 6 times the price per pound of live hogs in Chicago when the normal ratio is 1 to 3½. They believe that a reduction of retail prices of ham and some other food products to properly correspond with the reductions of prices received by farmers would do much to stimulate consumption and reduce surplus stocks, and restore normal conditions.

Henry A. Wallace wrote in 1934 (*22*):

Out of this 1922 conference came 37 legislative recommendations * * *. One of the recommendations looked a long way ahead, for it directed Congress and the President to "take steps immediately to reestablish a fair exchange value for all farm products with that of other commodities." The idea of fair exchange value had been described in a pamphlet under the title, "Equality for Agriculture," and the authorship was unknown—until a second edition appeared addressed to J. R. Howard, then president of the American Farm Bureau Federation. On this edition the names of the authors appeared—George N. Peek and Hugh S. Johnson. * * * At the time Peek and Johnson were pamphleteering for equality for agriculture, both were connected with the Moline Plow Co.

It was the purpose of the new Farm Bureau Federation to meet the pressing economic problems of agriculture. It did not believe that there was any cure-all for the economic ills of farmers. No one then dreamed that agriculture's economic problems would become so acute as they did 12 years later, in 1932. The educational purpose of the first county Farm Bureaus was not lost sight of in this crisis. It has always been an important secondary activity. In this work the State Farm Bureaus and the national organization continued to cooperate closely with the State extension services and the United States Department of Agriculture.

Under its organization plan, the Farm Bureau Federation was designed to be farmer-controlled. Its governing body is the board of delegates, which meets annually and formulates policies. Each State Farm Bureau has at least one delegate, with the number of additional delegates based on the size of its membership. The board of directors, which is the governing body between annual meetings, is so set up as to give adequate representation to each section of the country. A similar set-up exists in each of the present 40 Farm Bureau States. At the base are the county Farm Bureaus, which often function with the aid of local community units.

At the outset the Farm Bureau Federation had to find out what needed to be done and how to do it. It recognized clearly from the beginning that what farmers needed above all else was adequate prices. Increased acres under the plow, failing export demand, and power farming were intensifying agriculture's difficulties. Farmers had long been told that the law of supply and demand was something they could not change. The Farm Bureau Federation saw that industry and organized labor controlled supply, and made that control result in higher prices and wages. So the new farm organization set to work to do the same thing for agriculture.

In 1921 the first farm bloc was organized in Congress by the Farm Bureau Federation. Two years later the organization made its first direct attack on farm surpluses by urging farmers to withhold 2,000,000 bushels of wheat from a glutted market. Of more far-reaching importance, it secured an amendment to the warehouse act, which permitted bonded storage on the farm and paved the way for the corn loans made since 1934. When the first Federal corn loan was announced, the price of corn rose from 22 cents to 45 cents almost overnight.

The Farm Bureau Federation soon concluded that the basic trouble with American agriculture was uncontrolled production and marketing. Farmers had been raising all they could, and then putting it on the auction block, to sell for whatever it would bring. Products that they bought were controlled and stabilized, no more being produced and offered for sale than could be sold at a profitable price. Business had learned that the law of supply and demand, like the law of gravitation, could be controlled by a good set of brakes.

So the Farm Bureau Federation went to work to relieve farmers from the effects of uncontrolled supply and demand. Its first plan was to dump surpluses abroad, levying an equalization fee on each basic commodity to pay the loss of dumping. It was believed that the removal of surpluses would cause prices on the proportion of the crop consumed at home to rise to satisfactory levels. With modifications as time went on, this plan was known for some years under the name of the McNary-Haugen bill, which was backed by a coalition of farm forces, under the leadership of George N. Peek and Chester C. Davis. Congress passed the bill in 1926 and again in 1928, and President Coolidge twice vetoed it. The Farm Bureau Federation was the only national farm organiztion that supported the bill.

A larger and larger share of the national income was diverted to cities. Money that should have painted barns, improved farm homes, and increased soil fertility went instead into speculation. During these hectic years, Farm Bureau Federation leaders stood almost alone pointing out that the cities were building their prosperity on sand, and that a prosperity in which farmers did not share could only result in disaster.

After 1929 the condition of agriculture became worse. Circumstances were forcing farmers toward a united front. President Edward A. O'Neal of the Farm Bureau Federation called a conference of leading national farm organizations to meet in Washington, D. C., January 9, 1932. Out of this meeting grew the National Farm Conference, composed of the Farm Bureau Federation, the National Grange, the National Farmers' Union, the National Cooperative Council, the Farmers' National Grain Corporation, and representatives of the farm press.

Meeting at frequent intervals during the succeeding 2 years, this group presented a fairly united farm front. On December 12, 1932, President O'Neal called the farm conference group into session, and a price-parity, production-control, processing-tax bill was prepared, similar in its essential features to the Agricultural Adjustment Act which was passed in the following summer. An effort was made to rush this measure through the short session of Congress, but it was defeated in the Senate after having been passed by the House. The succeeding weeks saw agriculture and business at their lowest ebb in history and the closing of every bank in the United States.

With 40 State Farm Bureaus, the national organization in 1940 has 400,000 members, a majority of whom live in the Corn Belt. Memberships are increasing. The Associated Women of the Farm Bureau Federation number 475,000 members, according to Mrs. Charles W. Sewall, director of this group. In 1930 the total Farm Bureau membership was 321,000, and in 1933 it had dropped to 163,246. Membership dues vary in different States. They run from $2 to $15 a family annually. The national organization receives 50 cents out of each member's dues. Illinois has the largest State Farm Bureau and the highest membership fee—$15. At the end of its fiscal year, November 30, 1939, the American Farm Bureau Federation reported collections from its 39 State organizations of $199,098.65, and total income of $253,878.67. Its total expenses for the same period were $228,204.61, leaving an excess of income over expenses of $25,674.06.

Since its inception the organization has had four presidents: James R. Howard, of Iowa, 1920–22; O. E. Bradfute, of Ohio, 1923–25; S. H. Thompson, of Illinois, 1926–31; and Edward A. O'Neal, of Alabama, who, elected in April 1931, had served as president for 8 years when he was reelected in December 1939.

Interview With Farm Bureau President

Edward A. O'Neal, president of the American Farm Bureau Federation, interviewed early in 1940, said:

Following the trend of the past 20 years, agriculture has become an intricate business, subject to national and world-wide influences. The whole world contributes to the pantry shelf. Extensive growers of head lettuce in new regions almost put out of business gardeners in other regions of the country which formerly supplied the big cities with this product.

Half of the cotton grower's market is foreign, and a third of the tobacco grower's market is across the seas. Prices of cotton in Alabama may fluctuate because of depressing conditions in India, where British spinners sell a lot of their product.

Increased costs of distribution have been taken out of the farmer in recent years. In 1920, farmers got 53 percent of the consumer's food dollar; in 1939 that figure had shrunk to 40.5 percent. Since farming is and always will be largely a business of family-size farms, large farm units will never dominate farm prices as industrial prices are dominated by a few large concerns. Therefore, farmers must organize to bring their group power into action. However, they must not use their power to secure undue advantages. I agree with Henry A. Wallace, Secretary of Agriculture, in that respect.

I am convinced that agriculture's problem is a national one, one that can be solved only through a national approach. Cooperative marketing of commodities is helpful, but it is of no help when a huge surplus drives prices down to bankruptcy levels.

The AAA program has been tremendously helpful, but it has not restored agriculture to parity, and that is the goal for which all farm organizations should work together. I say this because I truly believe that no permanent national prosperity is possible unless agriculture is first made prosperous.

Up to the time when the McNary-Haugen plan for farm relief became dominant, the underlying philosophy of the Farm Bureau Federation gave strong support to cooperation. It started the United States Grain Growers' Corporation and the Producers' Livestock Commission Associations. It was responsible for other cooperatives, such as the American Cotton Cooperative Association, Inc., the Land O'Lakes Creameries, Inc., and the Twin-City Milk Producers' Association. After these cooperatives were organized, they pulled away from the Farm Bureau Federation, which made no effort to hold and control them. The Farm Bureau Federation is not now involved in any cooperative enterprise. It has nothing to do with any cooperative.

In about 1924 the organization changed its basic point of view. It had once thought that cooperative marketing by farmers would solve the agricultural problem. Later, it was convinced that cooperation could not solve the surplus problem. It regarded the Federal Farm Board's operations as being powerless to cope effectively with surpluses. It looked for something else, specifically production control, for which it is stronger than ever before. It is solidly for marketing agreements. It wants agriculture under one roof.

The Farm Bureau Federation wants county agents to captain the whole local show. It wants all agricultural programs and agencies to work outward from local Farm Bureau offices to farmers. It believes in the old notion of the Extension Service as a vehicle for carrying the job to be done to farmers, leaving policy making to a voluntary membership as a foundation.

In recent years there has developed a large volume of cooperative buying by Farm Bureau subsidiaries—although farm leaders in some States do not believe that this is an adequate argument for farmers to organize. If Farm Bureau members in Illinois took advantage of all their buying activities, their patronage dividends would amount to three times the cost of their membership, or $45, yet full-time organization men must be employed to keep up membership. Illinois spends more than any other State to keep up its membership in the Farm Bureau; 70,000 farmers in the State pay over $1,000,000 a year to belong.

Mr. O'Neal said that he was in agreement with the main points of an article by D. Howard Doane in the Nation's Agriculture for October 1939 (*13*). Mr. Doane, according to the magazine, is the "head of an organization specializing in farm management and research for the past two decades." Mr. O'Neal drew particular attention to parts of the article. Mr. Doane notes that a big change in farm management has occurred in the last 20 years. Production was stressed 20 years ago; now it is distribution. He continues:

Formerly we pointed to those with high unit yields as our best farmers. * * * To me one of the most distressing statements that I hear these days is: "That is where Jones used to live. See what a fine farm and home he had. He lost it because he farmed too well." By that our informant means that the money Jones put into good buildings, lime, legumes, drainage, and the like, built up a capital structure that abundant production and low prices would not sustain. Jones spent his reserves to *produce* for a generation that paid him but 20 cents for corn, 30 cents for wheat, and 2 to 3 cents for hogs. His modern plant with increased costs for insurance, taxes, and interest could not meet the situation. During periods of declines, the one who does least succeeds best. * * *

Today those who are succeeding are those who are paying primary attention to two major factors, i. e., low costs of production and efficient marketing. * * *

A modern plan calls for high efficiency. This means, among other things, labor efficiency, hence labor-saving machinery. Twenty years ago we gave each cropper a mule and a set of tools to plow, plant, and cultivate his 20 acres of crop land. Today one man on a four-row tractor prepares the land, plants and cultivates from 200 to 250 acres of cotton. Combines, corn harvesters, and other similar machines contribute to less field labor per unit of operation, hence lower costs.

High yields are still important. With restricted acreages and well-planned soil building programs, we till less acres and get more product. In 1930 on one of our cotton plantations we produced 1,892 bales of cotton on 3,867 acres and in 1937 we produced 3,287 bales on 2,467 acres.

Modern machines have not been the only factors contributing to low production costs. Our livestock programs now emphasize cost per pound of milk, beef or pork, rather than maximum production per day or year or animal unit. More pigs per litter, more hogs marketed per sow. * * * Low labor costs made possible by good systems of barn and lot management. More grazing and less feed and manure hauling, also lower costs of a pound of milk or beef. Better livestock health reduces veterinary and medicine bills, and sends more calves, lambs, and hogs to market per unit of breeding animal.

Farmers are accused of always working for higher prices while the car manufacturer tells us that today he sells us a better car for half the dollars he charged a few years ago. The chief difference in these comparisons is that while the farmer has lowered his costs, neither he nor the consumer has been the beneficiary. The middle groups who do more storing, hauling, processing, packing, advertising, and other handling not only charge more for their services but uselessly in many cases continue to add more and more, often duplicating services.

223761°—40——62

* * * As producers we can be individualistic. As such we used to boast about it but today it has become an expensive luxury that few of us can afford.

* * * The existence of a secure and sound agriculture in this country is directly dependent on the degree to which we maintain control of our products beyond the first stages of production.

The lowest paid workers in the world are those closest to pure production. The farmer who sells at once after the product is produced makes little or nothing. On some of our most profitable farms where we keep accurate records of all costs, we find that the cost of production almost always exceeds the selling price if we sell it immediately after it is produced. Our profits come from our own hauling, storing, insuring, ginning, distributing, financing and marketing. On one property of 7,000 acres we can perform many of these services for ourselves without the help of others. However, even here we are generous cooperators in both selling and processing.

If the last 20 years have taught us as farm managers one lesson above all others it is that we must follow our products beyond pure production.

When we compete as producers we are competing with a group which seldom figures labor costs, never adds a profit before pricing, and does not set the price. When we compete with commercial groups they make their financial calculations and additions thus:

Cost of materials	$
Cost of all labor	
Cost of overhead	
Profit	
Total cost	$
Final price	

From this tabulation and comparison it is quickly apparent why we can show farm profits on the handling and servicing of our products when we cannot if we are producers alone.

Large operators have many ways in which they can provide for themselves the services which others might furnish in handling their own products beyond production. Small operators can obtain the same objectives by cooperating. The small community processing plant, cooperative hauling, storing, and otherwise servicing are necessary steps in a sound agriculture. These last 20 years have shown us the high cost of individualism. It is so high it will break us all if we insist on its retention. * * *

Legislative methods have changed tremendously in the last 20 years. Formerly farmers appeared to need little representation in State Capitols or at Washington. Within the recent past we find that Government is more and more the result of pressure groups. Labor, manufacturers, exporters, bankers, professionals, and all others press for legislation favorable to their interests. Farmers must press *in* also or they will be pressed *out*.

More and more I realize that our job as farm managers is primarily business management, perhaps 15 to 25 percent. The business of farm operation is today's farm management problem. It is the one thing that the last 20 years have brought from a minor to a major position.

As I look forward I seem to see in the future a declining soil fertility; greater tax and other overhead costs; new laws, customs, and business practices which will tend to force agriculture farther into the field of pure production; a low or declining price level (except for a war) for the next 10 to 15 years, and smaller margins, more restrictions, and less volume of production.

These should place a premium on good land and further depress poor land; call for better and more efficient management, and reward the best management; and add to the attractiveness of agriculture as a place of security but make it unattractive for the *average* man who looks upon it as a means of obtaining substantial profits.

Farm Bureau Federation's 1939 Program

At its twenty-first annual meeting, held in Chicago, December 3–7, 1939, the Farm Bureau Federation's resolutions committee consisted of Earl C. Smith, of Illinois; Frank White, of Minnesota; Hassil E. Schenck, of Indiana; O. O. Wolf, of Kansas, Francis Johnson, of Iowa; R. E. Short, of Arkansas; Howard Gray, of Alabama, J. F. Porter, of Tennessee; H. P. King, of New York; John M. Bailey, of West Virginia, George H. Wilson, of California; and Mac Hoke, of Oregon.

The committee reviewed the recommendations of the commodity conferences and resolutions submitted by various individual delegates at the meeting and made the following statement:

> Insofar as the subject matter of these recommendations is not covered by the report of the committee, they seem to require further and appropriate study, and we therefore recommend that they be referred to the board of directors for its consideration, with authority to act within the limitation of the policies and resolutions adopted by the Federation.[9]

Resolutions

Considerably abridged, the foreword to the resolutions and the resolutions themselves follow:

> The fight of organized agriculture * * * has been and is now for equal opportunity and parity position with the other great groups. * * * The creation and maintenance of fair economic balance is essential to the attainment of national prosperity. * * * Military and naval armaments must be limited to a size which will meet the reasonable requirements of national defense. Federal income and credit must not be dissipated in expenditures for unnecessary implements of war. * * * Our national assets must be conserved for creative and reproductive purposes. Consistent with the necessary reasonable restraints which our complex economy requires, economic freedom must be maintained. Consistent with our rights of assemblage and free speech, freedom must not be dishonored through the diffusion of subversive alien theories and philosophies.
>
> *Farm parity and national prosperity.*—A year ago the Federation made the uncompromising statement that prosperity could not and would not be restored except through the attainment of a sound, economic balance to permit the free exchange of goods and services between respective population groups on a fair price and income basis.
>
> With much greater emphasis we reiterate that position. Either there must be a readjustment of industrial and labor policies to bring industrial prices to a level in relation to farm prices which will insure maximum consumption of the products of both agriculture and industry; or agriculture will be forced to demand of Congress appropriations adequate to make the AAA fully effective in bringing farm income to a level which will permit farmers to buy the products of industry in normal volume.
>
> The parity price concept of agriculture as set forth in the Agricultural Adjustment Act of 1938 attests the sincerity of farmers because in that act they ask only for farm prices high enough to insure a fair exchange of farm products for the products of industry. We reaffirm our uncompromising support of the broad principles set forth in the AAA of 1938, which is the most comprehensive and effective law ever written by and for farmers.
>
> Under the AAA program, progress toward parity has been made, but we are still far from our goal, because we have tried to pull a six-horse load with a two-horse team. Control of production has not been rigid enough to raise market prices to parity levels, although it has kept them considerably above the levels to which they would have otherwise fallen. At the same time, appropriations for parity payments have been inadequate to bridge the gap between open market prices and parity.
>
> * * * We believe that failure to raise agriculture's income to parity is the major cause of the unemployment which has cost the Federal Government billions of dollars in relief appropriations. Furthermore, billions have been spent for pump priming, without solving the fundamental problem. This approach has failed because most of the priming has gone into the wrong pumps. Labor needs more jobs and business needs more customers. Both of these needs

[9] Commodity committees were subsequently appointed for livestock, poultry, fruits and vegetables, and dairying.

can be met if the buying power of agriculture, the basic industry, is restored to a fair position. This buying power can come only from parity prices.

* * * If industrial and labor policies are not modified so as to bring industrial prices into fair relation with farm prices, then agriculture must ask for adequate appropriations or other equally effective means of bringing farm prices and industrial prices into mutual focus at a level which will permit maximum exchange of goods and services by all groups.

To the extent that Federal appropriations appear to be the only available means of bringing about fair economic balance between farmers and other groups, we authorize the board of directors of the American Farm Bureau Federation to insist upon adequate appropriations therefor and, if necessary, to support such tax measures as may appear to be most feasible and most effective to assist in raising the required revenue.

We are deeply conscious of the public demand for substantial reduction in Federal expenditures, and farmers completely agree that the business of Government must be put on a sound basis. Nevertheless, we believe that the present excessive cost of meeting emergency needs is the result of failure to solve the farm price problem. * * * It is costing the Government billions because it is not doing the one thing which will solve at once the twin problems of low farm prices and widespread unemployment.

The unsettled condition of the world makes it increasingly imperative that the United States should put its domestic affairs in order without further delay. The cost of accomplishing this by restoring agriculture to complete parity is hardly a drop in the bucket compared to the cost of neglecting to do the one thing which will solve our difficulties. We have temporized with this vital question too long. We must not delay action longer.

Rural credit.—The present cooperative system of rural credit, including Land Bank Loans, production loans, loans to cooperative associations and intermediate credit, has been built up through almost 25 years of struggle and experience of farmers in an endeavor to attain and preserve a fair, effective, sound, permanent and independent farm credit system. This achievement must not be compromised in any manner. We urge that the cooperative features of this system be expanded in the interest of economy, effective administration and service to its member borrowers. Until the parity position of farmers is greatly improved, we further recommend continuation, subject to congressional review, of the present emergency interest rates on Federal Land-Bank loans and commissioner loans, extension of the authority to make Land Bank Commissioner loans, and an amendment to the Bankhead-Jones Farm Tenant Purchase Act to extend the same consideration to worthy distressed farm owners now extended to tenants.

Administrative coordination.—Throughout recent years there has developed from the enactment of laws and amendments thereto the several lines of agricultural credit and the various types of action programs and administrative agencies for the improvement of agricultural commodity prices and rural conditions generally. They are well merited and have accomplished much for the betterment of agricultural conditions. Being developed at different times, it was only natural that what appear to be more lines of administrative machinery than are necessary should have been put into operation that now reach into the respective States and the various counties therein. In the interest of greater economy, a higher degree of efficiency, the removal of duplication of effort, better understanding and permanency, we recommend * * * careful consideration of the advisability of securing such modification of law or laws as seems necessary to provide for placing the full administrative responsibility of all lines of cooperative farm credit and all types of agricultural commodity programs under the direction of two independent Federal boards operating within or properly correlated with the Department of Agriculture.

Local coordination of agricultural programs.—We view with deep concern the growing tendency of governmental agencies to set up special field personnel to contact farmers every time a new program is to be developed or a new job is to be done. The Extension Service of our Land Grant Colleges has definitely proved itself the best qualified agency to carry out the educational work in connection with Federal programs affecting rural people. In the interest of economy and efficiency, and to avoid duplication, confusion and conflicts of policy, we urge that the Extension Service in the States and counties be utilized as the educational and coordinating agency to contact and assist farmers in planning and carrying out all agricultural programs, exclusive of their regulatory and enforcement aspects, in cooperation with farmer committees or other cooperating groups; and that adequate funds be transferred to the Extension Service in States and counties to provide the necessary personnel for such service.

Trade agreements policy.—In giving our support to the continuance of reciprocal trade agreements, we renew, with increased emphasis, our demand that no agreement be consummated the effects of which might be to force or hold domestic prices for any farm commodity below parity level. Any other course would justify the condemnation of and opposition to such agreement by all agricultural groups. We further insist that in the negotiation of trade agreements, economic factors be given consideration equivalent to the weight accorded to the factors of diplomacy and statecraft. To this end we urge that the Reciprocal Trade Act be amended to provide that no agreement be consummated unless unanimously approved by the Secretaries of State, Commerce, and Agriculture.

Transportation.—We reiterate our insistence upon the maintenance of highly efficient, economical systems of transportation under private ownership, with only such reasonable regulation, where it is in the public interest, to assure fair and reasonable rates and services; provide adequately for safety; encourage rather than restrict sound and orderly development and operation; provide reasonable freedom and flexibility to management in fixing rates and in adopting economies in operations, including consolidations, eliminations, and improvements in services and methods; eliminate discriminatory rates or regulations against any commodity or region; and provide relative treatment of different types of transportation, so as to preserve the inherent advantages of each.

Labor.—The American Farm Bureau Federation has always supported organized labor in all reasonable and legitimate efforts to improve the income of workers, and, where necessary, to achieve these ends, their full rights through collective bargaining. We shall continue to support the rights of working people in this respect. However, we deplore the use of violence, boycotts, lockouts, failure to recognize duly constituted governmental authority, disregard of contracts and other irresponsible acts, or any form of intimidation or coercion, either by labor or employers, any or all of which may result in the obstruction of the orderly flow of goods and services to the detriment of the public. For the protection of the public interest, consideration should be given to the creation of impartial arbitration and judicial tribunals for the settlement of jurisdictional and all other labor disputes and grievances, and, in industries handling and processing perishable or semiperishable agricultural commodities, the submission of disputes to such tribunals should be made mandatory. We insist upon early action by Congress to provide a proper definition of agricultural labor in the National Labor Relations Act, and to clarify the exemptions in the Fair Labor Standards Act (Wage and Hour Law) relating to "area of production" and the seasonal and perishable commodities.

Illegal restraints.—We heartily commend and support the Department of Justice in its efforts to enforce the antitrust laws against unlawful restraints, illegal monopolies and practices whether fostered by labor, industry or agriculture.

Transfer of Forest Service.—We reiterate our uncompromising opposition to the transfer of the Forest Service from the Department of Agriculture to any other branch of government. We insist that all the functions of government relating to plant and animal life be retained in or returned to the Department of Agriculture.

Agricultural Advisory Council.—We commend the action of the Secretary of Agriculture in creating a National Advisory Council, composed of producers, processors, and distributors of farm products, and representatives of labor and the general public, to advise with him regarding the problems which have resulted or may result from the present European war. We recommend that the Council use its influence to bring about the coordination of all agencies in the Federal Government toward maintaining parity price standards among the basic commodities of the Nation. Because of its widespread organization of trained personnel, reaching into States, counties and communities, and because of its long years of experience in this field, the Department of Agriculture is better qualified than any other agency of government to handle all emergencies relating to the food and fiber supply for domestic or foreign use; therefore, we urge that whatever action may become necessary in that field be carried on through the United States Department of Agriculture.

Monetary policies.—We commend the action of the United States Senate authorizing its Banking and Currency Committee to make a special study of monetary problems and policies and their effect upon commodity price levels.

Extension of Marketing Agreements Act.—We urge early enactment by Congress of pending legislation to extend the order provisions of the Agricultural Marketing Agreements Act of 1937 to any agricultural commodity.

Tobacco grading.—We urge that the Federal Government appropriate adequate funds for tobacco grading under the Tobacco Inspection Act.

Feed legislation.—We urge that Congress pass necessary livestock and poultry feed control legislation to prevent the movement in interstate and import commerce of feeds containing live noxious weed seeds, and to prevent misrepresentation of feeds in interstate and import commerce.

Marketing service.—We urge that the United States Department of Agriculture, the Land Grant Colleges and the Extension Service place increased emphasis upon research in the field of marketing and distribution of farm products, and to further assist in fostering, developing, and improving marketing services for farm commodities. To the extent necessary, additional funds should be provided by Congress for this purpose. If carried out, current proposals that appropriations be made available to other agencies of Federal or State Governments for this purpose would only result in duplication and confusion, and would not be conducive to the greatest measure of attainment.

Forest conservation.—We reaffirm forest conservation resolutions adopted at Nashville, Tenn., in December 1934, and supplemented annually, with special emphasis on farm forestry; adequate and regular funds for administration of the Prairie States Forestry Project; more adequate control of forest fires, insects, and diseases on private lands through full Federal participation under the principle of the Clarke-McNary Act; Federal research in all phases of forestry; early completion of the Forest Survey; speeding up acquisition and addition to the national forests of forest and submarginal lands mainly unsuited to private ownership, with equitable compensation to local governing units for loss of taxes; improved administration of the national forests, especially in management of range, wild life, and recreation areas, in control of fire and diseases, in developing roads and in other improvements.

Fertilizer program of Tennessee Valley Authority.—American farmers must restore and maintain the fertility of their farms. It is recognized that the necessary processes of husbandry are gradually reducing the store of essential mineral elements in our soils. In particular, the universal deficiency in phosphate is being felt and the urgency of its replacement made evident. Experimental concentrated phosphate products from the Muscle Shoals plant are being made available to agricultural colleges, and to associated groups of farmers throughout the Nation for educational use in practical farm programs which farmers themselves evolve under the guidance of the county agent, and through the agricultural conservation program as grants of aid for soil building practices. We recognize the soundness of the Tennessee Valley Authority's experimental large-scale production of concentrated fertilizers and their distribution for widespread educational use by State agricultural colleges and practical farmers. We recommend the introduction of improved plant food products in those areas which have not yet benefited by their use. In areas where these fertilizers have proved their value, we recommend more extensive use through A.A.A. distribution, such as is now in effect cooperatively with the Authority and private industry. We urge adequate congressional support of the fertilizer program of the Tennessee Valley Authority.

Marketing of livestock.[10]—Through the appointment of a representative committee of livestock farmers and ranchmen, the American Farm Bureau Federation set in motion in 1920 a comprehensive study covering the field of livestock market-

---

[10] According to the Prairie Farmer for May 4, 1940 (*6*): "A much-to-be-desired movement has been started to study present-day livestock marketing. Since the forming of cooperative livestock commission companies some 20 years ago, great changes have come in the way packers get their supplies of meat animals.

"Then, the need of the producers was to have their own commission companies in the great central yards, so that they might know more about the way business was handled in these markets.

"Now, with a high percentage of meat animals bought by packers at small country concentration points, without the aid of a commission firm in any of the central yards, the producers and the yards, too, have another problem. They have talked in and out of season against direct buying by packers. Men with fat hogs to sell have sold them where they found the high dollar, without great regard for loyalty, either to their own commission company or to the great central markets.

"Under American Farm Bureau Federation leadership, an able committee has been appointed to start a new attack on these problems. Farm organizations and farmer-owned marketing agencies will pay the expenses. If as good a job is done now, as was done 20 years ago, under the guiding hand of the late Dean Herbert W. Mumford, then working for the Illinois Agricultural Association, this committee's work will be well worth while."

ing. The results of this study and the action of this committee were comprehensive, and have had the continuous support of the American Farm Bureau Federation. Changes since 1920 in the field of marketing livestock and livestock products have been many and far-reaching in their influence upon livestock producers. It would appear that these changes fully justify a reappraisement of conditions in livestock marketing by a representative committee of livestock producers. We believe the need is so great and the moment so timely that the board of directors of the Federation should take the necessary steps to appoint a committee in cooperation with other interested groups with authority and direction to carry on the study and make recommendations, with appropriate arrangements made to finance adequately such a project.

Truth-in-Fabrics.—We commend the United States Senate for passing the Truth-in-Fabrics bill to require the honest labeling of wool products, and we urge early approval of such legislation by the House. We insist that Congress no longer delay action on this bill to protect wool growers and the consuming public against deception and misrepresentation.

Sugar legislation.—Conditions within the sugar industry of the United States seem to require enactment of legislation for its sound economic adjustment, giving due consideration to the rights of the consuming public. The Federation will support such legislation.

Philippine independence.—We oppose any extension of time for the complete independence of the Philippines, and insist that future trade relations be consistent with the reciprocal-trade policies of the Federation.

Farm Bureau-Extension relationships.—In a large number of States, county Farm Bureaus have been established by law or by mutual agreement as the official local unit of the cooperative Extension Service in agriculture and home economics. In many others, although not so designated, the county Farm Bureaus work in close cooperation with the county farm agents, home demonstration agents, and 4–H Club agents. The county Farm Bureau movement was organized for this and other service to farmers. This friendly working relationship should be maintained and strengthened in these States and extended to such other States in which it is possible for the Farm Bureau to cooperate with the Extension Service in developing and carrying out agricultural programs. We will resist all efforts to destroy or impair this fundamental teamwork of education and organization which has meant so much to the welfare of farm people throughout the years.

Reaffirmation.—We reaffirm the following resolutions adopted at the annual meeting in 1938: Democracy and balance, cooperatives, domestic and foreign quotas, State barriers to trade, discriminatory taxes, freight rates on imports and exports, farm-to-market roads and relief labor, agricultural representation, rural youth, agricultural planning and all other annual meeting resolutions of the Federation that are now in force except insofar as they are modified or supplemented by the resolutions adopted at this annual meeting. We approve the resolutions adopted and recommended by the Associated Women of the American Farm Bureau Federation, as follows:

Rural-urban relations.—The widespread interest in conferences of rural and urban women demonstrates the possibility of achieving better understanding between farm and city through extension of such discussion groups in every section of America. Rural and urban groups are definitely dependent one upon the other; a better understanding between the two will result in benefit to both. We endorse discussion meetings between leaders, men and women, of rural and urban groups.

Discussion.—A great spiritual leader makes the statement that democracy is based upon the conviction that there are extraordinary possibilities in ordinary people. Only through democratic organizations, such as our farm bureaus, can these extraordinary possibilities be discovered and trained to benefit the individual and his community. Open discussion allows everyone a chance to express his ideas and be influenced but not dominated by the ideas of his neighbor. We endorse the discussion type of meeting and pledge our efforts to extend its use in our meetings.

Local units.—The farm home and the family who constitute it must be brought to a fuller realization of the power of organization in the solution of their common problems. In the local units the farm women can bring a notable contribution by careful planning of programs and meetings designed to call attention to the need of concerted effort and the fuller use of their organization to meet these needs.

Coordinated agencies.—Economic conditions have brought to every rural community numerous agencies set up to serve agriculture. Duplication of effort and lack of coordination between these agencies have resulted in a great deal of confusion in the public mind with respect to these agencies. We respectfully suggest that local administrators of these programs consider the possibilities of the county farm bureaus as clearing houses through which the different programs may be coordinated and made more effective.

Health.—The health of the individual is the concern of the Nation. Until every child in America is given the advantage of proper care of his mother before his birth; followed by provisions for pure water, milk, and food in ample quantity; protective and preventive measures against communicable disease; periodic health examinations and correct dental care through his adolescence and adult years, we cannot say we have adequate health programs in our land. To this end our studies should be continued and our efforts redoubled to use every means already at hand to alleviate suffering and improve the physical and mental status of our citizenry. In this, as in many other programs, we will need the cooperation, advice, and support of other groups, and pledge our best endeavors to find solutions to these pressing problems. We therefore reaffirm our position as set forth in our 1938 convention resolutions on health.

Libraries.—Library service is an invaluable aid in the educational and cultural development of children, youth and adults; therefore, we endorse the greater expansion of library facilities for rural people.

Neutrality.—We herewith reaffirm the historic position of our organization in supporting all honorable methods of maintaining peaceful relations with the nations of the world, and we pledge our support to President Roosevelt in his policy of using all just and rightful means to keep this Nation out of the present European conflict.

Cooperative education.—Inasmuch as rapidly changing conditions are definitely affecting farm life in America, it is imperative that broader educational programs be developed along economic lines. Since cooperative endeavor occupies an important place in the preservation of democracy and in the preservation of country life, it is recommended that the American Farm Bureau Federation be asked to enlarge its program to include this cooperative education, emphasizing the following features:

(*a*) Development of business leadership among farm people wherein would be developed successful cooperative activities.

(*b*) Development of education in cooperative principles among rural youth and adults.

To that end we recommend that a committee be appointed from the American Farm Bureau Federation and the Associated Women to urge the possibilities of such a program.

Associated Country Women of the World.—The Associated Women of the American Farm Bureau Federation, assembled in their fifth annual meeting, in cooperation with the twentieth anniversary of the American Farm Bureau Federation, in Chicago, December 3–7, 1939, take this occasion to express genuine welcome to the Associated Country Women of the World, in case they should move their headquarters, temporarily, from London to the United States, as contemplated. The Associated Women of the American Farm Bureau Federation reaffirm their faith in the noble purposes of the Associated Country Women of the World, and pledge their cooperation in helping to preserve this international organization during the present world crisis, because of the significance of the Country Women of the World in cultivating international friendships and in carrying forward education that is dedicated to the eventual substitution of peace for war.

Reaffirmation.—We reaffirm the resolutions adopted at the fourth annual meeting of the Associated Women of the American Farm Bureau Federation, except insofar as they have been modified or supplemented by the resolutions heretofore adopted by this annual meeting.

LEGISLATIVE AND INFORMATION WORK OF THE NATIONAL FARM ORGANIZATIONS

Each of the three national farm organizations maintains Washington, D. C., headquarters, in charge of its own representative, and for use by its executive head while at the Nation's capital on official business. Emulating the established policy of many business, labor, and other organizations, the men who in Washington and at many State capitals represent national or State farm organizations, study and oppose or support legislation affecting the business and welfare of farmers. As "pressure groups," all of these organizations devote realistic efforts to achieving economic equality for agriculture.

Leadership in the State units that finance the national farm organizations through membership fees is not always in full accord with all of the objectives of the national organization. Differences of opinion among members from the bottom to the top of the organized structure often arise, but, it is said, frank discussion usually enables the parties involved to arrive at a common understanding. Serious dissensions within the local, State, and national bodies are decreasing.

A State Farm Bureau Federation, reflecting the sentiment of its membership, sometimes goes on record as favoring or opposing an adopted or proposed policy with respect to which the national organization holds an opposite or different view. Usually, however, the State and national organizations work harmoniously together. State Federations sometimes speak frankly in resolutions on questions having more than State-wide significance; as, for example, the following resolution by the Utah Farm Bureau in 1939:

> We are apprehensive of the effectiveness in solving the farm problem of the efforts of groups of farm people not selected by farmers through democratic processes but which are brought into existence by State and Federal agencies through a process of appointment. These groups are not satisfactorily serving agriculture upon a continuing basis because they lack the support of the farm population and, in many instances, the allegiance of such groups is to the agencies which appoint and subsidize them rather than to the farm people whom they should represent. It is our attitude that State and Federal agencies should recognize the fundamental necessity of having the farm population actively interested in the development of agricultural programs and organization, and in the selection of the personnel who shall direct the same. We deem it essential to the success of any agricultural program that the Farm Bureau or other voluntary farm organizations, and the cooperative marketing, bargaining, service and educational organizations be utilized as the contact agencies in representing and assisting the agricultural producers of the State.

An apparent trend is toward a division of territory among the Grange, Farmers' Union, and the Farm Bureau Federation. The Farm Bureau Federation has recently withdrawn from Pennsylvania, where the Grange has long been comparatively strong, but in a number of States two or all of the organizations are active. Their officials report that memberships have increased substantially since 1933. Some of these officials point out that thousands of young farmers, through their work as county and community committeemen charged with administering Agricultural Adjustment Administration farm programs in every agricultural county in the United States, have received practical training for cooperation and leadership in farm organizations.

Each national farm organization publishes a nationally circulated newspaper or magazine, dealing with subjects of importance to members. The National Grange Monthly, now in its thirty-first year, is printed at Springfield, Mass. Its circulation among members is between 70,000 and 100,000. Master Louis J. Taber is a regular contributor. President John Vesecky of the Farmers' Union contributes editorials, written in the first person, from his official headquarters at Salina, Kans., to the National Union Farmer. In its eighteenth volume and printed semimonthly in newspaper form at Oklahoma City, it has a circulation of 20,500. The Nation's Agriculture, the Farm Bureau Federation's official monthly magazine, edited at the organization's Chicago headquarters, is in its fifteenth volume. Its circulation exceeds 430,000 copies a month. President Edward A. O'Neal writes occasional signed articles for it. John J. Lacey is the editor. He is also director of the organization's department of information.

Where membership in the Farmers' Union is sufficient to justify the expense involved, the organization's State units publish monthly or semimonthly newspapers for State or regional circulation. A national monthly published by the organization serves each State that has no Farmers' Union paper of its own, and goes to locals in unorganized States. Each of the following 12 States has a Farmers' Union paper: Montana, Oregon, North Dakota, South Dakota, Nebraska, Kansas, Oklahoma, Iowa, Wisconsin, Colorado, Arkansas, and Louisiana. L. S. Herron edits the organization's State newspaper in Nebraska; A. W. Ricker is the editor of the Farmers' Union Herald, which circulates in the trade area served by St. Paul, Minn.; and Harvey Solberg edits the Colorado Farmers' Union paper. These men are members of an editorial committee which, in a report to the national organization's convention at Madison, Wis., in 1938, anticipated—

> a mass farm movement toward our ranks, for the reason that all essential factors for growth seem to be present: unanimity, harmony, and an awakening consciousness of the imperative need of farm organization on the part of those who need it most—unorganized farmers. * * * We urge that in every State efforts be made to get our paper for that territory into the hands not only of dues-paying members * * * but also * * * of prospective members, and particularly the patrons of all our cooperatives.

In each of 12 States—South Carolina, Pennsylvania, Ohio, Michigan, Minnesota, Wisconsin, Washington, Oregon, California, Idaho, Kansas, and Colorado—the State Grange publishes a weekly, monthly, or semimonthly paper for its membership. Similar periodicals for members are published by State Farm Bureaus in Alabama, Arkansas, California, Illinois, Indiana, Iowa, Georgia, Kansas, Kentucky, Louisiana, Maryland, Massachusetts, Michigan, Minnesota, Mississippi, Missouri, Nebraska, New Hampshire, Nevada, North Carolina, Ohio, Tennessee, Texas, Utah, Vermont, Washington, Oregon, West Virginia, Wisconsin, and Wyoming. Many of the editors of these State Grange and State Farm Bureau publications devote much of their time to other affairs.

All of these national and State farm organization publications, or house organs, with one exception, receive advertising from private individuals and companies or may compete for it with privately owned farm papers. The Illinois Agricultural Association's Record, a monthly magazine, confines its advertising patronage to the group of cooperative business services which that association performs for Farm Bureau members in Illinois.

Editors of the privately owned farm papers and farm magazines in the United States are in active accord with most of the work and objectives of one or more of the national farm organizations. Readers of the farm press are periodically urged by these editors to identify themselves with a vigorous, growing farm organization. In the Southern Agriculturist for June 1939, an editorial typical of farm press support of an organized agriculture is headed, "Farmers Lose if Unorganized," and the opening sentence reads: "The most consistent loser is the unorganized, noncooperating farmer." Continuing, the editor, J. E. Stanford, says:

Ever since civilization began, people have found it necessary to resort to group action, in order to protect themselves and further their common interests. Communities, cities, and nations that have been best organized and secured the highest degree of cooperation from the citizenship are those that were able to offer the greatest security for their citizens, the best education for their children, and the highest standard of living for all classes.

Farmers, as a whole, have failed to learn this lesson, and are still trying to solve many of their gigantic problems without working together in accord. Much progress has been made in recent years, with many resulting major benefits, but the vast majority of farmers still seem to believe that they can successfully fight their battles single-handed. * * * Agriculture must meet efficient, closely organized, well-directed industry and labor with weapons of a like nature—efficiency, leadership, and organization. Through organized efforts farmers can write into law beneficial legislation that is fair to all other groups.

Clarence Poe, editor of the Progressive Farmer, under the title "Join Organizations for Life," in the May 1940 issue of that southern monthly, says:

The curse of agriculture has been our "in-and-out"—first "in" and then "out"—attitude toward farm organizations. What we need to do now is to develop a lifelong habit of organization right straight on "from the cradle to the grave." We need to enlist boys and girls in 4–H Clubs as soon as they are old enough; then in Future Farmer and Future Homemaker groups; then in juvenile sections of farm organizations, and finally in Farm Bureau, Grange, etc., which they should join as they would join the church—"for life."

TREND TOWARD UNITY

In 1933 the heads of the three national farm organizations—the Grange, the Farmers' Union, and the Farm Bureau Federation—approved the Agricultural Adjustment Act. At their respective annual conventions in 1939, the three organizations were in agreement with respect to agriculture's share of the national income.

Grange: Proper steps should be taken to increase the farmers' share of the national income, giving agriculture equality with other groups. The program should be built on a basis of voluntary cooperation rather than a Government strait jacket.

Farmers' Union: To permit no blackout of our objective to attain parity income for agriculture sufficient to cover production costs, to provide a home free from threat of dispossession, and a decent standard of living for ourselves and our families. No one law or even several laws can make farmers permanently prosperous. We must have effective legislation to insure to our farmers prices high enough to give them their fair share of the national income.

Farm Bureau: The parity price concept of agriculture as set forth in the Agricultural Adjustment Act of 1938 attests the sincerity of farmers, because in that act they ask only for farm prices high enough to insure a fair exchange of farm products for the products of industry.

Concerning tariff protection and trade agreements, the organizations went on record as follows at their 1939 annual meetings:

Grange: If the Reciprocal Tariff Act is to remain in force, trade agreements should be ratified by the United States Senate before becoming effective. * * *

On the whole, the reciprocal agreements negotiated by the Government have not resulted in any increase of farm exports, but have added to the volume of agricultural imports.

Farmers' Union: Protection of the domestic market for American agriculture.

Farm Bureau: * * * we urge that the Reciprocal Trade Act be amended to provide that no agreement be consummated unless unanimously approved by the Secretaries of State, Commerce and Agriculture.

Referring to unity of purpose and action on the part of the national farm organizations, Editor Estes P. Taylor, in the January 1940 issue of the Agricultural Leaders' Digest, says (*19*):

Resolutions passed in 1939 by the National Grange * * * and those passed by the American Farm Bureau Federation * * * show honest attempts to better conditions for farmers. There are many points of similarity and common causes in their fight for the welfare of agriculture. Both came out for the parity principle between agriculture and industry which is perhaps the most fundamental of all rural-urban issues. The most noticeable divergence in national viewpoints is perhaps over foreign trade agreement policy. The Farm Bureau stands with Secretary Hull and Secretary Wallace in favor of a continuance of reciprocal foreign trading arrangements already in effect between the United States and 19 nations. The Grange is opposed to these agreements, believing that the American farmer gets the worst of these trades.

In spite of these differences, the two great farm organizations, and the less influential National Farmers' Union speak for agriculture. Farm organizations are not at serious loggerheads over vital issues. In fact, they evidently present a more solid front than either labor or industry.

In an article on the history of farm legislation, A. W. Ricker said in the National Union Farmer in 1939 (*17*) that—

the Agricultural Adjustment Administration is the product of an agreement on the part of the farm organizations, including John A. Simpson, then president of the Farmers' Union; Edward A. O'Neal, president of the Farm Bureau Federation, and L. J. Taber, master of the National Grange. These heads of farm groups, along with the cooperative organizations, did not agree on details of a program, but they did agree on principles.

Unity, however, may be more apparent than real. A. W. Ricker, editor of the Farmers' Union Herald, says in the February 1940 issue of that monthly (*4*):

William Hirth, one-time president of the Grain Belt Federation of Farm Organizations, still president of the Missouri Farm Association, and editor of The Missouri Farmer, in a recent issue of that paper makes the following prediction:

"In my opinion * * * it is not unlikely that the farm relief of recent years * * * will come to an end * * * and that farmers will once more be left wholly to root hog or die. * * * And yet if the farm men and women of the United States were willing to ignore partisan politics, and would speak with one voice, they could make demands for economic justice to agriculture which neither party would dare ignore, and the time is close at hand when farmers must act in this manner if the Republic is to be preserved."

In California the State Grange and the State Farm Bureau Federation are in conflict over certain intrastate issues:

Deputies of the California State Grange voted unanimously in their annual convention at Sacramento, October 17, 1939, to oppose the return of relief to the counties [on the ground that] such a change in the administration of relief would be pushing taxes back on the home-owners, besides increasing the cost of relief administration. * * * The deputies also came out strongly against the use of the Extension Service as a "tool of any one farm organization." This was a direct attack on the * * * State Farm Bureau Federation (*5*).

With regard to relief, the California Farm Bureau endorses the following among other principles:

Care for the transient indigent is neither a responsibility of local government nor within its powers to finance, and adequate funds must be provided by the Federal Government for this purpose; but its administration must be tied in with other forms of relief under local control.

Farmers should be encouraged and assisted in providing adequate housing facilities for their help.

MOVING TOWARD MORE COOPERATION

During the 1938–39 marketing season, 10,700 farmers' marketing and purchasing cooperatives in the United States, with a total membership of 3,300,000, transacted business amounting to $2,100,000,000, according to R. H. Elsworth of the Farm Credit Administration. Cooperatives handling dairy products led with a $610,000,000 business, followed by grain cooperatives, with an estimated business of $383,000,000.

All national organizations of farmers encourage cooperation. Secretary Henry A. Wallace said in 1939:[11]

> The continued development of the cooperative movement by farmers within the last few years represents a groping on their part for solution of their problems in a truly American way. * * * I sometimes wonder what our corporations would be like, if in the beginning they had been organized like the cooperatives, with each stockholder having only one vote, regardless of how many shares of stock he held, and with proxy voting barred.

Murray D. Lincoln, secretary of the Ohio Farm Bureau, when interviewed by the writer in September 1939, said:

> People have the tools to fashion their own destinies. These tools are the daily purchases of goods and services, bank deposits, and insurance policies. We must redirect the motivation of our economic system. People who use the goods should manage the business and return the profits back to themselves, so that they can buy the products of industry. This is the only way to do it within the framework of our system. The end of all economic acvitity is consumption. Mobilize consumption needs and fill them. Production separates labor, industry, and agriculture into competing groups. Their common interest as consumers should get them together.
>
> Now, due to what science has accomplished in the production of food, and in manufacturing articles, we have arrived at an age of real plenty, so far as production goes. But we have inadequate consumption because of the lack of purchasing power, because of high distributive costs, and because of the profit system with its tariffs, its monopolies and its restrictions. Because of the competition of groups of producers, as well as nations, to control production of both raw materials and manufactured products for their consumptive benefits, we have the paradox of dire poverty amidst great accumulations of wealth.
>
> The farmer is a consumer first and a producer second; his interests as a consumer are identical with the consumer interests of industrial and white-collar workers, and of professional people, but often in conflict with the producer interests of these groups. Consumer action is more effective than producer action. I have personally become convinced of the necessity for farmers to work with urban groups to solve the farm problem, half of which is in the city.

Hassil E. Schenck, president of the Indiana Farm Bureau, says:

> Organization was born of conditions growing out of the World War that threw agriculture out of equality with other groups. When the war ended, farm products declined to ruinous price levels, but things that farmers needed remained high. A protective tariff system keeps a fence around industry. Immigration laws keep a protective fence around labor. If all legislation favoring industry and labor were abolished, American agriculture could take care of itself. The

---

[11] WALLACE, HENRY A. COOPERATION IS THE REAL AMERICAN WAY. Address before the American Institute of Cooperation, Chicago, August 7, 1939.

AAA program gives us something like the protection that has long been given to industry and labor. Every cooperative effort that farmers have made has grown out of a situation in which unfair advantage was taken of farm people.

A. C. Adams, president of the district bank for cooperatives at Spokane, Wash., says (*7*):

Monopoly control of the supply of farm goods, or the fixing of a market price, has little place in modern cooperatives. Instead they must set the pace for their competitors. Good management and adequate financing are not enough for the successful operation of a cooperative. A successful foundation is built on the individual member and his attitude of mind. He must have a stake in the business; he must know the problems of the business. A member should not expect special services for himself that are not available to everybody. Most failures come from the inside.

An editorial in the Washington Farmer (*3*) comments on the expansion of the Grange Livestock Marketing Association into western Washington.

A writer in the Ohio Farm Bureau News in 1939 summed up the views of farmers' organizations as follows (*1*):

The cooperative movement will remove some of our biggest obstacles to prosperity and a higher standard of living. We must develop every possible cooperative service, and we must join hands with other groups of workers—industrial laborers, professional people who are similarly interested. But we must not lose sight of the problems we have as farmers that we can solve only through group action as farmers.

LITERATURE CITED

(1) Anonymous.
1939. FARM BUREAU EXISTS FOR A PURPOSE. (Editorial.) Ohio Farm Bur. News 19 (2): 34.

(2) ———
1939. FARMERS AND ORGANIZATIONS. (Editorial.) Dairymen's League News 23 (42): 4.

(3) ———
1939. GRANGE PLANS COOPERATIVE STOCKYARDS. Wash. Farmer 64 (16): 5.

(4) ———
1940. "AGRICULTURE FACING A NEW CRISIS." (Editorial.) Farmers' Union Herald 14 (2): 4.

(5) ———
1940. GRANGE DEMANDS STATE RELIEF. (Editorial.) Rural Observer 3 (3): 4.

(6) ———
1940. LIVESTOCK MARKETING PROBLEMS. (Editorial.) Prairie Farmer 112 (9): 8.

(7) ———
1940. MOST COOP. FAILURES COME FROM INSIDE. (Editorial.) Wash. Farmer 65 (2): 7.

(8) ———
1940. STREAMLINING THE NATIONAL FARMERS' UNION. (Editorial.) Farmers' Union Herald 14 (1): 4.

(9) ———
1940. STRONGER FARM ORGANIZATIONS. (Editorial comment.) South. Planter 101 (2): 8.

(10) Andrews, John.
1939. F. U. GRAIN TERMINAL HAS REMARKABLE GROWTH. Farmers' Union Herald 13 (12): 3.

(11) Atkeson, Thomas Clark.
1916. SEMI-CENTENNIAL HISTORY OF THE PATRONS OF HUSBANDRY. 364 pp., illus. New York.

(12) Clark, Thomas D.
1937. A HISTORY OF KENTUCKY. 702 pp., illus. New York.

(13) DOANE, D. HOWARD.
1939. TWENTY YEARS OF FARM MANAGEMENT. Nation's Agr. 14 (9): 5–6.
(14) GREGORY, CLIFFORD V.
1938. THE GOOD OLD DAYS. 24 pp. [Chicago.]
(15) HARDING, T. SWANN.
1931. THE DEGRADATION OF SCIENCE. 386 pp. New York.
(16) PHILADELPHIA SOCIETY FOR PROMOTING AGRICULTURE.
1939. MEMOIRS * * *. v. 6.
(17) RICKER, A. W.
1939. HISTORY OF FARM LEGISLATION. Natl. Union Farmer 18 (16):1–2.
(18) TABER, L. J.
1939. MARKETS FOR AMERICA. Amer. Agr. 136 (20): 1, 7.
(19) TAYLOR, ESTES P.
1940. FARM BUREAU AND GRANGE ADOPT 1940 PROGRAMS. Agr. Leaders' Digest 21 (1): 8.
(20) TAYLOR, H. C.
1940. EARLY HISTORY OF AGRICULTURAL ECONOMICS. Jour. Farm Econ. 22 (1): 84–97.
(21) THOMSEN, F. L.
1940. "—FOR THE AMERICAN FARMER." U. S. Bur. Agr. Econ., Agr. Situation 24 (4): 13–15.
(22) WALLACE, HENRY A.
1934. NEW FRONTIERS. 314 pp., illus. New York.
(23) ———
1937. TECHNOLOGY, CORPORATIONS, AND THE GENERAL WELFARE. 83 pp. Chapel Hill, N. C.

PART 5

What Some Social Scientists Have To Say

Cultural Anthropology and Modern Agriculture

by ROBERT REDFIELD and W. LLOYD WARNER [1]

A GREAT deal of our modern understanding of the ways of life of different communities of people has come from the studies made by anthropologists. They have developed new ideas about how communities meet their problems successfully and how a given culture or "civilization" affects the attitudes of all the individuals living in it. For the most part anthropologists have studied primitive societies or the more simple modern communities; but their methods and viewpoint should be valuable aids to understanding the life of groups in a highly complex civilization. Here two well-known anthropologists explore the possibilities tentatively and tell us what our civilization looks like from their point of view. They lay special emphasis on the need for viewing rural community life as a whole and argue that solutions for economic problems cannot be considered apart from this whole.

FARMERS, like other people, live in communities and have traditional ways of getting along. Farmers make adjustments to their natural environment and also adjustments to one another. They have ways of securing a livelihood; they have characteristic relations with one

[1] Robert Redfield is Professor of Anthropology and W. Lloyd Warner is Associate Professor of Anthropology and Sociology, University of Chicago.

another and with persons outside the community; and they have ambitions and ideals and conceptions of what is good and what is bad. The customary ways of life of a community, including the faiths and standards that are current in it, taken in their entirety, may be regarded as solutions developed for problems of survival. People everywhere must live together and must perpetuate themselves. These are the problems that are fundamental and universal.

The cultural anthropologist looks at problems of modern agriculture in the light of such a view of the farming community. Considering a community in relation to what is known of many societies, primitive and modern, is a way of understanding human problems. The social anthropologist thus compares one society with another to find out in what respects all societies are alike. It has been learned that much the same scheme of analysis may be applied to all communities. If the social anthropologist has a contribution to make to the understanding of rural problems it lies in two circumstances—his disposition scientifically to study any one community, as, for example, an agricultural community in the United States, with reference to what is known of all other human societies; and the conception he holds of the customary ways of life of any one community, as these ways are integrated with one another.

The problems of the American farmer have been attacked chiefly on the side of agricultural technology, credit, and marketing, and to some extent in terms of the varied and special efforts at rural betterment sometimes called social welfare. From the viewpoint of social anthropology, the agricultural techniques, farm credits, land tenure, social organizations, and morale of a farming community are all more or less interdependent parts of a whole. This whole, as such, can be objectively studied.

WHY SOCIETIES ARE ALIKE

Societies are all alike, most obviously, in that they provide ways for meeting the fundamental problems. Men—and animals, too—must feed themselves and their young, must reproduce and rear their offspring to sufficient maturity and in large enough numbers to enable their group to survive, and must protect themselves and their offspring from other species and from other groups of their own species. These three general headings cover thousands of separate problems which must be faced wherever people are found living together. Living together is an adaptation in which man adjusts himself to the rest of the physical world, to other men, and to himself.

One preliminary point that the anthropologist is likely to make about man's adaptation to the physical world is that it is accomplished not through changing his physical nature, but through the existence of society. Animals and plants have made adjustments, over long periods, by the development of radical changes in their very organisms. Hereditary differences have come about which are variously adjusted to the needs of various environments. But among the races of men, differences in skin color and in head form and in other physical features are not, in most cases, clearly adaptive. Nor is it clear that the mental capacities of races are different. So far as we know, the races of man are equally intelligent and equally capable of solving their problems of living together. Their varying ways of life are, it seems, social and learned differences and not physical and inherited differences. Therefore, man's adjustment to his surroundings is to be studied in custom and institution, not in anatomy and neural structure.

Perhaps the most basic aspect of man's adjustment to the physical world is the relation between population and resources. Any human community—a farming community, for example—is, very simply, an aggregate of organisms competing with others for food and the other necessaries of life. The ways of life of any settlement depend on or are conditioned by the possibilities for livelihood which the environment offers. And, though men always work out some way of feeding themselves, the ways do not, and in the nature of things cannot, remain adequate indefinitely. The very increase of population that tends to come with success in developing natural resources disturbs the balance between resources and population and in turn demands new adaptations. If the tools and methods for exploiting the resources are modified, these modifications in turn bring changes in the institutions and social organization of the people.

Thus, the presence of the bison enabled a certain number of Indians to live successfully on the Great Plains. The introduction of the horse greatly increased the power of the Indian to hunt bison and so made it possible for more Indians to live on the Plains. It was, no doubt, as a result of the development of cooperative hunting, in a situation in which entire tribes depended upon accessible herds of buffalo, that special groups—soldier societies—with police functions were established among the Indians to prevent individual action on the hunt from endangering the welfare of all. When the gun was added to the horse, the bison were hunted so effectively that they were almost exterminated. This reduction of the herds destroyed the older economic base for Indian life on the Plains, and, with the suppression of warfare by the whites, was largely responsible for the decline or disappearance of the soldier societies and of those military and hunting virtues which had been stressed in the older life.

The present-day situation of many an Oklahoma farmer is quite comparable. Whatever will turn out to be the relative importance of the many contributing factors in bringing about large numbers of deprived and insecure migratory laborers, the interaction of these same interrelated factors will be found to be involved: (1) Population increase, either locally or more generally; (2) accelerated use of limited or marginal resources; (3) strong social and economic pressures operating from without; (4) technical changes, as in the mechanization of agriculture, and important developments in marketing and financing in agriculture; and (5) corresponding repercussions on the institutions of the farmers and their outlook on life.

HOW THE ANTHROPOLOGIST LOOKS AT SOCIETIES

The anthropologist may make a claim to usefulness in the consideration of such matters because of his practice of studying intensively the adjustment of people to the physical environment in its relation to their adjustment to one another. The anthropologist is accustomed to analyzing the interconnections between the land and the people on the land. The ecologist [2] emphasizes the interaction on a biological level. The human geographer carries the matter up to at least the economic institutions of the society. But, for full understanding of many social problems, a complete consideration of the interaction of resources and the many elements of human society is required. In the case cited this would show not only how the resources—bison—were used by the Indians, but how the bison hunting conditioned and was conditioned by the form of society and indeed the very religious and ethical conceptions of the bison-hunting tribes.

It is this view of society as a rounded whole, built upon the land, that is here offered as of significance. Anthropology had its beginnings, like many another science, in speculative philosophy. It became a discipline responsible to fact, in considerable part, as one of the earth sciences—a study of human society as one of the elements in a habitat. It is capable of dealing with the simple question of how a simple community makes a living. And it is, or ought to be, able to carry forward analysis to reach valid and useful conclusions as to how social organization and even the will to live are affected or are likely to be affected by changes in the business of making a living.

In some simple communities the practical problem confronting the administrator may center in a question of getting enough food to enable even a very modest form of living to continue. In such a case the determination of the facts with reference to resources, population, and technology may be enough, for the purpose of dealing with that problem. If a community is starving, it is practically enough to find a way for them to get food. One is not encouraged first to make an exhaustive study of the effects of progressive starvation upon the social institutions of the people. On the other hand, a study of the interrelations of technology and social institutions may be of great practical value. People live not only by eating but also by having relations with one another which they understand and which seem to them right and by having conceptions of extranormal power and good, often specified as gods, in which they believe. The anthropologist might put this aspect of the nature of society somewhat as it appears in the following paragraphs.

DIFFERENCES BETWEEN SIMPLE AND COMPLEX SOCIETIES

Men must not only control nature, but they must also adjust and control their own relations among themselves. They must do this successfully if they are to survive. Social adjustments among the members of a group are made by means of such organizations as the family, the neighborhood, and economic and political organizations.

Each society has built up through the past and present experiences of its members, including their relations with individuals of their own and other groups, a way of life which regulates the lives of the individuals in it and gives these individuals a set of values by which they live. Certain actions are approved and others disapproved by the members of the group, which means that certain ways of behavior

---

[2] Ecology: The branch of biology which deals with the mutual relations between organisms and their environment. (Webster.)

are considered good and others bad, and these evaluations of all activities in the larger sense of the term constitute a body of rules of conduct. Such rules consist of obligations, duties, rights, and privileges by which the individuals who compose the group are controlled.

The social organization of a people not only regulates the relations of the members but also controls the division of labor necessary for the manipulation of the skills and tools. In some societies the labor is equally divided, but in others the division is unequal, and some individuals are given the more pleasant tasks while others, less fortunately placed, do the more unpleasant jobs. These differences in tasks are usually associated with corresponding differences in status. All of the complex societies, including our own, have some kind of status system. A caste system, such as that of India, is so rigidly fixed that every individual is born to perform a certain task and to occupy a corresponding social position.

As we recognize comparatively simple and complex technical systems, it is also possible to speak of simple, or undifferentiated, social structures as compared with complex, or differentiated, social structures. A socially differentiated society is divided into a large number of social institutions, while the simple societies have few social institutions. The family system is often the only formally organized social structure that many of these simple communities possess. The more differentiated communities, such as our own, develop different kinds of institutions to perform different kinds of social functions. The family system, instead of organizing the economic and political activities of the community life, chiefly controls sexual behavior and the early training of the resulting offspring. In primitive societies in Australia, the old men, by virtue of their age and sex, dominate the rest of the group. In complex communities this control is distributed among a great variety of people. Some of them may be politicians, factory owners, administrators, teachers, professors, soldiers, ministers, and church officials.

In complex societies, the appearance of many kinds of people that are not found in the simpler communities means that there is an increase in (1) the specialization of the social activities in the group, (2) the number and kinds of social status, and (3) the amount of individualism.

The increase in specialized activities means that more activities are carried on in a given group but that fewer of them are performed by any individual. The automobile factory performs a highly specialized activity since it makes but one article, and specialization is carried to its ultimate on the assembly line where the workers perform but one or two activities out of the thousands necessary to make the automobile. In the development of automotive manufacture the number of activities has increased, while the number of operations performed by the average worker has diminished. A similar specialization occurs among farmers. One region grows corn, another cotton, and still others the fruits, vegetables, and other crops that supply our needs. An entire community living on the production of one specialized crop will be dependent on a general economic system in which other communities (which in their turn are dependent on other specialized crops) supply the first community with its goods.

The social differentiation of a community gives the people in it a greater and greater variety of situations in which they can act. This tends to produce individualism. Since the variety of relations and situations in which men must live is sufficiently extreme that no two men receive exactly the same training or live in exactly the same social situation, each man is different from all other men.

THE FARMER'S PROBLEMS IN COMPLEX COMMUNITIES

What is the significance of all this for the study of the problems of the farmers? It amounts to the simple fact that the greater heterogeneity in such a life as our own greatly enlarges the problem of maintaining any kind of satisfactory working behavior among the various parts of our huge supercommunity. Some of the problems of social maladjustment that are encountered in the United States are not of the sort found in isolated primitive societies. The problems are functions of our bigness, our rapid change, and the extension of urban characteristics over large parts of the Nation.

The problem of maintaining order here is further complicated by our continuous social change. In our case, social change seems to be stimulated by very rapid shifts in the technical system, which in turn force changes in the social system. Therefore an anthropologist, used to studying problems in the neat capsule of an isolated village, must expand and extend his vision and his methods if he is to be fully useful in connection with problems of the American farm. For whole communities here are strongly affected by events originating quite outside themselves, such as new agricultural inventions or changes in money and finance.

There is another general fact that follows from the comparison of all societies with one another, and especially from comparison of the simple primitive societies with our own, which is significant in considering the contribution of the anthropological viewpoint to the study of the farmer's problems. The comparative view of societies, sketched above, is not complete without reference to the universal existence of sacred beliefs and rituals. These conceptions relate the members of the society to the supernatural, and offer explanations and evaluations of their relations to one another. In part these conceptions center around deities, superior supernatural beings. When men attempt to conform, in their ordinary activities, to the demands of what they believe to be the rules of the gods, they are obeying a sacred ideology, a sort of absolute control over the secular affairs of the community.

There is reason to suppose that these conceptions lose their effectiveness as society becomes very mixed in its elements and as changes become rapid and frequent. Partly this is because people lose understanding of the supposed reasons for their own conduct. "In the old days," said the Indian after he had been put on the reservation, "there was no law; everybody did what was right." By this he meant that actions, being explained and justified by myth, ritual, and the everyday approval of all his fellows, seemed both natural and right. Where a society is left alone long enough, things shake down, so to speak, so that beliefs and customs become harmonious and interdependent. One aspect of contemporary social problems is the result of the break-down of common understandings, especially moral understandings.

In simple agricultural communities such as those of the aborigines of the northern Philippines, or the Pueblo Indians of our own Southwest—at least before the advent of the white man—everyone tends to do part of all the things essential to be done, and all men tend to have similar views of life. Although the practical activities of men tend to be pretty sharply distinguished from the practical activities considered appropriate to women, anything one man does is much like what another does, and the same may be said of the activities of women. If it is a farming community, every man farms, and every man farms in the same way as the others. Furthermore, in such simple societies, every man carries on rituals to assure the security of his crops and also to satisfy his demand for inner well-being, and these are the same rituals his neighbor believes in and practices. The ideas of the gods and of good conduct and bad conduct are substantially the same for every person, man or woman, in the community. Therefore, when a student of such a society discovers what goes on in the mind of any adult in the community, he has learned much of what goes on in the minds of all the others.

The point just made may be briefly put by saying that in such a society the habits of individuals tend to be the same as the customs of the community. But there is more to be said. Not only is it true that there is relative uniformity as one individual is compared with another, but the ways of life of any individual tend to form a whole, and a whole that lies within the comprehension of every individual. Every man has knowledge that covers all the essential activities of life. Each area of knowledge or of practice is related to other areas, so that one is supported by others, and the entire view of life carries conviction to the individual. The view of life is like a network, within which there is a design or pattern to guide each man and to offer him reasons and authorization for what he does.

Thus, to cite one example, the agriculture of the Maya Indians of southeastern Yucatan is not simply a way of securing food. It is also a way of worshiping the gods. Before a man plants, he builds an altar in the field and prays there. He must not speak boisterously in the cornfield; it is a sort of temple. The cornfield is planted as an incident in a perpetual sacred contract between supernatural beings and men. By this agreement, the supernaturals yield part of what is theirs—the riches of the natural environment—to men. In exchange, men are pious and perform the traditional ceremonies in which offerings are made to the supernaturals. These ceremonies are dramatic expressions of this understanding. The world is seen as inhabited by the supernaturals; each has his appropriate place in the woods, the sky, or the wells from which the water is drawn. The village is seen as a reflection of the quadrilateral pattern of the cosmos; the cornfield too is oriented, or laid out east, west, north, and south, with reference to the supernaturals that watch over the cardinal points; and the table altars erected for the ceremonies again remind the individual of this pattern. The stories that are told at the time when men wait to perform the ceremony before the planting of the corn or that children hear as they grow up are largely stories which explain and further sanction this traditional way of life. So we may say of these Indians that each one lives within a system of knowledge and belief and practice that is self-consistent and covers most of the world of which the people have knowledge or with which they have relations of any kind. Not merely, then, are habits with them much the same as customs, but customs and habits form a whole of interrelated parts that covers the round of life. The local community, which produces what it consumes, is composed of people who share this integrated conception of life, a conception which ties together work, play, worship, and all the ways of life from the cradle to the grave.

In the complex societies, in contrast, where the division of labor is high, no one person does more than a small part of everything that needs to be done in order that all may live as the total organization provides. Like the manufacturer and the businessman, the agriculturist carries on specialized functions. All these functions together make up an enormous economic whole. The dweller in the modern community, therefore, is an element in a system for the division of labor which is nation-wide if not world-wide.

The people who participate in this division of labor are not homogeneous, as is the case in a self-sufficient primitive society. They include many kinds of men with different traditions and conceptions. They have different customs and religions. No man understands it all. And if attention is directed to any one local community, such as a farming community in the United States, two important differences will be recognized as that local community is compared with a primitive society. The understanding of no member of that community covers the area and the people included within the system of division of labor of which he is a part. And the ideas and understandings of any one member of that farming community, adapted though they be to the mode of life that is there current, do not have the completeness of interrelationship that is characteristic of the habits and customs of people in self-sufficient primitive societies.

LACK OF COMMON VALUES AND IDEALS IN COMPLEX COMMUNITIES

So a limitation must be put on the statement made early in this article to the effect that in all societies the customary ways of life are integrated with one another; or the statement must be reinterpreted. Societies are always organized in the sense that people divide labor and exchange goods and both compete and cooperate with one another. But there are important differences among societies in the degree to which the people so connected also share common values and social institutions and the degree to which these values and institutions form a well-integrated, self-consistent whole. The hypothesis of the anthropologist is that a tendency to mutual adaption of customs and institutions does indeed exist. But it is also observed that the economic order, or the division of labor, tends to expand beyond the area within which common values and ideals are shared. Therefore, in the case of the rural and the urban communities of modern times, the member of a community of either type may not be capable of thinking beyond the needs of the immediate local community. We seem to recognize this condition when we observe that legislation tends to be a component of pressure exerted by a number of local or occupational groups. Each thinks in terms of its own special needs, but none is concerned with the needs of the entire society.

The anthropologist, if confronted with a particular problem in some particular farming community, such as, for example, the success or failure of a program of land settlement or a new marketing provision, will investigate that new institution in its relations to other elements of the ways of living of that community. He will ask himself: With what other elements of living was the old program of marketing custom connected and how does the substitution affect the work, play, or social structure of the community? Assuming the tendency of customs and institutions to be conditioned by one another, he will consider the new feature in terms not merely of its practical efficiency or its theoretical outcome, but of the values and understandings of the people of that community. He will seek to discover what the new device means to the people, and what changes in their customary ways have followed or are likely to follow as a result of using it. Especially is it common to find that a change in technology brings with it changes in the social organization or in the system of values of the community. The readjustment of the whole body of ways to the effects of the novelty is a matter which can be studied and reported.

Another way of stating this point of view is to declare that provision for human welfare naturally begins with assuring a livelihood and establishing economic security, but it does not end there. Certain employees of a tropical fruit company known to the writers are assured a living wage and are protected from disease. Yet their form of living is not one to which we are likely to aspire. The population in question is heterogeneous; outside of working hours there is little organization in their lives; the people live, and live reasonably well, but they do not have much to live for. Most of us, comparing the condition of these people with that of many a primitive or peasant group in which the social organization is high although the standard of living is low, would prefer the condition of the peasants. A man must eat and be protected from catastrophe; but beyond this, he wants to know why he lives and to have an ideal and a goal.

So the anthropologist is disposed to regard the larger problems of agricultural America—not, of course, the smaller particular problems of local farming communities—as necessarily concerned with this discrepancy between the economic order and the moral or cultural order. The introduction of new tools or new inventions causing restriction or stimulation of production, let alone the construction from the beginning of a new settlement by outside leadership, is likely to have effects upon the moral and cultural order. What these effects will be it may not be possible to predict, but it is always possible to study them and so to improve our understanding of them. The complexity of modern society makes modern social behavior difficult to examine; yet we must study it and study it successfully if we are to control the world around us. A principal contribution from social anthropology is to be found in its methods for studying the relation, or the relative lack of relation, between the technical and economic order, on the one hand, and the moral and cultural order on the other.

From what has been learned from the comparative study of societies it appears that the adequate functioning of an agricultural community, as of any other, is favored when its members share common traditions, ideals, and objectives. In the case of primitive societies the development of common understandings comes about naturally by reason of the fact that the members of the community have lived long and intimately together, facing common difficulties and working out solutions in which everyone participates. To a considerable extent the same result occurs in the growth of rural communities in the United States. Nevertheless, as the foregoing remarks have already indicated, the fact that the farmer's life may be, and actually has been, severely affected by circumstances outside his immediate community and perhaps outside of his comprehension at the least breaks down the common understandings upon which adequate functioning depends and at the most destroys the community entirely.

COMMUNITIES MUST BE VIEWED AS WHOLES

To what extent policy and deliberate action can bring about the development of new common understandings is uncertain. Our rural problems are more complex than those which Grundtvig, in Denmark, went a great distance to solve when, by promoting folk schools for young adults, he strengthened and deepened Danish culture. Nevertheless the method of science is still available for the better understanding of our problems. This method is the objective analysis of subject matter by the use of hypothesis and proof. The practical advantages of science, paradoxically, lie in the abstract and theoretical character of science. By having general ideas, by minimizing the personal bias through the use of formal methods for study and for description, the scientist arrives at more widely acceptable descriptions than those that result from inspiration or prejudice or simply the urge to reform. His descriptions are more acceptable because he offers ways to test his conclusions and a means by which the relations between observation and inference may be made plain.

The cultural anthropologist is simply a scientist who studies human communities as wholes. He has practice in analyzing the interrelations of parts of that whole. He has compared many societies so as to arrive at general ideas as to the nature of all societies. A scientifically trained person from another field might well do what anthropologists do in the study of communities, and some are indeed doing it. Those trained in the study of societies as complete wholes have, however, other things being equal, some advantage. The recurrent forms of social institutions, the ways—to mention a point at random—in which a change in technology is likely to affect the assignment of status in a community, and many related subjects, are matters of which they are aware in advance. The peculiar contribution of anthropology to practical problems may come, if it comes at all, from its long tradition and experience with many kinds of societies, treated both comparatively and theoretically. It has not had to attend solely or chiefly to matters requiring action. It has systematic techniques of field observation and recording. It has terms and categories with which to describe social situations so that hypotheses about them are made accessible to checking and proof.

Useful knowledge is knowledge that is verifiable and complete. To acquire knowledge about societies, it is necessary to make use of such scientific methods of studying societies as exist. To one who wishes to study farming societies as wholes because he believes that farming problems go beyond such matters as markets, credits, and the techniques of production, cultural anthropology offers useful procedures and experience.

Democracy in Agriculture—Why and How?

by Rensis Likert [1]

MODERN agriculture, like modern industry, has enlisted many scientific aids and viewpoints in its service. Among the newest servants of agriculture are psychologists, who have long done useful work in industry and other fields. One of the significant recent contributions of psychology has been the development of procedures for sampling the experience and attitudes of people. Agriculture has begun to use this method to assist administrators to make local adjustments in programs more democratically. It accomplishes this by providing an accurate expression of the felt needs and difficulties of those affected by the programs. Here a psychologist shows how carefully the method must be used and tells what it does. He also furnishes some other sidelights on the problems of democracy as a psychologist sees them.

[1] Rensis Likert is Head, Division of Program Surveys, Bureau of Agricultural Economics.

DEMOCRACY AND THE BASIC HUMAN MOTIVES

ONE of the strongest urges of human nature is a desire to feel secure or safe (*9*).[2] Change and new conditions have a marked tendency to make us feel insecure. Even change that may be to our advantage affects us in this way. The farm in the Dust Bowl that has not had a cash crop in years still is "home," and therefore is familiar and dear to the family living on it. It takes real courage for them to pull up stakes and try their luck elsewhere. Our fear of insecurity, as Shakespeare said long ago, "makes us rather bear those ills we have than fly to others that we know not of."

A situation that makes us feel insecure usually arouses an emotional response. In most people the response is fear; in a few, it is anger. It is characteristic of people under the influence of anger to try to solve a problem by attempting to smash through it. Under the influence of fear, on the other hand, people are apt to try to run away.

These emotional reactions have a profound effect on the mental processes of the person involved. If the emotional reaction is marked, the thinking parts of his brain practically cease functioning, or at least are completely overshadowed and dominated by emotion (*2*). When this happens the individual is indeed handicapped, for he deprives himself of his greatest asset, his ability to think, at the time when he most needs it.

All the changes, confusion, and distress that have occurred throughout the world since the last war have created a marked sense of insecurity, accompanied in the minds of many people by fear. This has caused them to seek to deal with their problems, in part, on an emotional level. Looking for a form of escape, they have in many cases tried to turn their problems over to someone else—a dictator—hoping that he would find a way out. This form of solution at first glance may appear both to solve the problems that are present and to satisfy the desire of the people for security. It may, in fact, do both to some degree, so long as the dictator is benevolent and able. Under such circumstances, the people involved tend to assume a child-parent relationship to the dictator and seem to feel the same sense of security that children enjoy in a patriarchal family.

As history and the experience of peoples today have shown, however, to turn to dictators or absolute rulers as a way of solving problems or escaping from frustrations or insecurities is in the long run an unsatisfactory solution. From the standpoint of the people they govern, dictators are rarely benevolent—though there have been some absolute rulers in the past who have been considered benevolent. More serious, however, is the fact that a dictatorship deprives those governed by it of fully satisfying some of the most powerful motives present in man.

Most absolute rulers rely primarily upon fear to control the behavior of their subjects. Obviously, no one can feel any real sense of security when his and his family's very existence is constantly being threatened. A dictatorship at its inception may temporarily give a sense of security by dealing rapidly and often efficiently with distressing problems caused by changed conditions. Fundamentally and

[2] Italic numbers in parentheses refer to Literature Cited, p. 1002.

over a long period of time, however, it cannot satisfy the basic desire for security, because security cannot be built on fear. Since a democracy does not rely upon fear as a method of control, it can fulfill our desire for security provided that it furnishes adequate economic opportunity and assurance of well-being.

In addition to the desire for security, another motive that exercises a very powerful influence over human behavior is the desire for ego recognition (*6*, *9*)—the desire to feel important and to be favorably regarded. A serious weakness in any absolute form of government is that this desire cannot achieve full satisfaction. A dictator can give partial ego satisfaction to those who will identify themselves with him and his policies. They can bask in his reflected glory. His victories can be theirs. To identify themselves with him, however, they must submerge their own egos to the point where they become practically nonexistent as separate personalities. The leader must be their all. This complete negation of the personality is difficult in the extreme even for many reared under the traditions of absolute dictatorship. For those brought up in the democratic tradition such willing submergence of personality is a virtual impossibility. Full satisfaction of the ego can come only when one feels important not for what someone else is or has done but for what he himself is or has accomplished.

Genuine democracy, on the other hand, makes ego satisfaction a possibility for all. The experience of expressing his opinions unreservedly, of casting his vote, of holding office, of being a member of committees, etc., gives each citizen a real and justifiable sense of participation both in shaping the broad policies of government and in guiding its more specific activities. He feels that its accomplishments and ideals are his rather than "yours" or "theirs." [3]

CONDITIONS NECESSARY TO THE EFFECTIVE FUNCTIONING OF A DEMOCRACY

Among all the forms of government, democracy appears to offer the best opportunity to each citizen to satisfy most adequately some of his strongest drives. For a democracy to function effectively, however, certain conditions must be fulfilled.

Emotionally Mature and Self-Reliant Citizens

In order to function, a dictatorship demands of its citizens a certain emotional immaturity. A democracy, on the other hand, requires that the majority of its citizens learn how to meet situations in an emotionally mature manner. This is the first condition that must be met if a democracy is to function satisfactorily.

Emotional maturity means in part a well-established habit of tackling problems with the brain in full control of the emotions. That is, an emotionally mature person has learned that while it is easier to

[3] The author realizes that his description of the characteristics of dictatorship and of democracy from a psychological standpoint is oversimplified. Since it would be impossible here to discuss the questions involved at length, this brief outline should perhaps be taken as the confession of faith of a psychologist who lives in a democracy. It is true that modern dictatorships have used psychology to achieve popular support for their objectives, often playing very shrewdly on such fundamental human traits as those mentioned here. In the author's belief democracy better fits the basic nature of human beings.

meet difficult situations with outbursts of fear or anger or by running away from them, problems are not satisfactorily solved that way. He has learned that when a problem confronts him he needs all the help the rational, thinking part of his brain can give him. To make democracy work, people must be trained to be emotionally mature in this sense.

Another characteristic of the emotionally mature person is that he takes responsibility for solving his own problems. Among many people, responsibility is avoided by assuming a dependent relationship to others. For example, the servant class in some of the European countries have for generations been taught to look to their masters for security. This pattern is so deeply ingrained that they feel unhappy and insecure in any other relationship. If a democracy is to succeed, its people must have learned to get their security and ego recognition not in a pattern of dependency like that of a child looking to his parent but in the self-reliance of an emotionally mature adult.

Training in Democratic Methods

The habits of people and the patterns in which they have been trained to satisfy some of their strong drives do not change suddenly. They change very slowly, and even then much conscious effort and teaching is required to change them. It is no accident that a nation that has long lived under an autocrat does not suddenly become completely democratic. This fundamental fact of human nature, that man can be trained to satisfy many of his most powerful motives, such as his drive for security, in many different though not equally satisfying ways, provides the basis for the second important condition that must be fulfilled if a democracy is to function with full effectiveness. The citizens of a democracy must have acquired habits of living and thinking that cause them to feel secure only when they are living under a government that requires maturity and self-reliance in its citizens. A democracy, then, must provide extensive facilities and opportunities for its citizens to develop these habits of living and thinking.

People do not suddenly acquire skill in thinking in groups or in the give-and-take of group discussion, nor do they suddenly acquire the habit of participating in such discussions, whether devoted to governmental or other problems. These and similar skills and habits, essential if a democracy is to continue to exist, are learned slowly and only by actual participation in the activities involved. Democracy must actively and continuously foster this participation on which these habits are built.

Machinery for Carrying Out Democratic Processes

The third condition necessary for the success of a democracy is closely related to the second. There must be well-established and well-tested machinery for carrying out the democratic processes. In the United States, this means machinery at every level of government, local, State, and Federal, for dealing with all the special problems of our society.

A democracy in today's world also requires machinery that will enable it to deal rapidly with the sudden problems that arise under

223761°—40——64

modern conditions; and it needs organized procedures whereby administrators can carry out democratically the policies laid down by legislative bodies.

HOW THE UNITED STATES IS FULFILLING DEMOCRATIC REQUIREMENTS

During the last decade the farm people of the United States have instituted important procedures that should enable our democracy to meet better the needs of its citizens. Not only should these procedures permit Government to function in an increasingly democratic manner; they should also provide added opportunity for citizens to gain experience and skill in the use of the democratic process—which in turn fosters habits of emotional maturity.

Many illustrations of these procedures can be cited. Important among them are the democratically elected county and State committees through which the Agricultural Adjustment Administration functions. The democratic procedure back of the soil conservation districts and the whole program of aiding and encouraging cooperatives are among other examples that might be given. Again, in land use planning, local groups are systematically studying problems and working out plans for using the land in such a way as to conserve resources and give to the people dependent upon it the best possible living. The work of these local groups is coordinated with State and national activities.

Increased Responsibility of Administrators

An even more recent development, made necessary by the accelerating complexity of modern life, has occurred in the Department of Agriculture.

A few decades ago, many of the present functions and agencies of Government in the United States did not exist. The great increase in the complexity of Government in modern times tends to make it less rather than more democratic. For one thing, the legislation enacted by the Congress has of necessity become more general. It is virtually impossible, for instance, to draft legislation that is highly specific and have it meet satisfactorily the great variety of conditions that exist between the potato farms of Maine and the irrigated truck farms of California's Imperial Valley. As legislation has become more general, those charged with its execution have been given more and more freedom of action. Instead of executing specific legislative orders, they have been required increasingly to make decisions of their own in order to achieve in local situations the intent of the Congress as expressed in the legislation it has enacted. Yet they have had no practical way of learning how the people desired particular legislation to be carried out. A referendum on this point would have been prohibitively costly; moreover, it would frequently have taken too much time.

Under these circumstances the administrator had no alternative but to select the particular lines of action which, in his judgment and that of his advisers, would be soundest and most nearly in keeping with what appeared to be the desires of the greatest number of people.

A NEW TECHNIQUE FOR MAKING ADMINISTRATION MORE DEMOCRATIC

This trend away from democracy resulting from the increased responsibility thrust upon administrators need not be continued and in fact can be reversed by using methods developed in recent years in the social sciences. These methods make it possible for administrators to find out quickly, accurately, and at very little expense precisely how the citizens of this country or any section of it desire to have any particular act of the Congress administered.

Recently the Department of Agriculture, through a small staff of specialists, has started securing for administrators the information needed to make decisions in accordance with the desires of the people. It is now possible, for example, for the Agricultural Adjustment Administration to secure information on how farmers in various parts of the country want the Agricultural Adjustment Administration program for a particular commodity conducted; or for the Farm Security Administration to learn how the farmers in a given locality want the tenant-purchase plan operated; or for the Soil Conservation Service to find out what assistance farmers in eroded areas desire in carrying out a conservation program.

The method used in obtaining information on these or other issues is what is known as "sampling." It consists in asking questions of a relatively small group of farmers carefully selected so that they will be representative of all farmers. In this way the information needed can be secured much more quickly and at much less cost than is possible through referenda or any other procedure. In fact, the method is the only one now known for securing this kind of information accurately, rapidly, and inexpensively enough to be practicable.

Accuracy of the Sampling Method

For the technique to yield accurate results, however, it must be used in a careful, scientific manner, and all the checks and safeguards that research has shown to be necesssary must be adhered to rigorously. If this is done, surprisingly accurate results can be obtained from relatively small samples of interviews with farmers. A

Table 1.—Possible error of measurement due to size of sample

Number of persons in sample	Error [1] of given answer when the percentage obtained for that answer [2] is—				
	10	30	50	70	90
	Percent	*Percent*	*Percent*	*Percent*	*Percent*
250	5.7	8.7	9.5	8.7	5.7
500	4.0	6.2	6.7	6.2	4.0
1,000	2.8	4.4	4.7	4.4	2.8
2,500	1.8	2.8	3.0	2.8	1.8
5,000	1.3	2.0	2.1	2.0	1.3
10,000	.9	1.4	1.5	1.4	.9

[1] The chances are 997 in 1,000 that the error due to size of the sample will be less than that shown.
[2] If 10 percent of those interviewed in a sample of 1,000 farmers mention a particular answer, the chances are 997 in 1,000 that if all farmers were interviewed the actual percentage that would be obtained would fall between 7.2 and 12.8 percent, i. e., between 10 percent plus or minus 2.8 percent. It will be noted from the table that the more evenly divided the answers, or the smaller the sample, the greater the probable error.

sample of only 1,000 farmers, for instance, will yield results in which any error due to the size of the sample will not exceed 5 percent; that is, if all farmers had been questioned the results would have been the same within 5 percent. Table 1 shows the maximum error likely to occur as a result of the size of the sample.

To many persons it will come as a distinct surprise that interviewing only 1,000 farmers will give results that would be virtually certain not to differ by more than 5 percent from that obtained by interviewing all farmers. Yet the correctness of the data given in table 1 has been amply proved by extensive research. The table itself is based upon a mathematical formula worked out by a Swiss scientist, Bernoulli, over 200 years ago. The laws of probable error that he and others formulated have been tested by many experiments in various fields of science. Recently the errors that occur in sampling the experience, behavior, or opinions of people have been checked in research studies and found to conform with the laws of probability (*1*, *4*); [4] that is, the chances are 997 in 1,000 that the results of sampling will have an error not greater than the amount shown in the table. Whenever an error larger than those shown in the table occurs, it is practically certain to be due to failure to follow properly the scientific procedures shown by careful experiments to be necesssary in obtaining a representative sample.

Thus it is now possible to secure in a relatively small number of interviews the information administrators require in order to direct in a thoroughly democratic manner any programs for which they are responsible.

Errors To Be Avoided

Certain errors must be avoided, however, if the information obtained is to be accurate. (1) Precaution must be taken to make sure that the sample used is typical in every way of the entire group it is supposed to represent. In other words, the sample must be a true cross section of the whole. (2) The interviewing procedure must be such that the report for each individual correctly states his experiences and desires or opinions. (3) Careful and accurate analysis must be made of the interviews secured from the field.

To be representative a sample must contain the same proportion of each of the different groups of people as are present in the farm population being studied. For example, it must have the same proportion of each age group as exists in the population being studied; the same geographical representation; the same distribution by income, type of farming, and size of farm; and the same proportion of owners, tenants, and wage hands.

To be sure that individual opinions are accurately represented, it is important that interviewers be carefully trained to secure accurate, unbiased statements and to report them faithfully (*3*). No leading questions can be asked. For example, an interviewer will not obtain an answer reflecting what a farmer really believes if he puts a question such as this: "Mr. Jones, I noticed the new terraces in that field of yours over there. Am I right in believing that you like them very much, not only because they keep your soil from washing but also

[4] See also: PSYCHOLOGICAL CORPORATION. HOW MANY INTERVIEWS ARE NECESSARY FOR RESULTS OF A CERTAIN ACCURACY. 25 pp. New York. 1934. [Processed.]

because the water they hold back will increase your crop yield?" This is an extreme form of leading question, but all degrees of this kind of error must be avoided. "How do you like your new terraces?" would carry no suggestion. Similarly, the interviewer must avoid all explanation of any question or related matter that would tend to predispose the person being interviewed toward a particular answer (*7*, *8*).

The interviewer introduces another kind of error when he predisposes the farmer toward a certain answer as a result of conversation preceding the question. If after discussing with a farmer his experience with the corn loan, the interviewer asks him which part of the Agricultural Adjustment Administration corn program has helped him most and why, he would in all probability receive a prejudiced reply. Under such circumstances the farmer would be much more likely to mention the corn loan than some other part of the program which had not been discussed.

Using emotionally charged words in the questions asked is another source of error that interviewers must be trained not to introduce. If an adjective, a name of a person, or an idea about which most people tend to have strong feelings is used in asking a question, the answer will be in part a response to the emotionally charged word or phrase and will not accurately represent how the farmer feels about the question itself.

Through careful training and close supervision of interviewers it is possible to eliminate errors like those just given. Another important safeguard to assure accurate results is to use several interviewers on the same survey. Errors introduced by one interviewer are minimized when his reports are combined with those of several others. The results can also be checked against each other and a careful analysis made to find the causes of discrepancies.

It is not necessary, as is sometimes thought, for every interviewer to use precisely the same words in asking a given set of questions (*1*). The words may vary so long as the question in each case represents exactly the same idea.

The third type of error to be avoided, it will be recalled, is that resulting from incorrect analysis of the interviews secured in the field. Procedures have been developed for condensing the great variety of statements always obtained whenever interviewing is used into a limited number of groups that can be readily classified and tabulated. These procedures, as well as others for checking by cross tabulation and similar devices, are all based on careful scientific research (*5*). The procedures require considerable time and effort, but it is necessary to use them if erroneous conclusions are not to be drawn from the field reports.

TOWARD MORE DEMOCRATIC ADMINISTRATION

The general procedure outlined here represents an inexpensive and satisfactory way to help make administration more democratic. It should enable administrators to fit national legislation to local conditions and adapt it to the problems created by the continually changing world in which we live. It is important that the administration of any farm program be carried out in the way desired by most farmers and that the farmers themselves determine the rapidity with which existing procedures shall be changed. Sudden or drastic changes rarely meet with approval and usually confuse the individual.

The rapid changes that occur in the modern world represent one of the most serious threats to the future of our democracy. Effective yet democratic methods must be found that will permit adjustments to these bewildering changes. The developments described in this article give evidence of being important steps toward a solution of this crucial problem.

LITERATURE CITED

(1) American Institute of Public Opinion.
n. d. THE NEW SCIENCE OF PUBLIC OPINION MEASUREMENT. 16 pp. Princeton, N. J.

(2) Bard, Philip.
1929. THE NEURO-HUMORAL BASIS OF EMOTIONAL REACTIONS. *In* Murchison, Carl, The Foundations of Experimental Psychology, pp. 449–487, illus. Worcester, Mass., London, and Oxford.

(3) Bingham, Walter VanDyke, and Moore, Bruce Victor.
1934. HOW TO INTERVIEW. Ed. 2, 320 pp., illus. New York and London.

(4) Brown, Theodore Henry.
1935. THE USE OF STATISTICAL TECHNIQUES IN CERTAIN PROBLEMS OF MARKET RESEARCH. Harvard Univ., Grad. School Business Admin. Business Res. Studies No. 12, 24 pp.

(5) Franzen, Raymond.
1936. TECHNICAL RESPONSIBILITIES INVOLVED IN CONSUMER RESEARCH. Market Res. 5 (4): 3–7, illus.

(6) Houser, J. David.
1938. WHAT PEOPLE WANT FROM BUSINESS. 250 pp., illus. New York and London.

(7) Jenkins, John G.
1940. THE QUESTIONNAIRE AS A RESEARCH INSTRUMENT. 23 pp. New York. (Reprint from N. Y. Acad. Sci. Trans. ser. 2, v. 2, No. 5.)

(8) Lazarsfeld, Paul F.
1935. THE ART OF ASKING WHY IN MARKETING RESEARCH: THREE PRINCIPLES UNDERLYING THE FORMULATION OF QUESTIONNAIRES. Natl. Marketing Rev. 1 (1): 26–38.

(9) Thomson, Mehren K.
1927. THE SPRINGS OF HUMAN ACTION: A PSYCHOLOGICAL STUDY OF THE SOURCES, MECHANISM, AND PRINCIPLES OF MOTIVATION IN HUMAN BEHAVIOR. 501 pp. New York and London.

The Cultural Setting of American Agricultural Problems

by RALPH TURNER [1]

THE AUTHOR of this article deals with the problems of agriculture from a somewhat different viewpoint from that of the economists. He is concerned with an attempt to define the American tradition, discover what conditions shaped it, show how it came into conflict with later movements in national life, and determine how the conflict can be resolved. He holds that this tradition was shaped originally by certain powerful factors in rural life; that later it was twisted and weakened by urban interests; but that it has lasting value and can again become dominant in our culture. The outstanding characteristic of the American tradition, he believes, was a high development of individual self-decision. If this is to be restored, one of the primary needs is an understanding of the true relationship between city and country under modern conditions.

ALMOST half a century ago Frederick Jackson Turner, in closing his now famous essay, The Significance of the Frontier in American History (*3, pp. 185–229*),[2] observed, "The frontier has gone, and with its going has closed the first period of American history." If at that time the first period of American history ended, what has been the character of the succeeding decades—for American life as a whole and for American agriculture in particular? Suggestions for the answer to this question must be based not only upon the study of recent developments but also upon their interpretation in terms of modes of analysis and synthesis not yet developed at the end of the nineteenth century. Among these modes, of which there are in fact more than a

[1] Ralph Turner is Economic Historian, Bureau of Research and Statistics, Social Security Board.
[2] Italic numbers in parentheses refer to Literature Cited, p. 1031.

few, the concept of culture, as developed in recent anthropological and sociological thought, appears to have special significance, for it provides the means of setting recent developments in dynamic relation to one another as well as to the national heritage.

This is the approach adopted in this article. The author believes, however, that the story of agricultural development in the United States can be told from the standpoint of the culture concept without too much use of the technical terminology of the anthropologists and sociologists. At any rate the attempt will be made in the following pages. At the end of the article a technical note for students explains the concept of culture.

Of primary significance in a discussion of agricultural problems in terms of the concept of culture is the understanding that the rural and urban aspects of national life must be seen together; they are merely related parts of the whole culture. In order to bring them into a common focus it is necessary to glance for a moment at the relative positions of rural and urban life in the past, first in general cultural development and second in the growth of American culture.

RELATIONSHIP OF RURAL AND URBAN LIFE

The main aspects of the relative positions of rural and urban life in general cultural evolution are suggested in the following quotation (*1*):

> Before cities can emerge and grow it is necessary that the agricultural system with which they are associated shall have developed powers of feeding a nonagricultural population and providing them with such agricultural raw materials as they require for clothing, shelter, and fuel. The prerequisite of each step in relative growth is a further increase in efficiency in agricultural production, with increase in output per person engaged, so that a greater nonagricultural population may be maintained. Increase in proportion of urban population is evidence of increasing efficiency of the agricultural population in the hinterlands of the cities concerned, whether these cover only the distances possible for horse and river transport as for many medieval cities, or cover an overseas empire as in the present case of Great Britain.
>
> The development of cities may not be inevitable, but if any society is to show marked advance in material civilization it is necessary that its system of agricultural production shall develop so that ever-increasing numbers of workers may be set aside for the production of goods other than foodstuffs and primary raw materials and to render services. The less people that any society requires to maintain in agricultural production, the greater may be its supplies of clothing, furniture, housing, transport, books and papers, musical instruments, and all the other things, and the greater and more varied may be the services of the professions in education, entertainment, literature and art, medicine, law, and religion.

From the time when cities began, therefore, rural life supplied the primary wealth for the support of urban populations, and because cities were never able to reproduce their populations, also provided a continuous stream of migrants to the cities. By the labor of those workers who could be withdrawn from agriculture, the goods and services which entered into an advancing standard of living were produced, so that urban life possessed a diversity of satisfactions unknown among rural dwellers. Furthermore, throughout the history of Asia and of Europe, urban life was the organizing factor in cultural development, shaping the state and the law; it was also the creative factor, giving rise to the professions, the arts, learning, and the higher types of religion. "Science and art, philosophy and higher religion may be regarded as the natural products of city life" (*5*). Especially noteworthy is the fact that the great ethical movements calling upon men to realize new forms of justice were always far more urban than rural in origin and diffusion; this was especially true in the case of early Christianity. Except insofar as urban achievements affected agricultural production, by organizing new modes of labor control or by technological innovations (both very few in number until modern times), rural life remained virtually without change through century after century.

The achievements and monuments by which past cultural developments are known and judged—architecture, sculpture, painting, literature, for example—are almost exclusively urban in origin, for the cities, where social intercourse was most intense, were the centers of cultural advance. The poets, historians, and commentators whose praises of agriculture and country life—as in the Eclogues and Georgics of Virgil—are so frequently quoted were mainly representatives of urban groups who did not engage in the arduous labor of agricultural production. Severe toil and low productivity were, it should be remembered, the leading characteristics of tillage and husbandry as occupations until modern technical developments made high productivity possible. For these panegyrists country life was actually an extension of the urban mode of aristocratic living—a pleasant one, no doubt, for it was free from both the hazards of rural occupations and the dietary crudity that went with almost complete dependence on local staples. Indeed, specialized production to serve their lords' tables was commonly carried on by agricultural laborers—sometimes slaves, sometimes peasants—who seldom, if ever, tasted the fruits they grew. As primary wealth producers, the rural masses were the economic support of city populations, and the latter were careful to hold them to the performance of their social function.

DOMINANCE OF THE RURAL ECONOMY IN EARLY AMERICA

If this fundamental difference of position is in the deep background of the rural and urban elements in American national life, which of course had its origins in Europe, in the immediate foreground is that peculiar relationship that had its roots in the social and economic development of this Nation.

This development began in that period of European cultural advance—the seventeenth century—which raised individualism, especially economic and religious, to dominance, at least in the nations that were most active on the North American Atlantic seaboard. Correlative with this advance was a steady rise in Europe of the political, economic, and intellectual influence of the middle classes, composed largely of independent urban tradesmen and manufacturers (entrepreneurs). From them came the main developments in political theory and organization, economic doctrine and practice, technology, science, and social attitudes which have given distinctive patterns to modern European culture. The changes which transformed European agriculture were also largely the result of middle-class influence on land usage. However, in the commercial countries of Europe, as well as in those which remained almost completely agricultural, this individualism penetrated only slightly among the agricultural laborers and peasants.

Once transplanted to the Atlantic seaboard of North America, though, the development of this individualism was nourished by social selection and conditioning among the colonial population.

Although people representing almost every European type[3] came to the Colonies, and certainly the most important European economic patterns were planted here, representatives of two types, and with them a certain new combination of economic and social patterns, quickly became prominent. These types were (1) small entrepreneurs—independent merchants and farmers—and (2) laborers, mainly agricultural and having the legal status of indentured servants. Production and trade were originally speculative. They aimed at high and quick profits after the manner of European investors in overseas trade. But when these profits did not materialize, the economic adjustment to the available wilderness resources quickly produced a trade and an agriculture based on the staple products of the several Atlantic seaboard areas, and these activities yielded relatively low profits or only a bare subsistence.

The profits of trade supported a growth of towns which, it is important to emphasize, contained a very small part of the total population; in the middle of the eighteenth century the five towns worthy of the designation—Boston, Newport, New York, Philadelphia, and Charles Town—had only 7 percent of the colonial population. But these towns were closer to London in their social and intellectual life than they were to the rural areas surrounding them; ideas, commodities, and fashions that became popular in Europe found in them a quick acceptance. Although some aristocratic practices and attitudes survived, the European middle-class achievements gave form to their ways of living. Thus the early American urban population quickly assumed the function historically performed by urban populations of carrying on the traditions of learning, refinement, and taste. Both commercial enterprise and the diffusion of European middle-class ideas and attitudes strengthened the individualism which the founders of the cities had originally planted in them.

In agriculture, because among the available wilderness resources land was most plentiful, soon the typical entrepreneur was the independent small farmer. Inasmuch as he won his acres and added to them mainly by clearing away forest and undergrowth with his own hands, he was quite as much a laborer as he was an entrepreneur. In fact, it is probably true that his gains were more the reward of labor than of capital investment. This labor, it should be understood, included the exertions of the members of his family, who, like him, received their reward mainly in subsistence.

The circumstance which gave this turn to the development of production and trade also affected the situation of laborers. It was difficult to keep skilled workers such as bricklayers, carpenters, coopers, and cobblers in the towns, because they found it easy to become farmers. Thus an urban working class developed slowly and, except for sailors and dock workers, hardly existed until the last

[3] The word "type" throughout this article is to be understood as meaning sociocultural type. See the Note for Students at the end of the article.

two decades of the eighteenth century. For agricultural laborers this circumstance was especially favorable. In this connection it should be recalled that probably as many as half of the white settlers who came to the Atlantic seaboard between 1607 and 1783 were indentured servants. At the end of their periods of service they became free. Since they were already poor, their chief social attributes were freedom and poverty—indeed, then as now, the typical American, in the sense of those who constitute the majority, is best described as "free and poor." From this social and economic source, as well as from the families of the small farmers, came continually the frontier or backwoods settlers, who, without paying too much attention to legal rights established by charters granted by a far-away king, pushed the area of settlement ever nearer to the Appalachian ridges.

Although these ridges were not difficult to cross, in the eighteenth century they served as a sheltering wall behind which a predominantly rural population, by adapting its economic, social, and intellectual life to the exploitation of wilderness resources, grew to nationhood. The life of this Nation, although it contained a small but highly significant urban element, was patterned by the application of labor to land. Moreover, since the prevailing technology was inefficient, labor was severe, and productivity was low. Also the products, mainly those of the field and the forest, were raw materials which were processed into consumable goods only by additional labor. Thus self-reliance and self-sufficiency were organized in the normal activities of the most numerous American type, the farmers. However, it should be understood that, at best, these qualities supported life but meagerly. Hard work was the common lot. Standards of living were bare. Life-expectancy was low. Manners were crude; and intellectual activity, stripped of sophistication, cast both God and man in the image of that stalwart, free individual whose behavior was shaped by these conditions of life.

Modifications of European Patterns

In the course of the agricultural expansion which produced this type, two significant modifications in the economic and social patterns transplanted from Europe were made. (1) An opposition to the system of quitrents—originally payments to a feudal overlord in lieu of services—manifested in some way in most of the Colonies, brought, toward the end of the colonial period, an almost universal acceptance of freehold tenure. This made possible, of course, the individualization of the ownership of land which permitted easy ascent from the ranks of agricultural labor to the status of independent farmer; it was the legal support of the so-called tenure ladder. (2) At the same time, contrary to the traditional immobility of the European agricultural population, men became free to move, and moving became a normal step in the struggle for economic advancement. Together these developments, one legal and the other social, may be seen as primary modifications of European patterns to the needs and opportunities of a people for whom, because they lived in the presence of wilderness resources, the use and acquisition of land formed the base of economic support, advancement, and security.

Bases of American Democracy

If one takes a functional view of life in this early economy, one may see certain of its aspects as having special significance for the shaping of the tradition [4] of American culture which exists today. Self-support based on the application of labor to land involved, besides self-exertion, what may be called self-decision. In concrete terms, the farmer determined what and when to plant, how to till, when to harvest, what and when to market, when and how to process, and when to consume, and from these decisions flowed his well-being, except as nature intervened. Thus in the area of economic functioning, the farmer's life was his own to manage.

From the point of view of the preceding paragraph, it is not difficult to understand how governmental functions, correlated with economic self-sufficiency, were reduced to the maintenance of the liberties which permitted the individual to do most for himself in terms of opportunities that were at hand because of the availability of wilderness resources. Frontier conditions which made each individual a fighter also restricted the need for government to maintain a military establishment. In one important respect, however, government was brought to act positively in economic terms favorable to the farmers—namely, in the disposal of the public domain.

When the public domain was transferred to the Federal Government, national land policy became an issue between various interests—the independent small farmer or would-be farmer, the owner of capital who sought profits in speculation, and the large-scale producer whose unit of operation was the large plantation. The struggle between these interests was long and bitter, but with the passage of the Homestead Act of 1862 the interest of the independent small farmer prevailed. If the circumstances of a crude technology, low productivity, and a simple community are remembered, the policy embodied in this act may be seen as establishing an economic democracy. But—and this is the important point—it was achieved only through the action of government, the Federal Government at that. In terms of their social order the Americans of the expanding rural economy made the Federal Government a means of promoting their economic security and advancement.

In the area of political functioning a somewhat similar circumstance prevailed. Local government was so simple—building roads and bridges, keeping open elementary schools, and protecting life and property—that every adult male was ordinarily able to participate in it fully, both in deciding what was to be done and in doing it. Since social interdependence, based on division of labor and exchanges in the market, was slight, the functions of State and Federal Governments were sharply limited. A further limitation existed in the fact that governmental action, except in the case of money and credit, was not required to offset controls exercised over individuals through widely operating private economic organizations such as those existing today. Thus the same circumstances which made self-dependency characteristic of the rural economy tended to limit the activities of government. These circumstances were not only (1) the availability

[4] The term "tradition" in this article is to be understood as meaning subjective tradition. See the Note for Students at the end of the article.

of wilderness resources, but also (2) the technology which gave low productivity with hard labor and (3) a simple community in which the members could know well the qualities of one another. This last aspect of life enforced individual responsibility for self-maintenance and self-advancement. At the same time, however, when distress came to an individual as a result of a natural disaster or an accident, the community commonly furnished collective relief through neighborhood action.

When the aspects of life noted in the preceding paragraphs are viewed together as the essential components of "American democracy" as it was created by the generations in whose lives these aspects were uppermost, a statement which draws them together in one concept would seem to run as follows: "American democracy is a way of life in which the ordinary adult has the right to participate in making the significant decisions which shape his life, and the opportunity, as well as the responsibility, to participate in the action necessary to carry out these decisions." The chief corollary of this general principle is that the individual must accept the conditions which such action brings.

It cannot be emphasized too strongly that under the circumstances of life prevailing in the rural economy, democracy in these terms was an economic and political fact, for both the individual and the Government. The individual acted economically and politically according to this principle, and the Government, in spite of the limitation of functions imposed by technological and community factors, was brought to act in economic areas in harmony with the interests of the dominant type among the population.

Growth of Cities and the Rise of Technology

The concentration of attention upon the expansion of the rural economy which produced an integration of American culture in terms of the principle noted has obscured the place of urban elements in the development of American culture. Throughout the period of the expansion of the rural economy the cities grew in social and intellectual significance. The proportion of the population concentrated in the cities constantly increased. At the root of this growth was the economic demand for capital and consumers' goods created as wilderness resources were exploited. This growth was accompanied by the multiplication of those engaged in independent urban trade and industry and the formation of an urban wage-earning group. The tradesmen and manufacturers were drawn from both urban and rural sources, and so were the wage earners, although many of them were immigrants from European countrysides. So great was the social mobility among these groups that a change of economic status became a normal expectation in American life.

Along with this development, new European influences began to play an important part in American life. The technological innovations summed up in the term "industrial revolution" were introduced and gave rise soon to native technological developments which ultimately transformed both urban and rural occupations. At the same time the growth of new industries in Europe, especially in England, created a growing market for American raw materials and foodstuffs. The expansion of the rural economy which culminated with the closing of the frontier in the late decades of the nineteenth century, noted by Frederick Jackson Turner as having ended the first period of American history, was largely stimulated by demands arising in this market or by the investment in the United States of capital accumulated by English enterprises operating in this market.

These developments also accelerated the rise of land values so that the rural economy, as it reached the end of its geographical extension, continued its economic expansion. The new terms which governed the expansion, however, were little noted while they were displacing the historic circumstance of creating new farms from wilderness land. At the same time technological innovation in agriculture increased the efficiency of labor so that proportionately fewer workers were required on the land than in the past. The pressure of a growing population on the land which this circumstance might have caused was averted by the movement of agricultural workers into urban wage jobs created by technological innovations that were organizing, potentially at least, a new standard of living.

Thus, after the passing of free land, social mobility, technological advance, urban growth, and individual effort combined to create a kind of life that harmonized with the tradition of the national culture.

DIFFUSION OF ECONOMIC LIBERALISM FROM EUROPE

While these economic and social developments organized the individualistic modes of thinking and behaving in the life of the American masses, European influences which penetrated in the main only urban circles gave this individualism a doctrinaire interpretation. American law, largely nourished on Blackstone's Commentaries, received a fair portion of the eighteenth-century philosophical belief that the individual mind is a rational entity. German and English romanticism declared individual sentiments the source of moral feeling. And an interpretation of Darwinism identified self-aggrandizement with nature's fundamental creative process. Between these ideas and the normal expectations of rural life there was a close conformity; in other words, American farmers understood these ideas without thinking them. Thus, in fact, they easily gave an emotional acceptance to doctrines which, having been developed mainly by the European middle class, became the social philosophy of the American tradesmen, manufacturers, and financiers.

This philosophy—"economic liberalism," it is correctly called—was a foreign "ism" and should be clearly distinguished from the historic individualism shaped among the masses of the American people in the expanding rural economy. A brief statement of the doctrines of economic liberalism is pertinent:

(1) The ideal state of human affairs is realized in the free activity of individuals, each pursuing his own self-interest according to his special abilities. First in order among individual interests is the desire for gain, and individuals compete with each other for profits. And wealth—legally established in private property—is the just reward of the individual's enterprise, thrift, and foresight, and is his to do with as he pleases. Only by insuring the individual an adequate reward

for his enterprise can his energies be called into action; thus his accumulation of wealth is the just reward for his services to society.

(2) The individual is not at all responsible for the failure of any competitor. Poverty is the consequence of imprudence, laziness, and a lack of thrift and foresight; the unequal distribution of wealth is not only natural but just. Public education offers to each individual that access to knowledge which, if he avails himself of the advantages of possessing it, will increase his chance of becoming a successful competitor.

(3) Government exists to protect individuals in the free exercise of their abilities and to maintain free competition among them; the intervention of government in economic affairs is bad, not only because it gives one competitor an advantage over another but because it also deprives society of the beneficent results of free competition. The government ought to promote the interests of enterprisers, for only as they prosper does society progress.

(4) The well-being of laborers depends on the prosperity of enterprisers, but laborers must protect themselves from the mistakes of their employers by their own thrift and foresight. The goal of every laborer is to become an enterpriser. This is possible because, since human wants are infinite, there is always opportunity for new ventures.

Economic liberalism asserts that as individual initiative establishes new enterprises to satisfy an ever-increasing number of wants, a constantly advancing well-being for society as a whole is promoted. Economic prosperity and social progress are thus the correlative results of the free competition of individuals.

Although there are recognizable points of contact between these doctrines and the historic national individualism, there are also sharp differences which, in view of the economic and social developments that have given rise to the present national problems, deserve more emphasis. At the heart of the historic individualism of the Nation was a belief in equality, both economic and political. If on the one hand this belief was naively expressed in the 1840's by a refusal of New England factory girls to accept an offer of a railroad fare lower than that open to the general public, on the other hand it was the prime motivation of the movements that led to the abolition of imprisonment for debt, of indentured servitude, and of slavery. It was also the source of the judicial opinion which set aside the common-law rule of conspiracy that was long the legal obstacle to the organization of wage earners for collective bargaining. In the political area the belief in equality led to the granting of suffrage to adult white males regardless of the property they possessed almost a half century before it was granted in European countries. If, in this connection, it is remembered that the first 10 amendments to the Federal Constitution—the so-called bill of rights—which guarantee the liberties of the individual, were proposed and adopted in the struggle for ratification, when the voters, few in numbers because of property and religious qualifications, had their only opportunity to shape the national instrument of government, it becomes clear that that combination of equality and liberty which originated in this Nation owed little to the doctrines of economic liberalism.

The significance of this fact is clear only when it is understood that in European countries political inequality was primarily a means of maintaining economic inequality, and the adoption of policies justified by economic liberalism contributed little to the disappearance of either kind of inequality. Although economic liberalism hastened the abolition of the vestiges of the economic controls by means of which the traditional European ruling classes, the landed aristocrats and the priests of established churches, had drawn support from the peasants, it created in their stead the free labor market in which economic inequality is the decisive factor in the relationship of individuals, considered as competitors. When European countries finally extended the franchise to propertyless adult males, their action was largely impelled by movements that arose in the free labor market in opposition to the existing circumstances of life. American democracy is both older than and different in content from the democracy of European countries. Besides the self-decision previously noted, its chief element is that one individual shall not wield power, economic or political, over another individual, at least not to the continuous advantage of the former or to the permanent disadvantage of the latter. If, under the conditions which permitted the continuous expansion of the rural economy, this concept had originally little meaning for wage earners, it was because their position was regarded as one from which ascent by the "tenure ladder" to economic independence was easy. This faith had its roots in the belief that land was available for an expansion that would come to an end only in a remote future—perhaps, as Jefferson believed, not for a hundred generations.

Urban and Rural Interpretations of Individualism

In the final phase of the expansion of the rural economy, the developments which brought about a great industrial growth made possible the steady advance, economically and politically, of urban enterprisers; this phase of national development is commonly designated the period of the rise of "big business." Because wealth in any form has always been able to purchase professional and intellectual services, urban enterprisers found at hand men who, having learned the doctrines of economic liberalism in the centers of higher education, wrought them into legislation, judicial rules, journalistic pronouncements, and educational dicta. Thus it was the fortune of economic liberalism to become identified socially and intellectually with those elements of society which historically contrasted with, if they did not oppose, the rural element. From this circumstance arose a conception of individualism among urban enterprisers which took its place alongside the national individualism.

It is important for the understanding of current developments in national life to make a clear distinction between the urban and the rural interpretations of individualism.

The practical result of the acceptance of economic liberalism was to shape a concept of liberty mainly in negative terms, that is, in terms of a freedom from social controls and a lack of responsibility for social conditions. Whereas in the historic rural economy—under conditions of wilderness resources, simple technology, and slight social interdependence—liberty was the positive fact of individual effort and responsibility, in the rising urban economy it became, at least in a major aspect, a lack of responsibility for the social consequences of individual economic action. A fundamental difference between the two interpretations becomes clear when it is realized that the urban interpretation offers a theoretical justification of economic inequality, while the rural interpretation embodies an emotional attachment to equality, both economic and political. The propositions of the urban interpretation of individualism bar action to abate economic inequality or ameliorate the evils that flow from it; the sentiments of the rural interpretation impel action to establish conditions under which individuals can behave and feel as if they are equals.

During the period of the final expansion of the rural economy and the rise of big business, the disharmony of these two interpretations of individualism gave rise to political movements. Populism was a rural resistance to the power of industrial enterprisers and financiers who were finding in economic liberalism the intellectual support of their economic and political aggrandizement, and Progressivism, in either Republican or Democratic form, was similar in character and purpose. Both sought to protect the national individualism by political and legal devices when economic and social forces were transforming the structure of living in which it had been shaped. The political changes of the late nineteenth and early twentieth centuries were not introduced merely to broaden democracy; rather, they were adopted with the intention of increasing the ability of the people to use government for the achievement of their welfare. However, from the point of view of today, the efforts of both Populism and Progressivism were rear-guard actions, in the sense that social and economic developments in national life were so transforming it that the historic individualism could not be maintained by the methods they advocated. A statement that suggests the intermingling of the rural and urban interpretations of individualism in current American mentality will be found in Lynd (*6, ch. 3, The Pattern of American Culture*).

Before sketching the transformation that has been occurring in national life and affects individualism however interpreted, a further distinction between the urban interpretation of individualism and the historic individualism of the Nation must be noted, for it, more than any of the aspects of either interpretation, has significance for the future. The urban interpretation of individualism—economic liberalism—is intellectual in quality; that is, it is a body of doctrines reasoned from certain assumptions. And as a body of doctrines based on what today must be recognized as a false psychology and integrated by logic rather than correlated with any body of observed data, this interpretation can be only an obstacle to a sound interpretation of American life. Its principles can only be considered as fiats to obstruct action, not as guides for dealing with conditions that differ from the circumstances the original English and European authors of the system assumed to exist. On the other hand, national individualism, as shaped under the expanding rural economy, exists among the American masses as emotional reactions to various life situations—a body of sentiments vivified by the history of the Nation, unless that history is distorted. National individualism is the feeling in terms of which the individual recognizes that he is an "American." Regardless of the conditions which arise in the life of the group, such a feeling tends to endure, finding expression in new forms.[5] What these forms may be can be determined only in terms of existing American life.

CURRENT PATTERNS OF AMERICAN CULTURE

Technological and Intellectual Patterns

From the elaboration of technology have come at least four significant elements in current life: (1) An increased capacity to produce wealth, (2) more rapid means of transportation and communication, (3) diversification of occupations, and (4) new physical routines in both old and new occupations. It is not difficult to comprehend that these elements establish new forms of consumption, new types of enterprise and work, new relationships among individuals, and new contacts with nature. As a whole they organize a behavior, both individual and social, quite unlike that which prevailed in the rural economy.

Closely related to the elaboration of technology is the advance of scientific knowledge from which have issued (1) new services which have made life more secure in the sense of postponing death and lessening the incidence of disease, and (2) new professions which, if the present economy and social order are to continue to develop, must be maintained by the selection and education of large numbers of specialists. Scientific knowledge can serve life only through the development of individuals able to behave in terms of it.

No less important than these elements in present-day life are the spread of literacy and the rise of educational attainment among the people. These have roots in the traditional American faith that education is the primary means of advancement of the individual, but they are also nourished by the fact that machine technology, science, and business all require a higher level of educational attainment than was required by the rural economy. The folklore and the folk techniques of the early national culture are being progressively replaced, under the influence of machine technology, science, and the doctrine of efficiency in business enterprises, by a recognition of the utility of scientific knowledge and the practicability of human control in ever-wider areas of living, and by the belief that the material circumstances of human life can be altered.

The supreme effect of these influences is to nourish the faith that man's power to shape the conditions under which he lives is far greater now than at any time in the past. But this power, it is also clear, can be exercised only in ways of behavior quite unlike those of the rural economy. In these various terms a fundamental reorganization of the mentality of individuals is occurring at all levels of economic functioning.

Social Patterns

At least four social changes have accompanied these intellectual developments which now, even more than formerly, pattern national life.

(1) Simplest among these changes is the specialization of economic

[5] From the point of view of the concept of culture such a feeling, as the psychological mode of group unity, integrates the group's culture.

callings. Most of the traditional trades and crafts have been destroyed or transformed, and thousands of new occupations have been created. Versatility in simple occupations was possible and highly rewarded in the old rural economy; today specialization is necessary if any distinctive reward is to be obtained. However, although the new technology requires numerous high skills for maintenance, it needs, in the main, only simple skills—semiskills, as they are called—for operation. From one point of view the diversification of callings opens many new opportunities for individuals; from another point of view it tends to close opportunities, because advancement depends far less on skill acquired in job performance than it does upon training in scientific subject matter. The movement from one economic level to another is probably far more difficult than it was in the traditional rural economy.

(2) Closely related to the specialization of economic callings, but less recognized, is the hierarchical organization of employment—that is, its organization in grades from top to bottom—which has spread ever more widely. The grades of employment have origin partly in technology and science and partly in the administrative structure of enterprise. As technological developments compelled the investment of ever-larger amounts of capital, the corporate organization of enterprise grew, and as a result more and more individuals found themselves working not as independent operators themselves or as the employees of small independent operators, but as employees in corporate hierarchies. For individuals so employed economic advancement comes to be a rising from grade to grade instead of a shift from the status of employee to that of independent operator. Moreover, since in these hierarchies economic power is exercised from the top downward and enforced through the "right to fire," the qualities of behavior that bring advancement become less and less those summed up in the phrase "individual initiative" and more and more those implied in the word "loyalty." Actually conformity rather than initiative is the quality increasingly desired in individuals.

It is also important to note that economic power exerted from the top of these hierarchies upon individuals in the lower levels of employment does interfere upon occasion with the exercise of personal liberties in areas of life quite beyond the economic functioning of the hierarchies. The effect of this interference is to impose upon more and more individuals a regimentation in terms of private interests. At this point in current life the conflict between the historic individualism of the Nation and the social order developed under the influence of technology and business organization and justified by the principles of economic liberalism becomes sharper and sharper.

(3) A truly unprecedented social interdependence has developed, although it is obscured by a constant assertion of the social efficiency of competition which as a matter of fact also masks the effects of the spread of the hierarchical organization of employment. This social interdependence has three main aspects:

(a) The production of goods and services is carried on through an increasingly intricate division of labor which makes it virtually impossible to determine accurately what an individual at any particular level of skill and supervisory authority contributes. Furthermore, this division of labor, organized in scientific technology, rests upon a complex body of knowledge which it is impossible for any individual to master completely or to call his own. At the base of the production of wealth in contemporary society is a continuous social and intellectual cooperation too little recognized or understood.

(b) Satisfaction of the needs and wants of an individual is to be had only through the continuous functioning of innumerable private enterprises and public agencies that the individual does not know how to direct or control. No matter how wealthy an individual may be it is hardly possible for him to own all of the enterprises that must supply him with goods and services if he is to enjoy a standard of living, however described, that is called "American." The well to do, like the poor, are dependent upon an almost infinite social cooperation organized and maintained through the market.

(c) Finally, this increasing interdependence of individuals exists in the changed character of private property as developed in corporate enterprises. In that great area of private ownership designated by the term "securities," where, indeed, the typical giant concentrations of wealth—the great fortunes—are held, the owner cannot identify either the tangible goods or the real property to which his evidence of ownership attaches. If the owner of a share or bond attempts to discover what he actually owns, he finds that no specific part of an enterprise can be identified as his; actually he finds that he owns a right to share in the income of an enterprise rather than any specific part of the enterprise. The interest of an owner of securities can be served only by the orderly operation of economic processes frequently and almost entirely beyond his control.

Thus, the employee, the consumer, and the owner are alike dependent to an ever greater degree upon a cooperation which, if not maintained, may leave them without support, and their economic security is best achieved not by the exercise of the right to ownership over the means of production but by the establishment of a right to receive constantly a portion of currently produced wealth. In the historic rural economy the effects, good and bad, of individual effort were mainly restricted to the individual and his dependents; today individual effort gives rise to wide reactions among an indeterminate number of persons and, more important, has results for the individual that are shaped by these reactions. Thus the orientation of individual effort, and consequently of individual responsibility, has greatly changed.

(4) Of special significance among these social changes is the altered economic position of an ever-increasing proportion of the American people. About 1870, when the older of the present-day Americans were born, over half of the gainfully employed population was engaged in agriculture. By 1890, when these Americans had just begun their earning careers, 40 percent of the gainfully employed population was still engaged in agriculture. By 1930, however, when the earning careers of this generation were coming to an end, only slightly more than 20 percent of the gainfully employed population was at work on the land. This decline in the proportion of the gainfully employed in agriculture was accompanied by a decrease of those engaged as independent operators in other fields of enterprise. Together these circumstances have meant the steady movement of more and more

individuals into the industrial labor market.

Thus, in the course of a single generation, the Nation shifted from a life patterned mainly by the application of labor to land to a life patterned by the sale of labor for a price. For the traditional self-decision, self-support, and self-sufficiency has been substituted a condition in which economic need is likely to compel individuals to take the jobs offered in the labor market and to remain unemployed if no jobs are available.

The effect of this development is to deprive the ordinary individual of the economic independence that was his in the expanding rural economy. The lack of capital forces him to accept whatever job and wage are offered if he is to obtain the means of subsistence. His quitting of a job in order to find another may result in a failure to find any job. Low earnings and loss of earnings occasioned by unemployment are likely to make impossible the saving by which he is supposed to acquire the capital necessary to become independent or to make provision for periods when he has no work or is unable to work. His prospect of passing from the status of an employee to that of an independent operator is very small indeed.

Thus, contrary to the theory of economic liberalism, need rather than rationally determined interest guides the behavior of an ever-larger number of individuals. What the individual works at, when he works, how long he works, and what he does while he is at work are not decided by himself but by his employer. This circumstance is at the root of the movement of wage earners to form unions. These organizations, therefore, should be understood not as devices to coerce employers but as the means by which individuals who must live by selling labor seek to recover some of that right to decide about the conditions of their work which individuals possessed under the historic individualism of the Nation. This loss of the conditions necessary for individual effort and responsibility of course accompanied the growth of regimentation in employment hierarchies; and together the individual's dependence on the labor market for subsistence and his regimentation in employment hierarchies form what are now the most pervasive patterns in national life.

Business Cycles and Unemployment

As the national economy came to be operated under policies shaped by the principles of economic liberalism, cyclical movements of business activity carried enterprise and employment through alternate periods of expansion and contraction only superficially similar to the panics that accompanied the expansion of the rural economy. Progressively, therefore, as more and more individuals have been drawn into the labor market, the effect of these cyclical movements has been to increase the proportion of the gainfully employed population likely to be without jobs in the periods of contraction, that is, the depressions. In the most recent periods of depression the proportion of the potentially gainfully employed population without jobs has been about 30 percent, and as a result an unprecedented burden of economic dependency has appeared. Not all of this burden can be charged directly to unemployment, but the greater part of it, even among the population on the land, is certainly an indirect byproduct of business fluctuations.

The huge number of the individuals who are thus dependent—about 20,000,000 per year on an average[6]—clearly belies the assertion that they are predominantly unfit or unwilling to work; of special significance, in this respect, is the fact that among the unemployed population in 1940 about 4,000,000 are individuals in the age group 15-24 years who have never had regular jobs. Actually this condition has origin in the developments that have transferred more and more individuals from the land to the labor market, given rise to the employment hierarchies, and made the principles of economic liberalism the guides of public policies. Inasmuch as the dependency of an individual physically able to work is condemned, for easily understood reasons, in the tradition of the national culture, it is especially necessary to recognize that the present burden of dependency has its origin not so much in the economic failure of individuals as in the displacement of the historic rural economy by an economy patterned by the developments that have been noted.

Urbanization

In any culture the patterns entering into the behavior of different types in the population are bound together in a community the special form of which depends on the varieties of the patterns. As a sociological and a psychological process the community organizes within the individuals who grow up in it a behavior and a mentality embodying its essential patterns. The community is the decisive agent of perpetuation of a cultural organization of life. The most fundamental change in national life, therefore, has been a movement away from the community structure of the rural economy to a new community organization in which the economic and social changes indicated in preceding pages establish the dominant patterns.

In the expanding rural economy the community was the "frontier" settled by a few individuals and families scattered in the wilderness but always in process of becoming a sparsely settled countryside. Towns and cities were few in number and contained only a small part of the population. In 1820, for example, 93 percent of the population was designated "rural," and in 1870, the year about which the birth dates of the present older generation of Americans cluster, as large a proportion as 73 percent of the population still lived on the land or in villages and towns classified as rural.

Since that time, however, the economic and social developments that were displacing the rural economy have not only made the city the dominant community in the national social structure but also have created a new kind of urban community, now commonly designated the "metropolitan urban area." In 1920, for the first time, over half the population was classified as urban, and in 1930, 56 percent was so designated. A more precise view of the changing community organization of national life is provided in table 1, which shows both the decline in the proportion of the rural population—which of course

[6] See table 1, p. 4, of: BURNS, ARTHUR E., and WILLIAMS, EDWARD A. A SURVEY OF RELIEF AND SECURITY PROGRAMS. 102 pp., illus. [U. S.] Works Progress Admin. 102 pp., illus. 1938. [Processed.] In January 1940 it was estimated that the recipients of assistance under the social security program, of general public relief in the States, of subsistence payments by the Farm Security Administration, or of wages from Civilian Conservation Corps, from the Work Projects Administration, from the National Youth Administration, or from other Federal work and construction projects constituted an unduplicated total of 18,164,000 persons in 6,342,000 households. (Social Security Board press release 790, March 18, 1940.)

includes more than those engaged in farming—and the increase since 1870 in the proportion of the population that is urban.

Table 1.—Distribution of population by type and size of community, 1870–1930 [1]

Type and size of community	1870	1880	1890	1900	1910	1920	1930
	Percent	*Percent*	*Percent*	*Percent*	*Percent*	*Percent*	*Percent*
Rural	73.8	70.5	64.6	59.9	54.2	48.6	43.8
Urban:							
2,500 to 100,000	15.4	17.0	20.0	21.3	23.7	25.4	26.5
100,000 and over	11.7	12.4	15.4	18.8	22.1	26.0	29.6

[1] [UNITED STATES] NATIONAL RESOURCES COMMITTEE. POPULATION STATISTICS 3. URBAN DATA. 1937. P. 8, table 1.

Cities having a population of 100,000 or more are the central cities of metropolitan urban areas; the census of 1930 counted 96 such areas in the United States. When the smaller satellite cities and adjacent rural districts bound to the central cities by social and economic ties are considered along with the central cities, the persons residing in metropolitan urban areas in 1930 formed 48 percent of the total population. Over 50 percent of the population between 25 and 44 years of age resided in them. Between 1920 and 1930, 74 percent of all population increase occurred in them. The central cities showed no excessive rate of increase, but the satellite cities increased at the rate of 40.2 percent for the decade and the adjacent rural areas at the rate of 57 percent. Indeed, there is reason to believe that the distribution of the rural population is taking a pattern more or less determined by the location of these metropolitan urban areas. The conditions which have slowed down the movement of individuals from farms to cities since 1929 probably have not altered significantly the proportions of the national population in the metropolitan urban areas (*7, pp. 22–27*).

CHANGES IN THE RURAL ECONOMY

The developments which have been reshaping national life have not been without effect upon the rural economy, which has not retained the patterns of the period of frontier expansion. At least four types of changes have occurred—(1) technological, (2) economic, (3) social, and (4) intellectual.

(1) Its technology has changed with the introduction of many machines and diverse methods and practices developed in terms of scientific knowledge, and as a result the capacity to produce has increased in agriculture as in other industries.

(2) Three economic effects are especially important: (a) A greater amount of capital is required to carry on agricultural production; (b) the need for labor has become less as the capacity to produce has increased; and (c) the dependence on a market for the disposal of the product has constantly grown.

(3) The social effects are closely related to the technological and economic effects. The need for a greater amount of capital, due partly to technological improvements and partly to rising land values, has made more difficult the shift from the status of farm hand to the status of tenant and from the status of tenant to the status of farm

owner; in other words, the tenure ladder of the historic rural economy has broken down. With increased dependency on a market for the disposal of the product, the farm family has lost its self-sufficiency; it no longer produces many of the real goods its members consume. Finally, without available wilderness land to which the rural population can spread, it has been forced to find economic opportunity away from the soil—necessarily, in urban economic callings. The capacity for greater production with less labor also has contributed to the movement of the rural population into urban economic callings.

(4) The intellectual effects, although less recognized, are not less important. First, the folklore and folk techniques of the historic rural economy are being displaced by scientific knowledge and machine technology; and, second, through the improvement of communication the traditional isolation of the rural community has almost completely disappeared. The mentality of its members, although not touched directly by the physical routines of urban life, is constantly played upon by stimuli originating in urban life. The mental organization of the farmer today is far more influenced by routines and impulses having origins in machines, science, the market, and the city than was that of his antecedent, who in the face of physical danger and by hard manual labor transformed the wilderness into tillable fields.

NEW PROBLEMS OF THE RURAL ECONOMY

The current problems of the rural economy are aspects of the changing national culture. They flow mainly from three sources: The persisting tradition shaped when wilderness resources were continually available; the developments that have transformed the historic rural economy; and the interaction between the rural economy as it now exists and the urban elements of the national culture. The problems fall into four main divisions: (1) Economic control, (2) production, (3) standards of living, and (4) population. Only brief comments on them can be made here.

Problems of Economic Control

The problems of economic control in agriculture have their origin in a conflict between the historic independence of the farmer and the circumstances that have brought about dependence upon the market and the need for a greater amount of capital. True to the tradition of the national culture, the farmer regards making and acting on his own decisions as essential elements of his calling. He finds more and more, however, that market factors over which he has no control and financial power, which is effective because he has need for more capital than he possesses, combine either to take away the capacity to make his own decisions or to deprive him of the results he had expected to come from acting on them. In the historic self-sufficient rural economy good crops meant a plentiful supply of simple consumers' goods if the members of the farm family were skillful in producing them from raw materials. Individual effort was immediately evident in tangible goods. Today good crops may mean low prices and, as a result, an inability to purchase consumers' goods to be obtained only in the market. Successful individual effort in production may actually mean a decreased income; this is the circumstance that justifies measures for the social control of agricultural production.

In fact, the situation of the farmer who sells his labor mainly in the form of products of the soil, both plant and animal, is not greatly different from that of the man who sells his labor for a wage, because when supply is great or demand is weak, for reasons not in any way the result of their respective individual acts, their incomes are likely to decline or disappear. The agricultural surplus and the labor surplus root in the same fundamental circumstance—that individual effort alone is no longer sufficient to achieve economic well-being. The persistence of the tradition shaped in the historic rural economy obscures the understanding of this circumstance, and as a result farmers especially have difficulty in thinking in terms of the social interdependence that has become more and more deeply organized in national life. This difficulty is significant as a factor shaping current agricultural problems because it prevents the farmer from accepting the social controls which can operate effectively in terms of the social interdependence which affects him. Furthermore the devising of these social controls, it must be realized, can be successfully undertaken only when the circumstances giving rise to the need for them are understood, for only then can they be developed in terms of the conditions under which they must operate.

Problems of Production

The problems of control in agriculture are complicated by the new conditions that have come with the increased capacity to produce. In terms of this increased capacity, individual effort is more successful than ever, but, for the reasons already indicated, its reward may be actually less.

This circumstance is particularly acute in the continuous formation of agricultural surpluses. These surpluses, like the goods said to be overproduced in manufacturing, are in many instances only supplies of goods that cannot be sold in the market at a profit. They are market, not consumers' surpluses; that is, they exist mainly because there is some demand which, because of a lack of purchasing power, cannot become active.

In view of the circumstances the primary point of attack upon the agricultural surpluses must be an increase of the purchasing power of the low-income consumers, who form the great body of urban dwellers. This in turn means that in the final analysis the problem of agricultural surpluses can be effectively dealt with only by action outside the agricultural part of the national economy.

Significance of the Increased Capacity To Produce

The circumstances which point to this general proposition also emphasize the significance for cultural development of agriculture's increasing capacity to produce. When this increasing capacity is seen in historical perspective it is discovered as the fundamental factor in whatever general social advance may now be possible. It is permitting the release of labor from the production of the kinds of wealth necessary for basic subsistence; and this labor when set to producing other forms of wealth makes possible higher levels of consumption, broadened social services, an enriched intellectual and artistic life, and a greater security. Low productivity of agriculture was the economic factor which in the past held the greater part of the population in poverty and impelled the concentration of the available economic surpluses in owning and ruling classes. These classes were few in number because the economic surpluses were small. With the rise of the capacity to produce in agriculture, neither the social effects of this factor nor the politics patterned by it need continue. If the original democratization of national life had origin mainly in the availability of wilderness land, the future elaboration of this democracy in terms of wider opportunities and richer satisfactions for individuals rests in the utilization of this increased capacity of agriculture to produce.

The tradition of our national culture supports the demand for this utilization, because in the historic rural economy increased production was the primary factor in a heightened well-being. However, the organization of agricultural production under the principles of economic liberalism, that is, according to the law of supply and demand as controlled by the prevailing maldistribution of the national income, has produced the current situation in which the utilization of this increased capacity, by contributing to the formation of agricultural surpluses, frustrates individual effort and denies society beneficial results. Inasmuch as the physical circumstances under which our national tradition was shaped no longer exist, the modes of the behavior with which it was correlated need no longer prevail. However, the human values it served can still be served; and, since the capacity to produce wealth has incerased, this service to human values can be greater than ever if modes of behavior suitable to the present circumstances can be devised. Not the determination of new human values but a new realization of the human values embodied in the historic national individualism is the central problem raised by the increased capacity to produce wealth in agriculture and industry.

Problems of Standards of Living

Although living standards among the rural population are as varied as among the urban population, it is agreed that they are generally lower than urban standards.[7] This condition is shocking because a romantic view of farm life has long obscured and now protests against it. The truth appears to be that rural standards of living, judged in terms of housing, medical service, educational attainments, and cultural opportunity, have always been low. Where the self-sufficient farm family is still found, as in the southeastern Appalachian highland, living standards are crude; this is probably quite as much a matter of survival of the modes of living of the historic rural economy as it is a matter of rural decay. The self-sufficient farm family possessed a high degree of economic security at a low level of living; it has been the loss of economic security, as commercial farming has developed and as more and more persons have entered the urban labor market, that has created the sharp contrast between present conditions of living, both rural and urban, and those of the historic rural economy.

[7] TAYLOR, CARL C., WHEELER, HELEN W., and KIRKPATRICK, E. L. DISADVANTAGED CLASSES IN AMERICAN AGRICULTURE. U. S. Farm Security Admin. Soc. Res. Rpt. 8, 124 pp. 1938. [Processed.] See p. 4.

The problems of standards of living today involve stabilizing the standards of living in cities at a level which science and technology will support and finding ways to raise rural standards to this level. The solution is not to be found in depressing any part of the urban population to the bare subsistence level that prevails among a large part of the present rural population. The economic means of solving these problems in both phases, urban and rural, are at hand in the increased capacity to produce wealth; the real problem is devising social controls under which this capacity can operate for the achievement of the desired end.

Problems of Population

The crucial problem of the rural economy has origin in the fact that the rural birth rate is far above that required to maintain the existing rural population; the most important agricultural surplus consists of young persons who, unless they are to be a burden on a population already living at too low a level, must find economic opportunities off the land. During recent depression years the normal flow of this population to cities was checked, with the result that the number of farms in the least favorable agricultural areas multiplied and the pressure of the population increased (*2, p. 78*). Any expansion of urban business activity will quickly set in motion an increased flow of individuals to cities, and if this occurs under conditions now existing or likely to arise in the immediate future, it may be expected to continue.

How is the phenomenon of a surplus rural population to be regarded? Are these persons to be counted as economic losses to the rural economy and forgotten? Are they to be seen only as members of farm families? As individuals trying to better their economic circumstances? As new entrants into the urban labor market? Or as human material involved in a fundamental adjustment in national life?

If they are to be counted merely as economic losses and forgotten, they have no further significance for the rural economy. However, if they are seen as individuals who, attached to families, are trying to improve their economic circumstances by entering the urban labor market, the approach to the problems of the rural economy must be made in new terms. If a farm family recognizes that some of its members must go into the urban labor market, it must also recognize that the improvement of the economic lot of these members turns upon their finding favorable conditions there. Thus all of those circumstances—unemployment, low earnings, and unfavorable working conditions—which make life insecure for urban wage earners become at once matters of concern to the farm family, as threats to the well-being of some of its members. In such terms farm families should understand that those movements by which urban wage earners win greater economic security, higher wages, and better living conditions are significant for them. Indeed, the direct way for them to insure the economic advancement of some of their members is to support such movements. Furthermore, the success of movements which give increased purchasing power to urban wage earners is the chief way to broaden the market for farm products. The interest of the rural population is doubly served by the success of urban wage earners in obtaining improved working conditions and increased earnings by (1) creating conditions in terms of which some members of rural families may advance themselves, and (2) expanding the market which is the essential outlet for agricultural products. Thus the urban labor movement is the most important single factor in national life working for the improvement of conditions among the rural population.

Similarly, improved conditions among the rural population are important to the advancement of urban wage earners. An increased rural income broadens the market for manufactured goods, thereby supporting earnings and lessening unemployment. Improved living standards and social services among the rural population also maintain the market for the products of urban labor and, what is more important, tend to hold individuals on the land, thereby reducing the competition for jobs in the urban labor market. From this point of view urban wage earners should support movements to ameliorate conditions of rural life, just as rural families should approve efforts to strengthen the economic position of urban wage earners.

The mutuality of interest between these two groups, which together form the bulk of the national population, is seen most clearly in the fact that the excess population on the land necessarily becomes a part of the urban labor force, and that, conversely, when unsatisfactory conditions prevail in the urban labor market, there is a movement back to the land. The members of these groups shift from the conditions of life of the country to those of the urban labor market, and vice versa, but they do not escape distress by such movements. The gap in the living conditions which exists between them is the primary factor in the persistence of this distress. Low economic opportunity on the land forces individuals into the urban labor market to compete for jobs already paid too little. Unemployment and low annual earnings among urban wage earners, in turn, decrease the farmers' income. The closing of this gap in living standards is the first step in the permanent amelioration of distresses among each group, and it can be closed only when they, having recognized their mutual interest, support each other.

RURAL PROBLEMS PART OF THE NATIONAL PROBLEM

These brief comments on the problems of the rural economy have suggested, first, that they cannot be considered only from the economic viewpoint and, second, that they are so bound into the general problems of national life that they cannot be handled merely as agricultural problems. Fundamentally these problems are not the problems of an industry or an occupation but of people who, having a certain economic calling, are under the influences now affecting the whole national culture. And, in contrast to the period which shaped the tradition of the national culture, in recent decades these influences have been more and more those arising in and organizing urban life. It has been the unfortunate result of the economic determinism embodied in economic liberalism that all national problems have been viewed mainly as dollars-and-cents matters. For the rural population this has meant the adoption of programs oriented too exclusively toward commercial farming and not enough toward the maintenance of the historic qualities of rural life as shaped under the influence of available wilderness resources. If these historic qualities are to be maintained now, they must be restored to rural life as well as organized in urban life, and one result cannot be achieved apart from the other. In this connection it is important to emphasize that even in the period when the rural economy was dominant, this mutuality of interest between the farm population and urban wage-earning groups was expressed in common support of the extension of the franchise, the establishing of public education, the freeing of the Negro slaves, the repeal of the imprisonment penalty for debt, and the enactment of a homestead law.

Inasmuch as the problems of the rural economy have origin mainly in the developments that have been transforming the national culture, it should be clear that the solution of these problems will come only as these developments are integrated into a new pattern. At the end of this discussion it is important, therefore, to consider the factors likely to contribute to this integration. However, since the factors significant for cultural integration are not clearly recognized (this point is discussed in the Note for Students at the end of the article), little more than conjectures are possible.

If one employed the mode of thought of Frederick Jackson Turner, who found free land a persisting and pervasive element that unified the original national culture, one would inquire into the persisting and pervasive elements in present life which, like free land, affect economic opportunity and consequently social organization. One may also conceive, following this mode of thought, that the psychological concomitants of behavior on the frontier entered into ethical attributes and intellectual qualities which became "American"; if this occurred, it may follow that today, accompanying those factors which are affecting economic opportunity and, consequently, social organization, are psychological elements which are entering into new ethical attributes and intellectual qualtities. If, for example, the low productivity of technology and wilderness resources together nurtured the qualities of self-support and self-reliance, the new division of labor and social interdependence may be shaping forms of cooperation and mutual aid. One may also suppose that, since frontier life modified institutions and modes of behavior transplanted from Europe, the factors now affecting economic opportunity and social organization may modify the institutions and modes of behavior transmitted from the original culture.

This line of reasoning leads to the view that the values of the historic tradition of the national culture will be reoriented in terms of pervasive elements of urban life as shaped by the innovations and conditions created by them. If the frontier was originally a milieu in which was shaped the historic national culture, today the city, especially the metropolitan urban area, is a milieu from which will issue a reorientation of the original individualism of the Nation, and in such a reorientation rural life will be affected as much as any other phase of national life.

Among the elements of the urban milieu which, as they enter into the lives of millions of persons, form in their feeling and thinking a frame of reference that may impel this reorientation are: (1) Bargaining in the market, (2) interdependence in the division of labor, (3) increased human control through technology and science in ever-wider areas of living, and (4) the increased capacity to produce wealth, which offers, potentially at least, a far richer satisfaction of individual wants than now prevails.

Of these four elements, at present only bargaining in the market is organized in individual behavior, and the results issuing from it are everywhere evident in social distress. These results—unemployment, low standards of living, ill-health, and dependency—set the problem into the solution of which the other pervasive elements in the urban milieu may enter. From the point of view of the concept of culture, it may be argued that the truly significant influence for change is not present distress but the development of these new pervasive elements in life; for in spite of distress, living conditions are today better in many respects than under the historic rural economy.

If the demands for social amelioration had no basis other than distress—that is, need—little could be done about them, but human control, social interdependence, and a high capacity to produce wealth offer means of dealing with these demands in new ways. But the means can be used only as they enter into an individual behavior which is more social than that which prevails in the market. The repudiation of the concept of economic man, which one meets even in conservative newspapers and journals, is evidence of the abandonment of the principles of economic liberalism, or, in other words, of the urban interpretation of individualism by which the conditions now distressful in national life have been justified. Once this justification is abandoned, the historic national individualism declaring equality and self-decision, especially as they release the individual from the economic power of others, will become free to enter into an organization of life in terms of the greater human control, social interdependence, and high capacity to produce wealth that are so fundamental in the urban milieu. The doctrine that neither the owners nor the employees of urban utilities have the right to stop the performance of a service necessary to the orderly living of thousands is an adaptation of individual behavior to these new factors.

In a sense, therefore, the urban milieu, at least at present, sets into individual life a conflict between a behavior oriented in the market and a behavior socially oriented in terms of interdependence, increased human control over the conditions of living, and the higher capacity to produce wealth. If the market factor remains dominant, present conditions of life will continue; if it is modified under the influence of the other factors, individual behavior will be given a new social orientation.

According to the culture concept individuals and groups of individuals receive patterns of thought and behavior from their ancestors and transmit them to their descendants; when an individual or a group of individuals is seen as receiving and transmitting a relatively stable set of patterns, the individual or the group is said to be a carrier of the patterns. In the historic culture of the Nation, the members of farm families as they lived in rural communities were the carriers of the fundamental patterns of national life. Inasmuch as the changes which have occurred in national life are organized most widely in urban life, the urban population becomes their carrier. The engineers and laborers whose lives are patterned by machine technology and the division of labor and who, because of this, are familiar with the potentialities of increased production are most distinctively the carriers of these patterns.

Inasmuch as the engineers have been bound to urban enterprisers by financial ties, they have held fast to the market orientation of behavior, while their technological procedures are carried on in terms of planning and controls quite opposed to the uncertainty of the market. The need for mental coherence (which, perhaps, may be considered the greatest of all needs because it defines sanity and insanity) will possibly bring more and more into the foreground of the thinking of engineers and technicians the role of planning and control in human affairs.

On the other hand, the urban workers, especially those engaged in industrial production, because they have tended to see their well-being achieved in terms of the new elements of the urban milieu, have been the spear head of movements for social amelioration; this they are likely to continue to be, especially as their distresses seem sharper in contrast with the potentialities for improved living opened up by the new factors in the urban milieu.

Because the members of these groups are spread throughout cities, the social interaction of urban life carries their modes of thinking and acting ever more widely among the whole population. Thus the metropolitan milieu promotes a reorganization of the behavior and thought of all who come under its influences. For this reason cultural change does not originate in the advent of a new social class seeking to adjust existing institutions to the service of its interest; rather it springs from an emerging structure of behavior and thought which, affecting all classes, belongs peculiarly to the populations of industrial cities. From this point of view the extension of the urban milieu into rural areas by occupational changes, improved communication, and increased social interaction and interdependence may be seen to have special importance, for it means that the rural structure of behavior and thought is being reshaped by the influences at work among the urban population. Historically this is supremely significant, for now the ancient social and intellectual differences between the rural and urban sections of national groups are being greatly altered if not completely worn away. In perspective, therefore, it appears that the opposition of the rural and urban groups and the conflict of urban classes that patterned the cultures of the past are being displaced in an emerging culture which, developing under the influence of the metropolitan milieu, brings rural and urban dwellers more and more into a common life and compels all classes to redefine their interests in terms of new social and economic conditions.

Under these circumstances urban and rural mentalities meet easily in terms of reactions to the insecurity of life that roots in the market organization of the economy and also in an understanding of the potentialities of increased production. In other words, they both understand that low prices for products and for labor mean loss and, possibly, deprivation; they also understand that in the long run the failure to produce, whether by reducing agricultural production or by shutting down factories, means less goods and consequently some wants not adequately satisfied. In terms of the market factor—economic instability—the common problem (low conditions of living) of the rural and urban sections of the national population is defined; in terms of the increased capacity to produce wealth and the greater social interdependence, the modes of its solution are indicated. The solution involves the organization of production under controls which, while they stabilize the economy, leave the individual free and provide more adequately for his support.

From the point of view of democracy this solution is possible if the traditional American right of the individual to participate in making and carrying out the significant decisions that affect his life is made the guide of action. Concretely this means (1) that over-all decisions about production shall be made in conformity with an economic policy determined by the political action of the national electorate, and (2) that the execution of these decisions in industries, urban as well as rural, and in local areas of production, shall be made with the participation of workers, consumers, and technicians, as well as of the owners of the industries. The procedures of the agricultural conservation program in fixing allotments of crop acreage approximate the modes of action by which this democratic administration of production may be achieved.

As a democratic way of organizing production, the procedures of this program testify to the vitality of the historic national individualism of American culture. In fact, probably the one certain fact about cultural development is the persistence of the attitudes and values fixed in the tradition of the group carrying the culture. This means for Americans that the attitudes and values of the historic rural economy, not its crude physical routines or its simple crafts, have lasting vitality; and these are the attitudes and values of a society in which the individual made and acted upon the chief decisions that shaped his life. They are the traditional elements of the national culture and cannot be destroyed except as the group carrying them is disintegrated. Indeed, their distortion, such as has occurred under the influence of doctrinaire economic liberalism, can be only temporary. For whenever national life becomes disturbed or distressed, these values emerge as the standards by which conditions and programs are judged.

It is the good fortune of the American people that the tradition of their culture, more than that of any other people, declares the right of the individual to participate in making the significant decisions that shape his life. The right to vote, civil liberties, equality of opportunity, and easy access to the basic means of production—all that is meant by "democracy" as historically created by the American people—are only means of realizing this principle. The original Americans realized this principle in a social order having at hand abundant wilderness resources; twentieth-century Americans must realize it in a social order possessing an unprecedented capacity to produce wealth. The modes of this realization must be different from those of the historic rural economy, but the values will be the same. The individual, recognizing the social interdependence which supports his life, will find that the social controls he accepts are the means of achieving for himself a higher well-being than he could possibly achieve alone. From the social point of view, these controls will operate on a national, not on a class or a regional, basis to maintain a common level of well-being and a free and equal opportunity for individual advancement in every activity that serves and enriches the common well-being. In this restoration of national individualism the rural and urban populations will close that gap in living standards which today is the chief factor in perpetuating and spreading distress among them.

A NOTE FOR STUDENTS ON THE CONCEPT OF CULTURE

The fundamental predication of the concept of culture is that human life is a socially organized and transmitted structure of behavior and thought. This structure, it is held, is integrated functionally; that is, its constitutent parts—generally called traits and patterns—provide a unity more than a conflict of services to life, and have coherence psychologically in terms of a relatively clearly focused outlook on life. A culture may be regarded, therefore, as a psychological entity, evolved historically and carried in social interaction.

For an individual a culture is almost entirely an acquired mode of life. For a group it is a persisting organization of life, subject to change as new elements enter into it and old elements are dropped from it. For the individual and the group alike it is, on the one hand, an adjustment to physical nature by which life is supported materially and, on the other hand, a complex of relationships within which individuals perform functions significant for the maintenance of life. Correlative with the acts making up this adjustment and these relationships are the interpretations of life or, in other words, the ideas and values which are the subjective contents of the traits and patterns of the cultures. These subjective elements are embedded in both the mores of the group and the learning carried by the intellectual segment of the group. In the integration which gives coherence to a culture, folk mentality and learning normally complement each other; together they form the subjective tradition, as contrasted with the material elements of a culture.

However, it is recognized that within a culture the degree of integration varies from time to time. A high degree of integration is considered an evidence of stability, while a low degree is regarded as a manifestation of change. Under some conditions a given integration may be long enduring, while under some others the changes may be numerous, rapid, and far-reaching. In the latter case, it may be assumed that ultimately a new integration will be formed. Normally cultural change, it may be noted, is recognizable as problems—distresses and conflicts—about which there is agitation and action. These problems may be understood as evidences of a loss of coherence in an existing cultural organization of life or as manifestations of the elements of a new cultural integration. They commonly share both aspects in some degree, and it is important to see them in both lights, although constructive action about them is probably far less a matter of understanding the forces that are disintegrating existing cultural organization than recognizing the elements of a new cultural integration. That cultural change occurs is well recognized; how it occurs,

223761°—40——66

at least from the point of view of the shaping of a new cultural integration, is quite obscure.

Although the students who have developed the concept of culture have paid more attention to the structure of relationships of traits and patterns than they have to the factors which shape a cultural integration, it may be stated that the material aspects of a culture are likely to change before its subjective elements give way, or, in other words, the traditional values of a culture may persist in folk mentality and learning for a considerable time after its manipulative practices are displaced. This broad fact has recognition in the widely accepted theory of cultural lag. Insofar as this situation exists in a period of cultural change, it has a decisive effect upon the shaping of a new integration, for it means that the material operations which belong to the new integration are long held within old patterns by a persisting subjective tradition. Indeed, this circumstance is probably the most important source of the human distresses that occur in a period of cultural change. However, once a subjective tradition breaks up, the new material operations may move quickly into the new integration, and subjective elements correlative with modes of living supported by the new material operations will coalesce into a new tradition. In this process, it should be emphasized, both old material and old subjective elements will survive, but they will be adapted to the new elements, not contrariwise.

To this process as a whole may be given the designation "cultural reorientation."

The culminating phase of cultural change then becomes the disorganization of the subjective values of an old culture and their reorganization, sometimes along with new subjective values, in a new cultural integration. In this form cultural development can be seen as consisting, in the main, of psychological movements, that is, thinking, feeling, and acting, which move from synthesis to synthesis, each synthesis possessing coherence in some form.

The primary materials of cultural change are innovations, that is, inventions and discoveries, which are made by individuals. But since an individual thinks and acts in terms of a socially evolved culture, the inventions and discoveries he can make are almost completely fixed by the cultural base; likewise his invention or discovery, whatever it may be, becomes a part of culture only as it is socially accepted and organized in an enduring mode of life. In effect, therefore, social factors guide cultural growth at every important point—innovating, accepting, and organizing. Indeed, the integration of traits and patterns in a total culture is achieved in terms of an outlook on life which projects over experience, on the one hand, a pervasive reaction to the physical circumstances of life and, on the other hand, an interest sufficiently powerful to establish itself as a norm of selection among culture traits. The pervasive reaction has origin mainly in the emotions of the most numerous of the sociocultural types that are organized by a culture, while the interest arises in the sociocultural type which exercises the essential controls in the group. Such a reaction or interest arrives at cultural expression only through a social intercourse which binds great numbers of men into a common life at some level of behavior, thinking, and feeling. And a shift in outlook occurs only as this level is altered in some significant way. The powerful factors in cultural development are, therefore, those occurrences and movements which give rise to new modes of social intercourse by which, in turn, an emotional reaction to changing circumstances of mass life or the assertion of a new interest can be assimilated in a new general outlook on life.

A culture becomes then, in final form, a socially evolved mentality which, having different aspects, is carried by individuals who are designated "sociocultural types." These types represent, first, the kind of adjustments made to the physical environment and, second, the main points of social integration within the culture. Under the play of innovations and changing circumstances of life, particularly as they affect one or the other of the leading sociocultural types or create a new one, the culture is subject not to complete displacement but to reorientation. And the study of the problem of cultural change is, as a result, a matter of ascertaining the factors which, giving rise not only to innovations but also to their assimilation through the formation of a new outlook on life, are shaping a new structure of behavior and thought. The objective manifestation of these changes, however diverse, is, in final form, the alteration of old sociocultural types and the creation of new ones. The culmination of the changes is the integration of these altered and new sociocultural types under a general outlook on life that embodies the common element of their modes of experience. It seems, therefore, that the understanding of the circumstances contributing to this cultural integration is the goal to be sought.

In applying the concept of culture to the analysis of any situation, at least three elements of the situation, it would seem, have special significance: (1) The persisting subjective tradition, (2) the current innovations, especially as they are shaping new patterns, and (3) the factors which, as these patterns form, may be giving rise to a reorientation of the persisting subjective tradition. These factors, although they may be difficult to identify, are the truly decisive forces in cultural changes.

LITERATURE CITED

(1) Ashby, A. W.
1939. THE EFFECTS OF URBAN GROWTH ON THE COUNTRYSIDE. Sociol. Rev. 31 (4): 345–369.

(2) Baker, O. E., Borsodi, Ralph, and Wilson, M. L.
1939. AGRICULTURE IN MODERN LIFE. 303 pp., illus. New York and London.

(3) Edwards, Everett E., compiler.
1938. THE EARLY WRITINGS OF FREDERICK JACKSON TURNER; WITH A LIST OF ALL HIS WORKS. 316 pp. Madison, Wis.

(4) Goodrich, Carter, Allin, Bushrod W., Thornthwaite, C. Warren, and others.
1936. MIGRATION AND ECONOMIC OPPORTUNITY; THE REPORT OF THE STUDY OF POPULATION REDISTRIBUTION. 763 pp., illus. Philadelphia and London.

(5) Kekoni, Karl.
1937. THE PROBLEM OF THE CITY THE FUNDAMENTAL PROBLEM OF HUMAN GEOGRAPHY. Sci. Monthly 45: 547–554.

(6) Lynd, Robert S.
1939. KNOWLEDGE FOR WHAT? THE PLACE OF SOCIAL SCIENCE IN AMERICAN CULTURE. 268 pp. Princeton, N. J.

(7) THOMPSON, WARREN S.
1937. RESEARCH MEMORANDUM ON INTERNAL MIGRATION IN THE DEPRESSION. 86 pp. New York. (Soc. Sci. Research Bul. 30.)

(8) WELLS, O. V.
1940. AGRICULTURAL SURPLUSES AND NUTRITIONAL DEFICITS: A STATEMENT OF THE PROBLEM AND SOME FACTORS AFFECTING ITS SOLUTION. Jour. Farm Econ. 22: 317-323.

Education for Rural Life

by EDWIN R. EMBREE [1]

HERE IS an eloquent plea for a new approach to rural education, not in superficial things but in fundamentals. "Hundreds of millions of dollars of taxpayers' money," the author says, "is going into schools that are not educational institutions at all but simply a species of jail for keeping children in order for a few hours each day. * * * In many ways the educational procedures of primitive men were more sensible and more effective than the schools of today." The function of the school, he points out, is to prepare young people for happy and successful living. Education is not simply the covering of a series of specified topics. We are at the beginning of what bids fair to be a rural renaissance. For the first time in a hundred years we are recognizing the desirable qualities of the countryside. The school succeeds only as it contributes to the community as well as to the skill and knowledge of individual pupils.

THE function of education has always been to prepare young people for happy and successful living in the communities of which they are a part. We are constantly forgetting this sole and essential purpose. We easily fall into a worship of certain subjects and certain methods of teaching as if these were in themselves the ends of education. If education is to be of real service to farm life and to rural children, we must cease to be awed by traditional subjects and procedures and

[1] Edwin R. Embree is President of the Julius Rosenwald Fund, which has been active in the improvement of rural education, especially in the American South.

build our schools on the essential needs of the countryside and the country child.

Education is no new enterprise. It has existed in all societies. And in many ways the educational procedures of primitive men were more sensible and more effective than the schools of today. At any rate the ancients knew what they wanted, and they went about it vigorously and directly. The boys learned warfare, hunting, and hardihood as well as many manual arts. The girls learned cooking, weaving, and other women's skills, and also the duties of wife and homemaker. Both boys and girls were steeped in the traditions and morals and ideals of their group. The societies of adolescents and the spectacular and often prolonged initiation ceremonies were for the sole and direct purpose of preparing young people for their coming responsibilities as members of the tribe. American Indians, Polynesian islanders, and African tribesmen went to school arduously and on the whole successfully centuries before the little red schoolhouse came into being in Europe and North America.

The formal schooling of western Europe and modern America grew from the same need as the home training and societies of adolescents of the ancient tribes. As the mechanics of life became more complex—especially with the growth of reading and writing and science and mechanics—the duties of the school became more onerous and time consuming. During the last century or two, with the upsurge of science and the industrial revolution, the obligations of the school became almost overwhelming. It was necessary to divide up the tasks and classify the studies. Specialists were called in to handle the skills of reading and figuring, others to teach the crafts, others to pass on the traditions and morals, and still others to foster such specialties as the languages of other groups, the fine arts, and especially the new and complicated tools of science and mechanics. Some of this education was given in the home, some of it by priests and preachers, most of it in special buildings called schools. About each department of learning grew up a special profession of teachers, special textbooks, special traditions and feelings of prestige.

Finally, in the modern world, classes or special divisions of subject matter became so sharply differentiated and so highly organized that the subjects themselves began to overshadow the purposes for which they had been created. Education, instead of preparation for life, came to be thought of as simply the covering of a series of specified topics. Heated arguments arose in defense of given classes, not as to whether they would help the child live happily and successfully in his society, but as to their tradition-hallowed place in something called Education—with a very large E. "No one can be called educated who has not studied Latin"; "hand skills and morals have no place in proper education"; "science is the basis of true education"—these are a few examples of the kind of statements made.

Recently the futility of all this scholastic hullabaloo has dawned upon us. Today most of us do not talk about the sacredness to education of any given subject. Instead, with the same directness as the primitives, we are trying to build our schools upon the needs of the children and of the society of which they are a part.

This does not mean that we are going back to the learning routines of the early Indians or the Pacific islanders. Our society is very different from theirs, and the schooling of our children must therefore be very different. Among other things, our life is much more complex. We have built upon the learning of the ancients great superstructures of written literature and of science and mechanics, and we have built a society in which each citizen is supposed to take part in the control of policy as well as in labor. Our schools have a tremendous task in preparing children for this complex modern world. But in its essence, the function of the school today is just the same as it has always been: To prepare young people for happy and successful living in their world.

THE RURAL RENAISSANCE

Not only did we for a time allow the school to run off into a plethora of formal, scholastic subjects poorly related to the needs of actual life, but during the last century we especially forgot or ignored the needs of country life and the rural child. A special task, therefore, as we reorganize education in this country is to consider the needs of the rural school and the possibilities of making life rich and full on the farm as well as in the city.

We are at the beginning of what bids fair to be a rural renaissance. Country life is receiving attention and interest in the United States unequaled since colonial days. For the first time in 100 years we are recognizing the desirable qualities of the countryside.

There has been a strange contradiction in American history and in American ambition throughout the whole period of our national growth. While our history has been the conquest and cultivation of ever new and greater territory, our economic and cultural interests have been increasingly urban and industrial. The new Nation came into being just as the industrial revolution was getting into full swing. We grew up with the Machine Age. So while we kept swallowing up huge new territories—the Western Reserve, the Mississippi Valley, Florida, Louisiana, the Southwest, the Northwest, California—our interest really was not in land but in machines.

The very riches and expanse of the land helped to magnify the urban industrialism. The underground deposits of coal and iron and oil fed the manufacturing plants. The spread of territory gave scope to the huge industries of railroading and later of motor traffic and airplanes. Cotton and tobacco and other commercial crops became such big items in the national economy that interest in them shifted from the farm to the office and the factory. Cattle raising developed its headquarters in Chicago and Kansas City rather than on the Plains and the ranches. Forests were ruthlessly denuded to furnish timber for the towns and newspaper pulp for the cities. The whole American countryside poured its interest and its wealth into the building up of a spectacular urban civilization. Today, although this Nation covers most of the temperate zone of a whole great continent, over half our population is classed as urban while about 30 percent of all the people live in cities of more than 100,000. But much more than in mere residence, our interests and our ambitions have centered in city life and in industry.

All that is beginning to change. It is not that any spectacular migration back to the soil has set in. Even during the depths of the depression there was no mass movement toward the nourishing bosom of Mother Nature. Mechanical invention still continues; industrial efficiency proceeds; the labor-saving devices of machinery and mass production are steadily developing. And no sensible man can regret the advances which make it possible for more and more necessities, conveniences, and luxuries to be produced so that greater numbers of the total population can share in this enlarging wealth. But the adulation of industrialism as the be-all and end-all of human life has passed its zenith.

Country people need no longer look upon migration to the city as an escape from isolation and inconvenience. For, interestingly enough, industry today is beginning to direct a great deal of its effort to the enrichment of the countryside. Electrification, one of the greatest of modern industries, is now finding its largest development in the rural regions. Movies and radio are transforming the art and the communications available to the rural dweller. Automobiles and good roads have brought easy mobility to rustic masses formerly almost plantlike in their restriction of movement from the local base. Big stores, formerly city phenomena, are extending the widest variety of purchasable goods to every hamlet through mail-order and retail chains. With comforts, conveniences, and ready communication, country life in many places is a very different thing from the stark and barren struggle for existence which our forefathers knew.

The present trend, however, is not so much back to the country as back to a regard for living as contrasted to exclusive devotion to making a living. We are freeing ourselves from the obsession for money as contrasted to real wealth; our eyes are no longer wholly blinded by the garish neon lights of "success"; there is a little mitigation in the mad rush to keep up with the Joneses. In this fresh regard for the content and quality of life itself, country living takes its place on its own merits, not necessarily above tenement and apartment living in cities, but simply as one of the potentially satisfying ways of life.

RURAL SCHOOLS AND THE NATION

What happens in the rural schools of the Nation is not the problem of rural communities alone. It concerns all of us. For one thing, if we can devise good educational practices anywhere, these may be expected in time to influence the whole school system.

Furthermore, the people who live in cities have a very direct interest in country schools because to a great degree the future citizens of the large centers are being educated not in the schools of those centers but in the rural communities. Urban populations are not reproducing themselves, and rural regions are continuing to produce surplus populations which are continually moving into cities. In the southern rural States, for example, the number of children under 5 years old per 1,000 native white women of childbearing age (20 to 44 years) is more than double that of northern industrial regions, figures for typical States being 827 for North Carolina, 786 for Alabama, 777 for South Carolina, and 740 for Mississippi, as contrasted to 363 for Rhode Island, 362 for New York, and 359 for Massachusetts. And during the three decades from 1900 to 1930, 3,500,000 of the people born in the rural States of the Southeast moved to other regions, chiefly the industrial North. This heavy migration from country to city occurred also in other rural sections, especially the Midwest and the Great Plains. Thus the education of rural children, many of whom will be the future citizens of Chicago, New York, and similar metropolitan centers, is a matter of concern to cities as well as to rural communities.

EDUCATION FOR RURAL LIFE

How then can we plan the rural school so that it will give the child what he needs for life in the farm community and also for citizenship in the modern complex world? The problem is to give him the basic tools of knowledge and to get him to put these tools to use for his own growth and for the improvement of the community in which he lives.

This article will not discuss special training in the science and vocation of agriculture. A great deal of that is given in American high schools and universities, on the whole very successfully, though much of it is still fragmentary and pseudo scholarly rather than practical. But questions of special vocational training and of research and teaching in the higher branches of agriculture are separate subjects. Most children, especially in the country, do not carry their formal education beyond the common school. Anyway, there is little doubt of our ability to master the science and techniques of agriculture. In fact, so far as the production of standard crops is concerned, we have already succeeded almost too well. The need in the United States today and the great task of the rural school is to give general rather than vocational equipment to children that they may live fully the rich life which we now realize is possible in the farm community.

THE BASIC THREE R'S, ESPECIALLY READING

First, whatever else is done, the school must provide skill in the use of the three R's. No child is prepared to take his place in the modern world without some competence in reading, writing, and arithmetic. Language and numbers are tools so basic to our civilization that they become the first tasks of any school. The only thing we need to remember in this connection is that language and numbers are, after all, simply tools to be used in various ways. They are not ends in themselves. The chief fault in the teaching of them is that the lessons in reading and writing and arithmetic become so formalized that the pupil scarcely understands why he is learning them. In fact, in spite of the great amount of time devoted to these primary subjects, a shocking number of children—especially in the rural regions—do not acquire even an elementary knowledge of them.

If a child really learns to read and puts his knowledge into practice, he can care for all the rest of his academic education by his own efforts. The difference between educated and uneducated people is largely the difference in the range and understanding of their reading. Abraham Lincoln was one of the best educated of men in spite of meager schooling because he read so avidly. Almost the whole of the subject matter of elementary schools may be regarded as practice in reading. And reading, by the same token, should be thought of not as a "lesson," something to be had from a special class or a special set of textbooks, but as the means of mastery of all the subjects and projects which make up school life and all life.

COUNTRY LIFE AS GENERAL EDUCATION

In addition to the three R's, the rural pupil should be made acquainted with two other fields: handcrafts and the processes of nature. These are not advocated as vocational subjects but simply as essential tools quite as general in their use as language or arithmetic.

Ability to use one's hands is a fitting supplement to ability to use one's wits. Manual arts run the whole gamut from homely hand labor to high expression in art and music. Certainly, the beginnings of hand skill should be a part of any child's preparation for life.

What is meant by the understanding of nature is harder to define, and it will probably be harder to work into the educational program. It is not merely instruction in gardening or animal husbandry or in the protection of our own health, although it should be applied in all of these. It is the beginnings of knowledge of how natural forces work. "Nature study" is probably the best term, in spite of the fact that this phrase has been put to some pretty sentimental uses. At any rate, what the writer urges is an introduction to the simple biological facts which are a vital part of all our lives and which are particularly important and conspicuous in the rural scene.

SKILL AND KNOWLEDGE MUST BE USED

Skill and knowledge—it cannot too often be repeated—are of no value unless they are put to use; children cannot learn even the elementary skills unless they practice them.

The three R's, for example, easily fall into a rote so perfunctory that no learning results. It is easy to give rules for reading and arithmetic and to set exercises or lessons. Children may be drilled week after week, year after year, without ever realizing that they are acquiring tools which are usable in many ways. In such cases skill in reading or writing or the manipulation of numbers is on a level with the skill of parrots who have been taught to call words or of dogs who have been taught to jump through a hoop or to sit up and shake hands. Much of our school work, it must be sadly confessed, does not go far beyond this animal-training level.

The autobiography of a southern country boy records that after going to school for several years he happened to pick up the family Bible. To his amazement he found that he could read it. Up to that moment, he said, it had never occurred to him that the rote drill in school called reading had any connection with something he might do out of school. Suddenly he discovered that what he had supposed was a scholastic trick was instead a generalized tool by means of which he could gain information and pleasure from the whole realm of literature.

This seems an extreme case. Yet the tests given to the drafted soldiers during the World War indicated that 25 percent of that cross section of American youth had never made a successful transfer from the school lessons to reading. One-fourth of the whole American draft army, although most of the individuals had spent several years in school, had not learned enough to carry over into life the ability to read simple sentences or to write their own names.

In mathematics the percentage of educational failure is even greater. Many pupils become skillful in performing the cunning tricks of addition, multiplication, and division, or even in handling what are so aptly termed improper fractions. But they gain no general mathematical ability. In many cases they do not even understand that the problems are intended not as ends in themselves but merely as exercises or examples, on the one hand, of simple dealings they will have every day of their lives and, on the other hand, of the highly sophisticated process of dealing with quantities by symbols.

The additional fields of interest suggested—manual dexterity and the understanding of nature—are happily less liable to rote training than the three R's. In fact these subjects are so generalized that they may better be introduced through related activities than through formal courses. Certainly the school lessons attempted, for example, in health or hygiene have proved to be almost as deadly as the ills they were supposed to correct. But stimulating activities that involve manual dexterity and natural processes can easily be arranged by any resourceful teacher. They do not require elaborate or expensive equipment. In fact the less formal the equipment the better, since the aim is to stir up the creative impulse and to develop resourcefulness. This is especially true for country children whose problem often is to create utility or beauty from meager materials.

If true education is learning from the doing of one task how to use similar processes in other problems, then hand work and activities with nature are almost necessarily educational. One can scarcely use a saw or a hammer without realizing that either tool is usable in many ways and for many ends; the handling of clay or cloth or a musical instrument is by its very nature general rather than rote. Similarly in the processes of nature variety rather than routine is the rule. The planting of a school garden, for example, involves so many variables (seed, soil, fertilizer, weather, parasites) that it is almost impossible for it to become routine.

Furthermore the introduction into the school course of these hand and nature activities tends to break down the rote learning in the three R's. When a child sees multiplication at work through the breeding of rabbits, he cannot keep from realizing that arithmetic is something more than a lesson. Reading becomes an active tool—not simply an exercise—when it is used in finding out how to plant flowers or cultivate vegetables. Figuring comes alive for a boy when he measures off a garden plot or computes the yield from seed corn.

EDUCATION VERSUS LESSONS

If rural children can gain some competence in these basic skills and can put them to active use, they will have some preparation for happy and successful living. Surely the learning of the three R's and some acquaintance with hand work and nature are not too much to expect of the 6 to 8 years of the common school. The reason these or any other subjects are not mastered is that instead of generalized study and practice of a few broad topics, the school attempts to cram a great multitude of lessons into the brief days. Subjects are artificially divided into fragments, which are rehearsed in tiny sections, grade by grade. In many rural schools one or two teachers rush through a whole day made up of lessons of less than 15 minutes each. No wonder that teachers, driven by fantastic schedules of rote lessons, fail to offer real education in any subject or that children, hurried from class to class, come to regard school as a place for reciting rather than for learning.

All this may seem to be arguing the obvious. It is. But the plain fact is that thousands of schools in the United States today are not attempting to give any application to the simplest of routine skills. Millions of children are merely learning scholastic tricks—just like parrots or trained fleas. Hundreds of millions of dollars of taxpayers' money is going into schools that are not educational institutions at all but simply a species of jail for keeping children in order for a few hours each day.

SCHOOL AND SOCIETY

The school today has one other significant task. Not only must it give its pupils knowledge and skill, it must in some way get this learning into practice by the children and by the community. The general welfare is today largely a question of education. Especially in rural regions the school is often the only organized social force able to exert general influence.

In this new world of science and democracy, education not only has to encompass new realms of learning but also has to assume much of the social responsibility previously cared for by the church, the home, and other constituted authorities. If it were possible to build afresh a well-balanced society, the designers of it would probably hesitate to concentrate so much responsibility in a single institution. But in the United States today, and especially in rural areas, there is no other institution to which we can turn.

The modern school has a number of simple and clear duties in behalf of the community. It is universally agreed that the children and the community should be healthy instead of undernourished or ridden with disease; it is desirable that the farms be productive, that the houses and barns be well built and in good repair, that the homes be centers of good living, that children who have learned to read have access to books and papers so that they can go on reading with pleasure and profit. In such items the connections between in-school teaching and community practice are clear and direct.

In health, for example, the duty of the school is to give the children some idea of how to avoid diseases and how to keep well and robust. But the relation between teaching and the practices of the community is immediately apparent, for health cannot be treated as an individual matter. Hookworms can be avoided only by general sanitary facilities. Typhoid is spread by impure water or bad food, no matter how careful each individual tries to be. Malaria flies on the wings of mosquitoes from house to house unless swamps are drained or screens carefully used. Tuberculosis, diphtheria, measles, spread from person to person. Public action and community cooperation are necessary if a village or countryside is to keep well. The school, as the emissary of modern knowledge, is the natural rallying ground for information and for action toward better health for the individual child and for the neighborhood.

Farming is another example of the natural transition from the classroom to the field. The processes of nature about which the child learns in school are the very foundation of agriculture. And the verbal learning takes effect only as it is applied. Of course small children cannot with impunity undertake to change the habits of their parents. But the school, working in unison with the agricultural extension teachers and the farm agents, can help both parents and children to follow better practice on the basis of modern knowledge. In fact the school may well become the focal point for cooperative action by many governmental agencies—public health, home demonstration, farm extension, library service. Coordination is badly needed in these public services, which mean so much to rural development but which at the moment suffer from the natural tendency of each to engage busily in its own activities without regard for the work of the others or the general needs of the communities.

The community is the practice ground for the school. And the school succeeds only as it contributes to the community as well as to the skill and knowledge of individual pupils.

The Contribution of Sociology to Agriculture

by Carl C. Taylor [1]

IT HAS OFTEN been said that the physical or "natural" sciences have been developed to a high state but that they are just as capable of wrecking as of creating civilization. What is needed, according to this view, is a social science that will show us how to use our knowledge for the good of man. But the social sciences are very young, and to a considerable extent they have been confined to the classroom and the professor's study. Can they be applied as an everyday practical matter to the problems that beset all of us in the everyday world? Here is an attempt to explore the possibilities of using sociology in the study of agricultural problems. The author gives us a sweeping survey of the fields covered by sociology and holds that it can throw a great deal of light on the problem of building a better rural life.

SOCIOLOGY has been developing for only a little over a generation, but during that short period it has been organized into fairly concrete fields of study and investigation focused upon social problems of which the general public has become conscious. The following specific fields of teaching and research, each of which will be described

[1] Carl C. Taylor is Head, Division of Farm Population and Rural Welfare, Bureau of Agricultural Economics.

later in this article, probably represent sociology as well as any: [2] Social organization and social structure; population study, or social demography; social ecology, or human geography; cultural or social anthropology; social psychology; social pathology.

In some of these fields considerable work has been done in relation to agriculture and rural life; in others, very little. In order to appraise the complete contribution which sociology should be making to agriculture, it is necessary to take into consideration fields of knowledge and techniques of study that have become current in general sociology, although not always in rural sociology.

Rural sociology has as its primary aim improving the well-being of the farm population. It originated as a recognized discipline in teaching and research less than 25 years ago as a part of the general impulse to improve agriculture technologically, economically, and socially. Since then it has developed quite an elaborate body of research findings, but it has not yet brought to bear the full impact of available knowledge either from general sociology or from studies made in fields other than agriculture. Until it surveys the possibilities of doing this, it will not be in a position to make its full contribution to agriculture. In practically all instances its services will be focused directly upon problems to be solved. Owing to the fact that social causes are complex and sometimes deeply laid in the past history of social situations, recognition of the existence of problems is the necessary first step in their solution. It is the function of sociology, therefore, to reveal problems as well as to assist in solving them.

The roots of some of our most distressing agricultural problems are in part social, in part psychological, and in part cultural. We have widespread soil erosion partly because some of the customs, habits, and attitudes of farm people, instead of contributing to the conservation of soil, have speeded its destruction. We have hundreds of thousands of farm families living on lands which will not support adequate standards of living partly because great population movements of the past swept these people into places where successful settlement cannot be sustained. We have recently had more than a million farm families on relief and have only slightly less than 3,000,000 farm-tenant families, many of them sharecroppers. This is because of a slow but apparently steady shift toward the bottom of the agricultural ladder on the part of hundreds of thousands of farm families who because of general economic and social conditions are unable to maintain an acceptable economic and social status. This fact and the causes of it were not recognized while the problems were developing.

We are today in the midst of even more rapid social change than in the past, and new problems are developing while we are in the process of correcting old maladjustments and seeking new adjustments. Both maladjustments and adjustments depend to a considerable extent on the habits and attitudes of rural people, and an understanding of this fact demands a knowledge not only of social problems as such but also of what rural people themselves think about their

---

[2] BUREAU OF AGRICULTURAL ECONOMICS. THE FIELD OF RESEARCH IN RURAL SOCIOLOGY. Prepared by a Committee of the Rural Sociological Society of America and the Bureau of Agricultural Economics. 47 pp. Washington, D. C. 1938. [Mimeographed.]

problems and the extent to which they can be mobilized to assist in the solution of them.

FIELDS COVERED BY SOCIOLOGY

In order to orient the present discussion as definitely as possible to agriculture and to the established body of sociological knowledge and techniques, some elaboration of the fields listed above may clarify the contribution of rural sociology to the promotion of rural welfare.

Social Organization and Social Structure

In many ways the study of social organization is the heart of sociology, for social organization constitutes the more or less formalized machinery by which people live their daily lives. Social organization in rural life is in many ways similar and in a number of ways dissimilar to that in urban life. Each rural grouping has a pattern affected or conditioned not only by geography and the means of transportation and communication but by inherited social patterns, sometimes ethnic or racial, sometimes religious, sometimes economic, but never by any one of these factors exclusively. Neighborhoods, communities, and villages; institutional and service groups, including families, schools, churches, and libraries, and health, recreational, and welfare agencies; class and commodity groupings; and even political groups, all constitute forms of human association and social organization. Participation in the activities of these groups is the chief concern of rural people, and the groupings therefore affect their behavior and attitudes in everything they do. People measure their social standing in terms of the extent to which they are able or are permitted to help operate these pieces of social machinery; and since everyone desires an acceptable social status, some of the deepest issues of rural welfare are involved in the problems of participation in social organizations.

At a time when the impact of the world at large on rural life is steadily increasing, it is important to know to what extent stable local organizations of various kinds contribute to the economic, social, and psychological stability, well-being, and contentment of farm people. In terms of time and energy, their major concern is with comparatively local community organizations. It is a question whether adequate consideration is given to this fact in agricultural programs, even though security in rural life is one of the objectives of these programs.

In no section of the world has rural life changed more rapidly or drastically than in the United States during the relatively short period of our national history. This is another way of saying that the structure of American rural society has always been and still is in process of change. Change is essential to progress and adaptation, but it also disturbs and sometimes destroys things which tend to be the bulwarks of a culture. Considerable study of the effect of social change upon social institutions and organizations has been carried on by sociologists and anthropologists at various times and places, but the knowledge and understanding gained from such studies have not been fully utilized in developing an understanding of what may be happening in the rural life of the United States.

The pattern of settlement in many places in the United States was at one time that of village communities, but most of these gave way to scattered farmsteads as population moved westward with the settlement of the continent. Thousands of towns and hundreds of cities sprang up. Communities disintegrated and died, and new ones were formed. Institutions changed, and new service agencies appeared. The class structure of rural society changed greatly. All these processes of change will probably continue, but the rate of change will be less rapid as a settled economy and culture are established. Both the rate and type of change will be affected by changes in the numbers, composition, and distribution of the population, and the readier infiltration of urban culture and world culture into rural regions. Agricultural programs and plans must be based upon guesses or calculations as to where these changes will lead.

Will we revert, as Professor Gras, agricultural historian at Harvard University, predicted, to a village economy? Are rural neighborhoods doomed? Must rural communities be larger and financially stronger in order to support an adequate set of social institutions and service agencies? Must local government boundaries be redrawn? Are special-interest groups superseding all neighborhood and community groupings? Are distinct and permanent classes—laborers, tenants, owner-operators—developing in our rural society? Are rural resettlement and urban-rural resettlement communities developing, and should they develop? If so, where and how and in what patterns? These and other questions are important in a changing society such as ours. Furthermore, the answers to these questions would be immediately useful in the projection and operation of action programs. For example, it would be valuable to know what form of social organization would be effective for a county which is adding to its previous activities an ever-increasing list of new programs, such as those of the Agricultural Adjustment Administration, the Soil Conservation Service, the Farm Security Administration, the Farm Credit Administration, the Social Security Board, and relief and welfare agencies.

Population, or Social Demography

Population studies have been made for thousands of years. At first these involved only the simple task of counting or taking censuses of relatively primitive people. Demography (from demos, people, and geography) is a field in which the sociologist claims no monopoly, for population analyses, with which it is concerned, are for certain purposes important to the economist, the political scientist, and even the geneticist. Demography is, however, fundamental to the study of vital and social statistics and thus is one of the basic fields of sociology. It consists of far more than census taking. It not only deals with the numbers, distribution, and composition of populations, but it is also a study of the characteristics of various segments of the population and their relationships to internal and external factors of change. It even ventures predictions concerning population trends and their cause-and-effect relationships to the physical, economic, and social environment.

Studies and analyses which will contribute to an understanding of the composition, characteristics, and trends of the farm population

223761°—40——67

are of unique importance, because farm populations practically everywhere throughout the world bear peculiar relationships to national populations and to national economic and social structures. The urbanization of society has been in process for generations and has stimulated an almost constant net flow of population from farms to towns and cities, out of agriculture into industrial, commercial, and professional occupations. The rural birth rate nearly everywhere is higher than the urban birth rate, and in many instances is highest in those rural areas with the poorest natural resources and the lowest standards of living. (See the article, The Rural People, p. 827.) Because persons born and reared in rural areas, including areas with relatively poor natural resources and poor economic and social opportunities, will continue to furnish workers and citizens to other segments of the national population and to the economic and social life of the Nation as a whole, all parts of our national society must be concerned with the character, composition, and opportunities of the farm population.

The population of the United States in gross numbers increased from fewer than 4 million in 1790, the time of the first census, to about 131 million on January 1, 1939. In 1790 the area of settlement was a strip averaging about 250 miles wide along the Atlantic Ocean; by 1910 it quite thoroughly covered the continent from the Atlantic to the Pacific. At that time the farm population was 32,076,960, the greatest ever recorded by the decennial census. It had increased each decade from the time of earliest settlement, despite the fact that during each decade it contributed thousands, and in the later decades hundreds of thousands, of people to the urban population by way of rural-urban migration. Farm population did not increase, however, during the two decades following 1910. In 1930 it was only 30,169,000, or approximately 1,908,000 less than in 1910, notwithstanding a national population increase of approximately 30,803,-000 for the 20-year period. Since 1930 the farm population has again increased by an average of about 200,000 a year.

What has occasioned these trends and shifts? What will happen during succeeding decades? What significance will growth and shifts in population have for programs of road construction, rural electrification, school expansion or contraction, land use adjustment, and rural relief and rehabilitation? Answers to these questions are being sought constantly by the agencies mentioned on page 1045 and by many others, governmental and private, the projection and planning of whose programs depend upon the best estimates obtainable concerning population growth and movements. The decennial general census and the 5-year census of the rural and farm population furnish considerable useful information Annual farm-population estimates add to this information. In the operation of action programs, a great deal of knowledge is accumulated about the nature of general and specific population situations, and sociology can use this knowledge in the interpretation of quantitative data. Sociology has major tasks ahead of it, however, if it is to develop information adequate for the guidance of agricultural programs and policies that are already in action and must continue for the sake not only of rural but of national welfare.

Social Ecology, or Human Geography

The social geography or ecology of rural life is the study of the way people distribute themselves over the land in developing and utilizing natural resources and in response to cultural and social forces. It goes further than physical or economic geography and is as important as either.

The pattern of land utilization—that is, the organization of the geographic base in terms of economic enterprises—strongly affects the total social structure of a region. The amount of land required or utilized per farm unit determines the density and spacing of the farm population and consequently affects all social institutions and all social contacts. The kind of community life, the adequacy of social institutions, and to a considerable extent the levels of living of the people of an area depend at least partly on the natural resources of the area. The man-land ratio, or the ratio of human resources to natural resources, therefore constitutes the most important equation in so-called land use planning. Such ratios are never fixed. They have constantly changed during our national development, and they are still changing. The chief factors causing change are depletion or development of resources; changes in science, technology, and markets; high or low birth rates; migrations; and sometimes changes in local, State, and Federal governmental programs. A number of these factors are social, and all of them separately and together influence certain types of social structure and social change.

Likewise the ownership and control of land and the tenure upon it condition social welfare. Unless tenure is relatively permanent and secure, the making of profits from an efficient use of the land will not in itself guarantee that the operator is enjoying social, psychological, and cultural security or welfare.

Cultural or Social Anthropology

Not least among the natural resources of a society or a nation is its social heritage. In a rapidly changing society this heritage may not only be lost sight of, but to some extent it may be actually lost. It is not possible, of course, for any society to break the ties between its past and present or its present and future completely, but it is relatively easy to fail to recognize the strength of these ties and to fail to understand their ever-present influence. Such failure is not only easy but quite common, especially among those who deal day by day with more exact and measurable phenomena. It is natural that new traits of culture, especially when they are physical or economic and therefore easily observed, should obscure the presence of old traits that lie deeply hidden in people's attitudes and their value judgments. It is not easy for some people to believe that these attitudes and judgments are the most persistent things in human experience, for the very reason that they are not exhibited and paraded on the surface of human behavior. Nevertheless they may constitute the inertias of any society and may, therefore, be brakes upon the wheels of change as well as conservators of the "sacred" tenets of the group. The more rationalized—that is, the more scientific, efficient, and planned—agriculture becomes, the more and not the less important it is to understand these forces of inertia because they are the forces that tend to thwart the complete rationalization or expertization of economic, political, and social programs.

The folk culture in a simple society is its most treasured possession. This is probably true of even the most complex societies, though people are not aware of it. When change is very rapid and diverse, however, the treasured possessions of culture are jostled out of their place in the life of the group because of the competition of new elements that temporarily obscure them. In our modern rural society, we undoubtedly desire many of the new things, but we would like to obtain them without sacrificing all of the treasures that have come to us by way of social heritage from the past. We want not only the economic but the social and psychological security people had when self-sufficient agriculture prevailed. We want the richness of rural life that many less commercial agricultures have because of their folk art, music, drama, recreation, and other community activities; we want those qualities of personality and those social values which we think grow only out of family, neighborhood, and community life; but we do not want the continuation of a large amount of irksome labor, the dire physical and social isolation, and the relatively low standards of living that can be eliminated by modern science, business, and technology.

We are not in a position to attain this happy combination of the things that come to us from the past and those that come by way of new inventions and scientific discovery unless we understand the folk processes as well as the scientific processes. We must be able to answer such a question as how far and how fast improvements can be made in the material standard of living by artificial stimulation or by demonstration. Sufficient understanding to answer such a question is not impossible. Cultural anthropologists have for decades been studying not only the components of cultures, but the entire cultures of relatively simple societies. Their techniques are applicable to the analysis of more complex societies.

Each agricultural region of the Nation was settled at a different time by different people and at a different stage of our technological, economic, political, and social development, and each in response to a different environmental situation. Each region, therefore, probably constitutes a more or less unique cultural area, the characteristics of which must be understood in the promotion of programs of adjustment in agriculture and rural life. These adjustments must be made through a process of adaptation to the culture of each separate region. Recently sociologists in increasing numbers have been giving attention to the problem of analyzing the cultural areas of the Nation, with the conviction that such analyses will contribute to an understanding of the adaptations that must be effected if adjustments in agriculture and rural life are to be successfully accomplished.

Social Psychology

While the cultural anthropologist studies human behavior more or less as a complex whole in terms of folkways, customs, traditions, and group values, the social psychologist goes one step further and attempts to understand these cultural processes as they manifest themselves in individual human behavior.

The field of social psychology deals with the way customs, traditions, institutions, unique life experiences, and the like are reflected in the attitudes and opinions of members of a group. Furthermore, it deals with group opinion or public opinion and attempts to analyze and understand the operation of public opinion as it functions in collective behavior.

The attitudes and opinions of farm people are the greatest conditioning factors in all agricultural programs. They are as important to the agricultural scientist and educator as they are to the politician, propagandist, and salesman. In a democratically operated society they are part and parcel of every agricultural adjustment, and any attempts at adjustment will be successful only to the extent that the opinions and the attitudes of those involved in the adjustments are understood and appreciated. Verbal opinions are easy to ascertain, but back of these opinions lie attitudes that are often hidden deep in the occupational and folk life of people, often not even recognized by the people themselves but nevertheless influential in their behavior. Social psychology has made considerable progress in the development of research techniques by which individuals and groups can uncover and understand these attitudes. As yet there has been very little application of these techniques in an attempt to discover basic rural or farm attitudes. The techniques are applicable, however, and their utilization in behalf of understanding situations with which action programs constantly grapple would undoubtedly yield fruitful results.

The approach of social psychology would enable us to get at least partial solutions to such problems as the attitudes of farmers toward the various agricultural programs and the economic and social adjustments which these programs seek to effect; how public opinion can be made to function and how other democratic processes can be made to work in programs that are promoted, at least partly, and in some cases quite dominantly, from above; what is happening to individual initiative and enterprise under such programs and under widespread public relief programs; and what is happening to the old rural neighborhood and folk attitudes and habits under the impact of mechanization and commercialization.

Because of the relative slowness with which new elements of culture have in the past penetrated rural areas, old forms of behavior and old ideas, especially when they have become institutionalized, have prevailed in rural areas for a considerable time after they have materially changed in urban centers. A thorough understanding of both the values and the inertias of rural institutions is essential to an understanding of the processes by which change can be accomplished by means of programs initiated either within or without rural communities.

As rural people are swept more and more into the price and market economy and through various means of transportation and communication become a part of the larger society, the scope and level of leadership must necessarily change. The areas of group action in which farmers participate have widened in terms both of geography and of the number of people involved. Leaders who were competent on a local, neighborhood, or community basis may not be capable of leading large farmer pressure groups or of representing even their local group in large cooperative economic undertakings. The scope of effective leadership must and does change to meet these situations, and techniques and levels of leadership not necessary in the old situations become necessary. In such cases the type of leader needed may not be merely the personable fellow who is a good neighbor, but that person who by training and experience is capable of dealing with economic and social issues of Nation-wide and even world-wide scope. If agricultural and rural-life planning are to be democratic, there is great need to understand all of the factors contributing to effective leadership. We must know, for instance, at what point, or at least under what circumstances, old leaders give way to new leaders in the process of social change. Social psychology should contribute this kind of understanding.

With the rapid expansion of agricultural research, education, and necessary regulatory activities, a tremendous growth of institutional machinery has taken place in rural life. Agricultural colleges and secondary schools, extension services and experiment stations, departments of agriculture and conservation have all developed fairly recently and with tremendous rapidity. In order to be efficient, they have rapidly become institutions, with a great corps of leaders, more or less standardized procedures and programs, and to a considerable extent policies that are already traditional. Over against this more or less rigid set-up, there is continual change in the techniques of production, transportation, communication, and the areas of human association. Social psychology has a contribution to make by way of assisting those in charge of these institutions and agencies to understand the eternal and inevitable conflict between the process of institutionalization and the process of change.

Farmers today are more a part of the general public than were any past generation of farmers. They frequently act as a class-conscious group or segment of the public. Farmers' organizations, farmer pressure groups, farm legislation, and farmer opinion are recognized parts of our national life and thinking. The historical, social, psychological, and institutional characteristics of farmer opinion should be studied on an area-wide, Nation-wide, and occupation-wide basis as people attempt to understand and wrestle with the adjustments they conceive to be necessary for agriculture and rural life. The field of social psychology has during the last decade developed elaborate techniques and accumulated wide experience in measuring public opinion, in studying agencies that form public opinion, and in understanding the pros and cons of pressure-group behavior. With the development of all of these phenomena in rural life and with the tremendous influence of public opinion in a democracy, a new field is open and is being rapidly entered by social psychology in an attempt to contribute to an understanding of farmers and farm groups in their relationships to the so-called general public.

Social Pathology

Social pathology is the study of social maladjustments; and while it is unpopular to emphasize the faults of any social order of which we are a part, it is only wisdom to understand what the sore spots in rural life are and where they are. In the rural districts of the United States, as in rural districts all over the world, crime has always been relatively slight and pauperism almost absent, but poverty has been much more widespread than is commonly known. As long as we were in a frontier and pioneering era, low material standards of living and even poverty were tolerated in the expectation that the maladjustments would be comparatively temporary and that economic success would in due time eliminate them. Today there are many social maladjustments in rural life of a sterner nature and of sufficiently long standing to merit, in fact to demand, the closest analysis.

If rural families living on a low material standard or even in poverty do not themselves resent this status, it ill behooves the sociologist or anyone else to be unduly worried about them unless the existence of such conditions jeopardizes the institutional and community life of other families or handicaps the future generation being born and reared in these homes. When a set of conditions making for rural poverty is of long standing, influences a large segment of the rural population, and comes to be recognized as socially unhealthy, however, it becomes desirable, even imperative, that measures for improvement be applied in the interest of general rural welfare. That such conditions do exist in American agriculture cannot be gainsaid.

Something approaching rural slums has apparently been developing through a number of generations, but this has not been obvious to the general public, or even to the rural public, because poverty-stricken farm families, unlike poverty-stricken urban families, have not lived in congested or crowded areas, and also because our pioneer psychology of hopefulness has blinded us to accumulating maladjustments. Housing, for instance, has probably always been the weakest spot in the rural material standard of living, but inadequate rural houses existing by the thousands have not been so concentrated geographically as to be obvious to the passer-by. Rural unemployment has most often existed in terms of underemployment or ineffective employment and has not been recognized because of the relatively self-sufficient mode of life on the farm. Consequently, little if any attention has been given to the problem of farm unemployment, and there has been insufficient study of the realistic functioning of the agricultural ladder, with all its implications for the entire farm population and the whole enterprise of agriculture. It is too often assumed that there is a steady stream of people moving up the agricultural ladder from laborer to tenant to owner, while there is considerable evidence that actually there is an ever-increasing number of persons who are being stalled on the lower rungs of the ladder and even a goodly number who are descending rather than climbing.

CONTRIBUTIONS SOCIOLOGY CAN MAKE TO RURAL LIFE

As long as the social problems of our rural people were pretty much solved by the comparative ease with which the current normal standard of living could be attained and as long as practically all social problems were limited to the local community, no great knowledge of the body of phenomena which constitutes the field of sociology seemed necessary in the successful conduct of agriculture and rural life. Each local community to a considerable extent lived an integrated life; the family and the neighborhood were the chief patterns of human association; and each local community was relatively self-sufficient. Today the majority of American farmers have become a part of the "great society." New areas of association, much wider in scope and involving a much more diverse and complex set of economic, political, social, and cultural relationships, have entered rural life. Thus the contribution which sociology has to make to an understanding of these relationships and areas of association is constantly expanding.

The desirability of studying simpler agricultural societies and even archaic forms in modern society has been recognized for decades, but thus far little has been done in the application of the same techniques of study to the analysis of contemporary rural society. These techniques can just as well be utilized in studying the hundreds of thousands of farm families and hundreds of rural communities which still follow to a considerable extent the economic and social habits of simpler agricultural societies. Five hundred thousand farm families live on self-sufficing farms, many of them in so-called problem areas, and these areas or communities offer sociologists opportunities for analysis involving only a little more difficulty than studies of primitive societies.

From the day when the majority of American farmers lived largely by means of self-sufficient farming and had a self-sufficient community life, to the present, when the majority of them are operating commercialized and mechanized farms and are living as members of the great society, many adjustments in the whole mode of rural life have been required. In some instances, the adaptations made necessary by economic change have been successful and easy; in other cases, they have been difficult and have disturbed older modes of living to such an extent as to create social maladjustments. These maladjustments range all the way from a relatively slight realinement of old neighborhood and community groups to an almost complete loss of the folk culture of rural life. Today changes are taking place more rapidly than in any previous generation, and it has become necessary to understand as fully as possible the impact of change on the basic institutional structure of rural life, the personalities of rural people, and the cultural values or the philosophies which many people believe to be the unique worth of rural life.

Above everything else, sociology has a contribution to make to an understanding on the part of rural people that they are living in a society composed to a considerable extent of comparatively new relationships which involve them in problems that were not a part of the rural life of past generations. The task of operating a modern commercial farm is an economic enterprise often involving a capital set-up of $20,000 or more, credit arrangements that follow channels all the way from the local community to the large banking centers of the world, a market economy tied in with a world economy, large contributions to government by way of taxes, and calculations and decisions of almost big-business proportions. The operation of such an enterprise is so different from that of a simple, self-sufficing farm that the customs and traditions handed down from the fathers do not offer adequate guidance for the daily and seasonal tasks.

The farmer's participation in the areas of governmental and political action has steadily increased because of his widened economic concern and because channels of communication—the telephone, the rural free delivery, the automobile, the daily paper, and the radio—have enlarged his world of behavior and understanding. He now knows that regional, national, and international factors and situations influence his life and that through public opinion and pressure groups he has some ability to influence State, national, and international policies. His areas of governmental and political concern and association have therefore steadily expanded from a local school district, township, and county, to State, national, and international proportions. These new areas of association are as real in influencing his life as are his neighborhood relationships or his individual farm enterprise, and the development of any body of knowledge which will help him to function more successfully in these new areas and processes of association is greatly to be desired. Sociology, together with the other social sciences, can contribute to this understanding.

Social and cultural stimuli originating in sources far removed from the local neighborhood are as definite a part of the farmer's new world as are the distant world markets that are today a part of his economic situation. In simpler agricultural societies the very essence of self-sufficiency inhered in the fact that economic, social, and aesthetic values were not separate things. Local community life was a unit, and because the reign of custom was automatic, competition between rival values seldom created problems. In modern American farm life, each farm family must constantly contend with and, as best it can, resolve the conflict between alternative uses of time, attention, and money. Desires for current levels of living, stimulated by standards set outside the local community and even outside of rural life itself, compete constantly with the desire for farm ownership; family and neighborhood activities compete just as dynamically for the time, attention, and energy of farm people as for the expenditure of funds; and the whole body of folk culture, including everything from farm practices to religious and aesthetic values, is thrown in competition with alternative ways of doing and thinking. Many farm persons are conscious of these conflicts, and there is continuous discussion and argument among students of farm life as to whether the steady loss of rural folk cuture is in fact a loss or a gain in general rural welfare. No matter which of these contending schools of thought may in the long run prove to be correct, it is highly desirable that farm people and farm leaders understand the changes that are in process and the factors at work. Sociology, cultural anthropology, and social psychology have no patented answers to the numerous questions these complex factors in contemporary civilization raise, but they can offer great assistance in understanding the situations and processes involved.

August Comte, the so-called father of sociology, offered encouragement rather than discouragement because of the complexity of the phenomena with which the sociologist deals. He said, "The practical applications of the sciences increase with their complexity," and gave as the reason for this conclusion the argument that "phenomena grow more susceptible to artificial modification with the increasing complexity of the phenomena."[3] Lester F. Ward emphasized this same truth when he said: "Although its phenomena are the most complex of all and the most difficult fully to understand, when understood, if they ever are, the results their study promises in the direction of their modification in the interest of man are beyond calculation."[3] What these two eminent early sociologists were saying was that the living phenomena which the sociologist studies are more susceptible to change and guided direction than any other body of phenomena. If this is true, then the science of sociology has outstanding contributions to make to the field of planning, and there is considerable likelihood that it can assist in guiding behavior toward the end of human welfare.

Now, as never before, sociology is being given an opportunity to offer counsel and render service in great public, especially governmental, programs. For many years the sociologist has conducted research and written books on normal social behavior and conditions, and for a number of decades he has rendered practical service in the field of social maladjustment, especially in connection with crime and poverty; but only during the last few years has he been called on to give actual counsel and service in guiding large public activity programs. Today he is asked not only to analyze and interpret social trends, study public institutions and movements, and furnish social statistics in many fields, but also to answer a large number of specific questions about normal effective social organization and behavior. Like every other scientist, he must admit that he cannot always answer certain questions specifically. He can, however, if given time to study trends and situations, give approximate answers to many of the questions arising out of the problems of which farm people and their leaders have recently become conscious. If his answers sometimes seem vague and general, it will be well to remember what Von Wiese says:[4]

> Behind the alleged obscurity of sociology there often lurks the mental obscurity of pseudo-sociological writers; they mouthe the word without comprehending its actual meaning. In some cases, they derive their intellectual credentials from other sciences, but like to demonstrate their intellectual superiority by dabbling in sociology and then casting aspersions on it.

In other words, contrary to the general opinion, the sociologist is quite unwilling to venture easy answers to difficult questions but is perfectly willing to accept the responsibility of studying the factors, trends, and situations out of which necessary answers may be obtained.

Different social sciences have established themselves in fields of research dealing with the same phenomena, but with different methods of analysis and different objectives. The economist, for example, studies such forms of human association as corporations, trade unions, and cooperative societies, but is interested in them primarily from the standpoint of their efficiency as means of production and the exchange of wealth. The sociologist studies them with regard to the differences in their structure and function, the processes that account for their

[3] Ward, Lester Frank. applied sociology. 384 pp. Boston. 1906. See pp. 8–9.

[4] Wiese und Kaiserswaldau, Leopold Max Walter von. systematic sociology, on the basis of his beziehungslehre und gebildelehre. Adapted and amplified by Howard Becker. 772 pp. New York. 1932.

origin, maintenance, and change, and their effect on the whole life of the people who constitute their membership. Because the habits, customs, traditions, and attitudes of the members are important to effective economic organization, sociology makes a practical contribution to the analysis of situations that are often thought of as purely economic.

In other words, rural sociology is but one of the sciences useful in attempting to build an adequate and satisfying rural civilization. It uses the scientific method for studying the ways in which rural people associate, with the conviction that through the application of the methods of science that have improved their material conditions, men may be able to improve their relations to each other; for it is in these relations, whether they are competitive or cooperative, expressive of conflict or fellowship, that they find their deepest satisfactions.

Because rural sociology is one of the recently developed fields in sociology, which itself is the youngest of the social sciences, its greatest contributions to agriculture are yet to be made. In the immediate future, the major contributions will probably come from the study of the amount, the direction, and the significance of shifts in farm population in the various geographic areas of the Nation and between rural and urban centers; the reorientation of the farm population to the potential productive land resources of the Nation; the various community and institutional organizations that are the chief day-by-day concerns of farm people; the facts about, and the significance of, the growing number of so-called disadvantaged persons and families in the farm population; the gradual stratification, in terms of economic and social classes, of the people who live on the land; the farmer as a personality and rural life as a body of folk culture; the behavior and thought processes by which farm people get into step with the larger world of which they have become a part; and the participation of farm people in more effective democratic planning for rural welfare.

A Philosophy of Life for the American Farmer (and Others)

by William Ernest Hocking [1]

"FOR THE MAN who cannot act for himself," says the author, "philosophy is a luxury; for a free man it is a necessity"—because philosophy is concerned with values, with the things that make life worth while, and the free man has to make his own choice among these things. This distinguished philosopher, who runs a farm of his own, here outlines the kind of philosophy that grows out of farm life as he sees it. He deals with fundamental attitudes toward family life, the ownership of property, the urbanization of the country, the industrialization of farming, absentee ownership, capitalism, democracy, as well as with what he calls "the wider horizon" of literature, drama, the arts, the sciences. "The most dangerous feature of contemporary life," he concludes, "is not its transition but the fact that in the course of change our capacity for serious thought has so far diminished." There is "an absence of depth, a fear lest meditation should show the emptiness of the affair we call life. Philosophy is the business of taking stock, at least once; it is the passage to manhood." It should be especially the right of the farmer, who stands near the earth.

[1] William Ernest Hocking is Professor of Philosophy, Harvard University.

ONE THING that distinguishes man from the animals is his imagination. Animals, so far as we know, make no plans for tomorrow, still less for a year ahead; imagination presents them no picture of an improved condition. Many an animal, like the squirrel, hoards for the winter; but the probability is that this is done from instinct rather than from foresight—since the squirrel, like the bee, will keep on hoarding after all need for it is past. Man, on the contrary, is always planning; he lives in his dreams unless his hopes are dashed by repeated failure or unless circumstances compel him to believe that planning for himself is useless.

In a social order built on the authority of upper levels over lower levels, imagination has little to do in this direction; for the majority, their planning is done for them. In the authoritarian states arising in central Europe, the state plans as much as possible for its citizens, the place of personal planning is by so much restricted, and imagination has accordingly little to do. In a democratic state, men are encouraged to think not alone for themselves, but for the state also (often, it must be admitted, beyond their capacity). In the United States, while we are asked to think for the state, the striking trait of our social life has been the scope offered to individuals to imagine and plan for themselves. It has been assumed that human individuals know what they want and can be trusted to find ways and means to realize it, if they have opportunity. The opportunities have been present in the great domain and the rapid social growth; our Constitution has provided the freedom for individual enterprise; the rest has been left to our own energy and wisdom. The energy has not been lacking; has the wisdom been as great? Have we known the kind of life most worth living?

As a Nation of free people, we have done well. But we have also made our mistakes, and as time goes on the business of steering our own living seems to become more difficult rather than less so. Changes have come faster than we could adjust ourselves to them. We have thought we knew what we wanted; but we have not always known what we wanted most: we have lacked a scale of values. We have been wobbly in our principles—by the way, what are our principles? We have, in short, been in need of a philosophy. For a man who cannot act for himself, philosophy is a luxury; for a free man, it is a necessity.

THE NATURAL PROGRAM OF LIFE

What makes a human life worth living? To a certain extent, nature takes care of this matter. There is no need for a theory to tell the boy during the years when he is burning to grow up to man's powers and estate, that he wants the command of his own capacities. There is no need to instruct him later on that he wants to make a living, and to find friends; still later, to find a mate, to beget children, care for them, educate them; then to have a standing in the community which he can give to his family as well as enjoy for himself; then to rest a bit and take his ease before he leaves the scene. This is what we might call the natural program of life. If these are the fundamental satisfactions of life, we have to say that in our part of the planet, where famines and wars have played comparatively little havoc, most men achieve something of them.

It is no disparagement of this program to say that, except for that item which we called standing in the community, most of it is had in common by man and the animals. The writer is not prepared to say that even in some animal societies there is not such a thing as a "standing in the community"—the swagger cock and the champion buck seem to have something of the sort; but in any case, it has no such importance or meaning as with the human being. The other items—growing up, food getting, mating, bringing up the young, exerting one's powers and sometimes displaying them with a certain pride—all of these have deep roots in the animal kingdom.

It is a help to self-understanding to compare human life and animal life on these matters, both for the great likenesses and also for the great differences between them.

The principle of evolution dwells on the literal kinship between man and the lower animals. In the early days of this theory, much of the hostility to it was due to a subtle injury to our pride in the confession of relationship. But we have learned that likeness, however profound, does not abolish difference. And in the practical management of animals, the farmer is in a peculiar position of advantage to appreciate both the likeness and the difference. He knows the natural control which the superior being can always establish; and he knows as well the mutual trust and kindness which can be established across the great barrier. There are few men who do not feel subtly flattered when they can win the confidence of a shy or skittish beast. Man can understand the animal; the animal can but dimly understand man, for the peculiar values of human living pass him completely by.

What are those peculiar values?

THE HUMAN VALUES

The peculiar human values arise from the fact that in the human being the instinctive drives are balanced, giving the human mind a chance to survey the whole scene as the animal mind does not.

For example, in the animal there is no physical self-consciousness and no shame, and hence no inhibition about carrying out any physical function at any time. In man, all the physical functions are held in conscious check and governed by a sense of fitness or privacy. In the animal there are three drives which are more or less sporadic, but which are intense and lead to conflict—food getting, acquisition, sex. No society could grow strong unless there were some restraint to the angry expressions of competition for food or property or the sex mate. In the human being all these impulses are balanced by counterimpulses or hesitations; even in respect to eating, when other interests are in the saddle the idea of eating is likely to be slightly displeasing. None of these drives can become so insistent that the man has to yield to them unless he encourages them to become insistent. And then, combativeness itself has a counterimpulse which checks the attack. The result is that man is capable of hesitation as the animal is not; and hesitation gives thought a chance. It allows, and even compels, the question: Which way do I really prefer?

Thus man, by his natural balance, is fated to look at the whole of things. It is only the human being who can form the conception of the whole of life, plans and prepares for death, and considers that there are things he would like to get accomplished in this limited time.

Together with this remarkable balance of instincts there goes another peculiarity of human nature, its unity.

The various drives that affect the animal—hunger, curiosity, fear, anger, love—take their turns; one excludes the other. The unity of the animal consists in the fact that there is a time for each of these activities, and as a rule no two try to take the field at the same moment. A hungry beast whose prey is in an exposed place may be torn between fear and his famished stomach; but the general rule of his life is, one impulse after another. In man, competition of various impulses is the rule rather than the exception; he has choices and decisions to make every hour of the day. This would be a racking business were it not that there is for man a dominating interest which takes the shape of a "purpose"; and this purpose sheds off all the irrelevant suggestions without effort. When the day's work is on, play, quarreling, love making, and food taking are simply shunted; they get no hearing.

More than this, the dominating interest substitutes for the rest. All primitive interests may be said to be forms of one deeper interest, the will to live, or the will to power. Thus curiosity gets its force (partly) from the fact that knowledge is power; the interest in work and workmanship comes (in part) from the enjoyment of power over the materials at hand, and indirectly from the prestige or social power which skill commands. A man wants chiefly to count for something, not to be a cipher in the world; and if this fundamental interest can be satisfied in the direction of his purpose, the more specific drives can be relatively neglected. Thus the human being can make out a satisfactory life if he has one region of effectiveness, one outlet for his "will to power," and no man who is ineffective can be happy no matter how much he possesses.

To put it in a nutshell, an animal (since he has no purpose) is satisfied if he lives through the usual round of momentary activities and successes; a man can be satisfied only if he can create. He may be satisfied with a minimum of instinctive success, provided he can accomplish a purpose, that is, can leave an effect in the world which contributes to human life as a whole.

For this reason, self-judgment holds a deciding hand in human values. Man is the only animal that looks at himself and judges himself; he is the only animal that can be made unhappy by self-contempt or made strong by self-respect. He is the only animal that makes pictures of anything, the only one that makes portraits of himself, writes diaries, or regards a clean conscience as having anything to do with his happiness.

This makes a man terribly vulnerable to social approval or social ostracism, much concerned about that standing in the community of which we were speaking, and ready to do a good deal which he would not do for dear No. 1 in order to keep the regard of his neighbors. But it also makes him, now and then, able to stand very much by himself if he is sure he is right and able to sacrifice almost anything to promote an idea which he believes needs his support or championship. This is the great thing about human nature which the usual theories about human instincts forget. It was the capacity for this sort of fanaticism which gave the United States, and the American farm, its first occupants; it was this force in them which leads us, when we look at the fields they cleared, the miles of stone wall they built, the deep wells they drove into glacial till, the granite rocks they built into cellar walls and even into pigpens, to say, "They were men," and to feel anything but sorry for them!

The kind of satisfaction they got out of life any man can have at their kind of cost, provided only he has also their kind of conviction and their kind of purpose growing out of it. This is not a very useful prescription, inasmuch as there is no use hunting around for a purpose in order to secure a human kind of happiness. Purposes have to grow on their own ground! However, I do not apologize: the present task is not to prescribe, but to report the truth about human values. And the truth is (no matter what the current Freudian or other natural-human-animal psychologizing of the moment may appear to indicate) that any set of values falls short of being a set of human values unless it is built around a self-respecting purpose that calls out the peculiar powers of the individual.

THE SATISFACTIONS OF FARM LIFE

One reason for the perpetual fascination of farm life is the tangible satisfaction it offers for this fundamental interest in putting ideas into effect, the interest in creation. The man in the city office may have endless ideas for changing his physical surroundings, but he is not free to use his muscles on them, not even to smash the furniture. The industrial laborer is using his muscles, but he is not free to carry out his own plans. The farmer's situation is free in both ways: it makes planning necessary, the imagination which belongs to forethought; and it provides the satisfaction of being able to work at these his own plans with all the power that is in him. Creating in this sense is his business.

And also in another sense. He effects the first transformation of the useless into the useful.

We say that the frontier is gone, the first transformation of the wilderness into the cultivable land. But there are numerous kinds of frontier in the world. There is the frontier of the craftsman, that is to say, the line where his skill meets the obstacle it cannot yet surmount. There is the frontier of the scientist, the line between knowledge and ignorance. And there is the frontier between barrenness and fertility, the frontier of the farmer, a line that is always being pushed back but which is never banished and forever threatens to return. This line is a line between life and death, both for the farmer and for the community; for unless the farmer can continue to make the soil yield enough living matter for living people, all human life stops. This is the commonplace miracle of the farming process. The city takes it for granted; the farmer knows its incessant risks and perils.

He is said to be conservative, and in a sense he is so; for he is not dealing with any simple matter of bolts and screws, he is dealing with the sensitive balance of forces affecting germination and growth, the most intricate processes of nature. He knows only too well that any onlooker can propose an improvement in his methods but that not one in a hundred can devise a real improvement. Hence he properly distrusts the salesman. But he remains the perpetual pioneer and innovator. No implement factory could survive two seasons unless farmers were prepared to try out new tools and to devise improvements on them. He is an ally of all the crafts and sciences in his efforts to improve the art of working his primary miracle of making things grow.

There is a great deal of nonsense talked about farming and the satisfactions of farming. It is especially foolish to speak of farming as though it were one sort of thing instead of a dozen very different sorts of thing, especially in North America. It is peculiarly silly to talk about the joys of being "next to Nature," without distinguishing between the times when Nature is a very agreeable companion and the times when her storms, her winter rigors, her excesses of dryness and wetness, her untamed irregularities turn the best plans into dust and ashes and empty pockets. But it remains true that farming survives, and will always continue to attract men to itself, because the farmer is, among all ups and downs, a successful creator in the sense that the ideas of his brain do get themselves built into visible living products and that this, his personal success, is at the same time an absolutely necessary social good.

There is another thing about farming which has struck me as important, though I am not sure how far my farming brethren will agree with me. That is, the all-around weariness which comes of farm labor. I stress the word "all-around." Every man gets weary in some spot or other if he works hard at his job. But he is likely to tire one set of muscles or nerves and come out an unevenly wearied man, looking for some equally unbalanced amusement to smooth him out. The farmer has no such need; at least in the summer evenings, he is not looking for any amusement. He is fatigued all over; and when he rests, he rests all over.

He does not shine in evening entertainments; if he goes out he is likely to get sleepy. He is not disposed to burn midnight oil or electric current keeping up his reading. He neither wishes to make speeches nor to listen to them. It is hard for him to keep up the Grange or any other social institution during these active months. He regrets it. I admit the disadvantage, but I wish to congratulate him for at least one consequence. He retains soundness of nerve, clearness of eye, and steadiness of judgment. He is relatively free from that onset of nervous disorders which is carrying so large a percentage of our city population into the asylums, public and private.

When the natural reservoir of energy is exhausted evenly, nature rises nobly to the occasion and fills it up again. Hence the large proportion of the finest specimens of mankind which the farm produces; physical breadth of beam joined with a corresponding mental and moral breadth—for the sound man thinks well rather than ill of his neighbors, his thoughts extend beyond himself, and he plots for the good of his village and his township. His sons replenish the worn-out stock of the businesses and professions.

223761°—40——68

There is a seamy side to this, of course. The physical work of the farm is never done, because its possibilities are infinite; and the effort to do it all breaks many a man, turns many another into a working machine with no springs, develops occasional individuals of great stature who work the weaker ones around them to death, perhaps their wives or their children. Farming does not of itself beget the wisdom of restraint in labor; and as respect for the seventh day wanes, the quieter necessities of relaxation are increasingly neglected.

The remedy for this lies not so much in preaching recreation as in carrying further our analysis of the things that make up the good life, whether on the farm or elsewhere.

I will speak of three elements of welfare or happiness—family life, property, and the wider horizon.

Family Life

The farm has an opportunity for normal family life which is still definitely superior to that of the city, in spite of rapid recent changes. This superiority lies in part in the fact that children are more welcome; there is less artificial restriction of birth; the sexual atmosphere is cleaner. It lies further in the facts that when children do arrive, the family relation is less distracted, and the home is less likely to be interrupted by the absence of the mother; the occupation of the father is before their eyes; the area of common life is greater. Then, further, with greater freedom of physical action there is the natural discipline of an early taking part in the common work of the family. Just because the community is less dense and outer associations less numerous and less near, the family has to be more nearly self-sufficient in its mental as well as physical resources, has to find its own way to fun and mutual help, is a more compact society. Wherever to the ordinary routine of farm life there are added what normal family life can supply—love, economy, good foodstuffs, good cooking, simple and abundant hospitality, and the inescapable relation of cause and effect, effort and reward—there is a primary education unsurpassed in its possibilities for forming not alone the character but the mind also.

For the farmer, his family is the chief enlarger of his life; and if he can find satisfaction in his children, it may be his chief reward.

The farmer is likely to define this satisfaction in terms of handing his farm on to a son; he likes to think of his occupation as hereditary. The early sharing of everybody in farm work, if it is well managed on his part, might naturally have the effect of creating an ambition in all the young ones for the farm as a joint enterprise and a certain ingrained desire to carry it on. It is at this point that a good many farmers fail.

A farmer may overburden his children and lead them to seek escape. He may explain too little and consult too little and so leave them in the position of laborers rather than of partners. He may forget that while everyone has in his constitution somewhere a hankering for the farm, the modern farm calls for a special talent. A first-rate farmer like a first-rate poet has to be born; not everyone can be either. We cannot make farming strictly hereditary and at the same time keep that respect for individual talent which is the very genius of American life. If the young men are not farmers by instinct, they ought not to be held to the farm. The only thing that ought to hold them is, again, that human value—the sense of power in the use of one's own imagination and thought. In the long run, the state must do its part to make farming a hopeful occupation, having its due respect and its due income; unless it does so the farms will be and should be deserted. But while the state labors on this intricate problem, the farmer as parent can do much to make farming an attractive outlook for, let us say, one of his sons. And if in their interest he curbs his all-work program, this effort will make him a larger, more liberal, and happier man.

While it is to the interest of the community that farming should be to a large extent hereditary, since the special skills and tempers involved can best be kept by a father-to-son transmission, and since the prospect of handing the farm on as capital gives the farmer a strong motive to conserve its soil and enhance its value, it is not to be expected or desired that farming should be wholly hereditary. We don't want any caste lines in North America; we want circulation. There must be a generation that leaves the farm and a generation that returns to it, with added appreciation because of its absence.

Even the tyro who comes from the city to start farming in complete ignorance of his own ignorance should be tolerated. The amateur who runs a subsistence homestead, the farmer-mechanic who raises his food and does day's labor when he can, the laborer-farmer who tries to dovetail the factory season with the farming season; yes, even the city man who runs a farm with hired skill as well as hired help—all of these intruders should be allowed a place in the wide variety of the farming way of life. Such marginal characters do diminish the market for the genuine farmer's cash crop. But they will never amount to more than a fringe of the farm population; and they help to maintain that kind of liaison between farm, industry, and city which is necessary for the sound unity of national life.

Property

Property is today's bread and butter, and if you have enough of it, the promise that there will be bread and butter tomorrow. Most men consider the accumulation of a small property chiefly in the light of a protection for the years of declining strength. For these purposes it makes very little difference whether it is in the form of land, personal effects, money, or securities. But property has other purposes, for which it makes a great deal of difference what kind it is. For these purposes property in land—real estate—is far more personal than property in money or tokens of money which go by the name of personal.

Property that one can handle, use, take care of, does a great deal to educate its possessor. A child who owns a toy learns in time to take care of toys (more or less) as the price of having them; and the boy who has made a whistle cares more for it than for a better whistle bought on the market. Tangible and durable property like a farm responds to treatment, and so carries on through the years a silent conversation with its owner, telling him what kind of man he is and what sort of head he has. Most men have much to learn from this quiet and unanswerable instruction; and most men make a fair start at learning it.

Whatever a man completely owns, whether it be a whole farm or but a single tool or animal, it is that bit of property which most completely reflects the kind of man he is. For this bit of property can be regarded as a small domain in which he is king. For whatever happens in that domain, he is responsible; and conversely, whatever he wants to do there, he is at liberty to do. If he wants to neglect, abuse, or even destroy his property, he is within his right, so long as he causes no suffering or nuisance by doing so. If he wants to experiment with it, he may. If he has an idea for increasing its value, he may put it into effect. In brief, he enjoys the privileges of rulership and learns by experience what kind of ruler he would make! This is an invaluable kind of experience for a democracy. For a democracy is workable only if its citizens are accustomed to command and to rule and know from experience the meaning, the difficulties and burdens of authority. Democracy does not consist in taking authority away from everybody, but in giving everybody a bit of authority. And everyman's bit of private property, be it large or small, is his special field for gaining experience in the use of authority. It furnishes apprenticeship in responsibility. It is for this reason that the farm, as an actual domain, has been so significant a training ground for our democracy.

It is significant also in another way. If the farmer through this experience learns something about himself, his neighbors also are learning about him. They can tell by the appearance of his horses or his barn floor, the condition of his tools, his harnesses, his silo, whether he is slack or one who loves his work and his stock. If you want to know about a man, you can often tell more by seeing his place than by seeing the man himself. This is a very important social meaning of property.

Let us put it this way: Property makes the man visible and accessible. I cannot see a man's mind or his character. But when I see what he has chosen and what he does with it, I know what he likes, and quite a good deal about his principles.

The moral importance of property lies in the fact that the owner is not compelled to do well with it; he may be mean, foolish, dissipated, selfish. The beauty of being hospitable is that it is a free act; one does not have to be. Try to compel citizens to be generous and public-spirited in the management of property, and generosity ceases to be a virtue. Property develops character because it allows the free expression of personal traits and invites the social judgment which follows mistakes in its use. The institution justifies itself because for the most part men learn through this social judgment to avoid the chief abuses and to make a respectable use of their freedom. It is only on this condition that the state can continue to recognize the right of property in its full extent.

RESPONSE TO SOCIAL AND ECONOMIC CHANGE

With these things in mind, it seems evident that the full meaning of property is hardly anywhere represented so well as in the ownership of farms. This ownership is not alone raising crops; it is making citizens. Any radical change in the form or extent of farm ownership becomes a matter of importance for the state as a whole. This is the basis of the economic theory of history, according to which changes in technique and in the accompanying forms of ownership are the major factors in social change.

Living as we do in an era of rapid economic development, it is important for us to inquire how far this theory is true. It seems obvious that changes in tools and methods must alter the habits of man; but does this change in habit carry a change in character? Take an example:

Time was when logs had to be yarded out by men and horses; now the tractor invades the winter woods and does its marvels, rides over obstacles that would use up the best team of horses. But who drives the tractor? Probably not the teamster, but a new kind of acrobat with a new variety of seat holding and steering, with knowledge of his mount, its powers and limits of performance, its anatomy, and the possibility of repair. His courage, hardihood, and skill are of a different sort from those of the teamster, but they are not less. Sympathy with the animal is transformed into sympathy with the machine and an understanding of the beast into mechanical intelligence. Endurance is called for in both cases; the rigors of winter are certainly not abated for the tractor driver, nor is his seat softened, and he with his machine has often to take a kind of punishment the old woodsman knew nothing about.

The point is that the change in the man which follows change in technique runs less deep than we sometimes fear, far less deep than the economic theory of history would have us suppose. The primary principles of initiative, competitive skill, team play, individualism, and loyalty are not changed by the simple course of technical advance.

But there is a side of this change that does affect character. That is, the change in the position of ownership. The operator of our logging tractor is not usually the owner—the machine may belong to the company. Logging has become a more impersonal affair than it used to be; large bodies of capital are involved, and the work is done by contract. As a result, men no longer risk their lives in the jams of the Androscoggin narrows for the sake of their local name and for the delivery of goods to an unknown purchaser. Heroism and greatness leak out of the business: a different morale reigns in the woods. This is typical of what is happening quite generally in North America, though newer ideals may arise to replace the old.

It is true that most of the changes that have swept over farm life in North America in the last quarter century have come because they were wanted. New tools have made their way because they were improvements. I have neighbors who still remember when my farm was plowed by oxen and the hay mowed by hand. Nobody banished the oxen from New England farms; that was done by the fact that the horse with lesser strength was a nimbler beast. And nobody banishes the horse except where the tractor can more than take his place. No improvement, to be sure, is quite all an improvement; there are still things the horse can do which the tractor cannot do, and there are still oxen to be found in odd corners. Improvements are only on the whole and with some loss. Admitting this, we may still say that most recent changes affecting farming have come with the farmer's approval and are to the good.

But individual changes have cumulative effects not foreseen by anybody. We can now see certain massive changes in the spirit of the American farm; the vast middle area of fertile land no longer presents anything like the traditional picture of the American farm. Even in the marginal farms of New England the alteration runs deep. Do these changes make the American farmer less independent in his character, less a person, less stable, less the rock he has hitherto been in the maintenance of our institutions?

The most conspicuous of these changes may be labeled the urbanization of the country and the industrializing (and capitalizing) of the farm. Let us look more closely at each of them.

The Urbanization of the Country

In all ages of human history there is a different temper of life (and a different tempo) in the country from that in the town. And in all ages there has been a tendency to import the spirit of the town into the country—to urbanize it. For city life, always based more completely than that of the country on a money economy, has been able to experiment with new elements of comfort which can slowly enter into the national standard of living everywhere; and the clash of talents in the centers brings about a vivid cultural life and inventiveness whose products the country is prone to desire. Such urbanization has often brought decay in the fiber of a people. Philosophers of history have often seen in the process a phase of an inevitable rhythm leading to decline in the birth rate and the inner decay of a civilization. For the country breeds a type of man in whom natural virtues are ingrained; whereas the man of the town, living at a distance from raw materials and relying on trade and wit, tends to assume that life is satisfactory in proportion to the success of the artifices by which pain and effort are avoided. These two types (it is believed) cannot be rolled into one. Human nature requires a moral division of labor, and the city type, however much it resembles a flower, is in reality a parasite and could not survive were not the foundation there to sustain it. No civilization survives when the urbanite becomes the model for all groups.

If this is the case, we are indeed in danger. For in no age of the world has the urbanization of farm life proceeded so fast and so far as in the United States in the last half century. This is due largely to the fact that among the most conspicuous changes are those in the instruments of attack whereby any part of the national life can be invaded by any other part. The telephone, the radio, and the automobile have put an end to loneliness; but they have also done much to put an end to privacy. The farm (which has had a surplus of loneliness, especially in the long northern winters) has not merely admitted, it has eagerly embraced these instruments of invasion. Whatever the conception of music, of news values, of entertainment, of sport may be at the broadcasting center, those conceptions thrust themselves on the listener, who feels that in listening he is sharing in the actualities of the life of his time. If being invaded is being corrupted, the country has revelled in being corrupted! We are far from asserting that this is the case; all that we here assert is that, by its own complicity, the country is actively mixing cityhood into itself at a rate never before realized in history.

And certainly each of these changes taken by itself is for the better. The average farm home has not all, but soon will have much of the equipment, convenience, quick communication, electric power, instant news, and home-borne amusement of the city. Things are moving that way. Building, heating, lighting, sanitation of the farm are planned on the same lines as those of the city. This is only to say that the common basis of our national civilization has risen all around to a higher level. A new sense of community of experience and ease of understanding between town and country has been created.

It is hard to believe that anyone would want these changes undone. The question remains whether, taken together, this urbanization has changed the character of the farmer in any way that should give us concern. This question will be reverted to shortly.

Industrialization and Capitalization

The second type of change is more obviously menacing for the quality of our civilization. For the invasion of the country by the absentee powers of organized capital, replacing resident ownership by tenancy or by industrialized operation, may possibly carry to the great farm areas some of the social distempers of industrial centers.

The primary social problem of our time relates to the destiny of capitalism as a system. It is a system of free initiative, depending on the free use of privately owned capital to produce wealth and incidentally provide employment for labor. This freedom of the individual capitalist is anything but capricious, since capital can only be employed by employing; but it is here that the chief difficulty is felt, since labor becomes dependent on an employment which it cannot directly control. Such dependent persons may reach the point where the right to work becomes the biggest thing in their lives; it becomes a craving to get access to tools, materials, land—to be able to make a living, where the will to labor is strong. If this demand remains unsatisfied, it tends to turn against capitalism as a system and to call for its replacement by some system in which the ownership of the means of production is less private and less free. To the insecure man, security may seem far more desirable than liberty, whether for himself or for others.

In its normal operation capitalism takes care of labor's will to work, and therefore does not breed a proletariat, that is, a body of men dependent on employment at another man's choice, insecure, detached, propertyless, discontented, unfulfilled. This is the disease, not the normal order and not the usual order; still, a disease not yet entirely mastered.

But suppose that this same process invades the farm, which has been (at least theoretically) the refuge of the man who determines at all costs to retain his independence and his power to work. Suppose farms are sold out (under pressure or otherwise) to interests which speculate on their productivity; suppose these interests let them to operators who are not owners; suppose these operators in turn lose their hopes and fail in their payments. Then a semitethered, disheartened, spiritless class arises ready to strike hands with the malcontents of the industries. Capitalism will then have bred a double group of critics bent less on its reform than on its overturn. And agriculture in that place will have ceased to develop the American citizen. The matter is of public concern from both angles.

Capitalism can maintain its health only on three conditions. (1) It must take the problem of employment as its collective responsibility: it must satisfy the will to work. (2) The owning and use of capital must be widespread through the community—the possibility of saving and of earning through saving must be general. (3) Ownership in its full sense must be widely diffused; this means the ownership of real property instead of mere abstract tokens such as money and securities. And real property comes to its best expression in the farm operated by its owner or owners; for here we have captial bearing its natural and unchallenged fruit in direct response to labor and intelligent investment. The present changes appear to lead away from this third condition in the direction of widespread dependency of the worker and disaffection from his work.

These changes of capitalization and industrialization do not affect all American farming to the same extent or produce everywhere the same results. They light most easily in the great prairie regions where yield may be tangibly increased by highly capitalized production and where production that is not capitalized appears to be wasteful. The more difficult farms of the border States, eastern and western, remain relatively untouched by these changes, though they are driven by Midwest competitition to new specializations. Thus the first result of these changes is simply to increase the diversity in the types of life covered by the word "farming"; the farm life of the great American Plains will be a type of its own.

But that type cannot continue to be based on tenancy and absentee ownership. Capitalization, when it cannot be carried by the individual farmer, can perhaps be carried by cooperating groups of farmers. However this may be, it has become a public concern that farm property, be it small or large, be it completely owned or partly owned, be it owned individually or (to some extent) collectively, shall continue to do its part in the building of the American individual and democrat.

And we have to remember that neither economic change nor its consequences are inevitable. There is no such mysterious thing as an economic force apart from the conscious desires of men. The more efficient method of production is inevitable only when and so far as there is no social interest against it. If there is such a contrary interest—if, for example, a given method of plowing and planting leads to soil ruin or if a new method of financing eats out the spirit of the human operator—these methods are to be altered by the free human will; and if they are too much for the individual, they become fit subjects of community, perhaps of governmental attention.

THE WIDER HORIZON

We have spoken of family life and of property; we have now to speak of the wider horizon.

Everyone knows that there is a wider horizon; everyone demands a frame for his laboriousness and is grateful for those glints of distance and wholeness that sometimes break into conversation through the factualities of a business deal or the noontime talk when men are stretched out together under a tree discussing such weighty matters as whether a good coon dog will be satisfied with treeing the coon or will sometimes tackle him and if so how. But everyone knows too that a life of labor can drain men of vitality and that this wider horizon calls for an effort which few by themselves are in a position to make.

The advantage of having a traditional religion was that this wider horizon was periodically opened up by an especially appointed person who was not worn out and who could rely on a good representation of the community setting aside a time for opening up the wider horizon. The writer is not prepared to say that there is any substitute for the regular, deliberate, habit-breaking, and sky-revealing operations of the Sunday service if it could only become sensible, pertinent to actual problems, and beautiful.

But let us assume for the moment that the church is going through a molting period and cannot, in any case, do all that is needed for the farmer of today. The farm community must come to the help of the individual since all the impulses to get a more vivid grasp of the whole scene in which our lives are placed are intensified when a group acts on them together. Individualism sometimes seems to set itself in contrast to the common life; but not the individualism that builds a democracy. For the democratic process does not consist in registering the separate votes of independent thinkers who neither know nor care what anyone else thinks; it consists in making everyone aware, through discussion, of what others think, so that each decision when it comes shall have the whole community of thought as its basis. The more solidly the community acts and feels together on the big issues of life, the more democracy there will be. Individualism grows in the soil of a common tradition, a common amusement (no one can say how much baseball has contributed to form the American spirit and to unite city and country), a common education, and a common culture.

And as for this common culture, there has never been a time so hopeful as the present for making this somewhat vague and slippery entity a solid fact for the life of the American farmer. We are at the moment getting over the superstition that culture is equivalent to schooling; we are finding the vital ways in which the human mind continues to nourish itself throughout life, largely aided by the maturity which comes of adult years and labor. The occupation of the farmer is bringing its own enlargement with it; agriculture is now as never before a world interest. As soon as a world market exists, planting in every country is governed to some extent by planting in every other; methods and standards of living in every country become a concern of every other. The Chinese rice fields, the jute of India, the rubber of Malaya, the wheat of the Ukraine, the wool of Australia have now, in addition to their romantic and pictorial interest, a direct meaning in terms of American livelihood. Knowledge of the world becomes the right of the farmer in a new sense; he is immediately affected by the fact that half the human race are on the land in India and China. And the means of making this a living and growing interest are in our hands.

Let me mention some of the elements of culture which belong especially to the farm.

Literature

The great literature of the world is now accessible to everybody in the United States. The periodical literature is also accessible, but there are no adequate guides to it for farm readers. The farmer's magazines do a fair job in the way of technical and political notes; but they have had to keep costs low, and they do little for the mind. There is room for a better type of rural journal, but there is also a need that some of the great American journals which are not specifically for the farm should take on the task of representing farm life, its interests, its inner greatness, its heroism, its dangers, its possibilities, as part of their function. This is the only way in which the wealth of resource which is at the disposal of our best journalism can come within reach of farm readers.

The Arts

The social arts and amusements are at home everywhere and have their own local flavors, though it may require a degree of conscious effort to keep some of the dancing and festival customs alive through the present period of reshuffling of habits. Music has a more universal reach, and if it is nursed, it can become a force in any American community, especially if there are a few of north-European stock to help the enterprise.

But the undeveloped gold mine lies in the drama. No one knows until he has tried to find out what persons in any community have the gift of acting; great surprises are in store for one who makes the first attempt. Acting is the most effective introduction to great literature; and there is hardly a village in the United States so poor in talent as not to be able to make a beginning.

The Sciences and Philosophy

Science and philosophy are no longer subjects that can be kept enclosed in the schools and colleges; they belong to the thinking public and therefore to the farm public. The farm is a consumer of scientific progress; the farmer can be a consumer of scientific truth without regard to its application. Is he not an inhabitant of the cosmos? Are not the stars for him, and the seasons, and the minute infinitudes within the atom? It requires the sciences to tell the actual situation of human life in the world. It requires philosophy then to inquire what it all means, and what kind of life can be made of it.

Our colleges might do more than they do in this way, whether for the student or for the mature citizen. They expend great labor on the finesse of argument; but they are likely to fail to give the one thing most needed—a simple statement of the commonplaces of value and of ethics. Just as in the art of living, it is the commonplaces of which we need to be reminded from time to time. Our American life would be richer and wiser in all its corners if every teacher were as aware of this as was "old Stanty," of Ames, under whom the writer studied mathematics. He was a great teacher of his subjects; but he was an even greater teacher of the common morals of the day's work. "We must keep our work on a high plane; we must not let it descend to this low level"—few of his students willingly heard that speech addressed to them more than once. None of them forgot the commonplace truth that there is in all work a level of performance which can give it dignity and honor. The writer suggests faculty conferences on the ethical commonplaces, which will take this great human interest out of the hands of professional philosophers and make it what it is, the invitation of every man to the ennoblement of his day's work.

Philosophy and religion share in the function of tapping the vein of seriousness with which the responsible man wishes to face his more difficult passes of experience. The most dangerous feature of contemporary life is not its transition but the fact that in the course of change our capacity for serious thought has so far diminished. The underlying sadness and hollowness of much modern life is due not to poverty nor to too great labor but to an absence of depth, a fear lest meditation should show the emptiness of the affair we call life. Philosophy is the business of taking stock, at least once; it is the passage to manhood. It should be especially the right of the man who, standing near the earth, knows it both in its threat and its promise, sees it both as the receiver of death and the producer of life, knows by direct handling how closely the tangible living body is welded to the intangible and infinite mystery of consciousness and of the soul.

PART 6

Democracy and Agricultural Policy

Public Information and the Preservation of Democracy

by ALFRED D. STEDMAN [1]

THE AUTHOR of this article is a seasoned newspaperman who had charge of information for the Agricultural Adjustment Administration throughout the most difficult period of the farm crisis. He then "graduated" into newspaper work again. Thus he deals with agricultural information services as both an insider and an outsider. In this article he draws a distinction between "promotional campaigns" connected with a specific action program and the publication of other information, scientific and factual. Conceding that the promotional campaigns are necessary, he argues that special care must be taken to keep them democratic; and he outlines certain safeguards so that they will not be even remotely suggestive of the methods of dictatorship. The objective of these safeguards is to prevent any stifling of opposing ideas; for "competition of ideas is the life of democracy."

GOVERNMENTAL functions of public information, which have become increasingly vital in the Department of Agriculture, now confront new problems created by recurrent wars and the ever-present threats of war abroad.

[1] Alfred D. Stedman was formerly Assistant Administrator and Director of Information, Agricultural Adjustment Administration. He presented his views on public-information policies in detail in the Agricultural Adjustment Administrator's report for 1937-38. Some of the ideas of that more detailed report have been used here.

Forcibly and repeatedly this generation has been made aware that major economic and political disturbances elsewhere in the world have far-reaching repercussions in the United States, with ultimately profound effects upon the course of governmental operations in this country.

Our people look out now upon a world environment characterized not only by war but by the spread of absolutism and the confinement of democracy within continually shrinking boundaries and populations. Democracy is at bay in the world. The democratic nations have had to fight for life on the battlefield. One by one, the totalitarian tide has engulfed them. In desperate self-defense, democracy has grasped weapons characteristic of dictatorship—brute force and discipline wielded by vast governmental power—but by a government not self-imposed but of democracy's own choosing.

Ominous changes elsewhere in the world call for a rededication of this Nation to the processes of democracy. We must maintain healthy and unimpaired our own devotion to those processes which we, like all other democracies, are now called on to defend.

The deep concern of the Department of Agriculture in this general problem has been made clear by Secretary Wallace and M. L. Wilson, and there is no need for a detailed discussion of it here.

But this concern does focus with peculiar force upon the informational and educational work of the Department. Because the Department of Agriculture is one of the greatest scientific institutions in the world, it very greatly depends for expanding its usefulness on maintaining democratic processes. Freedom of inquiry is the essence of progress in its scientific laboratories and experiment stations. Freedom of access to the results of its researches is the basis for taxing the public to pay the cost. Freedom to disseminate the information assembled by the scientific branches to all farmers and to all the people everywhere, without any discrimination, is vital to the continued public service of the Department. The bedrock foundations of the Department of Agriculture are democratic freedom of inquiry, freedom of thought, and freedom of education.

WAR THREATENS DEMOCRATIC INSTITUTIONS

But the outbreak of a new war and the switch of the European democracies to totalitarian methods are having deepening effects in the United States. This country's internal and external trade relationships have been changed and distorted, necessitating large adjustments in agriculture and industry. A partial emergency has been declared to exist, and the near approach of war has led to suggestions of changing relationships between the Government and its citizens.

The basic difference between democracy and dictatorship is this: In the first the state is the servant of the people; in the second the people are the servants of the state. In the first there is unlimited competition of ideas among citizens through free speech, free press, and free religion, and agencies of information are free from dictation by the government as to what may be written, said, or printed about public affairs. In the second, the government tells the people what to think, the press what to write, and the radio what to say.

In a democracy the search for truth takes the form of a struggle of diverse opinions among its citizens. In a totalitarian state, truth is regarded as an absolute and purports to be whatever the government says it is at any given time. The subjects of the totalitarian state are compelled to accept as truth whatever combination of fact and fiction the rulers think it is to the government's advantage to have believed.

The freedom of each person to think, to search for knowledge, and to speak the truth as he sees it is the air in which civilization lives and breathes. If the liberty to beget ideas is smothered, civilization dies.

When, in the absolutist state, competition in ideas is throttled and freedom of thought and expression are suppressed, that part of the people who are opposed to the government's course lose every method of opposition except force. The rulers therefore live in constant fear, go from one excess to greater excesses in desperate efforts to protect themselves, and finally fall victims of the methods of violence which among vigorous men are the invariable alternative of the peaceable competition of democracy.

One circumstance making the course of world events so ominous is that when totalitarianism reaches its ultimate natural stage of war and comes into violent collision with democracy, the democracies themselves, in opposing force with force, adopt more and more of the methods of dictatorship.

Gaining the totalitarian strength of unified will and striking power, the democracies also acquire the weaknesses that come from stifling the processes of democracy, particularly freedom of information.

Censorship is imposed to keep the enemy ignorant of events. But whatever its effectiveness in this respect, it places a blindfold over that clear vision which is democracy's greatest strength. Doubt and fear born of public ignorance of large events replace the confident courage that comes to the people from knowing that they are being told the facts. Relieved of the cautioning influence that democracy provides through an ever-present and alert opposition, the rulers make mistakes that would otherwise be avoided, and the unchecked blunders of the military in every war cause untold losses of life and property, because in war errors are paid for in human lives.

The hunt for enemies within tends to become a hunt for all who have ideas at odds with the ideas of the official huntsmen, until it becomes unsafe for citizens to reveal even a devotion to the democratic processes for the protection of which the war is supposedly being fought. Government, which in a democracy should ever staunchly defend the rule of reason, relying on that rule and on the free venting of opinions to quell public passions and avert the hysterias which transform a rational people into a mob, in war may go in for the deliberate lashing of public passions, the creation of hate, and the incitement of the frenzied desire to kill. A democratic state may find that war has clothed the government with the powers of a dictatorship, that individual rights have been extinguished, and that the people have become, more or less temporarily, the servants of the state. War in defense of democracy may extinguish democracy. With flags flying and bands playing and cannon roaring, all in defense of democracy, nations in the past have set forth on a march to dictatorship.

223761°—40——69

THE UNITED STATES DEPARTMENT OF AGRICULTURE AND ITS DEMOCRATIC FUNCTIONS

Looking across the oceans toward such a world environment, this Nation needs to take stock of its democratic institutions.

Among those agencies whose functions lie close to the heart of the democratic process, the fact-finding and fact-disseminating units of the Department of Agriculture are important.

The informational and educational work of the Department has a large part to play in the maintenance of the democratic institutions of free expression in the critical period ahead.

Department's Background of Experience in Information Work

Relying naturally on its wealth of past experience, the Department will be in a strong position to carry on. The closer the emergency comes, the greater will be the need and the opportunity of the Department's informational agencies to maintain their democratic ideals and their already firm devotion to them.

When in 1933 Congress started the national farm programs that sought to implement the knowledge of farmers and experts and to enable farmers to act in concert for the protection of their incomes and their soil, new responsibilities were imposed upon the informational agencies of the Department. It became the Department's duty to supply farmers with information necessary to the formulation and operation of the programs. This could be done in the United States because here in a democracy the freedom of circulation of information had led to establishment of matchless facilities for rapidly disseminating facts and opinions among the people. Over the years, the Department and the States have built, in the Extension Service, a system reaching into every county and to nearly every farm.

Prior to the present spread of war over so much of the earth, the Department had met and largely or wholly solved most of its pressing information problems with methods in keeping with democratic processes. As the years went by, the Department constantly increased the efficiency of its methods of preparing and distributing among farmers information concerning its scientific work, and the farmers became accustomed to making larger and larger use of this help. Moreover, the ground had been broken and the pioneering work had been done in carrying through some of the greatest educational efforts ever undertaken within the requirements of democracy in acquainting 6,000,000 farmers with information about the national farm programs of the Agricultural Adjustment Administration.

Informational Functions of the Department, as Visualized by Its Informational Agencies

The informational agencies of the Department will without doubt continue to strive to make available to the press and the radio truthful, concise, and prompt information as to the operations of the Department. These agencies will not try to interpose themselves as barriers but, on the contrary, will aid those seeking to go to the technical and official sources of information in the Department. Independent scientific institutions outside the Department also will be given ready access to information at the source when they desire it.

Though having a normal human dislike for hostile criticism, the Department's informational agencies will no doubt also retain an appreciation of the function in a democracy of unfettered criticism and even outright opposition to the Government, without which democracy would become a dictatorship. They will have no patience with censorship and will shun all suggestions of using the immense informational machinery of government to undermine or destroy the free dissemination of information through the press, the radio, and the public forum.

Having a growing appreciation of the increasing value of their work in the Department and a healthy pride in seeing that it is well done, the Department's informational agencies will, I feel sure, maintain their high standards and, in order to do this, will define and differentiate their several functions.

Hence they will recognize, I believe, that in the final stages of an educational campaign for widespread participation of farmers in an action program, they are engaging in a type of effort essentially different from the publication of scientific and factual information which has been carried on by the Department for many years. Although making use of scientific information, these educational campaigns are promotional in character, and are frankly propaganda in the sense that they emphasize one point of view and subordinate others in matters which are to some extent controversial.

Need for Safeguards Recognized

Certain safeguards adopted by the Department as to the action programs are vital. The programs must be in accord with scientific facts; they must be in accord with the wishes of the farmers; they must serve the interests of the general public as well as the farmers as a group.

Additional safeguards with respect to the educational campaigns for the action programs are also vital.

Tied to a program which is in itself in the public interest, the educational campaign should be truthful and factual in character. It should not be mere ballyhoo. While striving for unity of action for a time among large numbers of farmers, with the object of cooperation to eliminate some of the destructive consequences of unbridled economic competition, the campaign managers should be always mindful that competition of ideas is the life of democracy.

The democratic processes have as their foundation the rule of reason based on this offsetting of ideas, on the opportunity of the opposition to vent itself in free expression, on the right of every man to have his day in the court of public opinion, and on calm tolerance. Therefore the educational campaign should not be high-pressure promotion. Nor should it be of a type calculated to arouse the group prejudices or mass emotions of great numbers of people to the extent of letting loose any hysterias even remotely suggestive of the mass hysterias employed by dictatorships abroad to keep the people in subjugation to their own emotions and to keep the national processes of democracy ineffectual and asleep.

Disbursing vast sums of money simultaneously with the conducting of great educational campaigns, the action programs must have strong and ever-present safeguards against political uses and prostitution for partisan purposes, which would quickly destroy the confidence of the farmers and the public in them. Just as payments to farmers must always be made in a fair, impersonal, and impartial way, and no payment can ever be made to anyone on any grounds of political influence or identification with party or party leadership, so the educational campaign must also be kept free from political taint. It is a lasting credit to the Department that the genuine public concern which resulted in enactment by Congress of the Hatch Act restricting the political activities of Federal employees was anticipated by several years in the safeguards written into the A. A. A. farm program and the articles of association of the farmers' county conservation associations.

Taken together, these various safeguards insure that the action programs shall not interfere in any degree with freedom of speech, freedom of the press, or the right of free assembly. The opponents are guaranteed a right to criticize and to present organized opposition. The Department's information agencies will supply them promptly and efficiently with all official information made available to others. The opponents have access to the radio, to the press, and to the public forums to get their ideas before the people.

THE DEPARTMENT CAN BE A STRONGHOLD OF DEMOCRACY

Democracy is a social system that depends upon the information and enlightenment of the people. It is a system in which differences are settled by a struggle of ideas, with the decision not by bullet but by ballot. While the government of every dictatorship in the world maintains itself by might and terror, and its rulers are in constant fear of the assassin, the United States Government has the confidence that a democracy reposes in a government of its own choosing.

In spite of a war-torn and dictatorship-ridden world environment, here on this continent the key institutions of democracy continue to function. If the Government does not try to undermine them, but cherishes their value and strives to make them stronger, then come what may in other parts of the world, democracy and civilization have a chance to survive in this Nation.

Because of its experience and past achievements, because of the high caliber of its personnel and their devotion to public service, because of the love of liberty among the farming people who are the constituency of the Department of Agriculture, this Department and its information agencies have a rare opportunity to serve democracy through the years to come in defense against the forces pressing in from other parts of the world.

Science and Agricultural Policy

by T. Swann Harding [1]

AS SCIENCE has shaped modern agriculture, it is one of the indispensable factors in shaping agricultural policy. Any policy that did not take science into account would be headed for the rocks. But, says the author of this article, both scientists and laymen are inclined to give lip service to this principle without knowing what it actually means. Specialists in the natural sciences do not understand, and often act as if they did not want to understand, social and economic problems. Laymen, on the other hand, often have only vague notions about what science is and the necessities it imposes. The main trouble with modern civilization, he argues, is that it has never learned how to make scientific use of science. He pleads for a new kind of scientific education; for a new kind of cooperation among specialists in the natural and social sciences; above all, for the development of a "science for making use of science." The author does not hesitate to attack what he regards as outworn notions. The article is amply documented with references to significant work in the field it covers.

THE UTILIZATION of knowledge acquired by fundamental research may be constructive or destructive. It may serve to build a civilization at peace or to destroy one at war.

[1] T. Swann Harding is Editor of Scientific Publications, Office of Information.

The impact of scientific discovery may be disruptive even of a society at peace. Wrongly applied scientific knowledge has often resulted in social confusion and economic disorder. But in the last analysis the form assumed by our social and economic system as a whole, and by agriculture in particular, depends primarily upon discoveries in natural science. The effect of such discoveries upon our society is, in turn, largely determined by the policies we adopt for their utilization.

WHAT IS SCIENTIFIC METHOD?

We commonly call this a scientific age and proudly point to our achievements through scientific method. What is scientific method as distinguished from the methods of magic or pre-science, or from what may be called ordinary, nonscientific methods? To help our understanding we might consider a theory of the nature of the universe held by certain philosophers in the sixth century.

According to this theory the earth was a flat parallelogram. In its center was the ocean, and the sky was glued to high walls on the edges. The proponents of this theory held it heretical to believe in the existence of the antipodes, to be misled by Greek fables, or to be deceived by human science. For man should appeal to authority, to the law, and to the testimony. Sacred writ said that man lived upon the face of the earth; hence he could not live upon more faces thereof than one, or upon the earth's back. Sacred writings compared the earth to a tabernacle; hence it must obviously have the shape of the tabernacle of Moses (*34*).[2]

Insofar as this reasoning seems strange to us as proof of the earth's shape we have been influenced by scientific method. The mere appeal to constituted authority does not, in itself, move us as it once might have. A similar appeal was made by the ancient physician Bernard Tornius who, finding the heart of a boy upon whom he performed an autopsy to be extraordinarily large, wrote:

"As to why his heart was large, I don't think it came from audacity inborn in him, for he seemed timid, rather, when he was in good health, but the heart was filled with a great quantity of blood, which made it turgid and inflated, but it may be he naturally had a large heart, which in man is a sign of audacity, though in hares it signifies timidity, as may be learned from the statements of Lord Avicenna * * *" (*85*).

Here the doctor did not set up a hypothesis based directly upon his autopsy. He performed an experiment and then appealed to traditional theory for its interpretation. This ultimately involved him in a rather ridiculous inconsistency, whereupon he fell back on authority.

But the full experimental testing of hypotheses, an integral part of the scientific method, was from time to time carried on, however imperfectly, rather early in history. Leonardo da Vinci (1452–1519), for instance, used the modern method of science to an amazing extent. Actually he discovered many general principles usually attributed to Galileo (1564–1642) and to others who came much later. But he

[2] Italic numbers in parentheses refer to Literature Cited, p. 1107.

described them in fragmentary notes full of ill-defined terms and never bothered to publish a logical, systematic treatise. Part of the scientific method consists in the complete and orderly statement of results.

Leonardo's method was scientific because he first observed phenomena, next tried to reproduce them artificially under controlled conditions, then sought relationships between their various factors, applied measurements to these relationships, and finally deduced general principles or laws. He wrote (*50, p. 78*): "Experience never deceives; it is only our judgment which deceives us, promising from it things which are not in its power * * * Before making this case a general rule, test it by experiment two or three times, and see whether the experience produces the same effect."

It certainly seems that Leonardo understood the experimental method as thoroughly as did Galileo a century later. But because he did not relate his findings in a system of logic or a pattern of truth, he did not produce a science (*27, 50*). Even a failure properly to disseminate scientific knowledge impedes the process of perfecting the method of science.

What, then, constitutes this method? The scientist first observes natural phenomena. Certain events in nature excite his curiosity. He faces a problem. His mind yearns for an explanation. So he formulates a hypothesis. He then tests this by experiment, performing certain operations under carefully controlled conditions. If the experiment casts doubt on his hypothesis he changes the hypothesis. Ultimately, after enough experiments have been performed, the scientist tentatively assumes that his hypothesis is sound and deduces from it certain general principles or laws. Finally he puts these principles together logically and systematically in a pattern.

Random observations and experiments, however accurate or informative, do not of themselves constitute a science. Atomic theories and theories of evolution abounded long before they could be established scientifically. The germ theory of disease was limned long before Pasteur. He, however, confirmed it as a fact by carefully controlled observation and experimentation. On the basis of this work he erected a new hypothesis which immediately ordered thousands of hitherto isolated facts and findings into a system that gave them all meaning.

THE NATURE OF SCIENTIFIC TRUTH

The truths established by science are never final. They are always subject to revision or elaboration, which usually makes them more comprehensive in scope.

J. S. Haldane has well written (*44*):

> In science we are always dealing with partial and incomplete aspects of reality—with abstractions which are not only convenient but ultimately unavoidable. Science is the application of abstract logical principles to a reality which they can never express fully. This is so not only in the mathematical, but also in the physical, biological, and any one of the humanistic sciences.

In the introductory chapter to his Grammar of Science, Karl Pearson briefly summarized the essentials of scientific method about as follows (*72*): Scientific method consists in the careful and accurate classification of facts, in the comparison of their relationships and sequences, in the discovery by aid of the disciplined, creative imagination of a brief statement or formula which in a few words sums up a wide range of facts, and, lastly, in the fearless use of objective self-criticism, with the understanding that the final product must have equal validity for all normal minds.

While the obligation of the scientist is to formulate hypotheses, to observe facts, to make experiments, and to substantiate or invalidate his hypotheses quite impersonally, something else may occur. When sufficient facts appear to favor a hypothesis the scientist tends to assume a new attitude toward it. He regards it as a law and develops a strong tendency to explain away recalcitrant facts found later. He thus tends to save the law rather than to surrender it and accept the brute fact as convincing. In doing this he is adopting a primitive, magical, or lay attitude and violating the principle of scientific method.

If a protective fetish worn by a primitive fails to be effectual in some emergency, the savage medicine man is not baffled. He retains his law and explains the fact away. He merely says that some more powerful but malignant magician produced a counter spell to which the individual fell victim, or that the victim wore or treated the charm incorrectly. Laymen untrained in science also tend to retain their assumption or hypothesis, once they are convinced of its truth, and to ignore or explain away facts that threaten to invalidate it.

At the same time they are prone to misapply scientific methods or instruments without consciousness of incongruity. Modern advertising daily surrounds us with grotesque misapplications of scientific method, for instance, and laymen generally are inclined to regard almost any sort of experiment, however ill-controlled, as conclusive, provided the result supports their preconception. Here also the spirit of science is lacking.

For the scientist exerts control in experiments by saying essentially: "Let us suppose that we shall get on best by completely ignoring such and such aspects of a certain object and by concentrating our attention on this one aspect only for the time being. We shall then be able to class it with other objects having this characteristic, and thus we may form groups." That process is abstraction.

In this way a considerable edifice of suppositions and fictions grows up in every science, and everything tends to fit rather too snugly in with everything else—because the process of abstraction is always functioning in the basement, so to speak. Scientists, like other people, like to fill up cracks and chinks in their knowledge of the universe. They must also believe in the simplest possible explanations, and in a form of determinism which, though purely statistical in inner nature, is perfectly rigid, or their experiments would become impossible. They must be able to say that, given a certain cause, a certain result will always follow.

In other words the laboratory scientist acts as if the world were such and such and as if its nature could be expressed in certain equations (*36*, *69*, *89*). As d'Abro has expressed it (*16*, *pp. 492–493*):

The fact is that science is necessarily deterministic, not through an act of faith, not because it has convinced itself that free will is nonexistent, but because determinism is for science a dire necessity if phenomena are to be coördinated and linked to one another. Regardless of what the future may hold in store, the physicist is therefore compelled to act as though a rigidly deterministic scheme were existent in nature, * * * even though he may doubt whether such is really the case.

What follows all this build-up of seemingly pure fiction?

More than 200 years ago Daniel Bernoulli guessed that the tendency of a gas to expand might be attributed to a rushing to and fro of small bits or molecules composing it. But he could offer no experimental proof in support of his assumption. Later Maxwell and Boltzmann investigated this theory mathematically, and they got credit for this because their theoretical anticipations were borne out by quantitative experiments performed in their day. Nevertheless Kelvin and Ostwald remained hostile to this so-called kinetic theory of gases for experimental reasons of their own.

But in 1827 Brown had observed that fine particles suspended in a liquid appeared under the microscope to be in constant, quivering, darting movement. These activities came to be called Brownian movements. Adherents of the kinetic theory explained these movements as due to the impacts of molecules in the fluid upon the tiny particles. Many years later Einstein supplied exhaustive proof that the Brownian movements were indeed in exact quantitative agreement with the kinetic theory of gases.

According to d'Abro (*16*), Perrin then sought experimentally to test Einstein's mathematical proofs on the assumption that the movements could not be such as they were if the kinetic theory held true. His results disagreed with Einstein's, a discrepancy later eliminated by the discovery of a miscomputation on Einstein's part. The kinetic theory was now no longer a guess. It had stood the test of logic and prolonged experimentation. It fitted neatly into the scientific pattern of truth even as related to the movements of tiny particles suspended in a fluid. It was confirmed as holding true with liquids as well as gases.

THE PATTERN OF SCIENTIFIC TRUTH

We should now consider the nature of scientific truth, and try to understand why a scientist may at times even maintain the right to hold, side by side, two theories that appear to be mutually exclusive—for instance those about the radiation of light—on the grounds that each is verifiable experimentally in a particular region. The scientist is doubly skeptical. He doubts both sense perception and pure thought. But he is always extremely skeptical of any alleged fact that is in logical contradiction to his theory. The observations he makes must be relevant, not merely to the particular question in mind, but more especially to the stage the theory has reached in its own development.

For a scientific fact is always a fact in relation to a theory or a pattern. An idea is true scientifically only insofar as it is useful or expedient for the specific purpose of effecting an orderly organization of experience. A new experience is treated as real or true only if it is found to be organizable, that is, if it can be incorporated as a unit in the existing system of knowledge. However, if any experiment turns out contrary to expectation, that is, if it does not fit the pattern and that lack of fit is repeatedly confirmed, the pattern itself must be altered. Thus scientific progress is possible.

Of two given systems of experience, both of them internally consistent, yet mutually incompatible, the scientist selects as true the more extensive system, his only test of truth thereafter being coherence with that system. But, even to convict the senses of error in a given case, the scientist must assume that sense perceptions are true fundamentally; similarly, to convict reason of error, he must assume the broad validity of reasoning.

Ideally every science should be presented as a body of doctrine that can be shown to follow with rigorous, logical necessity from a relatively small number of original postulates that have necessarily to be assumed to be true without proof. There should be the smallest possible number of such basic axioms. To "explain" a new fact or happening is to incorporate it in a logically integrated set of scientific propositions. Every science is based upon ultimate axioms which must be accepted as true sans proof (*39*).

Science thus offers us a pattern of truth. It maps the universe for us. The map is not the universe, but it helps us vastly in finding our way around in the universe without too much stumbling into disaster. It is a thought- and labor-saving device. Science also acts as an evaluating mechanism in the sense that it aids us to measure the validity of other systems by comparison (*28, 83*).

THE POWER INHERENT IN ABSTRACTIONS

Very often the knowledge that has proved most useful has been discovered by workers in science who concerned themselves primarily with trying to perfect the pattern of scientific truth, and thought neither of practical applications nor of financial reward. In his Science and Method (*73*), Henri Poincaré remarks how the triumphs of industry that have enriched so many "practical" men would never have seen the light if practical men only had existed. For the so-called practical man has always been preceded by what Poincaré called "unselfish devotees who died poor, who never thought of utility, and yet had a guide far other than caprice."

As Mach expressed it "these devotees have spared their successors the trouble of thinking" (*73, p. 363*). Later Mach is again quoted by Poincaré as saying that "the role of science is to produce economy of thought, just as a machine produces economy of effort" (*73, p. 371*).

These conceptions, patterns, or maps the scientist evolves have definite utility, even monetary value. We naturally interpret the world pictorially, but our private picture may have little meaning. Science offers a more universalized picture, though one highly abstract in all fields. Yet abstraction is a source of political and economic power. Such abstractions are made, as was said earlier, by separating out or taking away certain elements of reality, or certain aspects of an event, and treating them as if they were the wholes. This method yields the scientist useful results though the abstraction never represents more than part of reality.

A farmer raises wheat or cotton. He does actual work. He feels, handles, lives with his crops, and we tend to think of him as close to reality and far from abstraction. He is, in a sense, closer to reality in performing direct manual operations. But a financier, whose dealings with this reality of cotton and wheat are as abstract as those of any physicist—even though he affects to regard himself as a very practical man—is actually more powerful than the farmer who raised the crops. He can deal with wheat and cotton abstractly, as figures on paper, without ever having seen either growing. His knowledge about price movements is abstract, but it has power.

The modern physicist works similarly. He knows nothing whatever of matter as the thing in itself. But he knows certain laws of its movements; he knows enough to manipulate it. After working through formidable strings of equations in which the esoteric symbols stand for things whose intrinsic nature he can never, never know, he arrives at a result that can be interpreted in terms of your perceptions and mine. It can be utilized to produce desirable effects in our lives (*78*).

A single important scientific generalization based on abstractions can carry the race far and save a great deal of fumbling around. George Stephenson invented a safety lamp for miners. He first made a kind of lamp he thought might do, then tested it, altered it, tried it, tested, altered, and tried again, and so on, until by this slow and tedious process he finally evolved a satisfactory lamp. That is the empirical method your inventor often uses.

But a gifted scientist, like Sir Humphry Davy, worked differently on the same problem. Instead of proceeding from isolated facts to general principles he started in the more economical way from a general principle that science had established. This told him that explosive mixtures of mine damp would not pass through small apertures or tubes. Hence, if you made a lamp tight on all sides and containing only a small aperture for the admission of air, it would obviously serve the purpose. Such a lamp Davy produced. "Davy discovered a principle and then constructed a lamp based upon it. Stephenson made a lamp and was led by it to a principle" (*43*).

Most investigators have to seek the solution of special problems before attempting to solve general problems. But they often pay a big penalty in needless experimentation through inability to handle time- and labor-saving scientific abstractions. The work of Luther Burbank as compared with that of a thoroughly trained scientific geneticist comes to mind as an example.

Moreover the purest of pure research, basic research undertaken merely to arrive at general principles—that is, to piece out a little more of the map we have utilized to symbolize the scientific pattern of truth—offers us knowledge of great value. Michael Faraday's discovery of electromagnetic induction was a triumph of pure reason to him, but it showed man how to harness electricity for heat, light, and power. An abstract mathematical equation devised by Clerk Maxwell gave us the radio and television, for Marconi was inevitable after Maxwell. Pure research, animated by plant explorers' curiosity, discovered cold-resistant alfalfa in Siberia, and Gibbs' abstract-phase rule underlies much modern metallurgy.

Though much pure knowledge is often abused or misapplied, human-

Figure 1.—An example of fundamental research with a practical objective—in this case, the use of byproducts. On the table are sugarcane bagasse, straw (in foreground), and corncobs—possible sources of molding powder like that in the beaker. In the foreground are plastics made from the molding powder.

ity benefits enormously when rationally planned use of it can be assured. Yet it all springs from a system of what the ordinary person would call very unrealistic abstractions.

Research may be conveniently divided into four classifications: [3]

(1) Background research with no practical objective consciously

[3] Huxley (*55*) sets up somewhat the same classifications.

in view, like Mendel's work in genetics, research in molecular structure, in atomic physics, on photosynthesis (*81*), or in experimental embryology, or some investigations undertaken in anthropology.

(2) Basic or fundamental research that has a distant practical objective—soil science, meteorology, animal breeding, the industrial utilization of agricultural byproducts and crop surpluses (fig. 1), or studies of price movements, mortality rates, or shifts in population.

(3) Research carried on to attain an immediate objective or to solve some specific problem—for example, to wipe out some harmful insect or to eradicate some plant or animal pest, to raise farmer purchasing power, or to introduce the use of a new agricultural machine without economic disruption.

(4) Development or pilot-plant research, the type needed to translate small-scale laboratory findings into full-scale agricultural or commercial practice, such as testing out a new laboratory method for making sweetpotato starch, trying the food-stamp plan in a single city, or seeking to rehabilitate certain impoverished farm families by making them relatively small character loans.

Clerk Maxwell and Heinrich Hertz performed research of type 1 but gave the world the fundamental principles underlying all modern applications of electrical science. The equations they developed about 1873 concerned the relationships between electricity and magnetism and the detection of magnetic waves. Michael Faraday's work also was in the field of what is commonly called pure science, or what is classified here as background research.

Such workers as these are largely animated by curiosity and an urgent desire to extend the field of human knowledge. Yet to them we owe this entire vast system of technology and mechanics which forms our environment today. Obviously abstract scientific knowledge is a far more powerful revolutionary force than the "radical ideas" which so often frighten us.

Viewed as an investment, pure research pays good dividends (fig. 2). Since the returns are paid socially, and since each bit of knowledge aids in producing still other knowledge, the dividends cannot be estimated with close accuracy. But A. F. Woods, when Director of Scientific Work of the Department of Agriculture, felt it conservative to hold that research in the Department paid at least a 500-percent dividend on the investment. Yields up to 10,000 percent have been estimated (*9*) by certain American industries and also by the British Department of Scientific and Industrial Research.

Research in the Department of Agriculture and the State experiment stations engages 7,000 to 8,000 scientists on about as many projects. It is almost certain that the annual value of the research performed by them would more than pay the cost of setting up these agencies, with all the land-grant colleges thrown in. The Federal Bureau of Plant Industry alone estimates that 22 of its research accomplishments add $230,000,000 annually to our income. If but 5 percent of all projects produce practical results the returns are large.

Oregon in 1933–34 had one central and nine branch agricultural experiment stations. These spent about $88,000 a year on research as compared with an annual cash income of $120,000,000 for Oregon farmers. The experiment station staff estimated the return on that

Figure 2.—Research pays good dividends. The utilization of soybeans, for example, rests on research findings. Here experimental soybean plants are receiving different kinds of nutrient solutions. The growth of the plants and the chemical composition of the seed are compared. Thus the scientists determine the effect that each fertilizer element has on growth and on the chemical composition of the plant.

$88,000 as $10,000,000, a 10,000-percent yield (*9*). Again, in October 1939 Science Service reported that an insecticide and agricultural-spray manufacturer had increased his employment 400 percent since 1929 by the research development of a highly concentrated liquid insecticide that could be applied by atomizing it into a foglike mist.

IS ONE SCIENCE BETTER THAN ANOTHER?

So far we have dealt chiefly with the so-called natural sciences, exemplified by physics, chemistry, and biology. But many hold to the idea that in the hierarchy of sciences certain ones are below the salt. Are the so-called social sciences—sociology and economics, for instance—fundamentally different? Many still feel that some sciences are better than others. They are prone to say, for example, that the social sciences differ from the physical sciences because in the latter the observer does not form part of his experiment and does not deal with volition and value.

But the physical scientist himself deals with volition and value. Furthermore all experimenters inevitably form an integral part of their experiments. As one eminent physicist (Bridgman) has reminded us, workers in physics tend to discover the results and relationships they expect to find. He adds also that pure determinism with sharp prediction of future states is no longer possible in physical systems. This view, differently expressed, will be found shared by such scientists as Einstein, Bragg, Neils Bohr, Jeans, Schrödinger, Bridgman, Lindsay, as well as the late Viscount Haldane in his final writings (*1, 23, 24, 25, 40, 56, 60, 79*). As Sir James H. Jeans said of physics (*56*): "Nature no longer forms a closed system detached from the perceiving mind; the perceiver and the perceived are interacting parts of a single system."

The physicist himself no longer plays the simple role of passive observer. He is now conscious of that. For he has initially in mind a certain pattern of thought and certain related ideas. He then abstracts from the totality of things a limited sphere for intensive exploration. His pattern of thought makes him frame only certain questions. To obtain the answers he performs specific, carefully thought-out laboratory operations. He resorts to mathematical symbolism. His difficulty, quite like that of the social scientist, arises when he seeks to make the transition from his abstract world picture to the rude world of experience.

Philosophy, mathematics, physics, sociology, economics, and anthropology also have their respective fundamental assumptions or postulates—just as do blacksmithing, preaching, and cooking. All scientists by nature tend to believe implicity in the eternal truth of their axioms, though of course no one tries to prove them, for no one can. Scientists also assume such things as that: The solution of problems is possible; the simplest solution is the true one; the method of science is the best to use in solving problems; the specific cases examined are true of all the infinity of cases that cannot be examined; the position of the stars and other uncontrollable factors does not affect the rightness of the solution; and so on.

Furthermore science almost habitually deals with a something that laymen would scarcely regard as reality. It often creates that very special kind of reality already referred to as an abstraction and studies that (*23, 26, 35, 38, 46, 51, 56, 63, 65, 75, 80, 84*). No science is absolutely exact in the sense of corresponding fully with reality as understood by laymen. The kind of exactitude mathematics attains is something quite different and is achieved by definition established beforehand. We usually regard physics as very "exact," but that is because it deals with high abstractions and with exceedingly large masses of very small units, not because it corresponds directly with what ordinary people regard as reality. The exactitude of physics is purely mathematical; so is that of economics (*45*).

In the sense of corresponding neatly and snugly with that which ordinary people regard as reality, the social sciences are more exact than physics. For physics merely gains such exactitude of this sort as it possesses by limiting its sphere of observation and by utilizing abstractions so extreme that laymen would not regard the physicist's private world as real.

But the spirit and method of science are the same in all sciences. The method consists broadly in only two things: (1) The observation of the totality of things as they are and of what happens when as many factors as possible are under control in a carefully planned experiment; (2) the use of rational processes and of logic to create causes to account for that which has been observed and to formulate generalizations or laws. What happens thereafter is an effort to apply findings to what the average man knows as the real world, but any exact correspondence is out of the question in any science.

In his experiments the scientist prefers to deal with aggregates of many units. These may be uncounted billions of atoms, electrons, or molecules, or dozens of guinea pigs or rats, or thousands of human beings, or, as in the work of the actuary, hundreds of thousands of items of comparable data. Since scientists of every type deal with such aggregates their ultimate conclusions can have only a mathematical kind of certainty. Insofar as they carry out their work carefully the chances are overwhelming that their hypotheses as finally stated in the form of a law are consistently verifiable.

But some factors either always elude control or else have always to be ignored. At any time one of these may turn out to be crucial, and the scientist's generalization may be invalidated. There is a strong, logical probability derived from science that the sun will rise tomorrow, but it does not amount to a material necessity. Some factor may have been overlooked. The sun might explode overnight. If for any reason it failed to rise, science (if any scientists survived) would create a hypothetical cause to account for that. For science must always find causes to account for the failure of its predictions to come true. This again is true of all sciences (*47*).

If the predictions of any science prove incorrect, new causes are in order, for a science must be a logical system explicitly designed to predict phenomena within its own sphere accurately. A scientific law does not need complete and ultimate verification, for that would make it axiomatic. If scientists finally manage to see electrons and atoms, that would in a sense verify the laws of physics. But if they do not, physicists can create causes to account for that. They may insist that electrons are mere mathematical abstractions with no material reality whatever.

Scientific theories are, by and large, simply groups of related hypotheses, based on axioms and experiments, that permit our reasoning machines (minds) to interpret certain events around us rationally. This applies also in social science. While the evolution of a social or economic state of a particular kind is no more predictable scientifically than the actual discovery of atoms or electrons, we can record the laws that would apply in such a state, even though it does not exist.

Again, we can never affirm that a certain law in any science will or will not become operative. A man falls from a height; the law of gravity becomes operative; something intervenes, however, and another law becomes operative. A certain step is taken which should make the prices of agricultural commodities rise, but they fall. We cannot interfere with economic any more than we can with physical laws, but we can influence the situation to some extent and thus have a say as to which law becomes operative.

Social scientists have been fallaciously accused of lack of precision. That is largely because their method is not well understood even by themselves. It has been said that because they cannot tell what an individual unit—a human being—will do in a given situation, they are inept at prediction. But neither can the physicist tell what an individual electron will do. He can only predict what great masses of electrons will do, and the social scientist, after sufficient investigation, can do the same for the units with which he deals (*77*).

Nor could phenomena in any social science be more unstable than those in physical science. Astronomy unfolds to us worlds forming and dissolving; geology, continents rising and falling; biology, species appearing and becoming extinct; physics, infinitesimal particles in external motion.

Thirty years ago one worker said: "I do not know what an atom of iron may be, but it must be as complicated in structure as a grand piano."

The scientific concepts in which all these phenomena are described also undergo change. Mendelian units of inheritance become gene complexes; hereditary traits are found to be modified by vitamins, hormones, and spontaneous mutations; "instincts" fall before "conditioned reflexes"; the eternal stability of the chemical elements is dissolved in the acid of radioactivity, and transmutation occurs; the electron has become an ever-changing, half-mystical, mathematical concept (*75, 90*).

It should be emphasized perhaps that physical constants are themselves fictions or abstractions. The principal constants of physics are: The velocity of light in a vacuum—but there are no vacuums, and the final, exact velocity of light remains to be determined; the electrical charge and mass of an electron at rest—but electrons never are at rest; the elementary quantum of energy—yet it seems doubtful that quanta never increase or decrease; the laws of gravitation, based on the manner in which unsupported objects fall at sea level in vacuums—though vacuums do not exist, and sea level is a variable (*75, 90*).

Some years ago Read Bain showed rather conclusively (*19*) that the social sciences were no more complex than the natural sciences. He demonstrated that social phenomena are not more numerous, more unstable, more disorderly, more intangible, or more difficult to understand than those of natural science.

We may conclude, then, that no science deals in absolute exactitude or certainty and that all sciences resort to mathematical approximations. Hence probability rules physics and chemistry as well as economics.

The random samples studied by the physicist and the chemist seem so much less variable than those studied by the economist and the sociologist because they consist of so vastly many more units. It is true that the individual items observed by social scientists are often apparently variable in the extreme. But it must always be remembered that if man A does not follow strictly determinate laws neither does electron B (*31, 61, 76*).

The need of social scientists is to develop a scientific method peculiar to their own field, a method that will enable them to assay the relative importance and influence of a variety of factors operating simultaneously in a dynamic situation. Their difficulty is not in

223761°—40——70

using unproved assumptions but in starting with unsuitable ones. They have so far failed to develop techniques rapidly enough to keep pace with needs. They have also erred frequently in trying to pattern their techniques upon the methods used in supposedly more precise and respectable sciences such as physics.

NEEDED—A NEW SCIENCE TO MAKE USE OF SCIENCE

Though science as a whole has done much to promote research, it has done very little to supervise scientifically the utilization of the knowledge that research produces. We have no science for making use of science, though sociology would be such a specialty if it performed the functions we have a right to expect of it.

Sometimes scientific discoveries are quickly applied in commercial practice before sufficient controlled work has been done on them to assure us of their value. At other times the lag is long between the fully authenticated scientific discovery and its widespread application. Too often the fruits of research can be supplied only to the few who can afford to purchase them.

Addressing the Royal Society of Arts on April 9, 1930, F. A. E. Crew stated that the lag between demonstrated scientific fact and its incorporation into practice was then usually from 20 to 50 years (*2*). He cited important genetic knowledge which was then available but which had not been applied in the livestock industry. Agriculture was depressed, yet scientific information that would aid agriculture went unutilized. Professor Crew mentioned those "who sell the quickest growing sows and keep the slowest for further breeding, not knowing that the economical conversion of food into pig is an inherited character, and that the quickest growers are the most economical feeders."

In March 1939 Frank G. Boudreau and H. D. Kruse deplored the lag in practical application of the newer knowledge of nutrition in the United States. Public-health programs were said still very largely to neglect nutrition. The methods used to detect malnutrition were antiquated, and the problem remained vague and ill-defined though many studies indicated a high percentage of undernourishment among school children and 4,000 people died annually from pellagra, an easily and economically preventable disease (*22*).

Some agency is needed the function of which is to oversee the entire process of applying research results in practice (*17*, *74*). Because we lack such an agency, confusion, disorder, and impoverishment tend to follow our unplanned, haphazard utilizations of scientific knowledge in commerce, industry, agriculture, and society generally. Thus, while originative scientific discoveries make many new jobs, intensive scientific discoveries abolish very many more.

The discovery of an important fundamental principle may result in the appearance of new industries and the creation of many derivative jobs. The telephone, the radio, and the automobile, motortruck, and tractor are examples. But intensive inventions or discoveries tend soon thereafter to displace labor. Increased production with fewer workers begins; technological unemployment appears. The further economic repercussions of this situation, including necessarily decreased mass purchasing power, are extremely disastrous. We have tended altogether too much to use science as an aid in the unwise exploitation of natural resources, also, rather than as a conserving social force. The conservation of human and natural resources should be paramount. Today, dislocation of the major balance between industrial and agricultural production threatens our entire civilization.

Sir Arthur Salter said in 1934: "Our material resources, technical knowledge, and industrial skill are enough to afford every man of the world's teeming population, physical comfort, adequate leisure, and access to everything in our rich heritage of civilization that he has the personal quality to enjoy." But, as Nature (London), quoting Salter, commented (*8*), "To secure such advantages revolutionary changes in our customary and accepted attitude to distribution, production, work, and leisure may well be required, and the control of many sectional and selfish interests, realizing that in the long run the common interest is the true interest of the individual."

Nature continued:

Our task of reconciling industrial and social practice with revised scientific thought will not be achieved without courage and vision. It may issue in a new economic structure for society which as yet we are unable to predict. No scientific worker who has glimpsed the possibilities which machine power has put within our grasp can, however, turn aside from the task of assisting society to avert the evils with which mechanization threatens us, and to translate those possibilities into achievement, without disloyalty to that spirit of adventure and honest endeavor which is an essential part of the scientific spirit itself.

That spirit is supremely important. In his Freedom and Culture (*37*) John Dewey says we can save democracy and improve upon it only by cultivating and disseminating the scientific spirit and morale—that is, the

willingness to hold belief in suspense; ability to doubt until evidence is obtained; willingness to go where the evidence points instead of putting first a personally preferred conclusion; ability to hold ideas in solution and use them as hypotheses to be tested instead of as dogmas to be asserted; and (possibly the most distinctive of all) enjoyment of new fields for inquiry and of new problems.

The permeation of our culture with the scientific spirit and attitude is the essential thing.

The immediate problem is posed by the fact that our mechanical equipment tends constantly, under present conditions, to outstrip our purchasing power and our ability to give work to all who are employable. A decade ago Sir William Pope was saying (*18*) that science had launched us into a new era which was understood neither by the public nor by the politicians, much less by the businessmen. That era cannot be called truly scientific while so many perish for want of science properly applied (*41*).

From 40 to 80 percent of the cost of agricultural crop production can be attributed to power and labor. The human- and animal-power epoch continued until about the middle of the eighteenth century. During that time it took about 75 to 95 percent of the people to produce the population's food supply (fig. 3, *A*). The work was largely drudgery. Vast changes came by the mid-nineteenth century, 1850 roughly marking the border between the human- and animal-power and the machine-power phases of agriculture—though rapid advance in agricultural technology was worrying experts a

Figure 3.—*A*, When hand power alone was used, it took 75 to 95 percent of the population to produce the Nation's food supply. *B*, With the development of machine power, the production of individual workers greatly increased. In some cases, 1 man can do the work that 30 used to do.

decade earlier. Farm population began to decline; farmers began to seek improved tillage and production methods.

After 1910 machine power began to have a very marked effect on agricultural economics. Decreases in farm population and in numbers of farm work animals continued. The production of individual workers greatly increased. One man with modern machines can harvest as much grain as 30 men could have a century ago (fig. 3, *B*). The same sort of thing is true for other crops.

From 1929 on about half of the farmers were producing about 90 percent of all farm products sold or traded—that is, half the farmers could, if equipped with proper machinery, clothe and feed the city people and themselves as well (*52*). In Texas alone 10,000 farm families had been displaced by tractors between 1935 and 1938. These people went on relief or became migratory.[4] Hence the introduction of technology was in some ways catastrophic in its effects upon the farm as an institution. Such things occur because we do not have a mechanism the function of which is to put science to work in a scientific way. We need not less science but more.

Neither the benefits of scientific knowledge nor the impacts of scientific discovery upon society—when such discovery is applied—have been considered objectively and from the standpoint of the public welfare. Inexplicably, all this has been left to chance. If some practical application of a new research discovery dislocated thousands upon thousands of workers, that was regarded as unfortunate but unavoidable. We urgently need to develop what Sir Josiah Stamp well called "The Science of Social Adjustment" in the title of his book on the subject (*82*). This would be a sort of modernized sociology functioning mainly as a science for the intelligent utilization of scientific knowledge. (See also (*86*).)

Any laboratory discovery may at any time revolutionize agriculture as a whole, or broad sections of it. It is impossible to tell which quiet research worker in his remote nook may produce a force wildly disruptive, unless it be properly handled. It is quite possible even now that if a million efficient farmers were fully equipped in the most modern way they could produce all the agricultural products and commodities we need. It is certain at least that the use of machines can cut the work requirement of many an unmechanized farm in half.

That is perfectly all right so long as the shock is cushioned and provision is made to retain those thrown out of employment in the ranks of consumers (*7*). But to do this requires plans and programs. It cannot be accomplished haphazardly. Under our form of government these programs must also be formulated through the democratic process. The scientific specialist must have the vision and the social consciousness to do his share. The research worker has too long been content to lay his discovery in the lap of chance and think little more about it.

But, as we have seen, even the most seemingly theoretical inferential knowledge the scientist procures can readily operate antisocially and disruptively unless due provision is made for its beneficial use. In

[4] BAKER, O. E. POPULATION TRENDS IN RELATION TO LAND USE. U. S. Dept. Agr., Ext. Serv. Cir. 311, 12 pp., illus. 1939. [Mimeographed.]

this process the natural sciences are basic. If atomic energy is ever released—and in 1940 we drew nearer that possibility than ever before—a cube of sugar, a teaspoonful of water, a silver dollar, or even the energy released from the passengers' tickets—would propel a huge liner across the Atlantic.

It is startling to think that a pound of matter contains a billion horsepower of energy that is utilizable if it can be released. That would step up the energy to be derived from coal a millionfold. Electricity would be as abundant as air. Central generative stations would no longer be needed. Each farm, home, and office could have its own little generator for heating and cooling. Agriculture would be revolutionized. The present value of all rare metals, including gold, would disappear. Production would be increased enormously with much lower costs and vastly less necessity for human labor. These things, or something like them, may soon happen. We should have well-thought-out methods for dealing with such eventualities.

Turning to agriculture specifically: while we do not know that the water-culture method of producing certain crops will actually effect the results claimed for it by enthusiasts, the potentialities of the method when scientifically applied in practice may be extraordinary. While the utilization of hormone injections to increase milk production has not yet been worked out in practice, it soon may be; experimentally lactation has been stimulated to the extent of 30 percent and butterfat production by 50 percent by such injections. Ultimately ductless-gland therapy may be used to determine the rate and limit of growth of farm livestock, to control the intensity and duration of lactation, the deposition of body fat, and other factors now dependent upon the slow process of selective breeding. Already high-yielding corn and disease-resistant wheat serve to aggravate the evils of agricultural surpluses.

The potentialities are bewildering. The use of auxins or plant hormones to promote plant growth; the possible discovery of new, powerful fertilizing principles, or of chemical elements, not as yet determined quantitatively in soil, that may enable plants and trees to protect themselves from diseases and insects; the observation that certain drugs promote rapid hybridization of plants, thus speeding up synthetic evolution—any of these may change methods of agricultural production tremendously. Think what the general-purpose tractor is doing for the family-size farm or what a perfected mechanical cotton picker might do. Consider how the motortruck transformed agricultural transportation problems. Think what developments in the bacteriology and chemistry of food preservation, coupled with more rapid means of transportation, have done to agriculture as an industry.

Obviously, sensible provision must be made to organize the reciprocal relationship between research and society. There must be smoother functioning, with far less friction, to prevent or reduce shock and imbalance. This can be accomplished only by pure and applied research in economics, sociology, political economy, human ecology, cultural anthropology, social psychology, and the social sciences generally. That, in turn, will mean a realization that all science is basically one.

THE SOCIAL IRRESPONSIBILITY OF SCIENTISTS

This brings us to the rigid compartmentalization that has done so much to sterilize scientific knowledge by depriving scientific specialists of broad social vision. So far the scientist has usually confined himself to making observations, formulating hypotheses, planning and carrying out experiments and further investigations to test his hypotheses, perfecting the hypotheses until he could enunciate a general principle or scientific law, and then stopping. Beyond that point he has professed little interest. Yet essentially the entire process must be carried on over again in the field of social science to apply the knowledge in practice scientifically.

In the past the research worker has left the process of applying the knowledge he produced to others who were poorly grounded in scientific method and who usually lacked the scientific spirit. He has taken little part in the formulation of broad plans and programs for the social good and almost none in making these programs effective (*20*, *32*, *33*, *41*, *57*, *66*, *75*). This is natural. Persons in all lines of activity tend to become compartmentalized. In the scientist's case this process is perhaps accelerated by the popular notion that every scientist is queer—an absent-minded-professor type not to be trusted to produce sound plans, not likely to have useful ideas. The work of Benjamin Franklin and many others sufficiently disproves this notion.

This has all been very unfortunate. To be sure, the research worker must carry on objectively and without prejudice. He must seek to avoid bias and emotional disturbances while working creatively. But he must learn to do more than merely produce new knowledge. For one thing he must learn to express himself clearly; he is also responsible for the dissemination of knowledge. Furthermore he must to some extent be an interpreter, for his austere technical formulations of knowledge may be meaningless to others who must aid in making it socially effective.

Thus a highly technical presentation may be made of the manner in which food elements migrate in growing plants at different stages of growth. But what farmers in a certain locality may want to know is how to eradicate bindweed least laboriously and most effectively. Properly interpreted, the scientific knowledge may be just what they need.

But the scientist must go even further than that. A scientific writer entitled a recent article "Physics, A Vicious Abstraction," and argued therein that the value of a fact cannot be separated from the existence of the fact (*42*). Hence, if the highly abstract physics of these days has no real value to humanity it is a mere vicious abstraction. The test of successful scientific functioning is, How well do these operations succeed? "The working definition of success can be nothing short of the conscious attainment of the good life and the good society." This author therefore held it naive on the part of many scientists to hold themselves aloof from the questions of good, of right and wrong, and of social values and relations. For such an attitude "incorporates a mixture of primitive supernaturalism and superstition about human relations in contrast with the attitude they (scientists) assume in the laboratory." Although one of our American journals of sociology argued editorially during 1939 that scientists must remain wholly aloof from choices, values, and human relations (*15*), as scientists, that is an obsolete attitude. The cult of scientific irresponsibility is on the way out.

In the United States we have long had fact-finding agencies in abundance, but we have been reluctant to follow their findings in the social sciences because of a traditional ivory-tower attitude on the part of social scientists and perhaps in part because of the excessive timidity of natural scientists. Earnest doctors of philosophy have long toiled prodigiously in splendid isolation, often only to their own self-satisfaction or to little purpose other than supporting themselves and their families.

In an address delivered before the Science Federation of the University of Manchester, January 23, 1933, Hyman Levy denounced all this under the title "The Irresponsibility of Science." He said (*7*) that the man of science must help to solve the problems of unemployment, consumption, and distribution which have arisen in modern times so largely because of his activities. He held it was part of the scientist's duty to face the ethical problems created by the application of scientific discoveries. He said further:

> The habit engendered in the scientific worker by his very method of endeavoring to isolate objects or causes and consider the influence of single factors in a problem, has a very real danger in that it leads scientific workers to assume that all scientific questions are independent of ethics. Practically all scientific work, however, has a social aspect and its social properties cannot be clearly separated from its scientific properties any more than theoretical and applied science can be sharply demarcated.

We are increasingly forced, both in agriculture and in industry, to consider the limit beyond which the process of improving the facilities for production may prove socially disturbing and eventually be destructive of the very scientific movement itself, as it has been already in certain European countries. Scientific workers cannot ignore the fact that what they intend to be a gift of more enjoyable leisure to humanity too often transforms itself into unemployment and privation. Scientists must aid in finding what factors serve best to create a stable society capable of using science beneficially. Otherwise science will be increasingly a disruptive factor.

In British Nature for January 5, 1929, A. G. Church thus severely condemned the kind of scientific aloofness that is here under discussion (*29*):

> Apparently the assumption is made that persons like scientific specialists, absorbed in an intellectual occupation for a great deal of their time, are necessarily consistently "mental, conscious, and voluntary," in their relations. The fact is that most scientific specialists are ruled by their prejudices and emotions in everything except their own small branches of study. They are neither rational nor realistic in most affairs of life, merely normal, which is a real misfortune to the world and the civilization which is due to their discoveries. Science has lost the art of leadership, if it ever possessed it. The scientist is afraid to be different, timidly afraid to accept the implications of the results of his own work and acquired knowledge, afraid to suggest that his own outlook of inquiry and patient observation, fearlessness to discard outworn or useless hypotheses, all of which he brings to bear on his own research, could with advantage be applied to our political, social, and economic institutions. Perhaps, however, indifference and not fear is the cause of it.

Something over a decade ago there was a meeting of agricultural economists at which the usual things were discussed—the effect of the gold supply on trade, the relationship between the abstraction "agriculture" and the abstraction "industry," the influence of the price of hogs on the delivery of hogs to market, the preference of potato buyers for clean over dirty potatoes.

Then suddenly a delegate arose and remarked that agricultural economics was an applied science. It was concerned with what has happened, what is happening, and, if possible, what is going to happen. But it should also pass judgment on what happens. It should try to influence what may happen. Implicit in all scientific investigation is the idea that the facts found will furnish guidance for intelligent judgment. Nearly all discussion leads to a consideration of possible policies and their relative values. Why then have agricultural economists and other scientists shied off from discussions of policy? What ends are they seeking? Why are they seeking them? How do these ends fit into one another? What kind of rural life, what kind of rural society, do the scientists concerned wish to produce, if any? What is their program for producing it? (*3*).

This forthright approach rather threw the meeting into consternation. Yet why was such discussion felt to be out of order? Why should not scientists set up goals for society, be promoters of good and opponents of evil? If they do not do this, others, perhaps less richly qualified, will. Even the most rigid physical scientists must from time to time pass judgment upon methods and procedures within restricted fields. But scientific narrowness has too long been the rule.

No scientist can entirely escape the stream of life. Knowledge is not what it should be unless it is permeated with a sense of values. Policies must be informed by detailed judgment. Ends stated in terms that are too abstract cease to be goals. Scientists simply cannot be impartial in all phases of their existence, however objective they must endeavor to be when engaged in laboratory or field work. They too must choose.

Julian Huxley wisely said in his Scientific Research and Social Needs (*54*):

> The chief moral of this book, it seems to me, is that science is not the disembodied sort of activity that some people would make out, engaged in the abstract task of pursuing universal truth, but a social function intimately linked up with human history and human destiny. And the sooner scientists as a body realize this and organize their activities on that basis, the better for both science and society.

Social scientists especially must learn to take a scientific view of the changes constantly occurring in a dynamic society, for the entire realm of social action is their laboratory. They must develop techniques to deal with that continuum. Otherwise they will become passive onlookers upon sequences of events that should be, in some measure, under their control. They must above all concern themselves with the problem of putting scientific knowledge efficiently to work. For all research ultimately produces useful and valuable practical information. If scientists do not see to it that this knowledge is used wisely, it will be used antisocially and exploitatively by those far less intelligent than its creators (*3*, *14*, *87*).

EVILS OF OVERSPECIALIZATION

The Federal Government had long done much important research in a wide variety of fields. Today it is making a serious effort to put science rationally to work on a broader basis than ever before. For that is essentially what the so-called action agencies of the Department of Agriculture are doing (*88*). Before these agencies came into existence basic scientific knowledge had been accumulated in abundance by research. In the early years of this century Dr. Seaman A. Knapp conceived the idea of the demonstration farm as a means of putting this information to work. This idea evolved by 1914 into that extraordinarily interesting and successful experiment in adult education in agriculture known as the Extension Service. The action agencies have simply carried this good idea a few steps further, trying to make it profitable for farmers to follow approved agricultural practices.

As soon as the scientist was called in to help make plans, though, the problem of specialization bobbed up. In most cases each expert was convinced of the unique importance of his own specialty, was inclined to think that that specialty had some peculiar significance in solving agricultural problems, and was disposed to look with some distrust upon specialties other than his own. That has happened before. As William James wrote many years ago (as quoted by More (*67, pp. 32–33*):

> Of all insufficient authorities as to the total nature of reality, give me the "scientists" * * * Their interests are most incomplete and their professional conceit and bigotry immense. I know no narrower sect nor club, in spite of their excellent authority in the lines of fact they have explored, and their splendid achievement there.

That there is necessity for scientific specialization goes without saying. Where there was one science in the past, the complexity of investigation has now given rise to half a dozen or even a dozen new or subsidiary sciences. But too rigid compartmentalization is to be deplored. There has been a tendency for each specialty to operate in an idea-tight compartment, completely isolated from other specialties, each making its isolation the more perfect by developing a highly technical language. This production of superfluous terminologies, coupled with abstruse mathematical devices, has often gone so far as to enable two groups of workers in closely related disciplines to talk about precisely the same thing in entirely different languages (*13, 30, 48, 58, 71*).[5]

While this has to some extent favored the analysis of problems, synthesis has been neglected. The concept that all science is one has been overlooked. Communication has become so impaired that prominent scientists in both Great Britain and the United States have protested against the incomprehensible character of the papers delivered before scientific bodies, pointing out that many of the speakers could be fully understood by only two or three persons present who happened to be members of the same esoteric cult or sect (*6, 10*). Julian Huxley commented feelingly on such overspecialization in his Essays in Popular Science (*53*). Occasionally scientific

[5] See also: HAYAKAWA, S. I. LANGUAGE IN ACTION. 100 pp. Armour Institute of Technology. 1939. [Processed.]

conferences, such as a White House conference on child welfare a few years ago, make little progress because schools of specialists spend the time warring with each other (*68*).

Workers in the various scientific specialties must learn first to communicate successfully with one another, then to cooperate for human welfare. Leaders of science like Sir William Bragg have openly condemned extreme specialization and horrendous terminologies (*13*).

Lay distrust of scientists and the popular tendency to deride "fool professors" or to ridicule "scientific cranks" have arisen in part because of the erudite isolationism practiced by so many scientific specialists. The public has tended alternately to distrust and then to adulate the scientific specialist blindly. Neither attitude is sound nor healthful. Often in the past, as Harold J. Laski wrote 10 years ago (*59*), the expert has lacked humility, has "sacrificed the insight of common sense to the intensity of his experience" in a limited field, and distrusted the appearance of novel ideas.

The specialist also frequently fails to see his own results in their proper perspective. He tends to be afflicted with the caste spirit. He fails then to understand the ordinary men and the politicians who must be in charge of the legislative and executive departments, though it is his duty to give them expert advice, and even in part to guide them. For they know usually what the people want and what they will not have. The specialist tends too much to measure life in terms of his own subject and often reveals himself as naive when asked for his opinion on broad matters of policy.

The plain man's judgment too is important. The dirt farmer knows many things the phytopathologist never will know, and vice versa. The expert cannot dominate, but he must take his part in the formulation of agricultural and social policies, using the democratic process. He must cease even to feel that his own specialty is the one of supreme importance, for, in the anatomy of science, physics does not have supremacy over biological chemistry any more than in the bodily anatomy the heart has supremacy over the lungs. The different scientific specialties are integral parts of a whole, and their basic importance lies in the fact that this whole is equal to more than the sum of its component parts.

The restricted, specialized outlook of scientific workers themselves has done much to hinder right relations between science and leadership. Few scientific specialists have progressive, intelligent opinions in fields outside their speciality. Very often they even lack the ability to express the results of their work in such manner as to contribute to the normal life and growth of the community.

A celibacy of intellect has characterized scientists that resembles the physical celibacy practiced by the learned of the Middle Ages. It often renders their professional organizations strangely ineffective. Yet it arises naturally. Even advertising men have been known to think as advertising men. In justice it should therefore be said that the same thing is frequently true of lawyers, clergymen, editors, and other groups of specialists. Scientists are not alone in their failing. The failing assumes greater importance in their case because of the paramount importance of science in our civilization.

LINKING KNOWLEDGE TO POWER

The future of our society and of our agriculture depends upon our ability to link administrative power with the knowledge of the scientific factors involved in the problems demanding solution. This combination can be secured only when scientists add to their knowledge the wisdom that is the fruit of balanced judgment. The difficulty goes back in considerable part to an educational system that encourages early specialization and ultimately leaves natural scientists almost devoid of political sagacity, social wisdom, or knowledge about social psychology, and social scientists equally devoid of knowledge of the physical universe (*4*, *64*). The fact that our educational system tends also to appeal rather consistently to authority, tacitly assuming that teachers and textbooks have the right answers to all problems, likewise impedes the spread of the scientific spirit of inquiry among laymen.

The necessity for scientific synthesis, in a broad sense, is most urgent. Methods must be evolved to bring together laymen, administrators, scientists, and experts of various kinds. The broad regional type of planning the Department of Agriculture now utilizes in its land use programs may well serve as an example of the process required. It is both intelligent and democratic. All concerned participate in making the plans—the farmer, the local people in general, State as well as Federal officials and administrators, and the scientific specialists. No one dominates. The resulting synthesis contains contributions from all.

Today scientific problems ramify into many fields. They are often to be solved only by teamwork on the part of several different kinds of specialists. Advances in one science also depend on those in another; thus for example, the understanding of the nature of viruses waited upon the invention of the high-speed ultracentrifuge. It becomes increasingly necessary that we have technical men, trained in two or more sciences if possible, to bridge the gap between specialties. Otherwise great opportunities will be missed.

Finally, we must develop a mechanism the function of which will be to put science efficiently to work—to formulate and carry out programs in the spirit of democratic cooperation and of better mutual understanding among experts. The idea is broached in Sir Josiah Stamp's Science of Social Adjustment (*82*), in which he discusses governmental and other agencies that would put scientific and technical knowledge into effective operation with as little social and economic maladjustment as possible. This would merely be a further application of scientific method and of the spirit of science.

Every depression brings the cry that we should abandon research, that we already have too much science. Actually we do not have enough science. That is what causes depressions. One trouble has been that practical problems have usually been approached by the research efforts of a single scientific dicipline. Agricultural research agencies have had imposed upon them an inelastic type of organization that produced specialists in narrow fields and set them to attack isolated fragments of big problems. Research must more and more concern itself with agricultural methods as a whole and with the possibilities of devising totally new techniques.

Science must be unified even while it is departmentalized into special sciences. These must be considered arrangements of convenience, not actual cleavages. Each special science must be unified within itself and in relation to science as a whole. Scientific language must be simplified and made more universally understandable, due attention being paid the denotative, or purely informational, and the connotative, or affective use of words.[6] Scientists must know themselves when they are imparting information (making factual reports) and when their words reflect emotional states within themselves or seek to arouse them in others. Complicated formulas must be correlated with everyday life by translating them into common language (*70*).

Early in 1932 it was announced (*5*) that the British Science Guild was preparing a volume to assist politicians, statesmen, financiers, administrators, and industrialists to realize the value of scientific contributions to national progress and the further potentialities of science. The guild declared that scientists must develop sufficient interest in the social, economic, and political implications of their work to fit them to undertake larger responsibilities. In 1938 there was being discussed (*12*) the formation and functions of the International Council of Scientific Unions, organized to survey the influence of science on the world picture and on human life and society, to review the progress of science and of its applications, and to promote the study of the social influence of science. Many British scientists discussed the general problem of the social relations of science in Nature (London) (*11*).

Such developments are suggestive. At its Richmond meeting late in 1938 and early in 1939 the American Association for the Advancement of Science moved in the same direction. It formulated a comprehensive plan "designed to utilize the best of our scientific resources in the solution of the Nation's social and economic problems, in cooperation with business, labor, agriculture, and other fields." This was done frankly because it was held that scientists had become "increasingly concerned with the social implications of their discoveries and have felt a growing sense of social responsibility." That marks progress.

The statement then issued by the association also said: "From the standpoint of the misuse of science, the scientist is and should be concerned lest his progress and inventions be used to destroy liberty and civilization itself." The Nation's problems are too complex for politicians and businessmen to carry on unaided. The scientists have no desire to dictate, but they do at last feel a definite urge to assist in a united cooperative effort "to strengthen and preserve democratic government" and to attain other socially beneficial objectives.

Two recent books contain much helpful information regarding the manner in which scientists can aid in the formulation of policies and the implementation of programs: Robert S. Lynd's Knowledge for What (*62*) and J. D. Bernal's Social Function of Science (*21*). Their general thesis is that unless scientists do actively aid in the utilization of the knowledge they have produced, other far less well informed people will thrust upon our agriculture, our industry,

[6] See the reference in footnote 5, p. 102.

and our very culture their own interpretations and thought patterns.

If, as Bernal calculated, 2 billion acres, or less than half the present cultivated area of the earth, would, under scientific agricultural methods, provide an optimum food supply for the entire population of the globe, we should stop and take thought. For in this calculation no account is taken of increased yields we may confidently expect from continued research by agronomists, plant geneticists, entomologists, experts in animal husbandry, forage crops, and soils. Scientists must be not only instruments of appraisal and direction finding, but actual guides. They must say what they think ought to be done, or others far more ignorant than they will dictate the action taken.

So far as the Department of Agriculture is concerned, it is apparent (1) that the present structure of the Department as reorganized should enable scientific knowledge and specialists to play their part more efficiently than in the past and (2) that the applied social sciences are now increasingly used in putting natural science to work effectively.

The nature of the research worker's discovery always leaves its imprint upon agricultural policy, but its influence is no longer left completely to chance. At the same time agricultural policy can now regularly affect the approach of the research worker to his investigations. This is nothing really new, because research has always, though oftenest unconsciously, followed the trend of the times. No research worker can live apart from his time.

Today the Department of Agriculture is further advanced in developing instrumentalities for making the scientific specialist and the results of his studies useful to an industry in its entirety than perhaps any other agency in world history (*49*). In its daily operations science regularly, actively, and continuously lends aid in the formulation of agricultural policies. Its scientific specialists are rapidly learning to visualize the process as a whole and to be increasingly helpful in the democratic technique of developing plans and carrying out programs based on sound scientific information.

The agricultural "problem" will be solved, however, only insofar as the industrial and the distribution problems are solved, for agriculture cannot live alone, isolated from the other activities of the Nation. We shall much more nearly approach that state of ideal perfection—which humankind can never really attain and which it would not relish if obtainable—when we decide, as ultimately we certainly shall, to perfect the kind of functional social and economic system that will render an intelligent solution of social, industrial, and agricultural problems possible. That will require, for one thing, less emotive use of word magic and more attention to human and social engineering purely from the standpoint of devising agencies that perform specific functions.

In the past we have assumed the permanency of our economic and social frame of reference and have insisted upon trying to cram into this frame, willy-nilly, the vast knowledge and potentialities the natural sciences have provided. Henceforth we must decide to take the knowledge natural science has given us as our frame of reference and deliberately, consciously, and scientifically devise the kind of social and economic system that will enable us to use it most fully and beneficially for promoting the public welfare.

LITERATURE CITED

(1) Anonymous.
1930. [chemistry and the quantum theory.] Nature [London] 125: 788–789.

(2) ———
1930. note on livestock improvement. Lancet 218: 819.

(3) ———
1930. scientists as leaders. New Repub. 64: 140–141.

(4) ———
1931. professionalism and science. Nature [London] 127: 961–963.

(5) ———
1932. science and imperial affairs. Nature [London] 129: 1–3.

(6) ———
1932. exposition and authority. Nature [London] 129: 145–147.

(7) ———
1933. the disturbing influence of science. Nature [London] 131: 162.

(8) ———
1934. social aspects of labour and leisure. Nature [London] 134: 265–267.

(9) ———
1935. farm research pays huge dividend. Oreg. Farmer 58: 124.

(10) ———
1936. don't strut. Indus. and Engin. Chem. 28: 1244.

(11) ———
1938. realistic social studies. Nature [London] 141: 135–136.

(12) ———
1938. social relations of science. Nature [London] 141 (Sup.): 723–742.

(13) ———
1939. [comment on "the unity of knowledge," an address by sir william bragg to the royal society.] Nature [London] 143: 391–392.

(14) ———
1939. news and views. Nature [London] 143: 550–551.

(15) ———
1939. science, values, and sociology. (Editorial) Amer. Sociol. Rev. 4: 560–565.

(16) Abro, A. d'
1927. the evolution of scientific thought from newton to einstein. 544 pp., illus. New York.

(17) American Medical Association, Council on Foods.
1939. report . . . Amer. Med. Assoc. Jour. 113: 127–128.

(18) Armstrong, Henry E.
1930. neglect of scientific method. Nature [London] 126: 869–871.

(19) Bain, Read.
1929–30. the concept of complexity in sociology. Social Forces 8: 222–231, 369–378.

(20) Baldwin, P. M.
1935. technological unemployment. Sci. Monthly 40: 44–47.

(21) Bernal, J. D.
1939. the social function of science. 482 pp., illus. London.

(22) Boudreau, Frank G., and Kruse, H. D.
1939. malnutrition—a challenge and an opportunity. Amer. Jour. Pub. Health 29: 427–433.

(23) Bragg, W. L.
1934. the physical sciences. Science 79: 237–240.

(24) Bridgman, P. W.
1927. logic of modern physics. 228 pp. New York.

(25) ———
1936. the nature of physical theory. 138 pp. Princeton.

(26) Burtt, Edwin Arthur.
1927. metaphysical foundations of modern physical science. 349 pp. New York.

(27) ———
1931. PRINCIPLES AND PROBLEMS OF RIGHT THINKING; A TEXTBOOK FOR LOGIC, REFLECTIVE THINKING, AND ORIENTATION COURSES. Rev. ed., 529 pp. New York.
(28) CARMICHAEL, R. D.
1930. LOGIC OF DISCOVERY. 280 pp. Chicago.
(29) CHURCH, A. G.
1929. SCIENCE AND LIFE. Nature [London] 123: 6–7.
(30) CLARK, W. MANSFIELD.
1934. EVOLUTION TOWARD A MATURE SCIENTIFIC LITERATURE. Jour. Bact. 27: 1–18.
(31) COHEN, JEROME B.
1938. THE MISUSE OF STATISTICS. Amer. Statis. Assoc. Jour. 33: 657–674.
(32) COMPTON, KARL T.
1934. SCIENCE MAKES JOBS. Sci. Monthly 38: 297–300.
(33) COOLIDGE, W. D.
1934. SCIENTIFIC DEVELOPMENTS AND THEIR APPLICATION. Sci. Monthly 38: 307–309.
(34) CURTIS, WINTERTON C.
1922. SCIENCE AND HUMAN AFFAIRS FROM THE VIEWPOINT OF BIOLOGY. 330 pp., illus. New York.
(35) DAMPIER-WHETHAM, WILLIAM CECIL DAMPIER.
1931. A HISTORY OF SCIENCE AND ITS RELATION WITH PHILOSOPHY AND RELIGION. 514 pp., illus. New York, and Cambridge, England.
(36) DANTZIG, TOBIAS.
1937. ASPECTS OF SCIENCE. 285 pp. New York.
(37) DEWEY, JOHN.
1939. FREEDOM AND CULTURE. 176 pp. New York.
(38) DINGLE, HERBERT.
1932. SCIENCE AND HUMAN EXPERIENCE. 141 pp. New York.
(39) DOTTERER, RAY HARBAUGH.
1929. PHILOSOPHY BY WAY OF THE SCIENCES; AN INTRODUCTORY TEXTBOOK. 469 pp. New York.
(40) EINSTEIN, ALBERT.
1933. THE METHOD OF THEORETICAL PHYSICS. Spencer Lecture at Oxford University, June 10, 1933. 20 pp. Oxford.
(41) FERGUSON, ALLAN.
1936. TRENDS IN MODERN PHYSICS. Science 84: 401–407.
(42) FRIES, HORACE S.
1939. PHYSICS, A VICIOUS ABSTRACTION. Phil. Sci. 6: 301–308.
(43) GREGORY, R. A.
1916. DISCOVERY; OR, THE SPIRIT AND SERVICE OF SCIENCE. 340 pp., illus. London.
(44) HALDANE, JOHN SCOTT.
1923. MECHANISM, LIFE, AND PERSONALITY. AN EXAMINATION OF THE MECHANISTIC THEORY OF LIFE AND MIND. 152 pp. New York.
(45) HARDING, T. SWANN.
1936. ALL SCIENCE IS ONE. Amer. Jour. Sociol. 41: 492–503.
(46) ———
1936. SCIENCE AND REALITY. Open Court 50: 115–125.
(47) ———
1938. ALLEGED IGNORANCE OF SOCIAL SCIENTISTS. Amer. Sociol. Rev. 3: 850–854.
(48) ———
1938. SCIENCE AT THE TOWER OF BABEL. Phil. Sci. 5: 338–353.
(49) ———
1939. PUTTING SCIENCE TO WORK. Jour. Social Phil. 4: 237–251.
(50) HART, IVOR BLASHKA.
1925. THE MECHANICAL INVESTIGATIONS OF LEONARDO DA VINCI. 240 pp., illus. London, Chicago.
(51) HOUSTON, W. V.
1937. THE PHILOSOPHY OF PHYSICS. Science 85: 413–419.

(52) HURST, W. M., and CHURCH, L. M.
1933. POWER AND MACHINERY IN AGRICULTURE. U. S. Dept. Agr. Misc. Pub. 157, 39 pp., illus.
(53) HUXLEY, JULIAN.
1926. ESSAYS IN POPULAR SCIENCE. 307 pp. London.
(54) ———
1934. SCIENTIFIC RESEARCH AND SOCIAL NEEDS. With an introductory chapter by Sir William Bragg . . . 287 pp., illus. London.
(55) ———
1935. SCIENCE AND SOCIAL NEEDS. 287 pp. New York.
(56) JEANS, SIR JAMES HOPWOOD.
1934. THE NEW WORLD-PICTURE OF MODERN PHYSICS. Science 80: 213–222. [Also pub. in Nature [London] 134: 355–365. 1934.]
(57) JEWETT, FRANK B.
1934. SCIENCE AND INDUSTRY. Sci. Monthly 38: 301–302.
(58) KOLMER, JOHN A.
1928. A CRITICAL REVIEW OF THE MECHANISM AND TERMINOLOGY OF ALLERGY. Jour. Lab. and Clin. Med. 13: 905–913.
(59) LASKI, HAROLD JOSEPH.
1930. THE LIMITATIONS OF THE EXPERT. Harper's Mag. 162: 101–110.
(60) LINDSAY, R. B.
1933. CAUSALITY IN THE PHYSICAL WORLD. Sci. Monthly 37: 330–337.
(61) LOUCASSE, WALTER W.
1927. PROGRESS IN THE SCIENCES. Sci. Monthly 25: 213–219.
(62) LYND, ROBERT STAUGHTON.
1939. KNOWLEDGE FOR WHAT? THE PLACE OF SOCIAL SCIENCE IN AMERICAN CULTURE. 268 pp. New York.
(63) MARGENAU, HENRY.
1935. METHODOLOGY OF MODERN PHYSICS. Phil. Sci. 2: 48–72; 164–187.
(64) MATHER, KIRTLEY F.
1940. THE FUTURE OF MAN AS AN INHABITANT OF THE EARTH. Sci. Monthly 50: 193–203.
(65) MEYERSON, EMILE.
1930. IDENTITY AND REALITY. (Transl.) 495 pp. New York.
(66) MILLIKAN, ROBERT A.
1934. THE SERVICE OF SCIENCE. Sci. Monthly 38: 303–307.
(67) MORE, LOUIS TRENCHARD.
1925. THE DOGMA OF EVOLUTION. 387 pp. Princeton.
(68) MURPHY, J. PRENTICE.
1930. WHEN DOCTORS DISAGREED. Survey 65: 311–315, 348–349, 351.
(69) NEEDHAM, JOSEPH.
1930. THE SCEPTICAL BIOLOGIST. 270 pp. New York.
(70) NEURATH, OTTO.
1937. UNIFIED SCIENCE. Phil. Sci. 4: 265–277.
(71) OGDEN, C. K., and RICHARDS, I. A.
1930. THE MEANING OF MEANING. 363 pp. New York.
(72) PEARSON, KARL.
1900. THE GRAMMAR OF SCIENCE. Ed. 2, rev. and enl., 548 pp., illus. London.
(73) POINCARÉ, H.
1913. THE FOUNDATIONS OF SCIENCE; SCIENCE AND HYPOTHESIS, THE VALUE OF SCIENCE, SCIENCE AND METHOD. Authorized transl. by George Bruce Halsted . . . 553 pp. New York.
(74) RAY, G. B., JOHNSON, J. R., and TAYLOR, M. M.
1939. THE EFFECT OF GELATINE ON MUSCULAR FATIGUE. Soc. Expt. Biol. and Med. Proc. 40: 157–161.
(75) RAYLEIGH, ROBERT JOHN STRUTT (RT. HON. LORD).
1938. VISION IN NATURE AND VISION AIDED BY SCIENCE: SCIENCE AND WARFARE. Science 88: 175–181, 204–208.
(76) REITZ, H. L.
1931. SOME REMARKS ON MATHEMATICAL STATISTICS. Science 74: 82–86.
(77) RUEFF, JACQUES.
1929. FROM THE PHYSICAL TO THE SOCIAL SCIENCES; INTRODUCTION TO A STUDY OF ECONOMIC AND ETHICAL THEORY. Transl. by Herman Green . . . 159 pp., illus. Baltimore and London.

223761°—40——71

(78) Russell, Bertrand.
1925. A, B, C of relativity. 231 pp. New York.
(79) Schrödinger, E.
1936. Indeterminism and free will. Nature [London] 138: 13–14.
(80) Seitz, Frederick.
1935. Alterations in the foundations of the exact sciences in modern times. Science 81: 198–200.
(81) Spoehr, H. A.
1924. Photosynthesis and the possible use of solar energy. Smithsn. Inst. Ann. Rpt. 1922: 175–185.
(82) Stamp, Sir Josiah.
1937. The science of social adjustment. 174 pp., illus. London.
(83) Swabey, Marie Taylor (Collins).
1930. Logic and nature. 384 pp. New York.
(84) Swann, W. F. G.
1931. Reality in physics. Science 75: 113–121.
(85) Thorndike, Lynn.
1929. Science and thought in the fifteenth century . . . 387 pp., illus. New York
(86) United States National Resources Committee, Science Committee.
1937. Technological trends and national policy, including the social implications of new inventions . . . Report of subcommittee on technology . . . 388 pp., illus. Washington, D. C.
(87) ———
1938. The future of state planning . . . A report to the Advisory Committee by the State Planning Review Group. 117 pp., illus. Washington, D. C.
(88) United States Department of Agriculture.
1939. Planning for a permanent agriculture . . . Prepared for community and county land use program planning committees. 71 pp. Washington, D. C.
(89) Vaihinger, H.
1925. The philosophy of as if. 370 pp. New York.
(90) Wolters, Albert William Phillips.
1933. Evidence of our senses. 88 pp. New York.

Schools of Philosophy for Farmers

by Carl F. Taeusch [1]

A MAJOR characteristic of American life and thought at the present time is a search for truly democratic methods in running our affairs. We are acutely conscious of the problem because we so strongly wish to avoid laying a trap for ourselves—the trap whose jaws are dictatorship. Here is an account of a significant democratic development in rural life—the growth of discussion groups in rural communities and of State-wide conferences, called "schools of philosophy," from one end of the country to the other. Farmers and their wives, farmer committeemen, and agricultural administrators all attend these "schools." Discussion is wide and free, and it covers the most fundamental problems affecting American life today. Both sides of controversial questions are attacked and defended vigorously. The general feeling among those who have attended these discussions is that they are not only stimulating and educational in the highest sense but that they are at the same time a democratic safety valve and a training ground in democratic methods.

THE FARMER is a natural-born philosopher. Not only does he have to be a philosopher to live through the many things farmers have to face, including the weather and economic depressions, but his work is of such a varied character that he has a better opportunity to "see life whole" than does the more specialized man in the city.

[1] Carl F. Taeusch is Head, Division of Program Study and Discussion, Bureau of Agricultural Economics.

And in recent years, it is the farmer who has been asking the deeper and broader questions that we generally associate with philosophy—What's it all about? Can we do something about it, or must we take what comes? If we do something about the economic side of agriculture, what will this do to our democracy? How did all this trouble come about? Can government interfere with economic trends? What about world relations? What adjustments do we need to make in our society to bring about a better rural life?

These are profound questions, and they cannot be answered by the agricultural scientist or specialist unless he too turns philosopher. Now, the farmer does not care whether this is philosophy or not; he wants these questions answered, or at least he would like to talk them over and find out what others think about them. For example, the farmer committeemen [2] of Vermont recently agreed, at a conference, that these questions were more important than the technical problems of farming or of the agricultural program. They practically repeated William Allen White's query, "What's the matter with Kansas? Should we raise more corn or more hell?" So did the farmer committeemen of the northern Great Plains push aside the more pressing problems and discuss the long-range history of that region—going back to the early cave dwellers, who left evidence that a well-established corn culture long ago gave way to duststorms and a grass culture. And, everywhere, the farmer and his wife are wondering about what kind of life their boys and girls will lead, especially if they stay on the farm.

Realizing the need of encouraging such thinking, the Department of Agriculture, in 1935, adopted a plan for developing study and discussion groups among farm men and women, boys and girls. The purpose of this plan was to stimulate even more thinking along the lines of the broader implications of the national agricultural program. It was felt that, just as with anything new, the study and discussion of these wider problems required educational help. The desire and drive were there, but assistance was needed in getting things started, in learning the few simple things that enable a conference or a discussion group to take best advantage of the time at its disposal, and in getting accustomed to hearing other sides presented without impatience or intolerance or anger. Farm people need to be shown that the way to go about having profitable discussions is simple, though it has almost been lost in the complexities of modern life.

THE SCHOOLS OF PHILOSOPHY

Growing out of this discussion-group program there developed a more formal project designed for the farm leaders of a State, who would assemble for a period of several days to discuss the broader phases of the agricultural program. The earlier meetings were attended by extension workers only—county agents, home demonstration agents, 4–H Club leaders, extension specialists. These meetings soon became popularly known as "schools of philosophy."

[2] Every rural community elects a committee of farmers to administer the Agricultural Adjustment Administration program. These local committeemen in turn elect a county committee for the same purpose. In addition, the Bureau of Agricultural Economics has a committee of farmers in each county, ranging in number from 5 to 30, whose function is to plan the agricultural work of the county. Both groups participate in the educational program discussed in this article.

So well did these schools meet the need of these field-staff workers that they later were extended to include farm leaders, especially committeemen, and the other staff members of most of the bureaus of the Department and of the colleges of agriculture; and they are now also being held for teachers of vocational agriculture and the professional and business men of towns in rural areas. The schools provide an opportunity for participating in discussion groups, and thus tie in closely with the more direct demonstration and leadership-training conferences held to prepare farm people to organize and conduct discussion groups in their homes.

The Educational Needs of the Administrator

The problem of educating the voter to take an intelligent part in elections has long been recognized as paramount in a democracy. But we are now rapidly coming to see that this objective is too limited. Of perhaps even greater importance is the problem of educating the administrator, private as well as public, potential as well as actual. For democracy is to be regarded as a continuous administrative process, not merely as a succession of elections separated by 2 or 4 years.

The need for educating the administrator is especially evident in an executive organization such as the Department of Agriculture. With a staff of some 65,000 persons, many of them administrators in the States and counties, and now with a group of 40,000 farmers acting as committeemen in the counties and communities and some 125,000 others who have so acted in recent years, the Department becomes actively expressive of the democratic process through the judgment exercised by its administrative officers. The very acts of these administrators, even when they are subject to criticism, serve to educate the American farmer and the agricultural field worker in the methods of conducting a democracy. And if this form of education is regarded as costly, let us remember that it is not so costly as would be the loss of our democratic processes themselves.

But the question may be raised, If education is a short-cut form of experience, why not educate our public administrators so as to eliminate much of this costly blundering? And this raises the further question, What has been the education of our administrators? And this leads to the query, What sort of education do these administrators need?

If we ask these people themselves, What do you wish you had studied to prepare you better for the work you are doing? we get some startling answers. We know without asking that not many of the farmer-committeemen have had the privilege of a 4-year college course, in agriculture or otherwise. Not only have our agricultural colleges not graduated as many persons as that in the past 25 years,[3] but only a small part of our agricultural graduates return to the farm; and the committeemen are farmers, elected by farmers. Some of these committeemen attended a college of agriculture for 1 or 2 years, or took short courses or extension courses. But even so, most of this work, as well as their agricultural work in high school, consisted of

[3] TAEUSCH, CARL F. CAREER TRAINING FOR AGRICULTURE. A report to the Committee on Career Training for Agriculture. 13 pp. 1938. [Mimeographed.]

practical agricultural subjects, and very little attention was paid to economics or social problems. They were not taught even the elements of public administration, social and political problems, foreign affairs. And, while these matters can be learned by experience or even come naturally to some people, a certain amount of education along such lines would do no harm and might be far less costly in the long run.

Questions were also asked the 8,700 extension workers of the Department,[4] the county agents, the home demonstration workers, the specialists, the 4–H Club leaders: What did you study in college? What helped you most in your present job? What do you now wish you had studied? Practically all of these people have had a 4-year course in a college of agriculture. Over one-half of their work in college was in practical agriculture, however, with little in the fundamental sciences and even less in economics and social studies. The judgment of these persons was almost unanimous that more time should have been spent on problems of economics and social policy. Similar comments were elicited from some 1,500 of the top-salaried officials of the Washington staff of the Department.[5] It was disclosed that a considerable and increasing number of these staff members have been coming from nonagricultural colleges, a recognition of the broadening functions of the Department as well as of the need of curricular adjustments in our colleges of agriculture.

How These Needs Are Being Met

It became evident, therefore, that there was need of some way of educating the agricultural administrator for the broader task he has been called on to perform in recent years. The colleges of agriculture have been moving in this direction, but institutional changes are slow. The Extension Service has been encouraging additional professional training for its staff members in summer schools and through annual leave, but the costs are high. And so, as a supplement to these and other developments, the proposal was adopted by the Department to carry to the States some form of education that would help satisfy the need for a broader outlook on agricultural problems. The first step was to hold 4-day sessions, or schools, in such States as requested them and for such groups as could readily be assembled for the purpose. The idea was not, of course, to try to "educate" people in that short time, but rather to open the way to a broader approach to the whole situation confronting agriculture; this opening could then be followed up by institutions better equipped to pursue a continuous educational program.

Schools of philosophy have now been held in some 39 States, for extension workers, county and community committeemen, teachers of vocational agriculture, and others; additional schools have been held for the various Washington bureau staffs, for the Department field administrators of regional or type-of-farming areas, and for districts within the various States. The schools, now (July 1, 1940) numbering 70, have had an aggregate attendance of some 14,000 farm

[4] Wilson, M. C., and Crile, Lucinda. PREPARATION AND TRAINING OF EXTENSION WORKERS. U. S. Dept. Agr. Ext. Cir. 295 25 pp., mimeographed, and 19 pp., multilithed, illus. 1938.
[5] See p. 3 ff. of the reference cited in footnote 3.

leaders. Acting as staff lecturers, with 6 or 7 participating in each school, has been a total of some 200 professors of philosophy, psychology, and education; of history, economics, political science, and sociology; ministers, editors, authors, and artists; and members of the Department and State agricultural staffs. The schools are held usually for 4 days, with lectures each morning and discussion groups each afternoon. Here is typical program, on the general theme, What is a desirable national agricultural program?

First day: Backgrounds.

1. What can philosophy contribute to a better understanding of the present situation?
2. General social and economic background of the present situation.
3. Immediate backgrounds of present agricultural policies and programs.

Second day: The Place of Government in Modern Society.

1. Individualism, democracy, and social control.
2. The relation of government to social and economic affairs.
3. The problem of continuing a program of agricultural adjustment.

Third day: Regionalism, Nationalism, and Internationalism.

1. Unity and diversity in society.
2. Political and economic considerations.
3. A desirable foreign-trade policy for American agriculture.

Fourth day: Problems of Social Adjustment and Administration.

1. Psychological problems in social adjustment.
2. Democracy and group leadership, or traditional economics and our present economy.
3. Sanctions, or the means by which a social program is administered.

These schools are held only on the invitation of a State or regional unit. After the date is set, the program topics are worked out cooperatively with the person or persons who will be responsible locally for the school; a list of desired lecturers is prepared in the same manner. In a typical session of 4 days, with three lectures each morning, six or seven lecturers are invited so as to have most of them speak twice. Well-known critics and opponents of the national agricultural programs are invited to be perfectly candid in their remarks, and they usually are. Perhaps this point will bear repeating: through these schools, the Department of Agriculture is conducting a forum in which friends, opponents, critics, and those who are undecided as to the wisdom of the agricultural programs are given complete freedom to discuss the matter frankly among themselves.

Hearing various points of view expressed in the morning lectures encourages free discussion in the afternoons; an average of 80 to 85 percent of those in attendance actively participate in the discussions. The discussion often discloses misunderstandings from passive listening to the morning lectures which would never otherwise be discovered. Thus these schools bear out the educational principle that learning is a reaction to what is learned, a participation in the process itself and not mere passive receptivity.

The character of the schools differs with place and time. Special interests develop and are expressed early in most of the schools; these are taken up cumulatively and are accentuated by succeeding lecturers and discussion groups. Sometimes the interest is focused almost exclusively on foreign relations, sometimes on nutritional problems; again the problem attracting most attention may be the effect of the adjustment policy on our democracy, or the struggle between nature and man, or rainfall and the water table. Some schools have pointed toward rural arts and crafts and their instrumental value in supplementing farm income as well as enriching rural life creatively and culturally; some attending the schools have persisted in a philosophical recasting of the fundamental frameworks of our ideas; some have been attracted by history and anthropology. But all have worked toward a better understanding of the relation between the intimate local problems of the State or the county or the community and the broader national and international implications.

"I'd like to talk about malaria," said a woman from tidewater South Carolina; "that's our main problem." The topic for the day was "Regionalism, nationalism, and internationalism." But we started with malaria; from that the discussion went to screening against mosquitoes, then to tighter floors and walls; these were seen to require more cash income, and there we were, talking about the exportation of cotton. Then someone told of organizing a community swamp-drainage area, with the help of the doctors, the engineers, and the lawyers. Both tenants and landlords were present, so the tenancy problem came in for a thumping all around. And every time the little lady from tidewater South Carolina became a bit confused, we went back to malaria and started off again. But in the course of that one discussion group were developed social policies affecting foreign relations, economic principles, and local government in its broadest aspects.

Here is a woman from the Dust Bowl, just in from "pulling fence posts" but leading with aplomb a New Mexico group discussing "Have we too much government?" An Illinois group wrestles with the problem of the smug farmer and still smugger Department field worker, blind to farming problems in less fortunate areas, which soon may be their problems. Here are a Virginia group discussing the mutual dependence of county agent and home demonstration worker and a Connecticut group extending the problem to the 4-H Club leaders. A New York group, one that happened to believe in certain monetary theories, finally comes around to admitting that probably not all farm problems can be solved by manipulating gold. Here is a Utah group debating whether to accept philosophically an inexorable nature, or to "do something about it." Here a Texas group is realizing for the first time the real import of the water table and planning to "have a law on the subject." And so it goes, with emphasis on "what it's all about," and yet with a realization of the need, later and elsewhere, of getting down to the business of planning and of acting.

These schools are obviously not a one-directional affair. Criticisms and questions are raised that lead directly back to the Department: Is all this local planning work in the counties and the communities taken seriously at Washington, or is it dumped into the wastebasket? What is all this Government regulation doing to our democracy? Are the committeemen elected democratically, or are they "hand-picked" beforehand? Are the newspapers accurate in their statements; and if not, why not? Are we really up against fate in our farming problems, or can we do something about it? And just what is laissez faire as a practical social-economic principle? Should farmers lead the way in following what the economists say is the right thing to do, or should they demand privileges such as those sometimes accorded to industry, whether they are socially justifiable or not? Is the Department staff at Washington utilizing to the best advantage the State and local governments in the administration of the farm program, or is it trying to reconstruct local and State government? And is not the danger there too much centralization? What is the difference between education and propaganda? How can we best encourage boys and girls to stay on the farm?

These are the problems with which farmers and farm leaders are concerned, and which they discuss in the schools of philosophy. Note how most of them involve problems of broad social policy, which not only should be channeled back to Washington, but which also involve subject matter that should be incorporated into the curricula of high schools and colleges, so as to enable the student to learn how to study and discuss these problems before he becomes responsible for acting on them. To introduce them into the pretraining period of potential administrators would seem, in a democracy, not merely desirable but necessary. And such consideration of the broader social and philosophical problems of public policies becomes an essential part of the "in-training" education of the farm leader as well as of the active administrator, especially if he has never had such an opportunity before.

FARMER DISCUSSION GROUPS

Such considerations are not confined to the schools of philosophy for agricultural workers. Farmer discussion groups have been devel-

Figure 1.—Farmers meeting as a discussion group in the Orangeburg, S. C., courthouse.

oped in various States for many years. During the last 4 or 5 years the Department has become interested in supplementing this State activity, especially by encouraging study and discussion in the farm home, among neighbors and friends, of the broader philosophical implications of farm programs and the wider social events that affect them. State extension directors have been encouraged to appoint a State discussion-group leader, and in 37 States they have done so. These men work in cooperation with the regional experts in the Division of Program Study and Discussion of the Bureau of Agricultural Economics, organizing meetings throughout the State for periods of a week, 10 days, or 2 weeks to train discussion leaders among farm people. At these meetings a demonstration discussion group is presented to the 40 or 50 farm men and women who are interested in organizing such a group in their local community; organization technique and methods are discussed, and the demonstration group is criticized. In connection with some of the schools of philosophy, as many as 30 or 40 different people are given an opportunity to actually lead a discussion group. In the leadership conferences, hundreds of farm men and women of a State are given training during the period.

In this way, some 2 million farm people have engaged in organized discussion groups which meet at least 4 times during the winter (fig. 1).

A few sidelights exemplify what goes on in farmer discussion groups.

When asked what was thought of the increasing importation of Argentine corn, a member of an Illinois discussion group asked in return, Don't you think that shows that the price is getting about right? [6] This illustrates the quality of thinking that is going on in our farming areas, as does also the remark of a farmer-member of a South Dakota discussion group: "If the farmers of this country raise only one hog, and they can't sell that hog, they've raised one hog too much." A Colorado group listed the things they needed most—they were better doctors, better schools, more books and music, better fences, better markets, in that order. Some of these discuscussion groups have broadcast during the Farm and Home Hour—a New Jersey group discussed farmers' organizations, a Virginia group the way they are handling their woodlands, a Utah group the pending farm legislation.

Discussion of the problems of the neighborhood encourages every person to enter the conversation; but no discussion of even the simplest farm problems can continue long without getting into the profound problems of statecraft, social policy, and economic principle. And the encouragement to discuss these problems has led to their further study. For example, in a Dakota group, no one knew whether there was a tariff on farm machinery, so a member was designated to find out before the next meeting. Further study has encouraged the farmer and his wife to speak up, so as to be heard in their neighborhood where policy is being made.

In Wisconsin the farmers are beginning to invite local businessmen to join with them in rural-urban meetings; and in many States the

[6] Agricultural imports into this country have increased and decreased as the price level has gone up or down. The high prices of the late 1920's attracted large quantities of agricultural products from abroad. In 1932 such imports reached their lowest level. Since then rising price levels have attracted increasing amounts of imports, even over high tariff walls.

rural-urban women's conferences are following the lead of the Secretary's Washington conference of 1939. This conference included women representatives of every State, from urban professional, business, club, and consumer groups as well as from farm organizations, to discuss consumer-producer problems. The follow-up State meetings, of a similar kind, are now being developed still further in the counties. Similar meetings are being planned for professional and business men and farmers, in cooperation with the United States Chamber of Commerce, the Junior Chamber of Commerce, and the United States Department of Commerce.

PROBLEMS AND CRITICISMS

It is not surprising that a program of adult education sponsored by the Government should be suspected, at least in the beginning, of being propaganda. Nor should any such charge be met by mere denials or excuses. But it might be well to point out the essential element in propaganda that is liable to make it undesirable—the nearness of the so-called educational campaign to the action the propagandist has in mind. A hurriedly called election by a well-prepared party in power, with all the resources of the Government directed toward securing an immediate and favorable result, especially by presenting only one side of the case, is propaganda of the worst sort; so is a business advertising program blatantly insisting "Buy now!" To say, however, that the long-time educational methods of church or state, especially among children, is propaganda, is straining the meaning of this term, as well as placing no faith in the ability of the adolescent mind in time to throw off unsound doctrines. This same principle applies to adult education; the more time the educational process allows the citizen to reflect before he acts, the less undesirable is the educational activity, even if it should happen to have a propaganda bias. And the fact that the schools and discussion groups sponsored by the Department are not connected with any action agencies, and only indirectly even with the planning groups, results in a considerable interval of time between these educational conferences and any action which may result from them. During that interval, the critical and reflective processes of the human mind, which are especially characteristic of farm people, have ample time to become operative.

Other factors contribute toward the freedom of these schools and discussion groups. The lecturers are chosen on the basis of their professional standing regardless of the attitude they have toward the Department or the Administration. On a number of occasions the persons invited to lecture before the schools have replied to the effect that "there has been some mistake, for I am opposed to the present administration and to most of the farm program." Such persons are at once told that that is all the more reason why they should be invited to appear on the school-of-philosophy program. Lecturers are permitted to change the wordings of the topics assigned them if they wish; and they may develop their topics in any way they see fit. Discussion leaders are selected by their own groups, and the discussion groups themselves determine what topics they are to discuss. No group conclusions are formulated, no showing of hands is called for;

each individual makes up his own mind, upon the basis of the assorted intellectual fare spread before him.

One great difficulty with this method of education is that it is not pursued far enough to enable people to satisfy themselves regarding the questions they ask. To overcome this the Division has issued some half-dozen methods pamphlets, telling how to organize and conduct a discussion group, and 18 subject-matter pamphlets.

Over 2 million copies of these pamphlets have been distributed. This distribution follows the same basic principle observed in the schools of philosophy and farmer discussion groups—the request or invitation comes from the people who want the service. The discussion pamphlets are frankly controversial, presenting contrary points of view in conversational form, and they include bibliographies of other free or inexpensive pamphlets on the same subjects. But farmers everywhere complain that they cannot obtain reliable information on many problems or printed material dealing with these problems in the broad and comprehensive way of the lectures of the schools. Following the schools or a particularly active discussion-group training period, we learn of increased demands on local libraries or increased buying of books. But there still remains much to be done to integrate this work with the activities of the public schools and libraries. For, after all, the test of this educational work is not the immediate enthusiasms of those who come in contact with it but rather their ability to continue the study of farm problems on their own initiative, the making up of their own minds on questions of public policy, and the leavening influence they exert in their own communities for further study and discussion.

The statement is frequently made regarding the study and discussion program that it never gets beyond the talking stage. What does it all lead to? and What action does it imply? are questions often asked. The very fact that the schools and discussion groups are not pointed more definitely toward the action or planning programs of the Department is frequently used as a basis for condemning these educational methods as pointless. But between this criticism and the opposite danger of engaging in propaganda, the former is preferable. More profound thinking among farm people is being encouraged, regardless of what they may finally decide; greater confidence in their own judgments, so that they will express themselves fearlessly; and a feeling that they are a part of government and society and should take a hand in controlling them.

SOCIAL IMPLICATIONS

Walter Bagehot, in his Physics and Politics,[7] pointed out the importance of discussion in democratic government. Beginning with the ancient Greeks, Western Europe has been developing this instrument of social control for over 2,000 years. Discussion is a quick and harmless way of considering many social policies the actual trying out of which would be not only expensive but perhaps even disastrous. Those beginnings in the Athenian Assembly culminated in the parliamentary form of government, which we have inherited from Eng-

[7] BAGEHOT, WALTER. PHYSICS AND POLITICS. 224 pp. London. 1872.

land. To maintain the spirit of this great democratic institution, not only in the Halls of Congress and our State legislatures but in local community meetings as well, increasingly devolves on us in the United States of America—especially now that elsewhere the enemies of democracy are in the saddle and riding fast and furiously.

Should care be taken as to what information is presented to adults in a democratic system of education? Obviously not, in general; for, in a democracy, a fundamental assumption is that the adult human being is capable of formulating his own judgments, including the selection of the facts and opinions he will believe and the rejection of those he considers untrustworthy. To deny this fundamental assumption is to lose faith in democracy; and to nibble at this assumption piecemeal by qualifying acts is to be inconsistent if not hypocritical. And the principle of the unrestricted distribution of information to adult persons applies with especial force to the governmental undertakings of a democracy in the field of education. Private educational institutions may be restricted by religious, economic, or other social principles of a unique type, which may even be contrary to democracy; and these institutions frequently do have such principles, whether they are announced or admitted or not. But the individual can choose whether or not he cares to enter such an institution or remain there; he has no such choice as regards government-sponsored education of any kind. The government, therefore, if it is a democracy, cannot limit the field of information in any such way as can private institutions. The only exceptions to this sweeping statement are, of course, the provisions of the Constitution as interpreted by the courts, and the laws of Congress—although the determination of both of these agencies as regards educational content or methods may be questioned in the courts by the individual citizen.

Potentialities of Adult Education

Inasmuch as education in this country has been regarded traditionally as a function of the States, of smaller political units, or of private, including religious, institutions, the Federal Government has had little to do with formal education below the adult level. Until recently the field of adult education has been little developed by any agency except the Extension Service. We have unfortunately assumed that education was not an adult problem; that it ended with a college or high-school or even grade-school commencement. But we have come to see in recent years the vast social and individual potentialities of adult education; and, prior to that, every agency which disseminated information of any sort assumed, consciously or unconsciously, that adults could be educated. This has been especially true of business advertising activities; but it has also been increasingly true of any organization, public or private, which has been interested in developing public opinion. Religious, business, professional, or other groups, whether engaged in gaining good will, securing new members, selling goods and services, or affecting public policy, have become more and more involved in adult education.

In many cases this process has consisted almost exclusively in the dissemination of information, inferential and opinionated as well as factual. Two unfortunate features have characterized it. One has been that it has been limited and biased, even when parading as scientific knowledge or unprejudiced advice. Each agency declares its goods or services to be the best, or advances only such facts as would lead to such a conclusion. This is defensible as long as every agency is free to do the same thing; it ceases to be socially defensible when disparaging or untruthful statements are made or implied about others without any chance for the others to have an equal hearing. It is a fundamental postulate of democracy that people generally can exercise good judgment, and hence that the dissemination of conflicting ideas should be permitted in spite of the risk of confusion.

The second characteristic of the dissemination of information is one of educational method, and this is more clearly subject to criticism. It consists in the very fact that information is disseminated—given out without any chance for the listener to respond in a give-and-take fashion. True, he may join the organization or not, he may walk out of the hall or turn off the radio, he may or may not "buy now," he may reserve his own opinions. But education requires more than this. It requires a response from the pupil that will register itself on the "educator" and perhaps modify the latter's thoughts and behavior, thereby resulting in a new reaction, which will still further stimulate pupil reactions, and so on, indefinitely.

The problem of education in this sense involves not only the reader of newspapers, books, and magazines or the listener to sermons, lectures, or broadcasts; it involves the active disseminator as well. Not only is there something essentially unfair about educators or lecturers who do not give their audience a chance to strike back, but such a one-directional system of education limits the capacity of the disseminator as well.

THE FEDERAL GOVERNMENT AND EDUCATION

Need the Federal Government concern itself at all with education, adult or otherwise? Obviously, a democracy cannot engage in propaganda without contradicting itself. But if a democracy rests in the last analysis on "confidence in the judgment of the common man," as Thomas Mann expressed it, then democracies need to be interested not only in implementing that judgment by holding elections, but also in encouraging and developing the free discussion of public policy. For the development of sound public policies in a democracy requires a groundwork of sound individual judgments, and these have to be developed as much as does the information that constitutes their materials. Furthermore, the relative stability of our democracy, nationally as well as locally conceived, depends in part on allowing all minority or opposition views to be aired, so that policies may be formulated with those views in mind. Such safety valves eliminate the explosive menace of revolutions, to which all dictatorships are constantly subject. Nor are sound public policies exhausted in the formulation of legislative programs; the citizen in a democracy not only needs to learn how to vote intelligently for his legislative representatives and in the initiative and referendum, but he also needs to learn how to participate intelligently in the administrative activities of his government. Frequently the real test of legislation lies in the administration of it.

This situation is especially important in the case of the Department of Agriculture. The administration of the national agricultural program is becoming increasingly decentralized and is more and more dependent on the county and community farmer committeemen, who, in a pragmatic sense, are the Department of Agriculture. These farmers, some 40,000 elected by farmers in local units, act as leaders in the development of community and county planning, which becomes incorporated in State, regional, and national plans and legislation; they administer the national farm legislation in their local units; and they act as judicial boards of review in all cases needing individual adjustment. The 165,000 or more farmers who are now acting or have acted as committeemen have established an enviable record of good sense in these activities—a record that strengthens one's confidence in democracy. But to assume that such involved administrative work can be carried on indefinitely by relying solely on the native sense of these committeemen runs counter not only to the best judgment of those who realize the complexities of the problems, but also to the expressed opinion of these farmers themselves. And, until other methods of education are devised, the most economical methods now available for encouraging farm leaders to study and discuss the broader problems of farm policy include the schools of philosophy and the supplementary discussion groups for farm men and women.

From this review of the broader educational policies of a democracy, certain points emerge as principles to be observed by any Federal agency sponsoring an educational program.

(1) There should be a wide and increasing dissemination of factual information. The Federal Government has long been engaged in this activity, and its reputation for reliability has been high, even though—or perhaps because—it has been constantly subjected to sharp criticism.

(2) Factual information is necessary to, but an inadequate substitute for, education—especially such educational activities as are concerned with the development of discrimination and judgment concerning public policies or social values or the facts themselves. Therefore, in the interest of developing sound public policy, the Federal Government is concerned with the encouragement and development, in a social medium, of individual opinions and judgments.

(3) Any program of education that aims to implement these objectives must include the opportunity for all sides to be heard and discussed. Just as the medical profession encourages public health programs, though they may seem to be against the interests of doctors engaged in private practice, so must a democratic government go out of its way to enable the critic of its current policies to be heard; paradoxically, only so can a real democracy be perpetuated, for only so can it discover mistakes that might be disastrous.

(4) Finally, any program of adult education aimed at the study and discussion of public policies must provide means of implementing the judgments formulated, not only sporadically, at the ballot box, but continuously, by channeling these judgments to the central authorities and thereby improving the administrative activities at Washington and in the field—a day-by-day task.

In this sense, education becomes not merely an activity for children, but for adults as well. It becomes not only a matter of "book l'arnin"—of academic subjects—but of the very life activities of the people. And it thereby is not confined merely to content or subject matter, memory and rote, but becomes instrumental to the daily task, to the solving of community as well as national problems, and to the formulation of sound judgments on matters of public policy. Any educational objective short of this would develop an inadequate conception of democracy.

Old and New in Agricultural Organization

by MILTON S. EISENHOWER and ROY I. KIMMEL [1]

WHATEVER else may be said about the decade since the depression of 1929, probably no other period in our history has seen such intensive thinking and such widespread experimentation in agriculture. New approaches to agricultural problems and new patterns of activity have taken shape under the pressure of inescapable need and popular demand. Some of these approaches and patterns will probably have a permanent effect on our attitudes and institutions; others will pass and be forgotten. In any case, they have forced major changes in agricultural organization, from local committees of farmers, through the counties and the States, to the Department of Agriculture, which is responsible for carrying out national policies. Here is the story of that reorganization—why it was necessary, how it was done, and what it was intended to accomplish.

ONE of the great problems in a large public agency that seeks to help meet the needs of a vast number of citizens, as does the Department of Agriculture, is the coordination of its activities. The more varied its services, the more complex its tasks, especially when these tasks lie in the social and economic fields, the more difficult this problem becomes.

Coordination must reach into all aspects of the work of the Depart-

[1] Milton S. Eisenhower is Land Use Coordinator of the Department of Agriculture, and Roy I. Kimmel is Chief Program Analyst, Bureau of Agricultural Economics.

223761°—40——72

ment of Agriculture. Without good coordination, research workers may fail to develop the facts most urgently needed, or administrators, unaware of the results of research, may find themselves trying to carry out programs at cross purposes with research findings. Or the general public may discover that one bureau recommends one thing and another recommends something quite different. Within a single area, the objectives of State and Federal agricultural agencies may vary widely. The net results of such conditions, were they permitted to continue, would be confusion, waste, and loss of public confidence.

In the Department of Agriculture, the problem of coordination really consists of four problems, each of them extremely important. There is first the problem of getting all the agencies within the Department to work toward common ends. Next there is the problem of getting the work of the Department coordinated with that of other Federal agencies, especially with other agencies that also deal with things affecting farmers—land use, for example. Then there is the problem of coordinating the Department's efforts with those of the 48 States and the Territories. Finally, there is the problem of coordinating Department work with the thinking, the attitudes, the ideas, and the ideals of farmers in local communities.

This last should perhaps be put first. It is in essence the problem of democracy. How can a great national public agency work with people in thousands of local communities, carrying out their desires, yet also helping them to formulate those desires by giving them information they could not themselves collect—information patiently gathered by hundreds of trained research workers in a score of different branches of science? Or how can national agricultural programs be carried out so as to achieve such broad objectives as stability of farm income, conservation of resources, and security of tenure, and at the same time be adapted to the widely varying conditions of every locality?

For the sake of greater simplicity the whole problem may also be looked at from another standpoint. In any deliberate human activity, individual or social, there are, or should be, five steps:

Get the facts.
Formulate a plan, based on the facts.
Try out the plan.
Refashion it to suit the facts better.
Carry out the revised plan.

In modern large-scale group activity, public or private—including industry, agriculture, finance, and everything else—these five steps are involved in research, planning, and administration. The over-all problem is to coordinate these three and to see to it that each one is genuinely related to the others.

Because this problem is crucial today, the Department of Agriculture has recently undergone a rather thoroughgoing reorganization, designed to bring about far better coordination and thereby to make the Department a more efficient public servant and also one more quickly and completely responsive to local needs. The purpose of this article is to describe this reorganization briefly and give something of its background. The reorganization is not to be regarded as finally settling any problems, even those it was specifically designed to meet. The Department is a dynamic organization responding to the needs of a dynamic society, of which it is a part. As that society changes and new problems arise, the Department will change again—and yet again. Experience with present methods also may indicate from time to time the need for changes in these methods. The best that can be hoped for is that the present steps are good steps for the present situation.

RESEARCH AND INFORMATION CAME FIRST

Agriculture in all its branches has been subjected to as searching analysis as any occupation of man. The Department of Agriculture began its first research projects the moment it was created, 78 years ago. Since then few agricultural problems have escaped the prying curiosity of the investigators.

For a long time nearly all of this work was in the field of natural science and was confined to the farm practices that depend directly on natural science. Agricultural workers were concerned with a world-wide search for crop plants adaptable to the United States, improved fertilizer and tillage practices, better feeding of animals, methods of combating destructive insects and diseases, the breeding of better plants and animals, better methods of preserving and storing foods for human beings and feed for animals, the discovery of facts about weather and climate, and thousands of detailed problems related to such main lines of activity as these.

Gradually, under the pressure of changing farm needs, the Department added economic research, grading and standardization of agricultural products, market reporting, and crop estimating to its work in the natural sciences.

In the course of a few decades it became a great research organization. It attracted many able workers, some of whom made notable discoveries. It achieved an international reputation. Its work was divided, for convenience, among various bureaus, which tended to operate independently of each other, largely because there was little need for closer integration of their activities. The Department was, in fact, a rather loose federation of bureaus.

The land-grant colleges and universities were created by Congress in the same year as the Department, 1862. In 1884, they too began carrying on agricultural research with Federal aid. Thirty years later, in 1914, the Extension Service, with its Nation-wide system of county agents bringing information to farmers, was set up, to be operated by the State colleges with assistance from the Federal Government.

Thus there were two complementary systems of agricultural research and education. One was Federal and had its eyes mainly on national needs. One was State, with its eyes mainly on local needs. It would be a mistake to think that there was no coordination in all this work, however. There was probably as much coordination as was necessary for the times and under the circumstances. The Department, for instance, set up an Office of Experiment Stations and later an office of Director of Research when the need arose to bring about greater coordination of research activities. The Department and the State experiment stations cooperated in planning and carrying on research projects. And the Department and the State colleges had a common link in the Federal and State extension services, which brought the results of both Federal and State investigations to bear on the problems of farmers in all localities.

If coordination was not lacking, neither were "action programs." They too fitted the needs of the times. The campaigns to wipe out the cattle tick, foot-and-mouth disease, and bovine tuberculosis; the quarantine regulations to keep out harmful insects; the meat-inspection service to prevent the marketing of bad meat in interstate commerce; the efforts to protect and develop forest and wildlife resources—these were action programs on a wide scale and of the most direct kind. On the whole, however, the action was largely in the form of programs of information, education, advice. The educational services of the Department and the States published and disseminated great quantities of useful material. The various bureaus answered an endless stream of inquiries from farmers. The State extension services conducted demonstrations and came into direct contact with groups of individuals everywhere.

It may be assumed that this set-up was reasonably adequate for the needs of our agriculture. Probably most farmers were directly or indirectly affected by the work of the Department or the State agricultural agencies. They used varieties of plants, fertilizer practices, tillage or drainage practices, methods of fighting pests, and information about the market which had been developed by the professional workers. The individual may not have been aware of the extent to which he used these public services, but he made use of them just the same.

Until the end of the World War, agriculture felt that it needed little else in the way of public services. The one big job that farmers could not do for themselves was to carry on certain kinds of research and gather certain kinds of information. If there had been a widespread need for other services, it would have been expressed in widespread pressure for them. Public services in general grow out of definite public demand.

After the World War, early in the 1920's, the pressure for other services did begin. It increased throughout that decade, for farmers were having hard times. Not that most farmers ever had very easy times; but this was different. Something drastic had happened to the farm market and farm income, and there was a growing clamor to have something done about it. Gradually this focused in a demand that something be done about the surplus products which were ruining prices.

During the boom period of the 1920's, however, there was a tendency for almost everyone else to look at this new rural demand as being unjustified, since almost everyone else was doing quite nicely and feeling very optimistic. But after the 1929 collapse, when drastic steps had to be taken to protect the whole national economy, the farmers' demands were more generally understood.

NEW FIELDS OF ACTION

During the next few years Congress authorized new kinds of "action" programs. It passed a score of laws designed to bring about specific economic, physical, and social adjustments in agriculture. The administration of these laws was turned over to the Department of Agriculture.

Anyone who was in the Nation's agricultural headquarters in Washington during the period of acute crisis will never forget the experience. New agencies—the first of which was the Agricultural Adjustment Administration, designed initially to bolster farm prices—were set up practically overnight. Thousands of new people had to be added to the pay roll. Old hands suddenly found themselves in new jobs with new duties. New employees and old alike soon found themselves digging into an extraordinary array of facts and problems about such things as the meaning of the closed frontier, the implications of our new status as a creditor nation, world trade and international trade barriers, falling prices, soil waste, droughts, floods, rural poverty, and the decreasing equities of farmers in their farms.

Men worked feverishly, far into the night, 7 days a week. Unavoidably, there was some confusion. But the main thing was to get the new programs started, reduce the chief surpluses, get some immediate financial help out to the farmers, and make a start in checking erosion and dealing with rural poverty.

It is no confession to say that all this was new to the Department of Agriculture. An agricultural era, one that it understood, had ended. A new one had begun. The old-line traditional Department had somewhat the same sensation of surprise that Jonah must have felt when he found himself suddenly swallowed by the whale and realized that life would never be the same again.

The causes back of this situation, particularly the maladjustments from which agriculture suffered, are discussed in other articles in this volume. There is no need to repeat the discussion here. The point is that new agencies necessarily arose out of new functions of the Department. Some of the agencies were created in a hurry, because they had to be; there was an emergency to be met. All of them worked in a hurry—everybody did in those days. Actually, there was little that was radically new about the ideas back of some of these agencies. As Chester C. Davis points out in a historical survey elsewhere in this book, some of these ideas had been in the air, in one form or another, for years. But putting them into practice was new.

Something else was new, too—the character of many of the principal activities of the Department. The new agencies were not engaged in the traditional types of research and information; they were carrying out new types of action programs. Congress had said in effect: Reach all the farmers you can; help them to control these surpluses of the major farm products; give them greater bargaining power in marketing their products; increase their income so it will be more nearly what it used to be when agriculture was decently prosperous.

To undertake this initial job, the Department had to get out in the highways and byways in a way it had never done before. Under the original Agricultural Adjustment Administration programs, for example, it had to make formal two-way contracts with millions of individual farmers. Such things cannot be done without considerable administrative machinery, local and national.

While the first problem tackled was the immediate price and income emergency, it was not long before the new services of the Department went beyond this. Our modern agricultural economy is not a simple affair. It is a complex machine. When it breaks down, it cannot be fixed merely by tightening up a few bolts and nuts. Weaknesses rapidly showed up during the very process of meeting the immediate emergency. Yet the weaknesses themselves were not new. Some of them had long been known to farmers, to agricultural leaders, to legislators, and to civil service workers who spend their lives dealing with farm problems. Now those weaknesses began to show up glaringly because of a combination of circumstances.

So in addition to the original agricultural adjustment program, Congress was soon inaugurating programs for rural rehabilitation to help people who were down through no fault of their own to get back on their feet; for controlling soil erosion and helping farmers make physical adjustments in the use of land; for the purchase of farms by tenants, as one means of arresting the growth of farm tenancy and restoring some of the broken rungs of the old agricultural ladder which used to lead to ownership; for treating land in the upper reaches of watersheds for flood control; for developing water facilities in the drier parts of the West so that farmers there might use their land resources to better advantage; for encouraging farm forestry; for bringing back into public ownership land unsuited for agriculture and developing it for other uses; for enlarging the public forest holdings and increasing the number of wildlife sanctuaries; for regulating the use of the public domain; and for achieving other adjustments through such means as marketing agreements and crop insurance.

STRESSES AND CONFUSIONS

These vigorous young programs sometimes stepped on one another's toes. This was especially awkward when it occurred on the same farm. The situation was worst in the Great Plains. Here something like this might occur:

Under the early Agricultural Adjustment Administration program, a farmer would have to take some of his land out of wheat in order to qualify for a benefit payment. But under the early Resettlement Administration program, he might have to put land into wheat to qualify for a rehabilitation loan. But whether he took the land out of wheat or left it in wheat it might blow away; therefore the Soil Conservation Service might advise him to restore the land to grass. The Bureau of Plant Industry and the State experiment station might be telling him not to plant wheat that year, because recent research showed that the crop would be a failure unless there was a certain amount of moisture in the soil at seeding time. Yet he could borrow the money for seed and, by attempting to grow some wheat, could qualify for a benefit payment on reduced acreage.

It is not hard to imagine the farmer's confused state of mind after listening to these various agencies. He would probably do whatever seemed best at the moment, regardless of the long-time capabilities of the land and the consequences of misuse.

This was one type of difficulty. It arose out of (1) the initial need of each agency to drive hard and fast for the single objective assigned to it; (2) lack of time to collect all the facts bearing on a given local situation; (3) lack of means for churning even the known facts into a consistent general plan; (4) lack of means for coordinating the objectives of all agencies and presenting them as a unified proposal to the farmer. The example here given is an extreme one; in fact, it is imaginary. But in many actual cases a farmer had to deal with two or more agencies whose programs, while consistent nationally, were not equally adapted to his particular situation. Nationally consistent programs were sometimes locally contradictory.

Another type of difficulty developed at the same time. As a result of long experience, the Federal Department and the State agricultural colleges and universities were working reasonably well together. The tasks in which they cooperated had been largely noncontroversial; the occasional differences that had arisen were over minor jurisdictional matters. Now, new and powerful Federal agencies were barging into almost every local community, administering action programs that strongly affected local affairs and dealt with things which were far from being noncontroversial. It was not surprising that some State officials did not always agree with the concepts or purposes of the programs. Some felt that the Federal workers were encroaching on the traditional functions of the State workers, were not acquainted with local conditions, and could not adapt national programs to specific local needs. Some State workers could perhaps see themselves gradually falling into what Grover Cleveland once called a condition of innocuous desuetude. The Federal agencies, meanwhile, were under a congressional mandate to attain certain objectives. They felt their responsibility keenly. They did not believe they could or should divest themselves of the responsibility the Congress had assigned. They knew that many of the problems were national in scope and could not be dealt with piecemeal on a purely local or State basis. Stresses and strains developed out of this situation, which was in fact a phase of the old, typically American problem of Federal versus State jurisdiction.

A third kind of difficulty was related to both of these. Although local committees of farmers played a part in the agricultural adjustment program from the beginning—some 165,000 farmers have been included in these committees to date—nevertheless, local needs and local sentiment were not always fully understood or taken into account when action was urgent. As a result, two things happened—farmers sometimes became resentful of the "bureaucrats" from Washington with their ready-made plans; and the "bureaucrats" soon came to realize some of the limitations of their own knowledge. Actually, many of these "bureaucrats" were old civil servants, students of agricultural problems for years, now catapulted into a new kind of responsibility, which they had to meet. These men knew how little they knew about many aspects of the intricate agricultural puzzle in this country, where the range of conditions is so great and the local variations are so numerous.

The picture here given deliberately emphasizes difficulties. They were great enough, but they do not by any means tell the whole story. Despite all handicaps and shortcomings, millions of farmers and thousands of local, State, and Federal workers have cooperated with increased force and effectiveness in one of the most intensive drives for fundamental readjustments that any civilization has witnessed. The wide rural and urban acceptance of the main elements of the farm programs seems to indicate that on the whole they have been considered reasonably sound in conception and reasonably successful in execution. Moreover, those who administer them are themselves products of the political and economic system that prevails in this country. When they are driven too far in one direction by the pressure of circumstances, their own inner convictions and their democratic conditioning, as well as public protests, tend to pull them back again. The willingness to recognize mistakes has more significance than the fact that mistakes are made. Indeed, if any human endeavor, even systematic research, were suddenly magnified to the proportion of the action programs in agriculture, mistakes would probably be made that would match those made in this new effort for adjustment.

OUT OF THE WILDERNESS

Planning in its broad social sense seems to have become a necessity in the modern world dominated by science and machinery. Probably there is not a nation on earth that has not yielded to the necessity in one way or another. Some people have an emotional reaction of antagonism to the very word "planning." They associate it with the completely planned societies represented by the dictatorships. But planning does not necessarily imply either dictatorship or completeness. In fact, it may in the long run succeed better in a democracy than in any other type of political system. By shutting off democratic criticism, dictators fail to discover fatal errors in their plans which might be quite clear to the opposition and which quickly come to light under a democratic system that permits opposing parties to function.

How far should planning go in a democracy? That is what the people of the United States are engaged in trying to discover. They believe that it need not and must not regiment their lives and thoughts. They believe that it can have a democratic base. They are engaged in a long-time experiment to test the truth of these ideas. The experiment, of course, is bound to have many ups and downs.

This seems to be a fair interpretation of the developments of the past few years in agriculture. The question, Is broad social planning necessary to correct and prevent certain profound maladjustments in agriculture? has certainly been decided in the affirmative by the American public. What is yet to be decided is how much territory the planning should take in, and how it can best be done democratically. In the very nature of democracy, these decisions cannot be made offhand by some central authority. They can only be made piecemeal, in the experimental spirit, by the mass of our citizens.

Efforts to solve the difficulties already described in the field of agriculture are part of this experimental process.

The first step toward solving some of these difficulties through better coordination was the appointment in 1935 of a Land Policy Committee, which brought together key officials of various Federal agencies in an effort to harmonize their operating policies. Later, a Coordinating Committee, headed by the Under Secretary of Agriculture, was established within the Department to tackle the job of administrative coordination. The executive officer of this group was given a small staff to work continuously on the whole problem. Then, in the spring of 1937, there was appointed a Coordinator for the southern Great Plains, where the critical and varied nature of the agricultural problems led to exceptional confusion as well as suffering. (Later a Coordinator was appointed for the northern Great Plains.) The initial functions of the first Coordinator were very general—he was simply to do all he could, in collaboration with a newly established southern Great Plains committee, to straighten out contradictions in the programs in the region. This has been done with a fair degree of success. So far as administration is concerned, the programs in the area are now unified, and the individual farmer no longer has to choose between contradictory proposals; he now cooperates in a single agricultural program for his farm, not a set of separate programs.

The experiment in the southern Great Plains was only a single step, of course. The next step, taken in July 1937, was a much broader one. It consisted in the setting up of an Office of Land Use Coordination in Washington. It is obvious that many of the problems of farmers can be expressed in terms of land use and that land use is one of the common denominators of the Federal and State programs for farm readjustment. For example, the Agricultural Adjustment Administration program for income stability and conservation calls for individual farm changes in land use, such as specific shifts from soil-depleting to soil-conserving crops; the heart of the rehabilitation program is the farm- and home-management plan on which loans are based; the erosion-control and flood-control programs are essentially land use programs based upon the physical and economic requirements of the land and the people who use the land. Therefore, if consistency could be attained in the land use phases of all public agricultural effort, a major step would have been taken in total program coordination.

The Office of Land Use Coordination brought together for the first time all the agencies of the Department dealing with land use problems. These agencies cooperatively determined upon a definite Nation-wide program for systematic coordination, with a view to achieving agreement on needs, aims, methods, and results. This systematic effort included these steps:

(1) All basic fact-finding work essential to the action program, such as soil, conservation, and land use surveys, would be coordinated by the appropriate agencies so as to avoid duplication and, more important, achieve agreement upon the relevant facts.

(2) Both general planning, involving farmer-cooperation, and detailed planning by experts would be coordinated by the agencies so as to get agreements on general and specific objectives.

(3) Current policies and programs would be scrutinized regularly so as to iron out conflicts.

(4) Shortcomings in organization, which hampered unification of programs, would be studied, and appropriate changes would be instituted, such as a gradual shift to common regional headquarters to encourage regional coordination.

(5) Uniform methods and policies in decentralization and in working with State and local agencies would be developed.

(6) All existing and proposed legislation would be carefully studied so that the Secretary could advise Congress of any inconsistencies in basic policy.

(7) The work of the Department of Agriculture would be coordinated with that of other Federal agencies and, especially, the Department would participate actively in the work of the National Resources Planning Board.

The Land Use Coordinator became a liaison officer to deal with other departments of the Government concerned with land use—for example, the Department of the Interior, which manages the public domain, administers the Taylor Grazing Act, and now includes the Bureau of Biological Survey; the Corps of Engineers of the Army, which improves rivers and harbors, an activity that should dovetail with the work of the Department of Agriculture in retarding waterflow and in preventing soil erosion in the watersheds above the rivers; and the National Resources Planning Board, whose committees deal in a broad way with the Nation's land and water resources. The need for agreement on facts, aims, and methods among these agencies was both obvious and urgent.

While these steps toward coordination within and among Federal agencies were being taken, considerable progress was made toward decentralizing some of the major land use activities of the Department of Agriculture. This was a response to the feeling that local communities were having plans and programs thrust upon them rather than initiating and carrying out what they themselves wanted to do. The Agricultural Adjustment Administration had depended from the first on farmer committees for local administration. In 1935 separate farmer committees made a beginning in helping plan the Agricultural Adjustment Administration program. Gradually these committees began studying erosion, tenancy, tax delinquency, and other problems, and they often expressed their convictions to the Department on these problems. In 1937 began the formation of soil conservation districts, operating under State laws and State and local auspices. Under these laws, the planning and action required to solve major conservation problems in many areas are squarely up to the local farmers. They can act or not act as they see fit, and they can work out programs adjusted to their local needs. Federal and State agencies serve in an advisory capacity and are on call to furnish all the technical information they have available. They can also provide some other assistance, such as lending equipment.

In the meantime, for a period of about 3 years committees of the Department and the land-grant colleges were meeting and trying to iron out their conflicts and difficulties. The Department Committee, headed by the Under Secretary, worked constantly with the States Committee for a solution to what had come to be called the Federal-States relations problem. Finally, representatives of both groups retired to the wilderness to wrestle with the problem, as the old-time prophets used to do when they were especially in need of wisdom. There is a remote, unused Weather Bureau station called Mount Weather, in Virginia, and here in July 1938 the groups gathered for a powwow. After 2 days of intensive discussion they emerged from the wilderness with a far-reaching agreement.

The gist of this agreement was simple. It declared that the traditional Federal-States relationships in research and extension were satisfactory and should continue. But it recognized that the action programs for agriculture, if they were to be correlated and localized effectively, required a new kind of function that should parallel the functions of research and education. This new function was planning, a kind of planning that pools the experience and judgment of farmers, specialists, and administrators. It was agreed that planning, with first emphasis on land use planning, was to begin in local communities with local committees. Local plans were then to be coordinated for an entire county by a county committee. County plans were to be coordinated for an entire State by a State committee, of which the State agricultural extension director was to be chairman. State programs were to be integrated for the entire United States by the Department of Agriculture. Community committees were to be made up wholly of farm men and women. County committees, however, were not only to be composed of farmer members but also were to include the county representatives of State and Federal land use programs; the county agent in each county would usually be the executive officer. State committees also were to have farmer members, but the Federal and State personnel would be increased at the State level.

Not all community plans, of course, would need to be considered by the county, nor all county plans by the State, nor all State plans by the Federal Government. Many phases of county plans, for example, could be carried out by farmers, or by the county commissioners, or by a local soil conservation district, or by a State agreement. There was much latitude for decentralized action in the Federal programs.

As a result of the Mount Weather agreement, committees are now at work in a large number of communities and counties, classifying land and developing plans to meet their own needs. A unified program, based on detailed study, was begun in 1940 in at least one county in each State. Forty-five States have appointed State land use planning committees.

It is, of course, much too early to say how this procedure will work out; but its establishment would seem to be one of the momentous events in the history of agriculture in the United States—probably far more important than any single agricultural program. Undoubtedly there will be snags and difficulties. But if the procedure works reasonably well, it should accomplish several things. It should result in integrated planning that begins at the bottom, following policies set forth by Congress and State legislatures. It should bring about more widespread agreement on the facts, on objectives and plans formulated in the light of the facts, and eventually on closely coordinated action that seeks to carry out the plans. It should go far to justify faith in the efficacy of democratic methods in dealing with great national problems.

THE REORGANIZATION OF THE DEPARTMENT

Local citizens have the fundamental responsibility in coordinated planning, since it begins with them. But the Department of Agriculture has a large responsibility too. In order to discharge its responsibilities effectively the Department had to be reorganized. This was done in October 1938.

A principal change made in the 1938 reorganization was to establish an agency in the Department which would keep in touch with all these local, county, and State committees, understand their difficulties and what they were trying to do, and act as a central clearinghouse where ideas and plans could be received, sorted out, reconciled with each other, and finally put together to make a sensible and practical whole.

The Bureau of Agricultural Economics became this central agency. It dropped certain functions, such as those connected with marketing, and was expanded enough to include trained personnel representing almost every major aspect of modern agriculture. If such an agency is to function effectively, it should at all times have the whole picture. It should know this country thoroughly. It should understand the problems of all classes and all interests in agriculture. It should have a grasp of all kinds of problems—soil conservation, land use, credit, marketing, and all the rest. It should know what information the natural and social sciences can furnish to help solve these problems. It should understand the relationships between agriculture and the rest of our economy. Finally, it should know how to find out what the opinions and desires of farmers really are; for its activities and policies should reflect a profound faith in democratic methods as the ultimate basis of agricultural planning.

More is involved here than planning and integrating plans. These functions cannot be carried out without constant, alert, aggressive research to discover facts, to bring the problems of agriculture out into the light of day, and to express them in terms everyone can understand.

This is a counsel of perfection. The reorganized Bureau of Agricultural Economics is engaged in discovering how far it can live up to this counsel. Among its duties is that of working with all other agencies of the Department. They feed it information and help carry on the planning service for all branches.

Other changes in the Department were also made in the 1938 reorganization. For example, the operations of the Agricultural Adjustment Administration were simplified. Programs involving physical land use adjustments on privately owned lands were placed under one management, in the Soil Conservation Service. Marketing activities were closely grouped, and a Director of Marketing was appointed to bring about coordination in that field. Some of the work of the older bureaus was rearranged to make a more logical distribution of functions; notably, all soils research was consolidated in the Bureau of Plant Industry. An Agricultural Program Board, made up of the heads of action agencies, the planning agencies, and several of the Directors, with the Land Use Coordinator as chairman, was set up as part of the Office of the Secretary of Agriculture to pass finally on all completed programs before they are put into effect.

This, then, is the arrangement that has grown out of the critical experiences and the pressing needs of the past few years, and also out of the multiplicity of the Department's functions and the great scope of the problems with which it now has to deal.

Much remains to be done in achieving coordination. For instance, the older bureaus carry on a mass of research in the natural sciences that is vital to agriculture. Some parts of this work can contribute more fully to current programs. At the same time, these programs themselves may need to be changed more than once under the impact of discoveries in the natural sciences. It will require wisdom to correlate this research as much as possible with immediate needs and at the same time to retain for research workers the freedom they require as scientists. Again, there is the whole field of the relationships of agricultural policies to policies affecting industry, finance, labor, foreign affairs. The work of the Office of Land Use Coordination in cooperating with other departments of the Government is only a foretaste of what will occur as this field is developed. Developed it must be if democracy is to meet the challenge presented by the current trend of world affairs.

Cooperative Land Use Planning—A New Development in Democracy

by Ellery A. Foster and Harold A. Vogel[1]

A MOVEMENT in democracy about which most people know very little is under way in the rural areas throughout the United States. It goes under the name of "county land use planning," but it is already becoming much more than this name implies—first, because it extends down to all the small local communities in the county; second, because it is not confined to land use but takes in educational conditions, medical care, and a host of other things that are important in each community. The movement is only in its early stages at present, but it goes back to democratic traditions deeply rooted in our early history. It is an effort, in fact, to vitalize these traditions in terms of modern life. Many people believe that it may turn out in the long run to be the most important agricultural development of the past few years—more important than any specific program. Here is the story in brief.

DEMOCRATIC PLANNING TO MEET NEW NEEDS

IN THE difficult years since 1918, the farmers of the United States have concluded that the democratic way of attacking their common

[1] Ellery A. Foster is Senior Agricultural Economist and Harold A. Vogel is Principal Agricultural Economist, Division of State and Local Planning, Bureau of Agricultural Economics.

problems was by common action, and that the Federal Government was one agency through which such cooperative action could be accomplished. But prerequisite to action are plans. State legislatures made some of the first such plans and passed them as laws. Among them were mortgage moratoria, which took the place of the shotguns peace-loving farmers in some sections had begun using to prevent foreclosures. In the national sphere, the Congress authorized broad new programs for agriculture and made Federal agencies directly responsible for their administration.

Early in the administration of these new programs, the agencies in charge recognized that farmers should take part in planning how the programs should be carried out in each community. Consultation with the farmers was necessary to determine the facts of each local situation and to obtain agreement on the adjustments needed and the local program for carrying them out.

Some of the agencies encouraged the organization of farmer committees to plan with the program administrators. Good results followed this move. For example, when local people objected because a certain forest purchase program involved planting some cleared land to trees, the local administrator went to the township board. He said, "If you agree that some of the lands in the township ought to be developed for forestry, will you make a plan for doing it? Will you take a map and color in the lands you believe should be in forest? You can use another color to show the lands you think should be used for farming, and if there are lands you are in doubt about, show them in a third color." The administrator then supplied the board with a map showing the roads and the existing settlement of the township.

The township supervisors were farmers who knew the lands in their town that were good for farming and those where farming had been tried and had failed. They made the plan. They even marked on the map some farms that were in isolated, cut-over areas and suggested that the farmers there ought to move to the more settled parts of the country. One of the town-board members himself was on such a farm, and he agreed it would be better for him and for the town if he moved nearer to his neighbors. On the basis of the plan thus developed, the Government agency traded off some of the land it had bought for isolated farms in the forest area. The families from these farms were thus enabled to get farms nearer to neighbors and to schools, churches, and markets, and the community benefited by reduced costs of schools, school-bus service, and road maintenance. The forestry program, in turn, was able to go ahead, restoring forests on land that local people agreed should be in forest.

This is only one of many instances in which an administrative agency found that their plans worked best when local representatives played a large part in making them and in deciding how the program was to be carried out, when action was to be taken, and how rapidly the adjustments were to be carried to completion.

Planning for each program separately, however, even with the fullest participation of local people, was not fully effective in coordinating different programs with each other and with local conditions. Moreover, coordination of action obviously meant coordination of planning. Not only the Department but the cooperating State agencies—land-grant colleges and others—as well as farmers, felt this need for coordinated, cooperative planning. Land use planning as it now operates is meeting these fundamental requirements.

COOPERATIVE PLANNING ON A COUNTY BASIS

After much consideration and discussion by people experienced in earlier types of agricultural planning, the Department and the State agricultural colleges agreed that the logical organization for coordinated planning should consist of farmers, administrators, and technicians working together. The county was chosen as a major unit of this cooperative planning because it was realized that the work must be done by people close to the local situation and because much of the agricultural work was already organized on a county basis.

The area method was adopted as the simplest and most practical approach to so complex a planning problem. Most counties have several kinds of areas. In some most of the land is fertile and arable, while in others most of it is poor. Some are thickly settled and others sparsely settled; some have little soil erosion, while in others erosion is severe. There are mountainous or hilly areas, rolling and flat areas. One area has one type of farming, a neighboring area a different type, and each has problems that differ from the others. It was believed that a common understanding and agreement on the location and characteristics of these different land use areas would provide a good starting point for coordinated planning.

After agreeing on the location and general characteristics of a land use area, the next step is to agree on the problems and the type of adjustment needed. This means determining, among other things, whether the present use of the land is the best use. Is the land being managed in the most effective way? What kind of adjustment, if any, is needed? Agreement must be reached on the particular adjustments needed for each area. In one area the major need may be a change in farm organization, perhaps requiring credit aids and technical advice to assist the farmers in making the change. In another it may be greater emphasis on soil conservation. In yet another it may be improved forest management to help support the people and their local institutions. Retirement of submarginal farms and aid to people in finding new opportunities may be needed elsewhere. In many cases a combination of several different kinds of adjustment might be needed in the same land-use area.

It was decided to undertake this cooperative planning in such a way that the land use plans for different counties would be comparable and could be put together or summarized for purposes of district, State, regional, and national planning. This meant agreeing on a common procedure that could be adapted to local conditions.

The broad outlines of such cooperative activities were incorporated formally into an agreement on July 8, 1938, between two committees that had been set up to study the problem, one representing the Association of Land Grant Colleges and the other the Department of Agriculture. The agreement was drawn at a conference of the two committees at Mount Weather, Va., and is known as the Mount Weather Agreement.

The general conclusion reached at Mount Weather was to develop a State land use committee in each State and to organize similar committees in the different counties. The Mount Weather Agreement was a starting point for working out individual cooperative land use planning agreements between the land-grant colleges and the Department. With minor variations, these agreements are much the same in all the 45 States that entered into them the first year. The work is organized with a State land use planning or advisory committee and county and community committees in each county where the process has been started. In the Department the planning organization includes the Agricultural Program Board and the Interbureau Coordinating Committee, which is composed of representatives of all Department of Agriculture agencies. (See Old and New in Agricultural Organization, p. 1125.)

The State committee is set up to develop State agricultural plans and programs and to advise and assist the county committees. The State director of agricultural extension serves as chairman of the State committee, and the State representative of the Bureau of Agricultural Economics is secretary. In addition to these officials and a group of representative farm men and women, the membership of the committees includes representatives of State and Department agencies which have responsibility for the management of land-use programs. These agencies include the agricultural experiment station, Agricultural Adjustment Administration, Farm Security Administration, Soil Conservation Service, Farm Credit Administration, Public Roads Administration, Forest Service, and State forestry department. In addition, in many States the State highway department, State conservation department, and other State agencies are represented.

The community and county committees develop plans for communities and counties. They also work directly with administrative and policy-making agencies in translating the plans into action. In an ideal organization of a community committee, the individual members represent all the different neighborhoods in the community. A county committee is normally composed of representatives from the different communities, together with local representatives of agricultural agencies. The county agricultural agent serves as secretary.

As the planning work develops, nearly every land-use committee finds that it has several outstanding problems that demand special attention. Frequently these are referred to appropriate subcommittees for detailed study and analysis.

The planning organization does not end with the committees. Its real foundation is the people of the different neighborhoods and communities. The people who are not members of planning committees take part through public meetings at which the committees report what they have been doing and free discussion is encouraged. They participate, too, through individual discussions with committee members in the course of frequent personal contacts.

STAGES OF "COUNTY PLANNING"

The planning work has been organized in three progressive stages. The first is preparatory work, which includes the organizing of com-

223761°—40——73

mittees. The second stage is intensive planning work in studying problems, agreeing on facts, and deciding upon goals and objectives for the improvement of agriculture and of rural life in the different land use areas in the county. The third and last stage is cooperating to decide specifically what will be done, and by whom, to achieve the goals and objectives; this stage aims to develop a unified program of action by all agencies concerned with agriculture in the county.

In the preparatory stage, public meetings are held, and the whole idea is talked over. Preparatory work should include a review and study of the information available for use in planning, of the various public programs now operating to assist agriculture, and of regional and national forces and trends that have a bearing on local problems. The public meetings are particularly helpful because cooperative planning relies heavily upon open discussion as a means of reaching understanding and agreement on what the problems are and what should be done about them.

The farmer representatives on the planning committee are sometimes elected at these meetings. Again, names are suggested by nominating committees. Occasionally the members are appointed. As planning work progresses, more and more committees are elected in order to assure a representative organization. Representative committees are essential if the planning is to be democratic and if the committees' recommendations are to have general support.

The opinions and attitudes of each neighborhood and community should be fully represented in the membership of community and county committees. Committee members should be men and women of broad vision, with a high sense of public responsibility and a genuine concern for the needs and viewpoints of all groups in the community. They must have the ability to work together in a democratic way, which means respecting the judgment of others and recognizing that intelligent compromise is an essential part of democracy. They must also be able to see and understand the interdependence of communities and of counties and to appreciate how an action that appears desirable from a purely local point of view may prove undesirable because of national and regional forces and conditions.

Ideally, the actual development of land use plans—the area method of planning—is not started until after thorough preparatory work. This is begun by studying and reaching an agreement on the significant land use areas of the county. The work is normally done by community committees whose members are familiar with local conditions. Each community committee uses a large-scale base map of the community showing the roads, farms, schools, towns, rivers, lakes, and similar features. In addition, it has other data and maps which have been assembled and reviewed in the preparatory stage.

Frequently several community committees meet together at a central point, each discussing and drawing on its base map the land use areas it considers significant for planning purposes in its territory. As the work progresses, the community committees check with each other to reconcile differences so that the community maps and recommendations for changes in land use will fit together on a county basis. When in doubt concerning any area, committee members often go out and examine it. Available data on physical features, economic factors, and social conditions are used for reference in drawing the area boundaries, in studying the local problems, and in reaching conclusions on needed adjustments. The knowledge and experience of farmers likewise supplies an important part of the basis for the agreements that are reached in this important stage of planning.

Specific adjustments needed in different areas are likewise determined by discussions in the committee. Farm-management advisers, tax experts, foresters, and other specialists participate and supply any useful data they may have available.

When a community committee has agreed on the different land use areas, the essential facts and problems of each, and the specific adjustments that may be needed, the map and a brief report are submitted to the county committee. The county group reviews and assembles the reports of the community committees, combining the community maps in a county land use map. Areas suitable, unsuitable, and questionable for farm use are classified and shown on the county map in different colors. Questions are frequently referred back to community committees for further consideration.

When the work has progressed to a stage where the county committee feels it is ready to have its findings and recommendations assembled and presented in report form, the county agent, with the assistance of committee members and of technicians from cooperating State and Federal agencies, prepares a working draft for a report. This is considered by the committee as a whole. Copies are sent to the State committee for comments and suggestions. Then, when the county committee has received the various suggestions and has agreed on any revisions that it desires to make, the report is reproduced and distributed to the committee members, the State agencies, and the Department of Agriculture as a basis for the next stage—getting action on the recommendations.

Unless there were definite arrangements for translating plans into action, there would be danger that the planning process might result largely in maps and recommendations, with little actual progress in getting things done to help farmers deal with their problems. Proposals for specific action are therefore formulated by the committees.

Since representatives of many of the action agencies are actually members of the county committee, they are in a position to cooperate closely. If the local administrator of a program agrees that what the committee recommends is desirable, and if the action is within his power, he goes ahead with it. If the decision must be made by a higher official, the local representative refers the proposal to him for approval or disapproval. If he approves, he is asked to propose steps for carrying out the proposed action; if not, to suggest modifications.

Various lines of action which appear to the committees to be desirable for individual farmers are explained and discussed at public meetings and in personal talks of committee members with their neighbors. Committee reports and recommendations, reproduced and distributed widely among local farm people, are proving very useful in developing a better understanding of common problems and of practical ways to meet them.

This process of translating plans into coordinated action throughout a county is known as unified program development. It does not mean centralized administration under one head. Rather it means agreement upon desirable changes in the different programs so that each may contribute most fully to achieving the needed adjustments; administration of the unified programs is still carried out by separate agencies. Nor does the cooperative planning effort lessen the need for advisory committees to work on administrative problems with individual agencies, such as the county agricultural conservation program committee, the Farm Security advisory committee, and others. It provides a local organization with which these administrative committees can work on problems requiring coordinated action.

As a beginning, it was proposed to carry out the unified-program idea in one county in each State. This concentration of effort in a few counties, it was believed, would help to indicate in a reasonable length of time the type of accomplishment possible. In most States the work is now being started in a second county. In addition, other counties have been active in translating plans into action. Many of them likewise have decided upon definite things that should be done on the basis of their plans and have worked with the different agencies in getting them done.

In developing plans and in finding ways of putting them into action the committees have dealt with individual farmers and with agencies of local, State, and Federal Government. A large part of the action that has already resulted from this cooperative planning is carried out by local agencies—county commissioners, assessors, soil conservation district supervisors, vocational-agriculture teachers, health officers, and groups of farmers. Frequently several agencies—local, State, and Federal—are involved, each doing a particular part of the job and all cooperating. The county agent and the agricultural college are often called on to do the educational work needed as part of a unified program. Very commonly, on the recommendation of a planning committee, special research programs are set up to obtain facts and study particular problems. Specialists in various fields are enlisted from the colleges and universities, the Department of Agriculture, and other sources.

PROGRESS IN THE FIRST YEAR

One year after the new planning effort was started, 45 States had made definite arrangements for cooperating in it, and 43 had organized States committees, with a total of 552 farmer members. The activity had reached 1,120 counties in 47 States, and there were 70,000 farm men and women cooperating as members of county and community committees. These committees in 566 counties had carried on area mapping and classification work. In 112 of them a preliminary draft of area maps and reports had been completed. The development of unified programs had been undertaken in 46 counties in 40 States.

These figures show that the program has been inaugurated on a large scale. To determine the amount of progress being made, however, it is necessary to know what has happened in the counties where the work is being done and what success committees are having in obtaining action that helps improve local conditions. Space permits describing only a few selected experiences of committees.

Land Use Planning in Culpeper County, Va.

Broadening out its existing program of farmer planning for extension work, the County Board of Agriculture of Culpeper County, which is in the northern Piedmont section of Virginia, took the leadership in organizing 8 community committees, blanketing the county. The committees then mapped the county into 11 different land use areas and agreed on the following recommendations:

Areas 1, 2, 3. Primarily subsistence-farming areas with a relatively small acreage of the individual farms suited to tillage and the remainder of the land most useful as improved pasture and woodland.

Areas 4, 5. Mostly rough land. Considerable serious erosion. Best adapted to large farm units for livestock production.

Areas 6, 7. Rolling to steep land in use for general farming, dairying, and livestock production. Crop yields good, but there is need for soil conservation and improved farming practices, pasture improvement, and better marketing methods.

Area 8. Level to rolling land, above average in quality. Farms very large. It would be desirable to increase the number of farms and thus support on better land a number of farmers now occupying land unsuited to farming. Soil conservation also a need.

Area 9. Broken, badly eroded land, thickly settled and characterized by subsistence and part-time farming, with comparatively low crop yields. Further settlement should be discouraged; lands not suited to farming should be developed as forest, and efforts should be made to develop additional opportunities for employment off the farm.

Area 10. Sparsely settled, with small farms heavily wooded and on relatively poor soil, much of which is poorly drained. Needs in this area are for more supplemental income, increased utilization of idle land as pasture and forest, and more home production of family food supplies.

Area 11. Similar to area 10, except that the farms are larger. Incomes are low. Farming should be intensified on the small acreage of better lands, and the poorer lands should be developed and managed as forest.

Having agreed on these basic objectives, the committees turned to translating the numerous recommendations into action. The need for soil conservation practices in most of the land use areas led the committees to work for the establishment of a county-wide soil conservation district and for the location of a Civilian Conservation Corps camp there to provide labor for soil conservation work. Both of these objectives have been realized. The soil conservation program is now under way, with the committees taking an active part in developing it.

Realizing that many of their objectives could be attained only through closer correlation and cooperation between agricultural agencies, the county committee decided that one way to get the agencies to work together would be to have them housed together. Through the cooperation of the county board of supervisors, a building was obtained at the county seat in which all the agencies could have their offices.

One of the problems with people in the subsistence-farming areas who needed part-time work off the farm was that once such people got Works Progress Administration jobs they were reluctant to leave them to do seasonal farm work because of uncertainty as to whether they could get their jobs back afterward. An improved understanding was worked out with the county welfare office whereby needy families may take advantage of seasonal work demands and yet be assured of eligibility for relief when not employed on private jobs.

Many low-income farmers in the subsistence areas were found to need some form of aid that would enable them to improve their farms. Arrangements were worked out with the Farm Security Administration to make "prestandard" loans to such farmers. Another need of the low-income farmers was for more adequate low-cost medical service. A special committee on this problem has developed a tentative agreement with the Culpeper County Medical Society that provides a group medical-care program in which all of the doctors in the county will participate.

Many of the needs in Culpeper County required action by farmers to change farming practices, conserve soil, raise home food supplies, improve pastures, and take other measures. This meant getting the committee's recommendations before farmers in the different communities and neighborhoods. The committee decided that to do this it needed to know more about the actual neighborhoods and communities to which the different farmers felt they belonged. To obtain this knowledge, it enlisted the cooperation of the State agricultural college and the farm-population experts of the Department of Agriculture. The facts assembled and presented by these agencies are the basis for reorganizing community committees so that each neighborhood can be represented. The neighborhood representatives reach nearby farmers.

The Culpeper County committee feels that additional facts are needed on a number of different subjects before the soundest plans of action can be developed for some of its problems. To get some of the needed information it worked out a plan whereby the United States census officials would select especially qualified enumerators to tabulate the county census data in a special way to meet the needs of the planning committee. The State statistician and the State commissioner of agriculture cooperated by training the census enumerators to obtain the data in the form required by the committee.

These various measures in action programs, community and neighborhood organization, and the collection of additional facts represent the committee's efforts thus far to achieve the objectives it decided upon as the appropriate ones for the different land use areas and for the county at large. It can be seen that not all of the objectives have been achieved. Many of them cannot be achieved in a single year. Culpeper County is working on a long-range program, and the progress so far gives the community and county committees confidence that eventually they will accomplish much in improving conditions.

Land Use Planning in Ward County, North Dakota

Of the many counties from which a second example might be chosen, semiarid Ward County, N. Dak., is selected because of the sharp contrast of conditions there with those in humid Culpeper County. Ward County is in the northern spring-wheat area and was hard hit by drought in the 1930's.

Work of organizing the land use-planning committees was initiated by the county agricultural program-planning committee, which had been in existence for some time. This committee decided to subdivide the county into 12 community areas. Public meetings were called in each community center to discuss the program and to elect a community committee. Every township was represented on the community committees, which were composed of 7 members in all communities except 1, which had 8 members. It was decided that the chairman of each community committee should automatically become a member of the county committee.

Cooperation was obtained from various agencies in supplying data to the committees for use in developing basic land use plans. The committees were furnished maps and data on soils, slope, soil erosion, tax delinquency, publicly owned lands, types of landownership, and assessed valuations of land parcels. Aerial photographs and tabulations of 1938 crop acreages for each township also were supplied. Using this information and their own knowledge of local conditions, the committees decided that the county, for practical planning purposes, consists of 23 distinct areas. After analyzing conditions in these different areas, 20 of them were grouped in 2 major classes: (1) Areas now in farms, recommended as suitable for general farming (67 percent of the land in the county); (2) areas now in farms, recommended as suitable for livestock farming (28 percent of the land). Of the remaining 3 areas, 1 is now in farms but is classed as questionable for farming, and 2 are Federal migratory waterfowl refuge areas covering 2 percent of the county.

The most pressing needs for adjustment were found to be largely centered in the areas of the second class, where overcapitalization and overtaxation result in an overemphasis on cash crops. A major need, the committees decided, was for greater emphasis on livestock. Factors designated as impeding this adjustment include absentee ownership, small size of farm units, and a shortage of capital for range improvement, fencing, livestock purchases, and reorganization of operating units. Problems of range management and soil and water conservation are important in these areas.

Many of the other problems in Ward County are virtually countywide, applying to nearly all the land use areas. These include crop rotations and tillage methods poorly adapted to conditions in the county, periodic shortages of feed for livestock, short-term leases, overcapitalization, heavy debt burdens, inadequate farm buildings, inequitable distribution of the tax burden, heavy tax delinquency, and difficulty in financing local government. Another problem recognized was that of increasing the opportunities for recreation and social activities as a necessary part of modern life.

Obviously these complex problems called for a long-time program. With that in mind the committee turned to the development of a comprehensive set of recommendations for adjustments, involving local, State, and Federal agencies. For example, the recommendations on the tax problem suggest local action to adjust taxation to the productive power of the land; more stringent tax collections, including the impounding of rentals on tax-delinquent lands; and coordination of school programs to eliminate costly and inefficient small units. Recommended State action on the tax problem deals largely with revenues to local government from lands controlled by various State agencies, and with homestead tax exemption. Recommended Federal action to ease the tax problem involves payments on Federal lands in lieu of taxes and Federal aid in providing school services to families located on a Federal homesteads resettlement project. A major objective of the committee's tax program is to distribute the total tax burden more equitably, on the basis of ability to pay.

A similarly broad program was outlined for achieving needed adjustments in land use. This includes action by individual farmers to use all available public aids in shifting to a greater dependence on livestock, through leasing tax-title lands, obtaining loans for fencing and development of stock water, and adjusting farm operations so as to produce sufficient feed crops and bring the land on every farm into its best use. The program also calls for a number of changes in the local application of the agricultural adjustment program, to increase emphasis on feed and forage crops and make broader provisions for summer-fallow practices.

Recommendations for action in several other fields were developed as part of the county's long-time program. With two-thirds of the farms in the county tenant-operated, the committee saw tenancy as one of its most important problems. To deal with this, it recommended long-term leases developed to fit the individual farm and asked for continued purchase of farms for tenants through the Farm Security Administration program. To relieve a serious situation caused by heavy debt loads on farmers, it recommended that the debt-adjustment service of the Farm Security Administration be expanded in the county. Another recommendation was that Government credit agencies develop a program to unify under one agency all debts owed to Federal agencies and to provide for amortizing the combined debts over a period of years. Increased efforts to obtain more effective price adjustments for crops, the expansion of farmer cooperatives, and development of suitable tax-deed lands for outdoor recreation are among the other recommendations.

With this broad list of objectives, the committee began the task of getting action. Among the first arrangements worked out was the agreement of the local taxing authorities to utilize the results of land use planning as a foundation for revising and adjusting assessed land valuations. Begun in 1939, this work is being continued in 1940. Another arrangement has been to obtain the aid of the State agricultural experiment station and the Bureau of Agricultural Economics in analyzing the school situation and farm-debt conditions to provide a basis for considering possible reorganization of the school system and for relating farm debts more closely to the earning power of the land. Arrangements worked out with various agencies for obtaining other action as part of a unified program include definite commitments from the county commissioners, county superintendent of schools, county treasurer, Ward County Welfare Board, Farmers' Union of Ward County, the Governor of North Dakota, Farm Security Administration, Extension Service, and Bureau of Biological Survey.

Coordination in Teton County, Mont.

In Teton County, Mont.—out where the Great Plains meet the northern Rocky Mountains—one of the things the committee determined in developing a basic plan was that 20,000 acres of land then in wheat were really unsuited for that crop. The average yield was less than 5 bushels an acre. Other land, equally poor, also was believed in danger of similar unwise development. After studying the history of the area and the prospects for wheat growing, the committee decided that the land should be resodded and used for grazing and that all similar land should be kept out of cultivation.

That was the general objective. The next step was to accomplish it, and the first part of the job was to find out what agencies could help and in what ways. The committee conferred with each agency in turn on what it could do and, mostly through the agency representatives on the committee itself, developed a program in which six different agencies have agreed on definite actions that each will perform.

The Agricultural Adjustment Administration offered to cooperate in several ways—for example, by not allowing low-grade sod lands to come into the A. A. A. program as cropland. It will also encourage the retirement and reseeding of low-grade lands now in wheat.

The Farm Security Administration will work with its clients in getting the poor land out of wheat and in keeping poor land now in grass from going into wheat, and will help farmers on small units to get enough additional acreage to make a unit of sufficient size.

The Farm Credit Administration is testing out the feasibility of loans to permit enlargement of units that are too small and will consider land productivity carefully before extending loans so as not to encourage farming on submarginal land.

The Montana State Land Department will discourage wheat growing on the submarginal land it controls, will endeavor to get the poor land into grazing use, and will encourage reseeding by lowering rental charges to renters who reseed the land.

Teton County is undertaking a comprehensive program of reclassifying lands for tax purposes which aims at lower assessments of submarginal wheat lands if they are used for grazing and higher assessments when they are used for wheat. Adjusting the use of county-owned land is another aim in the program.

The county extension agent will direct extension work toward informing people about the program and enlisting the cooperation of local and nonresident landowners.

Other Values of Cooperative Planning

These examples indicate how cooperative planning unites farmers and agencies through common goals and how they operate as a team in achieving objectives. Similar results have been attained in a broad field of activities, including conservation, health, location of public services and facilities, carrying out State and local government policies, and educational programs. Formation of State and local government policies also has been facilitated through work of the committees.

A primary need in many cases was the fitting of programs to local conditions and to each other. Experience thus far shows that this is accomplished to a large extent through cooperatively developed basic plans. For example, highway agencies have been quick to utilize the land use plans as a guide for farm-to-market road programs. In fact the interest of highway agencies in these plans has led them to give substantial assistance to the planning committees. One of their major contributions is the large-scale maps used by many committees in mapping land use areas. These highway base maps show not only the existing roads but the location of farms, schools, towns, rivers, lakes, and other features, on a scale well suited to the committees' use. Guidance in placing new schools and in locating rural electrification lines is among the other important functions served by land use plans.

The cooperative planning process has proved of major value, too, in aiding extension work aimed directly at the specific problems in different areas. Special committees have been formed in a number of agricultural colleges to help redirect extension activities in the light of land use plans developed in the counties. County agents are consulting regularly with county and community committees in fitting extension programs to the objectives developed in land use planning.

One of the major contributions of planning to education is through the duplication and distribution of the planning committees' reports among farm people. The community meetings which are held to consider the committees' findings are of course educational in a high degree. The planning process itself is an educational experience for those who engage in it. Even the highly trained technician gains by seeing his own specialty as part of a local situation and learning how the many different subjects fit together in given local situations.

Another link between land use planning and education is the use of county planning reports in the public schools. In Kansas the agricultural teachers are receiving planning reports as soon as completed. In Belmont County, Ohio, the agricultural teacher is using the land use map and report in an adult education course. In Florida representatives of the State board of education are advocating that land use planning reports be utilized in the public-school curriculums. In Washington the agricultural teachers are helping to develop a revised course of study that will stress land use planning in the rural high schools. A number of State supervisors of agricultural education are planning to offer special courses on the philosophy and techniques of land use planning at their regular summer conferences for teachers of vocational agriculture.

Private Action on Common Problems

Joint private action to achieve agreed-upon goals and objectives may, in the long run, be a more significant result of the cooperative planning process than the coordination and unification of public programs, which was the initial purpose. Of course, it is nothing new for farmers to act together in doing things which cannot be done by the individual farmer acting alone, or which can be done more sociably by working together. In the early days farm people worked together in such things as logrollings and corn huskings. In more recent times there have been neighborhood threshing rings and cooperative creameries.

Planning together, in community and county committees, and later discussing the committees' findings and recommendations in community and neighborhood meetings and across fences lead to agreement on various things. Many of these things are in fields where Government action is needed. Many other objectives and goals, however, though too big for individual action, can be achieved by the joint action of local people with little or no Government assistance. For example, there is a need in many communities for purebred sires to replace inferior and scrub sires. Frequently, no individual farmer is in a position to own a really good sire. Commonly also, farms are too small to justify the individual ownership and use of power equipment, such as a tractor. Yet if a tractor or other equipment could be shared among several farms it might be a thoroughly economical investment. These problems obviously require some kind of joint action. For instance, agreement is frequently reached that one of the farmers in a community will buy a purebred sire and that the other farmers will contribute to the cost, through service charges or in some other way. A tractor can be obtained under a similar arrangement, or a cooperative association may be formed to buy and own it and to coordinate its use among the individual members. Many local groups have obtained purebred sires and tractors in this way. Often they have been aided by credit extended by the Farm Security Administration.

Numerous examples could be cited in which county planning has led to group or cooperative action of this type. In Uintah and Juab Counties, Utah, the work of planning committees led to the establishment of cooperative sawmills, enabling farmers to work together in getting out lumber for their own use. In Pend Oreille County, Wash., the planning committee has arranged for rental of a privately owned bulldozer for use in land clearing. Group purchases of farm supplies and livestock, establishment of cold-storage locker plants, and cooperative marketing are among the other kinds of joint private action to achieve definite objectives agreed upon in such county planning.

LOOKING AHEAD WITH COUNTIES AND COMMUNITIES

Cooperation by farmer committeemen, technicians, and representatives of agricultural agencies in developing common basic plans and determining how the plans are to be effectuated is new. It will be successful to the extent that farmers take an active interest in the work and responsibility for it. Farmers must help decide on the best ways to obtain the general planning and coordination needed for agricultural programs. This involves, for one thing, the broadening out of the planning activity to include counties that have not yet started it. Even more important is continued and sustained effort after it is started, for planning is a continuing process. The problems with which it deals are constantly changing. Out of the planning process itself there must evolve leadership that is increasingly competent to deal with problems and increasingly skilled in the democratic process of reaching a mutual agreement on what is to be done.

Many of the major problems of our times are agricultural or affect agriculture. Our country is "on the spot" to show that it can deal with its problems in a democratic and civilized way and do it better than the nations that have abandoned democracy. Democracy cannot survive in the modern world unless it solves the problems of farmers without land who lack opportunity and of all citizens who are overburdened with rent, interest, and taxes or are unable to make ends meet because of low incomes and high costs. Nor can it succeed unless there are economic and social opportunities for young people and means available for the common man to have a good life and the security that is made possible by science in the modern world. Cooperative land use planning is a means of attacking such of these problems as belong to agriculture.

It may be argued that planning by counties and communities cannot get at some of the larger agricultural problems, such as price parity, foreign markets, and the relation of effective to potential demand for farm products. It is true, of course, that all of the planning that is needed for agriculture cannot be done in the counties and communities. Some of the broader planning has to be done by State land use committees, State legislatures, the Congress of the United States, and the United States Department of Agriculture.

It is also true that many of the things farm people should have cannot be obtained through programs for agriculture alone. For example, additional alternative opportunities are needed for rural young people whose work is not required for farming and who do not desire to stay on farms.

Although agriculture is vitally concerned with these larger problems that cannot be solved within the county and community alone or within agriculture alone, the broad approach of the committees to their problems helps even in these cases. Problems are threshed out, ideas are formulated, and the State and national policies and plans are carefully checked, to see whether they improve the situation locally.

Local planning also helps in understanding the exact nature of basic problems. For example, the committees find many land use areas that have more people than the land can support in current production operations. This is one of the most frequent findings of county planning committees. Mechanization has made the family-size commercial farm unit larger than formerly, which means there would be fewer farms under an ideal program of commercial farming. In addition, many people have crowded onto cheap, poor land for subsistence farming because good land or other opportunities were not available.

The first conclusion usually has been that these "surplus" farm people must be taken care of "somewhere else." [2] Although some of the committees are finding undeveloped areas that might be used for farming, these are greatly outnumbered by the areas now in farms recommended by land use committees for retirement from commercial farming. Adequate opportunities in industry for large numbers of farm people do not now exist. At present there is no utopian somewhere else for all the surplus farm people to go to.

Areas now in farms but classed as unsuited for commercial farming present a special problem when the lack of opportunities elsewhere is considered. Getting people out of such areas is a poor solution for the problem if the people find themselves no better off, or perhaps even worse off, in the new location.

---

[2] JOHNSTONE, PAUL H. SOMEWHERE ELSE. U. S. Bur. Agr. Econ., Land Policy Rev. 2 (6): 1–9. 1939.

The fact is, of course, that a large proportion of the surplus farm people will have to remain where they are, at least for the present. In view of this prospect, it is clear that unless constructive employment is found in activities other than commercial crop production, continued heavy outlays for relief will be necessary in many rural areas. This situation calls for a fresh look at possibilities for constructive local employment in other lines. It seems also to call for consideration of a more adequate program for maintaining our agricultural resources, through conservation linked up closely with the employment needs of local people; there is need for perhaps 750,000 men in conservation.[3] It calls, too, for thinking in terms of an agriculture that consists of more than commercial farming. This might be a combination of commercial farming with live-at-home farming and part-time farming. It would include a long-time program of adjustment for families in submarginal areas. For example, special educational programs for those areas might aim to equip the young people for vocations other than agricultural production. These vocations might include agricultural services such as catering to the recreation trade, conservation, and rural industries of various types, as well as preparation for city jobs. The final retirement of submarginal land from farming would be postponed until the young folks had found opportunities in other fields and the old folks were done with the land. In the meantime, rehabilitation of natural resources and of the people might reduce the need for the people to move elsewhere.

Such a program might be supplemented in considerable degree with rural industries. There are also substantial but undetermined possibilities in utilizing a vast acreage of land now largely idle which might substantially help support unemployed and underemployed farm people in ways that would not add to the problem of surpluses. Much of this land not generally suited for farming is suited for other uses, notably timber growing, recreation, wildlife production, watershed protection, and in some cases stock grazing. Land of this character makes up more than 75 percent of the area of about 500 counties. It embraces 50 to 75 percent of the land in some 700 other counties, and 25 to 50 percent of another 700. This land does not include desert and semidesert areas, but rather the unimproved lands that are of real potential value for forestry or other agricultural uses. Many of these 1,900 counties (there are roughly 3,000 counties in the 48 States) are among those where the surplus of farmers is greatest. Altogether they include two-thirds of all farms in the United States. Whether this unimproved land is in farms or outside of them, it usually has had little or no real management or care.

Planning for Idle People and Idle Lands

The problem of unemployed and underemployed farm people seems linked up in many cases with these idle and partly idle lands. The problem also concerns the farmers outside the idle-land counties, because the high cost of relief for these needy people adds to the tax burden. What are the possibilities of rehabilitating the land and the people together in counties having a surplus of people and a large

[3] GOODRICH, CARTER; ALLIN, BUSHROD W.; THORNTHWAITE, C. WARREN; and others. MIGRATION AND ECONOMIC OPPORTUNITY. 763 pp., illus. Philadelphia and London. 1936. See p. 409.

acreage of idle land? There are many areas, for example, where people are poorly housed and buildings are in need of repair when nearby forest lands might be producing timber to meet their requirements as well as providing additional cash income. Similar forest lands in Europe support families at the rate of one worker for approximately 100 acres. There, in many instances, forest work is combined with part-time farming.[4] In the United States the surface has scarcely been scratched in managing this kind of land to support a better rural life.

The land use committee in Parke County, Ind., decided that 75,000 acres of "woods pasture" in the county is neither good woods nor good pasture and that it is not contributing as it should because of the way it is used. The committee decided that one of its jobs is to develop a program of better use for this land.

The committees in Belknap and Coos Counties in New Hampshire have decided that a way to make unimproved lands in farms contribute more is to have a joint pasture- and woodland-improvement project. The program has already spread to several other counties. It involves making a definite decision as to what part of the unimproved land is to be developed as improved pasture and what part as forest. Then it involves managing each tract for the use to which it is best suited.

Other problems involved in bringing unimproved lands under constructive development and use are those of commercially owned forest land and of large acreages of abandoned cut-over lands that are tax-delinquent.

The problem of surpluses, of course, is encountered in all plans for putting land to work. While long-time planning must be guided primarily by potential demand rather than by current effective demand, any increase in current production needs to be accompanied by an increase in effective demand. The new production naturally should be directed toward things for which a potential demand exists. Consistent effort is necessary to keep these considerations in view in formulating basic plans. The essential fact in connection with the development of programs to use idle land in rural areas is that in large part they are best adapted to producing things of which many people do not have enough. Much of this potential demand exists in the same locality with the idle land. Housing, fuel, outdoor recreation, and wildlife are some of the needs that might be filled better through a program of wise land use. In many areas public action of various kinds, especially a rural works program, doubtless would be required in reclaiming this land.

Institutional Adjustments

In addition to measures directly concerned with the physical use of land, land use planning committees will continue and probably increase their interest in institutional adjustments. One of the major fields of interest may be modifying or broadening rural educational systems to aid stranded farm youth in preparing for vocations other than agricultural production. More equitable assessment of farm property and debt adjustments doubtless will be primary fields of

[4] SPARHAWK, W. N. FOREST EMPLOYMENT IN GERMANY. U. S. Dept. Agr. Cir. 471, 52 pp. 1938.

interest. Other fields are those of recreational and social facilities and activities, rural electrification, tax delinquency, marketing problems, cooperative enterprises, changes in the type of farming, road programs, and the powers, functions, and organization of local government.

In the field of land tenure, committees will probably continue to find some of the greatest opportunities for constructive work. They will be concerned with the fact that for farmers the real basis of both security and liberty is stable tenure of land. They will deal with absentee versus local farm ownership of land and with improving the relations between landlord and tenant in the interests of both. Reducing the size of large holdings, if done with just concern for all interests, might at times be deemed necessary to make conditions better for farmers as a whole. On the other hand, in cases where large operations have marked advantages in efficiency, cooperative methods might be preferred by farm people.

Any agricultural adjustments required by war conditions in the rest of the world and in the interest of national defense will, of course, have the close attention of planning committees.

These are only a few of the problems with which planning committees will continue to concern themselves. Great diversity of action that can help improve the condition of agriculture and of farm people has already been indicated in the results obtained in the planning process.

Private Action as Well as Public

In looking ahead, one of the most fascinating things to consider is how the adjustments agreed upon in land use planning will be achieved. Of particular interest is the probable division of the work between private and public agencies. Private action already resulting from cooperative planning indicates some of the possibilities.

As planning work goes on and more committees agree upon goals and objectives, the question "Now what do we do?" seems bound to lead farmers, technicians, and administrators to thinking more and more of how the goals may be achieved by private as well as by Government action. Gradually this practical approach to problems may broaden the field of private action. In this way, cooperative planning may possibly make its greatest contribution by helping people to help themselves through private action rather than in the original purpose of coordinating and unifying the programs of Government agencies.

The achievement of many goals and objectives, of course, requires combined private and public action. Yet the possibilities of private action alone in dealing with diverse problems present a major challenge to planning committees. Perhaps ways will be found for private agencies to handle problems that are now looked upon as requiring Government action, and which people dread because of the public cost. Predictions are hazardous, and we should not become overconfident of what might be accomplished to achieve needed adjustments without governmental aid. The land use planning process will not be complete, however, unless it involves a consideration of the possibilities of action by farmers among themselves and in cooperation with other private groups to deal even with such difficult problems as agricultural surpluses, production control, submarginal croplands, reemployment of farmers displaced by technology, and the creation of opportunities for farm youth. At the very least, cooperative planning holds the major hope of developing measures of private-public cooperation that will keep the public cost within reasonable bounds and aid in balancing both public and private budgets.

NEW MEANS TO OLD ENDS

All these details of planning for agriculture and of translating plans into action are aimed at a single result—a better life, including security, through the development of a better agriculture and a better adjustment of the institutions that affect agriculture. The details of agricultural planning are like the parts of an automobile. The operation of an automobile looks simple and unified. But much painstaking work of design, construction, and maintenance goes into making it possible. Its production requires the cooperative work of many people. Without this painstaking cooperative work we would still be riding behind horses.

A good life likewise seems a simple and unified thing to those who have it. But if people are to have a good life and security, in the modern world, much painstaking cooperative work is needed. People who believe in democracy desire to do this cooperative work voluntarily, without regimentation. For them a good life has to include liberty as well as security. Voluntary cooperation in planning is a way to avoid regimented action planned by a dictator.

The desire for a good life is not new. The difference is that today it must be sought in new ways. That is what agricultural planning, through the cooperative efforts of farmers, technicians, and administrators working together in the agricultural counties, seeks to accomplish.

PART 7

Essentials of Agricultural Policy

Some Essentials of a Good Agricultural Policy

by HOWARD R. TOLLEY [1]

IN THE farm problem as a whole and in this book which tries to present the farm problem as a whole, there are many tangled threads of facts, ideas, struggles, needs, and dreams. Straightening out these threads and weaving them into a strong fabric of agricultural policy suited to democracy is the job of farmers and statesmen. This article attempts to disentangle some of the threads and show the kind of American homespun they can make. The author begins by asking what farm people today want in terms of a good life. He tries to define these wants and show the sources from which they spring. Then he asks, what would be the fundamentals of an agricultural policy in which these wants of the people were the warp of the fabric? Next he gives the broad pattern of policy shaped by these wants during the past decade. The fabric, he says, is far from perfect; it must be and can be strengthened and improved; but because its warp threads are the needs and wants of today, it will not change basically in character so far as we can now see. If we face the present honestly and do not fool ourselves and if the trend of events is not violently twisted by such developments as might occur in a world war, we can look a little way into the future.

[1] Howard R. Tolley is Chief of the Bureau of Agricultural Economics. The author wishes to acknowledge the assistance of O. V. Wells and Russell Smith, of the Bureau of Agricultural Economics, in the prepation of this paper.

THE dominating fact in any consideration of American economic problems is perhaps that in many ways our economy is approaching maturity. There are many signs of this maturity, such as our change, still comparatively recent, from a debtor to a creditor status among the great states of the world; the prospect of our having fairly soon a stable population; and especially the passing of the physical frontier. All of these have important implications for policy, as they have in our thinking as a Nation, but none is more important than the end of the frontier. Many of the major trends of contemporary agricultural policy—of national policy, for that matter—stem directly or indirectly from the consequences of the passing of the frontier. Moreover, this maturing process is characterized by a growing complexity. Far more than was true of past societies, every part of ours is interwoven with every other part, until the impact of change anywhere sends tremors through the whole network.

Until a few decades ago most people were born, grew up, and died in relatively stable surroundings, physical and cultural. To people living today, on the other hand, change has become as familiar a fact of everyday life as space and time themselves. This awareness of change tempers all our thinking. We are conscious that the consequence of drift, the passive acceptance of change, sometimes is disastrous; we have seen the effects of change upon the individual; finally we have been forewarned by events around us that those things we look upon as good must be guarded more zealously than would be the case in a more stable time. On the other hand the very fact that the past is the seedbed of the future means that work done today will bear fruit tomorrow. We of today may labor amid a changing order confident that what we do will have its influence. Upon the wisdom and energy with which we deal with our problems hangs the issue of whether that influence will be for good or ill.

It is within the context of such a time that the essentials of agricultural policy are to be considered. The first article in this volume (The Farmer's Changing World, p. 103) called attention to the sharp departure in governmental policy involved in the efforts of Government to meet the demands with which agriculture taxed it at the beginning of the decade just past, and to the need for a reexamination of the issues presented in those efforts. The author continued:

> Perhaps the most effective way to do this is to resurvey the position of agriculture in relation to our whole national and economic structure, with a view particularly to determining the forces that tend to affect agriculture adversely. In so doing, we should be able to determine how, and at what points, agriculture is out of balance with the rest of the economy and to appraise the various lines of action most appropriate for meeting the situation.

Some of the subsequent articles in the Yearbook are devoted to this objective. They bring out the need for action to deal with the problems dictated by change. And in the world of the middle twentieth century, in which the march of events has been telescoped beyond previous human experience, this need becomes imperative in other fields besides agriculture. A sense of the immediacy of contemporary problems runs throughout contemporary thought and literature.

But the implication of the material in this Yearbook is not that government by sweeping fiat should move militantly upon the Nation's problems, agricultural or otherwise. Rather, the emphasis is upon the encouragement of democratic channels of national energy and confidence, national consultation and decision, national tolerance and accommodation of views, together with the recognition that international affairs also have their bearing here.

THE "GOOD LIFE" FOR FARM PEOPLE—WHAT DOES IT MEAN TO THEM?

Before one considers what is desirable in agricultural policy, it is appropriate to define "desirable" and to glance at the sources of policy. In the long run, the desires of the people themselves must be the determinant. It is they who issue the charters of policy. These charters are often mutually contradictory; sometimes they are no more than a vigorous negation of an unpopular policy, without approval of a substitute. Through the processes of legislation and administration, policy is hammered out into detailed form and becomes concrete in programs. Yet, in the last analysis, these concrete details are accepted or rejected by the people, so that policy rests ultimately upon their desires as a base.

If policy is looked at as an expression of popular will, the thing to do is to try to arrive at some understanding of what the people, the farm people in common with their fellow citizens of other groups, think it should try to achieve for them.

In the effort to understand what farm people want, few objects of study are more rewarding than the ways in which Government has attempted to meet the demand of farmers for equal economic status with other groups in an industrialized world. As the impact of the Machine Age began to be fully felt after the Civil War, the Farmers' Alliance succeeded the Granger movement, the Populists succeeded the Farmers' Alliance, and still other vehicles of agrarian unrest followed the Populist movement. The Spanish-American and World Wars silenced the outcries briefly, but always they were renewed with increasing volume, because none of the responses of Government fully sufficed to right what the farmers regarded as their inferior economic position. Throughout the earlier years, the clamor of the farmers was for regulation of railroads and trusts, for credit and currency reform, for innumerable other actions by Government, but always it was for some action that would restore the economic dignity enjoyed by agriculture before the Civil War. In this century an extension of governmental efforts to comply with those demands has been apparent.

What are the common denominators in all these waves of action and reaction? What does the farmer want in terms of his own life when he insists upon equality for agriculture? What, in brief, does he regard as the elements that would go to make his life a good life?

Food, Clothing, and Shelter

To start with the most common of all common denominators, the average rural American wants food. He wants it three times a day and enough of it. His unfavorable reaction to the existence of agricultural commodities in quantity too great to be distributed by our economic system while at the same time great numbers of persons suffer want has been clearly expressed in recent years. Food, even more than houses or clothing, is the great fundamental necessity.

The inability of this country thus far to make its economy get food to these who need it and are willing to work for it is more dramatic than the corresponding inability to make houses and clothing available to those who need them. Yet both failures are of the same character. The disastrous effects of weakened purchasing power, perhaps aggravated by the imbalance of costs and prices, upon the housing and clothing industries have been clear to everyone in recent years. The need and demand for more and better houses, for more and better clothing, has persisted. It is unnecessary to pile up such evidence as the figures on housing shortages, even for those people who are well above the average in income, or the estimates of the acres that would be required to produce fibers to clothe the ill-clothed.

The Newer Fundamentals

But to the classic triumvirate of past generations—food, clothing, houses—ours has added other necessities that it regards as so basic that they must be grouped with those three. For one thing, it has become clear in the last few years that the great majority of people in this country need better medical care than has been available to them and that included in their broad demands for higher living standards is a desire for better health. The success of governmental attempts to bring more nearly adequate medical facilities to rural people, the development of group-health movements, and the wide agitation for a new national health policy all indicate the genuineness of this desire and the need to satisfy it in one way or another.

For our times, too, it has become equally essential for people to have means of ready transportation. The expansion of living standards that has gone on steadily in the United States and is considered by most people the outstanding characteristic of this country is dependent in large part upon facility of movement. Hence, good roads and means of using them must now be included among the necessities if we are to move toward the spread of this higher standard of living among all the people. Means of communication are almost equally important, from this point of view, and are rapidly becoming more significant. It is impossible, too, to ignore the growing desire for devices for home and farm that will reduce the drudgery too often associated with farm life. Obviously, the rural people of this country, more than any other group, stand in need of the essentials enumerated in this and the preceding paragraphs.

"Not by Bread Alone"

There is an intangible to be added to these tangibles, partly produced by them and in turn influencing them. Rural people, like everybody else, must feel at least some measure of security in the enjoyment of the fundamentals of the good life. This does not mean the kind of stability that conditions have imposed upon some other countries, the quiet of a strangulating economy or the rigidities of a society laid down in unchanging strata. It means that the average man wants to be able to look forward to the conduct of his life free from fear of events over which he has no control. If this assurance can be added to the elements outlined here, then truly the citizen will be prepared to live well.

For it is true that no man ever remains satisfied with bread alone, once he has achieved enough of that. In any passably adequate definition of the true desires of the people, therefore, those elements are to be included that do not contribute simply to material welfare.

Prominent among these essentials are schools. It is perhaps the greatest contradiction between the democratic theory and its practice that the rural schools of this country are as poor as they are. The country child today does not have the opportunity to obtain schooling as adequate as that afforded most city children. Yet from the rural areas come the majority of the country's children. The eagerness of rural people to take advantage of schools when they are available is attested from all sources and in turn attests that educational opportunity is one of the elements of the good life that they are striving to obtain for themselves.

The desire of farm people for improved transportation and communication for economic reasons has already been mentioned. Those two necessities are likewise important for a social reason. The drudgery of farm life is stressed no more often in modern writing dealing with agriculture than is the isolation, and this isolation is one of the most difficult barriers to the achievement of the good life individually and a strong, rich, homogeneous culture nationally Greater opportunity to take part in social activities, however, involves other elements than transportation and communication. Indeed, nearly every factor involved in raising standards of living contributes to this greater opportunity, as do more leisure, the development of group participation in political and economic life, and many others. Of the urgent need for a better social life there seems to be no doubt, if the reaction of farm people when the opportunity is offered is a gage.

Thomas Jefferson wrote 130 years ago: [2]

> I have often thought that nothing would do more good at small expense than the establihsment of a small circulating library in every county to consist of a few well-chosen books, to be lent to the people of the county under such regulations as would secure their safe return in due time. These should be such as would give them a general view of other history and particular view of that of their own country, a tolerable knowledge of geography, the elements of natural philosophy, of agriculture, and mechanics. Should your example lead to this it will do great good.

Few rural people even now have access to more than an infinitesimal part of the reservoirs of human thought stored in books new and old. Only infrequently are they able to have even the newspapers and periodicals that city people take for granted.

Many others of the softer threads woven into the rough fabric of living and enjoyed by other groups of our population are not for most farmers. Even the more well-to-do farmers may be without some of the advantages of city people merely because of the circumstances of rural life. For the poorer farmers this lack is aggravated by their poverty. The point is not that any particular activities are necessarily to be sponsored by the Government. If government makes it possible for people to have more leisure or greater income, the point

[2] WASHINGTON, H. A., ed. WRITINGS OF THOMAS JEFFERSON . . . v. 5. 1853. Letter to John Wyche, pp. 448–449.

would be the same. The provision of the opportunity for people to build a desirable life is what is important. It is not important whether this is done by government or otherwise; nor is it important whether government directly provides employment in cultural enterprises or merely makes it easier for people to share in them.

Very significant has been the development by rural people of their own means of self-expression, even when their material circumstances would apparently make it difficult for them to interest themselves in such things. Some investigators have cited the survival, through times of poverty and distress, of native folk arts such as square dances and handicrafts and the revival in late years of folk singing to illustrate the latent resources of our rural culture. Where highly commercialized agriculture has not altered the basic patterns of rural thought, these folk arts seem to flourish with vigor. Such response means that people are hungry for the interpretations of themselves and their own lives that the arts can give. The Nation may be only dimly aware of the richness of the cultural soil that awaits seeding. Here is a factor in the good life that farm people miss more than most others.

One of the great essentials for such a life is that a man have the opportunity to feel valuable, to feel that his work is of use and worth Men do not like to feel that they are the victims of forces over which they have no control. The farmer, for instance, does not want to feel that great cyclic depressions will rob him of the chance to make a living or that other unmanageable disasters hang over him daily or yearly. In a sense, this is the same desire for security mentioned earlier. Not that men demand absolute assurance that their efforts will be successful; what they want is the assurance that they can work and struggle for some reasonably achievable end.

Finally, every man needs to feel that he is working with and is part of a group of his fellow men. Partly, this feeling arises from self-interest. The farmer has learned that he can ordinarily achieve more for himself as a member of a group than he can working alone. But, equally, cooperative endeavor in work, as in social activity, satisfies a deep-rooted desire.

There has been abundant evidence of this in recent years. There are the remarkable records of participation by farmers in the various referenda that have been held in connection with Government programs, and the eagerness with which farmers for a quarter century have availed themselves of the chances to get together afforded by the State and Federal extension services and other organizations. The pronounced development in the last 25 years of cooperative-marketing groups illustrates the desire of farmers to work together for collectively beneficial ends. Finally, there has been a strong response by farmers to the new opportunities offered them to participate in community undertakings, to function as members of committees dealing with farm problems and helping to administer farm programs, and in other group activities not previously available to them. They have almost uniformly seized the opportunity not merely to attend meetings and sessions but to function with enthusiasm and effectiveness, and have demonstrated clearly that the traditional individualism of the agriculturist is not of the kind that prohibits successful cooperation.

It seems clear that the opportunity to assume the full dignity of the mature citizen of a democracy is one of the things that people desire. Therefore this opportunity should be included among the elements that make up the good life.

THE NATION'S STAKE IN THE GOOD LIFE ON THE FARM

Up to this point we have considered elements pertaining primarily to individuals and secondarily to farmers as a group. What is the Nation's interest in the attainment of the good life both by individual farmers and by agriculture as a whole? The Nation's principal interest in agriculture, aside from its interests in farmers as citizens like other citizens and in the production by farmers of an adequate supply of food and fibers, is that agriculture assume a status equal with those of other elements in the economy. A depressed agriculture obviously is a millstone about the Nation's neck. Agriculture must prosper if the Nation is to prosper—though the converse is true also, of course. The Nation also looks to agriculture to contribute to a well-rounded national culture, fully representative of the national life. Then, too, it must look primarily to agriculture for conservation of natural resources and for the cultivation of another resource—human values—among people engaged in agriculture. The Nation has a definite interest in the reinforcement of the sense of personal dignity, of the citizen's importance as a citizen. Indeed, this may be regarded as a dominant interest, for the health of any state depends upon the free intelligent functioning of its citizens.

The entire Nation, then, has a stake in seeing that its farm people have a chance at the good life. How far is it possible to say that the constituents of such a life, as roughly outlined, have so far been made attainable to the farmers of the United States? If the yardstick of what rural people want is applied to what they now have, much remains to be done before it can be said that any large number of them have attained very many of these elements of the good life or attained them in any large proportion.

For a generation or more the slogan of vocal farm groups has been "equality for agriculture." This has arisen from the feeling of farm people that they cannot now earn enough from their labor to enable them to buy for themselves, individually or as a group, to the same extent as other groups, these elements of a good life.

For instance, to take the denominator that is most readily usable, agriculture represents about 25 percent of the population, yet has less than 10 percent of the national money income, despite some progress in late years toward giving agriculture proportional status. Since farm families rear about one-third of the Nation's children, it is obvious that many of those children, in a money economy such as now exists, start life at a grave disadvantage compared with other children in the Nation. It has been estimated that 22 percent of American children suffer from malnutrition, and there is little evidence, even inferential, that rural children are much if any better off than urban in this respect. The prevalence of cash-crop farms as well as bitter poverty imposes an ill-balanced diet upon great groups of farm people. The evidence points to a relatively worse position for the farmer with respect to clothing and housing. As many as 50 percent of farmers are believed to live in inadequate dwellings, and probably one-third of them are poorly clothed.

Aside from the over-all inequity of the status of agriculture, there is imbalance within agriculture. It has been estimated that about 24 percent of all farm families in 1935–36 had less than $500 on which to live for a year, that at least 15 percent were "in dire physical need," and that "one-fourth to one-third of all our farm families are still below the poverty line."[3] Erosion still claims, despite great efforts, 3 billion tons of soil a year. So much for the material situation of agriculture. Figures upon many nonmaterial elements are hard to obtain, but it is known that rural school terms are shorter on an average than those of city schools and that teachers in rural schools are paid less than their urban colleagues. More than 70 percent of the entire rural population is without public-library service. And observation shows that all too few country families have any opportunity to enjoy music, pictures, plays, or movies. As citizen and worker, the farmer is still without effective control over the fruits of his labor, and he is still unsure that he can act to make his needs and desires known.

In conclusion this may be emphasized: The wants and desires of those who people the countrysides of the Nation are not static and will not go unvoiced. Their conception of what makes up a good life will continue to evolve with the changing times, and their struggle to convert that concept into reality will go on.

FUNDAMENTALS OF A GOOD AGRICULTURAL POLICY

Once some agreement has been reached as to the elements that rural people regard as essential to living a good life, the next question that logically arises is, how are they to obtain these elements? In terms of this discussion, how do these desires become translated first into policy and then into action designed to obtain the things they want? There can be little debate as to the ways in which they have obtained in recent years such of these elements as they have obtained. The last decade has given convincing demonstration to farmers of the value of group organization that moves aggressively on their behalf. There is no doubt whatever that the disposition of agriculture is to continue and expand this type of action. Symptomatic of this state of mind is this statement by the editor of a farm periodical:[4]

> The farmer today demands a standard of living in keeping to the contribution he makes to the national economy. He sees no reason why he should not enjoy most of those conveniences found in our cities and towns as a matter of course. But to obtain all those things takes money, far more money than farmers 40 years ago dreamed of having. Automobiles, tractors, radios, bath tubs, washing machines, refrigerators, etc., must be bought. To buy and maintain them the farmer must produce far above the animal needs of his family, and he must sell his products at a fair exchange value.
>
> When farm prices were low back in 1920–25, the farmer faced a choice. He could take what might be dished out to him and sink back into a state of chronic

---

[3] Maddox, James G. suggestions for a national program of rural rehabilitation and relief. Jour. Farm Econ. 21: 881–896. 1939. (Figures used by Maddox from: [United States] National Resources Committee. consumer incomes in the united states: their distribution in 1935–36. 104 pp., illus. 1939. Washington, D. C.)

[4] Roberts, Clarence. this isn't 1900 down on the farm. Daily Oklahoman Dec. 3, 1939, sec. D, p. 4. 1939.

poverty. Or, he could make a fight for a share of the national income which would permit him to live in decency and on a level comparable to men in town who render a like service to the nation. In the good old traditional American spirit he decided to fight. He is demanding government aid, not because he believes in aid as such, but because it seems at the moment the only attack on his problem that will get results.

Thus farmers have learned that group pressure will yield certain results, and few will deny that in justice they richly deserve the results they have obtained. New devices of consultation, cooperation, and administration looking toward the satisfaction of these demands will become major components of agricultural policy in the future if that policy mirrors the wishes of the people.

Discussion of such questions as these inevitably brings up related questions as to the interrelation of the popular will, the legislative process, and the administrative process; perhaps even of the place, in this framework, of the judiciary and of the great body of technical competence available in contemporary culture. Where do all these things fit into the makings of national policy? Perhaps the matter will be clarified somewhat by this quotation from Charles A. Beard, setting forth what he calls a "bill of axioms or aphorisms for public administration":[5]

(1) The continuous and fairly efficient discharge of certain functions by government, central and local, is a necessary condition for the existence of any great society.

(2) As a society becomes more complicated, as its division of labor ramifies more widely, as its commerce extends, as technology takes the place of handicrafts and local self-sufficiency, the functions of government increase in number and in their vital relationships to the fortunes of society and of individuals.

(3) Any government in such a complicated society, consequently any such society itself, is strong in proportion to its capacity to administer the functions that are brought into being.

(4) Legislation respecting these functions, difficult as it is, is relatively easy as compared with the enforcement of legislation, that is, the effective discharge of these functions in their most minute ramifications and for the public welfare.

(5) When a form of government, such as ours, provides for legal changes, by the process of discussion and open decision, to fit social changes, then effective and wise administration becomes the central prerequisite for the perdurance [continuance] of government and society—to use a metaphor—becomes a foundation of government as a going concern.

(6) Unless the members of an administrative system are drawn from various classes and regions, unless careers are open in it to talents, unless the way is prepared by an appropriate scheme of general education, unless public officials are subjected to internal and external criticism of a constructive nature, then the public personnel will become a bureaucracy dangerous to society and to popular government.

(7) Unless . . . an administrative system is so constructed and operated as to keep alive local and individual responsibilities, it is likely to destroy the basic well-springs of activity, hope, and enthusiasm necessary to popular government and to the flowering of a democratic civilization.

Can it not be said, in the light of these words, that policies are, in the first place, proposed by the people, and that, in the last place, they are judged by their effectiveness in the daily lives of the people? A corollary would seem to be that the more continuously and the more in detail policies are proposed and judged by the people, the better will be the chances of those policies for success. In other words,

[5] BEARD, CHARLES A. ADMINISTRATION, A FOUNDATION OF GOVERNMENT. (Extension of remarks of Hon. James A. Shanley, quoting Beard's speech before the Society of Public Administration.) Cong. Rec. Jan. 15, 1940, p. 557.

policies are outlined by the people in broad sweeping mandates, often inconsistent within themselves and usually very general in terms. The legislative branch of government gives these policies form and, to a certain extent, harmonizes them. The administrative arm develops and administers programs to give effect to the policies. But the "well-springs of activity, hope, and enthusiasm necessary to popular government" will be tapped throughout all these stages in "the flowering of a democratic civilization."

Policy, therefore, cannot be taken to mean simply a rule laid down by the people or their legislative or administrative representatives and then left to operate in a vacuum untouched by the necessities of circumstance. The mere statement of such a view seems to refute it. The realistic view is that policy making is a part of the daily, detailed living of the people and the functioning of their government in all its branches. If the formation of policy is conceived as being of this character, the powerful directive force of popular will throughout the process is apparent.

POLICIES IN ACTION

In turning from the general to the specific in policy, the present may be serviceable as a key to the future. If it does no more than instruct us in mistakes that can be avoided, such a survey will be useful. In this instance, we can discover much more than mistakes. In the policies of today, formed as they have been in response to emphatic though generalized instructions of the people as a whole, it is possible to see, at least partly, the shape of some of the things to come.

Contemporary agricultural policies have been pursued in a time when many nonagricultural influences exerted strong pressure upon farmers for good or ill. Agriculture is of course bound up inseparably with the total economy. This fact and others have limited and will continue to limit the directions that agricultural policy may take.

In the first place, agriculture has been faced since 1929 with an industrial situation in which available labor has far outrun available employment. This has meant that the rural population has backed up on the farm simply because alternative opportunities for employment could not be found. So long as this condition continues, a very considerable portion of the agricultural population is likely to engage in what is essentially subsistence rather than commercial farming. The result is a popular demand for the solution of problems associated with subsistence and submarginal types of farming and with such groups as migrant laborers and sharecroppers. If full employment is again reached in this country, with a prospect for sustained expansion, the measures proposed for today or for the several years immediately ahead may be altered.

A second limitation that conditions policy is the fact that, although agricultural production is becoming increasingly efficient, the market for agricultural products is no longer unlimited. Since the World War a number of forces have tended to increase either the efficiency of production or the actual quantity of products. The demand for the products has not increased at the same rate as the farmers' ability to produce them. Our foreign market has been severely curtailed, and it is doubtful whether any sustained improvement can be expected until an enduring peace is achieved in the world. Even then it is unlikely that the foreign market will absorb all the surpluses this country would like to sell. But a potentially large market at home among those who at present have inadequate purchasing power remains to be fully explored.

A third condition governing policy is the diversification of American agriculture; each commodity, region, and class of producers has its particular problem. This diversification is due in part to the fact that farmers of the United States supply one of the greatest free-trade markets in the world—their domestic market—and in part to the extremely wide range of physical conditions that affect or limit crop production.

A review of some of the objectives that contemporary policies seek to attain will be more enlightening if the forces just discussed are kept in mind. Broadly, these objectives may be said to be of three general types: (1) Activities designed to increase incomes of farmers who produce commodities for sale on a commercial scale; (2) the efforts to raise incomes and to improve the living conditions of migrant laborers, sharecroppers, subsistence farmers, victims of drought or flood, and others at a disadvantage within agriculture itself; and (3) activities designed to encourage better land use and more efficient production.

Most governmental programs of both the distant and the recent past have been directed toward improvement in the condition of commercial agriculture. It appears now that the last two of the groups of activities just listed will receive increasing attention in the immediate future, but to a considerable degree all three are interwoven. The problems of none of these will be solved separately; to some extent whatever approaches are made to solutions will be interdependent.

Issues of two kinds have been dominant in commercial American agriculture in the last quarter century: (1) Those associated with maintaining prices of the things farmers produce and incomes of the farmers who produce them; and (2) those associated with the existence of a large potential market for farm products that could not summon the buying power to buy the things farmers could and did produce, though this domestic market was badly needed because of declining foreign markets. Along with these two most prominent problems of the last 25 years there has been a whole complex of difficulties associated with credit, taxes, debt, land values, high risk in proportion to return, and other similar factors. These difficulties may be considered as a third major problem partly arising from and partly influencing the two others.

A previous article in this Yearbook (The Development of Agricultural Policy Since the End of the World War, p. 297) has recited in illuminating detail the history of the fight of farmers in the past two decades to attain "equality for agriculture" in the Nation—a fight for improvement all along the front indicated by the three groups of problems just named. This struggle illustrates the manner in which the desires of the people progressed from scattered, relatively ineffectual expression to legislative recognition and finally to actual administration. First, popular demand forced farm organizations to get together and agree upon their principal aims; then it pressed heavily upon public agencies concerned with agriculture; next it urged remedial measures through the legislative branch; and finally, when thwarted by executive action, it helped to bring about a change in the national administration itself.

As a result of the vast educational program to which this struggle subjected the whole Nation over many years, farmers and other groups have become conscious of the tremendous untapped consuming power of the American people. The loss of a great volume of export trade naturally has underlined this interest. Efforts to deal with the problem of unsalable surpluses and hungry people no doubt will receive increasing attention in the years ahead. This development will be discussed first.

Efforts to Increase Buying Power

At present, efforts to increase market demand include the development of the surplus purchase and other programs, especially the food-stamp program, designed to increase consumption among the low-income groups of the Nation; the encouragement of research in an effort to lower marketing costs and to improve marketing methods; and a wide variety of devices used to hold or regain the foreign market for such agricultural products as cotton and wheat.

One of the biggest marketing problems is to find a way to dispose of surpluses. Recently the use of these surpluses to improve the diets and living standards of low-income families has been explored. The Federal stamp plan has been an extension of this idea. Investigation of its possible application to cotton illustrates that it has potentialities for other commodities than food. A marketing program of this kind not only improves health and living standards but should be decidedly profitable to the farmer by moving into consumption many surpluses that now depress market prices. The surplus-commodities stamp program is still in the experimental stage. Further experience may show the need for many changes in detail, but something of this kind appears to offer distinct benefits to both farmers and consumers. In principle the food-stamp plan is similar to an export dumping program—with the one important difference that domestic consumers get the advantage of it.

In general, it may be said that consumption subsidies will be used to bring about better diets, better health, and better living standards generally for those families that are not now able to buy enough good food and clothing. The people of the country have evinced a growing concern for the conservation of surplus agricultural products in the widest sense—that is, use. Not only are farmers interested in stabilizing market prices through the disposal of surpluses; providing machinery to aid the underfed and undernourished has taken on the quality of a moral interest as well.

The steps that will be taken to hold or regain the export market for agricultural products will depend in part upon the extent to which any such device may be of help over a short period. Export subsidies have been used to retain the Nation's position in the world markets for cotton, wheat, and some minor commodities, and what are essentially barter arrangements have been resorted to in order to move some surplus agricultural products into the export market. Any satisfactory development of foreign trade depends chiefly upon the achievement of an enduring peace among the nations of the world in order that the fight for national self-containment may be stopped. The United States itself has contributed in considerable degree to the decline of its foreign market, and in the last few years the reciprocal trade agreements program has been in part an effort to undo some of the things which this country itself did earlier.

Involved in the whole problem of the export trade are certain emotional attitudes of people, including farmers. Notably, it is a human trait to ignore the fact that trade means an exchange of commodities—that it means buying as well as selling. Thus the tendency is to ignore the fact that if a Nation wants to sell its products abroad it must buy products from abroad. Then, too, there is a strong emotional pull among all groups of people toward economic as well as political isolation, and this pull exerts an influence upon any effort that might be made toward extension of foreign markets for agricultural commodities.

Control of Production and Marketing

A major phase of the policy of maintaining prices and incomes in agriculture has been the attempt to adjust supplies to market demand. This attempt, it may be said parenthetically, was in direct response to the insistence of farm groups. The working out of this policy has led to the development of what is known as the ever-normal-granary program. This program includes acreage allotments or conditional grants and benefit payments, commodity loans, and marketing quotas for use in years when supplies are excessively high. Taken together, these devices are designed to stabilize acreage, production, and marketings in such a fashion as to increase farm incomes while at the same time insuring adequate supplies for both the domestic and the foreign market.

A great deal of progress has been made in the application of policies such as that embodied in this program, but much is still to be worked out. Certainly, crop acreages can be controlled, marketing quotas can be administered, and commodity loans can be effective devices for preventing wide fluctuations in prices. Acreage control tends to increase efficiency of production, since it is usually so administered as to allow farmers to maintain their best land in production and since a reduction in the chief cash crops is also a reduction in the acreage of the chief soil-depleting crops, so that the farm plant is usually improved and potential yields are increased. This means, of course, that unless new consuming power is tapped, the control problem will become increasingly difficult as the program is continued.

Marketing quotas, in turn, ordinarily cannot be invoked unless a critical condition exists, and even then farmers usually operate under quotas so adjusted as to allow them to market all the products grown on their acreage allotments. A considerable degree of control is thus lost, and commodity loans must be depended upon to obtain a considerable part of the desired market adjustment.

The commodity loan is essentially a device to stabilize prices. Loans can be set at rates that will result in undue accumulation of stocks. On the other hand, the loan rate may be fixed at such a level that it will offer genuine support in years when supplies are excessively large; the rate also may be restrained from following prices up in years when supplies are reasonable.

So long as appropriations can be obtained for payments to supplement income from the market place, the question as to how they shall be distributed among the different commodities will be raised. To the extent that such payments are made, they can be used to supplement returns from the sale of those commodities the prices of which are lowest in relation to the prices of other agricultural products. Payments of this kind may be regarded as an integral part of an agricultural program, the separate phases of which are harmonized. Such questions are already receiving the attention of administrators of agricultural programs.

It is now realized that the process of marketing involves a large number of difficult and important problems, which can perhaps be classified in two groups: (1) Regulating or adjusting the existing market machinery to make it operate as smoothly as possible, and (2) encouraging fundamental changes to improve the system itself.

For many years the Department has been responsible for several kinds of regulation and service work, including, for example, the regulation of commodity exchanges, the inspection of food products, the provision of grades and standards, the development of a Nation-wide market news service, and many others that are important. Since 1933 the Department has developed an additional program of market regulation through marketing agreements and orders (see p. 638). This device makes possible more effective cooperation among farmers in the interests of orderly marketing. The agreements and orders appear to have a permanent place in the marketing of dairy products, fruits, and vegetables. They enable producers of these crops to regulate the amount and rate of shipment to market and to exercise a certain amount of control over the quality of the products marketed, which in many cases has proved profitable to farmers.

Less progress has been made, however, in bringing about any fundamental changes in the marketing system. Research and regulatory programs have been concerned with adjustments to make the present system operate as well as possible, but there is a growing realization that the farmer, the middleman, and the consumer would all benefit from more fundamental changes to increase the efficiency of the marketing system as a whole. The farmer is getting less than 50 cents of each dollar the consumer spends for foods. This does not mean that all middlemen are getting rich. It does mean that a thoroughgoing analysis of the marketing process is needed, along with a careful study of possible improvements in transportation, processing, and distribution.

A fair start on this problem has been made during the last few years—enough to show that very substantial savings could be made. But if much is to be accomplished in this direction an intelligent interest on the part of the public, as well as more research, is needed. If efficient marketing is desired, the growth of interstate trade barriers and various forms of price fixing will be stopped, and policies will encourage the growth of any type of marketing that is efficient and will not attempt to maintain inefficient types.

Financial Adjustments

The third problem that dominates efforts to bring about a healthy commercial agriculture is really a complex of problems, including those connected with credit, land values, debt, costs in relation to income, the risk of loss through natural causes, and many others. Two of these problems will be considered at this point—insurance against risk and the provision of credit.

Crop insurance is a comparatively new field of governmental activity, and few developments of the last decade are more attractive to the commercial farmer. The possibility of insuring crops against loss from natural causes would have excited derisive comment a half century ago in the belief that even if the plan were feasible, it would be madness to underwrite farming in this way. Such crop insurance systems as are now operating appear to have met this criticism adequately. But it seems safe to say that farm people will not want crop insurance used as a method of permanently underwriting farming in areas not adapted to farming or of bulwarking waste of the soil.

The provision of adequate credit is another element on which there is likely to be continued popular insistence. The fight for a more nearly adequate agricultural credit system was started shortly before the outbreak of the World War in 1914 and has continued to the present. As a result, a reasonably adequate system exists for commercial agriculture. The problems in this field, however, are by no means solved.

The several governmental credit agencies that serve the commercial farmer are finding it increasingly necessary to coordinate their programs and their efforts with those of agencies carrying on other parts of the agricultural program. To a considerable extent, these governmental credit agencies now provide certain yardsticks against which the credit charges and the policies of commercial lending agencies can be measured. One of the most important of these yardsticks is the method of appraisal used in extending farm-mortgage credit. The appraisal of farm-land values on the basis of normal yields and normal prices exerts a stabilizing influence. It seems clear that more attention will be paid to the systems of farming followed, especially as they affect conservation. The adoption of a variable amortization schedule would be a further stabilizing influence in that it would allow farmers to decrease their indebtedness at a rapid rate in good years and to carry on in bad years when their means of repayment were limited.

The Importance of Conservation

Conservation of soil and of human resources is inextricably bound up not only with the practices of commercial farming but with the condition of the generally underprivileged noncommercial farming group. It is a truism nowadays that education of farmers by itself is inadequate as a means of enabling them to maintain their resources. Poverty, the farm-tenure system, the economy of the individual farm and of whole farming areas and regions, and a host of other factors all have a bearing on the extent to which conservative methods can be used in production. Economic conditions affect conservation of natural resources, and on the other hand soil waste affects the economic condition of farmers, commercial and noncommercial.

223761°—40——75

Since the extension of farming into areas subject to recurrent drought and the realization that many farm people in some of the rougher and more broken sections of the country can never expect to attain the standard of living they desire, there has been a growing public demand for acquisition or control of considerable areas of submarginal land by some public agency, county, State, or Federal.

One of the major methods of obtaining better land use is through the acquisition and operation of forest and submarginal farm land by public agencies where such lands are of a character that makes private operation clearly inadvisable or inefficient.

The more commonly advocated programs of this sort are those for Federal acquisition of submarginal land and for county and State control of tax-reverted land, usually also submarginal. Federal acquisition has proved slow, complex, and subject to many restrictions, some of which are not inherent. Federal purchase has been a slow process because, for one thing, some people do not want to sell their land and because title must be obtained through a cumbersome legal process. Even more important, there is a feeling on the part of many county governments that Federal purchase destroys the tax base for county and State revenues. Most important of all, there is always the problem of where the people who are to be evacuated from the submarginal areas can relocate.

County and State control of tax-reverted lands offer much for the future. Aggressive action by these agencies can go far toward achieving genuine national conservation of resources, especially if reasonably adequate standards can be established for the repossession of such lands and for methods of operation. A pronounced popular trend in this direction has been apparent in recent years, and it may become strong enough to promote aggressive action. If that occurs, programs for public purchase of land can profit by the lessons of the past. Popular opinion also points toward the supplementing of purchase programs by some specific program for giving displaced people a means of livelihood.

Only recently has there been widespread realization that our land resources are limited, or at least that the greater portion of the more productive, more easily cultivated land is already under cultivation and that soil erosion has been taking an enormous toll. This popular realization commands the Nation, even though conservation means more efficient production and, perhaps, added unmarketable supplies, to try to stop soil erosion and to adopt such conserving practices as are needed to maintain the productivity of the land.

Conservation is required because we are unable to forecast future land needs, because the better lands are now occupied and it would require more labor and increased costs to shift production to poorer land, if that became necessary, and because of the popular demand for stabilizing agriculture on the better land in order that adequate housing and operating facilities may be supplied and community life may achieve its best possibilities.

Current policies designed to relate conservation with the acreage-allotment and conditional-grant approach to income raising and crop control have met with favorable popular response. Perhaps the national interest will require that those obtaining benefit or price-adjustment payments in connection with the allotment program follow a system of farming that will more fully conserve the soil or control erosion than do their present systems.

Public credit agencies are giving increased attention to the problem of conservation, and indeed some of the private lending agencies, especially insurance companies, are already experimenting in this field. It may be, for example, that the present wastage clause in the farm mortgages of public agencies will be replaced by a specific requirement that land be protected from wind and water erosion by the carrying out of certain specified practices. Perhaps farmers will call for new ways of handling foreclosed farms and farm lands. The transfer of farm lands in submarginal areas to public control and the sale of farm land in certain areas only in units of sufficient size to provide for commercial operation are other instances of the avenues that the people may feel that Government should take.

Social Adjustments

When policy turns from the problems of the commercial farmer and of conservation to those associated with what has been called noncommercial agriculture, it abandons familiar for less charted pathways.

The thesis of the following paragraphs is that agricultural policy in the future will take into account many elements that it has ignored or dealt with only lightly in the past, but that have been brought to the forefront of national thinking by the trend of popular opinion. Put in another way, this thesis is that the old patterns have proved insufficient for new or newly recognized problems. The pressure of the people upon the land and of wasting land upon people; the stride of technology across the country, smashing old ways of living, in seven-league boots; the drive, engendered by the economic environment, for efficiency in agriculture at the expense of humanity; the altered state of the world at large—these are some of the problems pressing upon individuals, and therefore upon groups and upon Government. The problems are of such a nature as to make it almost certain that people will demand new approaches for their solution—approaches in line with our own traditions but capable of developing new patterns of American life and opening new opportunities for achieving the things our farm people want.

It will help to promote agreement upon the nature of the problem, and perhaps on policy, if some facts about noncommercial or subsistence farmers are surveyed. The major aspects of the problem are the poverty of the people in this group and the possibility that this poverty will be aggravated in the future unless current programs change the outlook. Fifty percent of all American farms produce only 10 percent of our commercial farm products. More than a million and a half men and boys of working age who lived on farms registered in 1937 as partly or wholly unemployed save for emergency public work—and 1937 was a relatively prosperous year for agriculture. Only one out of six received public employment, while considerably more than half were wholly unemployed. Other statistics that would emphasize the plight of this group could readily be given.

The prospects for the future are less generally recognized than the present situation. Although knowledge of the effects of technology upon the employment of farm labor is fragmentary at best, enough is known to indicate clearly that nothing has happened to reverse the trend of the past century. In that time, the number of man-hours required to produce 100 bushels of wheat from 5 acres dropped from 288 in 1830 to 125 in 1880; and at last accounts it stood at 49. The same kind of thing has happened in the case of other commodities and other aspects of agriculture besides production. Every year about 400,000 farm boys reach working age, 18 years. Yearly, about 110,000 farmers die, and somewhere near the same number go into other occupations or retire. Allowing for other factors, it appears that every year until 1960 at least, about 200,000 farmers between 18 and 65 years of age will be added to the number now on farms. In other words, there will be a 23-percent increase in the number of farmers in the next 20 years unless the movement of farmers to cities accelerates.

The immediate conclusion that emerges from recent experience in dealing with such problems as these figures imply is that there is emphatic public endorsement of programs for the rehabilitation of farm people. Americans are nearly unanimous in their hostility to direct relief if they can find any other way out of pressing miseries, and the use of rehabilitation instead of direct relief seems to fit in with that sentiment. A successful rural rehabilitation program requires a combination of vocational guidance and credit based on character. This means, in effect, that in granting a man credit, his character is more important than the collateral he can offer and that a representative of the rehabilitation agency sits down with him and works out a farm plan that offers both the farmer and the agency a good prospect of success in a mutual venture. The general approval of such work in the past argues for its extension and elaboration in the future.

Further developments may include new ways of combining loans and outright grants of aid, still with rehabilitation as the end in view; and new techniques for fitting plans of operation to the farms. By such means the present method of rehabilitation can be made more useful.

The reestablishment of tenant families as owners provided for in current programs, also appears to have popular endorsement; and despite the relative slowness of this method, it is likely to be expanded in the future. The use of subsidies or direct governmental action to deal with certain kinds of problems has had wide popular support in recent years. The social-security program and the various proposals for a Federal health program are examples. Rural education is likely to be included in this group, especially since farmers bear much more than their proportionate share of the cost of rearing and educating the young people of the Nation.

There is a vigorous general opinion to the effect that rural young people, whether they are to remain on farms or to migrate to the cities, where they help to maintain the urban population, should be brought up in homes in which at least a minimum standard of living prevails and that they should be properly educated. There is also considerable demand for the development of better medical facilities in most rural areas. There are now enough doctors and nurses in the Nation to supply adequate medical service for all of our population, but both doctors and nurses, as well as hospital and laboratory facilities, are concentrated in the larger cities. It is likely that more attention will be given to means of attaining a better distribution and providing medical service at a reasonable cost for farmers with low incomes.

The provision of better educational facilities involves a reconsideration of our whole system of rural education. Possibly there will be a demand for establishing minimum educational standards in length of the school term, subjects taught, and training of the teaching personnel. For the present, certainly, it is doubtful whether any considerable number of rural States can or will go forward in this field, and for this reason there may be increased sentiment for some kind of Federal program that, while not infringing on State and local prerogatives, will guarantee minimum standards, even though it involves an increased subsidy or grants-in-aid.

Rural housing and living conveniences present another problem in this group. In this field the most striking recent experiment has been public action to make electric power more widely available to farmers. Within a short time the number of farm users of electricity has approximately doubled, and there have been notable advances in methods of distributing electricity and electrical appliances at prices that farmers can afford.

The various developments touched on here can be summed up from the standpoint of a broad attitude or approach.

Government in the past decade has assumed the responsibility for rectifying as nearly as it can the unequal position of agriculture within the national economy. This was in response to overwhelming mass demand. There may be a similar demand within the next decade for rectifying inequities within agriculture itself.

An illustration is the demand from many rural sections for better housing. Another is the demand for a program that will give work and supplementary income to unemployed and disadvantaged rural folk, doing for them what various programs have done for some urban groups. This is not the place to enter into debate as to the cost of such programs, or their self-liquidating character, or other controversial details. Use of such a method by Government, when it becomes necessary, does appear to be as legitimate for rural as for urban people.

There may also be a more insistent demand in the future for further development of part-time farming, subsistence homesteads, and cooperative farms, with which there has been a limited amount of experimenting in recent years. A large and increasing number of farm people, especially near cities and towns and along the principal highways, have sources of income that are partly agricultural and partly nonagricultural. Many farmers are practicing a very primitive and essentially subsistence type of agriculture. There are many migrant laborers and tenants who can never hope to become owners. All of these groups are likely to press harder for a solution of their problems in the years ahead.

In other words, policy will make use of the crude patterns developing in society itself. The trend toward part-time farming already exists. If farm families can become part of a community organization, if the spread of industry into rural areas can be stimulated, then part-time farming that is underwritten, at least to some extent, by Government may be one of the most effective cushions against economic shocks.

Similarly, the patterns of subsistence farming and of the family-size farm already exist. Subsistence farming of the type common in, say, pre-Civil War days has no significance now. But a type of farming designed to make use of technological advances, community planning, group organization, and new avenues to some supplementary income—this kind of subsistence farming holds much promise as a way out of difficulties for thousands of farmers. It would also carry on the tradition of the family-size farm, which has been a symbol of free agrarianism throughout this country's history.

The success of cooperative loans for equipment and for medical services and of related testings of group action encouraged by Government leads to the belief that people may demand more energetic and persistent efforts in this direction as a part of agricultural policy in the future. Perhaps the most interesting of the discoveries growing out of experimentation in this work has been the effect of cooperative activity upon the people themselves, aside from questions of the improvement of their economic status. The evidence seems clear that group endeavor has promoted a healthful attitude, socially and psychologically, and this is a very real though imponderable gain for individual and Nation alike.

Among the depressed groups in agriculture are farm laborers. Unless their situation is improved through such means as have already been discussed, the prospect is that they will present a problem distinct from those of other agricultural groups. They are increasing in numbers and becoming increasingly industrialized. The agricultural ladder, by which they formerly climbed to tenancy or ownership, has been shattered ever since the World War. Unless it is repaired quickly, there will be a demand for wage and hour legislation for a more or less permanent class of agricultural laborers at present exempted from legislation designed for industrial workers. For migrant laborers there is already a demand that the States or the Federal Government at the very least provide labor camps that will give these people a decent place to live and that their children be given educational opportunities that will enable them to become valuable citizens of a democracy.

POLICIES OF THE FUTURE

The current agricultural programs and the policies from which they spring have been examined in some detail in this article in a search for conclusions as to what the future may hold in store. What broad generalizations can be made from such a summary?

One such generalization is that the policies of the future will tend to reconcile the old and the new in the political, economic, and social aspects of agriculture. This task of reconciliation has been described by M. L. Wilson as follows: [6]

> The solution, as I see it, lies in combining the best of the new with the most enduring of the old, and in political-social-economic-educational policies that strive to keep the social mechanism sufficiently simple for fundamental popular

---

[6] BAKER, O. E., BORSODI, RALPH, and WILSON, M. L. AGRICULTURE IN MODERN LIFE. 303 pp., illus. New York and London. 1939.

understanding—whether in terms of reason or of prevailing folklore. Otherwise democracy cannot survive, and violent clashes of interest and ideologies will follow. The practical social understanding that was provided by the folklore of the self-sufficing culture does not apply to the new world of specialization and interdependence. The environments are almost complete opposites. The abruptness of the transition is fundamentally responsible for the greatest social tragedies of this age. The task of today is one of compromise and qualification. Our future now lies . . . in combining *some* dependent specialization with *some* individual responsibility, in joining *some* group and cooperative activity with *some* personal self-sufficiency. This will give mankind a chance to assimilate culturally the great mass of novelty that science and technology have already created.

Consideration of one major policy of the present, the maintenance of farm income through crop control, calls for a look at the future of acreage and marketing control, of commodity loans and price-adjustment payments as they apply to the basic commodities. Agriculture's ability to produce these commodities in quantities equal to or in excess of domestic and foreign requirements clearly indicates that adjustment and stabilizing efforts may be expected to continue, though the results achieved may not always be entirely satisfactory even to those who are most directly benefited.

Given different conditions from those to be expected within the more or less predictable future, the necessity for such controls may disappear. One such set of conditions would be the full employment of the working population, whether in industry or in agriculture. Perhaps domestic measures or free flow of world trade may bring about such conditions. Perhaps it will be possible for the Nation to work out ways of supplying its needs with reduced manpower and at the same time of giving all employables useful work and a high standard of living. But, to be realistic about the matter, none of these developments can be expected within any reasonable period. Until they occur, the problem the controls are designed to cope with will remain. It is to be expected that these mechanisms will be refined, perhaps modified, as experience dictates, but to discuss policy under the assumption that we can dispense with them does not seem profitable.

After all, such programs are essentially equalizing devices designed to provide farmers with an opportunity to obtain the advantages that labor obtains through organization and that business obtains through concentration of financial control, with a structure that allows costs to be cut by reducing production when demand is depressed.

Although increasing attention will be given, perhaps necessarily, to price maintenance, the effort to maintain prices at a reasonable cost to the Treasury is almost certain to drive attention back toward acreage and marketing adjustment and regulation. It seems, too, that in response to farmer insistence upon continuance of programs of this type, some way must be found of affording a stable financial base for them.

Controversy has centered for two decades around policies for price maintenance and crop control. The main stream of thought thus may be said to be reasonably well defined, except for those unpredictable shifts and changes which are continually being dictated by the exigencies of the moment.

Credit policy for agriculture will continue to be important. In part, the modifications in this field will be in terms of revising the more purely commercial types of credit that have developed through the last quarter of a century so as to relate them more closely to agricultural policies in fields other than credit. Other changes may be expected in the direction of further developing the credit functions now performed by the Farm Security Administration as part of its program of rural rehabilitation. This involves reasonably liberal loans to farmers whose resources are limited, based in considerable part on character and on the preparation of detailed farm- and home-management plans accompanied by technical supervision.

Efforts to develop better regulatory policies in marketing also will continue. Farmers feel that marketing and transportation charges are too high and too inflexible. Commodity speculation, especially, has long been a traditional devil for farmers and farm politicians. Speculation is now regulated, and we find ourselves increasingly concerned for marketing reform and improvement. But it must be remembered that marketing costs are chiefly compounded of wage rates, transportation charges, and the physical efficiency of the marketing system itself. Therefore any significant drop in the cost of marketing can be made only by bringing about greater physical efficiency—that is, by the utilization of fewer man-hours to perform each of the marketing functions mentioned. A spectacular reorganization that will greatly lower marketing costs in the near future is not to be expected. Consumers are demanding costly services. Some wage rates have increased. The quality of food has improved. With these trends we may do well to prevent further increases in marketing costs in the next few years. Nevertheless, farmers and consumers alike are becoming increasingly aware of the importance of marketing problems, and many groups of middlemen are becoming convinced that inefficiencies are unprofitable to them.

So far as better land use and soil and water conservation are concerned, it seems reasonable to expect a continuation of research and discussion, with a relatively slow but continued development in the field of action.

The idea of conservation, of saving the great natural resources of the Nation that, once gone, can never be replaced, and the argument that men should not be forced to spend their lives or their labor on land that is too poor to yield them a living even under favorable price conditions—such an idea and such an argument appeal very strongly to most men, if public response to these views in recent years may be taken as a guide.

But despite the sentiment and logic of the argument for conserving the soil and forests and working toward better patterns of land use, it is certain that the soil disappears slowly, that people are hesitant to question anything they are used to, and that the actual implementing of action programs of this kind can only gradually be achieved. In fact, if conservation policy is to be most fruitful, some way will be found for bringing the skills and services of technical conservationists to bear on other agricultural activities to the fullest extent. And if submarginal and forest lands are to be retired from cultivation, the farmers who are now on such lands will want, and their fellow farmers will want them to have, some place to go—where they can find some new land to operate or can develop a new way of agricultural life.

The third great stream of agricultural policy includes questions of dealing with the great mass of low-income farmers and farm people and the problems primarily associated with them. These are the people who are least vocal, and theirs are the problems that are least clearly understood in an environment where it was once an accepted maxim that every honest man would die rich if only he were willing to work hard enough.

These are the prople—and they account for one-third to one-half of all the farmers in the United States—who are most poorly organized and most frequently forced to depend upon the social conscience of others for support. From the preceding discussion, it may be said that the policies most likely to break new ground in the decade ahead will be the policies designed to benefit these disadvantaged classes.

First of all, it may be expected that the programs for commercial agriculture will give greater recognition to the small-scale producer and the family-size farm and greater security to certain classes of farmers whose operating risks are relatively high. This means increasing attention in the form of allotments, exemptions, and bonuses to the small-scale operators, and the continuation of crop insurance on wheat and its extension to other crops.

Second, a modification of some of our existing ideas with respect to conservation appears in prospect, as it becomes increasingly apparent that the land available to many farmers is so limited that they must usually seek to conserve soil through the use of farming practices rather than by shifting from soil-depleting to soil-conserving crops, about which so much has been heard during the past decade.

Third, the continued attention directed toward tenancy and the recognition of the evils of tenancy should gradually work toward the evolution of an intelligent tenancy policy. Traditionally, of course, Americans cherish the ideal of an unbroken agricultural ladder—of the farm boy starting as a laborer, working through several stages of tenancy and part ownership, and finally ending as full owner of a farm. This idea will persist and with it the effort to obtain increasing sums to finance a tenant purchase program.

But tenancy is not universally an evil, and there is little hope of appreciably bettering the condition of the 42 percent of farmers who are now tenants or sharecroppers if the country pins its hopes solely to an ownership program. Probably this fact will lead to popular insistence upon an intelligent and sustained drive for improving and stabilizing landlord-tenant relationships. This matter is also bound up with the success of some other agricultural programs and with the opening up of industrial opportunities.

Fourth, unless there is a marked expansion in commercial and industrial employment, the problems of a rational rural relief policy will be pressed more vigorously by a larger and larger number of people. So far, dependence has been placed upon a combination of Federal work projects, local relief, the Civilian Conservation Corps, and subsistence grants provided by the Farm Security Administration. Perhaps it is time to develop a rural conservation works program.

Certainly statistics given earlier on available farm manpower and its prospective utilization in present systems of agriculture point strongly toward increasing pressure for some such method of cushioning the impact of social and technological change.

Fifth, the rural rehabilitation program or its equivalent will be continued, but this is another field in which policy will be reoriented. Rural rehabilitation will be asked to do more than simply pick up members of farm families whose lives have been shattered by our current economic organization and endeavor to stick them back into the same kind of situation out of which they have just been forced.

That is, although rural rehabilitation will be continued, the general view is likely to be that the rehabilitation program should not be handicapped by being obliged to carry a burden for which it is not fitted. Perhaps one of the more important public debates of the decade ahead will turn on the question of how the acreage available and the payments made can be better distributed within agriculture.

But it may be that it will not be possible to find for many farm families the additional land and market necessary to supply a decent level of employment and even a minimum standard of living measured in American terms or the things other than land that many of them need. If not, in all likelihood the desires of the people will take two different directions. In the first place, they will seek ways of providing adequate medical care, education, and certain essential standards of living, including housing, roads, and the chance for amusement and relaxation for all the people. This demand probably will not be diminished by the opposing argument that considerable subsidies will be involved. In the second place, the prospect is that there will be popular insistence on devoting increased attention to the new way of agricultural life that is quietly developing in our midst—the combination of part-time agricultural employment in small-scale farming with other employment, in agriculture, in industry, or in a rural conservation program of the type mentioned.

Births in rural areas are currently running ahead of deaths by at least 400,000 annually. If our excess farm population remains on the land, it will demand employment of some sort. In part, this may take the form of producing goods and services for home use. But the old ideal of a completely self-sufficing farm economy is vanishing, if it has not already vanished, before the rising tide of urbanization; accompanying this urbanization is an abandonment of the old shibboleth of thrift and an acknowledgment of the great gulf between the nature of public spending and that of private spending. The constant infiltration of urban traits into the action and thinking of farm people is one of the most striking characteristics of contemporary rural life.

And why not? Why should farm people live in houses without the modern conveniences that city people take for granted? Why should farm women in some sections be forced to work in the field as well as do all the housework, when women of other groups do not? Why should farm people be expected to do without radios or that active comprehension of the modern scene which is fostered by the movie and the automobile? Why, even, should they limit themselves strictly to home-grown foods when the rest of the Nation eats fresh fruits and vegetables at times when they cannot be produced locally?

In the answers to these and other questions suggested in the earlier pages of this article, it may have seemed at times as if too much emphasis were being placed upon the responsibility of Government for trying to set the world right. Such an emphasis is in part inevitable. For one thing, it is only in recent decades that Government has assumed some of the responsibilities it should have assumed earlier; for another, in a discussion of policy in relation to Government, the role of the latter as compared with the role of the individual may bulk larger than it does in reality. If there appears to be too much of this emphasis, let it be said here that in the quest for a new way of life for farm people, Government's job ends when it has done what it can to free human potentialities. Government cannot confer success upon anyone; it can only help to give him a fair chance. In the performance of that function, Government has been forced to turn more and more directly to the people, as current national farm programs show. So long as this holds true, Government will not loom larger in the Nation's life than is proper.

The development of this new way of agricultural life will involve many experiments, but it seems to be foreshadowed in the demands of the people. Perhaps farming will never be an entirely stable way of life. All ways of farming, indeed all ways of life have their hazards, and this new way of life for the lower economic groups in agriculture means in the long run a strengthening of the economic base of rural society in all its phases. In turn, this cannot but benefit the Nation at large. Such a policy will be the product of the interactions that have been described earlier in this article, but if it is to be an agricultural policy that can be truly designated as "good" it will deal with the needs of every group in the agricultural population because it will reflect as fully as possible the desires of all groups. So shaped, this policy will at once give farmers of this generation a chance at the good life and at the same time conserve the human and natural resources from which will spring the life of the future.

Appendix

A Brief Chronology of American Agricultural History

COMPILED BY DOROTHY C. GOODWIN, UNDER THE DIRECTION OF PAUL H. JOHNSTONE [1]

HERITAGE

OXEN and horses were used for power, the wooden plows were crude, all sowing was done by hand, hoes were used for cultivating, hay and grain cutting was done with sickles, and threshing with flails. (Compare with later technological developments.)

All forms of domestic livestock except turkeys were at some time imported from Europe.

Plants imported from Europe included small grains, many fruits and vegetables, fiber plants, timothy and clover.

Plants borrowed from the Indians included maize, sweetpotatoes, tomatoes, pumpkins, gourds, squashes, watermelons, beans, peas, grapes, berries, pecans, black walnuts, peanuts, maple sugar, tobacco, and cotton. White potatoes were indigenous to South America.

Northern farmers tended to be self-sufficing. The plantation economy of the South was largely commercial.

Tobacco was the chief cash crop and principal agricultural export of the colonial South.

Rural-urban antagonisms had their roots in the colonial period in the conflicts between the politically powerful commercial interests of the cities and the self-sufficient farmers of the hinterlands.

Eighteenth-century ideas of progress, human perfectibility, rationality, and scientific improvement flourished in the New World as in the Old. Benjamin Franklin, George Washington, Thomas Jefferson, and others exemplified this spirit and encouraged its application to American agriculture and rural life. (See Jefferson, 1793; and George Washington, 1796.)

Jared Eliot (1685–1763), of Connecticut, wrote Essays upon Field Husbandry.

DEVELOPMENT

1785. The Philadelphia Society for the Promotion of Agriculture was founded. It was an example of the new spirit of scientific improvement.

1786. In Shays's Rebellion the farmers of western Massachusetts revolted against deflation and the financial policies of their Boston creditors.

1789. The first tariff act, for revenue only, was passed.

1790. The settled area extended westward an average of 255 miles.
Over 90 percent of all persons gainfully employed were engaged in agriculture. Many industrial functions which were later to be taken over by factories were at this time a regular part of the farm economy.

The sale of public lands was one of the money-raising devices resorted to by the newly formed States. This gave impetus to specula-

[1] Dorothy C. Goodwin is Junior Social Scientist, and Paul H. Johnstone is Senior Agricultural Historian, Bureau of Agricultural Economics.

tion in new lands, which rose in value, sometimes spectacularly, as population increased and as improved means of transportation and communication were developed. The financial success of many such ventures and the repeated experience of rising land values tended to emphasize, particularly in the newer sections of the country, the speculative aspects of land ownership.

In the last years of the eighteenth century the cradle and scythe, which had been brought in from Europe, came into wide use.

1793. The cotton gin was invented, paving the way for a tremendous increase in cotton production.
Jefferson tested his moldboard of least resistance.
The first Merino sheep were imported.

Northern farmers continued to be largely self-sufficient, while the plantation economy of the South remained largely commercial.

1794. In the Whiskey Rebellion, western farmers revolted against a tax on grain in the form of whiskey.

This was the period of aristocratic agricultural and scientific societies.

1796. George Washington suggested to Congress the establishment of a National Board of Agriculture.
1797. Newbold patented the first cast-iron plow.

In the late 1790's the sheep industry began to assume importance in New England. By 1810 the interest in Merino sheep had reached the proportions of a craze. This development resulted principally from the separation of America from the British textile industry during the Revolution and was stimulated by the Napoleonic Wars, which hampered trade with Europe. In 1816, after the end of the War of 1812 and the Napoleonic Wars, the price of wool collapsed and the sheep industry began to decline.

1800. The frontier had crossed the Appalachians.
1803. The Louisiana Purchase added 827,987 square miles to the territory of the United States.
1790–1820. The era of turnpike (toll-road) building improved communication and commerce between the settlements.

Aristocratic agricultural and scientific societies began to be replaced by more democratic societies and fair associations.

1804. The first modern agricultural fair was held in Washington, D. C.
1807. Fulton demonstrated the practicability of the steamboat.
Elkanah Watson exhibited Merino sheep in Pittsfield, Mass. As a result of the public response to this exhibition, he initiated the movement for agricultural fair associations.

Sorghum was brought in from Africa on a slave ship at an unknown date, probably in the first or second decade of the nineteenth century. It was not widely cultivated until about the fifties.

1810. The first American agricultural periodical, the Agricultural Museum, began publication.

Cotton began to take the place of tobacco as the chief cash crop of the South.

During the period between 1810 and 1830 the transfer of manufactures from the farm and home to the shop and factory was greatly accelerated. Farming became a less self-sufficient and a more specialized and commercial enterprise as a result of this change. The farmers began to need cash in order to buy the things they had formerly produced, and the growing urban and industrial populations required specialized agricultural production to support them.

1812–14. The War of 1812 and a war depression.
1814–16. Period of prosperity following the war.
1816. The first protective tariff act was passed.

Antagonism between the commercial and farming interests tended to increase. The farming interests of the South especially began to wage a losing fight against the protective tariff, which increased the cost of many of the manufactured goods they had to buy. (See The Tariff of Abominations, 1828; The tariff, 1857; and The Morrill Tariff Act, 1861.)

1819. Florida and other lands were acquired by treaty with Spain.
Jethro Wood patented an iron plow with interchangeable parts.
The Plough Boy and the American Farmer began publication.
The Secretary of the Treasury instructed consuls to collect seeds, plants, and agricultural inventions for introduction into this country. There was no appropriation.
The New York State Board of Agriculture was set up by the State legislature. It was the first organization of this sort.
1819–21. A period of depression came after the temporary prosperity that followed the War of 1812.
1820. About 83 percent of all persons gainfully employed were engaged in agriculture.
1821. Edmund Ruffin published his first Essay on Calcareous Manures (lime). Expanded editions of this essay based on further experimentation appeared from time to time until 1852.
1822. The first issue of the New England Farmer appeared.

Popular and agricultural education was becoming the most important rural issue.

1822–25. This period, during Monroe's second presidential term, was called the Era of Good Feeling because of the comparative prosperity and internal political peace which characterized it.

The value of new lands continued to rise as the population grew and as communication developed.

About 50 to 60 man-hours of labor were required to produce 1 acre (20 bushels) of wheat with a walking plow, a bundle of brush for harrow, hand broadcast of seed, harvesting by sickle, and threshing by flail. (Compare with labor requirements about 1890 and about 1930.)

Poland-China and Duroc-Jersey swine were being developed.

Berkshire swine were being imported.

Cotton was established as the chief cash crop of the Old South.

Competition with western farm areas began to force New England farmers out of meat and wheat production into dairying, truck, and later, tobacco.

1825. The Erie Canal was opened. This was the climax of the canal-building era.
1825–29. Depression.
1826. Josiah Holbrook organized Branch No. 1 of the American Lyceum at Millbury, Mass.

This was the period of manual-labor schools based on the educational system worked out by Fellenberg in Hofwyl, Switzerland. Students in these schools helped to make the institutions self-supporting by working on school farms and in workshops.

Rural-urban issues began to play an increasingly important part in national politics. (See Rural-urban antagonisms, under Heritage, p. 1184.)

1828. The "Tariff of Abominations" was enacted. This was an extremely high protective tariff sponsored by the Jacksonians, as a political move, and by the woolen interests. It was opposed by the South. (See South Carolina directed the Nullification Ordinance, 1832.)
The first issues of the New York Farmer and the Southern Agriculturist appeared.
1830. The Mississippi River formed the approximate boundary of the frontier.
1830–37. Land-speculation boom.
1831. Peter Cooper's railroad steam engine, the "Tom Thumb," ran 13 miles.

The beginning of the railroad era.

1831. The first issue of the Genessee Farmer appeared.
By this time 900 towns had Lyceums—associations for providing adult and community education in agriculture and other subjects and for training teachers.

Popular and agricultural education continued to be the most prominent rural issue, and the movement for agricultural education began to gather strength. The self-education vogue was associated with this movement.

Many schools and colleges began to offer courses in agriculture and sciences helpful to agriculture.

Agricultural spokesmen began to demand formal recognition by the Government of the special needs of agriculture. Government support was asked for agricultural societies and fairs, agricultural education, and State boards of agriculture. (See The Patent Office, 1839.)

1832. The renewal of the charter of the Second National Bank, whose existence had always been a point of contention between the creditors of the cities and the debtors of the South and West, was made a campaign issue.
South Carolina directed the Nullification Ordinance at the "Tariff of Abominations" of 1828. The tariff issue thus evolved into a States' rights issue. (See The Morrill Tariff Act, 1861; and Civil War, 1861–65.)
1833. John Lane began to manufacture steel plows.
1834. The McCormick reaper was patented.
The first issue of the Cultivator appeared.
1835–37. The bank-credit land boom became intensified.
1836. The Patent Office, which later took on agricultural functions, was created in the State Department.
1837. A State university providing general and agricultural education was legally established in Michigan.
Panic. The end of the land-speculation boom.
A practical threshing machine was invented.
John Deere began manufacturing steel plows. (See John Lane, 1833.)

The development of the reaper, the steel plow, the threshing machine, and other farm implements during this period involved changes in economic and social organization as well as in technology. The manufacture of farm implements was driven out of local blacksmith shops and into specialized factories because of the capital required for the efficient production of the new machinery. Moreover, as farmers gradually found it economically advantageous to make the heavy capital investment necessary for the new machines, their need for cash and their dependence upon the market increased. This trend has continued for more than a hundred years as mechanical technology has been constantly improved and specialized.

1837. Morse developed the first practical telegraph machine.
1839. Cotton boom.
The Patent Office received an appropriation of $1,000 for work with agricultural statistics.
1840. 77.5 percent of all those gainfully employed were engaged in agriculture.
Liebig's Chemistry appeared. It had a great influence on scientific thought and on agricultural experimentation in Europe and this country. (See Edmund Ruffin, 1821.)
3,320 miles of canal had been constructed.
1840–45. Depression.

Free land was becoming an important issue.

1841. The Preemption Act, providing for the sale of public lands at $1.25 an acre, was passed.

Agitation for popular and agricultural education and rural interest in self-improvement continued.

There was a growing tendency for farmers to organize along occupational lines.

1841. The Union Agriculturist and Western Prairie Farmer started publication.
By this time agricultural journalism was permanently established.
A practical grain drill was patented.
1842. The first grain elevator was constructed, in Buffalo.
1844. A mowing machine was patented.

The potato famine in Ireland in the 1840's and the German Revolution of 1848 brought a tremendous influx of immigrants.

1845. Texas was added to the Union.
1846. The Oregon question was settled, and Oregon was added to the Union.
Protective duties were lowered, and the system of computing duties was changed from specific to ad valorem by the Walker Tariff Act.

The value of new lands continued to rise as the population grew and as communication developed.

1846. The first herd book, for Shorthorns, was compiled.
The Howe sewing machine was patented.

In the forties and fifties Herefords, Ayrshires, Galloways, Jerseys, and Devons were being imported and bred.

Commercial corn and wheat belts began to develop. Wheat occupied the newer and cheaper areas and was constantly being forced westward by rising land values and the encroachment of corn. But New York, Pennsylvania, and Ohio were still the chief wheat-producing States.

As the frontier moved out onto the prairies and the Plains, subsistence farming became more difficult and agriculture became necessarily more commercial.

Cotton was the only great agricultural export until after 1860. (See The exportation to Europe of foodstuffs, about 1865.)

1846–48. The Mexican War and war prosperity.
1848. The Mexican Cession was added to the Union.
1849. The California Gold Rush began.
The Patent Office was transferred from the State Department to the newly created Interior Department. Distributing free seeds and collecting agricultural statistics were the principal agricultural functions of the Patent Office.

Jonathan Turner of Illinois began to campaign for "industrial universities." This campaign was part of the long struggle for popular and agricultural education which culminated in the passage of the Land Grant College Act in 1862. The industrial universities were to be practical colleges for common men to prepare them for agricultural or industrial jobs.

1850. The frontier had jumped the Great Plains and the Rockies from the Mississippi River to the Pacific coast, following the discovery of gold in California.

1850–56. California gold inflation prosperity.

About 30 to 35 man-hours of labor were required to produce 1 acre of corn (40 bushels) with a walking plow, a harrow, and hand planting. (Compare with labor requirements about 1890 and about 1930.)

Alfalfa was grown on the west coast.

1853. The Gadsden Purchase was made.

In the fifties kerosene lamps began to be popular.

"Uncle Sam has land enough for all of us." Free land became a more and more urgent issue, especially among urban working people who wanted to become freehold farmers. (See The Preemption Act, 1841; The Homestead Act, 1862; United States Census statement, 1890; and Land shortage, about 1933.)

The interests of agriculture were promoted through the Patent Office during this period.

The fifties, sixties, and seventies were the period of the farmers' clubs.

1855–60. The average annual value of agricultural exports was $229,371,600, or 82.4 percent of all exports.

1856. The two-horse straddle-row cultivator was patented.

In the fifties the South was in the political saddle. The contentions between the industrial North and the plantation South became steadily more intense.

1857. The tariff was revised downward to the lowest level since 1815, reflecting the political dominance of the South.
Panic.
An agricultural college was opened in Michigan.

Steam tractors were tried unsuccessfully.
Grimm alfalfa was introduced.

1859. Darwin published Origin of the Species, which had a great influence on biological science.
Maryland Agricultural College was opened to students.
"Pike's Peak or bust." The miners' frontier began moving eastward toward the westward-moving farmers' and ranchers' frontier.

1860. East Texas was first reported as an important cotton area.
30,000 miles of railroad track had been laid.

1861. The Morrill Tariff Act was passed. It raised the tariff barrier to a new high level, setting the precedent for later high protective tariffs, and it was bitterly opposed by agricultural interests, especially in the South.

1861–65. Civil War.

1861–62. Secession depression.

1862. The Department of Agriculture was set up but remained without Cabinet status until 1889.
The drive for agricultural education culminated in the passage of the Morrill Land Grant College Act.
The Homestead Act was passed; farmers and workingmen had won the free-land issue.

1862–65. War prosperity.

During the Civil War period the Corn Belt began to become stabilized in its present area, Wisconsin and Illinois were the chief wheat States, and the Wheat Belt began to move across the Mississippi. The prosperous Cotton Belt had already begun to move westward out of the exhausted lands of the old Southeast.

The exportation to Europe of foodstuffs produced in the North increased greatly, while the South, for the time being, could not export her cotton.

1865–66. Primary post-war depression.
1865–75. Gang plows and sulky plows came into use.

As a result of the Civil War there was a great expansion of industry in the North. In the South the sharecropping system tended to grow up in place of the old plantation slave system.

This was the beginning of a period of active revolt by farmers against their economic disadvantages. After the Civil War farm organizations and agricultural issues were destined to be primarily concerned with economic matters to a much greater degree than had been the case before the war.

1867. The first Grange was organized.
1869. Illinois passed the first of the so-called Granger laws, regulating railroads.

Women's suffrage and prohibition began to be important issues.

1869. Wyoming adopted women's suffrage.
The Union Pacific Railroad was completed. (See The Crédit Mobilier scandal, 1872.)
1870. 47.4 percent of all persons gainfully employed were engaged in agriculture. The 1870 census was the first which showed the farmers as a minority among the gainfully employed.

Commercial values of farm land continued to rise as cities and agricultural markets expanded.

1870–90. The days of the cattlemen on the Great Plains.
1870. Foot-and-mouth disease was first reported in the United States.
1871. The National Grange gave its sanction to a cooperative enterprise.
1872. The Crédit Mobilier scandal was made public, bringing to light the bribing of Congressmen by the construction company of the Union Pacific Railroad.
1873. Panic.

Settlement on the Great Plains was accelerated by the cattle boom and the panic of 1873.

1873. The grasshopper plagues in the West became serious. (See The United States Entomological Commission, 1877.)
A successful wire binder was on the market. (See Deering, 1880.)
Silver was demonetized in what came to be known among western farmers as "the Crime of '73." Free silver became a prominent rural issue.

Hard money, high freight rates, and monopoly were the most prominent agricultural issues of the day. They reflected the shift in power from the agrarian to the financial and industrial interests that was a result of the Civil War.

1874. The Glidden barbed-wire patent was granted. Barbed wire contributed greatly to the agricultural settlement of the Great Plains.
1874. The first Chautauqua was formed. The Chautauqua movement started as a device for training Sunday-school teachers and developed into an adult-education program.

Many State colleges of agriculture began to do experimental work, partly in order to improve farming methods and production and partly to build up a science of agriculture that could be taught in the agricultural colleges.

Silos and refrigerator cars began to come into use in the seventies.

The Grange was at its height during the middle seventies. It had started out as a fraternal order, but the economic circumstances in which farmers found themselves in that period forced the Grange to take a stand on such economic issues as railroad regulation and hard money.

The Farmers' Alliance movement began during the middle seventies in response to the farmers' economic distress. The original purposes of the Alliance, unlike those of the Grange, were wholly economic and political.

1875–80. The average annual value of agricultural exports was $525,902,400, or 78.8 percent of all exports.

1877. The United States Entomological Commission was established for work on grasshopper control.

1880. The estimated average equity of farm operators in the land they farmed was 62 percent. This figure was destined to decline from this time on at an average rate of 4 percent each decade until 1935. (See items concerning land values about 1920 and land shortage about 1933.)
Deering put 3,000 twine binders on the market.
The Mississippi River traffic reached its peak.

The cooperative movement began to assume some importance. Farmers' organizations such as the Grange (1867), the Farmers' Alliance (the middle seventies), the Agricultural Wheel and the Farmers' Mutual Benefit Association (1882), the Farmers' Union and the American Society of Equity (1902) took up the movement one after the other in an effort to give farmers bargaining power in their dealings with industry.

Plow agriculture was beginning to extend into the Great Plains. This movement, encouraged by population pressure and facilitated by the development of barbed-wire fencing, advanced in spite of the resistance of many cattlemen.

1880–83. Following the resumption of specie payment in 1879, which put an end to the greenback days of the Civil War, there was a brief period of prosperity.

1882. The German bacteriologist, Koch, isolated the tubercle bacillus, thereby taking the first step in the direction of control of tuberculosis in dairy herds.
The Agricultural Wheel, a farmers' organization similar to the Alliance and later absorbed into it, was organized.
The Farmers' Mutual Benefit Association, an organization for bettering the farmer's economic status and committed to the cooperative principle, was organized.
Bordeaux mixture, a fungicide, was discovered in France and soon introduced into the United States.

A few States began to institute inspection of dairy products.

1884. Depression.

1886–90. Railroad prosperity. This was the period of railroad consolidation.

1886–87. Overgrazing, drought, and blizzard brought disaster to the Great Plains cattle industry. Thereafter the extension of plow agriculture into the semiarid and arid sections of the Great Plains was accelerated.

1887. The Interstate Commerce Act was passed in response to the agitation of farmers and others for the control of railroads.
The Hatch Experiment Station Act was passed. At this time 15 States had 17 formally organized experiment stations.

Spring-tooth harrows were available for seedbed preparation. They began to replace the cultivators previously used for this purpose.

Cream separators began to come into wide use.

1889. The carrier of tick fever was determined by the Bureau of Animal Industry.

The agricultural pressure groups gathered strength. Hard money, high freight rates, trusts, and monopoly continued to be dominant issues.

1889. The Alliance evolved the subtreasury plan, whereby the Government was to grade and store farm products in Government warehouses. The farmers were to receive a year's loan for produce so deposited and were to be able to redeem it for sale in the open market when it seemed advantageous to do so.
The Department of Agriculture was raised to Cabinet status.

This was the height of the period of the Chautauquas. The Chautauqua movement was a part of the same self-education movement which founded Lyceums in 1826 and farmers' clubs in the fifties.

1890. "There can hardly be said to be a frontier line," said the United States Census. This is the date commonly selected to mark the end of the historic era of cheap and free lands open to agricultural settlement.
The estimated average equity of farm operators in the land they farmed was 59 percent.

Agriculture was becoming increasingly mechanized and commercialized.

Horse-drawn combines were in use in the Pacific coast grain areas.

Eight to ten man-hours of labor were required to produce 1 acre (20 bushels) of wheat with a gang plow, a seeder, a harrow, a binder, a thresher, wagons, and horses. (Compare with labor requirements about 1825 and about 1930.)

Fourteen to sixteen man-hours of labor were required to produce 1 acre (40 bushels) of corn with a two-bottom gang plow, a disk and peg-tooth harrow, and a two-row planter. (Compare with labor requirements about 1850 and about 1930.)

By 1890 most of the basic potentialities of agricultural machinery dependent on animal power had been discovered.

1890. The Babcock butterfat test was devised.
The McKinley Tariff Act was passed as a result of the campaign of 1888. Under it the tariff barrier was raised and a tariff on agricultural products was inserted as a sop to farmers.
The Sherman Antitrust Act was passed in an effort to stem the growing tide of monopolistic control in industry which worked to the disadvantage of the consumer.
There was a short, sharp crisis precipitated by the financial difficulties of an English banking firm, the Baring Brothers.

1892. The Farmers' Alliance became the "People's Party," or "Populist Party," to champion the rights of farmers.
It was reported that the last case of pleuropneumonia in cattle had been disposed of.

Kansas was becoming the center of the Wheat Belt and Texas the chief cotton State.

A beginning was made in the development of secondary agricultural education locally and by States.

1893. Panic.
There were 49 permanent experiment stations under the Hatch Act.

1894. The Wilson-Gorman Tariff Act was passed. President Cleveland, who had been elected on a pledge of a low tariff, considered this only slightly lowered tariff an example of "party perfidy and dishonor."

1895. The Selden patent for automobiles was granted.

1895–1900. The average annual value of agricultural exports was $752,120,200, or 66.4 percent of all exports.

1896. The rural free delivery system was started.

1897. In the Dingley Tariff Act the Republican Party raised the tariff wall above the McKinley tariff level.

1897–1901. Normal economic period.
1898. Trap nesting was begun for the selection of hens.
1899. An improved method of anthrax inoculation was devised.

The boll weevil crossed the Rio Grande and began to spread North and East.

1900. 35.7 percent of all persons gainfully employed were engaged in agriculture.
The estimated average equity of farm operators in the land they farmed was 54 percent.
Mendel's work on heredity was rediscovered.

Farmers began to have telephones. Many cooperative country lines were established.

Urban influences on rural life were becoming greatly intensified. The vast improvements and extension of transportation and communication, the growing use of urban industrial products by farm people, the increasing dependence of the farmer on the urban market, the increasing distribution of metropolitan newspapers and magazines among farmers, the growth of both formal and informal educational institutions, all tended to reduce the differences between rural and urban life.

1901–3. A period of industrial prosperity followed the development of the holding-company technique of consolidation.
1902. The Farmers' Union was formed.
The American Society of Equity, a farmers' organization devoted largely to improving marketing practices, was formed.
The Reclamation Act was passed.
De Vries announced the mutation theory, of great importance in the field of genetics.
1903. A serum for hog cholera was developed.
1904. A "rich man's panic" followed the conviction, under the Antitrust Act, of the Northern Securities Co., a holding company.

Soybeans began to be an important crop.

Agricultural settlement on the Great Plains continued, and a dry-land farming boom appeared as a result of experimentally developed dry-land farming practices.

1905–10. The average annual value of agricultural exports was $962,708,600, or 54.9 percent of all exports.
1905. The California Fruit Growers' Exchange was formed.
1905–6. A period of prosperity.
1906. The Food and Drugs Act was passed.
1907. Panic.
1908. The Wright brothers demonstrated the airplane.
1900–1929. Road building was stimulated following the invention of the automobile.

Agricultural credit, with the growth of commercialism in agriculture and the increasing need for cash among commercial farmers, became a more and more important rural issue.

1908. President Roosevelt organized the Country Life Commission.
1909. The Payne-Aldrich Tariff Act, which placed duties at the highest level up to this time, was passed.
1909–12. Normal economic period.
1910. 33.2 percent of all persons gainfully employed were engaged in agriculture.
The estimated average equity of farm operators in the land they farmed was 50 percent.
Morgan announced the gene theory.

Experimental work to breed disease- and drought-resistant varieties of plants, to improve plant yields in some cases, and to increase the productivity of farm-animal strains was becoming more and more extensive.

By 1910, 35 States and Territories required testing for tuberculosis of all entering cattle.

This was the period of the Country Life Movement.

1911. The first Farm Bureau was formed in Broome County, N. Y. (See Smith-Lever Act, 1914.)
1912. Marquis wheat was introduced.
1913. Panic.
The sixteenth amendment to the Constitution, permitting the levying of a Federal income tax, was ratified.
The seventeenth amendment to the Constitution, providing for direct election of Senators, was ratified.
The Underwood-Simmons Tariff Act, passed during a Democratic administration, represented some reduction in tariff rates but remained protectionist in principle.
The Federal Reserve Act was passed.
1914. The Cotton Futures Act was passed.
The Smith-Lever Extension Act was passed, providing for a Nation-wide extension of the county-agent system along the lines first worked out by the Farm Bureau of Broome County.
1915. The Non-Partisan League was formed.

Big, open-geared gasoline tractors came into use in areas of extensive farming and were soon used with the combine, which had been brought in from the Pacific coast.

1915–20. Movie houses were becoming common in rural areas.
The average annual value of agricultural exports was $2,637,853,000, or 41 percent of all exports.
War prosperity. Agricultural production was vastly increased to supply a tremendous foreign market.
1916. The Federal Farm Loan Act was passed.
1917. The Smith-Hughes Vocational Education Act was passed.
Entry of the United States into the war.
The Food Control Act, a war measure affecting agriculture, was passed.
Kansas Red wheat was developed.
1917–27. Grain production reached into the most arid sections of the Great Plains. (See Severe drought conditions, 1934.)
1918. Ceres wheat was developed.
1920. The American Farm Bureau Federation was organized.
26.3 percent of all persons gainfully employed were engaged in agriculture.
The estimated average equity of farm operators in the land they farmed was 46 percent.
The foreign market for farm products began to decline, wartime agricultural prices collapsed, and the long-time agricultural depression began.

There was a general though uneven decline in the value of farm land. The era of unearned increment was over, and the long-time trend of rising farm land values was at last broken.

1920–22. Primary post-war depression.

Enclosed gears were developed for the tractor.

1920. The nineteenth amendment to the Constitution, granting suffrage to women, was ratified.
1921. The Packers and Stockyards Act was passed.
A farm bloc was organized in Congress.
1922. A national agricultural conference was called in Washington, D. C.

The cooperative movement spread.

1922. The Capper-Volstead Act was passed, exempting production cooperatives from the restrictions of the antitrust law.
The Grain Futures Act was passed.

The surplus became the chief agricultural issue. It was first attacked primarily as a marketing and later as a marketing-and-production problem.

1922. The Illinois Agricultural Association attempted voluntary corn-acreage reduction.
The fear of the dumping of foreign products in this country following the war stimulated the passage of the highly protective Fordney-McCumber Tariff Act.
1923–27. "Coolidge prosperity."
1923. The Agricultural Credits Act was passed, setting up a Federal Intermediate Credit Bank in each Federal Reserve District for the purpose of making loans to farmers for periods intermediate between the usual long-term and short-term loans.
1925. The work of the Department of Agriculture was by now divided between research, service, and regulation under more than 30 regulatory laws. (See entries under 1819, 1839, 1862, and 1889.)
The Purnell Act, providing funds for economic and sociological research to be carried on by experiment stations, was passed.
The Master Farmer movement began under the auspices of the Prairie Farmer.
1925–30. The average annual value of agricultural exports was $1,791,529,800, or 37.1 percent of all exports.
1926. The first hybrid seed-corn company was organized.

A successful light tractor was developed.

1926. The export-debenture plan was first proposed. (See The surplus, about 1922, and The agricultural export market, about 1930.)
1927. The first McNary-Haugen bill was vetoed.
1928. The second McNary-Haugen bill was vetoed.
There were nearly 12,000 cooperatives in the country.
1929. The Federal Farm Board was established.
Panic.
1930. 21.5 percent of all persons gainfully employed were engaged in agriculture.
The estimated average equity of farm operators in the land they farmed was 41 percent.
58 percent of all farms had cars, 34 percent had telephones, 13 percent had electricity (including home generating plants).
262,713 miles of railroad were in operation.

The agricultural export market after the 1920's suffered increasingly serious competition from the newer agricultural regions of the world.

1930. The Hawley-Smoot Tariff Act, which was highly protective, was passed.

Three to four man-hours of labor were required to produce 1 acre (20 bushels) of wheat with a 3-bottom gang plow, a tractor, a 10-foot tandem disk, a harrow, a 12-foot combine, and trucks. (Compare with labor requirements about 1825 and about 1890.)

Six to eight man-hours of labor were required to produce 1 acre (40 bushels) of corn with a 2-bottom gang plow, a 7-foot tandem disk, a 4-section harrow, a 2-row planter, a 2-row cultivator, and a 2-row picker. (Compare with labor requirements about 1850 and about 1890.)

Multiple-row cultivators, corn planters, and pickers came into wide use.

The all-purpose rubber-tired tractor with complementary machinery came into wide use.

1930–40. The use of hybrid corn became general in the Corn Belt.
1933. The Farm Credit Act was passed.
The first Agricultural Adjustment Act was passed. (See The surplus, about 1922.)

Soil conservation was recognized as a growing problem.

Land shortage, surplus rural population, and farm-security problems began to attract attention. (See The Preemption Act, 1841; The Homestead Act, 1862; the end of the frontier, 1890.)

1934. The Reciprocal Tariff Act was passed.
Severe drought conditions and dust blowing developed on the Great Plains. (See Grain production, 1917–27.)

1935. The estimated average equity of farm operators in the land they farmed was 39 percent. (Compare with 1880.)

1936. The Supreme Court, in the Hoosac Mills decision, outlawed the processing taxes in the Agricultural Adjustment Act.
Congress immediately passed the Soil Conservation and Domestic Allotment Act as a substitute measure for the Agricultural Adjustment Act.

Soil conservation problems received increased attention.

The plight of the Dust Bowl refugees and migratory workers received Nation-wide attention. (See Land shortage, about 1933).

Attempts were made to reestablish some portions of the Great Plains as a cattle region.

The long-time agricultural depression continued.

1937. Business recession.

1938. The "ever-normal granary" was written into the Agricultural Adjustment Act.

1939. The food-stamp plan for distributing surplus food products was tried out in some cities.

Trade barriers between States began to attract attention.

1939. War began again in Europe.

Index